PRENTICE HALL

SCIENCE EXPLORER

Focus on Earth Science

PRENTICE HALL
Needham, Massachusetts
Upper Saddle River, New Jersey
Glenview, Illinois

PRENTICE HALL
SCIENCE EXPLORER

Focus on Earth Science

Program Resources
Student Edition
Teacher's Edition
Teaching Resource Box:
- Unit Resource Books, including
  - Lesson Plans
  - Section Summaries
  - Review and Reinforcement Worksheets
  - Enrichment
  - Labs and Projects
- Interdisciplinary Explorations
- Color Transparencies
- Guided Reading and Study Workbook
- Laboratory Manual, Student Edition
- Laboratory Manual, Teacher's Edition
- How to Manage Instruction in the Block

California Standards-Based Lesson Plans
California Standardized Test Preparation Book
Chapter and Unit Tests
Performance Assessment
How to Assess Student Work
Study Guides in English and Five Languages
Spanish Section Summaries
Reading in the Content Area with Literature Connections
Guided Reading English Audiotapes
Consumable Materials Kit
Nonconsumable Materials Kit
Spanish Guided Reading and Study Workbook

Program Components
Inquiry Skills Activity Book
Student-Centered Science Activity Book
Prentice Hall Interdisciplinary Explorations
Spanish Guided Reading Audiotapes and Section Summaries

Media/Technology
Spanish Student Edition on Audio CD
Assessment Resources with CD-ROM and Dial-A-Test®
Interactive Student Tutorial CD-ROMs
Resource Pro® (Standards-Based Lesson Plans and Teaching Resources on CD-ROM)
Lab Activity Video Libraries
Science Explorer Videotapes
Science Explorer Videodiscs
Internet Site at www.phschool.com/state_focus/california/

Other Support
Interactive Earth CD-ROM
Odyssey of Discovery (CD-ROMs for Life, Earth, and Physical Science)

Acknowledgments
Activity on pages 98–99 is from *Exploring Planets in the Classroom*, copyright © Hawaii Space Grant Consortium. Used with permission.

Excerpt on page 710 is from *The Amateur Naturalist* by Gerald Durrell. Copyright © 1982 by Dorling Kindersley Ltd., London. Reprinted by permission of Alfred A. Knopf, Inc.

Cover: Glaciers carved the sheer granite walls of El Capitan, which rises above Yosemite Valley in Yosemite National Park, California.

ISBN 0-13-044347-6
14 15 08 07 06

Program Authors

Michael J. Padilla, Ph.D.
Professor
Department of Science Education
University of Georgia
Athens, Georgia

Michael Padilla is a leader in middle school science education. He has served as an editor and elected officer for the National Science Teachers Association. He has been principal investigator of several National Science Foundation and Eisenhower grants and served as a writer of the National Science Education Standards.

As lead author of *Science Explorer,* Mike has inspired the team in developing a program that meets the needs of middle grades students, promotes science inquiry, and is aligned with the National Science Education Standards.

Ioannis Miaoulis, Ph.D.
Dean of Engineering
College of Engineering
Tufts University
Medford, Massachusetts

Martha Cyr, Ph.D.
Director, Engineering Educational Outreach
College of Engineering
Tufts University
Medford, Massachusetts

Science Explorer was created in collaboration with the College of Engineering at Tufts University. Tufts has an extensive engineering outreach program that uses engineering design and construction to excite and motivate students and teachers in science and technology education.

Faculty from Tufts University participated in the development of *Science Explorer* chapter projects, reviewed the student books for content accuracy, and helped coordinate field testing.

Book Authors

Joseph D. Exline, Ed.D.
Former Director of Science
Virginia Department of Education

Fred Holtzclaw
Science Teacher
Oak Ridge High School
Oak Ridge, Tennessee

Linda Cronin Jones, Ph.D.
College of Education
University of Florida
Gainesville, Florida

Steve Miller
Science Writer
State College, Pennsylvania

Barbara Brooks Simons
Science Writer
Boston, Massachusetts

Carole Garbuny Vogel
Science Writer
Lexington, Massachusetts

Thomas R. Wellnitz
Science Teacher
The Paideia School
Atlanta, Georgia

Contributing Writers

Alfred B. Bortz, Ph.D.
School of Education
Duquesne University
Pittsburgh, Pennsylvania

Rose-Marie Botting
Science Teacher
Broward County School District
Fort Lauderdale, Florida

Jeffrey C. Callister
Science Teacher
Newburgh Free Academy
Newburgh, New York

Colleen Campos
Science Teacher
Laredo Middle School
Aurora, Colorado

Holly Estes
Science Teacher
Hale Middle School
Stow, Massachusetts

Edward Evans
Former Science Teacher
Hilton Central School
Hilton, New York

Theresa K. Holtzclaw
Former Science Teacher
Clinton, Tennessee

Greg Hutton
Science and Health Curriculum Coordinator
School Board of Sarasota County
Sarasota, Florida

Jan Jenner, Ph.D.
Science Writer
Talladega, Alabama

Lauren Magruder
Science Teacher
St. Michael's Country Day School
Newport, Rhode Island

Emery Pineo
Science Instructor
Barrington Middle School
Barrington, Rhode Island

Karen Riley Sievers
Science Teacher
Callanan Middle School
Des Moines, Iowa

Sharon M. Stroud
Science Teacher
Widefield High School
Colorado Springs, Colorado

Reading Consultant

Bonnie B. Armbruster, Ph.D.
Department of Curriculum and Instruction
University of Illinois
Champaign, Illinois

Interdisciplinary Consultant

Heidi Hayes Jacobs, Ed.D.
Teacher's College
Columbia University
New York, New York

Safety Consultants

W. H. Breazeale, Ph.D.
Department of Chemistry
College of Charleston
Charleston, South Carolina

Ruth Hathaway, Ph.D.
Hathaway Consulting
Cape Girardeau, Missouri

California Reviewers

Stephanie Anderson
Sierra Vista Junior High School
Canyon Country, California

John W. Anson
Mesa Intermediate School
Palmdale, California

Dawn Smith Burgess, Ph.D.
Department of Geophysics
Stanford University
Palo Alto, California

Judy D'Albert
Harvard Day School
Corona Del Mar, California

Melody Law Ewey
Holmes Junior High School
Davis, California

Debra J. Goodding
Kraemer Middle School
Placentia, California

Jason Ho
Walter Reed Middle School
Los Angeles, California

Judy Jernstedt, Ph.D.
Department of Agronomy and Range Science
University of California, Davis
Davis, California

Dennis K. Lieu, Ph.D.
Department of Mechanical Engineering
University of California
Berkeley, California

Carol Ann Lionello
Kraemer Middle School
Placentia, California

Jaime A. Morales
Henry T. Gage Middle School
Huntington Park, California

Edward D. Walton, Ph.D.
Department of Chemistry
California State Polytechnic University
Pomona, California

Tufts University Program Reviewers

Behrouz Abedian, Ph.D.
Department of Mechanical Engineering

Wayne Chudyk, Ph.D.
Department of Civil and Environmental Engineering

Eliana De Bernardez-Clark, Ph.D.
Department of Chemical Engineering

Anne Marie Desmarais, Ph.D.
Department of Civil and Environmental Engineering

David L. Kaplan, Ph.D.
Department of Chemical Engineering

Paul Kelley, Ph.D.
Department of Electro-Optics

George S. Mumford, Ph.D.
Professor of Astronomy, Emeritus

Jan A. Pechenik, Ph.D.
Department of Biology

Livia Racz, Ph.D.
Department of Mechanical Engineering

Robert Rifkin, M.D.
School of Medicine

Jack Ridge, Ph.D.
Department of Geology

Chris Swan, Ph.D.
Department of Civil and Environmental Engineering

Peter Y. Wong, Ph.D.
Department of Mechanical Engineering

Content Reviewers

Jack W. Beal, Ph.D.
Department of Physics
Fairfield University
Fairfield, Connecticut

W. Russell Blake, Ph.D.
Planetarium Director
Plymouth Community Intermediate School
Plymouth, Massachusetts

Howard E. Buhse, Jr., Ph.D.
Department of Biological Sciences
University of Illinois
Chicago, Illinois

A. Campbell, Ph.D.
Assistant Professor
Davidson College
Davidson, North Carolina

Elizabeth A. De Stasio, Ph.D.
Associate Professor of Biology
Lawrence University
Appleton, Wisconsin

John M. Fowler, Ph.D.
Former Director of Special Projects
National Science Teacher's Association
Arlington, Virginia

Jonathan Gitlin, M.D.
School of Medicine
Washington University
St. Louis, Missouri

Dawn Graff-Haight, Ph.D., CHES
Department of Health, Human Performance, and Athletics
Linfield College
McMinnville, Oregon

Deborah L. Gumucio, Ph.D.
Associate Professor
Department of Anatomy and Cell Biology
University of Michigan
Ann Arbor, Michigan

William S. Harwood, Ph.D.
Dean of University Division and Associate Professor of Education
Indiana University
Bloomington, Indiana

Cyndy Henzel, Ph.D.
Department of Geography and Regional Development
University of Arizona
Tucson, Arizona

Greg Hutton
Science and Health Curriculum Coordinator
School Board of Sarasota County
Sarasota, Florida

Susan K. Jacobson, Ph.D.
Department of Wildlife Ecology and Conservation
University of Florida
Gainesville, Florida

John L. Kermond, Ph.D.
Office of Global Programs
National Oceanographic and Atmospheric Administration
Silver Spring, Maryland

David E. LaHart, Ph.D.
Institute of Science and Public Affairs
Florida State University
Tallahassee, Florida

Joe Leverich, Ph.D.
Department of Biology
St. Louis University
St. Louis, Missouri

Cynthia J. Moore, Ph.D.
Science Outreach Coordinator
Washington University
St. Louis, Missouri

Joseph M. Moran, Ph.D.
Department of Earth Science
University of Wisconsin–Green Bay
Green Bay, Wisconsin

Joseph Stukey, Ph.D.
Department of Biology
Hope College
Holland, Michigan

Seetha Subramanian
Lexington Community College
University of Kentucky
Lexington, Kentucky

Carl L. Thurman, Ph.D.
Department of Biology
University of Northern Iowa
Cedar Falls, Iowa

Robert S. Young, Ph.D.
Department of Geosciences and Natural Resource Management
Western Carolina University
Cullowhee, North Carolina

Edward J. Zalisko, Ph.D.
Department of Biology
Blackburn College
Carlinville, Illinois

Teacher Reviewers

Pamela Arline
Lake Taylor Middle School
Norfolk, Virginia

Lynn Beason
College Station Jr. High School
College Station, Texas

Richard Bothmer
Hollis School District
Hollis, New Hampshire

Jeffrey C. Callister
Newburgh Free Academy
Newburgh, New York

Betty Scott Dean
Guilford County Schools
McLeansville, North Carolina

Sarah C. Duff
Baltimore City Public Schools
Baltimore, Maryland

Sherry L. Fisher
Lake Zurich Middle School North
Lake Zurich, Illinois

Melissa Gibbons
Fort Worth ISD
Fort Worth, Texas

Jack Grande
Weber Middle School
Port Washington, New York

Steve Hills
Riverside Middle School
Grand Rapids, Michigan

Patsy Partin
Cameron Middle School
Nashville, Tennessee

Deedra H. Robinson
Newport News Public Schools
Newport News, Virginia

Bonnie Scott
Clack Middle School
Abilene, Texas

Charles M. Sears
Belzer Middle School
Indianapolis, Indiana

Barbara M. Strange
Ferndale Middle School
High Point, North Carolina

Jackie Louise Ulfig
Ford Middle School
Allen, Texas

Kathy Usina
Belzer Middle School
Indianapolis, Indiana

Heidi M. von Oetinger
L'Anse Creuse Public School
Harrison Township, Michigan

Pam Watson
Hill Country Middle School
Austin, Texas

Activity Field Testers

Nicki Bibbo
Russell Street School
Littleton, Massachusetts

Connie Boone
Fletcher Middle School
Jacksonville Beach, Florida

Rose-Marie Botting
Broward County School District
Fort Lauderdale, Florida

Colleen Campos
Laredo Middle School
Aurora, Colorado

Elizabeth Chait
W. L. Chenery Middle School
Belmont, Massachusetts

Holly Estes
Hale Middle School
Stow, Massachusetts

Laura Hapgood
Plymouth Community Intermediate School
Plymouth, Massachusetts

Sandra M. Harris
Winman Junior High School
Warwick, Rhode Island

Joanne Jackson
Winman Junior High School
Warwick, Rhode Island

Mary F. Lavin
Plymouth Community Intermediate School
Plymouth, Massachusetts

James MacNeil, Ph.D.
Concord Public Schools
Concord, Massachusetts

Lauren Magruder
St. Michael's Country Day School
Newport, Rhode Island

Jeanne Maurand
Glen Urquhart School
Beverly Farms, Massachusetts

Warren Phillips
Plymouth Community Intermediate School
Plymouth, Massachusetts

Carol Pirtle
Hale Middle School
Stow, Massachusetts

Kathleen M. Poe
Kirby-Smith Middle School
Jacksonville, Florida

Cynthia B. Pope
Ruffner Middle School
Norfolk, Virginia

Anne Scammell
Geneva Middle School
Geneva, New York

Karen Riley Sievers
Callanan Middle School
Des Moines, Iowa

David M. Smith
Howard A. Eyer Middle School
Macungie, Pennsylvania

Derek Strohschneider
Plymouth Community Intermediate School
Plymouth, Massachusetts

Sallie Teames
Rosemont Middle School
Fort Worth, Texas

Gene Vitale
Parkland Middle School
McHenry, Illinois

Zenovia Young
Meyer Levin Junior High School (IS 285)
Brooklyn, New York

State of California Science Content Standards
Focus on Earth Science

To Parents and Students:

The State of California has established guidelines, or standards, describing science knowledge and skills for which students in grades six through eight are responsible. State assessments of student achievement in science will be based on the content and skills described in these standards. The earth science portion of the standards are listed below. The chapter and section references show where you can find specific support for each standard in this book.

To continue to develop proficiency in these content and skills standards, students may use the Chapter Assessments at the end of each chapter, the Interactive Student Tutorial CD-ROM, and the program's Web site at **www.science-explorer.phschool.com.**

1. Plate tectonics explains important features of the Earth's surface and major geologic events. As the basis for understanding this concept, students know:

- **a.** the fit of the continents, location of earthquakes, volcanoes, and midocean ridges, and the distribution of fossils, rock types, and ancient climatic zones provide evidence for plate tectonics. *(Sections 1.3–1.5, 5.2–5.4, 5.5, 5.6, 13.1)*
- **b.** the solid Earth is layered with cold, brittle lithosphere; hot, convecting mantle; and dense, metallic core. *(Sections 1.1, 1.2, 6.1)*
- **c.** lithospheric plates that are the size of continents and oceans move at rates of centimeters per year in response to movements in the mantle. *(Sections 1.3, 2.1, 17.3, 19.3)*
- **d.** earthquakes are sudden motions along breaks in the crust called faults, and volcanoes/fissures are locations where magma reaches the surface. *(Sections 1.5, 2.1, 3.1, 3.2, 3.4, 4.2)*
- **e.** major geologic events, such as earthquakes, volcanic eruptions, and mountain building result from plate motions. *(Sections 1.4, 1.5, 2.1, 3.1, 3.3, 13.1, 13.3)*
- **f.** how to explain major features of California geology in terms of plate tectonics (including mountains, faults, volcanoes). *(Sections 1.4, 1.5, 2.1, 2.4, 3.1–3.3, 4.2)*
- **g.** how to determine the epicenter of an earthquake and that the effects of an earthquake vary with its size, distance from the epicenter, local geology, and the type of construction involved. *(Sections 2.2–2.4)*

2. Topography is reshaped by weathering of rock and soil and by the transportation and deposition of sediment. As the basis for understanding this concept, students know:

- **a.** water running downhill is the dominant process in shaping the landscape, including California's landscape. *(Sections 6.1, 7.1, 8.1–8.3, 10.1)*
- **b.** rivers and streams are dynamic systems that erode and transport sediment, change course, and flood their banks in natural and recurring patterns. *(Sections 6.3, 7.1, 8.2–8.4, 8.6, 9.1, 9.3, 10.1, 10.2, 16.3)*
- **c.** beaches are dynamic systems in which sand is supplied by rivers and moved along the coast by wave action. *(Sections 8.2, 8.5, 12.1)*
- **d.** earthquakes, volcanic eruptions, landslides, and floods change human and wildlife habitats. *(Sections 2.3, 2.4, 3.2, 3.3, 8.1, 8.2, 8.5, 10.1, 11.4, 14.2, 16.3, 19.5)*

3. Heat moves in a predictable flow from warmer objects to cooler objects until all objects are at the same temperature. As the basis for understanding this concept, students know:

- **a.** energy can be carried from one place to another by heat flow, or by waves including water waves, light and sound, or by moving objects. *(Sections 2.2–2.4, 8.5, 11.3, 11.4, 12.1, 12.4, 15.1, 15.2, 15.4, 16.1, 16.2)*
- **b.** when fuel is consumed, most of the energy released becomes heat energy. *(Sections 21.1, 21.4)*

c. heat flows in solids by conduction (which involves no flow of matter) and in fluids by conduction and also by convection (which involves flow of matter). *(Sections 1.2, 9.2, 9.3, 15.2, 16.1, 16.2, 21.4)*

d. heat energy is also transferred between objects by radiation; radiation can travel through space. *(Sections 1.2, 15.1, 15.2)*

4. Many phenomena on the Earth's surface are affected by the transfer of energy through radiation and convection currents. As the basis for understanding this concept, students know:

a. the sun is the major source of energy for phenomena on the Earth's surface, powering winds, ocean currents, and the water cycle. *(Sections 9.3, 15.1, 15.3, 15.4, 17.1, 17.3, 21.2)*

b. solar energy reaches Earth through radiation, mostly in the form of visible light. *(Sections 14.1, 14.4, 15.1, 21.2)*

c. heat from Earth's interior reaches the surface primarily through convection. *(Sections 1.2, 3.1, 3.2, 4.2, 5.2, 21.2)*

d. convection currents distribute heat in the atmosphere and oceans. *(Sections 12.3, 12.4, 15.2–15.4, 16.1, 16.2, 17.1, 17.2)*

e. differences in pressure, heat, air movement, and humidity result in changes of weather. *(Sections 14.4, 15.3–15.5, 16.1, 16.2, 16.4)*

5. Organisms in ecosystems exchange energy and nutrients among themselves and with the environment. As the basis for understanding this concept, students know:

a. energy entering ecosystems as sunlight is transferred by producers into chemical energy through photosynthesis, and then from organism to organism in food webs. *(Sections 9.1, 10.2, 10.3, 13.2, 13.3, 18.1, 19.1, 19.2)*

b. over time, matter is transferred from one organism to others in the food web, and between organisms and the physical environment. *(Sections 5.4, 7.2, 11.1, 11.3, 14.1, 18.1, 18.2, 19.1, 19.2)*

c. populations of organisms can be categorized by the functions they serve in an ecosystem. *(Sections 7.2, 18.1, 18.3, 19.1, 19.5)*

d. different kinds of organisms may play similar ecological roles in similar biomes. *(Sections 7.2, 13.2, 13.3, 18.3, 19.3, 19.4)*

e. the number and types of organisms an ecosystem can support depends on the resources available and abiotic factors, such as quantity of light and water, range of temperatures, and soil composition. *(Sections 7.3, 8.4, 9.1, 10.2, 10.3, 11.1–11.3, 12.3, 12.4, 13.2, 13.3, 14.2, 15.5, 17.2, 17.3, 18.1–18.3, 19.1, 19.3–19.5, 20.2, 20.3)*

6. Sources of energy and materials differ in amounts, distribution, usefulness, and the time required for their formation. As the basis for understanding this concept, students know:

a. the utility of energy sources is determined by factors that are involved in converting these sources to useful forms and the consequences of the conversion process. *(Sections 3.2, 11.2–11.4, 12.2, 13.4, 14.1, 14.2, 17.4, 20.1, 21.1–21.4)*

b. different natural energy and material resources, including air, soil, rocks, minerals, petroleum, fresh water, wildlife, and forests, and classify them as renewable or nonrenewable. *(Sections 4.1–4.3, 5.1–5.6, 7.3, 8.2, 8.3, 8.6, 9.1, 9.3, 10.3–10.5, 11.1–11.3, 12.2, 12.4, 13.2–13.4, 14.1–14.3, 17.4, 20.1–20.4, 21.1, 21.2, 21.4)*

c. natural origin of the materials used to make common objects. *(Sections 4.1–4.3, 5.1–5.3, 5.5, 13.4, 20.2–20.4)*

7. Scientific progress is made by asking meaningful questions and conducting careful investigations. As a basis for understanding this concept, and to address the content in the other three strands, students should develop their own questions and perform investigations. Students will:

a. develop a hypothesis. *(Sections 3.3, 5.6, 7.1, 7.3, 8.1, 8.2, 9.2, 14.1, 15.1, 16.1, 17.1, 17.4, 19.3, 20.1, 21.4, Chapter Projects 7, 17, 19)*

b. select and use appropriate tools and technology (including calculators, computers, balances, spring scales, microscopes, and binoculars) to perform tests, collect data, and display data. *(Sections 4.3, 5.5, 7.2, 10.5, 11.1, 11.2, 15.3, 19.3–19.5, Chapter Projects 11, 19)*

c. construct appropriate graphs from data and develop qualitative statements about the relationships between variables. *(Sections 2.2, 4.1, 9.3, 10.1, 12.3, 13.1, 15.5, 16.2, 17.1, 17.2, 18.2, 18.3, Chapter Projects 9, 15, 18)*

d. communicate the steps and results from an investigation in written reports and verbal presentations. *(Sections 1.5, 2.4, 4.3, 5.6, 6.4, 11.4, 21.4, Chapter Projects 1, 2, 3, 4, 5, 6, 11, 21)*

e. recognize whether evidence is consistent with a proposed explanation. *(Sections 1.1, 1.2, 1.5, 2.1, 8.6, 10.5, 12.4, 13.4, 18.1, 19.3, 20.2, 21.2, Chapter Projects 8, 10, 12, 13)*

f. read a topographic map and a geologic map for evidence provided on the maps, and construct and interpret a simple scale map. *(Sections 6.1–6.4, 7.3, 8.2, 10.1, 10.5, 16.4, 17.1, 17.2, Chapter Projects 6, 10)*

g. interpret events by sequence and time from natural phenomena (e.g., relative ages of rocks and intrusions). *(Section 1.4)*

h. identify changes in natural phenomena over time without manipulating the phenomena (e.g., a tree limb, a grove of trees, a stream, a hill slope). *(Sections 5.5, 14.3, 14.4, 16.4, 20.4, Chapter Projects 14, 16, 20)*

PRENTICE HALL SCIENCE EXPLORER

Contents

Unit 1 Plate Tectonics and Earth's Structure

Laser-ranging device on the San Andreas fault, Parkfield, California

San Andreas fault

Death Valley

Chapter 3 Volcanoes

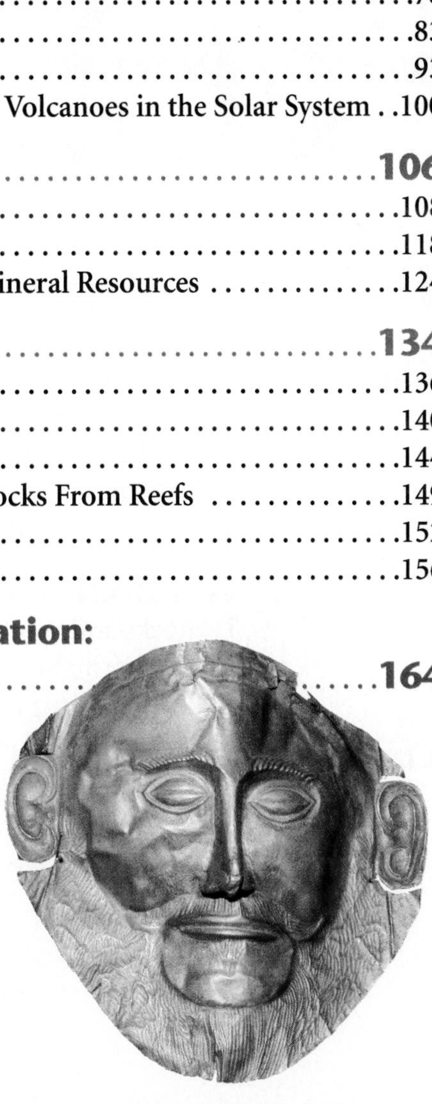

PRENTICE HALL SCIENCE EXPLORER

Sierra Nevada mountains

Unit 2 Shaping Earth's Surface

Unit 3 Earth's Waters

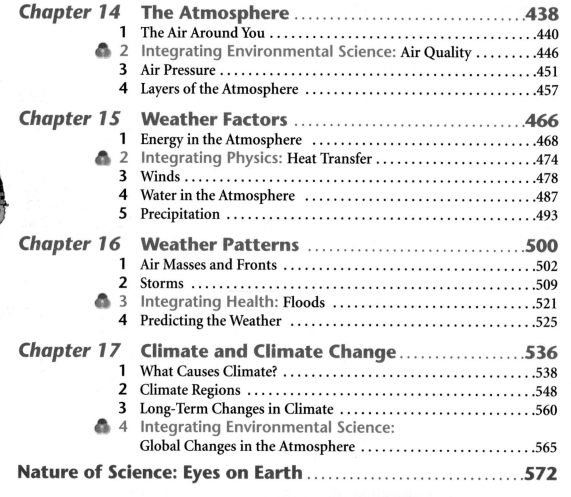

Unit 4 Weather: Energy in the Earth System

Lost Palms Oasis, Joshua Tree National Park

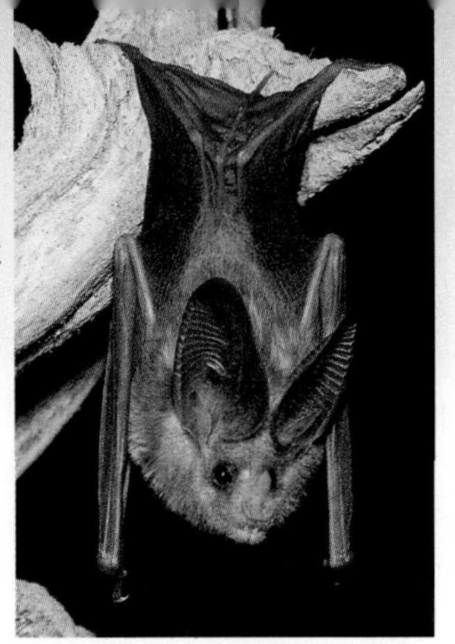

California leaf-nosed bat

Unit 5 Ecology and Resources

Reference Section

Mono Lake

Activities

Inquiry Activities

CHAPTER PROJECT

Opportunities for long-term inquiry

DISCOVER

Exploration and inquiry before reading

DISCOVER

continued

Sharpen your Skills

Practice of specific science inquiry skills

Try This

Reinforcement of key concepts

Skills Lab

In-depth practice of inquiry skills

Real-World Lab

Everyday application of science concepts

EXPLORING

Visual exploration of concepts

Wind farm in Mojave Desert

Interdisciplinary Activities

Science and History

Science and Society

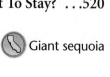

Giant sequoia

Math Toolbox

Connection

STATE OF CALIFORNIA
THE RESOURCES AGENCY
DEPARTMENT OF FISH AND GAME
BOLSA CHICA
ECOLOGICAL RESERVE
PROPERTY ACQUIRED BY
STATE LANDS COMMISSION
BOUNDARY
ECOLOGICAL
RESERVE

FOCUS ON FAULTS

"When I was about fourteen, my family was living in Taiwan," Geologist Carol Prentice recalls. "One day I was playing pinball, and a little earthquake happened. It tilted my pinball machine."

Unlike most people experiencing their first quake, her reaction was not fright but fascination. "*What in the world is that?* I wondered. That was the first time I consciously remember thinking that earthquakes were something interesting." Later, she recalls, "When I was teaching earth science in high school, I realized that my favorite section to teach was on earthquakes and faults."

During an earthquake, forces from inside Earth fracture, or break, Earth's crust, producing a powerful jolt called an earthquake. As Earth's crust moves and breaks, it forms cracks called faults. Over the centuries, the faults may move again and again. Geologist Carol Prentice climbs into these faults to study the soil and rocks. She hunts for clues about the history of a fault and estimates the risk of a serious earthquake in the future.

Carol Prentice studied geology at Humboldt State University and the California Institute of Technology. She is currently a Research Geologist for the United States Geological Survey in Menlo Park, California.

Finding Clues to Ancient Earthquakes

Today, Dr. Prentice is an expert in the field of paleoseismology. *Paleo* means "ancient" and *seismology* is "the study of earthquakes." So it's the study of ancient earthquakes. "Paleoseismologists search for evidence of earthquakes that happened hundreds or thousands of years ago," explains Dr. Prentice.

There are written records about earthquakes that happened years ago. But the real story of a quake is written in the rocks and soil. Years after an earthquake, wind, rain, and flowing water can wear the fault lines away from Earth's surface. Then the evidence of the quake is buried under layers of sediment. But the fault is still there.

Choosing a Site

How do you pick a site to research? "First we study aerial photographs, geological maps, and satellite images of the fault line," Dr. Prentice explains. "We will have some sites in mind. Then, we go out and look at the sites and do some digging with a shovel to get samples."

"We look for places where sediments, such as sand and gravel, have been building up. If sediments have been depositing there for many thousands of years, you're likely to have a good record of prehistoric earthquakes at that site. When you dig, you're likely to see not only the most recent earthquake buried and preserved in the sediments, but also earlier earthquakes. That's a really good site." Once the site is established, the geological team begins digging a trench across the fault.

The cracks of recent earthquakes, such as the Gobi-Altay fault shown here, are sometimes visible for hundreds of kilometers. Because this quake happened in the Mongolian desert, it is especially easy to see.

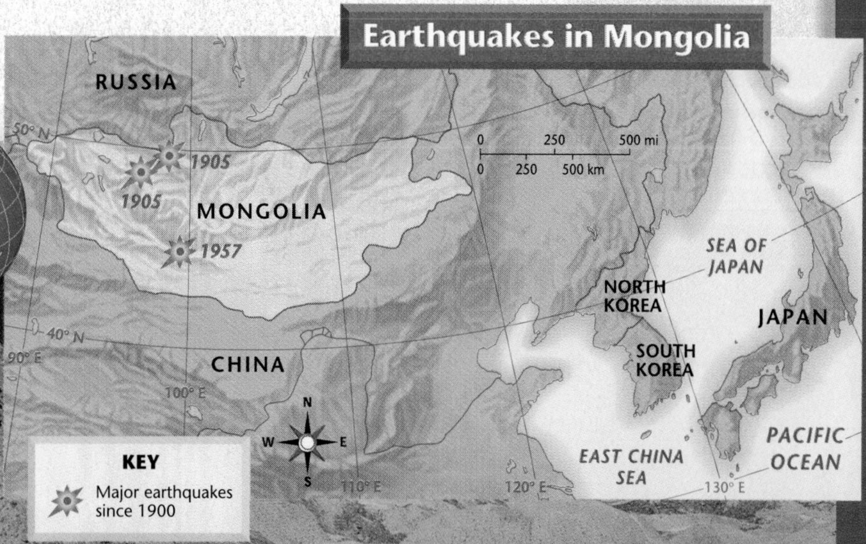

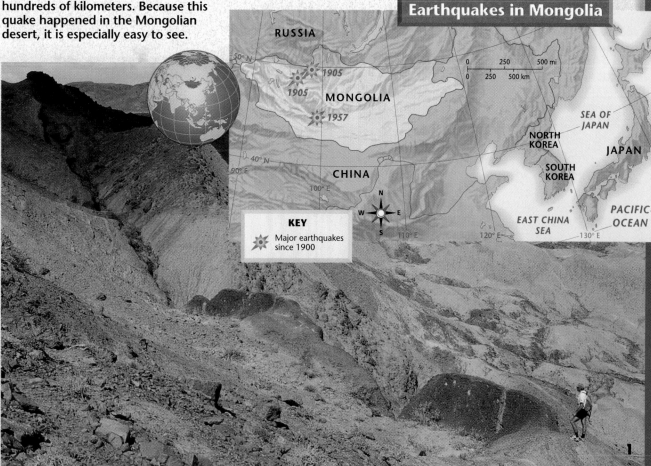

Earthquakes in Mongolia
RUSSIA
MONGOLIA
CHINA
1905
1905
1957
50° N
40° N
90° E
100° E
110° E
120° E
130° E
0 250 500 mi
0 250 500 km
SEA OF JAPAN
NORTH KOREA
SOUTH KOREA
JAPAN
EAST CHINA SEA
PACIFIC OCEAN
N
S
E
W
KEY
Major earthquakes since 1900

Working in the Trenches

What's it like to work in a spot where Earth's surface ruptured? Does Carol Prentice ever think that an earthquake might occur when she is digging in the fault? "It's always in the back of your mind when you are working in the trench," she admits.

But, she says, "The trenches are dangerous, not so much because there might be an earthquake while you are working there but because the trench can cave in. If a trench is 4 to 5 meters deep, or just over your head, it needs shores—braces and supports— or it might cave in. When sediments are soft, and the trench is deep, it's more likely to cave in. That could happen in a place like Mongolia."

Carol (in back) and another geologist in a deep trench.

String grid lines are used to map out sections of the trench.
Shores support the trench walls.

In Mongolia, in northeast Asia, it's difficult for geologists to find the right materials to support a deep trench. It could cave in while someone is in it. "That would be very frightening," she says.

Looking at the Gobi-Altay Quake

Carol Prentice travels to earthquake sites around the world—Dominican Republic, Thailand, Mongolia—as well as to the San Andreas fault in California. One of Dr. Prentice's most recent research expeditions was to the site of the monster Gobi-Altay earthquake of 1957 in the Mongolian desert. In earthquakes like this one, the faults are easy to see. "We're taking a look at this Gobi Altay earthquake and seeing whether the next-to-last earthquake had the same pattern," Dr. Prentice says.

The faults of the Gobi-Altay earthquake are similar in some ways to the San Andreas fault and to the faults of other earthquakes in the United States. That's one of the reasons the Gobi-Altay is so interesting to geologists.

Interpreting the Data

When Dr. Prentice finds evidence of several earthquakes in one spot, she takes measurements that tell her when the layers of rocks, sand, and gravel were deposited and when they split. From that she knows when and how frequently earthquakes have occurred there.

She also determines how fast the opposite sides of the fault are slipping past each other. "Those two pieces of information— the dates of prehistoric earthquakes and the slip rate—are very, very important in trying to

An earthquake is caused by movement on a fault deep beneath Earth's surface. If this movement is large enough, it can cause cracks in the ground surface. Over the years, layers of sediment are deposited on top of the crack. The next earthquake causes a new crack in the surface, and new sediments are deposited. By studying evidence of the cracks in these layers of sediment, geologists learn about past earthquakes along the fault.

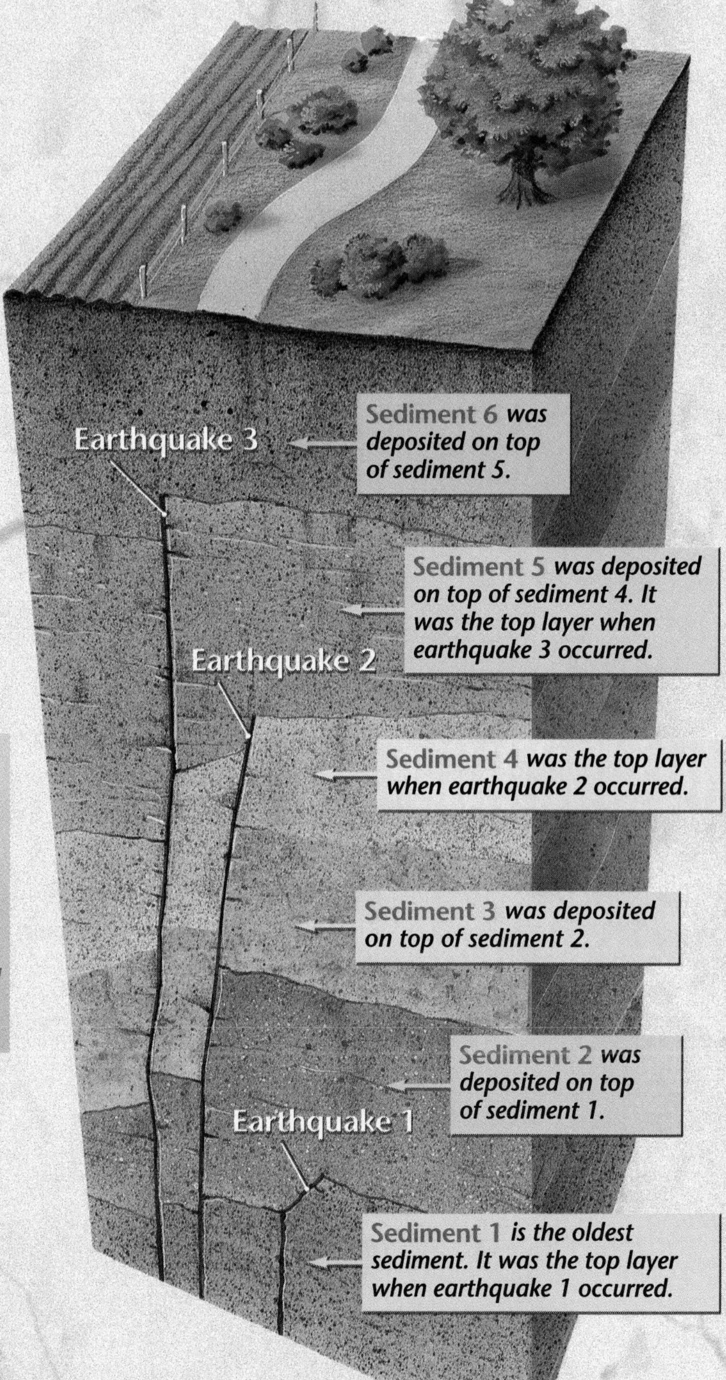

Earthquake 3
Sediment 6 was deposited on top of sediment 5.
Sediment 5 was deposited on top of sediment 4. It was the top layer when earthquake 3 occurred.
Earthquake 2
Sediment 4 was the top layer when earthquake 2 occurred.
Sediment 3 was deposited on top of sediment 2.
Sediment 2 was deposited on top of sediment 1.
Earthquake 1
Sediment 1 is the oldest sediment. It was the top layer when earthquake 1 occurred.

figure out how dangerous a particular fault is," Dr. Prentice explains.

Since faults don't move every year, but over thousands of years, you can figure out the average slip per year and make some predictions. The faster the fault is moving, the greater the danger. "We can look at the landforms around a fault.

> **" . . . the real story of a quake is written in the rocks and soil. "**

We can look at what our instruments record, and say: This is an active fault. Someday it might produce a big earthquake, but what we really want to know is when. Is that earthquake likely to happen in the next fifty years, in the next hundred years, or is it going to be a thousand years before the next big earthquake?"

In Your Journal

Carol Prentice relies on close observation and making inferences in her study of earthquakes. Write a paragraph describing some of the other skills that Dr. Prentice needs to do her work as a paleoseismologist.

CHAPTER 1

Plate Tectonics

This is a satellite image of the San Francisco Bay area. The row of lakes below marks the line of the San Andreas fault, a crack in Earth's crust.

CALIFORNIA SCIENCE CONTENT STANDARDS

The following California Science Content Standards are addressed in this chapter:

1. **Plate tectonics explains important features of the Earth's surface and major geologic events.**
   - a. The fit of the continents, location of earthquakes, volcanoes, and midocean ridges, and the distribution of fossils, rock types, and ancient climatic zones provide evidence for plate tectonics.
   - b. The solid Earth is layered with cold, brittle lithosphere; hot, convecting mantle; and dense, metallic core.
   - c. Lithospheric plates that are the size of continents and oceans move at rates of centimeters per year in response to movements in the mantle.
   - f. How to explain major features of California geology in terms of plate tectonics (including mountains, faults, volcanoes).

3. **Heat moves in a predictable flow from warmer objects to cooler objects until all objects are at the same temperature.**
   - c. Heat flows in solids by conduction (which involves no flow of matter) and in fluids by conduction and also by convection (which involves flow of matter).

PROJECT 1

Cut-Away Earth

Along the San Andreas fault in California, two vast pieces of Earth's crust slowly slide past each other. In this chapter, you will learn how movements deep within Earth cause movements on the surface. These movements help to create mountains and other surface features. You will build a model that shows Earth's interior and how the interior affects the planet's surface.

Your Goal To build a three-dimensional model that shows Earth's surface features as well as a cutaway view of Earth's interior.

To complete this project, you must

- build a scale model of the layers of Earth's interior
- include at least three of the plates that form Earth's surface, as well as two landmasses or continents
- show how the plates push together, pull apart, or slide past each other and indicate their direction of movement
- label all physical features clearly
- follow the safety guidelines in Appendix A

Get Started Begin now by previewing the chapter to learn about Earth's interior. Brainstorm a list of the kinds of materials that could be used to make a three-dimensional model. Start a project folder in which you will keep your sketches, ideas, and any information needed to design and build your model.

Check Your Progress You will be designing and building your model as you study this chapter. To keep your project on track, look for Check Your Progress boxes at the following points.

Section 1 Review, page 14: Begin sketching and designing your model.

Section 4 Review, page 29: Revise your design and start building the base of your model.

Section 5 Review, page 37: Complete the final construction of your model.

Wrap Up At the end of the chapter (page 41), you will present your completed model to the class and discuss the features you included.

d. Heat energy is also transferred between objects by radiation; radiation can travel through space.

4. Many phenomena on the Earth's surface are affected by the transfer of energy through radiation and convection currents.

c. Heat from Earth's interior reaches the surface primarily through convection.

7. Scientific progress is made by asking meaningful questions and conducting careful investigations.

d. Communicate the steps and results from an investigation in written reports and verbal presentations.

e. Recognize whether evidence is consistent with a proposed explanation.

g. Interpret events by sequence and time from natural phenomena (e.g., relative ages of rocks and intrusions).

SECTION 1

Earth's Interior

DISCOVER

ACTIVITY

How Do Scientists Determine What's Inside Earth?

1. Your teacher will provide you with three closed film canisters. Each canister contains a different material. Your goal is to determine what is inside each canister—even though you can't directly observe what it contains.
2. Stick a label made from a piece of tape on each canister.
3. To gather evidence about the contents of the canisters, you may tap, roll, shake, or weigh them. Record your observations.
4. What differences do you notice between the canisters? Apart from their appearance on the outside, are the canisters similar in any way? How did you obtain this evidence?

Think It Over

Inferring Based on your observations, what can you infer about the contents of the canisters? How do you think scientists gather evidence about Earth's interior?

GUIDE FOR READING

- **What does a geologist do?**
- **What are the characteristics of Earth's crust, mantle, and core?**

Reading Tip **Before you read, rewrite the headings in the section as what, how, or why questions. As you read, look for answers to these questions.**

In November 1963, the people of Iceland got to see how the world begins in fire. With no warning, the waters south of Iceland began to hiss and bubble. Soon there was a fiery volcanic eruption from beneath the ocean. Steam and ash belched into the sky. Molten rock from inside Earth spurted above the ocean's surface and hardened into a small island. Within the next several years, the new volcano added 2.5 square kilometers of new, raw land to Earth's surface. The Icelanders named the island "Surtsey." In Icelandic mythology, Surtsey is the god of fire.

Figure 1 The island of Surtsey began to form in the Atlantic Ocean near Iceland in 1963.

The Science of Geology

Figure 2 The work of geologists often takes them outdoors—from mountainsides to caves beneath the surface. *Observing What are the geologists in each picture doing?*

Newspapers reported the story of Surtsey's fiery birth. But much of what is known about volcanoes like Surtsey comes from the work of geologists. **Geologists** are scientists who study the forces that make and shape planet Earth. Geologists study the chemical and physical characteristics of **rock,** the material that forms Earth's hard surface. They map where different types of rock are found on and beneath the surface. Geologists describe landforms, the features formed in rock and soil by water, wind, and waves. **Geologists study the processes that create Earth's features and search for clues about Earth's history.**

The modern science of **geology,** the study of planet Earth, began in the late 1700s. Geologists of that time studied the rocks on the surface. These geologists concluded that Earth's landforms are the work of natural forces that slowly build up and wear down the land.

Studying Surface Changes Forces beneath the surface are constantly changing Earth's appearance. Throughout our planet's long history, its surface has been lifted up, pushed down, bent, and broken. Thus Earth looks different today from the way it did millions of years ago.

Today, geologists divide the forces that change the surface into two groups: constructive forces and destructive forces. **Constructive forces** shape the surface by building up mountains and landmasses. **Destructive forces** are those that slowly wear away mountains and, eventually, every other feature on the surface. The formation of the island of Surtsey is an example of constructive forces at work. The ocean waves that wear away Surtsey's shoreline are an example of destructive forces.

Two hundred years ago, the science of geology was young. Then, geologists knew only a few facts about Earth's surface. They knew that Earth is a sphere with a radius at the equator of more than 6,000 kilometers. They knew that there are seven great landmasses, called **continents,** surrounded by oceans. They knew that the continents are made up of layers of rock.

These layers can sometimes be seen on the walls of canyons and the sides of valleys. However, many riddles remained: How old is Earth? How has Earth's surface changed over time? Why are there oceans, and how did they form? For 200 years, geologists have tried to answer these and other questions about the planet.

Figure 3 This cave in Georgia may seem deep. But even a deep cave is only a small nick in Earth's surface.

Finding Indirect Evidence One of the most difficult questions that geologists have tried to answer is, What's inside Earth? Much as geologists might like to, they cannot dig a hole to the center of Earth. The extreme conditions in Earth's interior prevent exploration far below the surface. The deepest mine in the world, a gold mine in South Africa, reaches a depth of 3.8 kilometers. But it only scratches the surface. You would have to travel more than 1,600 times that distance—over 6,000 kilometers—to reach Earth's center.

Geologists cannot observe Earth's interior directly. Instead, they must rely on indirect methods of observation. Have you ever hung a heavy picture on a wall? If you have, you know that you can knock on the wall to locate the wooden beam underneath the plaster that will support the picture. When you knock on the wall, you listen carefully for a change in the sound.

When geologists want to study Earth's interior, they also use an indirect method. But instead of knocking on walls, they use seismic waves. When earthquakes occur, they produce **seismic waves** (SYZ mik). Geologists record the seismic waves and study how they travel through Earth. The speed of these seismic waves and the paths they take reveal how the planet is put together. Using data from seismic waves, geologists have learned that Earth's interior is made up of several layers. Each layer surrounds the layers beneath it, much like the layers of an onion.

☑ *Checkpoint* ***What kind of indirect evidence do geologists use to study the structure of Earth?***

A Journey to the Center of the Earth

If you really could travel through these layers to the center of Earth, what would your trip be like? To begin, you will need a vehicle that can travel through solid rock. The vehicle will carry scientific instruments to record changes in temperature and pressure as you descend.

Temperature As you start to tunnel beneath the surface, you might expect the rock around you to be cool. At first, the surrounding rock is cool. Then at about 20 meters down your instruments report that the surrounding rock is getting warmer. For every 40 meters that you descend from that point, the temperature rises 1 Celsius degree. This rapid rise in temperature continues for several kilometers. After that, the temperature increases more slowly, but steadily.

Pressure During your journey to the center of Earth, your instruments also record an increase in pressure in the surrounding rock. The deeper you go, the greater the pressure. **Pressure** is the force pushing on a surface or area. Because of the weight of the rock above, pressure inside Earth increases as you go deeper.

As you go toward the center of Earth, you travel through several different layers. **Three main layers make up Earth's interior: the crust, the mantle, and the core. Each layer has its own conditions and materials.** You can see these layers in *Exploring Earth's Interior* on pages 12–13.

Language Arts CONNECTION

Imagine taking a trip to the center of Earth. That's what happens in a novel written by Jules Verne in 1864. At that time, scientists knew almost nothing about Earth's interior. Was it solid or hollow? Hot or cold? People speculated wildly. Verne's novel, called *Journey to the Center of the Earth*, describes the adventures of a scientific expedition to explore a hollow Earth. On the way, the explorers follow caves and tunnels down to a strange sea lit by a miniature sun.

In Your Journal

Write a paragraph that describes the most exciting part of your own imaginary journey to Earth's center.

Pressure Increases
Depth
0
.5m
1m
1.5m
2m

Figure 4 The deeper this swimmer goes, the greater the pressure from the surrounding water. ***Comparing and Contrasting*** *How is the water in the swimming pool similar to Earth's interior? How is it different?*

A
B

Figure 5 Two of the most common rocks in the crust are basalt and granite. **A.** The dark rock is basalt, which makes up much of the oceanic crust. **B.** The light rock is granite, which makes up much of the continental crust.

The Crust

Your journey to the center of Earth begins in the crust. The **crust** is a layer of rock that forms Earth's outer skin. On the crust you find rocks and mountains. But the crust also includes the soil and water that cover large parts of Earth's surface.

This outer rind of rock is much thinner than what lies beneath it. In fact, you can think of Earth's crust as being similar to the paper-thin skin of an onion. The crust includes both the dry land and the ocean floor. It is thinnest beneath the ocean and thickest under high mountains. The crust ranges from 5 to 40 kilometers thick.

The crust beneath the ocean is called oceanic crust. Oceanic crust consists mostly of dense rocks such as basalt. **Basalt** (buh SAWLT) is dark, dense rock with a fine texture. Continental crust, the crust that forms the continents, consists mainly of less dense rocks such as granite. **Granite** is a rock that has larger crystals than basalt and is not as dense. It usually is a light color.

The Mantle

Your journey downward continues. At a depth of between 5 and 40 kilometers beneath the surface, you cross a boundary. Above this boundary are the basalt and granite rocks of the crust. Below the boundary is the solid material of the **mantle,** a layer of hot rock.

The crust and the uppermost part of the mantle are very similar. The uppermost part of the mantle and the crust together form a rigid layer called the **lithosphere** (LITH uh sfeer). In Greek, *lithos* means "stone." The lithosphere averages about 100 kilometers thick.

Figure 6 At the surface, Earth's crust forms peaks like these in the Rocky Mountains of Colorado. Soil and plants cover much of the crust.

Next you travel farther into the mantle below the lithosphere. There your vehicle encounters material that is hotter and under increasing pressure. In general, temperature and pressure in the mantle increase with depth. The heat and pressure make the part of the mantle just beneath the lithosphere less rigid than the rock above. Like road tar softened by the heat of the sun, the material that forms this part of the mantle is somewhat soft—it can bend like plastic.

This soft layer is called the **asthenosphere** (as THEHN uh sfeer). In Greek, *asthenes* means "weak." Just because asthenes means weak, you can't assume this layer is actually weak. But the asthenosphere is soft. The material in this layer can flow slowly.

The lithosphere floats on top of the asthenosphere. Beneath the asthenosphere, solid mantle material extends all the way to Earth's core. The mantle is nearly 3,000 kilometers thick.

☑ *Checkpoint* ***How does the material of the asthenosphere differ from the material of the lithosphere?***

The Core

After traveling through the mantle, you reach the core. Earth's core consists of two parts—a liquid outer core and a solid inner core. The metals iron and nickel make up both parts of the core. The **outer core** is a layer of molten metal that surrounds the inner core. In spite of enormous pressure, the outer core behaves like a thick liquid. The **inner core** is a dense ball of solid metal. In the inner core, extreme pressure squeezes the atoms of iron and nickel so much that they cannot spread out and become liquid.

The outer and inner cores make up about one third of Earth's mass, but only 15 percent of its volume. The inner and outer cores together are just slightly smaller than the moon.

Sharpen your Skills

Creating Data Tables

ACTIVITY

Imagine that you have invented a super-strong vehicle that can resist extremely high pressure as it bores a tunnel deep into Earth's interior. You stop several times on your trip to collect data using devices located on your vehicle's outer hull. To see what conditions you would find at various depths on your journey, refer to *Exploring Earth's Interior* on pages 12–13. Copy the table and complete it.

Depth	Name of Layer	What Layer Is Made Of
20 km		
150 km		
2,000 km		
4,000 km		
6,000 km		

EXPLORING *Earth's Interior*

Earth's interior is divided into layers: the crust, mantle, outer core, and inner core. Although Earth's crust seems stable, the extreme heat of Earth's interior causes changes that slowly reshape the surface.

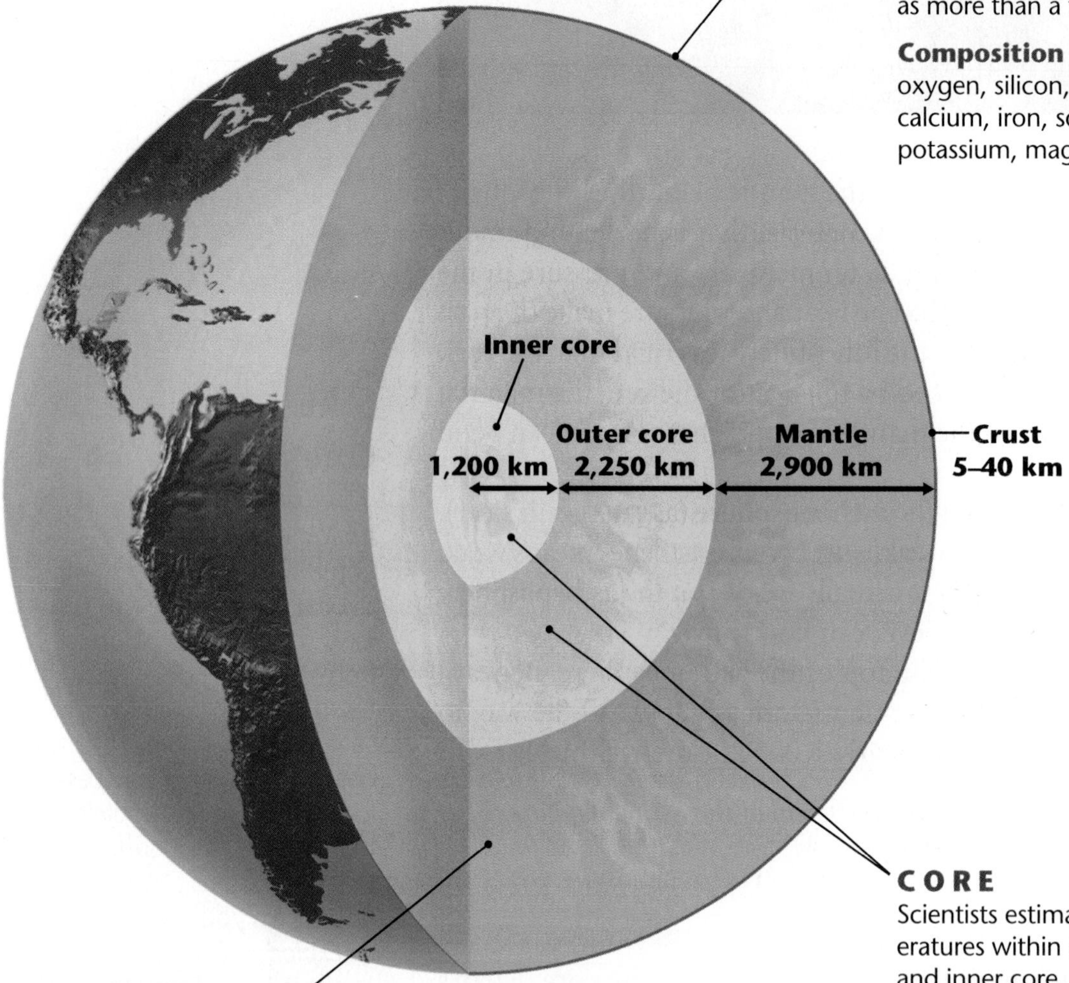
Inner core
Outer core
Mantle
Crust
1,200 km
2,250 km
2,900 km
5–40 km

CRUST
The crust is Earth's solid and rocky outer layer, including both the land surface and the ocean floor. The crust averages 32 km thick. At the scale of this drawing, the crust is too thin to show up as more than a thin line.

Composition of crust:
oxygen, silicon, aluminum, calcium, iron, sodium, potassium, magnesium

MANTLE
A trip through Earth's mantle goes almost halfway to the center of Earth. The chemical composition of the mantle does not change much from one part of the mantle to another. However, physical conditions in the mantle change because pressure and temperature increase with depth.

Composition of mantle:
silicon, oxygen, iron, magnesium

CORE
Scientists estimate that temperatures within Earth's outer core and inner core, both made of iron and nickel, range from about 2,000°C to 5,000°C. If these estimates are correct, then Earth's center may be as hot as the sun's surface.

Composition of core:
iron, nickel

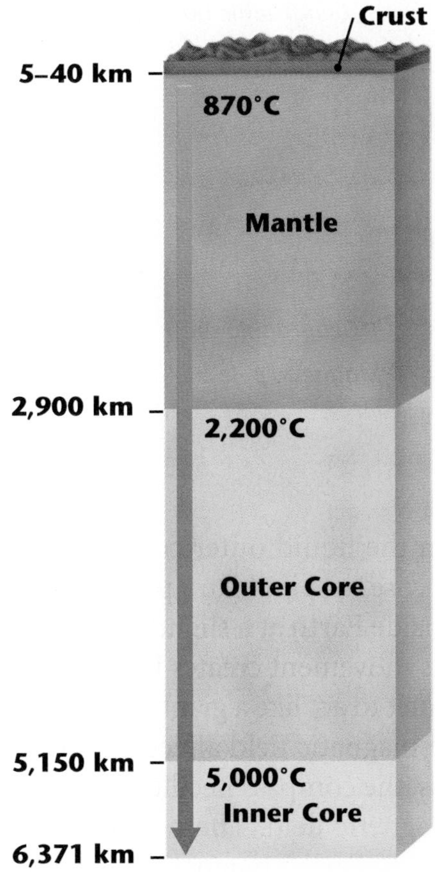
Crust
5–40 km
870°C
Mantle
2,900 km
2,200°C
Outer Core
5,150 km
5,000°C
Inner Core
6,371 km

◀ CROSS-SECTION FROM SURFACE TO CENTER

From Earth's surface to its center, the layers of Earth's interior differ in their composition, temperature, and pressure. Notice how temperature increases toward the inner core.

CRUST-TO-MANTLE

The rigid crust and lithosphere float on the hot, plastic material of the asthenosphere. Notice that continental crust, made mostly of granite, is several times thicker than oceanic crust, made mostly of basalt. ▼

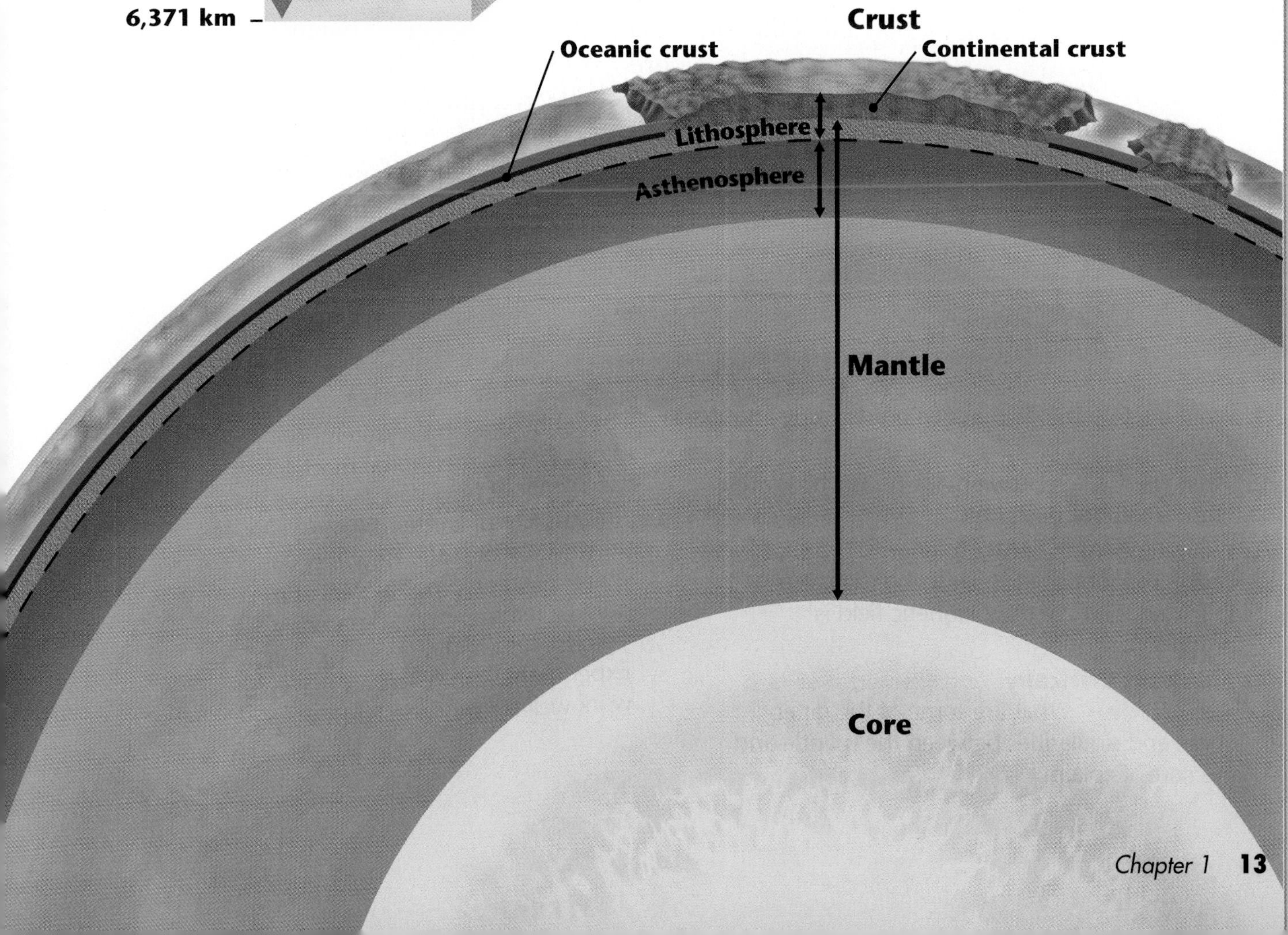
Crust
Oceanic crust
Continental crust
Lithosphere
Asthenosphere
Mantle
Core

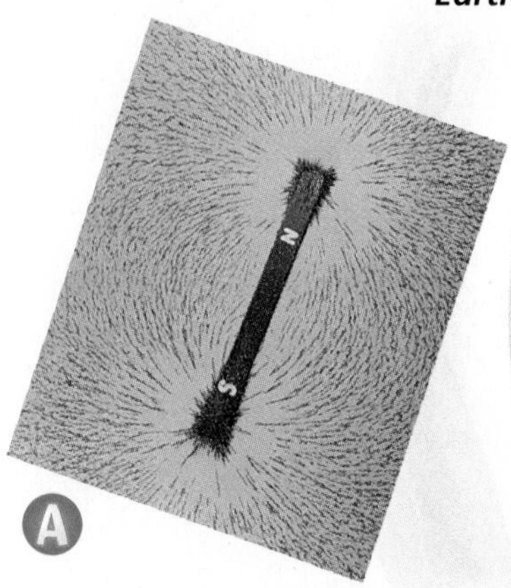

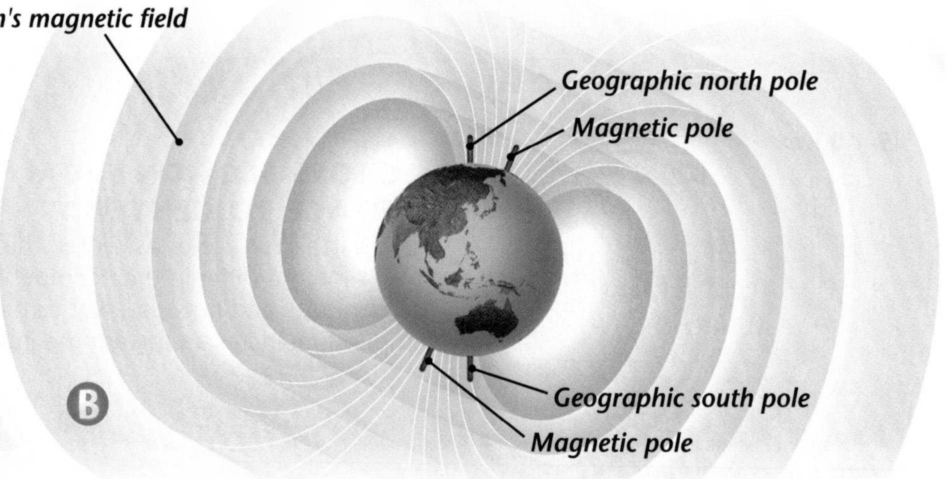
Earth's magnetic field
Geographic north pole
Magnetic pole
Geographic south pole
Magnetic pole

Figure 7 **A.** The pattern of iron filings was made by sprinkling them on paper placed over a bar magnet. **B.** Like a magnet, Earth's magnetic field has north and south poles. *Relating Cause and Effect If you shifted the magnet beneath the paper, what would happen to the iron filings?*

Earth's Magnetic Field

INTEGRATING PHYSICS Currents in the liquid outer core force the solid inner core to spin. Like a planet within a planet, the inner core spins inside Earth at a slightly faster rate than the rest of the planet. This movement creates Earth's magnetic field, which causes the planet to act like a giant bar magnet. As you can see in Figure 7, the magnetic field affects the whole Earth. When you use a compass, the compass needle aligns with the lines of force in Earth's magnetic field. The north-seeking end of the compass needle points to Earth's magnetic north pole.

Consider an ordinary bar magnet. If you place it beneath a piece of paper and sprinkle iron filings on the paper, the iron filings line up with the bar's magnetic field. If you could cover the entire planet with iron filings, they would form a similar pattern.

Section 1 Review

1. What are two things that geologists study about Earth?
2. What are the layers that make up Earth? Write a sentence about each one.
3. What happens in Earth's interior to produce Earth's magnetic field? Describe the layers of the interior where the magnetic field is produced.
4. **Thinking Critically Comparing and Contrasting** What are some of the differences and similarities between the mantle and the core? Explain.

CHAPTER PROJECT

Check Your Progress

Begin by drawing a sketch of your three-dimensional model. Think about how you will show the thicknesses of Earth's different layers at the correct scale. How can you show Earth's interior as well as its surface features? What materials can you use for building your model? Experiment with materials that might work well for showing Earth's layers.

SECTION 2

Convection Currents and the Mantle

DISCOVER

ACTIVITY

How Can Heat Cause Motion in a Liquid?

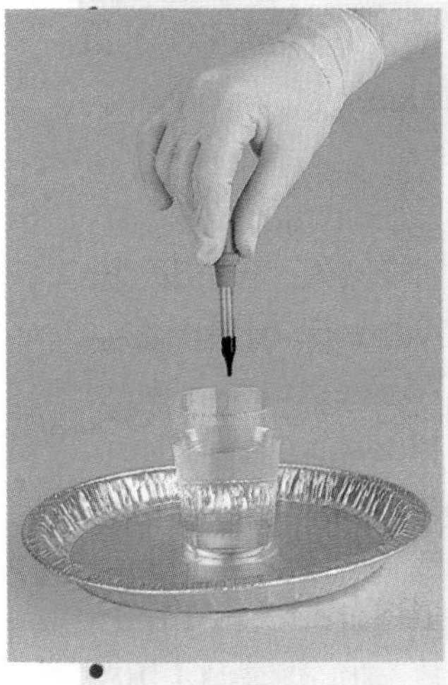

1. Carefully pour some hot water into a small, shallow pan. Fill a clear, plastic cup about half full with cold water. Place the cup in the pan.
2. Allow the water to stand for two minutes until all motion stops.
3. Fill a plastic dropper with some food coloring. Then, holding the dropper under the water surface and slightly away from the edge of the cup, gently squeeze a small droplet of the food coloring into the water.
4. Observe the water for one minute.
5. Add another droplet at the water surface in the middle of the cup and observe again.

Think It Over

Inferring How do you explain what happened to the droplets of food coloring? Why do you think the second droplet moved in a way that was different from the way the first droplet moved?

GUIDE FOR READING

- **How is heat transferred?**
- **What causes convection currents?**

Reading Tip **As you read, draw a concept map of the three types of heat transfer. Include supporting ideas about convection.**

Earth's molten outer core is nearly as hot as the surface of the sun. To explain how heat from the core affects the mantle, you need to know how heat is transferred in solids and liquids. If you have ever touched a hot pot accidentally, you have discovered for yourself (in a painful way) that heat moves. In this case, it moved from the hot pot to your hand. The movement of energy from a warmer object to a cooler object is called **heat transfer.**

Heat is always transferred from a warmer substance to a cooler substance. For example, holding an ice cube will make your hand begin to feel cold in a few seconds. But is the coldness in the ice cube moving to your hand? Since cold is the absence of heat, it's the heat in your hand that moves to the ice cube! **There are three types of heat transfer: radiation, conduction, and convection.**

Radiation

The transfer of energy through empty space is called **radiation.** Sunlight is radiation that warms Earth's surface. Heat transfer by radiation takes place with no direct contact between a heat source and an object. Radiation enables sunlight to warm Earth's surface. Other familiar forms of radiation include the heat you feel around a flame or open fire.

Figure 8 In conduction, the heated particles of a substance transfer heat to other particles through direct contact. That's how the spoon and the pot itself heat up.

Conduction

Heat transfer by direct contact of particles of matter is called **conduction.** What happens as a spoon heats up in a pot of soup? Heat is transferred from the hot soup and the pot to the particles that make up the spoon. The particles near the bottom of the spoon vibrate faster as they are heated, so they bump into other particles and heat them, too. Gradually the entire spoon heats up. When your hand touches the spoon, conduction transfers heat from the spoon directly to your skin. Then you feel the heat. Look at Figure 8 to see how conduction takes place.

Convection

Conduction heats the spoon, but how does the soup inside the pot heat up? Heat transfer involving the movement of fluids—liquids and gases—is called convection. **Convection** is heat transfer by the movement of a heated fluid. During convection, heated particles of fluid begin to flow, transferring heat energy from one part of the fluid to another.

Heat transfer by convection is caused by differences of temperature and density within a fluid. **Density** is a measure of how much mass there is in a volume of a substance. For example, rock is more dense than water because a given volume of rock has more mass than the same volume of water.

When a liquid or gas is heated, the particles move faster. As the particles move faster, they spread apart. Because the particles of the heated fluid are farther apart, they occupy more space. The density decreases. But when a fluid cools, its particles move more slowly and settle together more closely. As the fluid becomes cooler, its density increases.

If you look at Figure 9, you can see how convection occurs when you heat soup on a stove. As the soup at the bottom of the pot gets hot, it expands and therefore becomes less dense. The warm, less dense soup moves upward and floats over the cooler, denser soup. At the surface, the warm soup spreads out and cools, becoming denser. Then, gravity pulls this cooler, denser soup back down to the bottom of the pot, where it is heated again.

Figure 9 In this pot, the soup close to the heat source is hotter and less dense than the soup near the surface. These differences in temperature and density cause convection currents.

A constant flow begins as the cooler soup continually sinks to the bottom of the pot and the warmer soup rises. A **convection current** is the flow that transfers heat within a fluid.

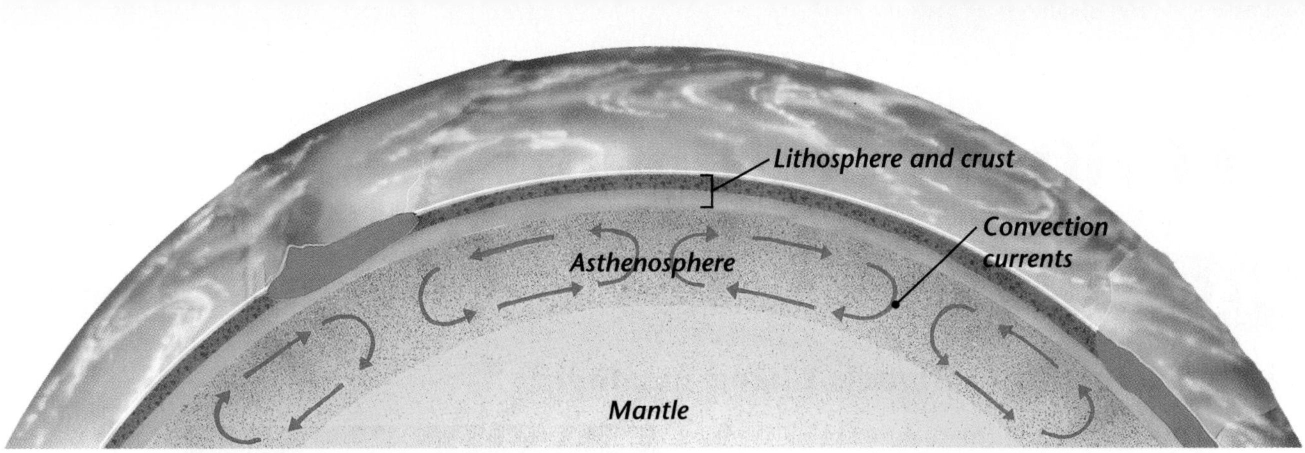
Lithosphere and crust
Convection currents
Asthenosphere
Mantle

Figure 10 Heat from Earth's mantle and core causes convection currents to form in the asthenosphere. Some geologists think convection currents extend throughout the mantle. ***Applying Concepts*** *What part of Earth's interior is like the soup in the pot? What part is like the burner on the stove?*

The heating and cooling of the fluid, changes in the fluid's density, and the force of gravity combine to set convection currents in motion. Convection currents continue as long as heat is added. What happens after the heat source is removed? Without heat, the convection currents will eventually stop when all of the material has reached the same temperature.

☑ *Checkpoint What is convection?*

Convection in Earth's Mantle

Like soup simmering in a pot, Earth's mantle responds to heat. Notice in Figure 10 how convection currents flow in the asthenosphere. The heat source for these currents is heat from Earth's core and from the mantle itself. Hot columns of mantle material rise slowly through the asthenosphere. At the top of the asthenosphere, the hot material spreads out and pushes the cooler material out of the way. This cooler material sinks back into the asthenosphere. Over and over, the cycle of rising and sinking takes place. Convection currents like these have been moving inside Earth for more than four billion years!

Section 2 Review

1. What are the three types of heat transfer?
2. Describe how convection currents form.
3. In general, what happens to the density of a fluid when it becomes hotter?
4. What happens to convection currents when a fluid reaches a constant temperature?
5. **Thinking Critically Predicting** What will happen to the flow of hot rock in Earth's mantle if the planet's core eventually cools down? Explain your answer.

Science at Home

Convection currents may keep the air inside your home at a comfortable temperature. Air is made up of gases, so it is a fluid. Regardless of the type of home heating system, heated air circulates through a room by convection. You may have tried to adjust the flow of air in a stuffy room by opening a window. When you did so, you were making use of convection currents. With an adult family member, study how your home is heated. Look for evidence of convection currents.

SECTION 3 Drifting Continents

DISCOVER ACTIVITY

How Are Earth's Continents Linked Together?

1. Find the oceans and the seven continents on a globe showing Earth's physical features.
2. How much of the globe is occupied by the Pacific Ocean? Does most of Earth's "dry" land lie in the Northern or Southern hemisphere?
3. Find the points or areas where most of the continents are connected. Find the points at which several of the continents almost touch, but are not connected.
4. Examine the globe more closely. Find the great belt of mountains running from north to south along the western side of North and South America. Can you find another great belt of mountains on the globe?

Think It Over

Posing Questions What questions can you pose about how oceans, continents, and mountains are distributed on Earth's surface?

GUIDE FOR READING

- **What is continental drift?**
- **Why was Alfred Wegener's theory rejected by most scientists of his day?**

Reading Tip **As you read, look for evidence that supports the theory of continental drift.**

Five hundred years ago, the sea voyages of Columbus and other explorers changed the map of the world. The continents of Europe, Asia, and Africa were already known to mapmakers. Soon mapmakers were also showing the outlines of the continents of North and South America. Looking at these world maps, many people wondered why the coasts of several continents matched so neatly.

Look at the modern world map in Figure 11. Notice how the coasts of Africa and South America look as if they could fit together like jigsaw-puzzle pieces. Could the continents have once been a single landmass? In the 1700s, the first geologists thought that the continents had remained fixed in their positions throughout Earth's history. Early in the 1900s, however, one scientist began to think in a new way about this riddle of the continents. His theory changed the way people look at the map of the world.

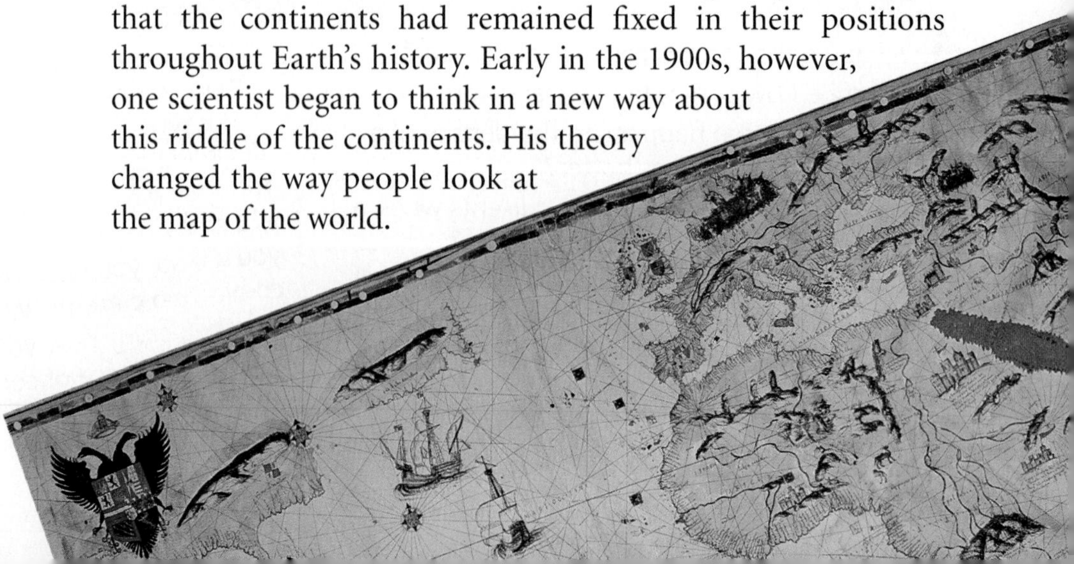

World map drawn by Juan Vespucci in 1526. ▶

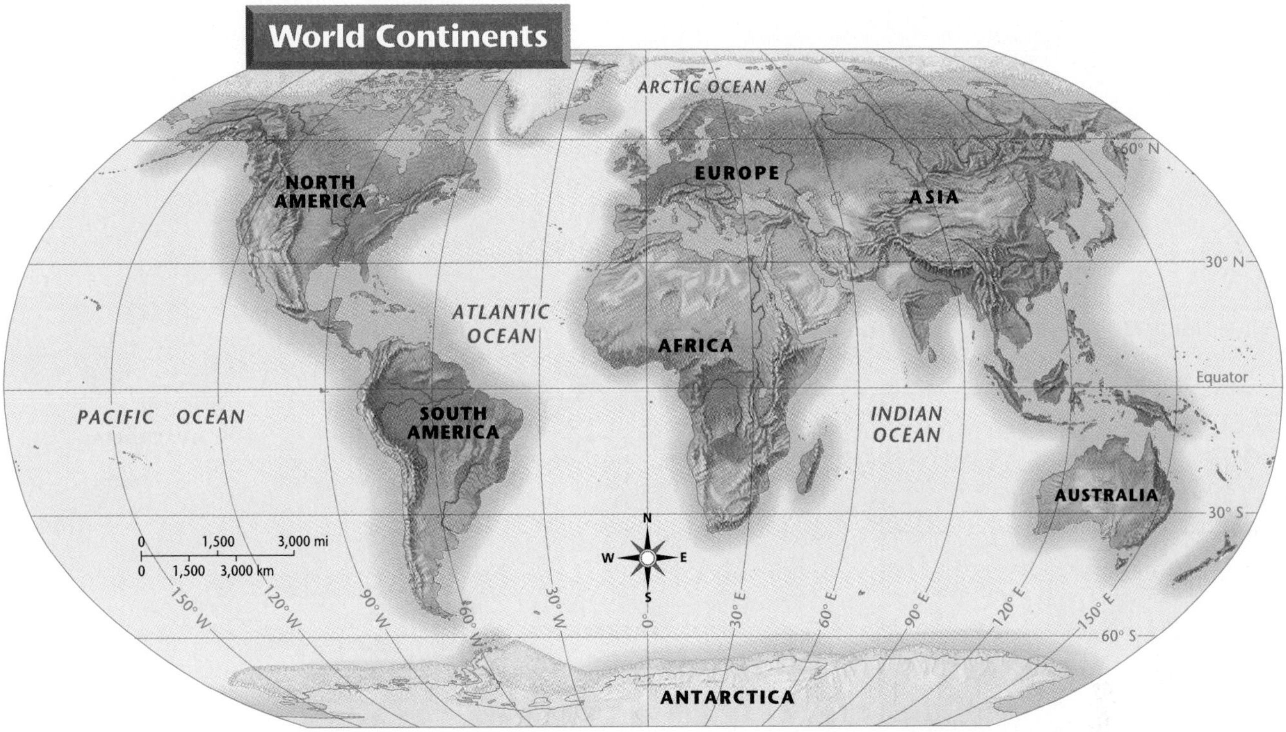
World Continents
ARCTIC OCEAN
NORTH AMERICA
EUROPE
ASIA
ATLANTIC OCEAN
AFRICA
PACIFIC OCEAN
SOUTH AMERICA
INDIAN OCEAN
AUSTRALIA
ANTARCTICA
Equator
60° N
30° N
30° S
60° S
0 1,500 3,000 mi
0 1,500 3,000 km
N
S
E
W
150° W
120° W
90° W
60° W
30° W
0°
30° E
60° E
90° E
120° E
150° E

Figure 11 Today's continents provide clues about Earth's history. *Observing Which coastlines of continents seem to match up like jigsaw-puzzle pieces?*

The Theory of Continental Drift

In 1910, a young German scientist named Alfred Wegener (VAY guh nur) became curious about the relationship of the continents. He formed a hypothesis that Earth's continents had moved! **Wegener's hypothesis was that all the continents had once been joined together in a single landmass and have since drifted apart.**

Wegener named this supercontinent **Pangaea** (pan JEE uh), meaning "all lands." According to Wegener, Pangaea existed about 300 million years ago. This was the time when reptiles and winged insects first appeared. Great tropical forests, which later formed coal deposits, covered large parts of Earth's surface.

Over tens of millions of years, Pangaea began to break apart. The pieces of Pangaea slowly moved toward their present-day locations, becoming the continents as they are today. Wegener's idea that the continents slowly moved over Earth's surface became known as **continental drift.**

Have you ever tried to persuade a friend to accept a new idea? Your friend's opinion probably won't change unless you provide some convincing evidence. Wegener gathered evidence from different scientific fields to support his ideas about continental drift. In particular, he studied landforms, fossils, and evidence that showed how Earth's climate had changed over many millions of years. Wegener published all his evidence for continental drift in a book called *The Origin of Continents and Oceans,* first published in 1915.

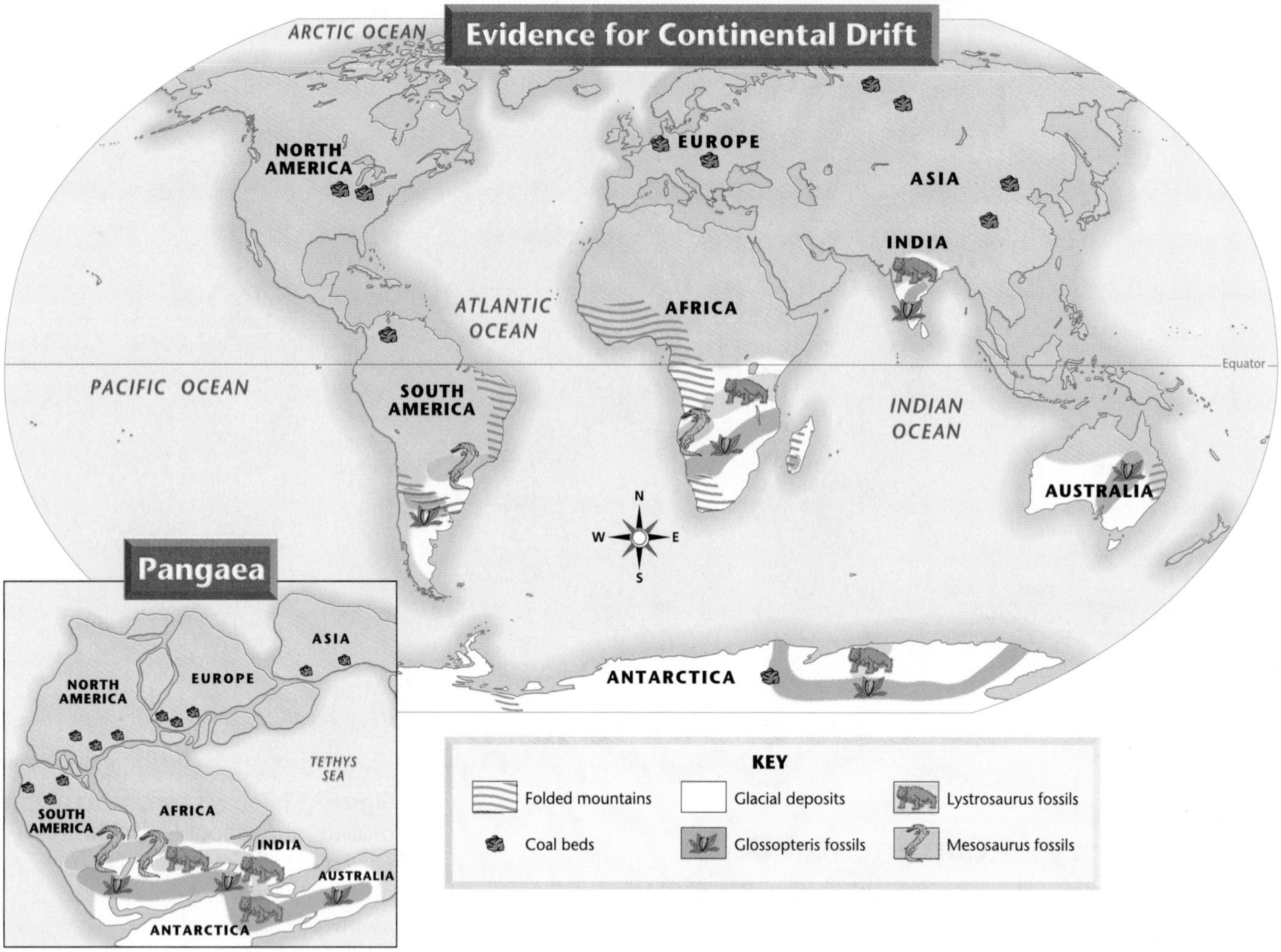
Evidence for Continental Drift
ARCTIC OCEAN
NORTH AMERICA
EUROPE
ASIA
INDIA
AFRICA
ATLANTIC OCEAN
PACIFIC OCEAN
SOUTH AMERICA
INDIAN OCEAN
Equator
AUSTRALIA
ANTARCTICA
N
S
E
W
Pangaea
ASIA
NORTH AMERICA
EUROPE
TETHYS SEA
SOUTH AMERICA
AFRICA
INDIA
AUSTRALIA
ANTARCTICA
KEY
Folded mountains
Glacial deposits
Lystrosaurus fossils
Coal beds
Glossopteris fossils
Mesosaurus fossils

Figure 12 Wegener used several types of evidence to support his idea that the continents were once joined in a single landmass called Pangaea. *Inferring According to Wegener's theory, what does the presence of similar mountain ranges in Africa and South America indicate?*

Evidence from Landforms Mountain ranges and other features on the continents provided evidence for continental drift. For example, when Wegener pieced together maps of Africa and South America, he noticed some remarkable things. A mountain range running from east to west in South Africa lines up with a mountain range in Argentina. European coal fields match up with similar coal fields in North America. Wegener compared matching these features to reassembling a torn-up newspaper. If the pieces could be put back together, the "words" would match.

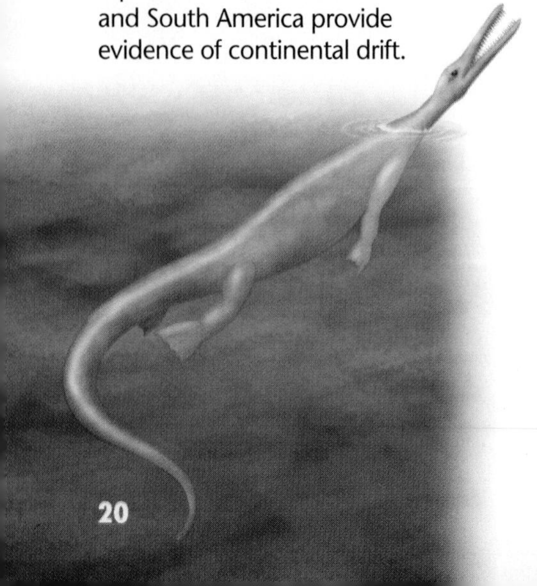

Figure 13 Fossils of the freshwater reptile *Mesosaurus* found in Africa and South America provide evidence of continental drift.

Evidence From Fossils Wegener also used fossils to support his argument for continental drift. A **fossil** is any trace of an ancient organism that has been preserved in rock. For example, fossils of the reptiles *Mesosaurus* and *Lystrosaurus* have been found in places now separated by oceans. Neither reptile could have swum great distances across salt water. It is therefore likely that these reptiles lived on a single landmass that has since split apart. Another example is *Glossopteris* (glaw SAHP tuh ris), a fernlike plant that lived 250 million years ago. *Glossopteris* fossils have been found in rocks in Africa, South America, Australia, India, and Antarctica. The occurrence of *Glossopteris* on these widely separated landmasses convinced Wegener that the continents had once been united.

Figure 14 Fossils of *Glossopteris* are found on continents in the Southern Hemisphere and in India.

INTEGRATING LIFE SCIENCE The seedlike structures of *Glossopteris* could not have traveled the great distances that separate the continents today. The "seeds" were too large to have been carried by the wind and too fragile to have survived a trip by ocean waves. How did *Glossopteris* develop on such widely separated continents? Wegener inferred that the continents at that time were joined as the supercontinent Pangaea.

Evidence From Climate Wegener used evidence of climate change to support his theory—for example, from the island of Spitsbergen. Spitsbergen lies in the Arctic Ocean north of Norway. This island is ice-covered and has a harsh polar climate. But fossils of tropical plants are found on Spitsbergen. When these plants lived about 300 million years ago, the island must have had a warm and mild climate. According to Wegener, Spitsbergen must have been located closer to the equator.

Thousands of kilometers to the south, geologists found evidence that at the same time it was warm in Spitsbergen, the climate was much colder in South Africa. Deep scratches in rocks showed that continental glaciers once covered South Africa. Continental glaciers are thick layers of ice that cover hundreds of thousands of square kilometers. But the climate of South Africa is too mild today for continental glaciers to form. Wegener concluded that, when Pangaea existed, South Africa was much closer to the South Pole.

According to Wegener, the climates of Spitsbergen and South Africa changed because the positions of these places on Earth's surface changed. As a continent moves toward the equator, its climate becomes warmer. As a continent moves toward the poles, its climate becomes colder. But the continent carries with it the fossils and rocks that formed at its previous location. These clues provide evidence that continental drift really happened.

☑ ***Checkpoint*** ***What were the three types of evidence Wegener used to support his theory of continental drift?***

TRY THIS

Reassembling the Pieces

ACTIVITY

Assembling a puzzle can reveal a hidden meaning.

1. Working with a partner, obtain one sheet of newspaper per person.
2. Tear your sheet of newspaper into six to eight large pieces. Trade your pieces with your partner.
3. Try to fit the pieces of newspaper together.

Making Models What evidence did you use to put the pieces together? How do your pieces of newspaper serve as a model of the theory of continental drift?

Figure 15 Although scientists rejected his theory, Wegener continued to collect evidence on continental drift and to update his book. He died in 1930 on an expedition to explore Greenland's continental glacier.

Scientists Reject Wegener's Theory

Wegener did more than provide a theory to answer the riddle of continental drift. He attempted to explain how drift took place. He even offered a new explanation for how mountains form. Wegener thought that when drifting continents collide, their edges crumple and fold. The folding continents slowly push up huge chunks of rock to form great mountains.

Unfortunately, Wegener could not provide a satisfactory explanation for the force that pushes or pulls the continents. Because Wegener could not identify the cause of continental drift, most geologists rejected his idea. In addition, for geologists to accept Wegener's idea, they would need new explanations of what caused continents and mountains to form.

Many geologists in the early 1900s thought that Earth was slowly cooling and shrinking. According to this theory, mountains formed when the crust wrinkled like the skin of a dried-up apple. Wegener said that if the apple theory were correct, then mountains should be found all over Earth's surface. But mountains usually occur in narrow bands along the edges of continents. Wegener thought that his own theory better explained where mountains occur and how they form.

For nearly half a century, from the 1920s to the 1960s, most scientists paid little attention to the idea of continental drift. Then new evidence about Earth's structure led scientists to reconsider Wegener's bold theory.

Section 3 Review

1. What was Wegener's theory of continental drift?
2. How did Wegener use evidence based on fossils to support his theory that the continents had moved?
3. What was the main reason scientists rejected Wegener's theory of continental drift?
4. **Thinking Critically Inferring** Coal deposits have also been found beneath the ice of Antarctica. But coal only forms in warm swamps. Use Wegener's theory to explain how coal could be found so near the poles.

Science at Home

You can demonstrate Wegener's idea of continental drift. Use the map of the world in Figure 11. On a sheet of tracing paper, trace the outlines of the continents bordering the Atlantic Ocean. Label the continents. Then use scissors to carefully cut the map along the eastern edge of South America, North America, and Greenland. Next, cut along the western edge of Africa and Europe (including the British Isles). Throw away the Atlantic Ocean. Place the two cut-out pieces on a dark surface and ask family members to try to fit the two halves together. Explain to them about the supercontinent Pangaea and its history.

SECTION 4

Sea-Floor Spreading

DISCOVER ACTIVITY

What Is the Effect of a Change in Density?

1. Partially fill a sink or dishpan with water.
2. Open up a dry washcloth in your hand. Does the washcloth feel light or heavy?
3. Moisten one edge of the washcloth in the water. Then gently place the washcloth so that it floats on the water's surface. Observe the washcloth carefully (especially at its edges) as it starts to sink.
4. Remove the washcloth from the water and open it up in your hand. Is the mass of the washcloth the same as, less than, or greater than when it was dry?

Think It Over

Observing How did the washcloth's density change? What effect did this change in density have on the washcloth?

GUIDE FOR READING

- **What is the process of sea-floor spreading?**
- **What happens to the ocean floor at deep ocean trenches?**

Reading Tip **Before you read, preview the art and captions looking for new terms. As you read, find the meanings of these terms.**

Deep in the ocean, the temperature is near freezing. There is no light, and living things are generally scarce. Yet some areas of the deep-ocean floor are teeming with life. One of these areas is the East Pacific Rise, a region of the Pacific Ocean floor off the coasts of Mexico and South America. Here, ocean water sinks through cracks, or vents, in the crust. The water is heated by contact with hot material from the mantle and then spurts back into the ocean.

Around these hot-water vents live some of the most bizarre creatures ever discovered. Giant, red-tipped tube worms sway in the water. Nearby sit giant clams nearly a meter across. Strange spiderlike crabs scuttle by. Surprisingly, the geological features of this strange environment provided scientists with some of the best evidence for Wegener's theory of continental drift.

Figure 16 **Tube worms cluster near hot water vents in the ocean floor.**

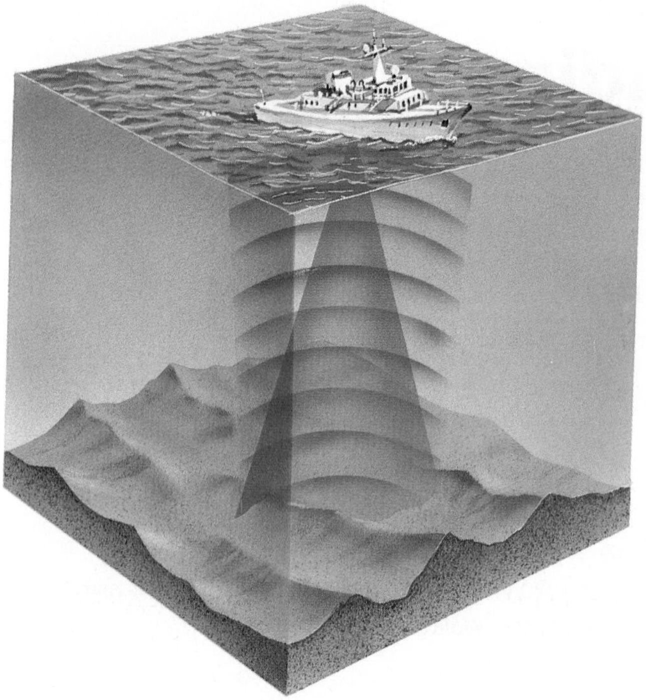

Figure 17 Scientists use sonar to map the ocean floor.

Mapping the Mid-Ocean Ridge

The East Pacific Rise is just one part of the **mid-ocean ridge,** the longest chain of mountains in the world. In the mid-1900s, scientists mapped the mid-ocean ridge using sonar. **Sonar** is a device that bounces sound waves off underwater objects and then records the echoes of these sound waves. The time it takes for the echo to arrive indicates the distance to the object.

The mid-ocean ridge curves like the seam of a baseball along the sea floor, extending into all of Earth's oceans. Most of the mountains in the mid-ocean ridge lie hidden under hundreds of meters of water. However, there are places where the ridge pokes above the surface. For example, the island of Iceland is a part of the mid-ocean ridge that rises above the surface in the North Atlantic Ocean. A steep-sided valley splits the top of the mid-ocean ridge for most of its length. The valley is almost twice as deep as the Grand Canyon. The mapping of the mid-ocean ridge made scientists curious to know what the ridge was and how it got there.

☑ *Checkpoint* *What device is used to map the ocean floor?*

Figure 18 The mid-ocean ridge is more than 50,000 kilometers long.

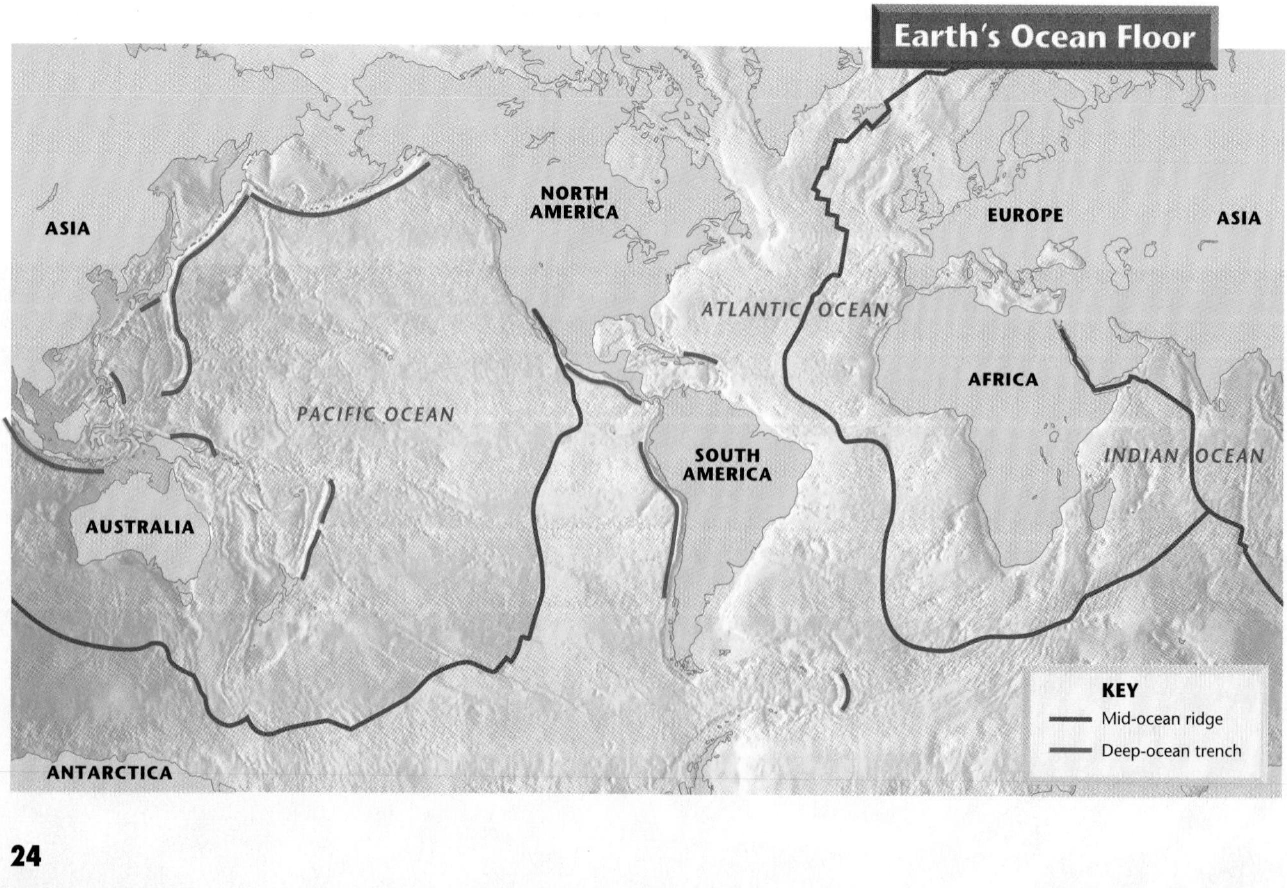
Earth's Ocean Floor
ASIA
NORTH AMERICA
EUROPE
ASIA
ATLANTIC OCEAN
AFRICA
PACIFIC OCEAN
SOUTH AMERICA
INDIAN OCEAN
AUSTRALIA
ANTARCTICA
KEY
Mid-ocean ridge
Deep-ocean trench

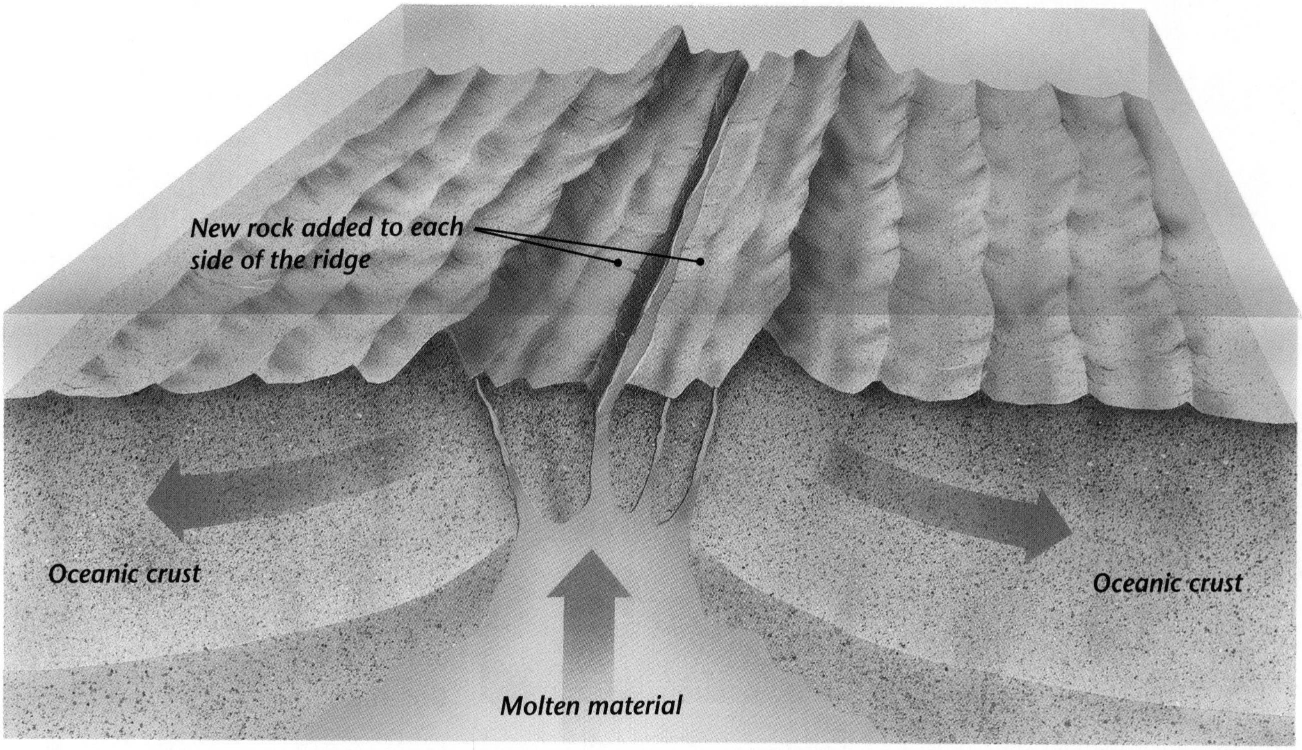
New rock added to each side of the ridge
Oceanic crust
Oceanic crust
Molten material

Figure 19 Molten material erupts though the valley that runs along the center of the mid-ocean ridge. This material hardens to form the rock of the ocean floor. **Applying Concepts** *What happens to the rock along the ridge when new molten material erupts?*

Evidence for Sea-Floor Spreading

Harry Hess, an American geologist, was one of the scientists who studied the mid-ocean ridge. Hess carefully examined maps of the mid-ocean ridge. Then he began to think about the ocean floor in relation to the problem of continental drift. Finally, he reconsidered an idea that he previously had thought impossible: Maybe Wegener was right! Perhaps the continents do move.

In 1960, Hess proposed a radical idea. He suggested that the ocean floors move like conveyor belts, carrying the continents along with them. This movement begins at the mid-ocean ridge. The mid-ocean ridge forms along a crack in the oceanic crust. **At the mid-ocean ridge, molten material rises from the mantle and erupts. The molten material then spreads out, pushing older rock to both sides of the ridge.** As the molten material cools, it forms a strip of solid rock in the center of the ridge. Then more molten material flows into the crack. This material splits apart the strip of solid rock that formed before, pushing it aside.

Hess called the process that continually adds new material to the ocean floor **sea-floor spreading.** He realized that the sea floor spreads apart along both sides of the mid-ocean ridge as new crust is added. Look at Figure 19 to see the process of sea-floor spreading.

Several types of evidence from the oceans supported Hess's theory of sea-floor spreading—evidence from molten material, magnetic stripes, and drilling samples. This evidence also led scientists to look again at Wegener's theory of continental drift.

ALVIN

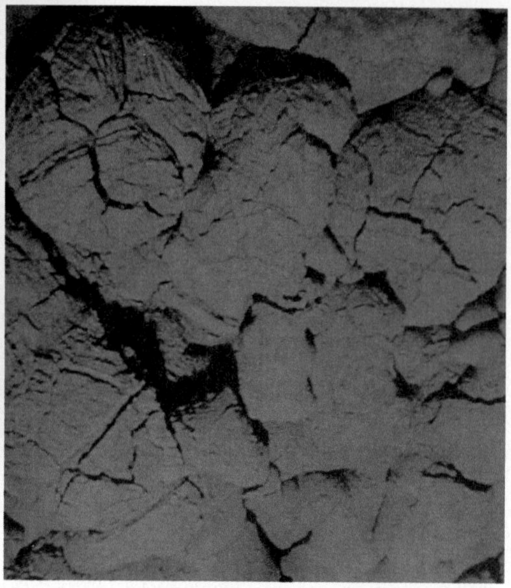

Figure 20 The submersible *Alvin* photographed pillow lava along the mid-ocean ridge. These "pillows" form under water when cold ocean water causes a crust to form on erupting molten material. Each pillow expands until it bursts, allowing molten material to flow out and form the next pillow.

Evidence From Molten Material In the 1960s, scientists found evidence that new material is indeed erupting along the mid-ocean ridge. The scientists dived to the ocean floor in *Alvin,* a small submersible built to withstand the crushing pressures four kilometers down in the ocean. In the central valley of the mid-ocean ridge, *Alvin's* crew found strange rocks shaped like pillows or like toothpaste squeezed from a tube. Such rocks can form only when molten material hardens quickly after erupting under water. The presence of these rocks showed that molten material has erupted again and again from cracks along the central valley of the mid-ocean ridge.

Evidence From Magnetic Stripes When scientists studied

INTEGRATING PHYSICS

patterns in the rocks of the ocean floor, they found more support for sea-floor spreading. In Section 1 you read that Earth behaves like a giant magnet, with a north pole and a south pole. Evidence shows that Earth's magnetic poles have reversed themselves. This last happened 780,000 years ago. If the magnetic poles suddenly reversed themselves today, you would find that your compass needle pointed south. Scientists discovered that the rock that makes up the ocean floor lies in a pattern of magnetized "stripes." These stripes hold a record of reversals in Earth's magnetic field.

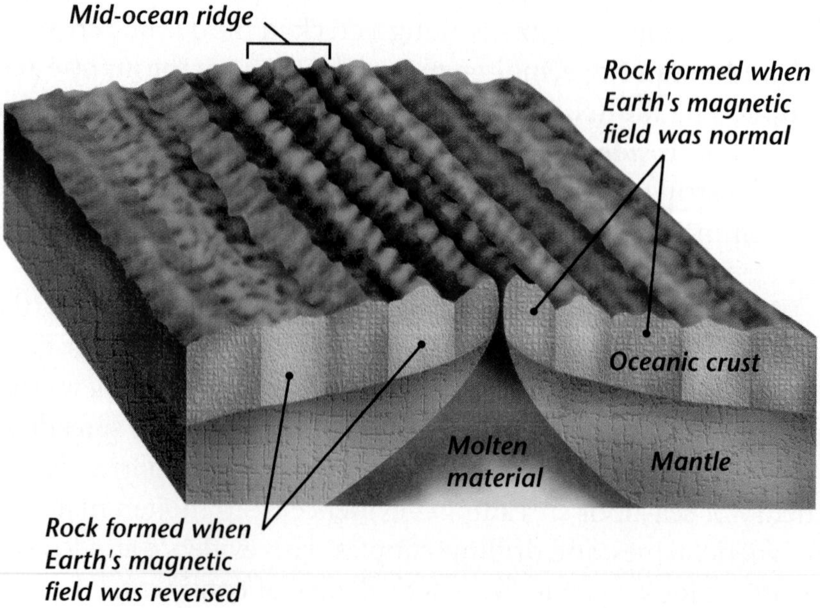
Mid-ocean ridge
Rock formed when Earth's magnetic field was normal
Oceanic crust
Molten material
Mantle
Rock formed when Earth's magnetic field was reversed

Figure 21 Magnetic stripes in the rock of the ocean floor show the direction of Earth's magnetic field at the time the rock hardened. *Interpreting Diagrams How are these matching stripes evidence of sea-floor spreading?*

The rock of the ocean floor, which contains iron, began as molten material. As the molten material cooled, the iron bits inside lined up in the direction of Earth's magnetic poles. When the rock hardened completely, it locked the iron bits in place, giving the rocks a permanent "magnetic memory." You can think of it as setting thousands of tiny compass needles in cement.

Using sensitive instruments, scientists recorded the magnetic memory of rocks on both sides of the mid-ocean ridge. They found that a stripe of rock that shows when Earth's magnetic field pointed north is followed by a parallel stripe of rock that shows when the magnetic field pointed south. As you can see in Figure 21, the pattern is the same on both sides of the ridge. Rock that hardens at the same time has the same magnetic memory.

Evidence From Drilling Samples The final proof of sea-floor spreading came from rock samples obtained by drilling into the ocean floor. The *Glomar Challenger*, a drilling ship built in 1968, gathered the samples. The *Glomar Challenger* sent drilling pipes through water six kilometers deep to drill holes in the ocean floor. This feat has been compared to using a sharp-ended wire to dig a hole into a sidewalk from the top of the Empire State Building.

Samples from the sea floor were brought up through the pipes. Then the scientists determined the age of the rocks in the samples. They found that the farther away from the ridge the samples were taken, the older the rocks were. The youngest rocks were always in the center of the ridges. This showed that sea-floor spreading really has taken place.

☑ *Checkpoint* ***What evidence did scientists find for sea-floor spreading?***

TRY THIS

Reversing Poles

ACTIVITY

1. Cut six short pieces, each about 2.5 cm long, from a length of audiotape.
2. Tape one end of each piece of audiotape to a flat surface. The pieces should be spaced 1 cm apart and line up lengthwise in a single line.
3. Touch a bar magnet's north pole to the first piece of audiotape. Then reverse the magnet and touch its south pole to the next piece.
4. Repeat Step 3 until you have applied the magnet to each piece of audiotape.
5. Sweep one end of the magnet about 1 cm above the line of audiotape pieces. Observe what happens.

Making Models What characteristic of the ocean floor did you observe as you swept the magnet along the line of audiotape pieces?

Figure 22 The *Glomar Challenger* was the first research ship designed to drill samples of rock from the deep-ocean floor.

Subduction at Deep-Ocean Trenches

How can the ocean floor keep getting wider and wider? The answer is that the ocean floor generally does not just keep spreading. Instead, the ocean floor plunges into deep underwater canyons called **deep-ocean trenches.** A deep-ocean trench forms where the oceanic crust bends downward.

Where there are deep-ocean trenches, subduction takes place. **Subduction** (sub DUK shun) is the process by which the ocean floor sinks beneath a deep-ocean trench and back into the mantle. Convection currents under the lithosphere push new crust that forms at the mid-ocean ridge away from the ridge and toward a deep-ocean trench.

New oceanic crust is hot. But as it moves away from the mid-ocean ridge, it cools and becomes more dense. Eventually, as shown in Figure 23, gravity pulls this older, denser oceanic crust down beneath the trench. The sinking crust is like the washcloth in the Discover activity at the beginning of this section. As the dry washcloth floating on the water gets wet, its density increases and it begins to sink.

At deep-ocean trenches, subduction allows part of the ocean floor to sink back into the mantle, over tens of millions of years. You can think of sea-floor spreading and subduction together as if the ocean floor were moving out from the mid-ocean ridge on a giant conveyor belt.

Figure 23 Oceanic crust created along the mid-ocean ridge is destroyed at a deep-ocean trench. In the process of subduction, oceanic crust sinks down beneath the trench into the mantle. *Drawing Conclusions Where would denser oceanic crust be found?*

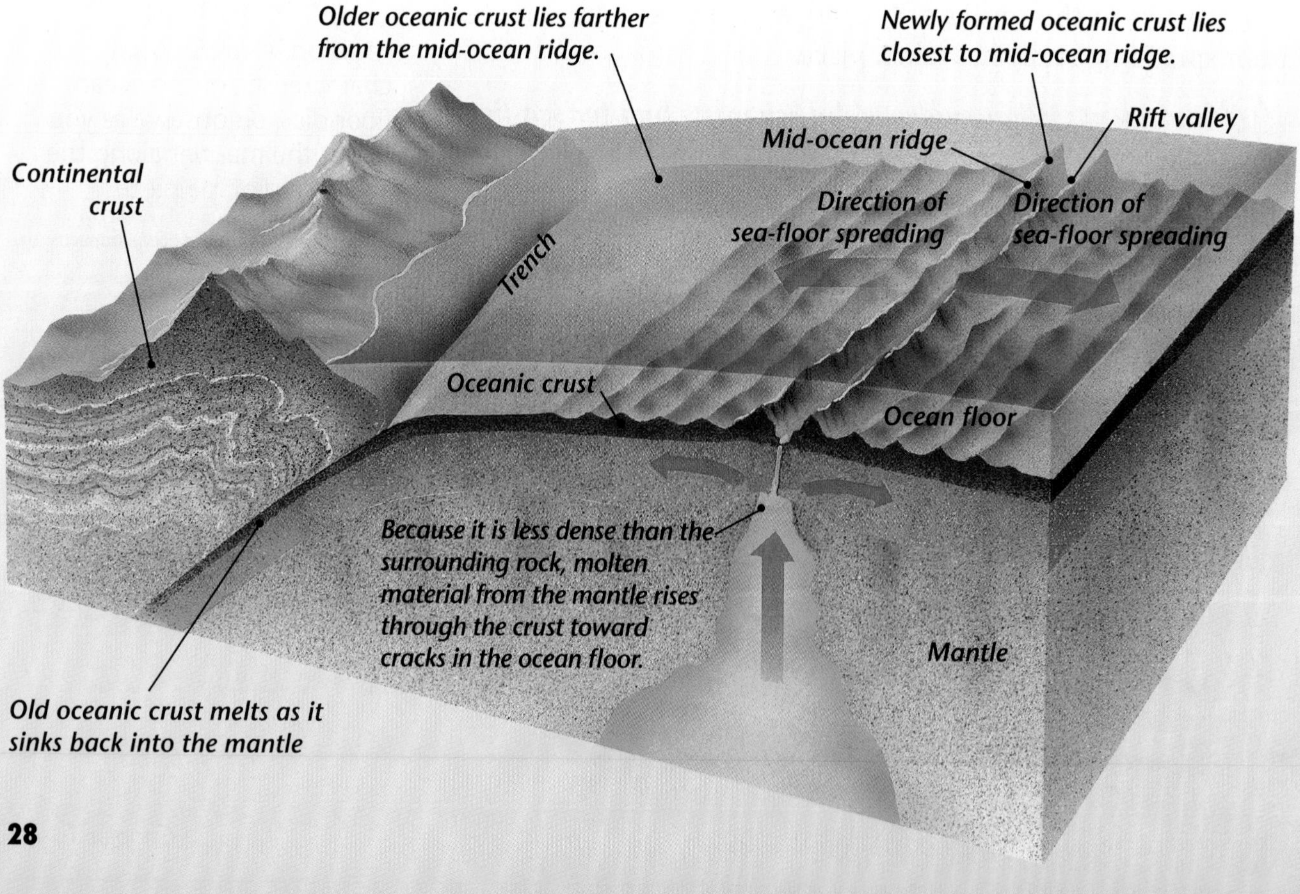
Older oceanic crust lies farther from the mid-ocean ridge.
Newly formed oceanic crust lies closest to mid-ocean ridge.
Rift valley
Mid-ocean ridge
Continental crust
Direction of sea-floor spreading
Direction of sea-floor spreading
Trench
Oceanic crust
Ocean floor
Because it is less dense than the surrounding rock, molten material from the mantle rises through the crust toward cracks in the ocean floor.
Mantle
Old oceanic crust melts as it sinks back into the mantle

Subduction and Earth's Oceans

The processes of subduction and sea-floor spreading can change the size and shape of the oceans. Because of these processes, the ocean floor is renewed about every 200 million years. That is the time it takes for new rock to form at the mid-ocean ridge, move across the ocean, and sink into a trench.

Figure 24 It is cold and dark in the deep ocean trenches where subduction occurs. But even here, scientists have found living things, such as this angler fish.

Subduction in the Pacific Ocean The vast Pacific Ocean covers almost one third of the planet. And yet it is shrinking. How could that be? Sometimes a deep ocean trench swallows more oceanic crust than the mid-ocean ridge can produce. Then, if the ridge does not add new crust fast enough, the width of the ocean will shrink. This is happening to the Pacific Ocean, which is ringed by many trenches.

Subduction in the Atlantic Ocean The Atlantic Ocean, on the other hand, is expanding. Unlike the Pacific Ocean, the Atlantic Ocean has only a few short trenches. As a result, the spreading ocean floor has virtually nowhere to go. In most places, the oceanic crust of the Atlantic Ocean floor is attached to the continental crust of the continents around the ocean. So as the Atlantic's ocean floor spreads, the continents along its edges also move. Over time, the whole ocean gets wider. The spreading floor of the North Atlantic Ocean and the continent of North America move together like two giant barges pushed by the same tugboat.

Section 4 Review

1. What is the role of the mid-ocean ridge in sea-floor spreading?
2. What is the evidence for sea-floor spreading?
3. Describe the process of subduction at a deep-ocean trench.
4. **Thinking Critically Relating Cause and Effect** Where would you expect to find the oldest rock on the ocean floor? Explain your answer.
5. **Thinking Critically Predicting** As you can see in Figure 18, the mid-ocean ridge extends into the Red Sea between Africa and Asia. What do you think will happen to the Red Sea in the future? Explain your answer.

CHAPTER PROJECT

Check Your Progress

Now that you have learned about sea-floor spreading, draw a revised sketch of your model. Include examples of sea-floor spreading and subduction on your sketch. Show the features that form as a result of these processes. How will you show what happens beneath the crust? Improve your original ideas and add new ideas. Revise your list of materials if necessary. Begin building your model.

Making Models

Modeling Sea-Floor Spreading

Along the entire length of Earth's mid-ocean ridge, the sea floor is spreading. Although this process takes place constantly, it is difficult to observe directly. You can build a model to help understand this process.

Problem

How does sea-floor spreading add material to the ocean floor?

Materials

scissors
metric ruler
2 sheets of unlined paper
colored marker

Procedure

1. Draw stripes across one sheet of paper, parallel to the short sides of the paper. The stripes should vary in spacing and thickness.
2. Fold the paper in half lengthwise and write the word "Start" at the top of both halves of the paper. Using the scissors, carefully cut the paper in half along the fold line to form two strips.
3. Lightly fold the second sheet of paper into eighths. Then unfold it, leaving creases in the paper. Fold this sheet in half lengthwise.

START
START

4. Starting at the fold, draw lines 5.5 cm long on the middle crease and the two creases closest to the ends of the paper.

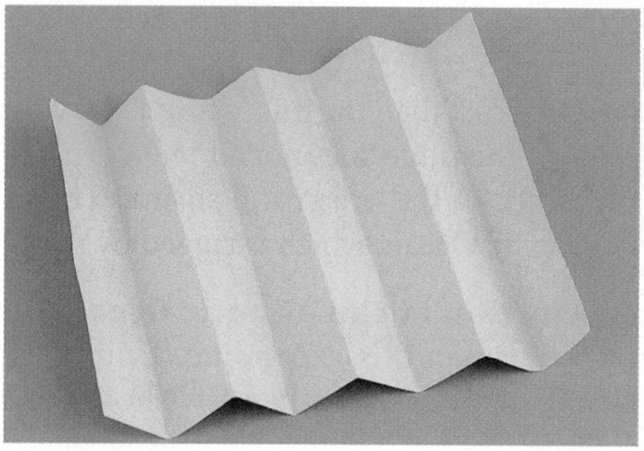

5. Now carefully cut along the lines you drew. Unfold the paper. There should be three slits in the center of the paper.

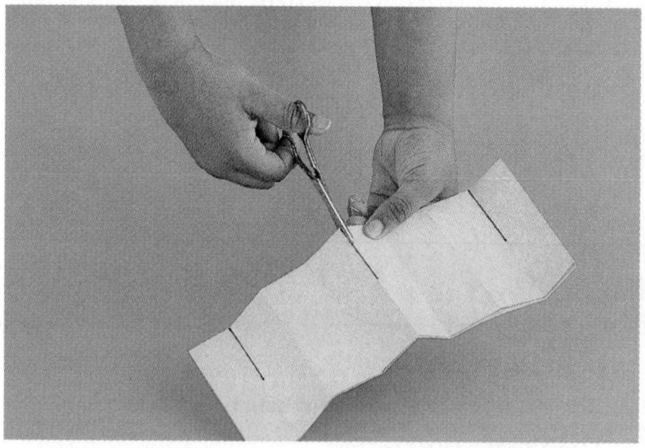

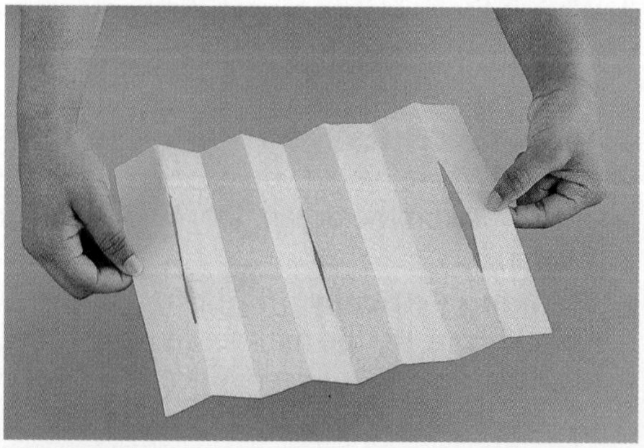

START
START

6. Put the two striped strips of paper together so their Start labels touch one another. Insert the Start ends of the strips up through the center slit and then pull them toward the side slits.
7. Insert the ends of the strips into the side slits. Pull the ends of the strips and watch what happens at the center slit.
8. Practice pulling the strips through the slits until you can make the two strips come up and go down at the same time.

Analyze and Conclude

1. What feature of the ocean floor does the center slit stand for? What prominent feature of the ocean floor is missing from the model at this point?
2. What do the side slits stand for? What does the space under the paper stand for?
3. How does the ocean floor as shown by the part of a strip close to the center slit differ from the ocean floor as shown by the part near a side slit? How does this difference affect the depth of the ocean?
4. What do the stripes on the strips stand for? Why is it important that your model have an identical pattern of stripes on both sides of the center slit?
5. Explain how differences in density and temperature provide some of the force needed to cause sea-floor spreading and subduction.
6. **Think About It** Use your own words to describe the process of ocean-floor spreading. What parts of the process were not shown by your model?

More to Explore

Imagine that so much molten rock erupted from the mid-ocean ridge that an island formed there. How could you modify your model to show this island? How could you show what would happen to it over a long period of time?

SECTION 5

The Theory of Plate Tectonics

DISCOVER — ACTIVITY

How Well Do the Continents Fit Together?

1. Using a world map in an atlas, trace the shapes of the continents North America, South America, Africa, and Europe, including Great Britain and Ireland.
2. Carefully cut apart the landmasses. When you cut out Europe, leave Britain and Ireland attached to Europe.
3. Piece together these landmasses as they may have looked before Pangaea split apart, creating the Atlantic Ocean.
4. Attach your partial reconstruction of Pangea to a piece of paper.

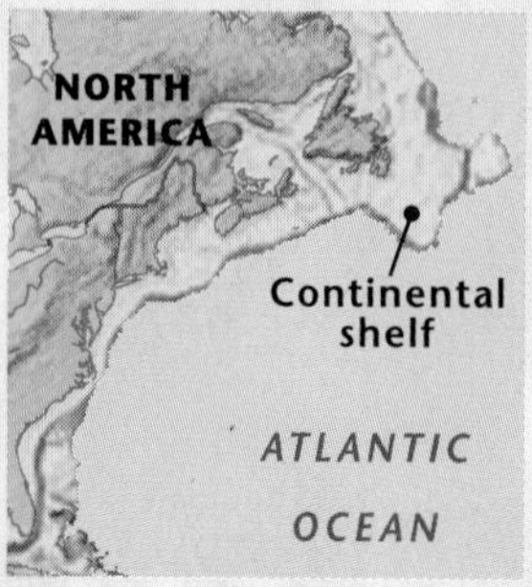
NORTH AMERICA
Continental shelf
ATLANTIC OCEAN

5. Obtain a map that shows the continental shelf. The continental shelf is the apron of continental crust that extends under water around the edges of the continents. Trace around the continental shelves of the same continents used in Step 1.
6. Repeat steps 2 through 4.

Think It Over

Drawing Conclusions Do your observations support the idea that the continents were once joined together? When did they fit together better: when you cut them out along their coastlines or along their continental shelves? Explain.

GUIDE FOR READING

- **What is the theory of plate tectonics?**
- **What are the three types of plate boundaries?**

Reading Tip **Before you read, preview *Exploring Plate Tectonics* on pages 36–37. Write a list of any questions you have about plate tectonics. Look for answers as you read.**

Have you ever dropped a hard-boiled egg? If so, you may have noticed that the eggshell cracked in an irregular pattern of broken pieces. Earth's lithosphere, its solid outer shell, is not one unbroken layer. It is more like that cracked eggshell. It's broken into pieces separated by jagged cracks.

A Canadian scientist, J. Tuzo Wilson, observed that there are cracks in the continents similar to those on the ocean floor. In 1965, Wilson proposed a new way of looking at these cracks. According to Wilson, the lithosphere is broken into separate sections called **plates.** The plates fit closely together along cracks in the lithosphere. As shown in Figure 26, the plates carry the continents or parts of the ocean floor, or both.

Figure 25 The Great Rift Valley in east Africa is a crack in Earth's crust where two pieces of crust are pulling apart.

A Theory of Plate Motion

Wilson combined what geologists knew about sea-floor spreading, Earth's plates, and continental drift into a single theory—the theory of plate tectonics (tek TAHN iks). A **scientific theory** is a well-tested concept that explains a wide range of observations. **Plate tectonics** is the geological theory that states that pieces of Earth's lithosphere are in constant, slow motion, driven by convection currents in the mantle. **The theory of plate tectonics explains the formation, movement, and subduction of Earth's plates.**

How can Earth's plates move? The plates of the lithosphere float on top of the asthenosphere. Convection currents rise in the asthenosphere and spread out beneath the lithosphere. Most geologists think that the flow of these currents causes the movement of Earth's plates.

No plate can budge without affecting the other plates surrounding it. As the plates move, they collide, pull apart, or grind past each other, producing spectacular changes in Earth's surface. These changes include volcanoes, mountain ranges, and deep-sea trenches.

Sharpen your Skills

Predicting

ACTIVITY

Study the map of Earth's plates in Figure 26. Notice the arrows that show the direction of plate movement. Now find the Nazca plate on the map. Which direction is it moving? Find the South American plate and describe its movement. What do you think will happen as these plates continue to move?

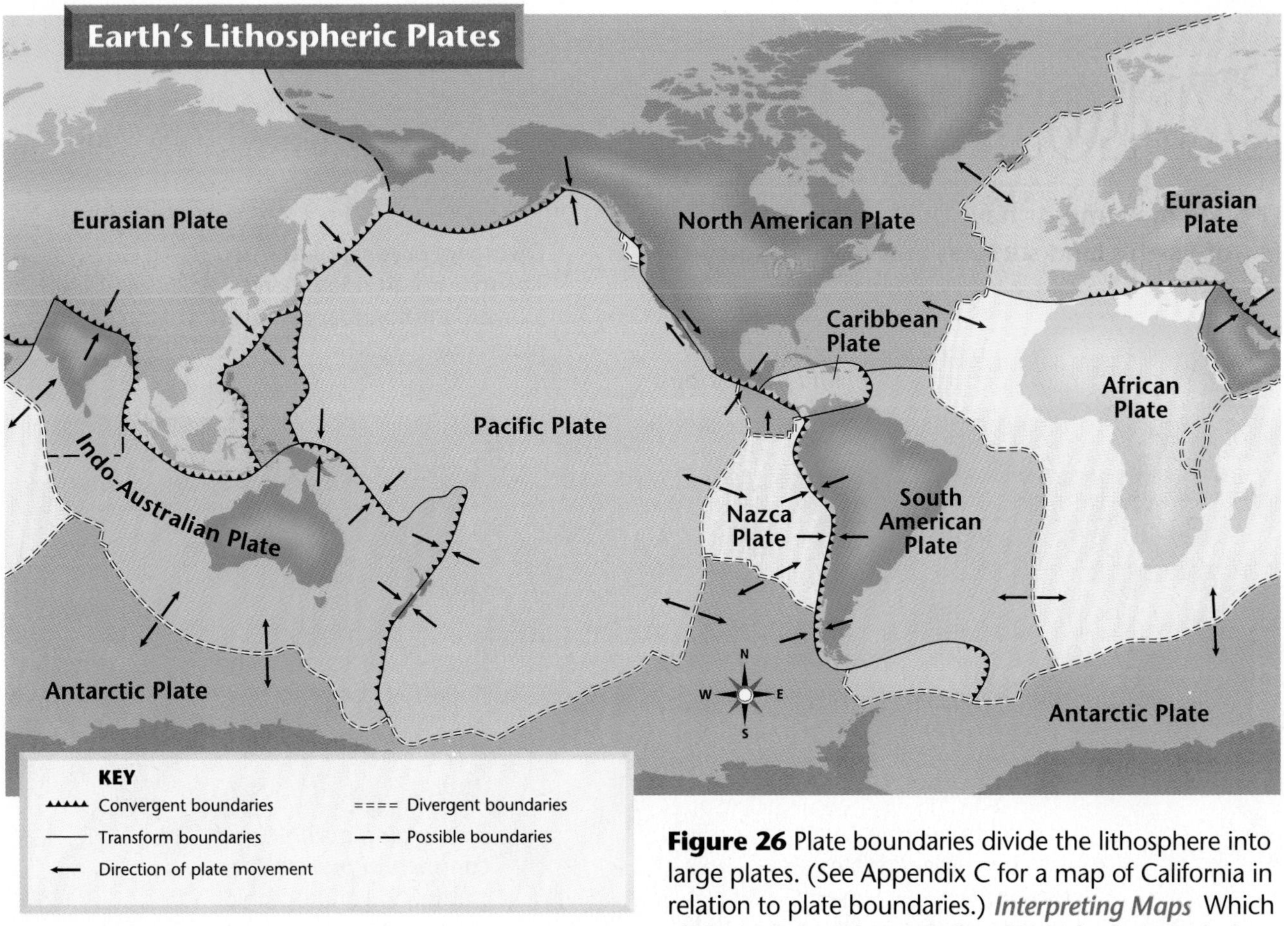
Earth's Lithospheric Plates
Eurasian Plate
North American Plate
Eurasian Plate
Caribbean Plate
African Plate
Pacific Plate
Indo-Australian Plate
Nazca Plate
South American Plate
Antarctic Plate
Antarctic Plate
N
S
W
E
KEY
Convergent boundaries
Transform boundaries
Direction of plate movement
Divergent boundaries
Possible boundaries

Figure 26 Plate boundaries divide the lithosphere into large plates. (See Appendix C for a map of California in relation to plate boundaries.) *Interpreting Maps* Which plates include only ocean floor? Which plates include both continents and ocean floor?

Plate Boundaries

The edges of different pieces of the lithosphere—Earth's rigid shell—meet at lines called plate boundaries. Plate boundaries extend deep into the lithosphere. **Faults**—breaks in Earth's crust where rocks have slipped past each other—form along these boundaries. There are three kinds of plate boundaries: transform boundaries, divergent boundaries, and convergent boundaries. For each type of boundary, there is a different type of plate movement.

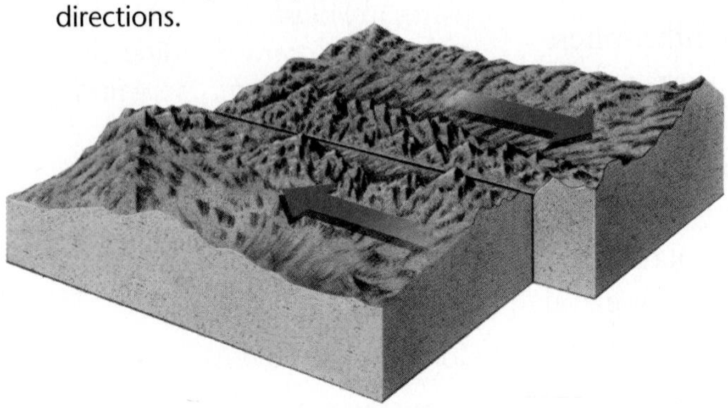

Figure 27 At a transform boundary, two plates move along the boundary in opposite directions.

Transform Boundaries Along transform boundaries, crust is neither created nor destroyed. A **transform boundary** is a place where two plates slip past each other, moving in opposite directions. Earthquakes occur frequently along these boundaries. Look at Figure 27 to see the type of plate movement that occurs along a transform boundary.

EXPLORING *Plate Tectonics*

Plate movements have built many of the features of Earth's land surfaces and ocean floors.

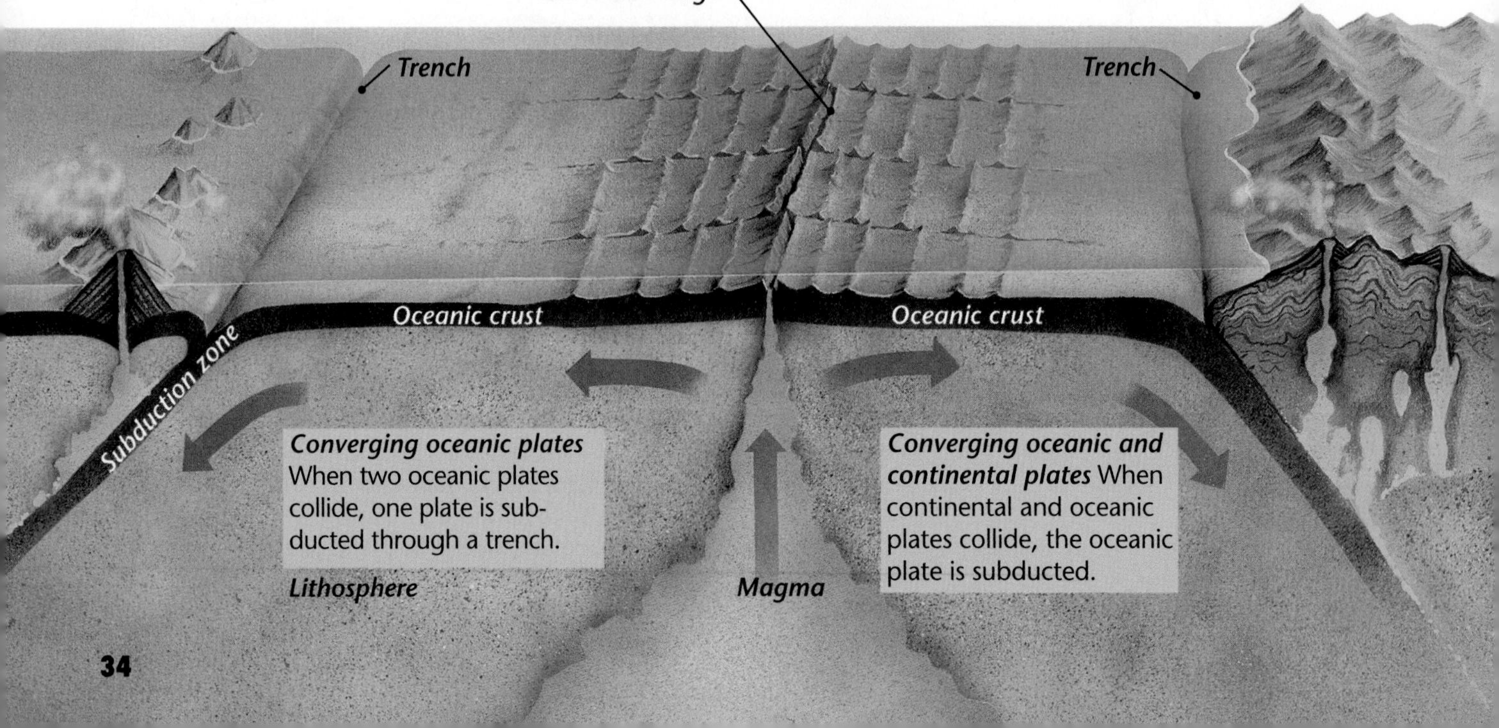
Diverging oceanic plates The mid-ocean ridge marks a divergent boundary where plates move apart.
Mid-ocean ridge
Trench
Trench
Oceanic crust
Oceanic crust
Subduction zone
Converging oceanic plates When two oceanic plates collide, one plate is subducted through a trench.
Converging oceanic and continental plates When continental and oceanic plates collide, the oceanic plate is subducted.
Lithosphere
Magma

Divergent Boundaries The place where two plates move apart, or diverge, is called a **divergent boundary** (dy VUR junt). Most divergent boundaries occur at the mid-ocean ridge. In Section 4, you learned how oceanic crust forms along the mid-ocean ridge as sea-floor spreading occurs.

Divergent boundaries also occur on land. When a divergent boundary develops on land, two of Earth's plates slide apart. A deep valley called a **rift valley** forms along the divergent boundary. For example, the Great Rift Valley in east Africa marks a deep crack in the African continent that runs for about 3,000 kilometers. Along this crack, a divergent plate boundary is slowly spreading apart. The rift may someday split the eastern part of Africa away from the rest of the continent. As a rift valley widens, its floor drops. Eventually, the floor may drop enough for the sea to fill the widening gap.

☑ *Checkpoint* *What is a rift valley? How are rift valleys formed?*

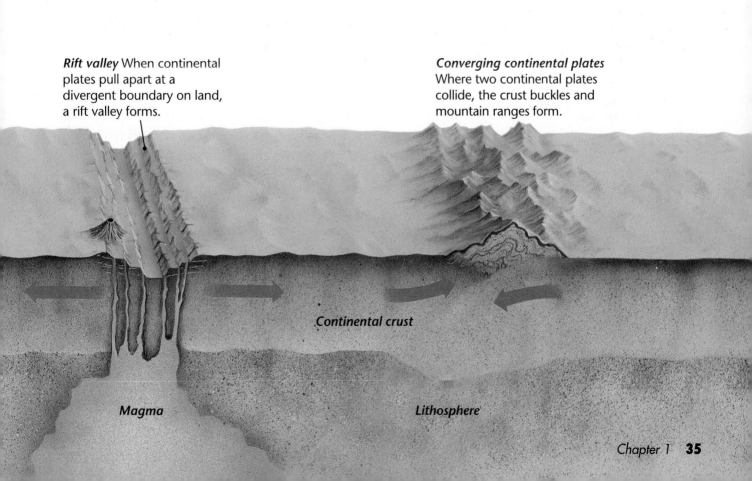

Rift valley When continental plates pull apart at a divergent boundary on land, a rift valley forms.

Converging continental plates Where two continental plates collide, the crust buckles and mountain ranges form.

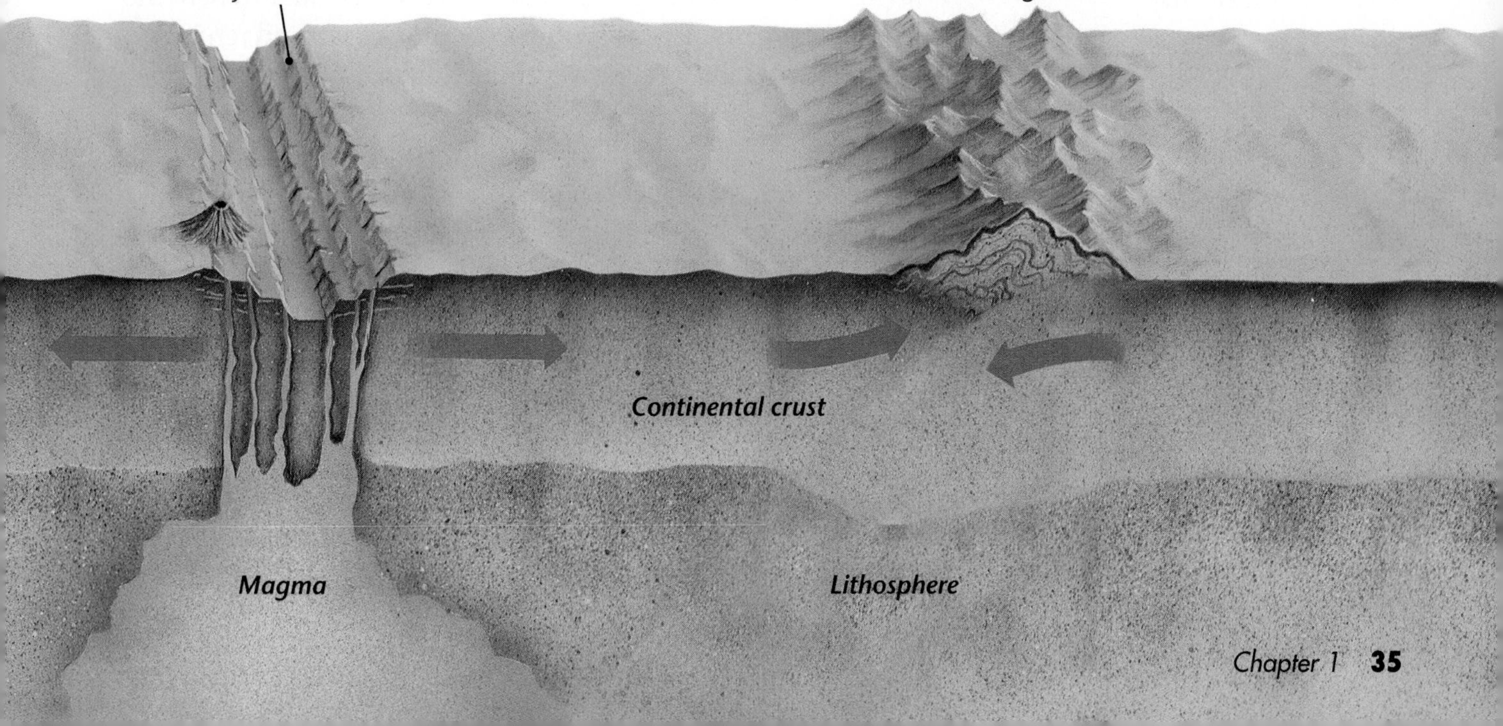
Continental crust
Magma
Lithosphere

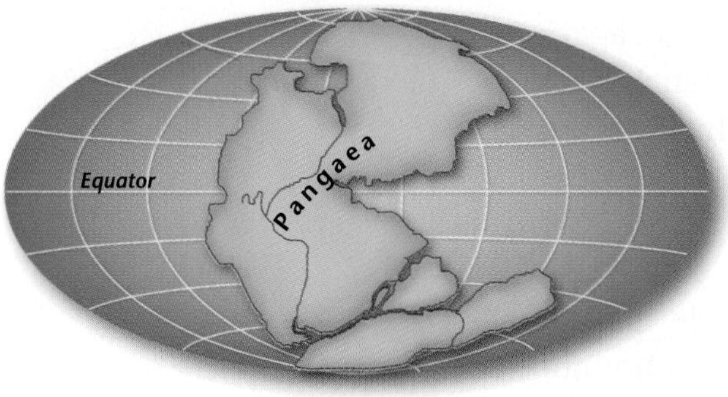
Equator
Pangaea

225 million years ago
All Earth's major landmasses were joined in the supercontinent Pangaea before plate movements began to split it apart.

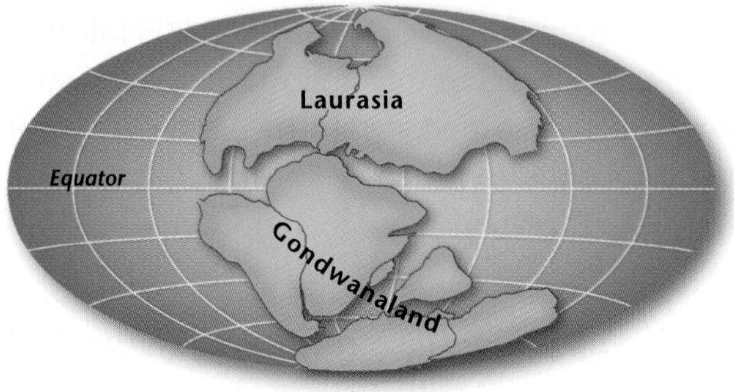
Laurasia
Equator
Gondwanaland

180–200 million years ago
Pangaea continued to split apart, opening narrow seas that later became oceans.

Convergent Boundaries The place where two plates come together, or converge, is called a **convergent boundary** (kun VUR junt). When two plates converge, the result is called a collision. Collisions may bring together oceanic crust and oceanic crust, oceanic crust and continental crust, or continental crust and continental crust.

When two plates collide, the density of the plates determines which one comes out on top. Oceanic crust, which is made mostly of basalt, is more dense than continental crust, which is made mostly of granite. And oceanic crust becomes cooler and denser as it spreads away from the mid-ocean ridge.

Where two plates carrying oceanic crust meet at a trench, the plate that is more dense dives under the other plate and returns to the mantle. This is the process of subduction that you learned about in Section 4.

Sometimes a plate carrying oceanic crust collides with a plate carrying continental crust. The less dense continental crust can't sink under the more dense oceanic crust. Instead, the oceanic plate begins to sink and plunges beneath the continental plate.

When two plates carrying continental crust collide, subduction does not take place. Both continental plates are mostly low-density granite rock. Therefore, neither plate is dense enough to sink into the mantle. Instead, the plates crash head-on. The collision squeezes the crust into mighty mountain ranges.

☑ *Checkpoint* *What types of plate movement occur at plate boundaries?*

Figure 28 A collision between two continental plates produced the majestic Himalayas. The collision began 50 million years ago, when the plate that carries India slammed into Asia.

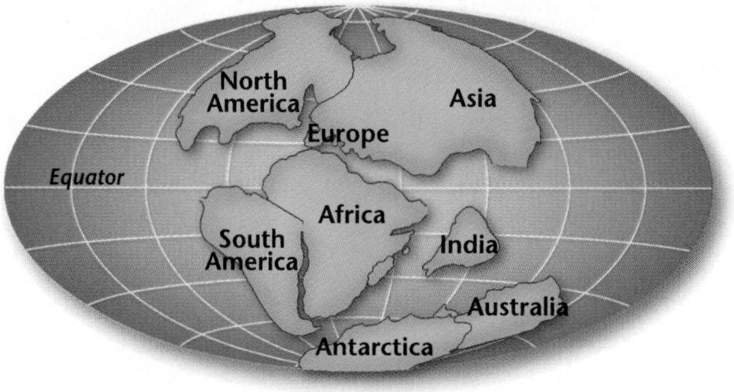
North America
Asia
Europe
Equator
Africa
South America
India
Australia
Antarctica

135 million years ago Gradually, the landmasses that became today's continents began to drift apart.

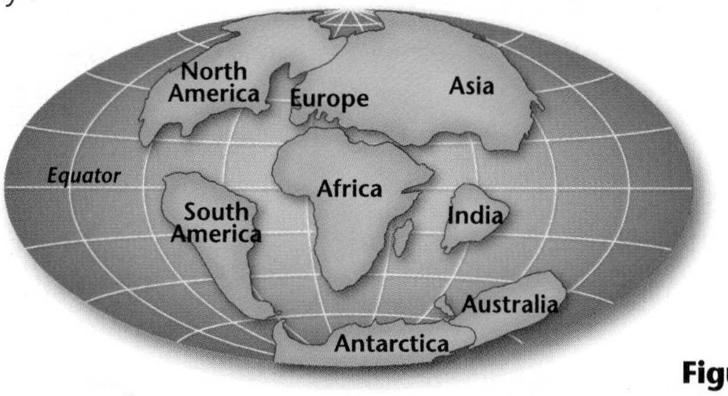
North America
Europe
Asia
Equator
Africa
South America
India
Australia
Antarctica

65 million years ago
India was still a separate continent, charging toward Asia, while Australia remained attached to Antarctica.

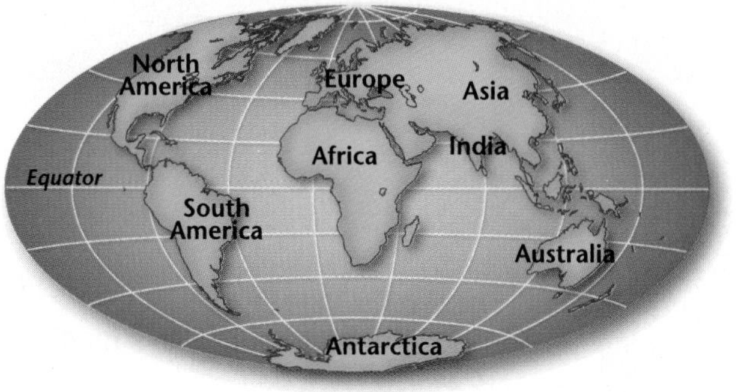
North America
Europe
Asia
Africa
India
Equator
South America
Australia
Antarctica

Earth today
Note how far to the north India has drifted—farther than any other major landmass.

Figure 29 It has taken about 225 million years for the continents to move to their present locations. *Posing Questions* What questions would you need to answer in order to predict where the continents will be in 50 million years?

The Continents' Slow Dance

The plates move at amazingly slow rates: from about one to ten centimeters per year. The North American and Eurasian plates are floating apart at a rate of 2.5 centimeters per year—that's about as fast as your fingernails grow. This may not seem like much, but these plates have been moving for tens of millions of years.

About 260 million years ago, the continents were joined together in the supercontinent that Wegener called Pangaea. Then, about 225 million years ago, Pangaea began to break apart. Figure 29 shows how Earth's continents and other landmasses have moved since the break-up of Pangaea.

Section 5 Review

1. What is the theory of plate tectonics?
2. What are the different types of boundaries found along the edges of Earth's plates?
3. What major event in Earth's history began about 225 million years ago? Explain.
4. **Thinking Critically Predicting** Look at Figure 26 on page 33 and find the divergent boundary that runs through the African plate. Predict what could eventually happen along this boundary.

CHAPTER PROJECT

Check Your Progress

Now that you have learned about plate tectonics, add examples of plate boundaries to your model. If possible, include a transform boundary, a convergent boundary, and a divergent boundary. Complete the construction of your model by adding all the required surface features. Be sure to label the features on your model. Include arrows that indicate the direction of plate movement.

Skills Lab

Observing

HOT PLATES

In this lab, you will observe a model of convection currents in Earth's mantle.

Problem

How do convection currents affect Earth's plates?

Materials

1 aluminum roasting pan
2 candles, about 10 cm long
clay to hold the candles up
6 bricks
2 medium-sized kitchen sponges
10 map pins
2 L water

Procedure

1. Stick ten pins about halfway into a long side of one of the sponges.
2. Place an aluminum pan on top of two stacks of bricks. **CAUTION:** *Position the bricks so that they fully support both ends of the pan.*
3. Fill the pan with water to a depth of 4 cm.
4. Moisten both sponges with water and float them in the pan.
5. Slowy nudge the two sponges together with the row of map pins between them. (The pins will keep the sponges from sticking together.)
6. Carefully let go of the sponges. If they drift apart, gently move them back together again.
7. Once the sponges stay close together, place the candles under opposite ends of the pan. Use clay to hold up the candles.
8. Draw a diagram of the pan, showing the starting position of the sponges.
9. Carefully light the candles. Observe the two sponges as the water heats up.

10. Draw diagrams showing the position of the sponges 1 minute and 2 minutes after placing the candles under the pan.

Analyze and Conclude

1. What happens to the sponges as the water heats up?
2. What can you infer is causing the changes you observed?
3. What material represents the mantle in this activity? What represents Earth's plates?
4. What would be the effect of adding several more candles under the pan?
5. **Think About It** How well did this activity model the movement of Earth's plates? What type of plate movement did you observe in the pan? How could you modify the activity to model plate movement more closely?

More to Explore

You can observe directly the movement of the water in the pan. To do this, squeeze a single drop of food coloring into the pan. After the drop of coloring has sunk to the bottom, place a lit candle under the pan near the colored water. How does the food coloring move in the water? How does this movement compare with convection currents in the mantle?

STUDY GUIDE

Section 1 Earth's Interior

Key Ideas

- A geologist studies the materials that make up the Earth and the processes that shape its surface and interior.
- Earth's interior is divided into the crust, the mantle, the outer core, and the inner core.
- The lithosphere includes the crust and the rigid upper layer of the mantle; beneath the lithosphere lies the soft layer of the mantle called the asthenosphere.

Key Terms

geologist	crust
rock	basalt
geology	granite
constructive force	mantle
destructive force	lithosphere
continent	asthenosphere
seismic wave	outer core
pressure	inner core

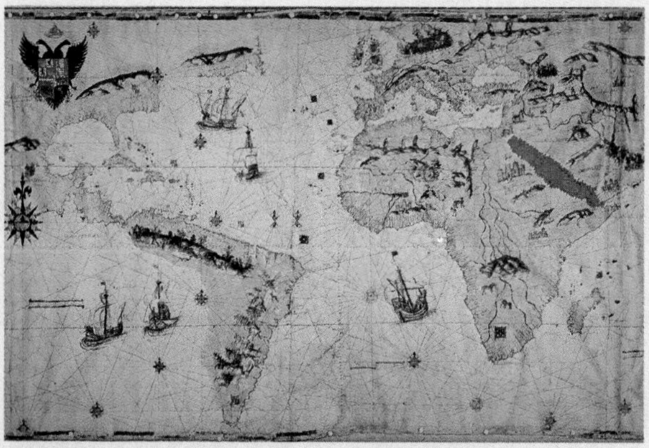

Section 2 Convection Currents and the Mantle

INTEGRATING PHYSICS

Key Ideas

- Heat can be transferred in three ways: radiation, conduction, and convection.
- Differences of temperature and density within a fluid cause convection currents.

Key Terms

heat transfer	convection
radiation	density
conduction	convection current

Section 3 Drifting Continents

Key Ideas

- Alfred Wegener developed the idea that the continents were once joined and have since drifted apart.
- Most scientists rejected Wegener's theory because he could not identify a force that could move the continents.

Key Terms

Pangaea   continental drift   fossil

Section 4 Sea-Floor Spreading

Key Ideas

- In sea-floor spreading, molten material erupts along the mid-ocean ridge and hardens to form rock.
- In subduction, the ocean floor sinks back to the mantle beneath deep ocean trenches.

Key Terms

mid-ocean ridge	deep-ocean trench
sonar	subduction
sea-floor spreading	

Section 5 The Theory of Plate Tectonics

Key Ideas

- The theory of plate tectonics explains plate movements and how they cause continental drift and sea-floor spreading.
- Plates slip past each other at transform boundaries, move apart at divergent boundaries, and come together at convergent boundaries.

Key Terms

plate	transform boundary
scientific theory	divergent boundary
plate tectonics	rift valley
fault	convergent boundary

ACTIVITY

USING THE INTERNET

www.phschool.com/state_focus/california/

CHAPTER 1 REVIEW

California Test Prep: Reviewing Content

Multiple Choice

Choose the letter of the answer that best completes each statement.

1. The layer of the upper mantle that can flow is the
   a. asthenosphere. **b.** lithosphere.
   c. inner core. **d.** continental crust.
2. Most scientists rejected Wegener's theory of continental drift because the theory failed to explain
   a. coal deposits in Antarctica.
   b. formation of mountains.
   c. climate changes.
   d. how the continents move.
3. Subduction of the ocean floor takes place at
   a. the lower mantle. **b.** mid-ocean ridges.
   c. rift valleys. **d.** trenches.
4. The process that powers plate tectonics is
   a. radiation. **b.** convection.
   c. conduction. **d.** subduction
5. Two plates collide with each other at
   a. a divergent boundary
   b. a convergent boundary
   c. the boundary between the mantle and the crust.
   d. a transform boundary.

True or False

If the statement is true, write true. If it is false, change the underlined word or words to make the statement true.

6. The Earth's outer core is made of basalt and granite.
7. The spinning of the asthenosphere, made of iron and nickel, explains why Earth has a magnetic field.
8. Convection currents form because of differences of temperature and density in a fluid.
9. Magnetic stripes on the ocean floor are places where oceanic crust sinks back to the mantle.
10. When two continental plates converge, a rift valley forms.

Checking Concepts

11. How is the inner core different from the outer core?
12. Why are there convection currents in the mantle? Explain.
13. What evidence of Earth's climate in the past supports the theory of continental drift?
14. What was the importance of the discovery that molten rock was coming out of cracks along the mid-ocean ridge?
15. How do magnetic stripes form on the ocean floor? Why are these stripes significant?
16. What happens when a plate of oceanic crust collides with a plate of continental crust? Why?
17. **Writing to Learn** Imagine that Alfred Wegener is alive today to defend his theory of continental drift. Write a short interview that Wegener might have on a daytime talk show. You may use humor.

Thinking Visually

18. To show the processes that link a trench and the mid-ocean ridge, copy the cycle diagram into your notebook and fill in the blanks. (For more on cycle diagrams, see the *Skills Handbook.*)

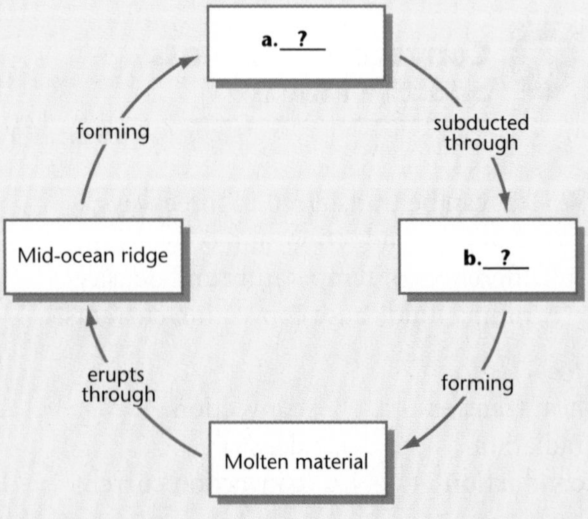

a. ?
subducted through
b. ?
forming
Molten material
erupts through
Mid-ocean ridge
forming

Test Prep: Skills

Geologists think that a new plate boundary is forming in the Indian Ocean. The part of the plate carrying Australia is twisting away from the part of the plate carrying India.

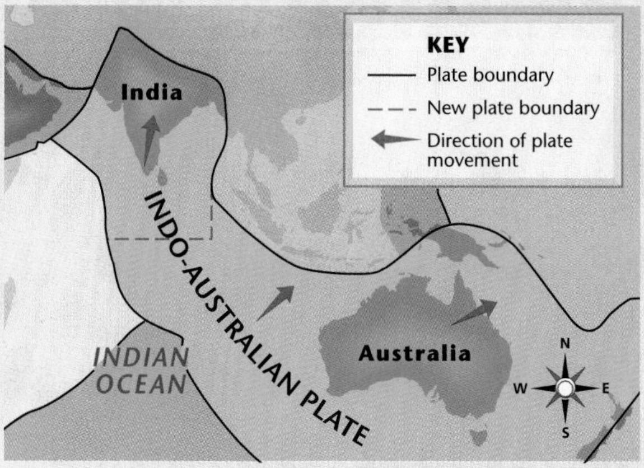

KEY
Plate boundary
New plate boundary
Direction of plate movement
India
INDO-AUSTRALIAN PLATE
INDIAN OCEAN
Australia
N
W
E
S

19. **Interpreting Maps** Look at the arrows showing the direction of plate motion. In what direction is the part of the plate carrying Australia moving? In what direction is the part carrying India moving?

20. **Predicting** As India and Australia move in different directions, what type of plate boundary will form between them?

21. **Inferring** On the map you can see that the northern part of the Indo-Australian plate is moving north and colliding with the Eurasian plate. What features would occur where these plates meet? Explain.

Thinking Critically

22. **Classifying** Classify these layers of Earth as liquid, solid, or solid but able to flow slowly: crust, lithosphere, asthenosphere, outer core, inner core.

23. **Comparing and Contrasting** How are oceanic and continental crust alike? How do they differ?

24. **Relating Cause and Effect** What do many geologists think is the driving force of plate tectonics? Explain.

25. **Making Generalizations** State in one sentence the most significant discovery that geologists established through their study of plate tectonics.

CHAPTER 1 ASSESSMENT

Performance Assessment

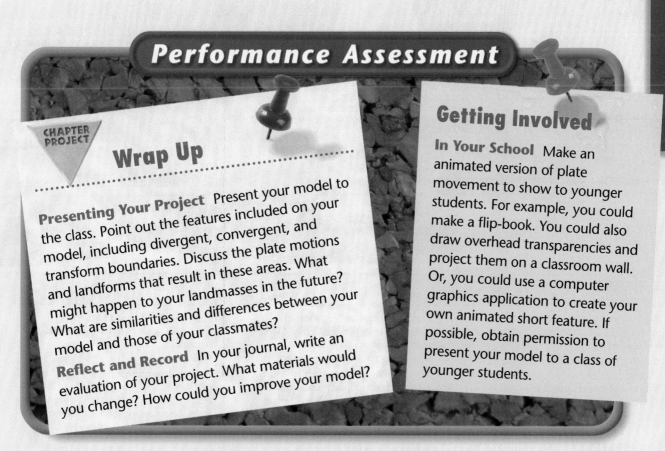

CHAPTER PROJECT

Wrap Up

Presenting Your Project Present your model to the class. Point out the features included on your model, including divergent, convergent, and transform boundaries. Discuss the plate motions and landforms that result in these areas. What might happen to your landmasses in the future? What are similarities and differences between your model and those of your classmates?

Reflect and Record In your journal, write an evaluation of your project. What materials would you change? How could you improve your model?

Getting Involved

In Your School Make an animated version of plate movement to show to younger students. For example, you could make a flip-book. You could also draw overhead transparencies and project them on a classroom wall. Or, you could use a computer graphics application to create your own animated short feature. If possible, obtain permission to present your model to a class of younger students.

CHAPTER

2 Earthquakes

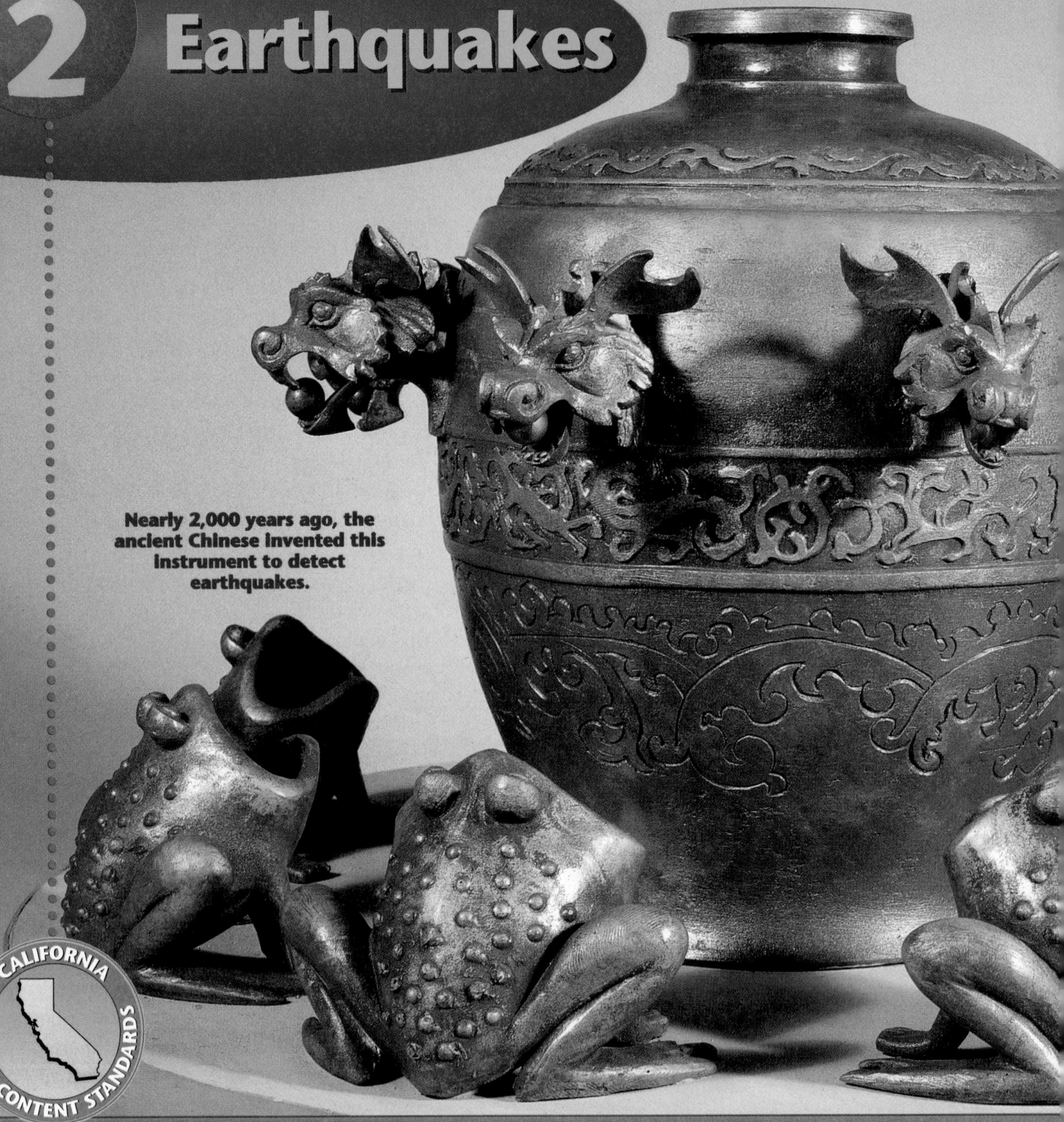

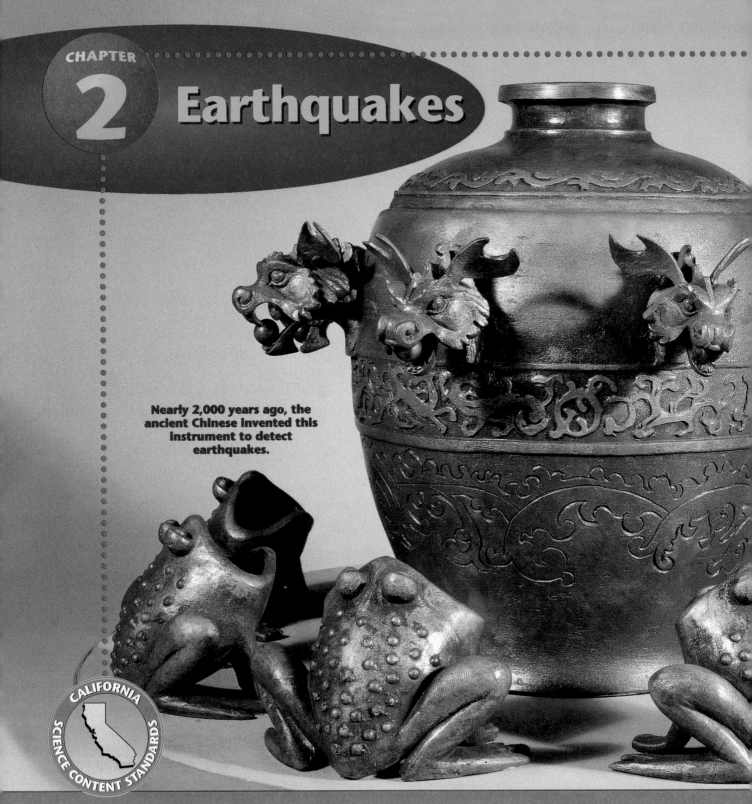

Nearly 2,000 years ago, the ancient Chinese invented this instrument to detect earthquakes.

The following California Science Content Standards are addressed in this chapter:

1. Plate tectonics explains important features of the Earth's surface and major geologic events.
   - **c.** Lithospheric plates that are the size of continents and oceans move at rates of centimeters per year in response to movements in the mantle.
   - **d.** Earthquakes are sudden motions along breaks in the crust called faults, and volcanoes/fissures are locations where magma reaches the surface.
   - **e.** Major geologic events, such as earthquakes, volcanic eruptions, and mountain building result from plate motions.
   - **f.** How to explain major features of California geology in terms of plate tectonics (including mountains, faults, volcanoes).
   - **g.** How to determine the epicenter of an earthquake and that the effects of an earthquake vary with its size, distance from the epicenter, local geology, and the type of construction involved.

PROJECT 2

Shake, Rattle, and Roll

The ground shakes ever so slightly. A bronze dragon drops a ball into the mouth of the frog below. Nearly 2,000 years ago in China, that's how an instrument like this one would have detected a distant earthquake. Earthquakes are proof that our planet is subject to great forces from within. Earthquakes remind us that we live on the moving pieces of Earth's crust.

In this chapter, you will design a structure that will withstand earthquakes.

Your Goal To design, build, and test a model structure that is earthquake resistant.

Your model should

- be made of materials that are approved by your teacher
- be built to specifications agreed on by your class
- be able to withstand several simulated earthquakes of increasing intensity
- be built following the safety guidelines in Appendix A

Get Started Before you design your model, find out how earthquakes cause damage to structures such as homes, office buildings, and highway overpasses. Preview the chapter to find out how engineers design structures to withstand earthquakes.

Check Your Progress You will be working on this project as you study this chapter. To keep your project on track, look for Check Your Progress boxes at the following points.

Section 1 Review, page 51: Design your model.
Section 2 Review, page 59: Construct, improve, and test your model.
Section 4 Review, page 71: Test your model again, and then repair and improve it.

Wrap Up At the end of the chapter (page 75), you will demonstrate how well your model can withstand the effects of a simulated earthquake and predict whether a building that followed your design could withstand a real earthquake.

2. Topography is reshaped by weathering of rock and soil and by the transportation and deposition of sediment.

d. Earthquakes, volcanic eruptions, landslides, and floods change human and wildlife habitats.

3. Heat moves in a predictable flow from warmer objects to cooler objects until all objects are at the same temperature.

a. Energy can be carried from one place to another by heat flow, or by waves including water waves, light and sound, or by moving objects.

7. Scientific progress is made by asking meaningful questions and conducting careful investigations.

c. Construct appropriate graphs from data and develop qualitative statements about the relationships between variables.

d. Communicate the steps and results from an investigation in written reports and verbal presentations.

e. Recognize whether evidence is consistent with a proposed explanation.

SECTION 1 Earth's Crust in Motion

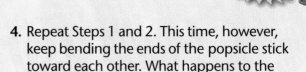

DISCOVER ACTIVITY

How Does Stress Affect Earth's Crust?

1. Put on your goggles.
2. Holding a popsicle stick at both ends, slowly bend it into an arch.
3. Release the pressure on the popsicle stick and observe what happens.
4. Repeat Steps 1 and 2. This time, however, keep bending the ends of the popsicle stick toward each other. What happens to the wood?

Think It Over

Predicting Think of the popsicle stick as a model for part of Earth's crust. What do you think might eventually happen as the forces of plate movement bend the crust?

GUIDE FOR READING

- **How do stress forces affect rock?**
- **Why do faults form and where do they occur?**
- **How does movement along faults change Earth's surface?**

Reading Tip **Before you read, use the headings to make an outline about stress in the crust, faults, and mountain building.**

You are sitting at the kitchen table eating breakfast. Suddenly you notice a slight vibration, as if a heavy truck were rumbling by. At the same time, your glass of orange juice jiggles. Dishes rattle in the cupboards. After a few seconds, the rattling stops. Later, when you listen to the news on the radio, you learn that your region experienced a small earthquake. Earthquakes are a reminder that Earth's crust can move.

Stress in the Crust

An **earthquake** is the shaking and trembling that results from the movement of rock beneath Earth's surface. The movement of Earth's plates creates powerful forces that squeeze or pull the rock in the crust. These forces are examples of **stress,** a force that acts on rock to change its shape or volume. (Volume is the amount of space an object takes up.) Because stress is a force, it adds energy to the rock. The energy is stored in the rock until the rock either breaks or changes shape.

Figure 1 Stress in the crust folded this rock like a sheet of ribbon candy.

Types of Stress

Three different kinds of stress occur in the crust—shearing, tension, and compression. **Shearing, tension, and compression work over millions of years to change the shape and volume of rock.** These forces cause some rocks to become brittle and snap. Other rocks tend to bend slowly like road tar softened by the heat of the sun.

Stress that pushes a mass of rock in two opposite directions is called **shearing.** Shearing can cause rock to break and slip apart or to change its shape.

The stress force called **tension** pulls on the crust, stretching rock so that it becomes thinner in the middle. The effect of tension on rock is somewhat like pulling apart a piece of warm bubble gum. Tension occurs where two plates are moving apart.

The stress force called **compression** squeezes rock until it folds or breaks. One plate pushing against another can compress rock like a giant trash compactor.

Any change in the volume or shape of Earth's crust is called **deformation.** Most changes in the crust occur so slowly that they cannot be observed directly. But if you could speed up time so a billion years passed by in minutes, you could see the deformation of the crust. The crust would bend, stretch, break, tilt, fold, and slide. The slow shift of Earth's plates causes this deformation.

☑ *Checkpoint* *How does deformation change Earth's surface?*

TRY THIS

It's a Stretch

You can model the stresses that create faults. **ACTIVITY**

1. Knead a piece of plastic putty until it is soft.
2. Push the ends of the putty toward the middle.
3. Pull the ends apart.
4. Push half of the putty one way and the other half in the opposite direction.

Classifying Which types of stress do Steps 2, 3, and 4 represent?

Figure 2 Deformation pushes, pulls, or twists the rocks in Earth's crust. *Relating Cause and Effect Which type of deformation tends to shorten part of the crust?*

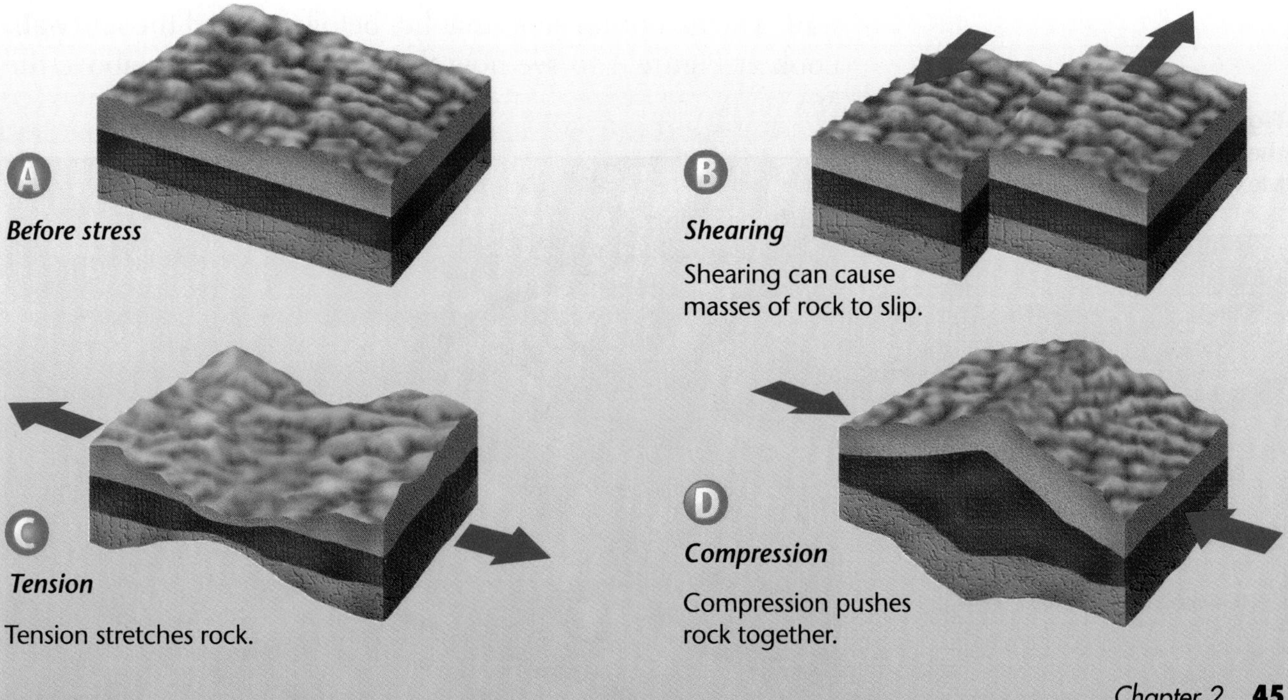
A
Before stress
B
Shearing
Shearing can cause masses of rock to slip.
C
Tension
Tension stretches rock.
D
Compression
Compression pushes rock together.

Kinds of Faults

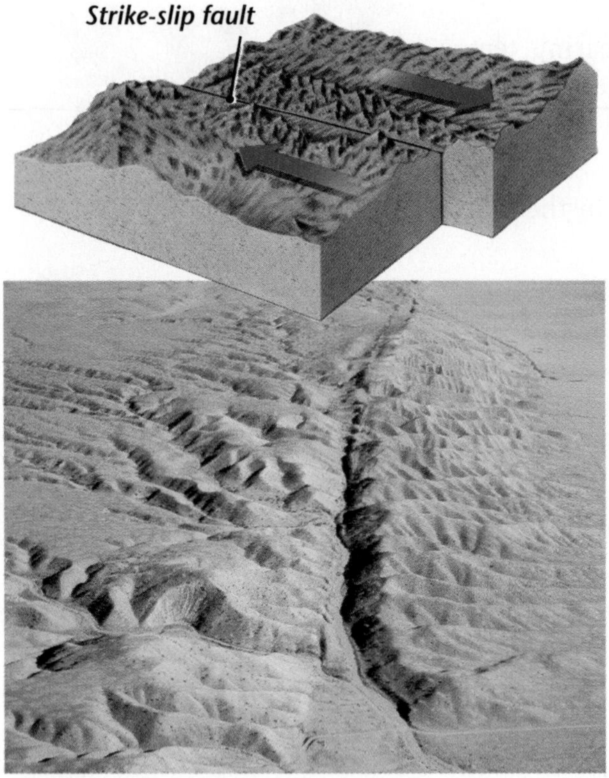
Strike-slip fault

Figure 3 A strike-slip fault that is clearly visible at the surface is the San Andreas Fault in California.

If you try to break a caramel candy bar in two, it may only bend and stretch at first. Like a candy bar, many types of rock can bend or fold. But beyond a certain limit, even these rocks will break. And it takes less stress to snap a brittle rock than it does to snap one that can bend.

When enough stress builds up in rock, the rock breaks, creating a fault. A **fault** is a break in Earth's crust where slabs of crust slip past each other. The rocks on both sides of a fault can move up or down or sideways. **Faults usually occur along plate boundaries, where the forces of plate motion compress, pull, or shear the crust so much that the crust breaks.** There are three main types of faults: strike-slip faults, normal faults, and reverse faults.

Strike-Slip Faults Shearing creates strike-slip faults. In a **strike-slip fault,** the rocks on either side of the fault slip past each other sideways with little up-or-down motion. Figure 3 shows the type of movement that occurs along a strike-slip fault. A strike-slip fault that forms the boundary between two plates is called a transform boundary. The San Andreas fault in California is an example of a strike-slip fault that is a transform boundary.

Normal Faults Tension forces in Earth's crust cause normal faults. In a **normal fault,** the fault is at an angle, so one block of rock lies above the fault while the other block lies below the fault. The half of the fault that lies above is called the **hanging wall.** The half of the fault that lies below is called the **footwall.** Look at Figure 4 to see how the hanging wall lies above the

Figure 4 A normal fault created the Sandia Mountains in New Mexico.

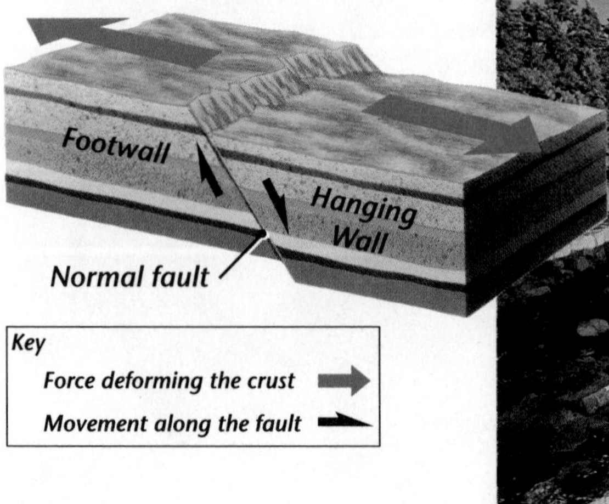
Footwall
Hanging Wall
Normal fault
Key
Force deforming the crust
Movement along the fault

footwall. When movement occurs along a normal fault, the hanging wall slips downward. Tension forces create normal faults where plates diverge, or pull apart. For example, normal faults occur along the Rio Grande rift valley in New Mexico, where two pieces of Earth's crust are diverging.

Reverse Faults Compression forces produce reverse faults. A **reverse fault** has the same structure as a normal fault, but the blocks move in the opposite direction. Look at Figure 5 to see how the rocks along a reverse fault move. As in a normal fault, one side of a reverse fault lies at an angle above the other side. The rock forming the hanging wall of a reverse fault slides up and over the footwall. Reverse faults produced part of the Appalachian Mountains in the eastern United States.

A type of reverse fault formed the majestic peaks in Glacier National Park in Montana shown in Figure 5. Over millions of years, a huge block of rock slid along the fault, moving up and over the surface rock. Parts of the overlying block then wore away, leaving the mountain peaks.

☑ *Checkpoint* ***What are the three types of fault? What force of deformation produces each?***

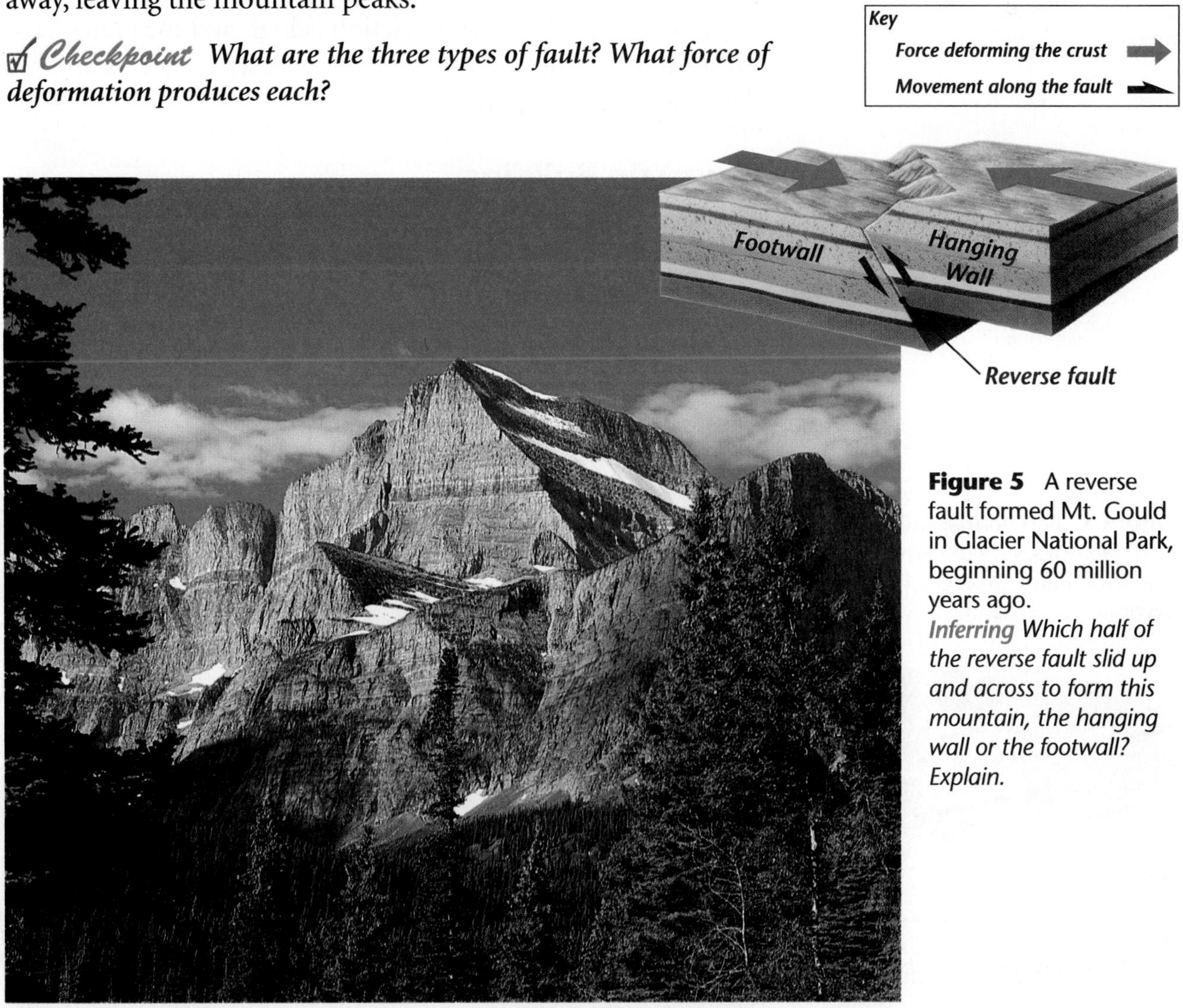
Key
Force deforming the crust
Movement along the fault
Footwall
Hanging Wall
Reverse fault

Figure 5 A reverse fault formed Mt. Gould in Glacier National Park, beginning 60 million years ago.
Inferring Which half of the reverse fault slid up and across to form this mountain, the hanging wall or the footwall? Explain.

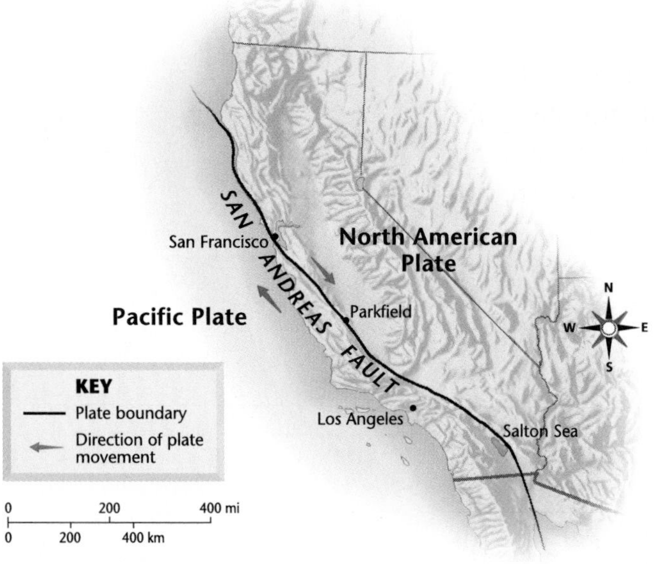
SAN ANDREAS FAULT
San Francisco
North American Plate
Pacific Plate
Parkfield
Los Angeles
Salton Sea
N
S
E
W
KEY
Plate boundary
Direction of plate movement
0
200
400 mi
0
200
400 km

Figure 6 The San Andreas fault extends from the Salton Sea in southern California to the point in northern California where the plate boundary continues into the Pacific Ocean. See Appendix C for a map of major faults and mountain ranges in California.

Friction Along Faults

Integrating Physics How rocks move along a fault depends on how much friction there is between the opposite sides of the fault. Friction is the force that opposes the motion of one surface as it moves across another surface. Friction exists because surfaces are not perfectly smooth.

Where friction along a fault is low, the rocks on both sides of the fault slide by each other without much sticking. Where friction is moderate, the sides of the fault jam together. Then from time to time they jerk free, producing small earthquakes. Where friction is high, the rocks lock together and do not move. In this case, stress increases until it is strong enough to overcome the friction force.

The San Andreas fault forms a transform boundary between the Pacific plate and the North American plate. In most places along the San Andreas fault, friction is high and the plates lock. Stress builds up until an earthquake releases the stress and the plates slide past each other.

Mountain Building

The forces of plate movement can build up Earth's surface. **Over millions of years, fault movement can change a flat plain into a towering mountain range.**

Mountains Formed by Faulting When normal faults uplift a block of rock, a **fault-block mountain** forms. You can see a diagram of this process in Figure 7. How does this process begin?

Figure 7 Two normal faults can form fault-block mountains, such as the Teton Range near the border of Wyoming and Idaho.

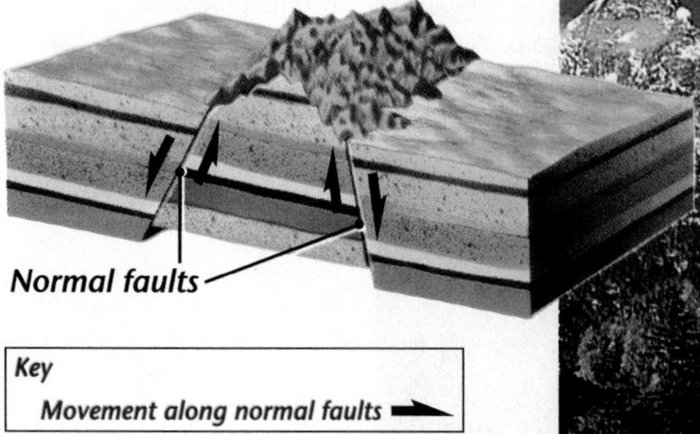
Normal faults
Key
Movement along normal faults

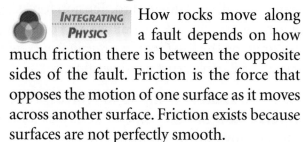

Where two plates move away from each other, tension forces create many normal faults. When two of these normal faults form parallel to each other, a block of rock is left lying between them. As the hanging wall of each normal fault slips downward, the block in between moves upward. When a block of rock lying between two normal faults slides downward, a valley forms.

The Sierra Nevada of California is a fault-block mountain range. The Physical Map of California in Appendix C, page 731, shows the Sierras as well as California's other mountain ranges. California's Central Valley formed when crust along the western side of the fault block dropped down.

If you traveled by car from Salt Lake City to Los Angeles you would cross the Great Basin, a region with many ranges of fault-block mountains separated by broad valleys, or basins. This "basin and range" region covers much of Nevada and western Utah. The region extends into California's Mojave Desert and the area east of the Sierra Nevada.

Mountains Formed by Folding Under certain conditions, plate movement causes the crust to fold. Have you ever skidded on a rug that wrinkled up as your feet pushed it across the floor? Much as the rug wrinkles, rock stressed by compression may bend slowly without breaking. **Folds** are bends in rock that form when compression shortens and thickens part of Earth's crust.

The collisions of two plates can cause compression and folding of the crust. Some of the world's largest mountain ranges, including the Himalayas in Asia and the Alps in Europe, formed when pieces of the crust folded during the collision of two plates. Such plate collisions also lead to earthquakes, because folding rock can fracture and produce faults. The mountains in California's northern Coast Range are partly the result of folding.

Sharpen your Skills

Measuring

ACTIVITY

You can measure the force of friction.

1. Place a small weight on a smooth, flat tabletop. Use a spring scale to pull the weight across the surface. How much force is shown on the spring scale? (*Hint*: The unit of force is newtons.)
2. Tape a piece of sandpaper to the tabletop. Repeat Step 1, pulling the weight across the sandpaper.

Is the force of friction greater for a smooth surface or for a rough surface?

B

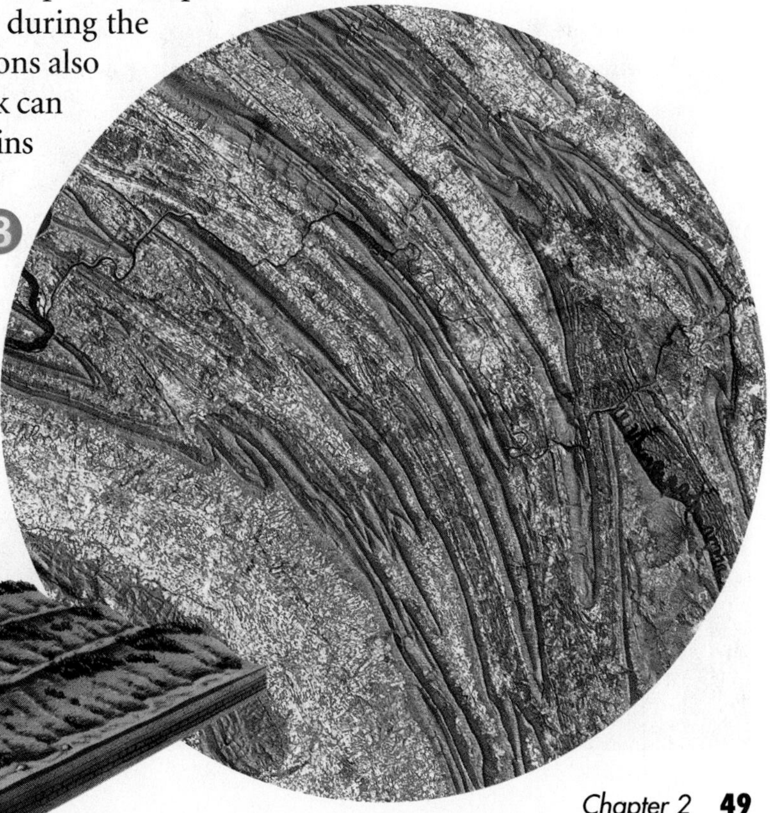

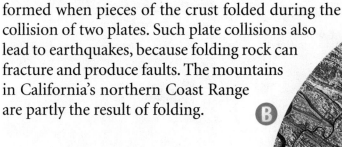

Figure 8 Compression forces cause folds in Earth's crust. **A.** Some mountains are made up of folded rock. **B.** The satellite image shows folded mountains west of Harrisburg, Pennsylvania.

A

Anticlines and Synclines Geologists use the terms anticline and syncline to describe upward and downward folds in rock. You can compare anticlines and synclines in the diagram in Figure 9. A fold in rock that bends upward into an arch is an **anticline.** A fold in rock that bends downward in the middle to form a bowl is a **syncline.** Anticlines and synclines are found on many parts of Earth's surface where compression forces have folded the crust.

One example of an anticline is the Black Hills of South Dakota. The Black Hills began to form about 65 million years ago. At that time, forces in Earth's crust produced a large dome-shaped anticline. Over millions of years, a variety of processes wore down and shaped the rock of this anticline into the Black Hills.

You may see a syncline where a valley dips between two parallel ranges of hills. But a syncline may also be a very large feature, as large as the state of Illinois. The Illinois Basin is a syncline that stretches from the western side of Indiana about 250 kilometers across the state of Illinois. The basin is filled with soil and rock that have accumulated over millions of years.

Figure 9 **A.** Over millions of years, compression and folding of the crust produce anticlines, which arch upward, and synclines, which dip downward. **B.** The folded rock layers of an anticline can be seen on this cliff on the coast of England.

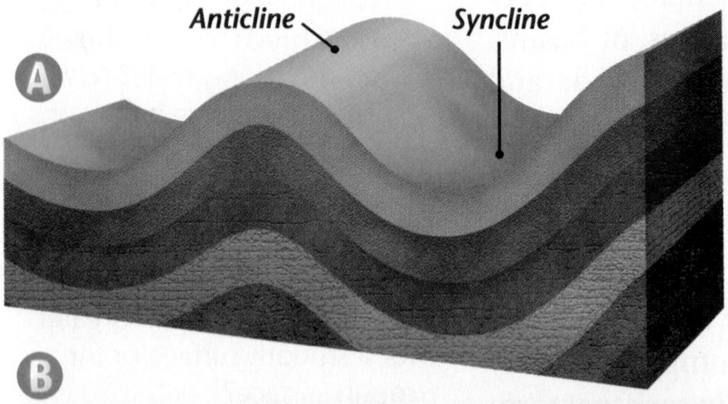
A
Anticline
Syncline

B

Figure 10 The flat land on the horizon is the Kaibab Plateau, which forms the North Rim of the Grand Canyon in Arizona. The Kaibab Plateau is part of the Colorado Plateau.

Plateaus The forces that raise mountains can also raise plateaus. A **plateau** is a large area of flat land elevated high above sea level. Some plateaus form when vertical faults push up a large, flat block of rock. Like a fancy sandwich, a plateau consists of many different flat layers, and is wider than it is tall.

Forces deforming the crust uplifted the Colorado Plateau in the "Four Corners" region of Arizona, Utah, Colorado, and New Mexico. The Colorado Plateau is a roughly circular area of uplifted rock more than 500 kilometers across. This vast slab of rock once formed part of a sea floor. Today, much of the plateau lies more than 1,500 meters above sea level.

Section 1 Review

1. What are the three main types of stress in rock?
2. Describe the movements that occur along each of the three types of faults.
3. How does Earth's surface change as a result of movement along faults?
4. **Thinking Critically** **Predicting** If plate motion compresses part of the crust, what landforms will form there in millions of years? Explain.

CHAPTER PROJECT

Check Your Progress

Discuss with your classmates the model you plan to build. What materials could you choose for your earthquake-resistant structure? Sketch your design. Does your design meet the guidelines provided by your teacher? How will you use your materials to build your model? (*Hint*: Draw the sketch of your model to scale).

Skills Lab

Making Models

MODELING MOVEMENT ALONG FAULTS

Faults are cracks in Earth's crust where masses of rock move over, under, or past each other. In this lab, you will make a model of the movements along faults.

Problem

How does the movement of rock along the sides of a fault compare for different types of faults?

Materials

Modeling compound in two or more colors
Marking pen
Plastic butter knife

Procedure

1. Roll some modeling compound into a sheet about 0.5 centimeter thick and about 6 centimeters square. Then make another sheet of the same size and thickness, using a different color.
2. Cut each square in half and stack the sheets on top of each other, alternating colors. **CAUTION:** *To avoid breaking the plastic knife, do not press too hard as you cut.* The sheets of modeling compound stand for different layers of rock. The different colors will help you see where similar layers of rock end up after movement occurs along the model fault.
3. Press the layers of modeling compound together to form a rectangular block that fits in the palm of your hand.
4. Use the butter knife to slice carefully through the block at an angle, as shown in the photograph.
5. Place the two blocks formed by the slice together, but don't let them stick together.
6. Review the descriptions and diagrams of faults in Section 1. Decide which piece of your block is the hanging wall and which is the footwall. Using the marking pen, label the side of each block. What part of your model stands for the fault itself?
7. What part of the model stands for the land surface? Along the top surface of the two blocks, draw a river flowing across the fault. Also draw an arrow on each block to show the direction of the river's flow. The arrow should point from the footwall toward the hanging wall.
8. Make a table that includes the headings Type of Fault, How the Sides of the Fault Move, and Changes in the Land Surface.

Type of Fault	How the Sides of the Fault Move	Changes in the Land Surface

9. Using your blocks, model the movement along a strike-slip fault. Record your motion and the results on the data table.
10. Repeat Step 9 for a normal fault.
11. Repeat Step 9 for a reverse fault.

Analyze and Conclude

Refer to your data table to draw a chart that will help you answer questions 1 through 4.

1. On your chart, show the direction in which the sides of the fault move for each type of fault.
2. On your chart, show how movement along a strike-slip fault is different from movement along the other two types of fault.
3. Add to your chart a column that shows how the river on the surface might change for each type of fault.
4. Assuming that the river is flowing from the footwall toward the hanging wall, which type of fault could produce small waterfalls in the surface river? (*Hint:* Recall how you tell which block is the hanging wall and which block is the footwall).
5. If you could observe only the land surface around a fault, how could you tell if the fault is a strike-slip fault? A normal fault?
6. If you slide the hanging wall of your fault model upward in relation to the footwall, what type of fault forms? If this movement continues, where will the slab of rock with the hanging wall end up?
7. From an airplane, you see a chain of several long, narrow lakes along a fault. What type of fault would cause these lakes to form?
8. **Think About It** In what ways does the model help you picture what is happening along a fault? In what ways does the model not accurately reflect what happens along a fault? How is the model still useful in spite of its inaccuracies?

More to Explore

On Earth's surface, individual faults do not exist all by themselves. With one or more of your classmates, combine your models to show how a fault-block mountain range or a rift valley could form. (*Hint:* Both involve normal faults.) How could you combine your models to show how reverse faults produce a mountain range?

SECTION 2

Measuring Earthquakes

DISCOVER ACTIVITY

How Do Seismic Waves Travel Through Earth?

1. Stretch a spring toy across the floor while a classmate holds the other end. Do not overstretch the toy.
2. Gather together about 4 coils of the spring toy and release them. In what direction do the coils move?
3. Once the spring toy has stopped moving, jerk one end of the toy from side to side once. In what direction do the coils move? Be certain your classmate has a secure grip on the other end.

Think It Over

Observing Describe the two types of wave motion that you observed in the spring toy.

GUIDE FOR READING

- **How does the energy of an earthquake travel through Earth?**
- **What are the different kinds of seismic waves?**
- **What are the scales used to measure the strength of an earthquake?**

Reading Tip **Before you read, preview the illustrations and captions. Predict how energy from earthquakes travels through the crust.**

Earth is never still. Every day, worldwide, there are about 8,000 earthquakes. Most of them are too small to notice. But when an earthquake is strong enough to rattle dishes in kitchen cabinets, people sit up and take notice. "How big was the quake?" and "Where was it centered?" are two questions just about everyone asks after an earthquake.

To know where an earthquake was centered, you need to know where it began. Earthquakes always begin in rock below the surface. Most earthquakes begin in the lithosphere within 100 kilometers of Earth's surface. An earthquake starts at one particular point. The **focus** (FOH kus) is the point beneath Earth's surface where rock that is under stress breaks, triggering an earthquake. The point on the surface directly above the focus is called the **epicenter** (EHP uh sen tur).

Seismic Waves

If you have ever played a drum, you know that the sound it makes depends on how hard you strike it. A drumbeat produces vibrations called sound waves. Sound waves carry energy as they travel outward from their source. During an earthquake, seismic waves race out from the focus in all directions. **Seismic waves** are vibrations that travel through Earth carrying the energy released during an earthquake. The seismic waves move like ripples in a pond. Look at Figure 11 to see how seismic waves travel outward in all directions from the focus.

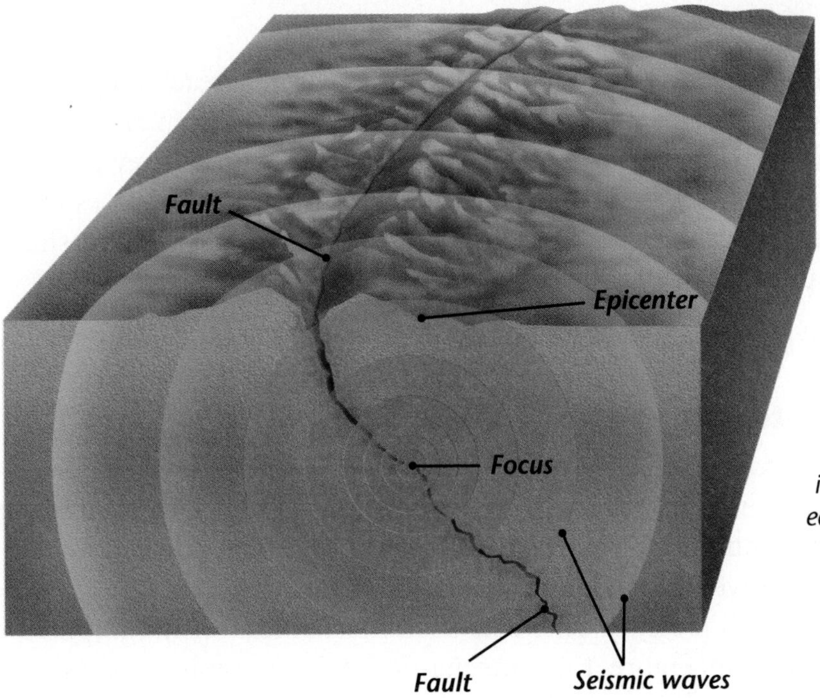
Fault
Epicenter
Focus
Fault
Seismic waves

Figure 11 An earthquake occurs when rocks fracture at the focus, deep in Earth's crust. *Interpreting Diagrams What point is directly above the focus of the earthquake?*

Seismic waves carry the energy of an earthquake away from the focus, through Earth's interior, and across the surface. The energy of the seismic waves that reach the surface is greatest at the epicenter. The most violent shaking during an earthquake, however, may occur kilometers away from the epicenter. The types of rock and soil around the epicenter determine where and how much the ground shakes. You will learn more about the effects of seismic waves in Section 3.

There are three categories of seismic waves: P waves, S waves, and surface waves. An earthquake sends out two types of waves from its focus: P waves and S waves. When these waves reach Earth's surface at the epicenter, surface waves develop.

Primary Waves The first waves to arrive are primary waves, or P waves. **P waves** are earthquake waves that compress and expand the ground like an accordion. P waves cause buildings to contract and expand. Look at Figure 12 to compare P waves and S waves.

Secondary Waves After P waves come secondary waves, or S waves. **S waves** are earthquake waves that vibrate from side to side as well as up and down. They shake the ground back and forth. When S waves reach the surface, they shake structures violently. Unlike P waves, which travel through both solids and liquids, S waves cannot move through liquids.

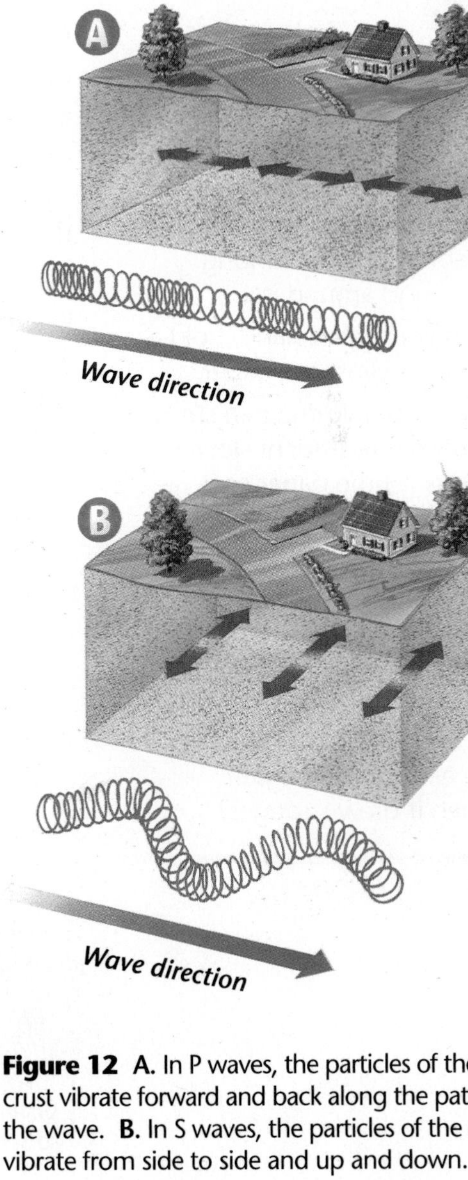
A
Wave direction
B
Wave direction

Figure 12 **A.** In P waves, the particles of the crust vibrate forward and back along the path of the wave. **B.** In S waves, the particles of the crust vibrate from side to side and up and down.

TRY THIS

Recording Seismic Waves

ACTIVITY

You and two classmates can simulate a seismograph.

1. Place a big book on a table.
2. With one hand, hold a pencil with a strip of paper about one meter long wound around it.
3. In your other hand, hold a pen against the paper.
4. As you hold the pen steady, have one student slowly pull on the paper so it slides across the book.
5. After a few seconds, have the other student jiggle the book for 10 seconds—first gently, then strongly.

Observing How did the line on the paper change when the earthquake began? When it grew stronger?

Surface Waves When P waves and S waves reach the surface, some of them are transformed into surface waves. **Surface waves** move more slowly than P waves and S waves, but they produce the most severe ground movements. Some surface waves make the ground roll like ocean waves. Other surface waves shake buildings from side to side.

☑ *Checkpoint* *What are the three types of seismic waves?*

Detecting Seismic Waves

To record and measure the vibrations of seismic waves, geologists use instruments called seismographs. A **seismograph** (SYZ muh graf) records the ground movements caused by seismic waves as they move through the Earth.

Until recently, scientists used mechanical seismographs. As shown in Figure 13, a mechanical seismograph consists of a heavy weight attached to a frame by a spring or wire. A pen connected to the weight rests its point on a rotating drum. When the drum is still, the pen draws a straight line on paper wrapped around the drum. During an earthquake, seismic waves cause the drum to vibrate. Meanwhile, the pen stays in place and records the drum's vibrations. The height of the jagged lines drawn on the seismograph's drum is greater for a more severe earthquake.

Today, scientists use electronic seismographs that work according to the same principle as the mechanical seismograph. The electronic seismograph converts ground movements into a signal that can be recorded and printed.

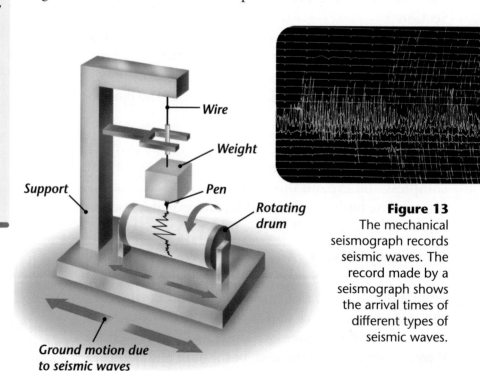

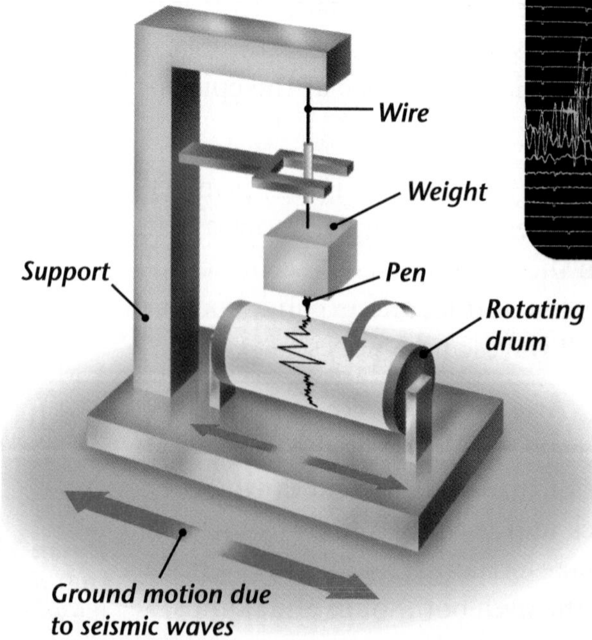
Wire
Weight
Support
Pen
Rotating drum
Ground motion due to seismic waves

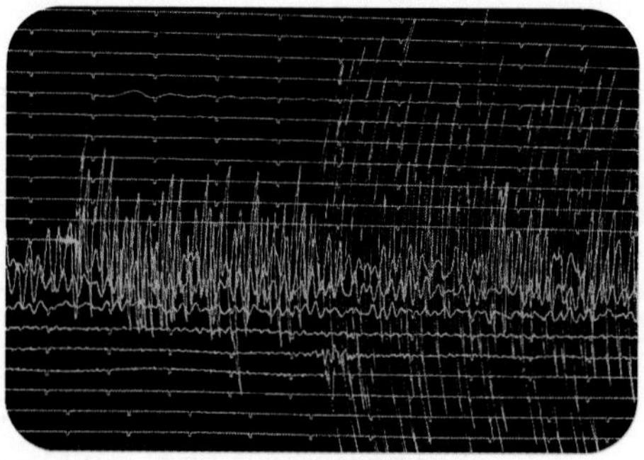

Figure 13 The mechanical seismograph records seismic waves. The record made by a seismograph shows the arrival times of different types of seismic waves.

The Mercalli Scale	
Earthquake Intensity	**Earthquake Effects**
I–II	Almost unnoticeable
III–IV	People notice vibrations like those from a passing truck. Unstable objects disturbed.
V–VI	Dishes and windows rattle. Books knocked off shelves. Slight damage.
VII–VIII	People run outdoors. Moderate to heavy damage.
IX–X	Buildings jolted off foundations or destroyed. Cracks appear in ground and landslides occur.
XI–XII	Severe damage. Wide cracks appear in ground. Waves seen on ground surface.

Figure 14 An earthquake in 1997 damaged the tower of this city hall in Foligno, Italy (left). The Mercalli scale (right) uses Roman numerals to rank earthquakes by how much damage they cause.
Applying Concepts How would you rate the damage to the Foligno city hall on the Mercalli scale?

Measuring Earthquakes

When geologists want to know the size of an earthquake, they must consider many factors. As a result, there are at least 20 different measures for rating earthquakes, each with its strengths and shortcomings. Three ways of measuring earthquakes, the Mercalli scale, the Richter scale, and the moment magnitude scale, are described here. **Magnitude** is a measurement of earthquake strength based on seismic waves and movement along faults.

The Mercalli Scale Early in the twentieth century, the **Mercalli scale** was developed to rate earthquakes according to their intensity. An earthquake's intensity is the strength of ground motion in a given place. The Mercalli scale is not a precise measurement. But the 12 steps of the Mercalli scale describe how earthquakes affect people, buildings, and the land surface. The same earthquake can have different Mercalli ratings because it causes different amounts of damage at different locations.

The Richter Scale The **Richter scale** is a rating of the size of seismic waves as measured by a particular type of mechanical seismograph. The Richter scale was developed in the 1930s. Geologists all over the world used this scale for about 50 years. Eventually, electronic seismographs replaced the mechanical seismographs used for the Richter scale. The Richter scale provides accurate measurements for small, nearby earthquakes. But the scale does not work well for large or distant earthquakes.

Earthquake Magnitudes	
Earthquake	**Moment Magnitude**
San Francisco, California, 1906	7.7
Southern Chile, 1960	9.5
Anchorage, Alaska, 1964	9.2
Loma Prieta, California, 1989	7.2
Northridge/ Los Angeles, California, 1994	6.7

Figure 15 The table lists the moment magnitudes for some of the twentieth century's biggest earthquakes.

The Moment Magnitude Scale Today, geologists use the **moment magnitude scale,** a rating system that estimates the total energy released by an earthquake. **The moment magnitude scale can be used to rate earthquakes of all sizes, near or far.** You may hear news reports that mention the Richter scale. But the magnitude number they quote is almost always the moment magnitude for that earthquake.

To rate an earthquake on the moment magnitude scale, geologists first study data from modern electronic seismographs. The data show what kinds of seismic waves the earthquake produced and how strong they were. The data also help geologists infer how much movement occurred along the fault and the strength of the rocks that broke when the fault slipped. Geologists combine all this information to rate the earthquake on the moment magnitude scale.

Earthquakes with a magnitude below 5.0 on the moment magnitude scale are small and cause little damage. Those with a magnitude above 5.0 can produce great destruction. A magnitude 6.0 quake releases 32 times as much energy as a magnitude 5.0 quake, and nearly 1,000 times as much as a magnitude 4.0 quake.

☑ *Checkpoint* *What are three scales for measuring earthquakes?*

Locating the Epicenter

Geologists use seismic waves to locate an earthquake's epicenter. Seismic waves travel at different speeds. P waves arrive first at a seismograph, with S waves following close behind. To tell how far the epicenter is from the seismograph, scientists measure the difference between the arrival times of the P waves and S waves.

Figure 16 In terms of magnitude, the 1906 San Francisco earthquake was not the strongest of the century. But it toppled buildings and caused fires that devastated the city.

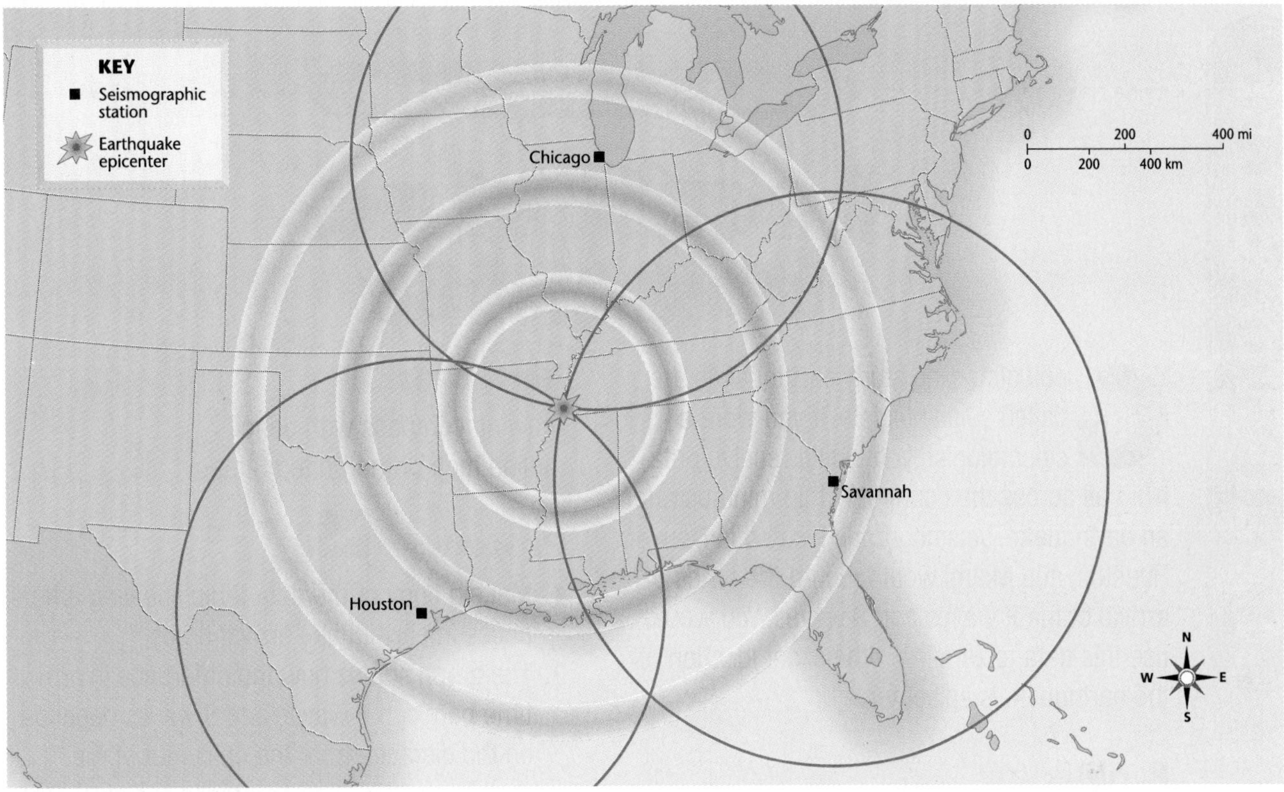
KEY
Seismographic station
Earthquake epicenter
Chicago
Savannah
Houston
0 200 400 mi
0 200 400 km
N
W
E
S

Figure 17 The map shows how to find the epicenter of an earthquake using data from three seismographic stations. *Measuring* *Use the map scale to determine the distances from Savannah and Houston to the epicenter. Which is closer?*

The farther away an earthquake is, the greater the time between the arrival of the P waves and the S waves.

INTEGRATING MATHEMATICS Geologists then draw at least three circles using data from different seismographs set up at stations all over the world. The center of each circle is a particular seismograph's location. The radius of each circle is the distance from the seismograph to the epicenter. The point where the three circles intersect is the location of the epicenter. If you look at Figure 17, you can see why two circles would not give enough information to pinpoint the epicenter.

Section 2 Review

1. How does the energy from an earthquake reach Earth's surface?
2. Describe the three types of seismic waves.
3. What system do geologists use today for rating the magnitude of an earthquake?
4. **Thinking Critically Relating Cause and Effect** Describe how energy released at an earthquake's focus, deep inside Earth, can cause damage on the surface many kilometers from the epicenter.

CHAPTER PROJECT

Check Your Progress

Now it is time to complete your design and construct your model. From what you have learned about earthquakes, what changes will you make in your design? Have a classmate review your model and make suggestions for improvements. When you have made the changes, test your model's ability to withstand an earthquake. Take notes on how well it withstands the quake.

Real-World Lab

Careers in Science

Locating an Epicenter

Geologists who study earthquakes are called seismologists. If you were a seismologist, you would receive data from all across the country. Within minutes after an earthquake, seismographs located in Denver, Houston, and Miami would record the times of arrival of the P waves and S waves. You would use this data to zero in on the exact location of the earthquake's epicenter.

Problem

How can you locate an earthquake's epicenter?

Skills Focus

interpreting data, drawing conclusions

Materials

drawing compass with pencil

outline map of the United States

Procedure

1. Make a copy of the data table showing differences in earthquake arrival times.
2. The graph shows how the difference in arrival time between P waves and S waves depends on the distance from the epicenter of the earthquake. Find the difference in arrival time for Denver on the *y*-axis of the graph. Follow this line across to the point at which it crosses the curve. To find the distance to the epicenter, read down from this point to the *x*-axis of the graph. Enter this distance in the data table.

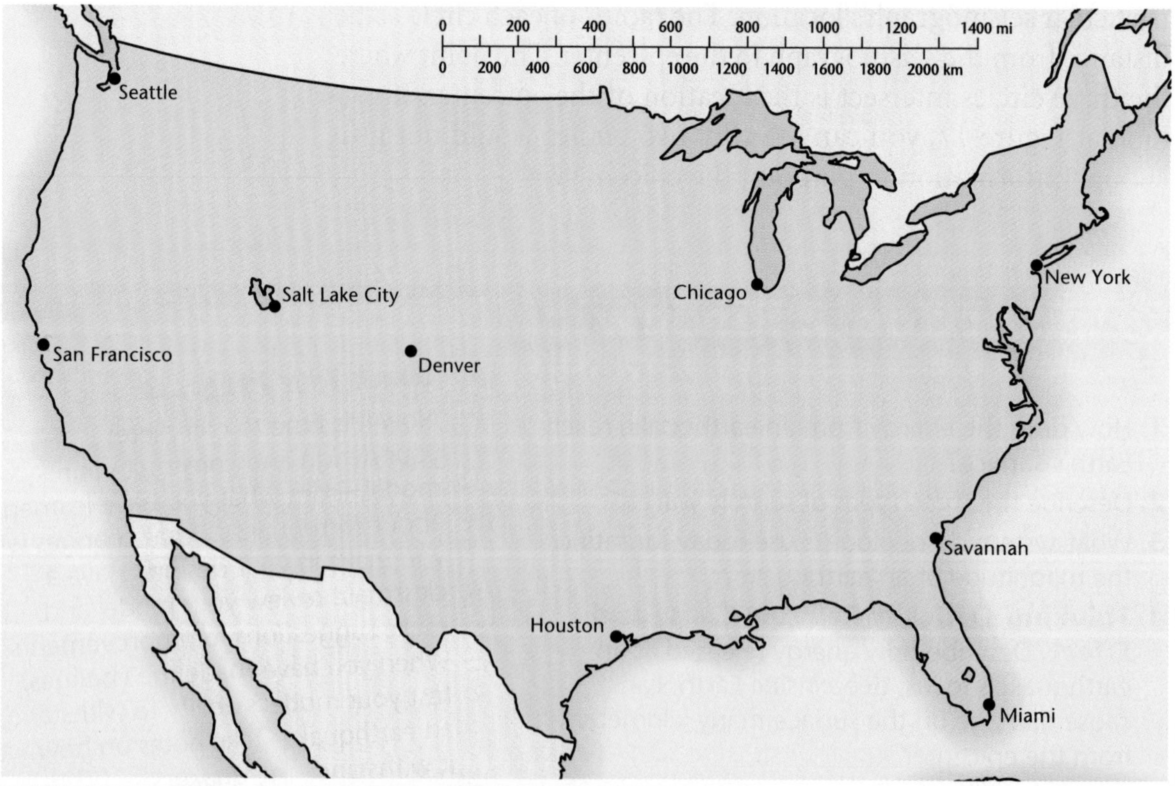
0 200 400 600 800 1000 1200 1400 mi
0 200 400 600 800 1000 1200 1400 1600 1800 2000 km
Seattle
Salt Lake City
San Francisco
Denver
Chicago
New York
Savannah
Houston
Miami

Data Table

City	Difference in P and S Wave Arrival Times	Distance to Epicenter
Denver, Colorado	2 min 10 s	
Houston, Texas	3 min 55 s	
Miami, Florida	5 min 40 s	

3. Repeat Step 2 for Houston and Miami.
4. Set your compass at a radius equal to the distance from Denver to the earthquake epicenter that you recorded in your data table.
5. Draw a circle with the radius determined in Step 4, using Denver as the center. Draw the circle on your copy of the map. (*Hint:* Draw your circles carefully. You may need to draw some parts of the circles off the map.)
6. Repeat Steps 4 and 5 for Houston and Miami.

Analyze and Conclude

1. Observe the three circles you have drawn to locate the earthquake's epicenter.
2. Which city on the map is closest to the earthquake epicenter? How far, in kilometers, is this city from the epicenter?
3. In which of the three cities listed in the data table would seismographs detect the earthquake first? Last?
4. When you are trying to locate an epicenter, why is it necessary to know the distance from the epicenter for at least three recording stations?
5. About how far is the epicenter that you found from San Francisco? What would the difference in arrival times of the P waves and S waves be for a recording station in San Francisco?
6. What happens to the difference in arrival times between P waves and S waves as the distance from the earthquake increases?
7. **Apply** Working as a seismologist, you find the epicenters of many earthquakes in a region. What features of Earth's crust would you expect to find in this region?

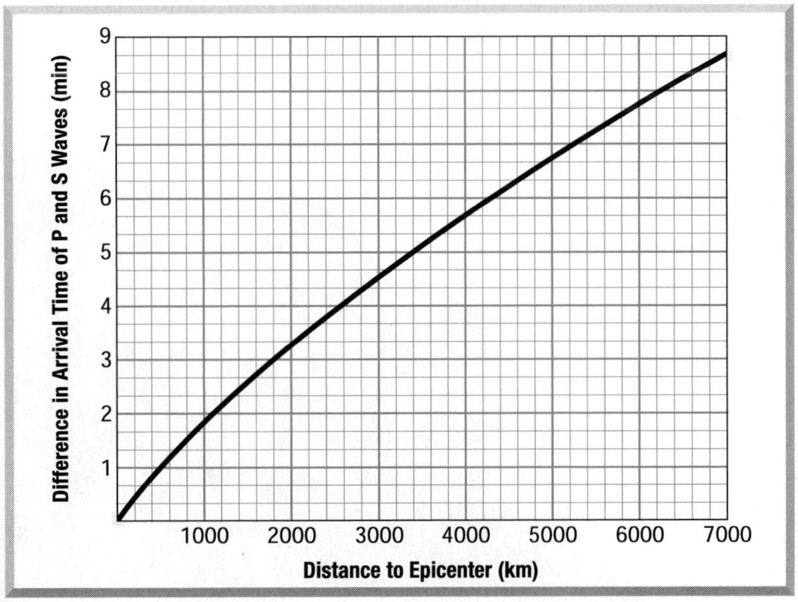
Difference in Arrival Time of P and S Waves (min)
1
2
3
4
5
6
7
8
9
1000
2000
3000
4000
5000
6000
7000
Distance to Epicenter (km)

More to Explore

You have just located an earthquake's epicenter. Find this earthquake's location on the earthquake risk map on page 71. Judging from the map, was this earthquake a freak event? What is the risk of earthquakes in the area of this quake? Now look at the map of Earth's plates on page 33. What conclusions can you draw from this map about the cause of earthquakes in this area?

SECTION 3

Earthquake Hazards and Safety

DISCOVER ACTIVITY

Can Bracing Prevent Building Collapse?

1. Tape four straws together to make a square frame. Hold the frame upright on a flat surface in front of you.
2. Hold the bottom straw down with one hand while you push the top straw to the left with the other. Push it as far as it will go without breaking the frame.
3. Tape a fifth straw horizontally across the middle of the frame. Repeat Step 2.

Think It Over

Predicting What effect did the fifth straw have? What effect would a piece of cardboard taped to the frame have? Based on your observations, how would an earthquake affect the frame of a house?

GUIDE FOR READING

- **What kinds of damage does an earthquake cause?**
- **What can be done to reduce earthquake hazards?**

Reading Tip **Before you read preview the headings of the section. Then predict some of the ways that people can reduce earthquake hazards.**

On a cold, bleak morning in January 1995, a powerful earthquake awoke the 1.5 million residents of Kobe, Japan. In 20 terrifying seconds, the earthquake collapsed thousands of buildings, crumpled freeways, and sparked about 130 fires. More than 5,000 people perished.

Most of the buildings that toppled were more than 20 years old. Many were two-story, wood-frame houses with heavy tile roofs. These top-heavy houses were about as stable in an earthquake as a heavy book supported by a framework of pencils. In contrast, many of the more modern buildings remained standing. The newer buildings had been designed to withstand intense shaking.

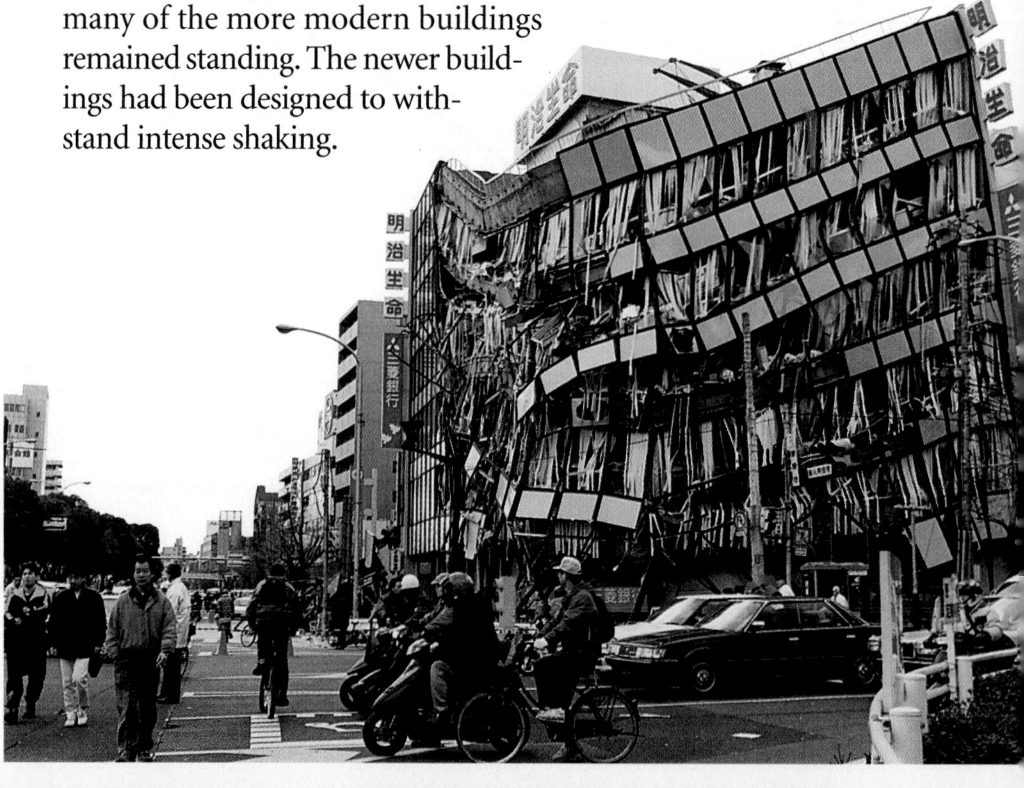
明治生命

Figure 18 Many buildings in Kobe, Japan, could not withstand the magnitude 6.9 earthquake that struck in 1995.

Figure 19 An earthquake caused the soil beneath this house to liquefy. Liquefaction caused by seismic waves can change solid soil to liquid mud within seconds. *Posing Questions What are some questions people might ask before building a house in an area that is at risk for earthquakes?*

How Earthquakes Cause Damage

When a major earthquake strikes, it can cause great damage. **The severe shaking produced by seismic waves can damage or destroy buildings and bridges, topple utility poles, and fracture gas and water mains.** S waves, with their side-to-side and up-and-down movement, can cause severe damage near the epicenter. As the twisting forces of S waves sweep through the ground, the S waves put enough stress on buildings to tear them apart. Earthquakes can also trigger landslides or avalanches. In coastal regions, giant waves pushed up by earthquakes can cause more damage.

Local Soil Conditions When seismic waves move from hard, dense rock to loosely packed soil, they transmit their energy to the soil. The loose soil shakes more violently than the surrounding rock. The thicker the layer of soil, the more violent the shaking will be. This means a house built on solid rock will shake less than a house built on sandy soil.

Liquefaction In 1964, when a powerful earthquake roared through Anchorage, Alaska, cracks opened in the ground. Some of the cracks were 9 meters wide. The cracks were created by liquefaction. **Liquefaction** (lik wih FAK shun) occurs when an earthquake's violent shaking suddenly turns loose, soft soil into liquid mud. Liquefaction is likely where the soil is full of moisture. As the ground gives way, buildings sink and pull apart.

Liquefaction can also trigger landslides. During the 1964 Anchorage earthquake, liquefaction caused a landslide that swept an entire housing development down a cliff and into the sea. Figure 19 shows the damage liquefaction can cause.

Aftershocks Sometimes, buildings weakened by an earthquake collapse during an aftershock. An **aftershock** is an earthquake that occurs after a larger earthquake in the same area. Aftershocks may strike hours, days, or even months later.

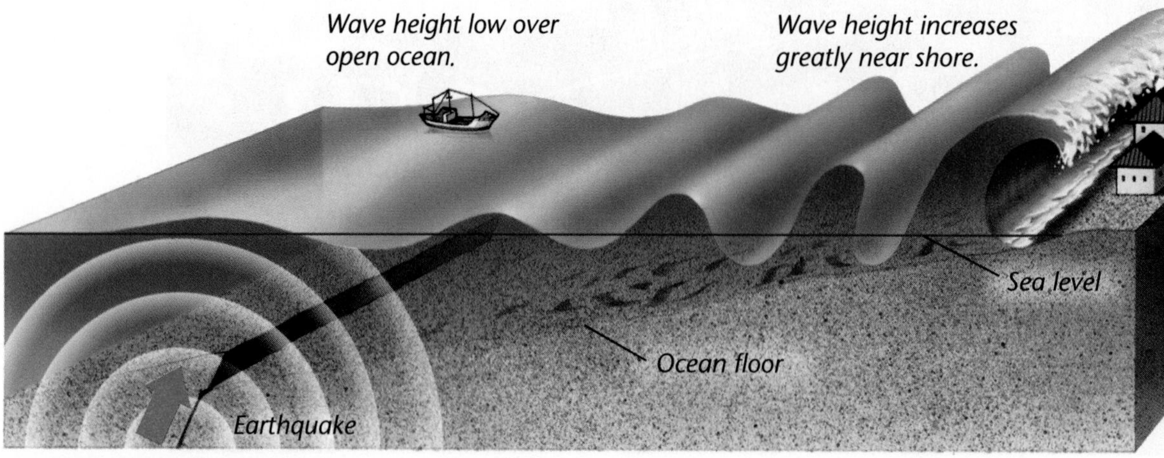
Wave height low over open ocean.
Wave height increases greatly near shore.
Sea level
Ocean floor
Earthquake

Figure 20 A tsunami begins as a low wave, but turns into a huge wave as it nears the shore.

Tsunamis When an earthquake jolts the ocean floor, plate movement causes the ocean floor to rise slightly and push water out of its way. If the earthquake is strong enough, the water displaced by the quake forms large waves, called **tsunamis** (tsoo NAH meez). Figure 20 follows a tsunami from where it begins on the ocean floor.

A tsunami spreads out from an earthquake's epicenter and speeds across the ocean. In the open ocean, the distance between the waves of a tsunami is a very long—between 100 and 200 kilometers. But the height of the wave is low. Tsunamis rise only half a meter or so above the other waves. However, as they approach shallow water near a coastline, the waves become closer together. The tsunami grows into a mountain of water. Some are the height of a six-story building.

☑ *Checkpoint* *What are the major causes of earthquake damage?*

Sharpen your Skills

Calculating ACTIVITY

The Tsunami Warning System alerts people who live near the Pacific Ocean. When geologists detect an earthquake on the ocean floor, they notify coastal areas.

An earthquake in the Gulf of Alaska occurs 3,600 kilometers from Hawaii. The quake's seismic waves travel about 560 kilometers per *minute.* The quake triggers a tsunami that travels at 640 kilometers per *hour.* The seismic waves arrive in Hawaii within minutes and are recorded on seismographs. The seismic waves' arrival warns of the dangerous tsunami that may follow. About how much advance warning will Hawaii have that a tsunami is on the way?

Making Buildings Safer

Most earthquake-related deaths and injuries result from damage to buildings or other structures. **To reduce earthquake damage, new buildings must be made stronger and more flexible. Older buildings must be modified to withstand stronger quakes.** A structure must be strong in order to resist violent shaking in a quake. It must also be flexible so it can twist and bend without breaking. *Exploring an Earthquake-Safe House* shows how a house can be made safer in an earthquake.

Choice of Location The location of a building affects the type of damage it may suffer during an earthquake. Steep slopes pose the danger of landslides. Filled land can shake violently. Therefore, people should avoid building on such sites. People should also avoid building structures near earthquake faults. As seismic waves pass through the earth, their strength decreases. So the farther a structure is from a fault, the less strong the shaking will be.

EXPLORING an Earthquake-Safe House

People can take a variety of steps to make their homes safer in an earthquake. Some steps strengthen the house itself. Others may help to keep objects from tipping or falling.

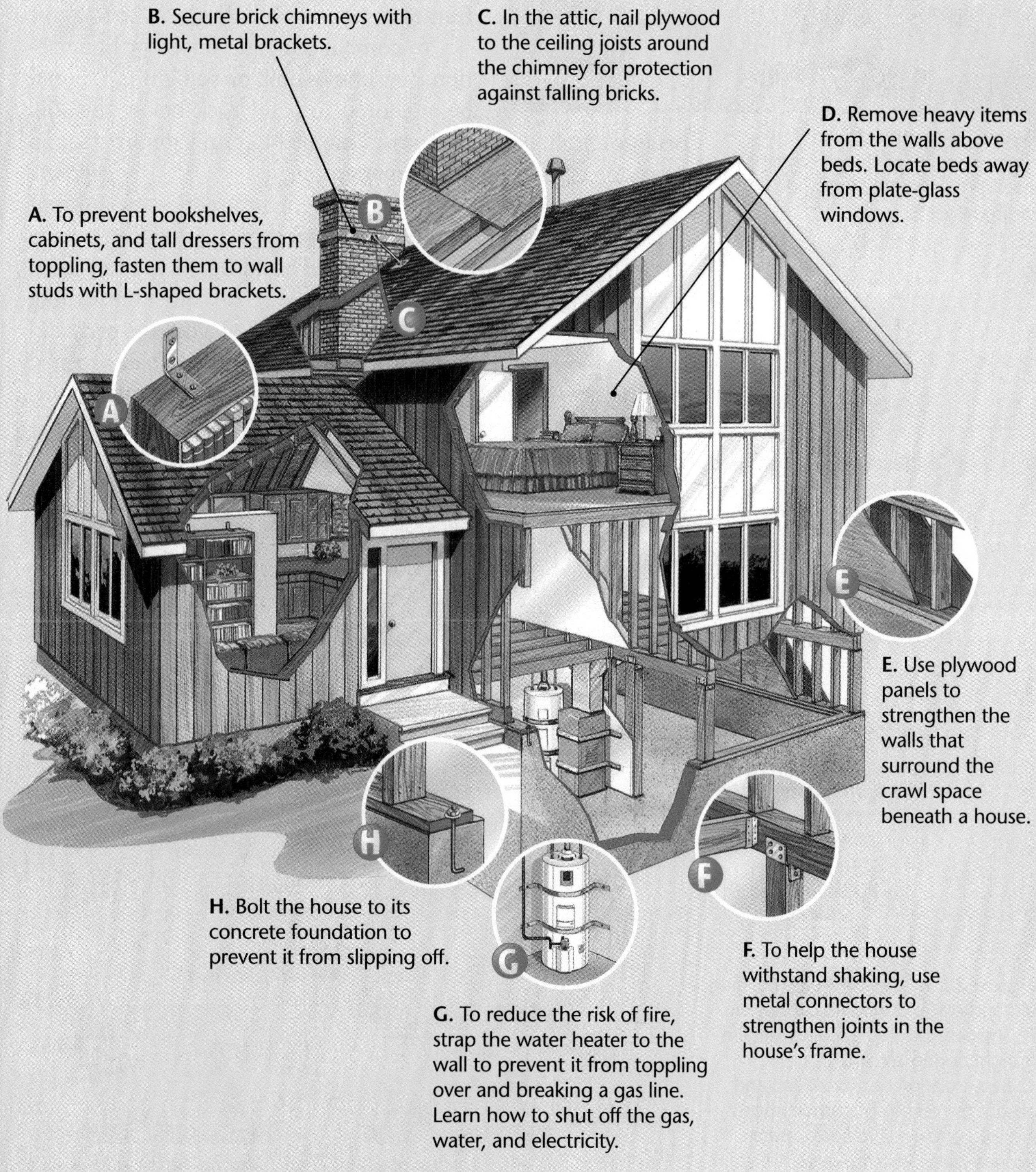
A. To prevent bookshelves, cabinets, and tall dressers from toppling, fasten them to wall studs with L-shaped brackets.
B. Secure brick chimneys with light, metal brackets.
C. In the attic, nail plywood to the ceiling joists around the chimney for protection against falling bricks.
D. Remove heavy items from the walls above beds. Locate beds away from plate-glass windows.
E. Use plywood panels to strengthen the walls that surround the crawl space beneath a house.
F. To help the house withstand shaking, use metal connectors to strengthen joints in the house's frame.
G. To reduce the risk of fire, strap the water heater to the wall to prevent it from toppling over and breaking a gas line. Learn how to shut off the gas, water, and electricity.
H. Bolt the house to its concrete foundation to prevent it from slipping off.

Figure 21 Architects and engineers work to design buildings that will be able to withstand earthquakes.

Construction Methods The way in which a building is constructed determines whether it can withstand an earthquake. During an earthquake, brick buildings as well as some wood-frame buildings may collapse if their walls have not been reinforced, or strengthened. Sometimes plywood sheets are used to strengthen the frames of wooden buildings.

To combat damage caused by liquefaction, new homes built on soft ground should be anchored to solid rock below the soil. Bridges and highway overpasses can be built on supports that go down through soft soil to firmer ground.

INTEGRATING TECHNOLOGY A building designed to reduce the amount of energy that reaches the building during an earthquake is called a **base-isolated building.** As you can see in Figure 22, a base-isolated building rests on shock-absorbing rubber pads or springs. Like the suspension of a car, the pads and springs smooth out a bumpy ride. During a quake, a base-isolated building moves gently back and forth without any violent shaking.

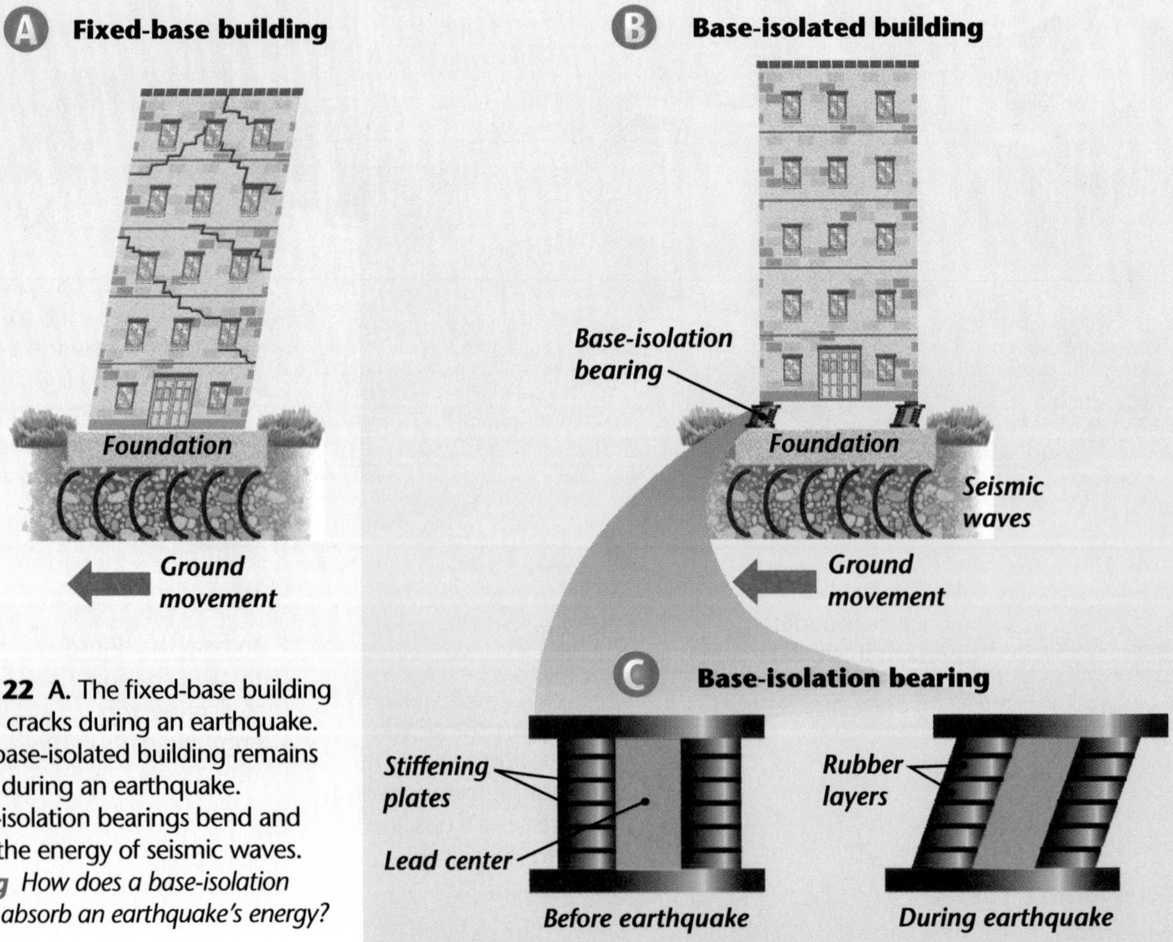
A Fixed-base building
Foundation
Ground movement
B Base-isolated building
Base-isolation bearing
Foundation
Seismic waves
Ground movement
C Base-isolation bearing
Stiffening plates
Lead center
Rubber layers
Before earthquake
During earthquake

Figure 22 **A.** The fixed-base building tilts and cracks during an earthquake. **B.** The base-isolated building remains upright during an earthquake. **C.** Base-isolation bearings bend and absorb the energy of seismic waves. ***Inferring*** *How does a base-isolation bearing absorb an earthquake's energy?*

Much earthquake damage is not the direct result of shaking. Earthquakes indirectly cause fire and flooding when gas pipes and water mains break. Flexible joints can be installed in gas and water lines to keep them from breaking. Automatic shut-off valves also can be installed on these lines to cut off gas and water flow.

Protecting Yourself During an Earthquake

What should you do if an earthquake strikes? The main danger is from falling objects and flying glass. **The best way to protect yourself is to drop, cover, and hold.** This means you should crouch beneath a sturdy table or desk and hold on to it so it doesn't jiggle away during the shaking. The desk or table will provide a barrier against falling objects. If no desk or table is available, crouch against an inner wall, away from the outside of a building, and cover your head and neck with your arms. Avoid windows, mirrors, wall hangings, and furniture that might topple.

If you are outdoors, move to an open area such as a playground. Avoid vehicles, power lines, trees, and buildings, especially ones with brick walls or chimneys. Sit down to avoid being thrown down.

INTEGRATING HEALTH After a major earthquake, water and power supplies may fail, food stores may be closed, and travel may be difficult. People may have to wait several days for these services to be restored. To prepare for such an emergency, families living in a region at high risk for damaging quakes may want to put together an earthquake kit. The kit should contain canned food, water, and first aid supplies and should be stored where it is easy to reach.

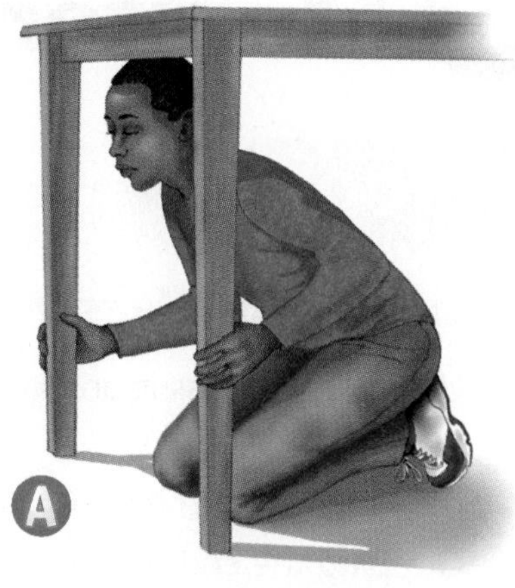
A

B

Figure 23 Drop, cover, and hold to protect yourself indoors during an earthquake. **A.** If possible, crouch under a desk or table. **B.** Or, crouch against an interior wall and cover your head and neck with your hands.

Section 3 Review

1. Explain how liquefaction occurs and how it causes damage during an earthquake.
2. What can residents do to reduce the risk of earthquake damage to their homes?
3. Describe safety measures you can take to protect yourself during an earthquake.
4. **Thinking Critically Problem Solving** You are a builder planning a housing development where earthquakes are likely. What types of land would you avoid for your development? Where would it be safe to build?

Science at Home

Show your family how an earthquake can affect two different structures—one with more weight on top, the other with more weight on the bottom. Make a model of a fault by placing two small, folded towels side by side on a flat surface. Pile a stack of books on the fault by placing the light books on the bottom and the heaviest ones on top. Then, gently pull the towels in opposite directions until the pile topples. Repeat the process, but this time with the heavier books on the bottom. Discuss with your family which makes a more stable structure.

SECTION 4 Monitoring Faults

DISCOVER ACTIVITY

Can Stress Be Measured?

1. Unfold a facial tissue and lay it flat on your desk.
2. Measure the length of the tissue with a ruler.
3. Grasping the ends of the tissue with both hands, gently pull it. As you are stretching it, hold the tissue against the ruler and measure its length again.
4. Stretch the tissue once more, but this time give it a hard tug.

Think It Over

Drawing Conclusions How is the tissue like the ground along a fault? How might measuring stress in the ground help in predicting an earthquake?

GUIDE FOR READING

- **How do geologists monitor faults?**
- **How do geologists determine earthquake risk?**

Reading Tip **As you read, make a list of devices for monitoring earthquakes. Write a sentence about each.**

The small town of Parkfield, California, lies on the San Andreas fault about halfway between Los Angeles and San Francisco. Geologists are fascinated by Parkfield because the town had a strong earthquake about every 22 years between 1857 and 1966. Scientists have not found any other place on Earth where the time from one earthquake to the next has been so regular.

In the early 1980s, geologists predicted that a strong earthquake was going to occur in Parkfield between 1985 and 1993. The geologists eagerly set up their instruments—and waited. They waited year after year for the predicted earthquake. But it didn't happen. Finally, several medium-sized earthquakes rumbled along the San Andreas fault near Parkfield in 1993–1994.

Did these quakes take the place of the larger earthquake that geologists had expected? Or had the San Andreas fault itself changed, breaking the pattern of 22 years between quakes? Geologists still don't know the answers to these questions. Nonetheless, geologists continue to monitor the San Andreas fault. Someday, they may find a way to predict when and where an earthquake will occur.

Figure 24 This laser beam detects movement along the San Andreas Fault in Parkfield, California.

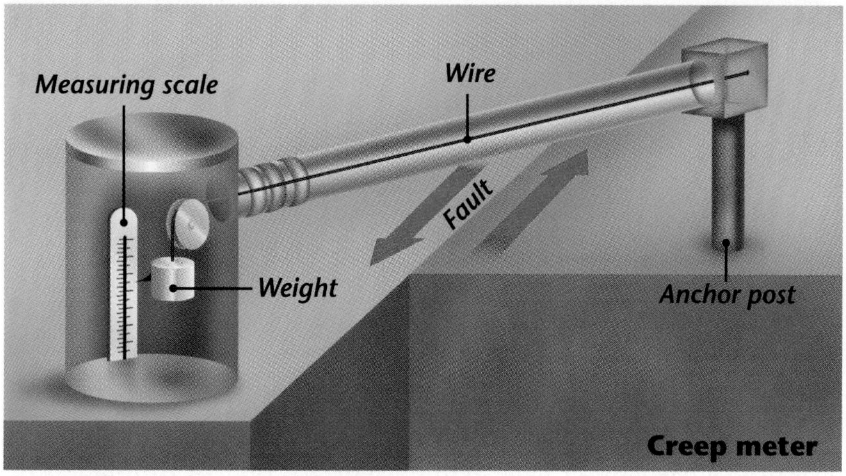
Measuring scale
Wire
Fault
Weight
Anchor post
Creep meter

Figure 25 A creep meter can be used to measure movement along a strike-slip fault.

Devices that Monitor Faults

In trying to predict earthquakes, geologists have invented instruments to record the ground movements that occur along faults. **To observe these changes, geologists put in place instruments that measure stress and deformation in the crust.** Geologists hypothesize that such changes signal an approaching earthquake.

Unfortunately, earthquakes almost always strike without warning. The only clue may be a slight rise or fall in the elevation and tilt of the land. Instruments that geologists use to monitor these movements include creep meters, laser-ranging devices, tiltmeters, and satellites.

Creep Meters A creep meter uses a wire stretched across a fault to measure horizontal movement of the ground. On one side of the fault, the wire is anchored to a post. On the other side, the wire is attached to a weight that can slide if the fault moves. Geologists can measure the amount that the fault has moved by measuring how much the weight has moved against a measuring scale.

Laser-Ranging Devices A laser-ranging device uses a laser beam to detect even tiny fault movements. The device calculates any change in the time needed for the laser beam to travel to a reflector and bounce back. Thus, the device can detect any change in distance to the reflector.

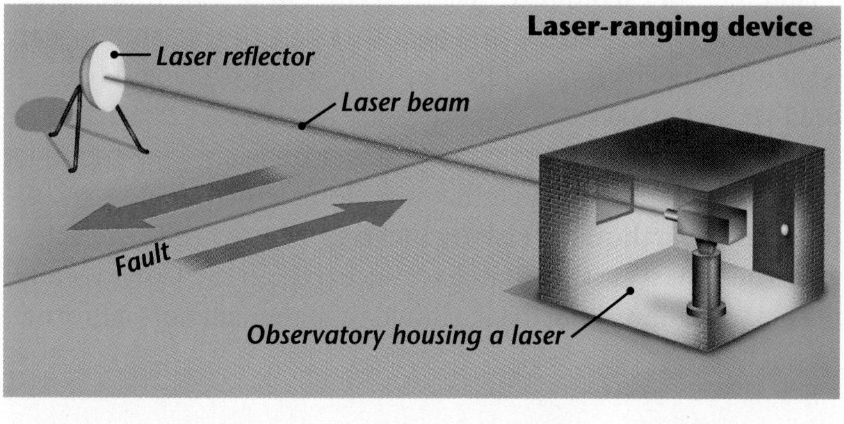
Laser-ranging device
Laser reflector
Laser beam
Fault
Observatory housing a laser

Figure 26 A laser-ranging device monitors fault movement by bouncing a laser beam off a reflector on the other side of the fault. ***Comparing and Contrasting*** *How are a laser-ranging device and a creep meter (shown above) similar? How are they different?*

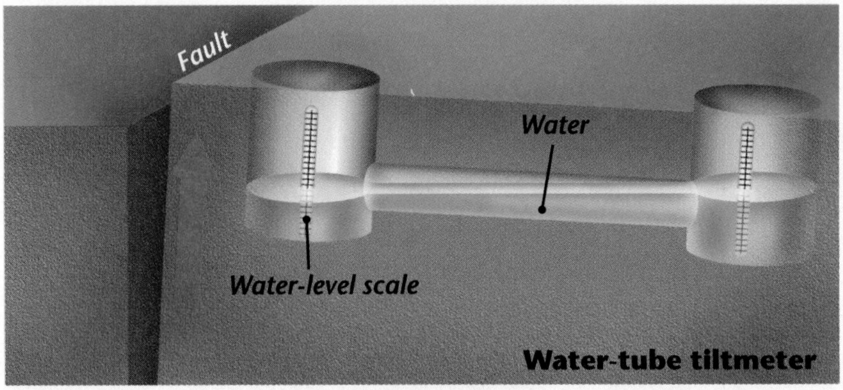
Fault
Water
Water-level scale
Water-tube tiltmeter

Figure 27 A tiltmeter monitors vertical movement along a fault.

Tiltmeters A tiltmeter measures tilting of the ground. If you have ever used a carpenter's level, you have used a type of tiltmeter. The tiltmeters used by seismologists consist of two bulbs that are filled with a liquid and connected by a hollow stem. Look at the drawing of a tiltmeter in Figure 27. Notice that if the land rises or falls even slightly, the liquid will flow from one bulb to the other. Each bulb contains a measuring scale to measure the depth of the liquid in that bulb. Geologists read the scales to measure the amount of tilt occurring along the fault.

Integrating Space Science **Satellite Monitors** Besides ground-based instruments, geologists use satellites equipped with radar to make images of faults. The satellite bounces radio waves off the ground. As the waves echo back into space, the satellite records them. The time it takes for the radio waves to make their round trip provides precise measurements of the distance to the ground. The distance from the ground to the satellite changes with every change in the ground surface. By comparing different images of the same area taken at different times, geologists detect small changes in elevation. These changes in elevation result when stress deforms the ground along a fault.

☑ *Checkpoint What do fault-monitoring instruments measure?*

Monitoring Risk in the United States

Even with data from many sources, geologists can't predict when and where a quake will strike. Usually, stress along a fault increases until an earthquake occurs. Yet sometimes stress builds up along a fault, but an earthquake fails to occur. Or, one or more earthquakes may relieve stress along another part of the fault. Exactly what will happen remains uncertain—that's why geologists cannot predict earthquakes.

Geologists do know that earthquakes are likely wherever plate movement stores energy in the rock along faults. **Geologists can determine earthquake risk by locating where faults are active and where past earthquakes have occurred.** In the United States, the risk is highest along the Pacific coast in the states of California,

Language Arts CONNECTION

In an emergency broadcast, the television newscaster must not only provide information on the disaster, but also grab the viewer's attention. To state the facts as briefly as possible, journalists use the 5 W's: Who, What, Where, When, and Why.

In Your Journal

You are a local newscaster presenting the news. During your broadcast, you receive information that a major earthquake has struck a city in another part of the country. You must interrupt the regular news to present an emergency news bulletin. Write that bulletin, following the 5 W's.

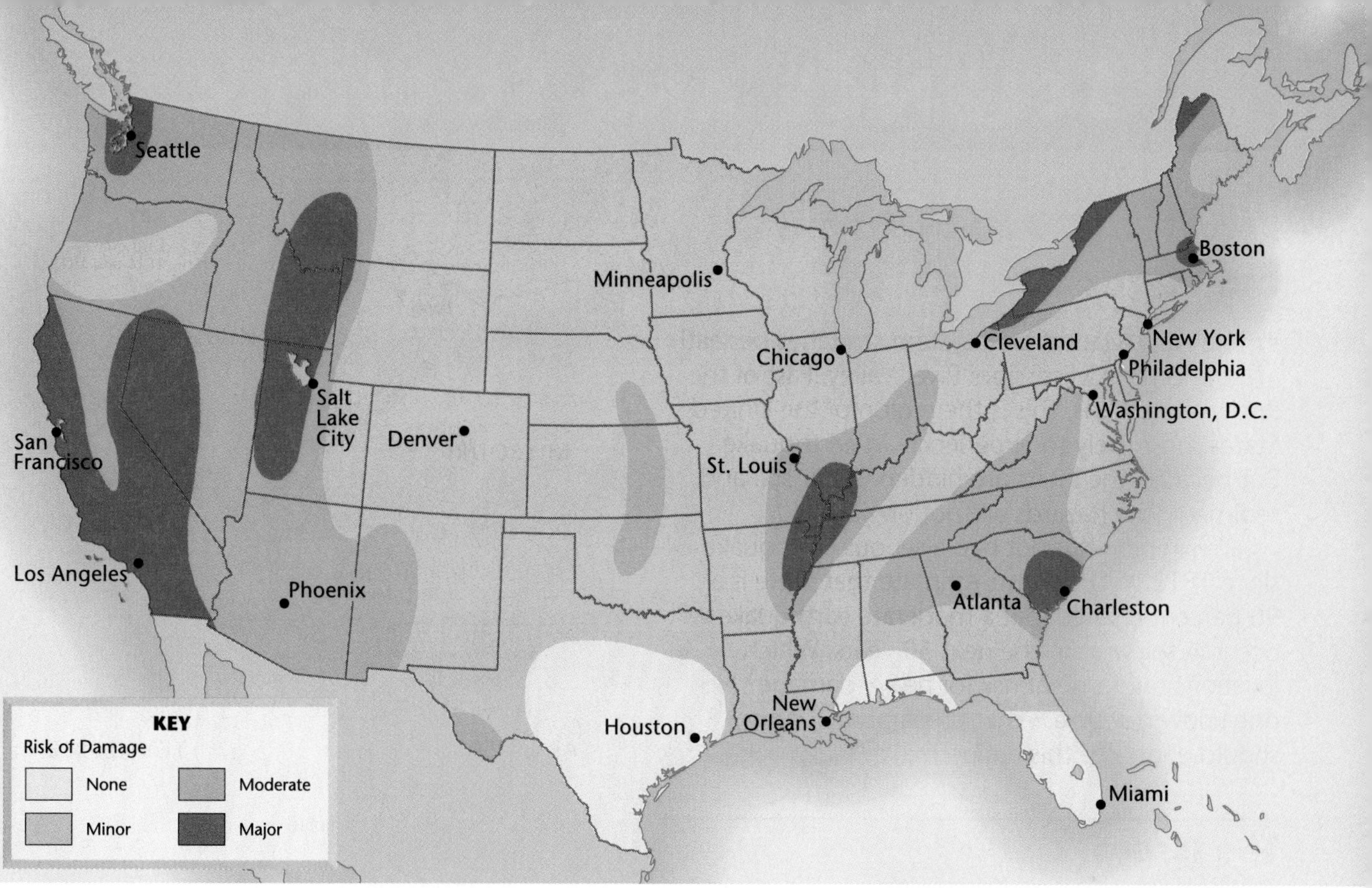
Seattle
Boston
Minneapolis
Cleveland
New York
Chicago
Philadelphia
Salt Lake City
Washington, D.C.
San Francisco
Denver
St. Louis
Los Angeles
Phoenix
Atlanta
Charleston
New Orleans
Houston
Miami
KEY
Risk of Damage
None
Moderate
Minor
Major

Figure 28 The map shows areas of the United States, excluding Alaska and Hawaii, where earthquakes are likely to occur and the relative damage they are likely to cause. *Interpreting Maps Where are damaging earthquakes least likely to occur? Most likely to occur?*

Washington, and Alaska. The risk of quakes is high because that's where the Pacific and North American plates meet.

Other regions of the United States also have some risk of earthquakes. Serious earthquakes are rare east of the Rockies. Nonetheless, the region has experienced some of the most powerful quakes in the nation's history. Scientists hypothesize that the continental plate forming most of North America is under stress. This stress could disturb faults that formed millions of years ago. Today, these faults lie hidden beneath thick layers of soil and rock. Find your state in Figure 28 to determine your area's risk of a damaging quake.

Section 4 Review

1. What equipment do geologists use to monitor the movement of faults?
2. What two factors do geologists consider when determining earthquake risk for a region?
3. Explain how satellites can be used to collect data on earthquake faults.
4. **Thinking Critically Making Generalizations** Why can't scientists predict the exact time and place an earthquake is going to occur?

CHAPTER PROJECT

Check Your Progress

Use what you have learned about making buildings earthquake resistant to repair and improve your structure. Test your model again. Are your changes successful in preventing damage? Make additional repairs and improvements to your structure.

What's the Risk of an Earthquake?

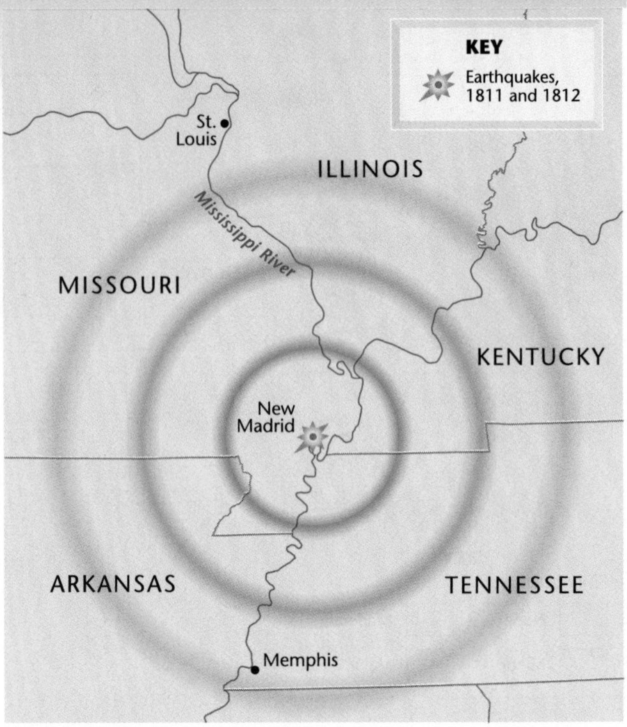
KEY
Earthquakes, 1811 and 1812
St. Louis
ILLINOIS
Mississippi River
MISSOURI
KENTUCKY
New Madrid
ARKANSAS
TENNESSEE
Memphis

The New Madrid fault system stretches beneath the central Mississippi River Valley. East of the Rocky Mountains, this is the region of the United States most likely to experience an earthquake. But because the faults are hidden under soil and sediment, the hazards are not obvious.

This region has not had a serious earthquake since 1812. Yet scientists estimate that there is a 90 percent chance that a moderate earthquake will occur in this area in the next 50 years. Which locations might be at risk for heavy damage? No one knows for sure. What preparations, if any, should people of this region make?

The Issues

How Much Money Should People Spend? In areas where earthquakes are rare, such as the New Madrid fault region, communities face hard choices. Should they spend money for earthquake preparation now in order to cut costs later? Or should they save the money and risk the consequences?

Which Buildings Should Be Modified? It's clear that the best way to save lives is to make buildings that can withstand severe shaking. Since damaged or collapsing buildings cause most injuries and deaths during earthquakes, modifying existing buildings could save lives. Unfortunately building renovations are costly.

Most new houses can withstand moderate earthquakes. But many older houses—especially brick or masonry houses—are not safe. Unfortunately, few homeowners can afford the cost of making their houses safer. They might need financial aid or a tax break to help them make these changes.

What Other Structures Need Improvement? Imagine what would happen if your community were without utility stations and lines for electricity, gas, and water, or without bridges, schools, and hospitals. Engineers who understand earthquake hazards have worked out design standards to reduce damage to these structures. Today, many cities follow these standards in their building codes. But not all structures can be made earthquake-safe. Furthermore, some structures are more crucial for public health and safety than others.

You Decide

1. Identify the Problem
Summarize the dilemma that communities face in regard to earthquake preparations. Which structures in a community are most important to make earthquake-resistant?

2. Analyze the Options
Consider what would happen if communities spent more money, less money, or nothing on earthquake preparations. In each case, who would benefit? Who might be harmed?

3. Find a Solution
Your community near the New Madrid fault system has received a large sum of money to spend on earthquake preparedness. Develop a plan for building and modifying structures. Explain and defend your use of funds.

Section 1 Earth's Crust in Motion

Key Ideas

- Stresses on Earth's crust produce compression, tension, and shearing in rock.
- Faults are cracks in Earth's crust that result from stress.
- Faulting and folding of the crust cause mountains and other features to form on the surface.

Key Terms

earthquake	hanging wall
stress	footwall
deformation	reverse fault
shearing	fault-block mountain
tension	folds
compression	anticline
fault	syncline
strike-slip fault	plateau
normal fault	

Section 2 Measuring Earthquakes

Key Ideas

- As seismic waves travel through Earth, they carry the energy of an earthquake from the focus to the surface.
- Earthquakes produce two types of seismic waves, P waves and S waves, that travel out in all directions from the focus of an earthquake.
- Today, the moment magnitude scale is used to determine the magnitude of an earthquake. Other scales that geologists have used to rate earthquakes include the Mercalli scale and the Richter scale.

Key Terms

focus	seismograph
epicenter	magnitude
seismic waves	Mercalli scale
P waves	Richter scale
S waves	moment magnitude scale
surface waves	

Section 3 Earthquake Hazards and Safety

Key Ideas

- Earthquakes can damage buildings and other structures through shaking or liquefaction of the ground, tsunamis, and landslides or avalanches.
- New buildings can be designed to withstand earthquakes; old buildings can be modified to make them more earthquake-resistant.
- For personal safety indoors during an earthquake, drop, cover, and hold under a desk or table, or against an interior wall.

Key Terms

liquefaction	tsunamis
aftershock	base-isolated building

Section 4 Monitoring Faults

INTEGRATING TECHNOLOGY

Key Ideas

- Geologists use instruments to measure deformation and stress along faults.
- Scientists determine earthquake risk by monitoring active faults and by studying faults where past earthquakes have occurred.

ACTIVITY

USING THE INTERNET

www.phschool.com/state_focus/california/

California Test Prep: Reviewing Content

Multiple Choice

Chose the letter of the answer that best completes each statement.

1. Shearing is the force in Earth's crust that
   a. squeezes the crust together.
   b. pushes the crust in opposite directions.
   c. forces the crust to bend and fold.
   d. stretches the crust apart.
2. When the hanging wall of a fault slips downward with respect to the footwall, the result is a
   a. reverse fault. b. syncline.
   c. normal fault. d. strike-slip fault.
3. A seismograph measures
   a. the depth of an earthquake.
   b. friction forces along a fault.
   c. ground motion during an earthquake.
   d. movement along a fault.
4. Geologists use the difference in the arrival times of P waves and S waves at a seismograph to determine
   a. the magnitude of the earthquake.
   b. the depth of the earthquake's focus.
   c. the strength of the surface waves.
   d. the distance to the epicenter.
5. To monitor the upward movement along a fault, geologists would probably use a
   a. laser-ranging device.
   b. tiltmeter.
   c. seismograph.
   d. creep meter.

True or False

If the statement is true, write true. If it is false, change the underlined word or words to make the statement true.

6. Deformation is the breaking, tilting, and folding of rocks caused by liquefaction.
7. Rock uplifted by strike-slip faults creates fault-block mountains.
8. An earthquake's epicenter is located deep underground.
9. As S waves move through the ground, they cause it to compress and then expand.
10. Tsunamis are triggered by earthquakes originating beneath the ocean floor.

Checking Concepts

11. How does stress affect Earth's crust?
12. Explain the process that forms a fault-block mountain.
13. What type of stress in the crust results in the formation of folded mountains? Explain your answer.
14. What are plateaus and how do they form?
15. Explain how the moment magnitude and Richter scales of earthquake measurement are similar and how they are different.
16. When geologists monitor a fault, what kinds of data do they collect? Explain.
17. **Writing to Learn** You are a geologist studying earthquake risk in an eastern state. Your data show that a major earthquake might happen there within 10 years. Write a letter to the governor of your state explaining why there is an earthquake hazard there and recommending how your state should prepare for the earthquake.

Thinking Visually

18. **Concept Map** Copy the concept map about stress on a separate piece of paper. Then complete it and add a title. (For more on concept maps, see the Skills Handbook.)

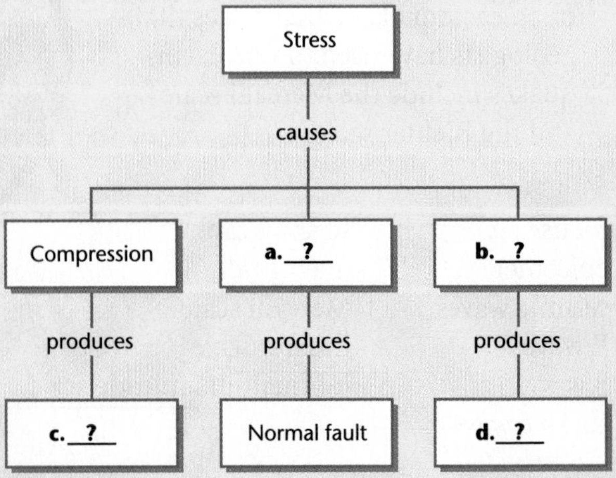
Stress
causes
Compression
a. ?
b. ?
produces
produces
produces
c. ?
Normal fault
d. ?

Test Prep: Skills

The graph shows the seismograph record for an earthquake. The y-axis of the graph shows the up-and-down shaking in millimeters detected at the seismograph station. The x-axis shows time in minutes.

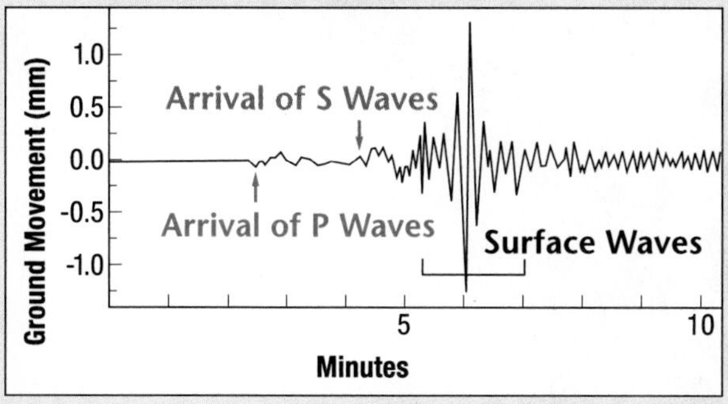
Ground Movement (mm)
1.0
0.5
0.0
-0.5
-1.0
Arrival of S Waves
Arrival of P Waves
Surface Waves
5
10
Minutes

19. Interpreting Diagrams In what order do the seismic waves arrive at the seismograph station? Which type of seismic wave produces the largest ground movement?

20. Interpreting Diagrams What is the difference in arrival times for the P waves and S waves?

21. Predicting What would the seismograph record look like several hours after this earthquake? How would it change if an aftershock occurred?

22. Drawing Conclusions If the difference in arrival times for P waves and S waves is 5 minutes longer at a second seismograph station than at the first station, what can you conclude about the location of the second station?

Thinking Critically

23. Classifying How would you classify a fault in which the hanging wall has slid up and over the footwall?

24. Comparing and Contrasting Compare and contrast P waves and S waves.

25. Predicting A community has just built a street across a strike-slip fault that has frequent earthquakes. How will movement along the fault affect the street?

26. Applying Concepts If you were building a house in an earthquake-prone area, what steps would you take to limit potential damage in an earthquake?

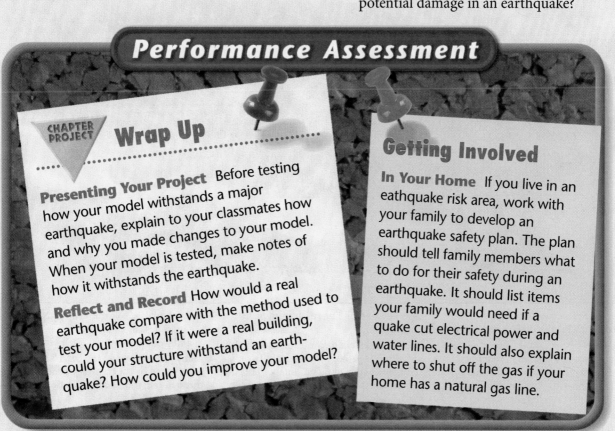

Performance Assessment

CHAPTER PROJECT

Wrap Up

Presenting Your Project Before testing how your model withstands a major earthquake, explain to your classmates how and why you made changes to your model. When your model is tested, make notes of how it withstands the earthquake.

Reflect and Record How would a real earthquake compare with the method used to test your model? If it were a real building, could your structure withstand an earthquake? How could you improve your model?

Getting Involved

In Your Home If you live in an eathquake risk area, work with your family to develop an earthquake safety plan. The plan should tell family members what to do for their safety during an earthquake. It should list items your family would need if a quake cut electrical power and water lines. It should also explain where to shut off the gas if your home has a natural gas line.

CHAPTER

3 Volcanoes

Kilauea volcano is on Hawaii, the largest of the Hawaiian Islands.

The following California Science Content Standards are addressed in this chapter:

1. **Plate tectonics explains important features of the Earth's surface and major geologic events.**
   - **d.** Earthquakes are sudden motions along breaks in the crust called faults, and volcanoes/fissures are locations where magma reaches the surface.
   - **e.** Major geologic events, such as earthquakes, volcanic eruptions, and mountain building result from plate motions.
   - **f.** How to explain major features of California geology in terms of plate tectonics (including mountains, faults, volcanoes).
2. **Topography is reshaped by weathering of rock and soil and by the transportation and deposition of sediment.**
   - **d.** Earthquakes, volcanic eruptions, landslides, and floods change human and wildlife habitats.
4. **Many phenomena on the Earth's surface are affected by the transfer of energy through radiation and convection currents.**
   - **c.** Heat from Earth's interior reaches the surface primarily through convection.

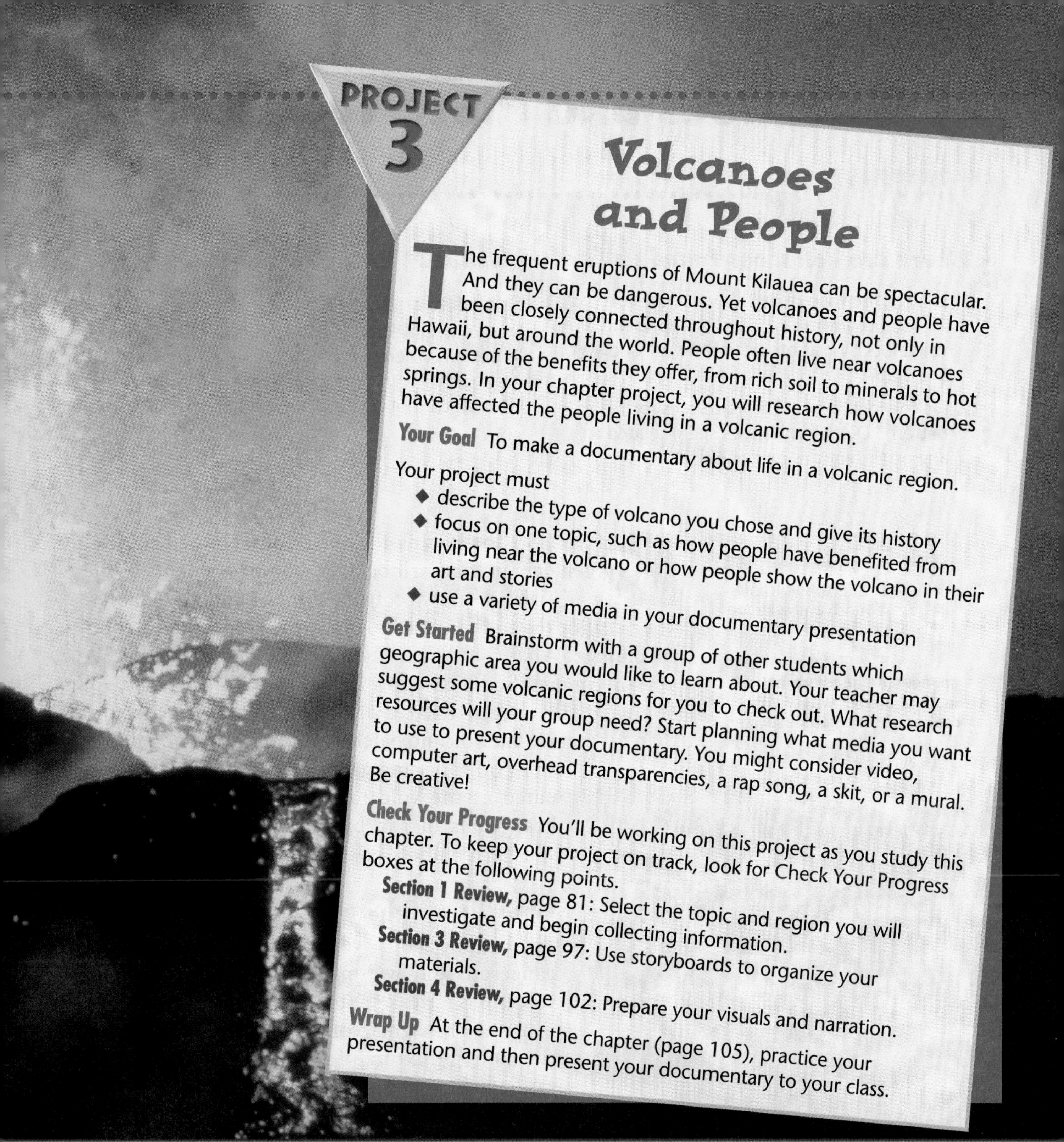

PROJECT 3

Volcanoes and People

The frequent eruptions of Mount Kilauea can be spectacular. And they can be dangerous. Yet volcanoes and people have been closely connected throughout history, not only in Hawaii, but around the world. People often live near volcanoes because of the benefits they offer, from rich soil to minerals to hot springs. In your chapter project, you will research how volcanoes have affected the people living in a volcanic region.

Your Goal To make a documentary about life in a volcanic region.

Your project must

- describe the type of volcano you chose and give its history
- focus on one topic, such as how people have benefited from living near the volcano or how people show the volcano in their art and stories
- use a variety of media in your documentary presentation

Get Started Brainstorm with a group of other students which geographic area you would like to learn about. Your teacher may suggest some volcanic regions for you to check out. What research resources will your group need? Start planning what media you want to use to present your documentary. You might consider video, computer art, overhead transparencies, a rap song, a skit, or a mural. Be creative!

Check Your Progress You'll be working on this project as you study this chapter. To keep your project on track, look for Check Your Progress boxes at the following points.

Section 1 Review, page 81: Select the topic and region you will investigate and begin collecting information.

Section 3 Review, page 97: Use storyboards to organize your materials.

Section 4 Review, page 102: Prepare your visuals and narration.

Wrap Up At the end of the chapter (page 105), practice your presentation and then present your documentary to your class.

6. Sources of energy and materials differ in amounts, distribution, usefulness, and the time required for their formation.

a. The utility of energy sources is determined by factors that are involved in converting these sources to useful forms and the consequences of the conversion process.

7. Scientific progress is made by asking meaningful questions and conducting careful investigations.

a. Develop a hypothesis.

d. Communicate the steps and results from an investigation in written reports and verbal presentations.

f. Read a topographic map and a geologic map for evidence provided on the maps, and construct and interpret a simple scale map.

SECTION 1 Volcanoes and Plate Tectonics

DISCOVER ACTIVITY

Where Are Volcanoes Found on Earth's Surface?

1. Look at the map of Earth's volcanoes on page 79. What symbols are used to represent volcanoes? What other symbols are shown on the map?
2. Do the locations of the volcanoes form a pattern? Do the volcanoes seem related to any other features on Earth's surface?

Think About It

Developing Hypotheses Develop a hypothesis to explain where Earth's volcanoes are located. Are there any volcanoes on the map whose location cannot be explained by your hypothesis?

GUIDE FOR READING

- **Where are Earth's volcanic regions found, and why are they found there?**

Reading Tip **Before you read, preview the headings in this section. Predict where volcanoes are likely to be located.**

Before 1995, the island of Montserrat sat like a beautiful green gem in the Caribbean Sea. Some residents of the small island grew cotton, limes, and vegetables. Tourists flocked to the island to enjoy the scenery and tropical climate. What could possibly spoil this island paradise? A volcano named Soufrière (soo free EHR) Hills did. In 1995, Soufrière Hills began a series of eruptions that lasted more than two years. The volcano belched volcanic ash that fell like snow on roofs and gardens. Residents were evacuated as the volcano continued to erupt, and heavy falls of ash buried entire towns on the southern half of the island.

◀ **Soufrière Hills volcano**

What Is a Volcano?

The eruption of a volcano is among the most dangerous and awe-inspiring events on Earth. A **volcano** is a weak spot in the crust where molten material, or magma, comes to the surface. **Magma** is a molten mixture of rock-forming substances, gases, and water from the mantle. When magma reaches the surface, it is called **lava**. After lava has cooled, it forms solid rock. The lava released during volcanic activity builds up Earth's surface. Volcanic activity is a constructive force that adds new rock to existing land and forms new islands.

Location of Volcanoes

There are about 600 active volcanoes on land. Many more lie beneath the sea. Figure 1 is a map that shows the location of Earth's volcanoes. Notice how volcanoes occur in belts that extend across continents and oceans. One major volcanic belt is the **Ring of Fire,** formed by the many volcanoes that rim the Pacific Ocean. Can you find other volcanic belts on the map?

Volcanic belts form along the boundaries of Earth's plates. At plate boundaries, huge pieces of the crust diverge (pull apart) or converge (push together). Here, the crust is weak and fractured, allowing magma to reach the surface. **Most volcanoes occur along diverging plate boundaries, such as the mid-ocean ridge, or in subduction zones around the edges of oceans.** But there are exceptions to this pattern. Some volcanoes form at "hot spots" far from the boundaries of continental or oceanic plates.

Volcanoes at Diverging Plate Boundaries

Volcanoes form along the mid-ocean ridge, which marks a diverging plate boundary. Recall from Chapter 1 that the ridge is a long, underwater rift valley that winds through the oceans. Along the ridge, lava pours out of cracks in the ocean floor. Only in a few places, as in Iceland and the Azores Islands in the Atlantic Ocean, do the volcanoes of the mid-ocean ridge rise above the ocean's surface.

Language Arts CONNECTION

The word *volcano* comes from the name of the Roman god of fire, Vulcan. According to Roman mythology, Vulcan lived beneath Mount Etna, a huge volcano on the island of Sicily in the Mediterranean Sea. Vulcan used the heat of Mount Etna to make metal armor and weapons for the ancient gods and heroes.

In Your Journal

Use the dictionary to find the definition of *plutonic* rock. Explain why the name of another Roman god was used for this term.

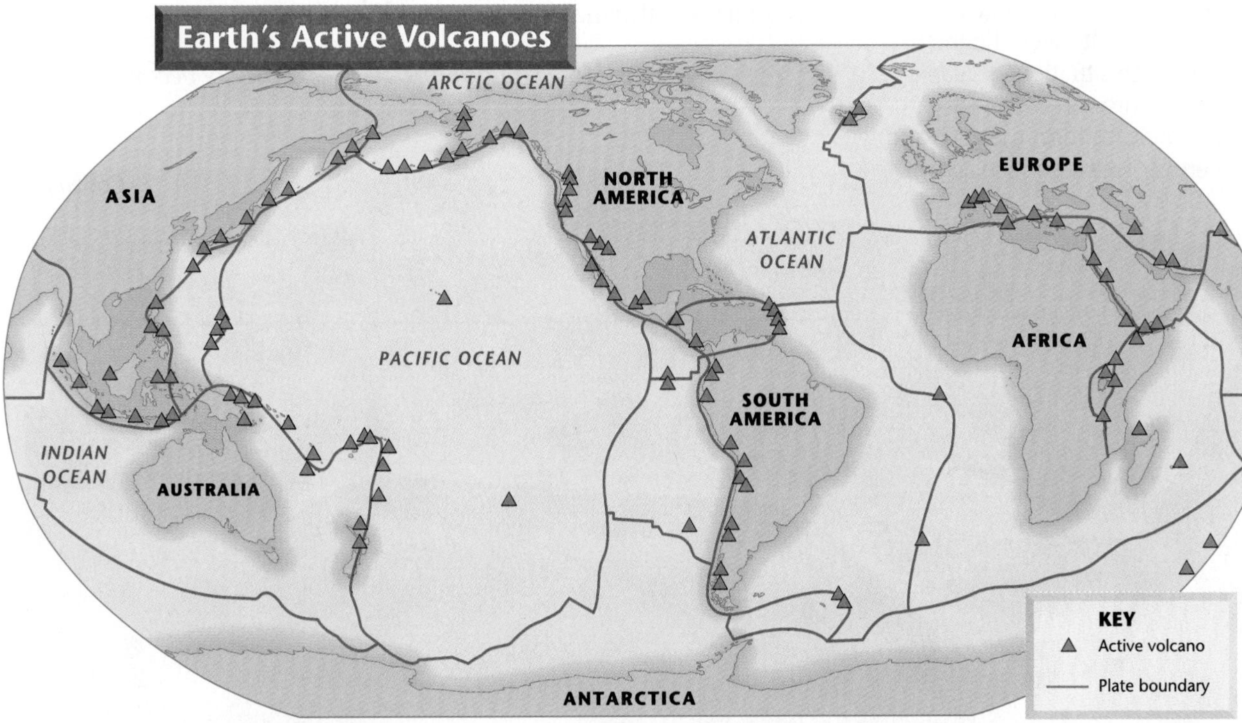
Earth's Active Volcanoes
ARCTIC OCEAN
ASIA
NORTH AMERICA
EUROPE
ATLANTIC OCEAN
PACIFIC OCEAN
AFRICA
SOUTH AMERICA
INDIAN OCEAN
AUSTRALIA
ANTARCTICA
KEY
Active volcano
Plate boundary

Figure 1 The Ring of Fire is a belt of volcanoes that circles the Pacific Ocean. **Observing** *What other patterns can you see in the locations of Earth's volcanoes?*

Volcanoes at Converging Boundaries

Many volcanoes form near the plate boundaries where oceanic crust returns to the mantle. Subduction causes slabs of oceanic crust to sink through a deep-ocean trench into the mantle. The crust melts and forms magma, which then rises back toward the surface. When the magma from the melted crust erupts as lava, volcanoes are formed. Figure 2 shows how converging plates produce volcanoes.

Many volcanoes occur on islands, near boundaries where two oceanic plates collide. The older, denser plate dives under the other plate, creating a deep-ocean trench. The lower plate sinks beneath the deep-ocean trench into the asthenosphere. There it begins to melt, forming magma. Because it is less dense than the surrounding rock, the magma seeps upward through cracks in the crust. Eventually, the magma breaks through the ocean floor, creating volcanoes.

The resulting volcanoes create a string of islands called an **island arc**. The curve of an island arc echoes the curve of its deep-ocean trench. Major island arcs include Japan, New Zealand, Indonesia, the Caribbean islands, the Philippines, and the Aleutians.

Subduction also occurs where the edge of a continental plate collides with an oceanic plate. Collisions between oceanic and continental plates produced both the volcanoes of the Andes mountains on the west coast of South America and the volcanoes of northern California, Oregon, and Washington.

☑ *Checkpoint* *How can oceanic crust eventually become magma?*

Figure 2 Converging plates often form volcanoes when two oceanic plates collide or when an oceanic plate collides with a continental plate. In both situations, oceanic crust sinks through a deep-ocean trench, melts to form magma, and then erupts to the surface as lava.

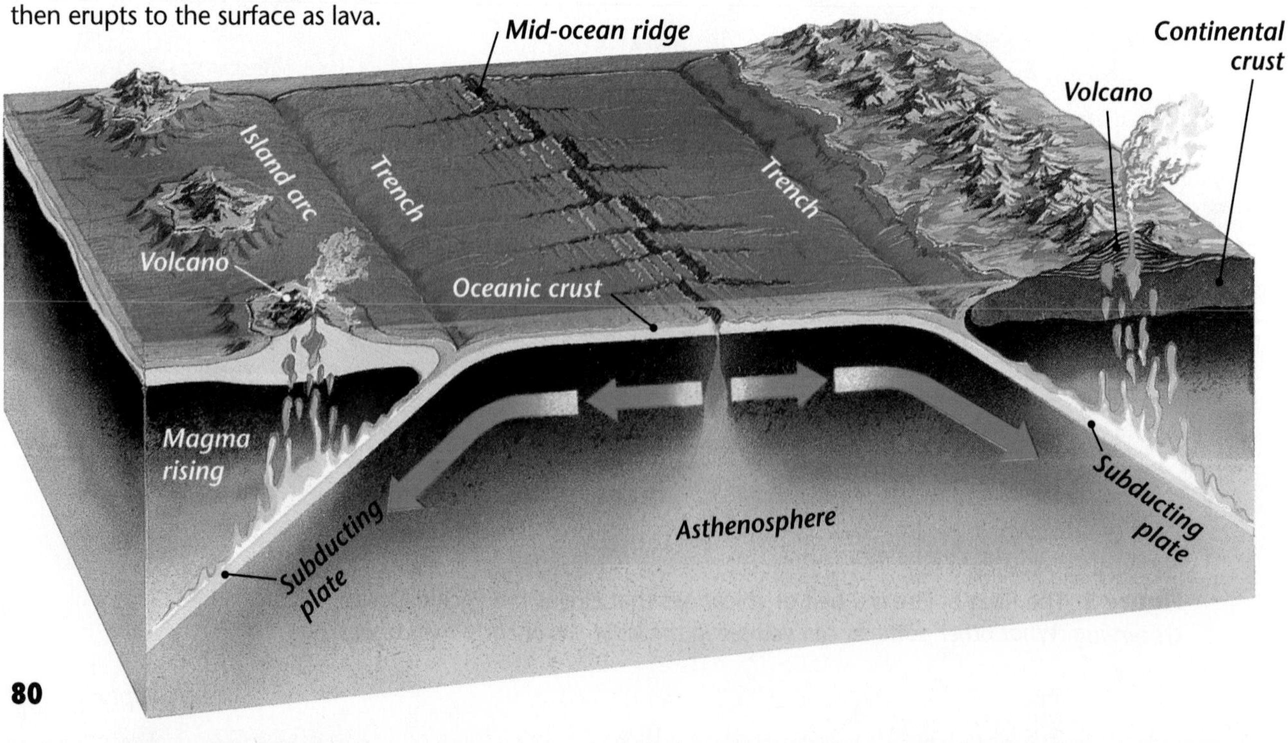
Mid-ocean ridge
Continental crust
Volcano
Island arc
Trench
Trench
Volcano
Oceanic crust
Magma rising
Subducting plate
Asthenosphere
Subducting plate

Pacific Ocean
Kauai
Oahu
Maui
Hawaii
Hawaiian Islands
Hot spot
Pacific plate

Figure 3 Hawaii sits on the moving Pacific plate. Beneath it is a powerful hot spot. Eventually, the plate's movement will carry the island of Hawaii away from the hot spot. *Inferring Which island on the map formed first?*

Hot Spot Volcanoes

Some volcanoes result from "hot spots" in Earth's mantle. A **hot spot** is an area where magma from deep within the mantle melts through the crust like a blow torch. Hot spots often lie in the middle of continental or oceanic plates far from any plate boundaries. Unlike the volcanoes in an island arc, the volcanoes at a hot spot do not result from subduction.

A hot spot volcano in the ocean floor can gradually form a series of volcanic mountains. For example, the Hawaiian Islands formed one by one over millions of years as the Pacific plate drifted over a hot spot.

Hot spots can also form under the continents. Yellowstone National Park in Wyoming marks a major hot spot under the North American plate. The last volcanic eruption in Yellowstone occurred about 75,000 years ago.

TRY THIS

Hot Spot in a Box

ACTIVITY

1. Fill a plastic box half full of cold water. This represents the ocean.
2. Mix red food coloring with hot water in a small, narrow-necked bottle to represent magma.
3. Hold your finger over the mouth of the bottle as you place the bottle in the center of the box. The mouth of the bottle must be under water.
4. Float a flat piece of plastic foam on the water to model a tectonic plate. Make sure the "plate" is floating above the bottle.
5. Take your finger off the bottle and observe what happens to the "magma."

Making Models Move the plastic foam slowly along. Where does the magma touch the "plate"? How does this model a hot spot volcano?

Section 1 Review

1. Where do most volcanoes occur on Earth's surface?
2. What process forms island arcs?
3. What causes hot spot volcanoes to form?
4. **Thinking Critically Predicting** What will eventually happen to the active volcano on the island of Hawaii, which is now over the hot spot?

CHAPTER PROJECT

Check Your Progress

Start by selecting the volcanic region you will study. Possible topics to investigate are myths and legends about volcanoes, the importance of volcanic soils, mineral resources from volcanoes, tourism, and geothermal power. Choose the topic that interests you the most. Begin your research and take notes on the information you collect.

Skills Lab

Interpreting Data

Mapping Earthquakes and Volcanoes

In this lab, you will interpret data on the locations of earthquakes and volcanoes to find patterns.

Problem

Is there a pattern in the locations of earthquakes and volcanoes?

Materials

outline world map showing longitude and latitude
4 pencils of different colors

Procedure

1. Use the information in the table to mark the location of each earthquake on the world map. Use one of the colored pencils to draw a letter E inside a circle at each earthquake location.
2. Use a pencil of a second color to mark the locations of the volcanoes on the world map. Indicate each volcano with the letter V inside a circle.
3. Use a third pencil to lightly shade the areas in which earthquakes are found.
4. Use a fourth colored pencil to lightly shade the areas in which volcanoes are found.

Analyze and Conclude

1. How are earthquakes distributed on the map? Are they scattered evenly over Earth's surface? Are they concentrated in zones?
2. How are volcanoes distributed? Are they scattered evenly or concentrated in zones?
3. From your data, what can you infer about the relationship between earthquakes and volcanoes?
4. **Apply** Based on the data, which area of the North American continent would have the greatest risk of earthquake damage? Of volcano damage? Why would knowing this information be important to urban planners, engineers, and builders in this area?

More to Explore

On a map of the United States, locate active volcanoes and areas of earthquake activity. Determine the distance from your home to the nearest active volcano.

Earthquakes		Volcanoes	
Longitude	Latitude	Longitude	Latitude
120° W	40° N	150° W	60° N
110° E	5° S	70° W	35° S
77° W	4° S	120° W	45° N
88° E	23° N	61° W	15° N
121° E	14° S	105° W	20° N
34° E	7° N	75° W	0°
74° W	44° N	122° W	40° N
70° W	30° S	30° E	40° N
10° E	45° N	60° E	30° N
85° W	13° N	160° E	55° N
125° E	23° N	37° E	3° S
30° E	35° N	145° E	40° N
140° E	35° N	120° E	10° S
12° E	46° N	14° E	41° N
75° E	28° N	105° E	5° S
150° W	61° N	35° E	15° N
68° W	47° S	70° W	30° S
175° E	41° S	175° E	39° S
121° E	17° N	123° E	13° N

SECTION 2

Volcanic Activity

DISCOVER ACTIVITY

Pumice
Obsidian

What Are Volcanic Rocks Like?

Volcanoes produce lava, which hardens into rock. Two of these rocks are pumice and obsidian.

1. Observe samples of pumice and obsidian with a hand lens.
2. How would you describe the texture of the pumice? What could have caused this texture?
3. Observe the surface of the obsidian. How does the surface of the obsidian differ from pumice?

Think It Over

Developing Hypotheses What could have produced the difference in texture between the two rocks? Explain your answer.

In Hawaii, there are many myths about Pele (PAY lay), the fire goddess of volcanoes. In these myths, Pele is the creator and the destroyer of the Hawaiian islands. She lives in the fiery depths of erupting volcanoes. According to legend, when Pele is angry, she releases the fires of Earth through openings on the mountainside. Evidence of her presence is "Pele's hair," a fine, threadlike rock formed by lava. Pele's hair forms when lava sprays out of the ground like water from a fountain. As it cools, the lava stretches and hardens into thin strands.

GUIDE FOR READING

- **What happens when a volcano erupts?**
- **How do the two types of volcanic eruptions differ?**
- **What are some hazards of volcanoes?**

Reading Tip **Before you read, preview *Exploring a Volcano* on page 85. Write a list of any questions you have about how a volcano erupts.**

How Magma Reaches Earth's Surface

Where does this fiery lava come from? Lava begins as magma in the mantle. There, magma forms in the asthenosphere, which lies beneath the lithosphere. The materials of the asthenosphere are under great pressure.

Magma Rises Because liquid magma is less dense than the surrounding solid material, magma flows upward into any cracks in the rock above. Magma rises until it reaches the surface, or until it becomes trapped beneath layers of rock.

Figure 4 Pele's hair is a type of rock formed from lava. Each strand is as fine as spun glass.

Figure 5 Molten lava from Kilauea volcano in Hawaii.

Gases in Magma

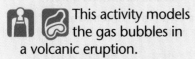

This activity models the gas bubbles in a volcanic eruption.

1. In a 1- or 2-liter plastic bottle, mix 10 g of baking soda into 65 mL of water.
2. Put about six raisins in the water.
3. While swirling the water and raisins, add 65 mL of vinegar and stir vigorously.
4. Once the liquid has stopped moving, observe the raisins.

Making a Model What happens after you add the vinegar? What do the raisins and bubbles represent? How is this model similar to the way magma behaves in a volcano?

A Volcano Erupts Just like the carbon dioxide trapped in a bottle of soda pop, the dissolved gases trapped in magma are under tremendous pressure. You cannot see the carbon dioxide gas in a bottle of soda pop because it is dissolved in the liquid. But when you open the bottle, the pressure is released. The carbon dioxide forms bubbles, which rush to the surface.

As magma rises toward the surface, the pressure decreases. The dissolved gases begin to separate out, forming bubbles. A volcano erupts when an opening develops in weak rock on the surface. **During a volcanic eruption, the gases dissolved in magma rush out, carrying the magma with them.** Once magma reaches the surface and becomes lava, the gases bubble out.

Inside a Volcano

All volcanoes have a pocket of magma beneath the surface and one or more cracks through which the magma forces its way. You can see these features in *Exploring a Volcano.* Beneath a volcano, magma collects in a pocket called a **magma chamber.** The magma moves through a **pipe,** a long tube in the ground that connects the magma chamber to Earth's surface. Molten rock and gas leave the volcano through an opening called a **vent.** Often, there is one central vent at the top of a volcano. However, many volcanoes also have other vents that open on the volcano's sides. A **lava flow** is the area covered by lava as it pours out of a vent. A **crater** is a bowl-shaped area that may form at the top of a volcano around the volcano's central vent.

Checkpoint *How does magma rise through the lithosphere?*

EXPLORING a Volcano

A volcano forms where magma breaks through Earth's crust and lava flows over the surface.

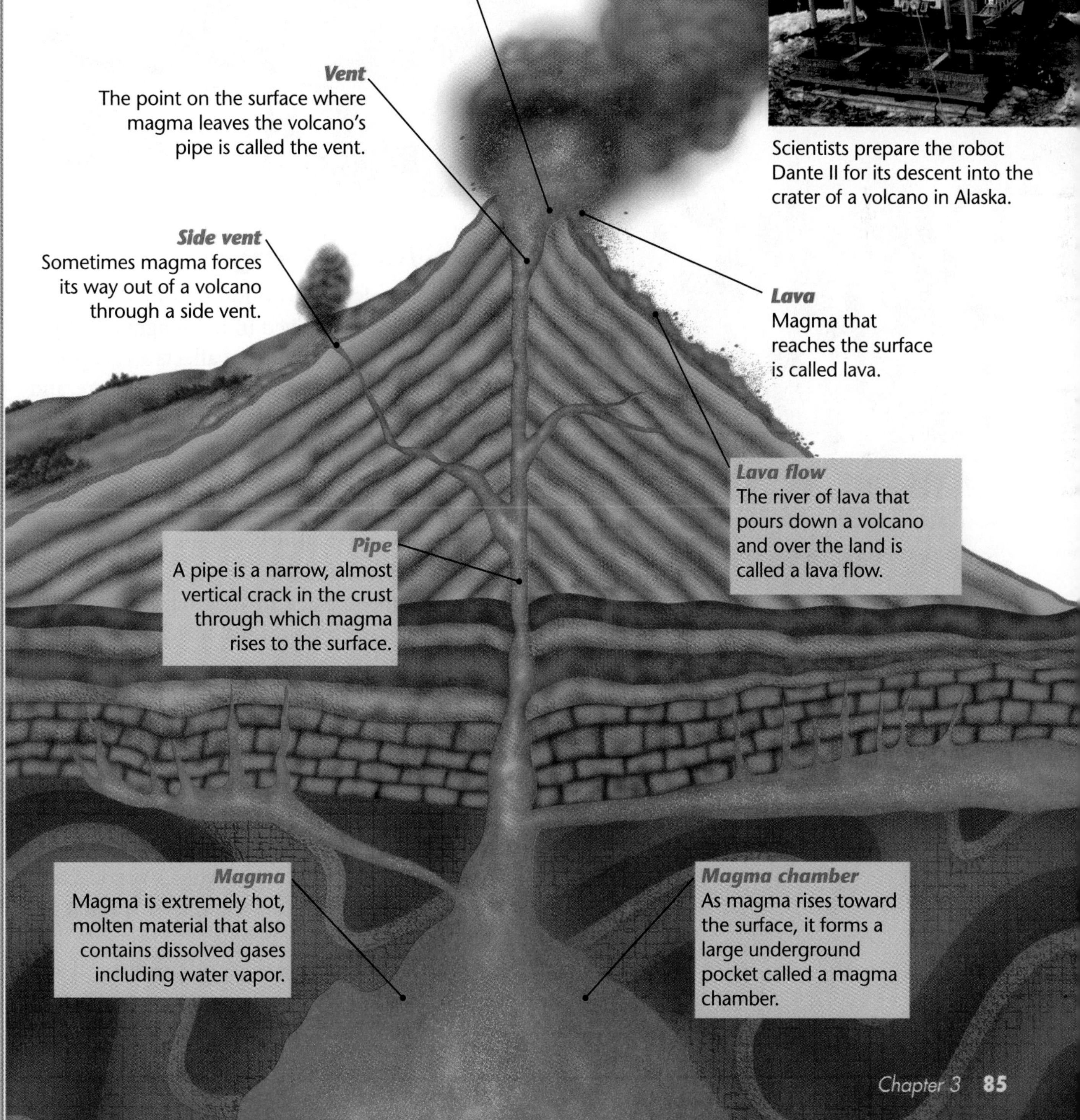

Crater
Lava collects in the crater, the bowl-shaped area that forms around the volcano's vent.
Vent
The point on the surface where magma leaves the volcano's pipe is called the vent.
Side vent
Sometimes magma forces its way out of a volcano through a side vent.
Lava
Magma that reaches the surface is called lava.
Lava flow
The river of lava that pours down a volcano and over the land is called a lava flow.
Pipe
A pipe is a narrow, almost vertical crack in the crust through which magma rises to the surface.
Magma
Magma is extremely hot, molten material that also contains dissolved gases including water vapor.
Magma chamber
As magma rises toward the surface, it forms a large underground pocket called a magma chamber.

Scientists prepare the robot Dante II for its descent into the crater of a volcano in Alaska.

Figure 6 Rhyolite (top) forms from high-silica lava. Basalt (bottom) forms from low-silica lava. When this type of lava cools, it sometimes forms six-sided columns like the ones in the picture.

Characteristics of Magma

The force of a volcanic eruption depends partly on the amount of gas dissolved in the magma. But gas content is not the only thing that affects an eruption. How thick or thin the magma is, its temperature, and its silica content are also important factors.

Some types of magma are thick and flow very slowly. Other types of magma are fluid and flow almost as easily as water. Magma's temperature partly determines whether it is thick or fluid. The hotter the magma, the more fluid it is.

The amount of silica in magma also helps to determine how easily the magma flows. **Silica,** which is a material that is formed from the elements oxygen and silicon, is one of the most abundant materials in Earth's crust and mantle. The more silica magma contains, the thicker it is.

Magma that is high in silica produces light-colored lava that is too sticky to flow very far. When this type of lava cools, it forms the rock rhyolite, which has the same composition as granite. Pumice and obsidian, which you observed if you did the Discover activity, also form from high-silica lava. Obsidian forms when lava cools very quickly, giving it a smooth, glossy surface. Pumice forms when gas bubbles are trapped in cooling lava, leaving spaces in the rock.

Magma that is low in silica flows readily and produces dark-colored lava. When this kind of lava cools, rocks such as basalt are formed.

Types of Volcanic Eruptions

A volcano's magma influences how the volcano erupts. **The silica content of magma helps to determine whether the volcanic eruption is quiet or explosive.**

Quiet Eruptions A volcano erupts quietly if its magma flows easily. In this case, the gas dissolved in the magma bubbles out gently. Thin, runny lava oozes quietly from the vent. The islands of Hawaii and Iceland were formed from quiet eruptions. On the Big Island of Hawaii, lava pours out of the crater near the top of Mount Kilauea (kee loo AY uh), but also flows out of long cracks on the volcano's sides. Quiet eruptions like the ones that regularly take place on Mount Kilauea have built up the Big Island over hundreds of thousands of years. In Iceland, lava usually emerges from gigantic fissures many kilometers long. The fluid lava from a quiet eruption can flow many kilometers from the volcano's vent.

Quiet eruptions produce two different types of lava: pahoehoe and aa. **Pahoehoe** (pah HOH ee hoh ee) is fast-moving, hot lava. The surface of a lava flow formed from pahoehoe looks like a solid mass of wrinkles, billows, and ropelike coils. Lava that is cooler and slower-moving is called **aa** (AH ah). When aa hardens, it forms a rough surface consisting of jagged lava chunks. Figure 7 shows how different these types of lava can be.

☑ *Checkpoint* *What types of lava are produced by quiet eruptions?*

B

A

Figure 7 Both pahoehoe and aa can come from the same volcano. **A.** Pahoehoe flows easily and hardens into a rippled surface. **B.** Aa hardens into rough chunks. *Inferring What accounts for the differences between these two types of lava?*

Figure 8 Mount St. Helens erupted at 8:30 A.M. on May 18, 1980. **A.** A large bulge that had formed on the north side of the mountain crashed downward.

B. As the mountainside collapsed, bottled up gas and magma inside began to escape.

Social Studies CONNECTION

In A.D. 79, Mount Vesuvius in Italy erupted. A thick layer of ash from Vesuvius buried the Roman city of Pompeii, which lay between the volcano and the Mediterranean Sea. Beginning in the 1700s, about half of the buried city was dug out, and we now know the following: Pompeii was a walled city with shops, homes, paved streets, a forum (or public square), temples, and public baths. Perhaps 20,000 people lived there.

In Your Journal

Research Pompeii to find out what scientists have learned about daily life in the city. Write a paragraph summarizing your findings.

Explosive Eruptions If its magma is thick and sticky, a volcano erupts explosively. The thick magma does not flow out of the crater and down the mountain. Instead, it slowly builds up in the volcano's pipe, plugging it like a cork in a bottle. Dissolved gases cannot escape from the thick magma. The trapped gases build up pressure until they explode. The erupting gases push the magma out of the volcano with incredible force.

The explosion breaks the lava into fragments that quickly cool and harden into pieces of different sizes. The smallest pieces are volcanic ash—fine, rocky particles as small as a grain of sand. Cinders are pebble-sized particles. Larger pieces, called bombs, may range from the size of a baseball to the size of a car. A **pyroclastic flow** (py roh KLAS tik) occurs when an explosive eruption hurls out ash, cinders, and bombs as well as gases.

Look at Figure 8 to see the 1980 eruption of Mount St. Helens in the state of Washington. It was one of the most violent explosive eruptions that has ever occurred in the United States.

☑ *Checkpoint* *What causes an explosive eruption?*

Stages of a Volcano

The activity of a volcano may last from less than a decade to more than 10 million years. Most long-lived volcanoes, however, do not erupt continuously. Geologists often describe volcanoes with terms usually reserved for living things, such as sleeping, awakening, alive, and dead. An **active,** or live, volcano is one that is erupting or has shown signs that it may erupt in the near future. A **dormant,** or sleeping, volcano is like a sleeping bear. Scientists expect a dormant volcano to awaken in the future and become active. However, there may be thousands of years between eruptions. An **extinct,** or dead, volcano is unlikely to erupt again.

C. Shattered rock and pyroclastic flows blasted out sideways from the volcano.

D. The blast traveled outward, leveling the surrounding forest and causing mudflows that affected a wide area around the volcano.

Other Types of Volcanic Activity

Hot springs and geysers are two examples of volcanic activity that do not involve the eruption of lava. These features may occur in any volcanic area—even around an extinct volcano,

A **hot spring** forms when groundwater heated by a nearby body of magma rises to the surface and collects in a natural pool. (Groundwater is water that has seeped into the spaces among rocks deep beneath Earth's surface.) Water from hot springs may contain dissolved gases and other substances from deep within Earth.

Sometimes, rising hot water and steam become trapped underground in a narrow crack. Pressure builds until the mixture suddenly sprays above the surface as a geyser. A **geyser** (GY zur) is a fountain of water and steam that erupts from the ground.

INTEGRATING TECHNOLOGY In volcanic areas, water heated by magma can provide a clean, reliable energy source called **geothermal energy.** The people of Reykjavik, Iceland, pipe this hot water directly into their homes for warmth. Geothermal energy is also a source of electricity in Iceland as well as northern California and New Zealand. Steam from deep underground is piped into turbines. Inside a turbine, the steam spins a wheel in the same way that blowing on a pinwheel makes the pinwheel turn. The moving wheel in the turbine turns a generator that changes the energy of motion into electrical energy.

Figure 9 Old Faithful, a geyser in Yellowstone National Park, erupts about every 33 to 93 minutes. That's how long it takes for the pressure to build up again after each eruption.

SCIENCE & History

Monitoring Volcanoes

Geologists have been somewhat more successful in predicting volcanic eruptions than in predicting earthquakes. Changes in and around a volcano usually give warning a short time before the volcano erupts. Geologists use tiltmeters, laser-ranging devices, and other instruments to detect slight surface changes in elevation and tilt caused by magma moving underground. Geologists monitor the local magnetic field, water level in a volcano's crater lake, and any gases escaping from a volcano. They take the temperature of underground water to see if it is getting hotter—a sign that magma may be nearing the surface.

Geologists also monitor the many small earthquakes that occur in the area around a volcano before an eruption.

The Power of Volcanoes

Within the last 150 years, major volcanic eruptions have greatly affected the land and people around them.

1883 Indonesia

The violent eruption of Krakatau volcano threw 18 cubic kilometers of ash skyward. The blast was heard 5,000 kilometers away.

1912

Alaska, U.S.A.

Today, a river in Alaska cuts through the thick layer of volcanic ash from the eruption of Mount Katmai. Mount Katmai blasted out almost as much ash as Krakatau.

1850 — 1900

1902

Martinique

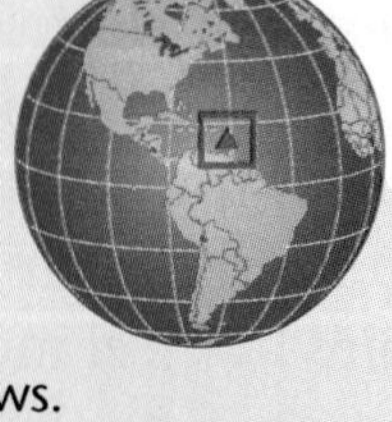

Mount Pelée, a Caribbean volcano, spewed out a burning cloud of hot gas and pyroclastic flows. Within two minutes of the eruption, the cloud had killed the 29,000 residents of St. Pierre, a city on the volcano's flank. Only two people survived.

The movement of magma into the magma chamber and through the volcano's pipe triggers these quakes.

All these data help geologists predict that an eruption is about to occur. But geologists cannot be certain about the type of eruption or how powerful it will be.

Volcano Hazards

The time between volcanic eruptions may span hundreds of years. So people living near a dormant volcano may be unaware of the danger. Before 1980, the people who lived, worked, and vacationed in the region around Mount St. Helens viewed it as a peaceful mountain. Few imagined the destruction the volcano would bring when it awakened from its 123-year slumber.

In Your Journal

People have written eye-witness accounts of famous volcanic eruptions. Research one of the eruptions in the time line. Then write a letter describing what someone observing the eruption might have seen.

1991 Philippines

Mount Pinatubo was dormant for hundreds of years before erupting in June 1991. Pinatubo spewed out huge quantities of ash that rose high into the atmosphere and also buried the surrounding countryside.

1950 — **2000**

1980 Washington, U.S.A.

When Mount St. Helens exploded, it blasted one cubic kilometer of rock fragments and volcanic material skyward. The eruption was not unexpected. For months, geologists had monitored releases of ash, small earthquakes, and a bulge on the mountain caused by the buildup of magma inside.

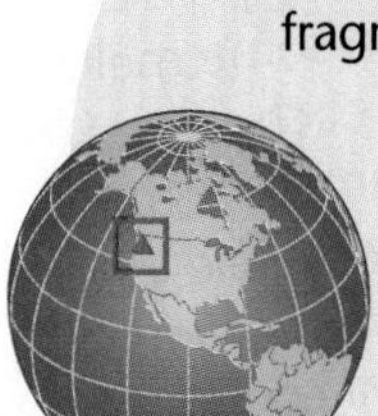

1995 Montserrat

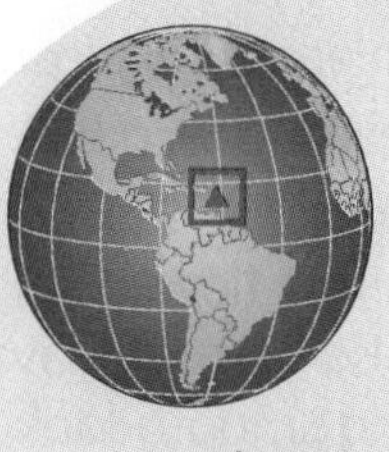

For more than two years, eruptions of volcanic ash from the Soufrière Hills volcano poured down on this small Caribbean island. Geologists anxiously waited for the eruption to run its course, not knowing whether it would end in a huge explosion.

Figure 10 A. Mudflows were one of the hazards of Mt. Pinatubo's 1991 eruption. **B.** People around Mt. Pinatubo wore masks to protect themselves from breathing volcanic ash.

Although quiet eruptions and explosive eruptions involve different volcano hazards, both types of eruption can cause damage far from the crater's rim. During a quiet eruption, lava flows pour from vents, setting fire to and then burying everything in their path. During an explosive eruption, a volcano can belch out hot, burning clouds of volcanic gases as well as cinders and bombs.

Volcanic ash can bury entire towns, damage crops, and clog car engines. If it becomes wet, the heavy ash can cause roofs to collapse. If a jet plane sucks ash into its engine, the engine may stall. Eruptions can also cause landslides and avalanches of mud, melted snow, and rock. Figure 10 shows some effects of mud and ash from Mount Pinatubo's eruption. When Mount St. Helens erupted, gigantic mudflows carried ash, trees, and rock fragments 29 kilometers down the nearby Toutle River.

Section 2 Review

1. What are the stages that lead up to a volcanic eruption?
2. Compare and contrast quiet and explosive eruptions.
3. Describe some of the hazards posed by volcanoes.
4. **Thinking Critically Drawing Conclusions** A geologist times a passing lava flow at 15 kilometers per hour. The geologist also sees that lava near the edge of the flow is forming smooth-looking ripples as it hardens. What type of lava is this? What type of magma produced it? Explain your conclusions.

Science at Home

Place cold water in one cup and hot tap water in another. **CAUTION:** *Handle the cup containing the hot water carefully to avoid spilling.* Ask members of your family to predict what will happen when some melted candle wax drops into each cup of water. Have an adult family member drip melted wax from a candle into each cup. Explain how this models what happens when lava cools quickly or more slowly.

SECTION 3
Volcanic Landforms

DISCOVER ACTIVITY

How Can Volcanic Activity Change Earth's Surface?

1. Use tape to secure the neck of a balloon over one end of a straw.
2. Place the balloon in the center of a box with the straw protruding.
3. Partially inflate the balloon.
4. Put damp sand on top of the balloon until it is covered.
5. Slowly inflate the balloon more. Observe what happens to the surface of the sand.

Think It Over

Making Models This activity models one of the ways in which volcanic activity can cause a mountain to form. What do you think the sand represents? What does the balloon represent?

GUIDE FOR READING

- **What landforms does lava create on Earth's surface?**
- **How does magma that hardens beneath the surface create landforms?**

Reading Tip **As you read, make a table comparing volcanic landforms. Include what formed each landform—lava, ash, or magma—as well as its characteristics.**

Volcanoes have created some of Earth's most spectacular landforms. For example, the perfect volcanic cone of Mt. Fuji in Japan and the majestic profile of snow-capped Mt. Kilimanjaro rising above the grasslands of East Africa are famous around the world.

Some volcanic landforms arise when lava flows build up mountains and plateaus on Earth's surface. Other volcanic landforms are the result of the buildup of magma beneath the surface.

Landforms From Lava and Ash

Rock and other materials formed from lava create a variety of landforms including shield volcanoes, composite volcanoes, cinder cone volcanoes, and lava plateaus. Look at *Exploring Volcanic Mountains* on page 95 to see the similarities and differences among these features.

Mt. Fuji, Japan

Shield Volcanoes At some places on Earth's surface, thin layers of lava pour out of a vent and harden on top of previous layers. Such lava flows gradually build a wide, gently sloping mountain called a **shield volcano.** Shield volcanoes rising from a hot spot on the ocean floor created the Hawaiian Islands.

Cinder Cone Volcanoes A volcano can also be a **cinder cone,** a steep, cone-shaped hill or mountain. If a volcano's lava is thick and stiff, it may produce ash, cinders, and bombs. These materials pile up around the vent in a steep, cone-shaped pile. For example, Paricutín in Mexico erupted in 1943 in a farmer's cornfield. The volcano built up a cinder cone about 400 meters high.

Composite Volcanoes Sometimes, lava flows alternate with explosive eruptions of ash, cinder, and bombs. The result is a composite volcano. **Composite volcanoes** are tall, cone-shaped mountains in which layers of lava alternate with layers of ash. Composite volcanoes include Mount Fuji in Japan and Mount St. Helens in Washington state. California's composite volcanoes, Mount Shasta and Lassen Peak, appear on the map in Appendix C.

Lava Plateaus Instead of forming mountains, some eruptions of lava form high, level areas called lava plateaus. First, lava flows out of several long cracks in an area. The thin, runny lava travels far before cooling and solidifying. Again and again, floods of lava flow on top of earlier floods. After millions of years, these layers can form high plateaus such as the Columbia Plateau, which covers parts of Washington, Oregon, and Idaho.

Figure 11 Crater Lake in Oregon fills the caldera formed after an eruption that destroyed the top 2,000 meters of Mount Mazama nearly 7,000 years ago.
Developing Hypotheses Develop a hypothesis to explain the formation of Wizard Island, the small island in Crater Lake.

Calderas Enormous eruptions may empty the main vent and the magma chamber beneath a volcano. The mountain becomes a hollow shell. With nothing to support it, the top of the mountain collapses inward. The huge hole left by the collapse of a volcanic mountain is called a **caldera** (kal DAIR uh). The hole is filled with the pieces of the volcano that have fallen inward, as well as some lava and ash. In Figure 11 you can see one of the world's largest calderas.

☑ *Checkpoint* ***What are the three types of volcanic mountains?***

EXPLORING *Volcanic Mountains*

Volcanic activity is responsible for building up much of Earth's surface. Lava from volcanoes cools and hardens into three types of mountains.

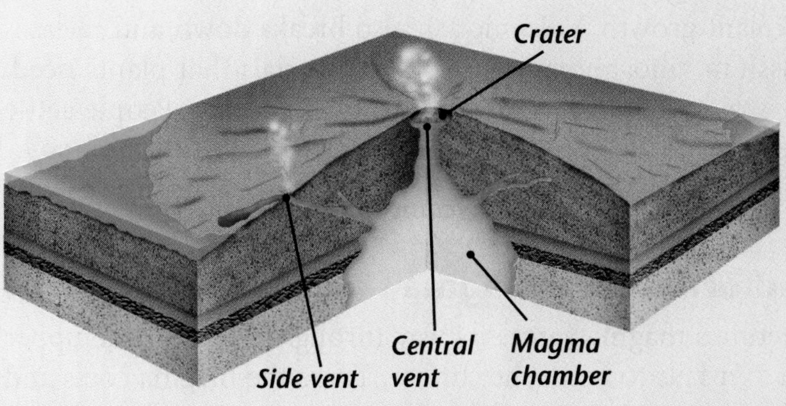

Crater
Side vent
Central vent
Magma chamber

Shield Volcano

Repeated lava flows during quiet eruptions gradually build up a broad, gently sloping volcanic mountain known as a shield volcano.

▲ *Mauna Loa is one of the shield volcanoes that built the island Hawaii.*

Cinder Cone Volcano

When cinders erupt explosively from a volcanic vent, they pile up around the vent, forming a cone-shaped hill called a cinder cone.

▲ *Sunset Crater is an extinct cinder cone in Arizona.*

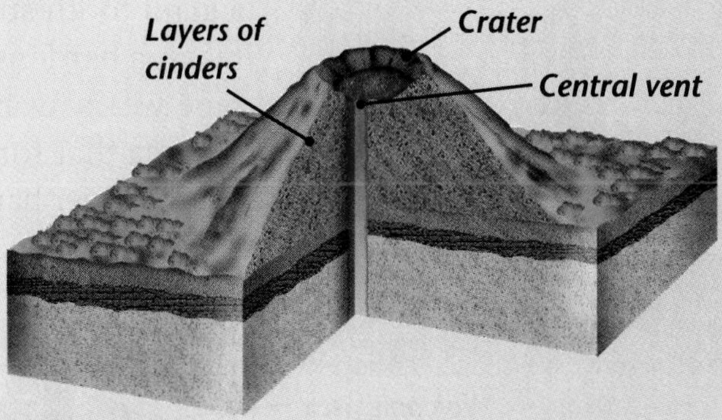

Layers of cinders
Crater
Central vent

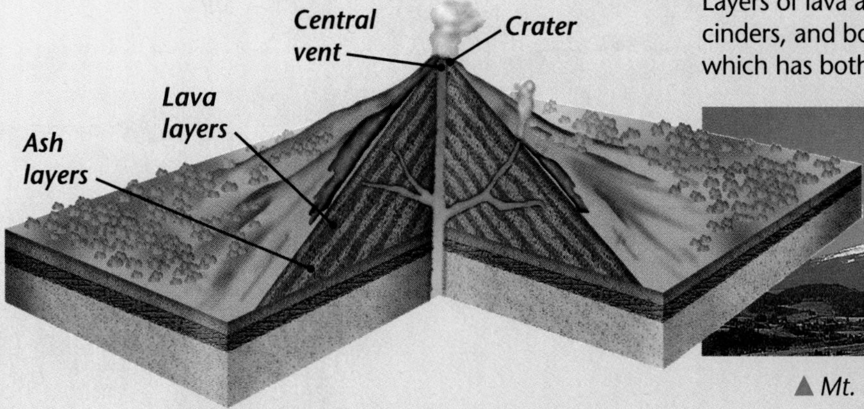

Central vent
Crater
Lava layers
Ash layers

Composite Volcano

Layers of lava alternate with layers of ash, cinders, and bombs in a composite volcano, which has both quiet and explosive eruptions.

▲ *Mt. Hood is a composite volcano in Oregon.*

Soils from Lava and Ash

Integrating Environmental Science

The lava, ash, and cinders that erupt from a volcano are initially barren. Over time, however, the hard surface of the lava flow breaks down to form soil. As soil develops, plants are able to grow. Some volcanic soils are among the richest soils in the world. Saying that soil is rich means that it's fertile, or able to support plant growth. Volcanic ash also breaks down and releases potassium, phosphorus, and other materials that plants need. Why would anyone live near an active volcano? People settle close to volcanoes to take advantage of the fertile volcanic soil.

☑ *Checkpoint* ***How does volcanic soil form?***

Landforms from Magma

Sometimes magma forces its way through cracks in the upper crust, but fails to reach the surface. There the magma cools and hardens into rock. Or the forces that wear away Earth's surface—such as flowing water, ice, or wind—may strip away the layers of rock above the magma and finally expose it. **Features formed by magma include volcanic necks, dikes, and sills, as well as batholiths and dome mountains.**

Volcanic Necks, Dikes, and Sills A volcanic neck looks like a giant tooth stuck in the ground. A **volcanic neck** forms when magma hardens in a volcano's pipe. The softer rock around the pipe wears away, exposing the hard rock of the volcanic neck. Magma that forces itself across rock layers hardens into a **dike.** On the other hand, when magma squeezes between layers of rock, it forms a **sill.**

Figure 12 Magma that hardens beneath the surface may form volcanic necks, dikes, and sills. *Compare and Contrast What is the difference between a dike and a sill?*

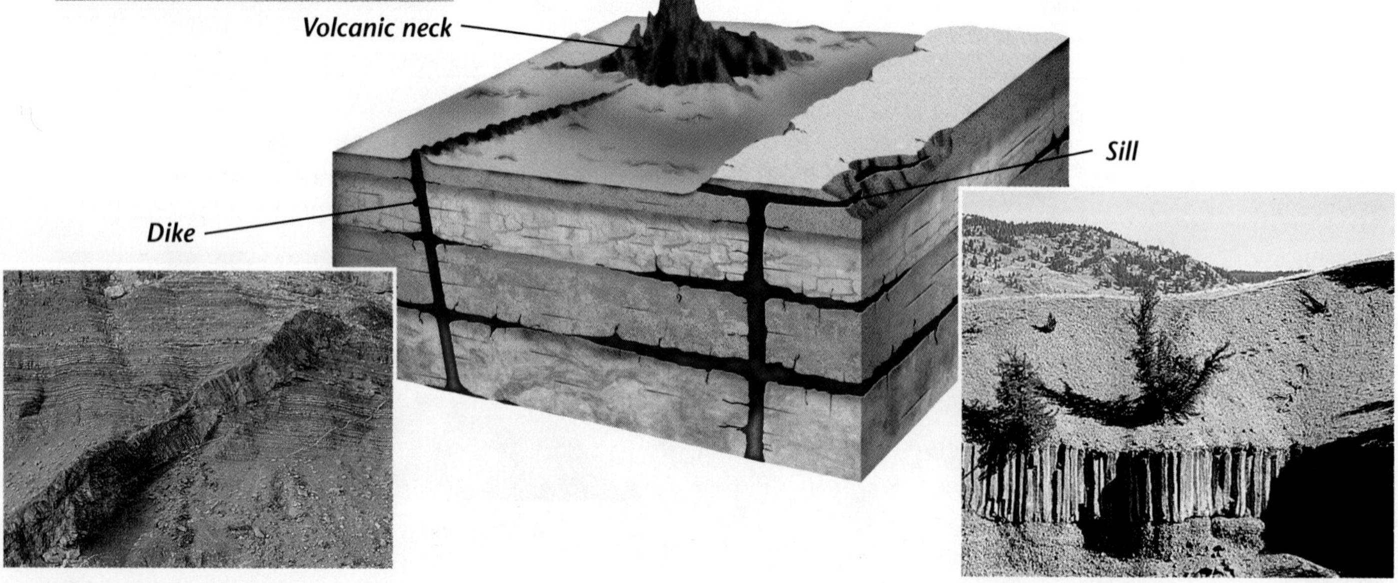
Volcanic neck
Sill
Dike

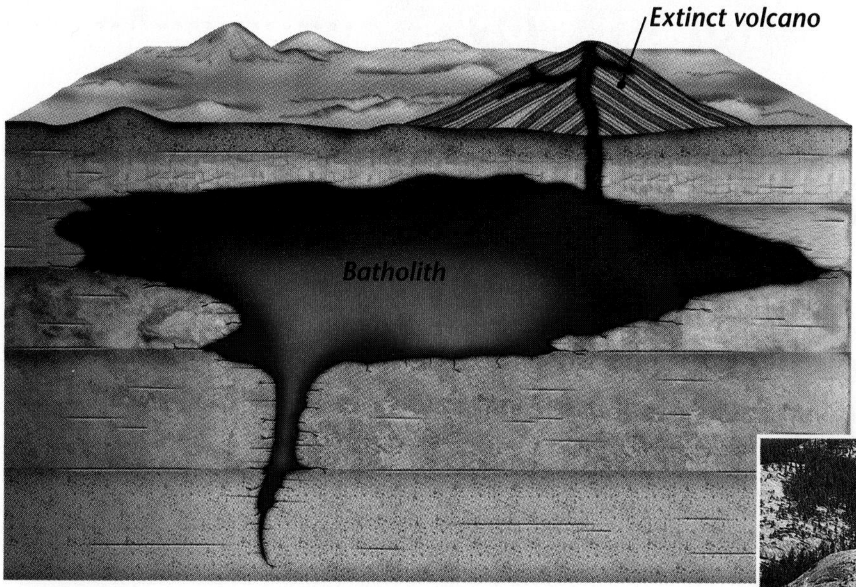
Extinct volcano
Batholith

Figure 13 A batholith forms when magma cools inside the crust. One of the largest batholiths in North America forms the core of the Sierra Nevada mountains in California. These mountains in Yosemite National Park are part of that granite batholith.

Batholiths Large rock masses called batholiths form the core of many mountain ranges. A **batholith** (BATH uh lith) is a mass of rock formed when a large body of magma cools inside the crust. The diagram in Figure 13 shows how a batholith looks when it forms. The photograph shows how it looks when the layers of rock above it have worn away.

Dome Mountains Other, smaller bodies of magma can create dome mountains. A dome mountain forms when rising magma is blocked by horizontal layers of rock. The magma forces the layers of rock to bend upward into a dome shape. Eventually, the rock above the dome mountain wears away, leaving it exposed. This process formed the Black Hills in South Dakota.

Section 3 Review

1. Describe five landforms formed from lava and ash.
2. Describe the process that creates a lava plateau.
3. What features form as a result of magma hardening beneath Earth's surface?
4. Describe how a dome mountain can eventually form out of magma that hardened beneath Earth's surface.
5. **Thinking Critically Relating Cause and Effect** Explain the formation of a volcanic landform that can result when a volcano uses up the magma in its magma chamber.

CHAPTER PROJECT

Check Your Progress

By now you should have collected information about what it's like to live in a volcanic region. Do you need to do more research? Now begin to plan your presentation. One way to plan a presentation is to prepare storyboards. In a storyboard, you sketch each major step in the presentation on a separate sheet of paper. Decide who in your group is presenting each portion.

Real-World Lab

How It Works

Gelatin Volcanoes

Does the magma inside a volcano move along fractures, or through tubes or pipes? How does the eruption of magma create features such as dikes and sills? You can use a gelatin volcano model and red-colored liquid "magma" to find answers to these questions.

Problem

How does magma move inside a volcano?

Skills Focus

developing hypotheses, making models, observing

Materials

plastic cup
tray or shallow pan
plastic knife
aluminum pizza pan with holes punched at 2.5-cm intervals
unflavored gelatin mold in bowl
red food coloring and water
plastic syringe, 10 cc
3 small cardboard oatmeal boxes
rubber gloves
unlined paper

Procedure

1. Before magma erupts as lava, how does it travel up from underground magma chambers? Record your hypothesis.
2. Remove the gelatin from the refrigerator. Loosen the gelatin from its container by briefly placing the container of gelatin in a larger bowl of hot water.
3. Place the pizza pan over the gelatin so the mold is near the center of the pizza pan. While holding the pizza pan against the top of the mold, carefully turn the mold and the pizza pan upside down.
4. Place the pizza pan with the gelatin mold on top of the oatmeal boxes as shown in the photograph.
5. Carefully lift the bowl off the gelatin mold to create a gelatin volcano.
6. Fill the syringe with the red water ("magma"). Remove air bubbles from the syringe by holding it upright and squirting out a small amount of water.
7. Insert the tip of the syringe through a hole in the pizza pan near the center of the gelatin volcano. Inject the magma into the gelatin very slowly. It should take at least 30 seconds to empty the syringe. Observe what happens to the magma.
8. Repeat steps 6 and 7 as many times as possible. Observe the movement of the magma each time. Note any differences in the direction the magma takes when the syringe is inserted into different parts of the gelatin volcano. Record your observations.
9. Look down on your gelatin volcano from above. Make a sketch of the positions and shapes of the magma bodies. Label your drawing "Top View."
10. Carefully use a knife to cut your volcano in half. Separate the pieces and examine the cut surfaces for traces of the magma bodies.
11. Sketch the positions and shapes of the magma bodies on one of the cut faces. Label your drawing "Cross Section."

Analyze and Conclude

1. Describe how the magma moved through your model. Did the magma move straight up through the center of your model volcano or did it branch off in places? Explain why you think the magma moved in this way.
2. What knowledge or experience did you use to develop your hypothesis? How did the actual movement compare with your hypothesis?
3. Were there differences in the direction the magma flowed when the syringe was inserted in different parts of the gelatin volcano?
4. **Apply** How does what you observed in your model compare to the way magma moves through real volcanoes?

Design an Experiment

Plan to repeat the experiment using a mold made of two layers of gelatin. Before injecting the magma, develop a hypothesis about the effect of layering on magma movement. Record your observations to determine if your hypothesis was correct. What volcanic feature is produced by this version of the model? Can you think of other volcanic features that you could model using gelatin layers?

SECTION 4 Volcanoes in the Solar System

DISCOVER ACTIVITY

What Forces Shaped the Surface of Io?

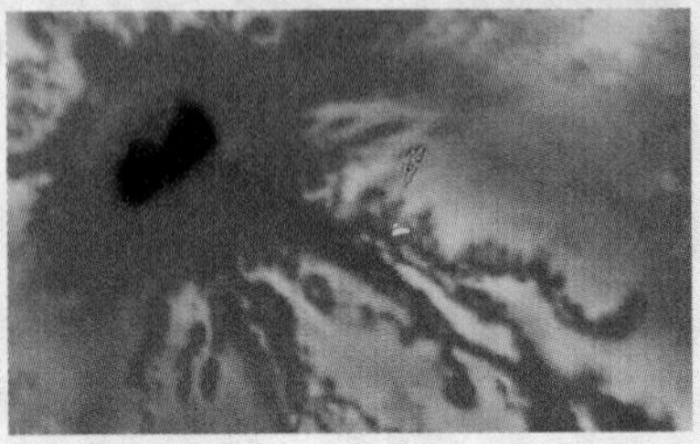

Io is a moon of Jupiter. Pictures taken by the *Voyager* space probe as it passed by Io in 1979 show signs of unusual features and activity on Io.

1. Observe the blue cloud rising above the rim of Io in the top photo. What do you think it could be?
2. Look at the feature on Io's surface shown in the bottom photo. What do you think it looks like?

Think It Over

Posing Questions Is the volcanic activity on Io similar to that on Earth? State several questions that you would like to answer in order to find out.

GUIDE FOR READING

- **How do volcanoes on Mars and Venus compare with volcanoes on Earth?**
- **What volcanic activity is found on the moons of Jupiter and Neptune?**

Reading Tip **Before you read, preview the headings in the section. Then predict where, besides Earth, volcanoes are found in the solar system.**

Earth is not the only body in the solar system to show signs of volcanic activity. Pictures taken by space probes show evidence of past volcanic activity on Mercury, Venus, and Mars. These planets—like Earth and its moon—have rocky crusts. Scientists think these planets once had hot, molten cores. The heat caused volcanic activity. But because these planets are smaller than Earth, their cores have cooled, bringing volcanic activity to an end.

Geologists are eager for information about other planets and moons. By comparing other bodies in the solar system with Earth, geologists can learn more about the processes that have shaped Earth over billions of years.

Earth's Moon

If you looked at the full moon through a telescope you would notice that much of the moon's surface is pockmarked with light-colored craters. Other, darker areas on the moon's surface look unusually smooth. The craters mark where meteorites have smashed into the moon over billions of years. The smooth areas are where lava flowed onto the moon's surface more than three billion years ago.

Figure 14 The dark areas on the moon's surface are flat plains made of basalt, a type of rock formed from lava.

Figure 15 The space probe *Magellan* observed volcanoes on Venus, but no recent or ongoing eruptions.

Volcanoes on Venus

Geologists were excited about the results of the space probe *Magellan's* mission to Venus in 1990. Venus shows signs of widespread volcanic activity that lasted for billions of years. Venus has thousands of volcanoes. There are about 150 large volcanoes measuring between 100 and 600 kilometers across and about half a kilometer high. The largest volcano on Venus, Theia Mons, is 800 kilometers across and 4 kilometers high. Scientists are trying to find evidence that volcanoes on Venus are still active.

Like Earth, Venus has volcanic mountains and other features that are probably made of thin, runny lava. Such lava produces gently sloping shield volcanoes with broad bases, as well as long, riverlike lava flows. One of the lava flows on Venus is more than 6,800 kilometers long!

☑ *Checkpoint* *What type of volcano is most common on Venus?*

Volcanoes on Mars

Mars is a planet with a long history of volcanic activity. However, there are far fewer volcanoes on Mars than on Venus. Volcanoes are found in only a few regions of Mars' surface.

Mars has a variety of volcanic features. **On Mars there are large shield volcanoes similar to those on Venus and Earth, as well as cone-shaped volcanoes and lava flows.** Mars also has lava plains that resemble the lava flows on the moon.

The biggest volcano on Mars is the largest mountain in the solar system. This volcano, Olympus Mons, is a shield volcano similar to Mauna Loa on the island of Hawaii, but much, much bigger! Olympus Mons covers an area as large as Ohio. This huge volcano, shown in Figure 16, is over eight times taller than Theia Mons on Venus.

Figure 16 Scientists estimate that Olympus Mons on Mars is about one billion years old. Around most of the base of Olympus Mons is a huge cliff that in places is 10 kilometers high—more than 5 times the height of the Grand Canyon.

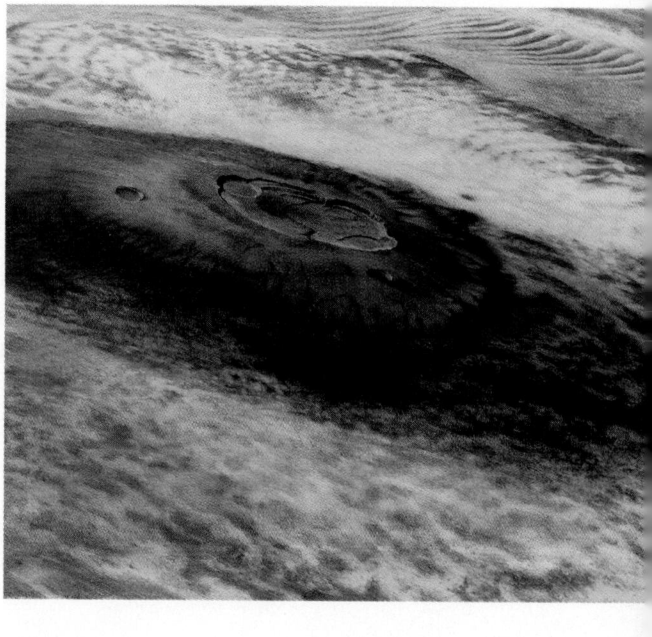

Figure 17 The surface of Neptune's moon Triton has areas covered by frozen "lava lakes" that show where liquid material erupted from inside Triton. *Posing Questions Imagine that you are observing Triton from a spacecraft. What questions would you want to answer about volcanic activity there?*

Scientists estimate that volcanic activity on Mars probably goes back about 3.5 billion years, to about the same time as the volcanic activity on the moon. Martian volcanoes don't seem to be active. Lava flows on Olympus Mons may be more than 100 million years old.

Volcanoes on Distant Moons

Besides Earth, there are only two other bodies in the solar system where volcanic eruptions have been observed: Io, a moon of the planet Jupiter, and Triton, a moon of the planet Neptune. *Voyager 1* photographed eruptions on these moons as it sped past them in 1979. Geologists on Earth were amazed when they saw these pictures. **Io and Triton have volcanic features very different from those on Earth, Mars, and Venus.** On Io, sulfur volcanoes erupt like fountains or spread out like umbrellas above the colorful surface.

The eruptions on Triton involve nitrogen. On Earth, nitrogen is a gas. Triton is so cold, however, that most of the nitrogen there is frozen solid. Scientists hypothesize that Triton's surface, which is made up of frozen water and other materials, absorbs heat from the sun. This heat melts some of the frozen nitrogen underneath Triton's surface. The liquid nitrogen then expands and erupts through the planet's icy crust.

Other moons of Jupiter, Saturn, and Neptune show signs of volcanic activity, but space probes have not observed any eruptions in progress on these moons.

Section 4 Review

1. Describe volcanic features found on Venus and Mars. Do volcanic features on these planets resemble volcanic features on Earth? Explain.
2. How is volcanic activity on the moons of Jupiter and Neptune different from volcanic activity on Earth?
3. What is the largest volcano in the solar system? What type of volcano is it?
4. **Thinking Critically Comparing and Contrasting** How do the volcanoes on Venus compare with the volcanoes on Mars?

CHAPTER PROJECT

Check Your Progress

By this time, your group should have planned your documentary and know what materials you will need. Put the finishing touches on your presentation. Make sure any posters, overhead transparencies, or computer art will be easy for your audience to read. If you are using video or audio, make your recordings now. Revise and polish any narrative, rap, or skit. (*Hint:* Check the length of your presentation.)

Section 1 Volcanoes and Plate Tectonics

Key Ideas

- A volcano is an opening on Earth's surface where magma escapes from the interior. Magma that reaches Earth's surface is called lava.
- The constructive force of volcanoes adds new rock to existing land and forms new islands.
- Most volcanoes occur near the boundaries of Earth's plates and along the edges of continents, in island arcs, or along mid-ocean ridges.

Key Terms

volcano
magma
lava
Ring of Fire
island arc
hot spot

Section 2 Volcanic Activity

Key Ideas

- An eruption occurs when gases trapped in magma rush through an opening at the Earth's surface, carrying magma with them.
- Volcanoes can erupt quietly or explosively, depending on the amount of dissolved gases in the magma and on how thick or fluid the magma is.
- When magma heats water underground, hot springs and geysers form.
- Volcano hazards include pyroclastic flows, avalanches of mud, damage from ash, lava flows, flooding, and deadly gases.

Key Terms

magma chamber
pipe
vent
lava flow
crater
silica
pahoehoe
aa
pyroclastic flow
active
dormant
extinct
hot spring
geyser
geothermal energy

Section 3 Volcanic Landforms

Key Ideas

- Different types of volcanic eruptions form different types of landforms.
- Lava on the surface creates landforms such as shield volcanoes, cinder cones, composite volcanoes, and plateaus.
- One benefit of volcanoes is fertile soil.
- Magma that hardens beneath the surface creates batholiths, dome mountains, dikes, and sills that are eventually exposed when the covering rock wears away.

Key Terms

shield volcano
cinder cone
composite volcano
caldera
volcanic neck
dike
sill
batholith

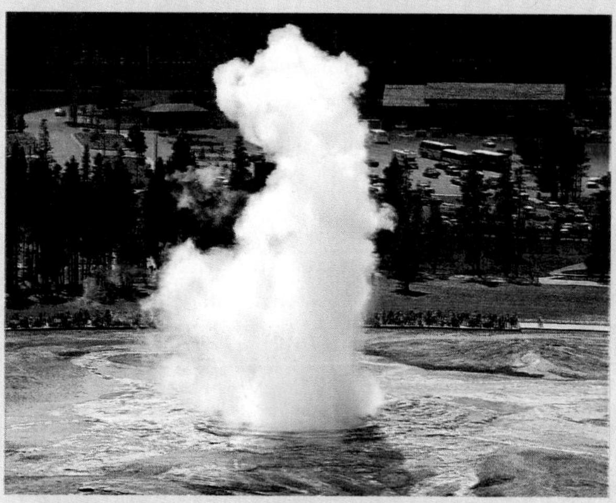

Section 4 Volcanoes in the Solar System

INTEGRATING SPACE SCIENCE

Key Ideas

- Venus and Mars both have extinct volcanoes similar to volcanoes on Earth.
- Spacecraft have photographed volcanic activity on moons of Jupiter and Neptune.

ACTIVITY

USING THE INTERNET

www.phschool.com/state_focus/california/

California Test Prep: Reviewing Content

Multiple Choice

Choose the letter of the best answer.

1. When two oceanic plates collide, the result may be
   a. volcanoes on the edge of a continent.
   b. a hot spot volcano.
   c. volcanoes in an island arc.
   d. a volcano along the mid-ocean ridge.
2. The force that causes magma to erupt at the surface is provided by
   a. heat.
   b. the shape of the pipe.
   c. geothermal energy.
   d. dissolved gases under pressure.
3. An eruption of thin, fluid lava would most likely be
   a. a cinder-cone eruption.
   b. an explosive eruption.
   c. a quiet eruption.
   d. a pyroclastic eruption.
4. Alternating layers of lava and volcanic ash are found in
   a. dome mountains. **b.** dikes and sills.
   c. shield volcanoes. **d.** composite volcanoes.
5. Which of the following has active volcanoes?
   a. Venus **b.** Mars
   c. Triton **d.** Earth's moon

True or False

If the statement is true, write true. If it is false, change the underlined word or words to make the statement true.

6. Many volcanoes are found in island arcs that form where two oceanic plates collide.
7. Thin, runny lava usually hardens into ash, cinders, and bombs.
8. An extinct volcano is not likely to erupt in your lifetime.
9. Hot spots form where a plume of magma rises through the crust from the mantle.
10. Olympus Mons, the largest mountain in the solar system, is found on Venus.

Checking Concepts

11. What is the Ring of Fire?
12. How does plate tectonics explain the volcanoes that form along the mid-ocean ridge?
13. Where are hot spot volcanoes located in relation to Earth's plates?
14. What effect does silica content have on the characteristics of magma?
15. How do hot springs and geysers form?
16. While observing a lava flow from a recently active volcano, you notice an area of lava with a rough, chunky surface. What type of lava is this and how does it form?
17. How does a shield volcano form?
18. Why can earthquakes be a warning sign that an eruption is about to happen?
19. **Writing to Learn** Pretend you are a newspaper reporter in 1980. You have been assigned to report on the eruption of Mount St. Helens. Write a news story describing your observations.

Thinking Visually

20. **Concept Map** Copy the concept map about types of volcanic mountains onto a separate sheet of paper. Then complete it and add a title. (For more on concept maps, see the Skills Handbook.)

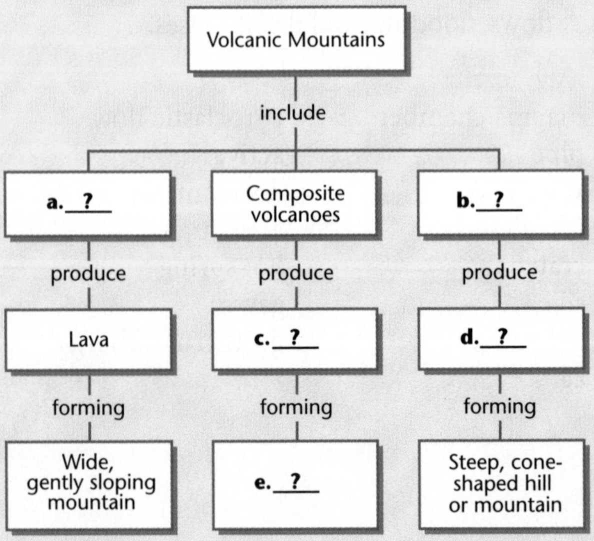
Volcanic Mountains
include
a. ?
Composite volcanoes
b. ?
produce
produce
produce
Lava
c. ?
d. ?
forming
forming
forming
Wide, gently sloping mountain
e. ?
Steep, cone-shaped hill or mountain

Test Prep: Skills

Refer to the diagram to answer Questions 21–24.

21. Classifying What is this volcano made of? How do geologists classify a volcano made of these materials?

22. Developing Hypotheses What is the feature labeled A in the diagram? What is the feature labeled B? How do these features form?

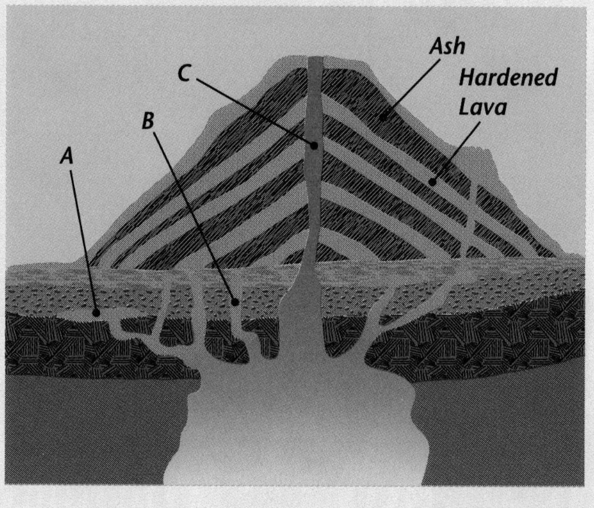
Ash
Hardened
Lava
C
B
A

23. Inferring This volcano is located where oceanic crust is subducted under continental crust. Would the volcano erupt quietly or explosively? Give reasons for your answer.

24. Predicting What is the feature labeled C in the diagram? If this feature becomes plugged with hardened magma, what could happen to the volcano? Explain.

Thinking Critically

25. Applying Concepts Is a volcanic eruption likely to occur on the east coast of the United States? Explain your answer.

26. Comparing and Contrasting Compare the way in which an island arc forms with the way in which a hot spot volcano forms.

27. Making Generalizations How might a volcanic eruption affect the area around a volcano, including its plant and animal life?

CHAPTER 3 ASSESSMENT

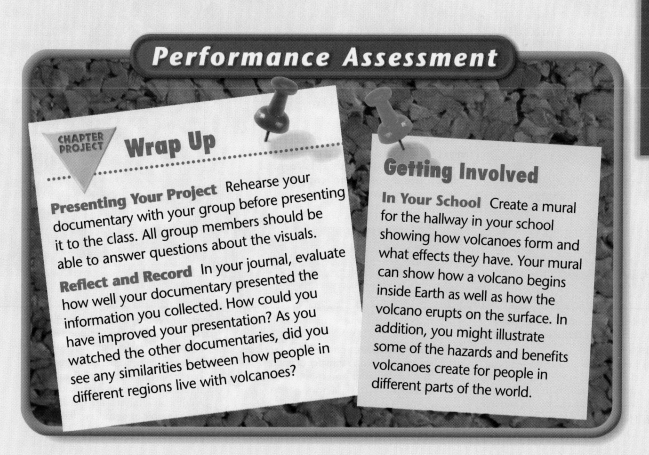

Performance Assessment

CHAPTER PROJECT Wrap Up

Presenting Your Project Rehearse your documentary with your group before presenting it to the class. All group members should be able to answer questions about the visuals.

Reflect and Record In your journal, evaluate how well your documentary presented the information you collected. How could you have improved your presentation? As you watched the other documentaries, did you see any similarities between how people in different regions live with volcanoes?

Getting Involved

In Your School Create a mural for the hallway in your school showing how volcanoes form and what effects they have. Your mural can show how a volcano begins inside Earth as well as how the volcano erupts on the surface. In addition, you might illustrate some of the hazards and benefits volcanoes create for people in different parts of the world.

CHAPTER

4 Minerals

CALIFORNIA
SCIENCE CONTENT STANDARDS

These aurichalcite (oh rih KAL syt) crystals were found in a copper mine in Mexico. This mineral is formed from the metals zinc, copper, and other elements.

The following California Science Content Standards are addressed in this chapter:

1. **Plate tectonics explains important features of the Earth's surface and major geologic events.**
   - **d.** Earthquakes are sudden motions along breaks in the crust called faults, and volcanoes/fissures are locations where magma reaches the surface.
   - **f.** How to explain major features of California geology in terms of plate tectonics (including mountains, faults, volcanoes).
4. **Many phenomena on the Earth's surface are affected by the transfer of energy through radiation and convection currents.**
   - **c.** Heat from Earth's interior reaches the surface primarily through convection.
6. **Sources of energy and materials differ in amounts, distribution, usefulness, and the time required for their formation.**
   - **b.** Different natural energy and material resources, including air, soil, rocks, minerals, petroleum, fresh water, wildlife, and forests, and classify them as renewable or nonrenewable.

PROJECT 4

Growing a Crystal Garden

Everyone has wondered at the beauty of minerals. Minerals occur in an amazing variety of colors and crystal shapes—from clear, tiny cubes of halite (table salt) to precious rubies and sapphires. Some crystals look like dandelion puffs. In this project, you will grow crystals to see how different types of chemicals form different crystal shapes.

Your Goal To design and grow a crystal garden.

To complete this project successfully, you must

- create a three-dimensional garden scene as a base on which to grow crystals
- prepare at least two different crystal-growth solutions
- observe and record the shapes and growth rates of your crystals
- follow the safety guidelines in Appendix A.

Get Started Begin by deciding what materials you will use to create your garden scene. Your teacher will suggest a variety of materials and also describe the types of crystal-growth solutions that you can use.

Check Your Progress You'll be working on this project as you study this chapter. To keep your project on track, look for Check Your Progress boxes at the following points.

Section 1 Review, page 116: Design and build a setting for your crystal garden and add the solutions.

Section 2 Review, page 122: Observe and record the growth of the crystals.

Wrap Up At the end of the chapter (page 133), display your finished crystal garden to your class. Be prepared to describe your procedure, observations, and conclusions.

c. Natural origin of the materials used to make common objects.

7. Scientific progress is made by asking meaningful questions and conducting careful investigations.

b. Select and use appropriate tools and technology to perform tests, collect data, and display data.

c. Construct appropriate graphs from data and develop qualitative statements about the relationships between variables.

d. Communicate the steps and results from an investigation in written reports and verbal presentations.

SECTION 1

Properties of Minerals

DISCOVER

ACTIVITY

What Is the True Color of a Mineral?

1. Examine samples of magnetite and black hematite. Both minerals contain iron. Describe the color and appearance of the two minerals. Are they similar or different?
2. Rub the black hematite across the back of a porcelain or ceramic tile. Observe the color of the streak on the tile.
3. Wipe the tile clean before you test the next sample.
4. Rub the magnetite across the back of the tile. Observe the color of the streak on the tile.

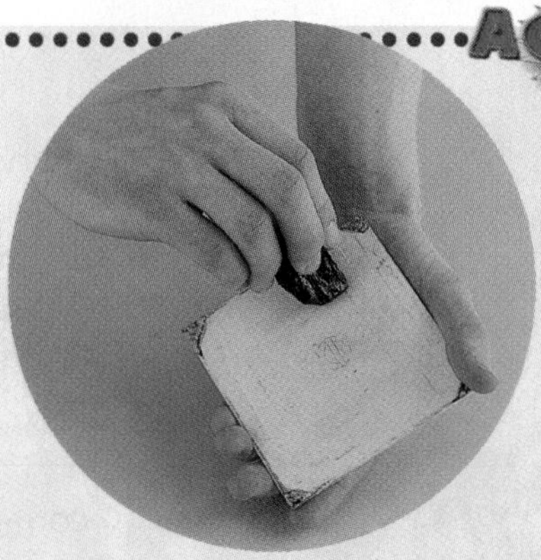

Think It Over

Observing Does the color of each mineral's streak match its color? How could this streak test be helpful in identifying them as two different minerals?

GUIDE FOR READING

- **What are the characteristics of a mineral?**
- **How are minerals identified?**

Reading Tip **As you read, use the headings to make an outline showing what minerals are and how they can be identified.**

If you visit a science museum, you might wander into a room named the "hall of minerals." There you would see substances you have never heard of. For example, you might see deep-red crystals labeled "sphalerite" (SFAL uh ryt). You might be surprised to learn that sphalerite is a source of zinc and gallium. These metals are used in products from "tin" cans to computer chips! Although you may never have seen sphalerite, you are probably familiar with other common minerals. For example, you have probably seen turquoise, a blue-green mineral used in jewelry.

Figure 1 The Hall of Minerals at the American Museum of Natural History in New York City contains one of the world's largest collections of minerals.

A

Figure 2 **A.** Red crystals of the mineral sphalerite are called ruby zinc. **B.** Borax is a mineral that forms in dry lake beds. **C.** Coal is not a mineral because it is made of the remains of ancient plants. **Comparing and Contrasting** *How are sphalerite and borax similar? How are they different?*

What Is a Mineral?

B

Sphalerite and turquoise are just two of more than 3,000 minerals that geologists have identified. Of all these minerals, only about 100 are common. Most of the others are harder to find than gold. About 20 minerals make up most of the rocks of Earth's crust. These minerals are known as rock-forming minerals. Appendix B at the back of this book lists some of the most common rock-forming minerals.

A mineral is a naturally occurring, inorganic solid that has a crystal structure and a definite chemical composition. For a substance to be a mineral, it must have all five of these characteristics. In Figure 2, you can compare sphalerite with another mineral, borax, and with coal, which is not a mineral.

C

Naturally Occurring To be classified as a mineral, a substance must occur naturally. Cement, brick, steel, and glass all come from substances found in Earth's crust. However, these building materials are manufactured by people. Because they are not naturally occurring, such materials are not considered to be minerals.

Inorganic A mineral must also be **inorganic.** This means that the mineral cannot arise from materials that were once part of a living thing. For example, coal forms naturally in the crust. But geologists do not classify coal as a mineral because it comes from the remains of plants and animals that lived millions of years ago.

Solid A mineral is always a solid, with a definite volume and shape. The particles that make up a solid are packed together very tightly, so they cannot move like the particles that make up a liquid. A solid keeps its shape because its particles can't flow freely.

Crystal Structure The particles of a mineral line up in a pattern that repeats over and over again. The repeating pattern of a mineral's particles forms a solid called a **crystal.** A crystal has flat sides, called faces, that meet at sharp edges and corners.

Sometimes, the crystal structure is obvious from the mineral's appearance. In other minerals, however, the crystal structure is visible only under a microscope. A few minerals, such as opal, are considered minerals even though their particles are not arranged in a crystal structure.

Definite Chemical Composition A mineral has a definite

INTEGRATING CHEMISTRY

chemical composition. This means that a mineral always contains certain elements in definite proportions. An **element** is a substance composed of a single kind of atom. All the atoms of the same element have the same chemical and physical properties.

Almost all minerals are compounds. In a **compound,** two or more elements are combined so that the elements no longer have distinct properties. The elements that make up a compound are said to be chemically joined. For example, a crystal of the mineral quartz has one atom of silicon for every two atoms of oxygen. Each compound has its own properties, which usually differ greatly from the properties of the elements that form it. Figure 3 compares the mineral cinnabar to the elements that make it up.

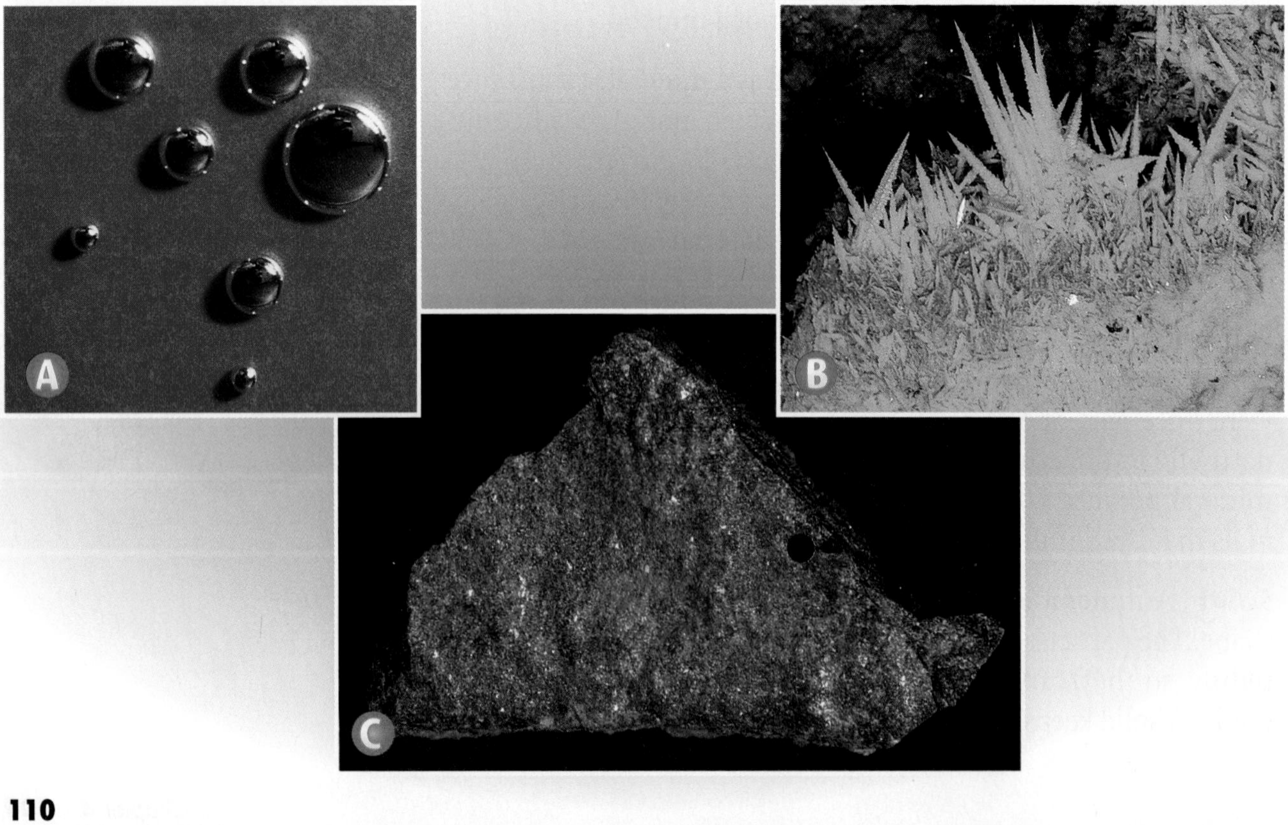
A
B
C

Figure 3 Minerals are usually a compound of two or more elements. **A.** Mercury is a metal that is a silvery liquid at room temperature. **B.** The element sulfur is bright yellow. **C.** The mineral cinnabar is a compound of the elements mercury and sulfur. Cinnabar has red crystals.

A
B
C

Figure 4 An old saying warns "All that glitters is not gold." **A.** Real gold can occur as a pure metal. **B.** Pyrite, or fool's gold, contains iron and sulfur. **C.** Chalcopyrite is a compound of copper, iron, and sulfur. ***Observing*** *These minerals are similar in color. But do you notice any differences in their appearance?*

Some elements occur in nature in a pure form, not as part of a compound with other elements. These elements, such as copper, silver, and gold, are considered to be minerals. Almost all pure elements are metals.

☑ ***Checkpoint*** ***What does it mean to say that a mineral has a definite chemical composition?***

Identifying Minerals

During the California Gold Rush of 1849, thousands of people headed west to find gold in the California hills. Some found gold, but most found disappointment. Perhaps the most disappointed of all were the ones who found pyrite, or "fool's gold." All three minerals in Figure 4 look like gold, yet only one is the real thing.

Because there are so many different kinds of minerals, telling them apart can be a challenge. The color of a mineral alone often provides too little information to make an identification. **Each mineral has its own specific properties that can be used to identify it.** When you have learned to recognize the properties of minerals, you will be able to identify many common minerals around you.

You can see some of the properties of a mineral just by looking at a sample. To observe other properties, however, you need to conduct tests on that sample. As you read about the properties of minerals, think about how you could use them to identify a mineral.

Hardness When you identify a mineral, one of the best clues you can use is the mineral's hardness. In 1812, Friedrich Mohs, an Austrian mineral expert, invented a test to describe and compare the hardness of minerals. Called the **Mohs hardness scale,** this scale ranks ten minerals from softest to hardest. Look at the

Sharpen your Skills

Classifying

ACTIVITY

1. Use your fingernail to try to scratch talc, calcite, and quartz. Record which minerals you were able to scratch.
2. Now try to scratch the minerals with a penny. Were your results different? Explain.
3. Were there any minerals you were unable to scratch with either your fingernail or the penny?
4. How would you classify the three minerals in order of increasing hardness?

Figure 5 Mohs hardness scale rates the hardness of minerals on a scale of 1 to 10. ***Drawing Conclusions*** *You find a mineral that can be scratched by a steel knife, but not by a copper penny. What is this mineral's hardness on the Mohs scale?*

Mohs Hardness Scale

Mineral	Rating	Testing Method
Talc	1	Softest known mineral. It flakes easily when scratched by a fingernail.
Gypsum	2	A fingernail can easily scratch it.
Calcite	3	A fingernail cannot scratch it, but a copper penny can.
Fluorite	4	A steel knife can easily scratch it.
Apatite	5	A steel knife can scratch it.
Feldspar	6	Cannot be scratched by a steel knife, but it can scratch window glass.
Quartz	7	Can scratch steel and hard glass easily.
Topaz	8	Can scratch quartz.
Corundum	9	Can scratch topaz.
Diamond	10	Hardest known mineral. Diamond can scratch all other substances.

table in Figure 5 to see which mineral is the softest and which is the hardest. A mineral can scratch any mineral softer than itself, but will be scratched by any mineral that is harder. How would you determine the hardness of a mineral not listed on the Mohs scale, such as sphalerite? You could try to scratch sphalerite with talc, gypsum, or calcite. But you would find that none of them scratch sphalerite. Apatite, the mineral rated 5 on the scale, does scratch sphalerite. Therefore, you would conclude that sphalerite's hardness is about 4 on Mohs hardness scale.

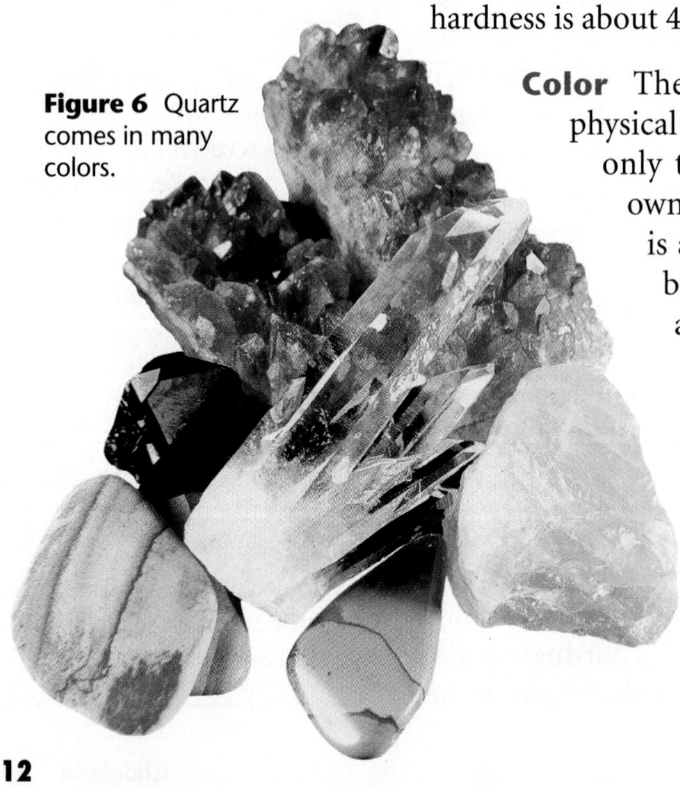

Figure 6 Quartz comes in many colors.

Color The color of a mineral is an easily observed physical property. But color can be used to identify only those few minerals that always have their own characteristic color. The mineral malachite is always green. The mineral azurite is always blue. No other minerals look quite the same as these. Many minerals, however, like the quartz in Figure 6, can occur in a variety of colors.

Streak A streak test can provide a clue to a mineral's identity. The **streak** of a mineral is the color of its powder. You can observe a streak by rubbing a mineral against a piece of unglazed tile called a streak plate. Even though the color of the mineral may vary, its streak does not. Surprisingly, the streak color

A

B

Figure 7 **A.** Galena, which contains lead, has a metallic luster. **B.** Malachite, which contains copper, has a silky luster.

and the mineral color are often different. For example, although pyrite has a gold color, it always produces a greenish black streak. Real gold, on the other hand, produces a golden yellow streak.

Luster Another simple test to identify a mineral is to check its luster. **Luster** is the term used to describe how a mineral reflects light from its surface. Minerals containing metals are often shiny. For example, galena is an ore of lead that has a bright, metallic luster. Look at Figure 7 to compare the luster of galena with the luster of malachite. Other minerals, such as quartz, have a glassy luster. Some of the other terms used to describe luster include earthy, waxy, and pearly.

Density Each mineral has a characteristic density. Recall from Chapter 1 that density is the mass in a given space, or mass per unit volume. No matter what the size of a mineral sample, the density of that mineral always remains the same.

You can compare the density of two mineral samples of about the same size. Just pick them up and heft them, or feel their weight, in your hands. You may be able to feel the difference between low-density quartz and high-density galena. If the two samples are the same size, the galena is almost three times as heavy as the quartz.

But heft provides only a rough measure of density. When geologists measure density, they use a balance to determine precisely the mass of a mineral sample. The mineral is also placed in water to determine how much water it displaces. The volume of the displaced water equals the volume of the sample. Dividing the sample's mass by its volume gives the density of the mineral.

Checkpoint *How can you determine a mineral's density?*

Language Arts CONNECTION

Geologists use adjectives such as glassy, dull, pearly, silky, greasy, and pitchlike to describe the luster of a mineral. When writers describe the surfaces of objects other than minerals, they also use words that describe luster. Luster can suggest how a surface looks. A new car, for example, might look glassy; an old car might look dull.

In Your Journal

Think of a familiar scene to describe—a room, building, tree, or street. Make a list of objects in your scene and a list of adjectives describing the surfaces of these objects. You might use some of the adjectives that geologists use to describe luster. Now write a paragraph using sensory words that make the scene seem real.

Crystal Systems The crystals of each mineral grow atom by atom to form that mineral's particular crystal stucture. Geologists classify these structures into six groups based on the number and angle of the crystal faces. These groups are called crystal systems. For example, all halite crystals are cubic. Halite crystals have six sides that meet at right angles, forming a perfect cube. Sometimes you can see that a crystal has the particular crystal structure of its mineral. Crystals that grow in an open space can be almost perfectly formed. But crystals that grow in a tight space are often incompletely formed. Figure 8 shows minerals that belong to each of the six crystal systems.

Figure 8 This chart lists some common minerals and their properties. ***Interpreting Data*** *Which mineral is lowest in density and hardness? Which mineral could you identify by using a compass?*

Properties and Uses of Minerals

					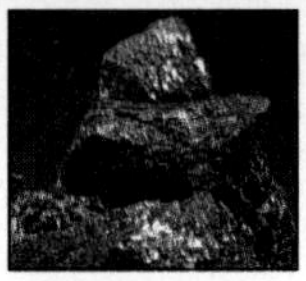	
Name	**Magnetite**	**Quartz**	**Rutile**	**Sulfur**	**Azurite**	**Microcline Feldspar**
Hardness	6	7	$6 - 6\frac{1}{2}$	2	$3\frac{1}{2} - 4$	6
Color	Black	Transparent or in a range of colors	Black or reddish brown	Lemon yellow to yellowish brown	Blue	Green, red-brown, pink, or white
Streak	Black	Colorless	Light brown	White	Pale blue	Colorless
Crystal System	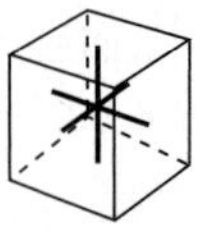 Cubic	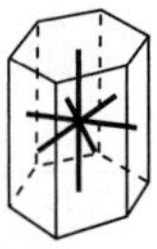 Hexagonal	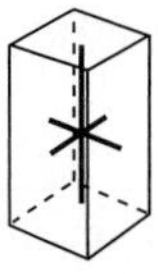 Tetragonal	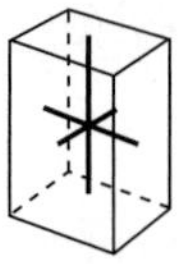 Orthorhombic	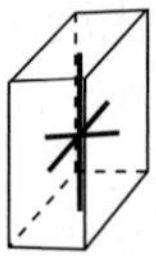 Monoclinic	 Triclinic
Luster	Metallic	Glassy	Metallic or gemlike	Greasy	Glassy to dull or earthy	Glassy
Special Properties	Magnetic	Fractures like broken glass	Not easily melted	Melts easily	Reacts to acid	Cleaves well in two directions
Density (g/cm^3)	5.2	2.6	4.2–4.3	2.0–2.1	3.8	2.6
Uses	A source of iron used to make steel	Used in making glass and electronic equipment, or as a gem	Contains titanium, a hard, lightweight metal used in aircraft and cars	Used in fungicides, industrial chemicals, and rubber	A source of copper metal; also used as a gem	Used in pottery glaze, scouring powder, or as a gem

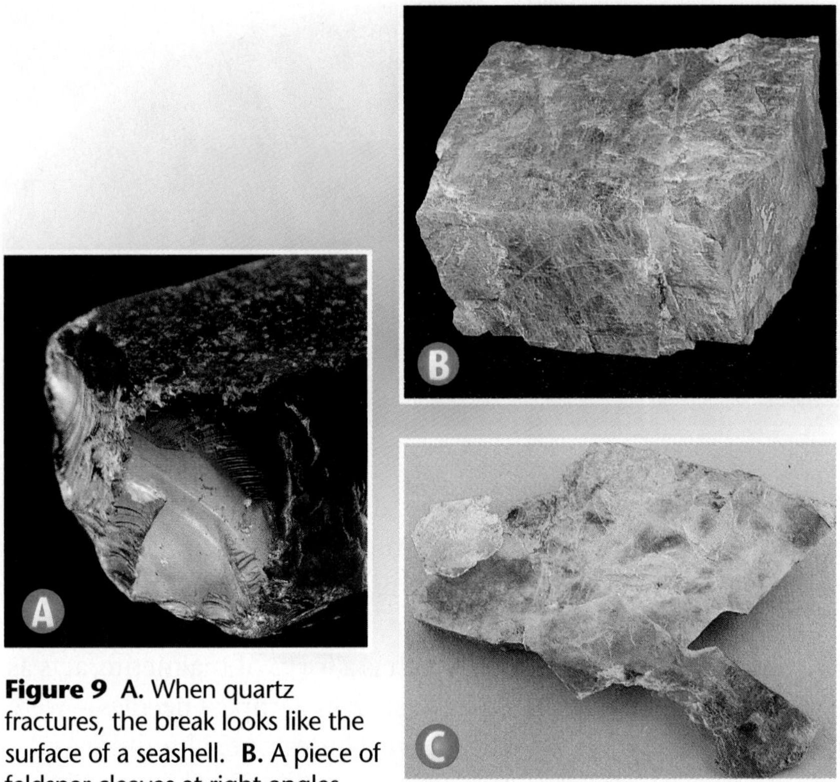
A
B
C

Figure 9 **A.** When quartz fractures, the break looks like the surface of a seashell. **B.** A piece of feldspar cleaves at right angles. **C.** Mica cleaves into thin, flat sheets that are almost transparent. *Applying Concepts How would you test a mineral to determine its cleavage and fracture?*

Cleavage and Fracture The way a mineral breaks apart can help to identify it. A mineral that splits easily along flat surfaces has the property called **cleavage.** Whether a mineral has cleavage depends on how the atoms in its crystals are arranged. Depending on the arrangement of atoms in the mineral, it will break apart more easily in one direction than another. Look at the minerals in Figure 9. Mica separates easily in only one direction, forming flat sheets. Feldspar splits at right angles, producing square corners. These minerals have cleavage.

Most minerals do not split apart evenly. Instead, they have a characteristic type of fracture. **Fracture** describes how a mineral looks when it breaks apart in an irregular way. Geologists use a variety of terms to describe fracture. For example, quartz has a shell-shaped fracture. When quartz breaks, it produces curved, shell-like surfaces that look like chipped glass. Pure metals, like copper and iron, have a hackly fracture—they form jagged points. Some soft minerals that crumble easily like clay have an earthy fracture. Minerals that form rough, irregular surfaces when broken have an uneven fracture.

☑ *Checkpoint How are cleavage and fracture similar? How are they different?*

TRY THIS

Crystal Hands

ACTIVITY

You can grow two different kinds of salt crystals.

1. Put on your goggles.
2. Pour a solution of halite (table salt) into one shallow pan and a solution of Epsom salts into another shallow pan.
3. Put a large piece of black construction paper on a flat surface.
4. Dip one hand in the halite solution. Shake off the excess liquid and make a palm print on the paper. Repeat with your other hand and the Epsom salt solution, placing your new print next to the first one. **CAUTION:** *Do not do this activity if you have a cut on your hand.* Wash your hands after making your hand prints.
5. Let the prints dry overnight.

Observing Use a hand lens to compare the shape of the crystals. Which hand prints have more crystals?

Figure 10 Scheelite looks quite ordinary in daylight, but glows with brilliant color under ultraviolet light.

Special Properties Some minerals can be identified by special physical properties. For example, minerals that glow under ultraviolet light have a property known as **fluorescence** (floo RES uns). The mineral scheelite is fluorescent. Magnetism occurs naturally in a few minerals. Lodestone, which is a form of magnetite, acts as a natural magnet. Early magnets—such as compass needles—were made by striking a piece of iron with lodestone. Uraninite and a few other minerals are radioactive. They set off a Geiger counter. Some minerals react chemically to acid. Calcite, a compound of calcium, carbon, and oxygen, fizzes and gives off carbon dioxide when a drop of vinegar is placed on it.

A few minerals, such as quartz, have electrical properties. Pressure applied to these crystals produces a small electric current. In addition, these crystals vibrate if they come in contact with an electric current. Because of these properties, quartz crystals are used in microphones, radio transmitters, and watches.

Section 1 Review

1. What characteristics must a substance have to be considered a mineral?
2. Describe how you can test a mineral to determine its hardness, density, and streak.
3. What is the major difference between an element and a compound?
4. **Thinking Critically Classifying** According to the definition of a mineral, can water be classified as a mineral? Explain your answer.
5. **Thinking Critically Making Generalizations** Explain why you can't rely on any single test or property when you are trying to identify a mineral.

CHAPTER PROJECT

Check Your Progress

Select a container for your crystal garden such as a plastic shoe box or a large-mouth jar. Make a sketch showing the shapes and locations of the "plants" you plan to grow. When you have designed your garden, decide what materials to put in the box for the crystals to grow on. Decide what crystal-growth solutions you will use. Halite, Epsom salts, and alum are possibilities. Check with your teacher to make sure the chemicals you plan to use are safe.

Measuring

The Density of Minerals

In this lab, you will use water to help you measure the density of minerals.

Problem

How can you compare the density of different minerals?

Materials (per student)

graduated cylinder, 100 mL
3 mineral samples: pyrite, quartz, and galena
water
balance

Procedure

1. Check to make sure the mineral samples are small enough to fit in the graduated cylinder.
2. Copy the data table into your notebook. Place the pyrite on the balance and record its mass in the data table.
3. Fill the cylinder with water to the 50-mL mark.
4. Carefully place the pyrite into the cylinder of water. Try not to spill any of the water.
5. Read the level of the water on the scale of the graduated cylinder. Record the level of the water with the pyrite in it.
6. Calculate the volume of water displaced by the pyrite. To do this, subtract the volume of water without the pyrite from the volume of water with the pyrite. Record your answer.
7. Calculate the density of the pyrite by using this formula.

$$\text{Density} = \frac{\text{Mass of mineral}}{\text{Volume of water displaced by the mineral}}$$

(Note: Density is expressed as g/cm^3. One mL of water has a volume of 1 cm^3.)

8. Remove the water and mineral from the cylinder.
9. Repeat steps 2–8 for quartz and galena.

Analyze and Conclude

1. Which mineral had the highest density? The lowest density?
2. How does finding the volume of the water that was displaced help you find the volume of the mineral itself?
3. Why won't the procedure you used in this lab work for a substance that floats or one that dissolves in water?
4. **Apply** Pyrite is sometimes called "fool's gold" because its color and appearance are similar to real gold. How could a scientist determine if a sample was real gold?
5. **Think About It** Does the shape or size of a mineral sample affect its density? Explain.

More to Explore

Repeat the activity by finding the density of other minerals or materials. Then compare the densities of these materials with pyrite, quartz, and galena.

DATA TABLE

	Pyrite	Quartz	Galena
Mass of Mineral (g)			
Volume of Water without Mineral (mL)	50 mL	50 mL	50 mL
Volume of Water with Mineral (mL)			
Volume of Water Displaced (mL)			
Density (g/cm^3)			

Skills Lab

SECTION 2 How Minerals Form

DISCOVER ACTIVITY

How Does the Rate of Cooling Affect Crystals?

1. Put on your goggles. Use a plastic spoon to place a small amount of salol near one end of each of two microscope slides. You need just enough to form a spot 0.5 to 1.0 cm in diameter.
2. Carefully hold one slide with tongs. Warm it gently over a lit candle until the salol is almost completely melted. **CAUTION:** *Move the slide in and out of the flame to avoid cracking the glass.*
3. Set the slide aside to cool slowly.
4. While the first slide is cooling, hold the second slide with tongs and heat it as in Step 2. Cool the slide quickly by placing it on an ice cube. Carefully blow out the candle.
5. Observe the slides under a hand lens. Compare the appearance of the crystals that form on the two slides.
6. Wash your hands when you are finished.

Think It Over

Relating Cause and Effect Which sample had larger crystals? If a mineral forms by rapid cooling, would you expect the crystals to be large or small?

GUIDE FOR READING

- **What are the processes by which minerals form?**

Reading Tip **Before you read, rewrite the headings of the section as how, why, or what questions. As you read, look for answers to these questions.**

Imagine digging for diamonds. At Crater of Diamonds State Park in Arkansas, that's exactly what people do. The park is one of the very few places in the United States where diamonds can be found. Visitors are permitted to prospect, or search, for diamonds. Since the area became a park in 1972, visitors have found more than 20,000 diamonds!

How did the diamonds get there? Millions of years ago, a volcanic pipe formed in the mantle at a depth of 120 kilometers or more. At that depth, great

Diamonds ▶

pressure and heat changed carbon atoms into the hardest known substance—diamond. Then the pipe erupted, carrying diamonds and other materials toward the surface. Today, geologists recognize this type of volcanic pipe as an area of unusual bluish-colored rock made up of a variety of minerals, including diamond. Volcanic pipes containing diamonds are found in only a few places on Earth. Most occur in South Africa and Australia, where many of the world's diamonds are mined today.

Processes That Form Minerals

You probably have handled products made from minerals. But you may not have thought about how the minerals formed. The minerals that people use today have been forming deep in Earth's crust or on the surface for several billion years. **In general, minerals can form in two ways: through crystallization of melted materials, and through crystallization of materials dissolved in water.** Crystallization is the process by which atoms are arranged to form a material with a crystal structure.

Minerals From Magma

Minerals form as hot magma cools inside the crust, or as lava hardens on the surface. When these liquids cool to the solid state, they form crystals. The size of the crystals depends on several factors. The rate at which the magma cools, the amount of gas the magma contains, and the chemical composition of the magma all affect crystal size.

When magma remains deep below the surface, it cools slowly over many thousands of years. Slow cooling leads to the formation of large crystals. If the crystals remain undisturbed while cooling, they grow by adding atoms according to a regular pattern.

Magma closer to the surface cools much faster than magma that hardens deep below ground. With more rapid cooling, there is no time for magma to form large crystals. Instead, small crystals form. If magma erupts to the surface and becomes lava, the lava will also cool quickly and form minerals with small crystals.

Figure 11 This crystal of the mineral spodumene is 24 cm long. But it's not the largest crystal. Spodumene crystals the size of telephone poles have been found in South Dakota.
Inferring *Under what conditions did such large crystals probably form?*

A

B

Figure 12 A. Silver sometimes occurs as a pure metal, forming delicate, treelike crystals.
B. Solutions containing dissolved metals form veins like the ones in this silver mine in Idaho.

Minerals From Hot Water Solutions

Sometimes, the elements that form a mineral dissolve in hot water. Magma has heated the water to a high temperature beneath Earth's surface. These dissolved minerals form solutions. A **solution** is a mixture in which one substance dissolves in another. When a hot water solution begins to cool, the elements and compounds leave the solution and crystallize as minerals. The silver shown in Figure 12A formed by this process.

Pure metals that crystallize underground from hot water solutions often form veins. A **vein** is a narrow channel or slab of a mineral that is much different from the surrounding rock. Deep underground, solutions of hot water and metals often follow cracks within the rock. Then the metals crystallize into veins that resemble the streaks of fudge in vanilla fudge ice cream. Figure 12B shows a vein of silver in a mine.

Many minerals form from solutions at places where tectonic plates spread apart along the mid-ocean ridge. First, ocean water

Figure 13 Many minerals form at chimneys along the mid-ocean ridge. Chimneys occur in areas where sea-floor spreading causes cracks in the oceanic crust. *Interpreting Diagrams What is the energy source for this process?*

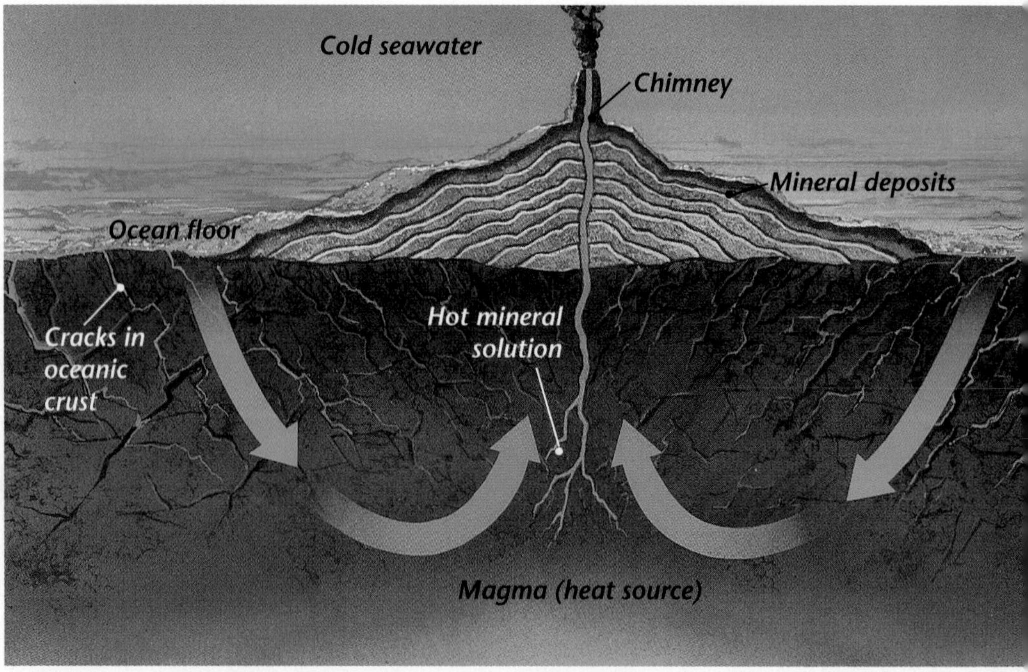
Cold seawater
Chimney
Mineral deposits
Ocean floor
Cracks in oceanic crust
Hot mineral solution
Magma (heat source)

Figure 14 In Death Valley, California, water carries dissolved minerals from the surrounding mountains into the valley. When the water evaporates under the blazing desert sun, the minerals form a crust on the valley floor.

seeps down through cracks in the crust. There, the water comes in contact with magma that heats it to a very high temperature. The heated water dissolves minerals from the crust and rushes upward. This hot solution then billows out of vents, called "chimneys." When the hot solution hits the cold sea, minerals crystallize and settle to the ocean floor.

Minerals Formed by Evaporation

Minerals can also form when solutions evaporate. You know that if you stir salt crystals into a beaker of water, the salt dissolves, forming a solution. But if you allow the water in the solution to evaporate, it will leave salt crystals on the bottom of the beaker. In a similar way, thick deposits of the mineral halite formed over millions of years when ancient seas slowly evaporated. In the United States, such halite deposits occur in the Midwest, the Southwest, and along the Gulf Coast.

Several other useful minerals also form by the evaporation of seawater. These include gypsum, used in making building materials; calcite crystals, used in microscopes; and minerals containing potassium, used in making fertilizer.

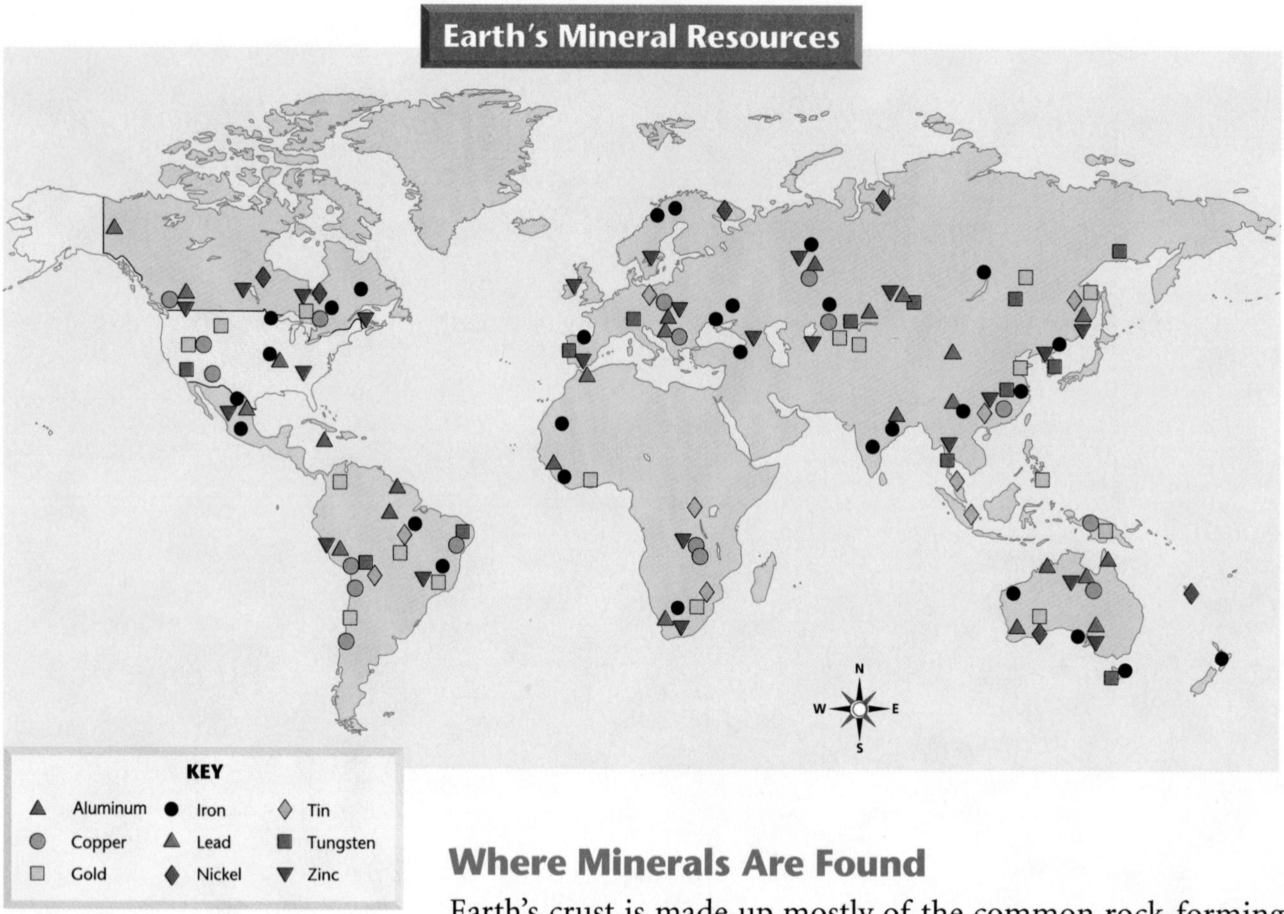
Earth's Mineral Resources
KEY
Aluminum
Copper
Gold
Iron
Lead
Nickel
Tin
Tungsten
Zinc
N
W
E
S

Figure 15 The map shows where important mineral resources are found throughout the world. ***Interpreting Maps*** *Which metals are found in the United States? Which ones must be imported from other countries?*

Where Minerals Are Found

Earth's crust is made up mostly of the common rock-forming minerals combined in various types of rock. Less common and rare minerals, however, are not distributed evenly throughout the crust. Instead, there are several processes that concentrate minerals, or bring them together, in deposits. Look at the map of the world's mineral resources in Figure 15. Do you see any patterns in the distribution of minerals such as gold and copper? Many valuable minerals are found in or near areas of volcanic activity and mountain building. For example, in the 1800s, California's rich gold deposits were found along the Sierra Nevada mountains.

Section 2 Review

1. What are the two main ways in which minerals form?
2. Describe how the cooling rate of magma affects the size of the mineral crystals formed.
3. What are the steps by which mineral deposits form along mid-ocean ridges?
4. **Thinking Critically Relating Cause and Effect** A miner finds a vein of silver. Describe a process that could have formed the vein.

CHAPTER PROJECT

Check Your Progress

Remember to record your daily observations of how your crystal garden grows. Sketch the shapes of the crystals and describe how the crystals grow. Compare the shapes and growth rates of the crystals grown from the various solutions. (*Hint:* If crystals do not begin growing, add more of the correct solution.)

SCIENCE AND SOCIETY

Who Owns the Ocean's Minerals?

Rich mineral deposits lie on and just beneath the ocean floor. Many nations would like to mine these deposits. Coastal nations already have the right to mine deposits near their shores. Today, they are mining materials such as tin, titanium, diamonds, and sulfur from the continental shelf—the wide area of shallow water just off the shores of continents.

But the ocean floor beyond the continental shelves is open for all nations to explore. Mineral deposits in volcanic areas of the ocean floor include manganese, iron, cobalt, copper, nickel and platinum. Who owns these valuable underwater minerals?

▲ This sample from the floor of the Pacific Ocean near New Guinea may contain copper and gold.

The Issues

Who Can Afford to Mine? Although the ocean floor is open to all for exploration, mining the ocean floor will cost a huge amount of money. New technologies must be developed to obtain mineral deposits from the ocean floor.

Only wealthy industrial nations such as France, Germany, Japan, and the United States will be able to afford these costs. Industrial nations that have spent money and effort on mining think that they should be allowed to keep all the profits. However, developing nations that lack money and technology disagree. Landlocked nations that have no coastlines also object.

What Rights Do Other Nations Have? As of 1996, 87 nations had signed the Law of the Sea treaty. Among other things, this treaty stated that ocean mineral deposits are the common property of all people. It also stated that mining profits must be shared among all nations.

Some people think that, because of the treaty, wealthy nations should share their technology and any profits they get from mining the ocean floor.

How Can the Wealth Be Shared? What can nations do to prevent conflict over mining the ocean floor? They might arrange a compromise. Perhaps wealthy nations should contribute part of their profits to help developing or landlocked nations. Developing nations could pool their money for ocean-floor mining. Whatever nations decide, some regulations for ocean-floor mining are necessary. In the future, these resources will be important to everyone.

You Decide

1. **Identify the Problem**
   In your own words, state the controversy about ocean mineral rights.
2. **Analyze the Options**
   Compare the concerns of wealthy nations with those of developing nations. How could you reassure developing nations that they will not be left out?
3. **Find a Solution**
   Look at a map of the world. Who should share the mineral profits from the Pacific Ocean? From the Atlantic Ocean? Write one or two paragraphs stating your opinion. Support your ideas with facts.

SECTION 3 Mineral Resources

DISCOVER ACTIVITY

How Are Minerals Processed Before They Are Used?

1. Examine a piece of the mineral bauxite and use your knowledge of the properties of minerals to describe it.
2. Examine an aluminum can. (The metal aluminum comes from bauxite.) Compare the properties of the aluminum can with the properties of bauxite.
3. Examine a piece of the mineral graphite and describe its properties.
4. Examine the lead in a pencil. (Pencil "lead" is made from graphite.) Compare the properties of the pencil lead with the properties of graphite.

Think It Over

Posing Questions How is each mineral similar to or different from the object made from it? What questions would you need to answer to understand how bauxite and graphite are made into useful materials?

GUIDE FOR READING

- **How are minerals used?**
- **What are the three types of mines?**
- **How are ores processed to obtain metals?**

Reading Tip **As you read, draw a concept map that explains how metal ores are located, mined, and smelted.**

More than a thousand years ago, the Hopewell people lived in the Mississippi River valley. These ancient Native Americans are famous for the mysterious earthen mounds they built near the river. There these people left beautiful objects made from minerals: tools chipped from flint (a variety of quartz), the shape of a human hand cut out of a piece of translucent mica, or a flying bird made from a thin sheet of copper.

To obtain these minerals, the Hopewell people traded with peoples across North America. The copper, for example, came from near Lake Superior. There, copper could be found as a pure metal. Because copper is a soft metal, this copper was easy to shape into ornaments or weapons.

Figure 16 The copper to make this Hopewell ornament may have come from an area in Michigan that is still a source of copper ore.

The Uses of Minerals

Like the Hopewell people, people today use minerals. You are surrounded by materials that come from minerals—for example, the metal body and window glass of a car. **Minerals are the source of metals, gemstones, and other materials used to make many products.** Are you familiar with any products that are made from minerals? You might be surprised at how important minerals are in everyday life.

Gemstones Beautiful gemstones such as rubies and sapphires have captured the imagination of people throughout the ages. Usually, a **gemstone** is a hard, colorful mineral that has a brilliant or glassy luster. People value gemstones for their color, luster, and durability—and for the fact that they are rare. Once a gemstone is cut and polished, it is called a gem. Gems are used mainly for jewelry and decoration. They are also used for mechanical parts and for grinding and polishing.

Figure 17 Gems like these red rubies and blue and yellow sapphires are among the most valuable minerals. These precious gems are varieties of the mineral corundum.

Metals Some minerals are the sources of metals such as aluminum, iron, copper, or silver. Metals are useful because they can be stretched into wire, flattened into sheets, and hammered or molded without breaking. Metal tools and machinery, the metal filament in a light bulb, even the steel girders used to frame office buildings—all began as minerals inside Earth's crust.

Other Useful Minerals There are many other useful minerals besides metals and gems. People use materials from these minerals in foods, medicines, fertilizers, and building materials. The very soft mineral talc is ground up to make talcum powder. Fluorite is important in making aluminum and steel. Clear crystals of the mineral calcite are used in optical instruments such as microscopes. Quartz, a mineral found in sand, is used in making glass as well as in electronic equipment and watches. Kaolin occurs as white clay, which is used for making high-quality china and pottery. Gypsum, a soft, white mineral, is used to make wallboard, cement, and stucco. Corundum, the second hardest mineral after diamond, is often used in polishing and cleaning products.

☑ *Checkpoint* *What is a gemstone? Why are gemstones valuable?*

Ores

A rock that contains a metal or economically useful mineral is called an **ore**. Unlike the copper used by the Hopewell people, most metals do not occur in a pure form. A metal usually occurs as a mineral that is a combination of that metal and other elements. Much of the world's copper, for example, comes from ores containing the mineral chalcopyrite (kal kuh PY ryt). Before metals, gemstones, and other useful minerals can be separated from their ores, however, geologists must find them.

Prospecting

A prospector is anyone who searches, or prospects, for an ore deposit. Geologists prospect for ores by looking for certain features on Earth's surface. These geologists observe what kind of rocks are on the land surface. They examine plants growing in an area and test stream water for the presence of certain chemicals.

Geologists also employ some of the tools used to study Earth's interior. In one technique, they set off explosions below ground to create shock waves. The echoes of these shock waves are used to map the location, size, and shape of an ore deposit.

Mining

The geologist's map of an ore deposit helps miners decide how to mine the ore from the ground. **There are three types of mines: strip mines, open pit mines, and shaft mines.** In strip mining,

SCIENCE & History

Advances in Metal Technology

For thousands of years, people have been inventing and improving methods for smelting metals and making alloys.

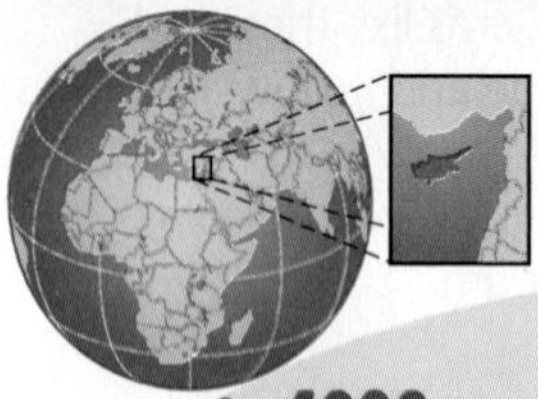

4000 B.C. Cyprus

The island of Cyprus was one of the first places where copper was mined and smelted. In fact, the name of the island provided the name of the metal. In Latin, *aes cyprium* meant "metal of Cyprus." It was later shortened to *cuprum*, meaning "copper." The sculptured figure is carrying a large piece of smelted copper.

4000 B.C. | 2500 B.C. | 1000 B.C.

3500 B.C.
Mesopotamia

Metalworkers in Sumer, a city between the Tigris and Euphrates rivers, made an alloy of tin and copper to produce a harder metal—bronze. Bronze was poured into molds to form statues, weapons, or vessels for food and drink.

1500 B.C.
Turkey

The Hittites learned to mine and smelt iron ore. Because iron is stronger than copper or bronze, its use spread rapidly. Tools and weapons could be made of iron. This iron dagger was made in Austria several hundred years after the Hittites' discovery.

earthmoving equipment scrapes away soil to expose ore. In open pit mining, miners use giant earthmoving equipment to dig a tremendous pit. Miners dig an open pit mine to remove ore deposits that may start near the surface, but extend down for hundreds of meters. Some open pit mines are more than a kilometer wide and nearly as deep. For ore deposits that occur in veins, miners dig shaft mines. Shaft mines often have a network of tunnels that extend deep into the ground, following the veins of ore.

INTEGRATING ENVIRONMENTAL SCIENCE Mining for metals and other minerals can harm the environment. Strip mining and pit mining leave scars on the land. Waste materials from mining can pollute rivers and lakes. In the United States, laws now require that mine operators do as little damage to the environment as possible. To restore land damaged by strip mining, mine operators grade the surface and replace the soil.

In Your Journal

When people discover how to use metals in a new way, the discovery often produces big changes in the way those people live. Choose a development in the history of metals to research. Write a diary entry telling how the discovery happened and how it changed people's lives.

A.D. 1860s
England

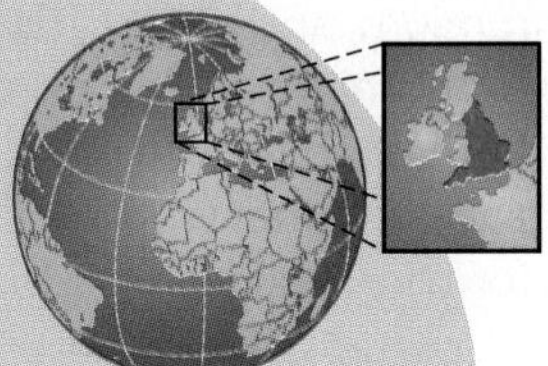

Steel-making techniques invented by Henry Bessemer and William Siemens made it possible to produce steel cheaply on a large scale. Siemens' invention, the open-hearth furnace, is still widely used, although more modern methods account for most steel production today.

A.D. 500 — A.D. 2000

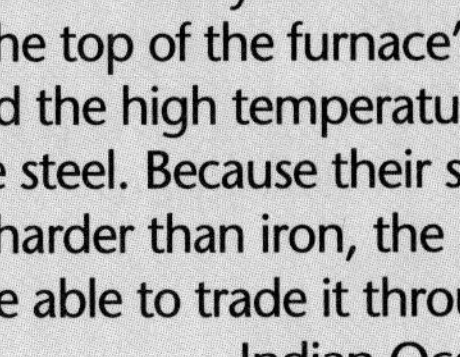

A.D. 600s
Sri Lanka

Sri Lankans made steel in outdoor furnaces. Steady winds blowing over the top of the furnace's front wall created the high temperatures needed to make steel. Because their steel was so much harder than iron, the Sri Lankans were able to trade it throughout the Indian Ocean region.

A.D. 1960s TO THE PRESENT
United States

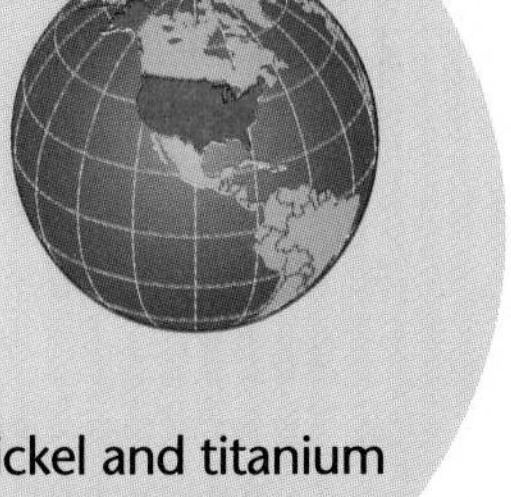

Scientists working on the space program have developed light and strong alloys for use in products ranging from bicycles to soda cans. For example, a new alloy of nickel and titanium can "remember" its shape. It is used for eyeglasses that return to their original shape after being bent.

Figure 18 Plain steel rusts easily. But stainless steel—an alloy of iron, chromium, and nickel—doesn't rust. The chromium and nickel slow down the process by which the oxygen in the air combines with iron in the steel to form iron oxide, or rust.

Smelting

Ores must be processed before the metals they contain can be used. **After miners remove ore from a mine, smelting is necessary to remove the metal from the ore.** In the process of **smelting,** an ore is melted to separate the useful metal from other elements the ore contains. People around the world have used smelting to obtain metals from ores. Look at the time line in *Science and History* to see how this technology has developed from ancient times to the present.

How does smelting separate iron metal from hematite, a common form of iron ore? In general, smelting involves mixing an ore with other substances and then heating the mixture to a very high temperature. The heat melts the metal in the ore. The heat also causes the metal to separate from the oxygen with which it is combined. Metalworkers can then pour off the molten metal. Follow the steps in *Exploring Smelting Iron Ore.*

After smelting, additional processing is needed to remove impurities from the iron. The result is steel, which is harder and stronger than iron. Steel is an **alloy,** a solid mixture of two or more metals. Steelmakers mix iron with other elements to create alloys with special properties. For stronger steel, the metal manganese and a small amount of carbon are added. For rust-resistant steel, the metals chromium and nickel are added. You can compare plain steel with rust-resistant stainless steel in Figure 18.

Section 3 Review

1. What are some of the ways that people use gems and metals?
2. Describe three different kinds of mines.
3. What process is used to separate useful metals from ores?
4. What are alloys, and why are they useful?
5. **Thinking Critically** In smelting, what causes a metal to separate from its ore?

Science at Home

You can demonstrate to your family how rust damages objects that contain iron. Obtain three iron nails. Coat one of the nails with petroleum jelly and coat the second nail with clear nail polish. Do not put anything on the third nail. Place all the nails in a glass of water with a little vinegar. (The vinegar speeds up the rusting process.) Allow the nails to stand in the glass overnight. Which nails show signs of rusting? Explain these results to your family.

EXPLORING *Smelting Iron Ore*

Iron usually occurs as the ores hematite or magnetite. Iron ores must be smelted to separate the iron from the oxygen and other substances in the ores. Then the iron is refined and processed into steel.

1. Iron ore is crushed and then mixed with crushed limestone and coke (baked coal), which is rich in carbon.

2. The coke and iron ore mixture is placed in a blast furnace, where extremely hot air is blown through, making the coke burn easily.

3. As the coke burns, chemical changes in the mixture produce carbon dioxide gas and molten iron.

4. The iron sinks to the bottom of the furnace. Impurities left in the ore combine with the limestone to create slag.

5. The slag and molten iron are poured off through taps in the blast furnace.

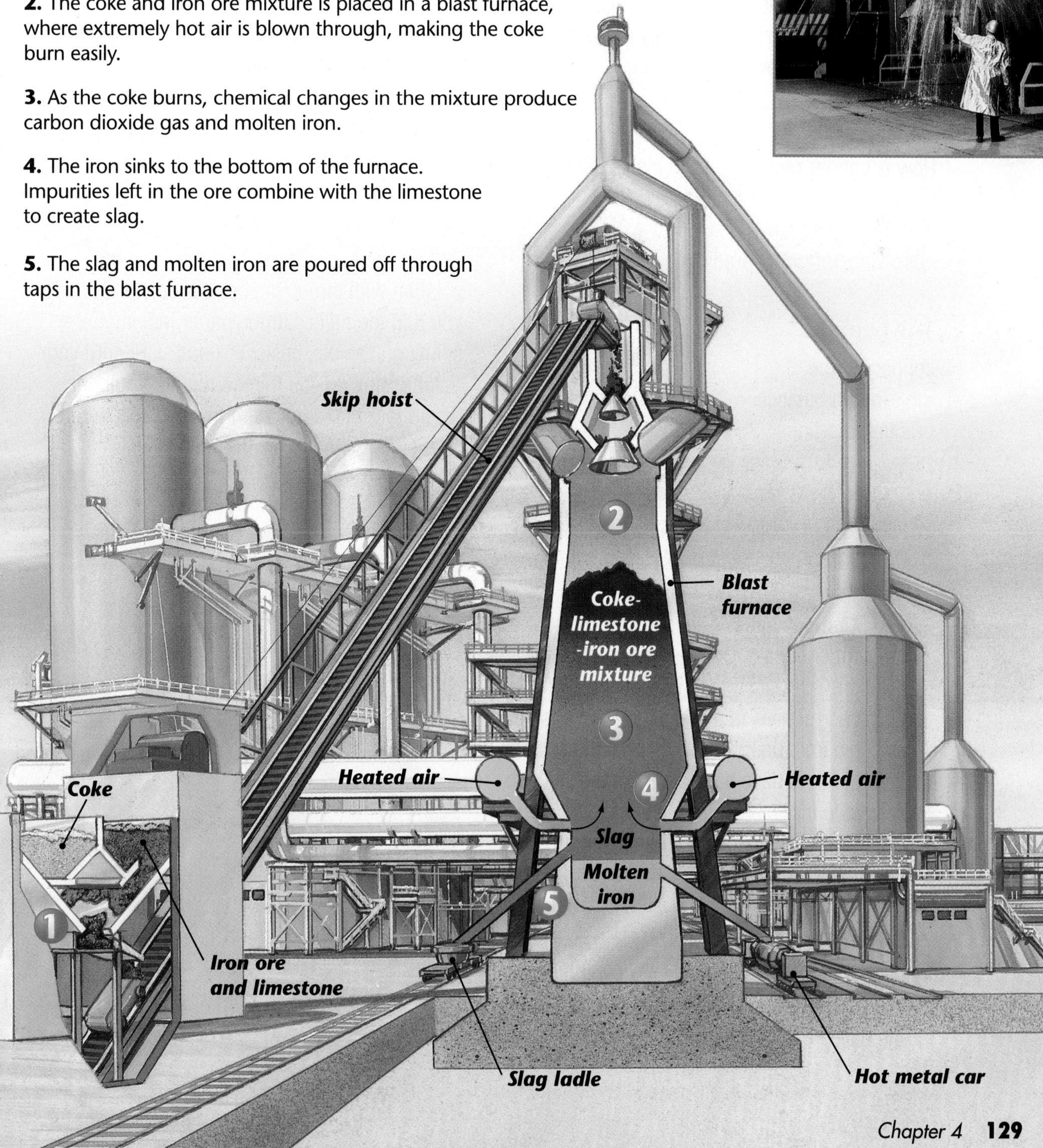

Skip hoist
2
Blast furnace
Coke-limestone-iron ore mixture
3
Heated air
4
Heated air
Coke
Slag
Molten iron
5
1
Iron ore and limestone
Slag ladle
Hot metal car

Real-World Lab

Careers in Science

COPPER RECOVERY

If you were a mining engineer, one of your tasks would be to make mining and processing ores more efficient. When copper ore is processed at copper mines, waste water containing copper sulfate is produced. Mining engineers have invented a way to recover copper metal from the waste water. They make the waste water flow over scrap iron.

Problem

How is copper recovered from a solution?

Skills Focus

observing, inferring, predicting

Materials

copper sulfate, 3 g
triple-beam balance
graduated cylinder, 200 mL
beaker, 400 mL
5 iron nails

Procedure

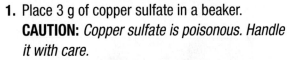

1. Place 3 g of copper sulfate in a beaker. **CAUTION:** *Copper sulfate is poisonous. Handle it with care.*
2. Add 50 mL of water to the beaker to dissolve the copper sulfate. Observe the color of the solution.
3. Add the iron nails to the beaker. The nails act as scrap iron. Describe the color of the solution after the nails have been added to the solution.
4. Follow your teacher's instructions for proper disposal. Wash your hands when you are finished.

Analyze and Conclude

1. What happened to the nails after you placed them in the solution? What is the material on the nails? Explain your answer.
2. How does the material on the nails compare with the copper sulfate?
3. Develop a plan that describes how a mine might recover copper from mine water using the method that you have just tried.
4. What additional step would you have to perform to obtain copper useful for making copper wire or pennies?
5. **Apply** Why do you think the operator of a copper mine would want to collect copper from the waste water?

Move to Explore

Repeat the experiment. This time test the solution with litmus paper both before and after you add the nails. Litmus paper indicates if a solution is acidic, basic, or neutral. Record your results. Why do you think a mining engineer would test the water from this process before releasing it into the environment?

SECTION 1 Properties of Minerals

Key Ideas

- A mineral is a naturally occurring inorganic solid that has a distinct chemical composition and crystal shape.
- Each mineral can be identified by its own physical and chemical properties.
- Some of the properties of minerals include hardness, color, streak, luster, density, cleavage and fracture, and crystal structure. Hardness is measured by the Mohs hardness scale.
- Minerals usually consist of two or more elements joined together in a compound.

Key Terms

mineral	Mohs hardness scale
inorganic	streak
crystal	luster
element	cleavage
compound	fracture
	fluorescence

SECTION 2 How Minerals Form

Key Ideas

- Minerals form inside Earth through crystallization as magma or lava cools.
- Minerals form on Earth's surface when materials dissolved in water crystallize through evaporation.
- Mineral deposits form on the ocean floor from solutions heated by magma along the mid-ocean ridge. The hot-water solutions containing minerals erupt through chimneys on the ocean floor, then crystallize when they come in contact with cold sea water.

Key Terms

solution
vein

SECTION 3 Mineral Resources

INTEGRATING TECHNOLOGY

Key Ideas

- Minerals are useful as the source of all metals, gemstones, and of many other materials.
- Geologists locate ore deposits by prospecting—looking for certain features on and beneath Earth's surface.
- Ores can be removed from the ground through open pit mines, strip mines, or shaft mines.
- Smelting is the process of heating an ore to extract a metal.

Key Terms

gemstone	smelting
ore	alloy

ACTIVITY

USING THE INTERNET

www.phschool.com/state_focus/california/

California Test Prep: Reviewing Content

Multiple Choice

Choose the letter of the answer that best completes each statement.

1. In a mineral, the particles line up in a repeating pattern to form
   a. an element. **b.** a crystal.
   c. a mixture. **d.** a compound.
2. The softest mineral in the Mohs hardness scale is
   a. quartz. **b.** talc.
   c. apatite. **d.** gypsum.
3. Halite is a mineral formed by
   a. sea-floor spreading.
   b. cooling of magma.
   c. evaporation.
   d. cooling of lava.
4. Metals are useful for tools because they
   a. are compounds.
   b. have a metallic luster.
   c. are hard yet can be easily shaped.
   d. are elements.
5. Minerals from which metals can be removed in usable amounts are called
   a. gemstones. **b.** crystals.
   c. alloys. **d.** ores.

True or False

If the statement is true, write true. If it is false, change the underlined word or words to make the statement true.

6. Luster is the term that describes how a mineral reflects light from its surface.
7. A piece of unglazed tile is used to test a mineral's hardness.
8. If magma cools very slowly, minerals with small crystals will form.
9. Minerals form from hot-water solutions at chimneys on the ocean floor.
10. The process of removing an ore deposit from the ground is known as prospecting.

Checking Concepts

11. What is the difference in composition between most minerals and a pure element?
12. How can the streak test be helpful in identifying minerals?
13. Compare cleavage and fracture.
14. Describe two different ways that minerals can form.
15. Describe the process used to extract metal from hematite ore. What metal would be obtained?
16. **Writing to Learn** You are a prospector searching for gold. In a letter home, describe where you plan to look, how you will know if you have found gold, and how you will feel about your discovery.

Thinking Visually

17. **Venn Diagram** Copy the Venn diagram comparing the mineral hematite and the human-made material brick onto a separate piece of paper. Then complete it and add a title. (For more on Venn diagrams, see the Skills Handbook.)

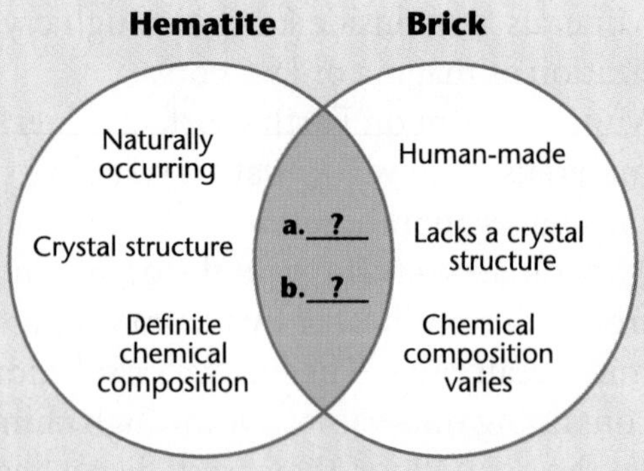
Hematite
Brick
Naturally occurring
Crystal structure
Definite chemical composition
a. ?
b. ?
Human-made
Lacks a crystal structure
Chemical composition varies

Test Prep: Skills

Working as a geologist, you have found a sample of the mineral wulfenite. Testing the wulfenite reveals that it has a hardness of about 3 on the Mohs hardness scale and a density of 6.8 grams per cubic centimeter. You also determine that the mineral contains oxygen as well as the metals lead and molybdenum.

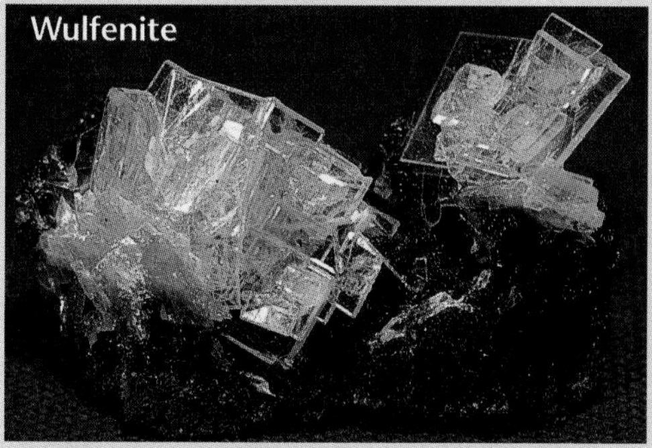
Wulfenite

18. **Observing** Describe wulfenite's color, luster, and crystal shape.
19. **Inferring** Did the wulfenite form slowly or quickly? Explain your answer.
20. **Drawing Conclusions** Is wulfenite hard enough for use as a gem? What would you use these crystals for? Explain.

Thinking Critically

21. **Comparing and Contrasting** Color and luster are both properties of minerals. How are these properties similar? How are they different? How can each be used to help identify a mineral?
22. **Classifying** Obsidian forms when magma cools very quickly, creating a type of glass. In glass, the particles are not arranged in an orderly pattern as in a crystal. Obsidian is a solid, inorganic substance that occurs naturally in volcanic areas. Should it be classified as a mineral? Explain why or why not.
23. **Relating Cause and Effect** Describe how a vein of ore forms underground. What is the energy source for this process?
24. **Applying Concepts** Explain the roles of elements, solutions, and compounds in the process that forms minerals along the mid-ocean ridge.
25. **Predicting** What would happen if steel-makers forgot to add enough chromium and nickel to a batch of stainless steel?

CHAPTER 4 ASSESSMENT

Performance Assessment

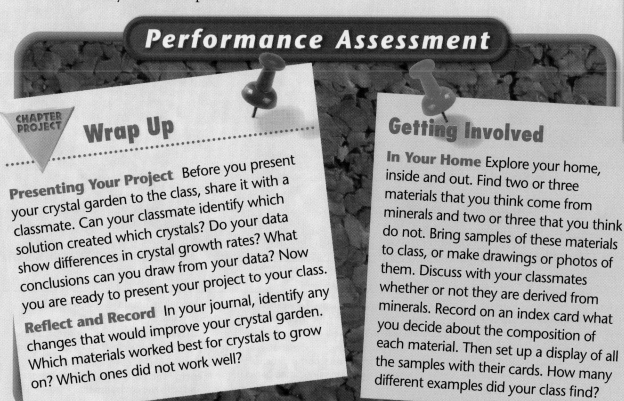

CHAPTER PROJECT

Wrap Up

Presenting Your Project Before you present your crystal garden to the class, share it with a classmate. Can your classmate identify which solution created which crystals? Do your data show differences in crystal growth rates? What conclusions can you draw from your data? Now you are ready to present your project to your class.

Reflect and Record In your journal, identify any changes that would improve your crystal garden. Which materials worked best for crystals to grow on? Which ones did not work well?

Getting Involved

In Your Home Explore your home, inside and out. Find two or three materials that you think come from minerals and two or three that you think do not. Bring samples of these materials to class, or make drawings or photos of them. Discuss with your classmates whether or not they are derived from minerals. Record on an index card what you decide about the composition of each material. Then set up a display of all the samples with their cards. How many different examples did your class find?

CHAPTER 5 Rocks

The following California Science Content Standards are addressed in this chapter:

1. **Plate tectonics explains important features of the Earth's surface and major geologic events.**
   - **a.** The fit of the continents, location of earthquakes, volcanoes, and midocean ridges, and the distribution of fossils, rock types, and ancient climatic zones provide evidence for plate tectonics.
2. **Topography is reshaped by weathering of rock and soil and by the transportation and deposition of sediment.**
   - **b.** Rivers and streams are dynamic systems that erode and transport sediment, change course, and flood their banks in natural and recurring patterns.
4. **Many phenomena on the Earth's surface are affected by the transfer of energy through radiation and convection currents.**
   - **c.** Heat from Earth's interior reaches the surface primarily through convection.
5. **Organisms in ecosystems exchange energy and nutrients among themselves and with the environment.**
   - **b.** Over time, matter is transferred from one organism to others in the food

Hikers cross a landscape of rock in the Cascade Range, a mountain range in Washington state.

PROJECT 5

Collecting Rocks

Each rock, whether a small pebble or a giant boulder, tells a story. By observing a rock's characteristics, geologists learn about the forces that shaped the portion of Earth's crust where the rock formed. The rocks in your own community tell the story of Earth's crust in your area.

In this chapter, you will learn how three different types of rocks form. You can apply what you learn about rocks to create your own rock collection and explore the properties of these rocks.

Your Goal To make a collection of the rocks in your area.

To complete this project, you must
- collect samples of rocks, keeping a record of where you found each sample
- describe the characteristics of your rocks, including their color, texture, and density
- classify each rock as igneous, sedimentary, or metamorphic
- create a display for your rock collection
- follow the safety guidelines in Appendix A

Get Started With your classmates and teacher, brainstorm locations in your community where rocks are likely to be found. Are there road cuts, outcroppings of bedrock, riverbanks, or beaches where you could safely and legally collect your rocks?

Check Your Progress You will be working on this project as you study the chapter. To keep your project on track, look for Check Your Progress boxes at the following points.

Section 1 Review, page 139: Plan your rock-hunting expeditions.
Section 3 Review, page 148: Collect your rocks.
Section 4 Review, page 151: Begin to describe, test, and catalog your rock collection.
Section 6 Review, page 159: Classify your rocks and plan your presentation.

Wrap Up At the end of the chapter (page 163), prepare a display of your rock collection. Be prepared to discuss the properties of the rocks you collected, how the rocks formed, and how people can use them.

web, and between organisms and the physical environment.

6. Sources of energy and materials differ in amounts, distribution, usefulness, and the time required for their formation.
   b. Different natural energy and material resources, including air, soil, rocks, minerals, petroleum, fresh water, wildlife, and forests, and classify them as renewable or nonrenewable.
   c. Natural origin of the materials used to make common objects.
7. Scientific progress is made by asking meaningful questions and conducting careful investigations.
   a. Develop a hypothesis.
   b. Select and use appropriate tools and technology to perform tests, collect data, and display data.
   d. Communicate the steps and results from an investigation in written reports and verbal presentations.
   h. Identify changes in natural phenomena over time without manipulating the phenomena (e.g., a tree limb, a grove of trees, a stream, a hill slope).

SECTION 1 Classifying Rocks

DISCOVER ACTIVITY

How Are Rocks Alike and Different?

1. Look at samples of marble and conglomerate with a hand lens.
2. Describe the two rocks. What is the color and texture of each?
3. Try scratching the surface of each rock with the edge of a penny. Which rock seems harder?
4. Hold each rock in your hand. Allowing for the fact that the samples aren't exactly the same size, which rock seems denser?

Think It Over

Observing Based on your observations, how would you compare the physical properties of marble and conglomerate?

GUIDE FOR READING

- **What characteristics are used to identify rocks?**
- **What are the three major groups of rocks?**

Reading Tip **Before you read, use the headings to make an outline about rocks. Then fill in details as you read.**

Between 1969 and 1972, the Apollo missions to the moon returned to Earth with pieces of the moon's surface. Space scientists eagerly tested these samples. They wanted to learn what the moon is made of. They found that the moon's surface is made of material very similar to the material that makes up Earth's surface—rock. Some moon samples are dark rock called basalt. Other samples are light-colored rock made mostly of the mineral feldspar.

Figure 1 Geology students collect and study samples of rocks.

How Geologists Classify Rocks

For both Earth and its moon, rocks are important building blocks. On Earth, rock forms mountains, hills, valleys, beaches, even the ocean floor. Earth's crust is made of rock. Rocks are made of mixtures of minerals and other materials, although some rocks may contain only a single mineral. Granite, shown in Figure 2, is made up of the minerals quartz, feldspar, mica, and hornblende, and sometimes other minerals.

Geologists collect and study samples of rock in order to classify them. Imagine that you are a geologist exploring a mountain range for the first time. How would you study a particular type of rock found in these mountains? You might use a camera or notebook to record

Granite

Quartz

Feldspar

Mica

Hornblende

Figure 2 Granite is made up of quartz, mica, feldspar, and hornblende. It may also contain other minerals. ***Observing*** Which mineral seems most abundant in the sample of granite shown?

information about the setting where the rock was found. (In classifying a rock, it's important for a geologist to know what other types of rock occur nearby). Then, you would use a chisel or the sharp end of a rock hammer to remove samples of the rock. Finally, you would break open the samples with a hammer to examine their inside surfaces. You must look at the inside of a rock because the effects of water and weather can change the outer surface of a rock.

When studying a rock sample, geologists observe the rock's color and texture and determine its mineral composition. Using these characteristics, geologists can classify a rock according to its origin, or where and how it formed.

Texture

As with minerals, color alone does not provide enough information to identify a rock. A rock's texture, however, is very useful in identifying the rock. To a geologist, a rock's **texture** is the look and feel of the rock's surface. Some rocks are smooth and glassy. Others are rough or chalky. Most rocks are made up of particles of minerals or other rocks, which geologists call **grains.** A rock's grains give the rock its texture. To describe a rock's texture, geologists use a number of terms based on the size, shape, and pattern of the rock's grains.

Figure 3 Texture helps geologists classify rocks. *Forming Operational Definitions* Looking at the rocks below, describe the characteristics of a rock that help you to define what a rock's "grain" is.

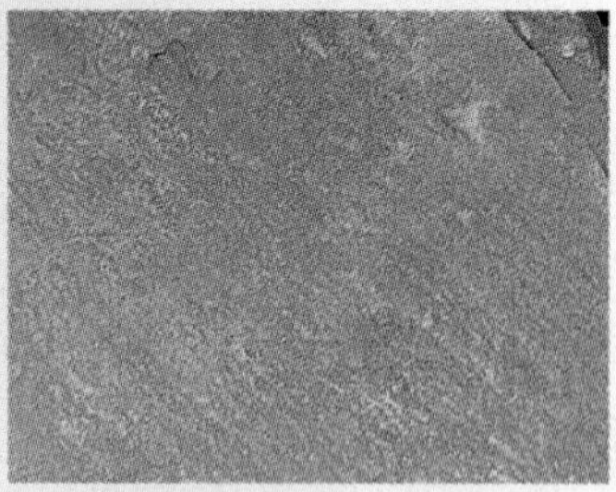

Fine-grained
Slate

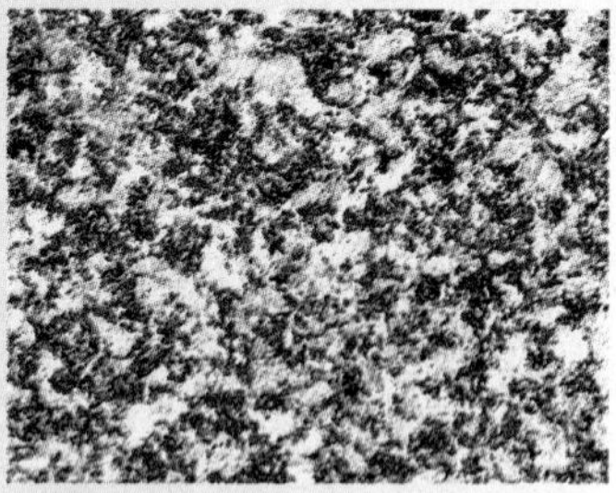

Coarse-grained
Diorite

No visible grain
Flint

Grain Size Often, the grains in a rock are large and easy to see. Such rocks are said to be coarse-grained. In other rocks, the grains are so small that they can only be seen with a microscope. These rocks are said to be fine-grained. Notice the difference in texture between the fine-grained slate and the coarse-grained diorite at left.

Grain Shape The grains in a rock vary widely in shape. Some grains look like tiny particles of fine sand. Others look like small seeds or exploding stars. In some rocks, such as granite, the grain results from the shapes of the crystals that form the rock. In other rocks, the grain shape results from fragments of other rock. These fragments can be smooth and rounded, like the fragments in conglomerate, or they can be jagged, like the fragments in breccia. You can compare conglomerate and breccia below.

Grain Pattern The grains in a rock often form patterns. Some grains lie in flat layers that look like a stack of pancakes. Other grains form wavy, swirling patterns. Some rocks have grains that look like rows of multicolored beads, as in the sample of gneiss shown below. Other rocks, in contrast, have grains that occur randomly throughout the rock.

No Visible Grain Some rocks have no grain, even when they are examined under a microscope. Some of these rocks have no crystal grains because when they form, they cool very quickly. This quick cooling gives these rocks the smooth, shiny texture of a thick piece of glass. Other rocks with a glassy texture are made up of extremely small particles of silica that settle out of water. One glassy-textured rock that forms in this manner is flint.

☑ *Checkpoint* ***What terms describe a rock's texture?***

Rounded grain
Conglomerate

Jagged grain
Breccia

Nonbanded
Quartzite

Banded
Gneiss

Mineral Composition

Often, geologists must look more closely at a rock to determine its mineral composition. By looking at a small sliver of a rock under a microscope, a geologist can observe the shape and size of crystals in the rock and identify the minerals it contains. To prepare a rock for viewing under the microscope, geologists cut the rock very thin, so that light can shine through its crystals.

In identifying rocks, geologists also use some of the tests that are used to identify minerals. For example, testing the rock's surface with acid determines whether the rock includes minerals made of compounds called carbonates. Testing with a magnet detects the elements iron or nickel.

Figure 4 A scientist is preparing to cut a thin slice from a piece of moon rock. He will then examine it under a microscope to determine its composition.

Origin

There are three major groups of rocks: igneous rock, sedimentary rock, and metamorphic rock. These terms refer to how the rocks in each group formed.

Rock belonging to each of these groups forms in a different way. **Igneous rock** forms from the cooling of molten rock—either magma below the surface or lava at the surface. Most **sedimentary rock** forms when particles of other rocks or the remains of plants and animals are pressed and cemented together. Sedimentary rock forms in layers below the surface. **Metamorphic rock** is formed when an existing rock is changed by heat, pressure, or chemical reactions. Most metamorphic rock forms deep underground.

Section 1 Review

1. What three characteristics do geologists use to identify a rock sample?
2. What are the three groups into which geologists classify rocks?
3. What is a rock's texture?
4. What methods do geologists use to determine the mineral composition of a rock?
5. **Thinking Critically Comparing and Contrasting** What do the three major groups of rocks have in common? How are they different?

CHAPTER PROJECT

Check Your Progress

Your neighborhood might be a good place to begin your rock collection. Look for gravel and crushed rock in flower beds, driveways or parking lots, and beneath downspouts. **CAUTION:** *If the area you choose is not a public place, make sure that you have permission to be there.* Begin to collect samples of rocks with different colors and textures. Plan with your teacher or an adult family member to visit other parts of your community where you could collect rocks.

Section 2 Igneous Rocks

Discover — Activity

How Do Igneous Rocks Form?

1. Use a hand lens to examine samples of granite and obsidian.
2. Describe the texture of both rocks using the terms coarse, fine, or glassy.
3. Which rock has coarse-grained crystals? Which rock has no crystals or grains?

Think It Over

Inferring Granite and obsidian are igneous rocks. Given the physical properties of these rocks, what can you infer about how each type of rock formed?

GUIDE FOR READING

- **What characteristics are used to classify igneous rocks?**

Reading Tip **As you read, make a list of the characteristics of igneous rocks. Write one sentence describing each characteristic.**

You are in a spacecraft orbiting Earth 4.6 billion years ago. Do you see the blue and green globe of Earth that astronauts today see from space? No—instead, Earth looks like a glowing piece of charcoal from a barbecue, or a charred and bubbling marshmallow heated over the coals.

Soon after Earth formed, the planet became so hot that its surface was a glowing mass of molten material. Hundreds of millions of years passed before Earth cooled enough for a crust to solidify. Then lava probably flowed from Earth's interior, spread over the surface, and hardened. The movement of magma and lava has continued ever since.

Figure 5 A lava flow soon cools and hardens to form igneous rock.

Figure 6 Igneous rocks can vary greatly in texture.
A. Rhyolite is a fine-grained igneous rock with a mineral composition similar to granite.
B. Pegmatite is a very coarse-grained variety of granite.
C. Porphyry has large crystals surrounded by fine-grained crystals.
Relating Cause and Effect What conditions caused rhyolite to have a fine-grained texture?

Characteristics of Igneous Rock

The first rocks to form on Earth probably looked much like the igneous rocks that harden from lava today. Igneous rock (IG nee us) is any rock that forms from magma or lava. The name "igneous" comes from the Latin word *ignis*, meaning "fire."

Most igneous rocks are made of mineral crystals. The only exceptions to this rule are the different types of volcanic glass—igneous rock that lacks minerals with a crystal structure. **Igneous rocks are classified according to their origin, texture, and mineral composition.**

Origin Geologists classify igneous rocks according to where they formed. **Extrusive rock** is igneous rock formed from lava that erupted onto Earth's surface. Basalt is the most common extrusive rock. Basalt forms much of the crust, including the oceanic crust, shield volcanoes, and lava plateaus.

Igneous rock that formed when magma hardened beneath Earth's surface is called **intrusive rock.** Granite is the most abundant intrusive rock in continental crust. Recall from Chapter 3 that granite batholiths form the core of many mountain ranges.

Texture The texture of an igneous rock depends on the size and shape of its mineral crystals. Igneous rocks may be similar in mineral composition and yet have very different textures. The texture of an igneous rock may be fine-grained, coarse-grained, glassy, or porphyritic. Rapid cooling lava forms fine-grained igneous rocks with small crystals. Slow cooling magma forms coarse-grained rock with large crystals.

Intrusive and extrusive rocks usually have different textures. Intrusive rocks have larger crystals than extrusive rocks. If you examine a coarse-grained rock such as granite, you can easily see that the crystals vary in size and color.

Some intrusive rocks have a texture that looks like a gelatin dessert with chopped-up fruit mixed in. A rock with large crystals scattered on a background of much smaller crystals has a **porphyritic texture** (pawr fuh RIT ik). How can a rock have two

Sharpen your Skills

Observing

ACTIVITY

You can learn about a rock's mineral composition by looking at a thin section.

1. The diagram shows a thin section of an igneous rock. The key identifies different minerals. Which mineral makes up most of this rock? How did you decide?
2. Which mineral is present in the smallest amount?

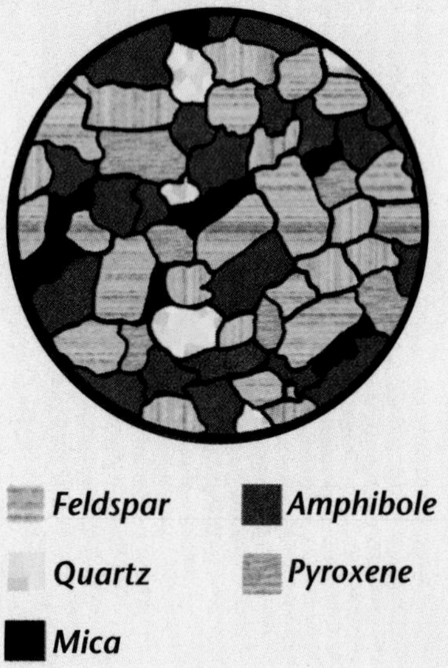

Feldspar
Amphibole
Quartz
Pyroxene
Mica

Figure 7 This thin slice of granite, viewed under a microscope, contains quartz, feldspar, mica, and other minerals.

textures? Porphyritic rocks form when intrusive rocks cool in two stages. As the magma begins to cool, large crystals form slowly. The remaining magma, however, cools more quickly, forming small crystals. The change in the rate of cooling may occur as magma moves nearer to the surface.

Extrusive rocks have a fine-grained or glassy texture. Basalt is an extrusive rock. It consists of crystals too small to be seen without a microscope.

Mineral Composition Recall from Chapter 3 that the silica content of magma and lava affects how easily the magma or lava will flow. Lava that is low in silica usually forms dark-colored rocks such as basalt. Basalt contains feldspar as well as certain dark-colored minerals, but does not contain quartz.

INTEGRATING CHEMISTRY Magma that is high in silica usually forms light-colored rocks, such as granite. However, granite comes in many shades and colors. Granite can be dark to light gray, red, and pink. Granite's color changes along with its mineral composition. Granite that is rich in reddish feldspar is a speckled pink. But granite rich in hornblende and dark mica is light gray with dark specks. Quartz crystals in granite add light gray or smoky specks. Geologists can make thin slices of granite and study each type of crystal in the rock to determine its mineral composition more exactly.

☑ *Checkpoint* *How do igneous rocks differ in origin, texture, and mineral composition?*

Uses of Igneous Rocks

Many igneous rocks are hard, dense, and durable. For this reason, people throughout history have used igneous rock for tools and building materials. For example, ancient Native Americans used obsidian for making very sharp tools for cutting and scraping.

Granite, one of the most abundant igneous rocks, has a long history as a building material. More than 3,500 years ago, the ancient Egyptians used granite for statues like the one shown in Figure 8. About 600 years ago, the Incas of Peru carefully fitted together great blocks of granite and other igneous rocks to build a fortress near Cuzco, their capital city. In the United States during the 1800s and early 1900s, granite was widely used to build bridges and public buildings and for paving streets with cobblestones. Thin, polished sheets of granite are still used in decorative stonework, curbstones, and floors.

Igneous rocks such as basalt, pumice, and obsidian also have important uses. Basalt is crushed to make gravel that is used in construction. The rough surface of pumice makes it a good abrasive for cleaning and polishing. Perlite, formed from the heating of obsidian, is often mixed with soil for starting vegetable seeds.

Figure 8 The ancient Egyptians valued granite for its durability. This royal couple at a temple in Luxor, Egypt, was carved in granite.

Section 2 Review

1. What are the three major characteristics that geologists use to identify igneous rocks?
2. What is the difference between extrusive and intrusive rocks? Give an example of each.
3. Explain what causes an igneous rock to have a fine-grained or coarse-grained texture.
4. Why are some igneous rocks dark and others light?
5. **Thinking Critically Comparing and Contrasting** How are basalt and granite different in their origin, texture, and mineral composition? How are they similar?

Science at Home

When you and a family member visit a pharmacy or large food store, observe the various foot-care products. What kinds of foot products are available that are made from pumice? How do people use these products? Check other skin and body care products to see if they contain pumice or other igneous rocks. Explain to your family how pumice is formed.

SECTION 3 Sedimentary Rocks

DISCOVER ACTIVITY

How Does Pressure Affect Particles of Rock?

1. Place a sheet of paper over a slice of soft bread.
2. Put a stack of several heavy books on the top of the paper. After 10 minutes, remove the books. Observe what happened to the bread.
3. Slice the bread so you can observe its cross section.
4. Carefully slice a piece of fresh bread and compare its cross section to that of the pressed bread.

Think It Over

Observing How did the bread change after you removed the books? Describe the texture of the bread. How does the bread feel? What can you predict about how pressure affects the particles that make up sedimentary rocks?

GUIDE FOR READING

- How do sedimentary rocks form?
- What are the three major types of sedimentary rocks?

Reading Tip Before you read, preview the headings in the section and predict how you think sedimentary rocks form.

Visitors to Arches National Park in Utah see some of the strangest scenery on Earth. The park contains dozens of natural arches sculpted in colorful rock that is layered like a birthday cake. The layers of this cake are red, orange, pink, or tan. One arch, named Landscape Arch, is nearly 90 meters across and about 30 meters high. Delicate Arch looks like the legs of a striding giant. The forces that wear away rock on Earth's surface have been carving these arches out of solid rock for 100 million years. The arches are made of sandstone, one of the most common sedimentary rocks.

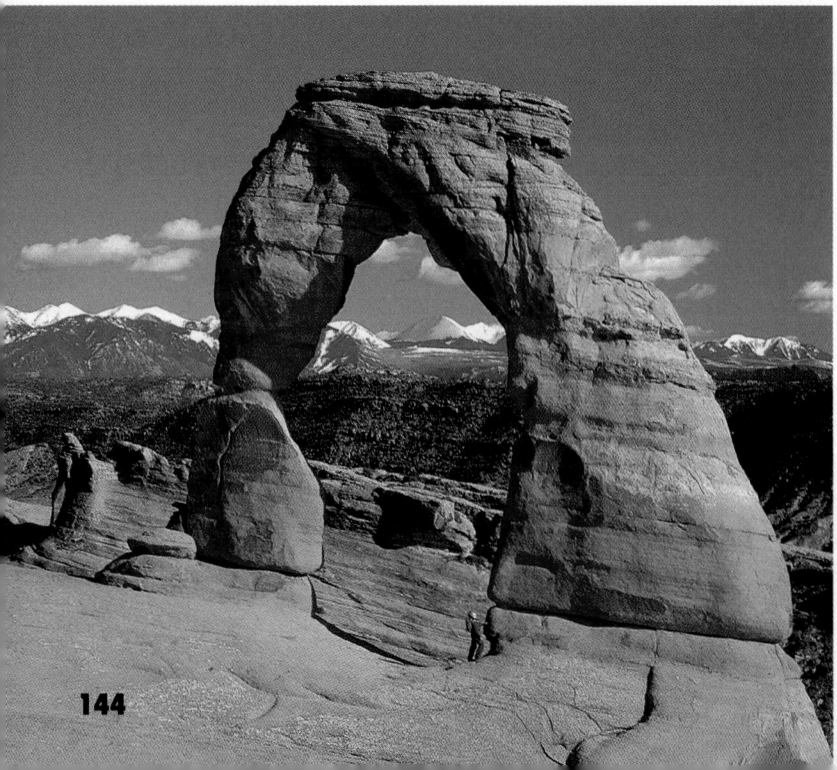

◀ Delicate Arch, Arches National Park, Utah

From Sediment to Rock

Sedimentary rocks form from particles deposited by water and wind. If you have ever walked along a stream or beach you may have noticed tiny sand grains, mud, and pebbles. These are some of the sediments that form sedimentary rock. **Sediment** is small, solid pieces of material that come from rocks or living things. Water, wind, and ice can carry sediment and deposit it in layers. But what turns these sediments into solid rock?

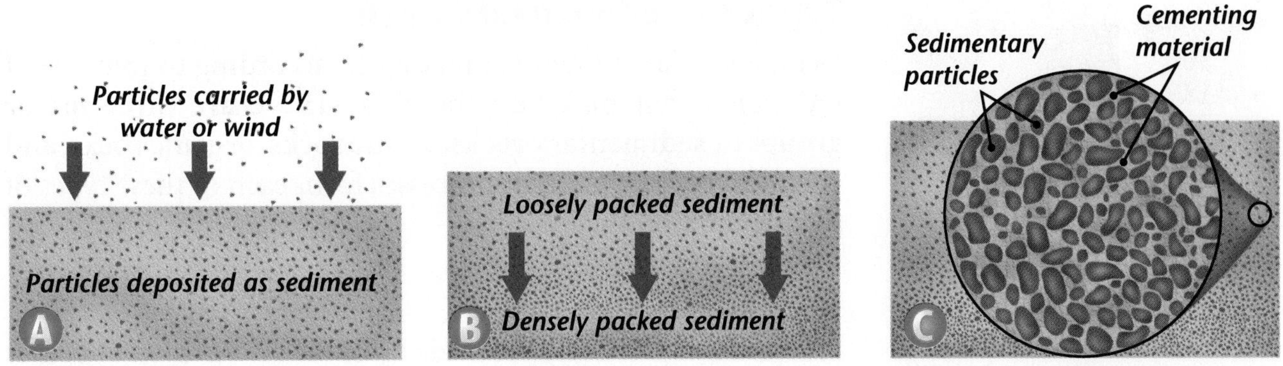
Particles carried by
water or wind
Particles deposited as sediment
A
Loosely packed sediment
Densely packed sediment
B
Sedimentary
particles
Cementing
material
C

Figure 9 Sedimentary rocks form through the deposition, compaction, and cementation of sediments. **A.** Water or wind deposits sediment. **B.** The heavy sediments press down on the layers beneath. **C.** Dissolved minerals flow between the particles and cement them together.
Relating Cause and Effect What conditions are necessary for sedimentary rock to form?

Erosion Destructive forces are constantly breaking up and wearing away all the rocks on Earth's surface. These forces include heat and cold, rain, waves, and grinding ice. **Erosion** occurs when running water or wind loosen and carry away the fragments of rock.

Deposition Eventually, the moving water or wind slows and deposits the sediment. If water is carrying the sediment, rock fragments and other materials sink to the bottom of a lake or ocean. **Deposition** is the process by which sediment settles out of the water or wind carrying it. **After sediment has been deposited, the processes of compaction and cementation change the sediment into sedimentary rock.**

In addition to particles of rock, sediment may include shells, bones, leaves, stems, and other remains of living things. Over time, any remains of living things in the sediment may slowly harden and change into fossils trapped in the rock.

Compaction At first the sediments fit together loosely. But gradually, over millions of years, thick layers of sediment build up. These layers are heavy and press down on the layers beneath them. Then compaction occurs. **Compaction** is the process that presses sediments together. Year after year more sediment falls on top, creating new layers. The weight of the layers further compacts the sediments, squeezing them tightly together. The layers often remain visible in the sedimentary rock.

Cementation While compaction is taking place, the minerals in the rock slowly dissolve in the water. The dissolved minerals seep into the spaces between particles of sediment. **Cementation** is the process in which dissolved minerals crystallize and glue particles of sediment together. It often takes millions of years for compaction and cementation to transform loose sediments into solid sedimentary rock.

☑ *Checkpoint* *What are the processes that change sediment to sedimentary rock?*

TRY THIS

Rock Absorber

Find out if water can soak into rock.

ACTIVITY

1. Using a hand lens, observe samples of sandstone and shale. How are they alike? How are they different?
2. Use a balance to measure the mass of each rock.
3. Place the rocks in a pan of water. Observe the samples. Which sample has bubbles escaping? Predict which sample will gain mass.
4. Leave the rocks submerged in the pan overnight.
5. The next day, remove the rocks from the pan and find the mass of each rock.

Drawing Conclusions How did the masses of the two rocks change after soaking? What can you conclude about each rock based on your observations?

Types of Sedimentary Rock

Geologists classify sedimentary rocks according to the type of sediments that make up the rock. **There are three major groups of sedimentary rocks: clastic rocks, organic rocks, and chemical rocks.** Different processes form each of these types of sedimentary rocks.

Clastic Rocks

Most sedimentary rocks are made up of the broken pieces of other rocks. A **clastic rock** is a sedimentary rock that forms when rock fragments are squeezed together. These fragments can range in size from clay particles too small to be seen without a microscope to large boulders too heavy for you to lift. Clastic rocks are grouped by the size of the rock fragments, or particles, of which they are made.

Shale One common clastic rock is shale. Shale forms from tiny particles of clay. For shale to form, water must deposit clay particles in very thin, flat layers, one on top of another. No cementation is needed to hold clay particles together. Even so, the spaces between the particles in the resulting shale are so small that water cannot pass through them. Shale feels smooth, and splits easily into flat pieces.

Sandstone Sandstone forms from the sand on beaches, on the ocean floor, in riverbeds, and in sand dunes. Sandstone is a clastic rock formed from the compaction and cementation of small particles of sand. Most sand particles consist of quartz. Because the cementation process does not fill all the spaces between sand grains, sandstone contains many small holes. Sandstone can easily absorb water through these holes.

Conglomerate and Breccia Some sedimentary rocks contain a mixture of rock fragments of different sizes. The fragments can range in size from sand and pebbles to boulders. If the fragments have rounded edges, they form a clastic rock called conglomerate. A rock made up of large fragments with sharp edges is called breccia (BRECH ee uh).

Figure 10 Puddingstone is a form of the clastic rock conglomerate. ***Observing*** *What types of particles can you observe in this sample of puddingstone?*

Organic Rocks

INTEGRATING LIFE SCIENCE Not all sedimentary rocks are made from particles of other rocks. **Organic rock** forms where the remains of plants and animals are deposited in thick layers. The term "organic" refers to substances that once were part of living things or were made by living things. Two important organic sedimentary rocks are coal and limestone.

Coal Coal forms from the remains of swamp plants buried in water. As layer upon layer of plant remains build up, the weight of the layers squeezes the decaying plants. Over millions of years, they slowly change into coal.

Limestone The hard shells of living things produce some kinds of limestone. How does limestone form? In the ocean, many living things, including coral, clams, oysters, and snails, have shells or skeletons made of calcite. When these animals die, their shells pile up as sediment on the ocean floor. Over millions of years, these layers of sediment can grow to a depth of hundreds of meters. Slowly, the pressure of overlying layers compacts the sediment. Some of the shells dissolve, forming a solution of calcite that seeps into the spaces between the shell fragments. Later, the dissolved material comes out of solution, forming calcite. The calcite cements the shell particles together, forming limestone.

Everyone knows one type of limestone: chalk. Chalk forms from sediments made of the skeletons of microscopic living things found in the oceans.

☑ *Checkpoint* *What are two important organic sedimentary rocks?*

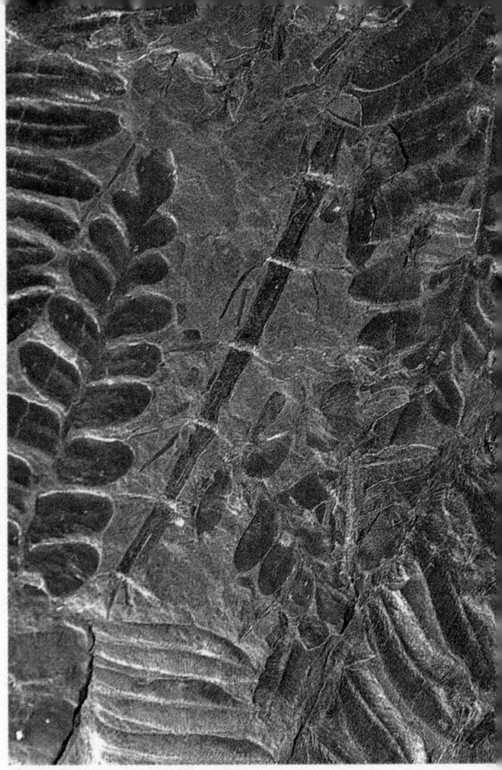

Figure 11 When broken apart, a piece of shale from a coal mine may reveal the impression of an ancient plant. Geologists estimate that it takes about 20 meters of decayed plants to form a layer of coal about one meter thick.

Figure 12 These limestone cliffs are along the Eleven Point River in Missouri.

Figure 13 These rock "towers" in Mono Lake, California, are made of tufa, a type of limestone. Tufa forms from solutions containing dissolved minerals. *Classifying What type of sedimentary rock is tufa?*

Chemical Rocks

Chemical rock forms when minerals that are dissolved in a solution crystallize. For example, limestone can form when calcite that is dissolved in lakes, seas, or underground water comes out of solution and forms crystals. This kind of limestone is considered a chemical rock.

Chemical rocks can also form from mineral deposits left when seas or lakes evaporate. Rock salt is a chemical rock made of the mineral halite, which forms by evaporation. Gypsum is another chemical rock formed by evaporation. Large deposits of rocks formed by evaporation form only in dry climates.

Uses of Sedimentary Rocks

For thousands of years, people have used sandstone and limestone as building materials. Both types of stone are soft enough to be easily cut into blocks or slabs. You may be surprised to learn that the White House in Washington, D.C., is built of sandstone. Builders today use sandstone and limestone for decorating or for covering the outside walls of buildings.

Limestone also has many industrial uses. Recall from Chapter 4 that limestone is important in smelting iron ore. Limestone is also used in making cement.

Section 3 Review

1. Once sediment has been deposited, what processes change it into sedimentary rock?
2. What are the three major kinds of sedimentary rocks?
3. Describe two ways in which limestone can form.
4. **Thinking Critically Comparing and Contrasting** Compare and contrast shale and sandstone. Include what they are made of and how they form.

CHAPTER PROJECT

Check Your Progress

With an adult, visit an area where you can collect samples of rocks. As you collect your samples, observe whether the rock is loose on the ground, broken off a ledge, or in a stream. Begin to classify your rocks into groups. Do any of your rocks consist of a single mineral? Do you recognize any of the minerals in these rocks? Notice the texture of each rock. Did you find any rocks made of pieces of other rocks?

SECTION 4

Rocks From Reefs

DISCOVER ACTIVITY

What Can You Conclude From the Way a Rock Reacts to Acid?

1. Using a hand lens, observe the color and texture of samples of limestone and coquina.
2. Put on your goggles and apron.
3. Obtain a small amount of dilute hydrochloric acid from your teacher. Hydrochloric acid is used to test rocks for the presence of the mineral calcite.
4. Using a plastic dropper, place a few drops of dilute hydrochloric acid on the limestone. **CAUTION**: *Hydrochloric acid can cause burns.*
5. Record your observations.
6. Repeat Steps 2 through 4 with the sample of coquina and observe the results.
7. Rinse the samples of limestone and coquina with lots of water before returning them to your teacher. Wash your hands.

Think It Over

Drawing Conclusions How did the color and texture of the two rocks compare? How did they react to the test? A piece of coral reacts to hydrochloric acid the same way as limestone and coquina. What could you conclude about the mineral composition of coral?

GUIDE FOR READING

- **How do coral reefs form?**
- **How do coral reefs become organic limestone deposits on land?**

Reading Tip **As you read, make a list of main ideas and supporting details about coral.**

Off the coast of Florida lies a "city" in the sea. It is a coral reef providing both food and shelter for many sea animals. The reef shimmers with life—clams, sponges, sea urchins, starfish, marine worms and, of course, fish. Schools of brilliantly colored fish dart in and out of forests of equally colorful corals. Octopuses lurk in underwater caves, scooping up crabs that pass too close. A reef forms a sturdy wall that protects the shoreline from battering waves. This city was built by billions of tiny, soft-bodied animals that have outer skeletons made of calcite.

Figure 14 A coral reef in the Florida Keys provides food and shelter for many different kinds of living things.

Figure 15 Coral animals feed on even smaller living things carried their way by the movement of ocean water. (This view has been magnified to show detail.)

Living Coral

Coral animals are tiny relatives of jellyfish that live together in vast numbers. Most coral animals are the size of your fingernail, or even smaller. Each one looks like a small sack with a mouth surrounded by tentacles. These animals use their tentacles to capture and eat microscopic creatures that float by. They produce skeletons that grow together to form a structure called a **coral reef.**

Coral reefs form only in the warm, shallow water of tropical oceans. Coral animals cannot grow in cold water or water low in salt. Reefs are most abundant around islands and along the eastern coasts of continents. In the United States, only the coasts of southern Florida and Hawaii have coral reefs.

Tiny algae grow within the body of each coral animal. The algae provide substances that the coral animals need to live. In turn, the coral animals provide a framework for the algae to grow on. Like plants, algae need sunlight. Below 40 meters, not enough light penetrates the water for the algae to grow. For this reason, almost all growth in a coral reef occurs within 40 meters of the water's surface.

How a Coral Reef Forms

Coral animals absorb the element calcium from the ocean water. The calcium is then changed into calcite and forms their skeletons. **When coral animals die, their skeletons remain, and more corals build on top of them.** Over thousands of years, reefs may grow to be hundreds of kilometers long and hundreds of meters thick. Reefs usually grow outward toward the open ocean. If the sea level rises or if the sea floor sinks, the reef will grow upward, too.

Figure 16 The island of Bora Bora in the South Pacific Ocean is ringed by a fringing reef. Someday, erosion will wear away the island, leaving an atoll. ***Inferring*** *As the sea floor beneath an atoll sinks, what happens to the living part of the coral reef?*

There are three types of coral reefs: fringing reefs, barrier reefs and atolls. Fringing reefs lie close to shore, separated from land by shallow water. Barrier reefs lie farther out, at least 10 kilometers from the land. The Great Barrier Reef that stretches 2,000 kilometers along the coast of Australia is a barrier reef. An **atoll** is a ring-shaped coral island found far from land. An atoll develops when coral grows on top of a volcanic island that has sunk beneath the ocean's surface. How can a volcanic island sink? As the oceanic crust moves away from the mid-ocean ridge, it cools and becomes more dense. This causes the sea floor to sink.

☑ *Checkpoint* *What are the three types of coral reefs?*

Figure 17 A striking band of white rock tops El Capitan Peak in the Guadalupe Mountains of Texas. This massive layer of limestone formed from coral reefs that grew in a warm, shallow sea more than 250 million years ago.

Limestone Deposits From Coral Reefs

Over time, coral buried by sediments can turn into limestone. Like modern-day coral animals, ancient coral animals thrived in warm, tropical oceans. Their limestone fossils are among the most common fossils on Earth. **Limestone that began as coral can be found on continents in places where uplift has raised ancient sea floors above sea level.**

In parts of the United States, reefs that formed under water millions of years ago now make up part of the land. The movement of Earth's plates slowly uplifted the ocean floor where these reefs grew until the ocean floor became dry land. There are exposed reefs in Wisconsin, Illinois, and Indiana, as well as in Texas, New Mexico, and many other places.

Section 4 Review

1. Explain how coral reefs form.
2. How does coral become limestone?
3. Why are living coral animals only found in water that is less than 40 meters deep?
4. **Thinking Critically Predicting** The Amazon is a great river that flows through the tropical forests of Brazil. The river dumps huge amounts of fresh water, made cloudy by particles of sediment, into the South Atlantic Ocean. Would you expect to find coral reefs growing in the ocean near the mouth of the Amazon? Explain your answer.

CHAPTER PROJECT

Check Your Progress

Begin to make an information card for each of your rocks, and decide how to store the rocks. Each rock's card should include the following information: where and when the rock was found; the type of geologic feature where you found the rock; a description of the rock's texture; a description of the minerals that make up the rock; and the results of any tests you performed on the rock. Are any of your rocks organic rocks? How could you tell?

SECTION 5

Metamorphic Rocks

DISCOVER ACTIVITY

How Do the Grain Patterns of Gneiss and Granite Compare?

1. Using a hand lens, observe samples of gneiss and granite. Look carefully at the grains or crystals in both rocks.
2. Observe how the grains or crystals are arranged in both rocks. Draw a sketch of both rocks and describe their textures.

Think It Over

Inferring Within the crust, some granite becomes gneiss. What do you think must happen to cause this change?

GUIDE FOR READING

- **Under what conditions do metamorphic rocks form?**
- **How do geologists classify metamorphic rocks?**

Reading Tip **Before you read, rewrite the headings in the section as questions. As you read, look for answers to those questions.**

Every metamorphic rock is a rock that has changed its form. In fact, the word *metamorphic* comes from the Greek words *meta*, meaning "change," and *morphosis*, meaning "form." But what causes a rock to change into metamorphic rock? The answer lies inside Earth.

How Metamorphic Rocks Form

Heat and pressure deep beneath Earth's surface can change any rock into metamorphic rock. When rock changes into metamorphic rock, its appearance, texture, crystal structure, and mineral content change. Metamorphic rock can form out of igneous, sedimentary, or other metamorphic rock.

Collisions between Earth's plates can push the rock down toward the heat of the mantle. Pockets of magma rising through the crust also provide heat that can produce metamorphic rocks.

The deeper rock is buried in the crust, the greater the pressure on that rock. Under pressure hundreds or thousands of times greater than at Earth's surface, the minerals in a rock can change into other minerals. The rock has become a metamorphic rock.

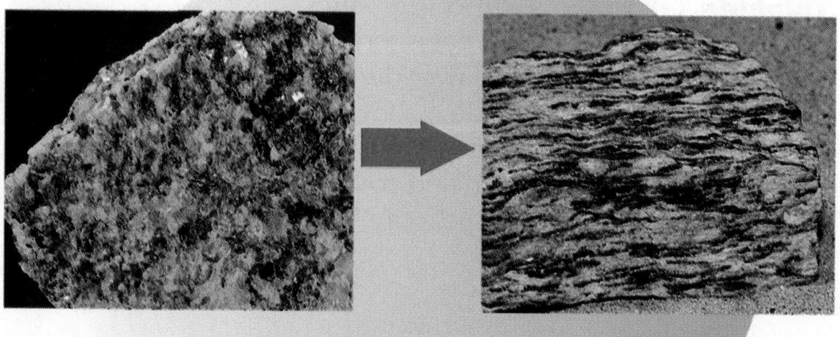
Granite
Gneiss

Figure 18 Great heat and pressure can change one type of rock into another. Granite becomes gneiss, shale becomes slate, and sandstone changes to quartzite. **Observing** *How does quartzite differ from sandstone?*

Classifying Metamorphic Rocks

While metamorphic rocks are forming, high temperatures change the size and shape of the grains, or mineral crystals, in the rock. In addition, tremendous pressure squeezes rock so tightly that the mineral grains may line up in flat, parallel layers. **Geologists classify metamorphic rocks by the arrangement of the grains that make up the rocks.**

Metamorphic rocks that have their grains arranged in parallel layers or bands are said to be **foliated.** The term *foliated* comes from the Latin word for "leaf." It describes the thin, flat layering found in most metamorphic rocks. Foliated rocks—including slate, schist, and gneiss—may split apart along these bands. In Figure 18, notice how the crystals in granite have been flattened to create the foliated texture of gneiss.

One common foliated rock is slate. Heat and pressure change the sedimentary rock shale into slate. Slate is basically a denser, more compact version of shale. During the change, new minerals such as mica and hornblende form in the slate.

Sometimes metamorphic rocks are nonfoliated. The mineral grains in these rocks are arranged randomly. Metamorphic rocks that are nonfoliated do not split into layers. Marble and quartzite both have a nonfoliated texture. Quartzite forms out of sandstone. The weakly cemented quartz particles in the sandstone recrystallize to form quartzite, which is extremely hard. Notice in Figure 18 how much smoother quartzite looks than sandstone.

☑ *Checkpoint* *What is a foliated rock?*

A Sequined Rock

1. Make three balls of clay about 3 cm in diameter. Gently mix about 25 sequins into one ball.
2. Use a 30-cm piece of string to cut the ball in half. How are the sequins arranged?
3. Roll the clay with the sequins back into a ball. Stack the three balls with the sequin ball in the middle. Set these on a block of wood. With another block of wood, press slowly down until the stack is about 3 cm high.
4. Use the string to cut the stack in half. Observe the arrangement of the sequins.

Making a Model What do the sequins in your model rock represent? Is this rock foliated or nonfoliated?

Sandstone
Shale
Slate
Quartzite

Figure 19 The pure white marble for the Taj Mahal came from a quarry 300 kilometers away. It took 20,000 workers more than 20 years to build the Taj Mahal.

Visual Arts CONNECTION

The architect of the Taj Mahal used symmetry and repetition to design a beautiful building. Notice how the left side mirrors the right side, creating balance. Also notice how different parts of the building, such as domes, arches, and minarets (towers), are repeated. Repetition of these shapes creates rhythms as you look at the building.

In Your Journal

Write a letter to a friend describing what you feel walking toward the Taj Mahal. Explain how the building's symmetry and other features help to create this effect.

Uses of Metamorphic Rock

Marble and slate are two of the most useful metamorphic rocks. Marble usually forms when limestone is subjected to heat and pressure deep beneath the surface. Because marble has a fine, even grain, it is relatively easy to cut into thin slabs. And marble can be easily polished. These qualities have led architects and sculptors to use marble for many buildings and statues. For example, one of the most beautiful buildings in the world is the Taj Mahal in Agra, India. An emperor of India had the Taj Mahal built during the 1600s as a memorial to his wife, who had died in childbirth. The Taj Mahal, shown in Figure 19, is made of gleaming white marble.

Slate, because it is foliated, splits easily into flat pieces that can be used for flooring, roofing, outdoor walkways, or chalkboards. Like marble, slate comes in a variety of colors, including gray, black, red, and purple, so it has been used as trim for stone buildings.

Section 5 Review

1. Describe the process by which metamorphic rocks form.
2. What characteristics are used to classify metamorphic rocks?
3. Which properties of a rock may change as the rock becomes metamorphic?
4. How does pressure change rock?
5. **Thinking Critically Relating Cause and Effect** Why are you less likely to find fossils in metamorphic rocks than in sedimentary rocks?

Science at Home

How are rocks used in your neighborhood? Take a walk with your family to see how many uses you can observe. Identify statues, walls, and buildings made from rocks. Can you identify which type of rock is used? Look for limestone, sandstone, granite, and marble. Share a list of the rocks you found with your class. For each rock, include a description of its color and texture, where you observed the rock, and how it was used.

Classifying

Mystery Rocks

Skills Lab

Problem

What properties can be used to classify rocks?

Materials

1 "mystery rock"
hand lens
2 unknown igneous rocks
2 unknown sedimentary rocks
2 unknown metamorphic rocks

Procedure

1. For this activity, you will be given six rocks and one sample that is not a rock. They are labeled A through G.
2. Copy the data table into your notebook.
3. Using the hand lens, examine each rock for clues that show the rock formed from molten material. Record the rock's color and texture. Observe if there are any crystals or grains in the rock.
4. Use the hand lens to look for clues that show the rock formed from particles of other rocks. Observe the texture of the rock to see if it has any tiny, well-rounded grains.
5. Use the hand lens to look for clues that show the rock formed under heat and pressure. Observe if the rock has a flat layer of crystals or shows colored bands.
6. Record your observations in the data table.

Sample	Color (dark, medium, light, or mixed colors)	Texture (fine, medium, or coarse-grained)	Foliated or Banded	Rock Group (igneous, metamorphic, sedimentary)
A				
B				

Analyze and Conclude

1. Infer from your observations which group each rock belongs in.
2. Decide which sample is not a rock. How did you determine that the sample you chose is not a rock? What do you think the "mystery rock" is? Explain.
3. Which of the samples could be classified as igneous rocks? What physical properties do these rock share with the other samples? How are they different?
4. Which of the samples could be classified as sedimentary rocks? How do you think these rocks formed? What are the physical properties of these rocks?
5. Which of the samples could be classified as metamorphic rocks? What are their physical properties?
6. **Think About It** What physical property was most useful in classifying rocks? Why?

More to Explore

Can you name each rock? Use a field guide to rocks and minerals to find the specific name of each rock sample.

SECTION 6

The Rock Cycle

DISCOVER

ACTIVITY

Which Rock Came First?

1. Referring to the photos below, make sketches of quartzite, granite, and sandstone on three index cards.
2. In your sketches, try to portray the color and texture of each rock. Look for similarities and differences.
3. To which major group does each rock belong?

Think It Over

Developing Hypotheses How are quartzite, granite, and sandstone related? Arrange your cards in the order in which these three rocks formed. Given enough time in Earth's crust, what might happen to the third rock in your series?

Quartzite

Granite

Sandstone

GUIDE FOR READING

- **What is the rock cycle?**
- **What is the role of plate tectonics in the rock cycle?**

Reading Tip **Before you read, preview *Exploring the Rock Cycle* on page 158. Write a list of questions you have about the rock cycle. Then look for answers to the questions as you read.**

The enormous granite dome that forms Stone Mountain in Georgia looks as if it will be there forever. The granite formed hundreds of millions of years ago as a batholith—a mass of igneous rock beneath Earth's surface. But this rock has stood exposed to the weather for millions of years. Bit by bit, the granite is flaking off. Washed away in streams, the bits of granite will eventually be ground down into sand. But that's not the end of the story. What will become of those sand particles from Stone Mountain? They are part of a series of changes that happen to all the rocks of Earth's crust.

A Cycle of Many Pathways

Earth's rocks are not as unchanging as they seem. **Forces inside Earth and at the surface produce a rock cycle that builds, destroys, and changes the rocks in the crust.** The **rock cycle** is a series of processes on Earth's surface and inside the planet that slowly change rocks from one kind to another. What drives the rock cycle? Earth's constructive and destructive forces—including plate tectonics—move rocks through the rock cycle.

The rock cycle can follow many different pathways. You can follow the rock of Stone Mountain along one of the pathways of the rock cycle.

Figure 20 Stone Mountain, near Atlanta, Georgia, rises 210 meters above the surrounding land.

One Pathway Through the Rock Cycle

In the case of Stone Mountain, the rock cycle began millions of years ago. First, a granite batholith formed beneath Earth's surface. Then the forces of mountain building slowly pushed the granite upward. Over millions of years, water and weather began to wear away the granite of Stone Mountain. Today, particles of granite still break off the mountain and become sand. Streams carry the sand to the ocean.

Over millions of years, layers of sediment will pile up on the ocean floor. Slowly, the sediments will be compacted by their own weight. Dissolved calcite in the ocean water will cement the particles together. Eventually, the quartz that once formed the granite of Stone Mountain will become sandstone, a sedimentary rock.

More and more sediment will pile up on the sandstone. As sandstone becomes deeply buried, pressure on the rocks will increase. The rock will become hot. Pressure will compact the particles in the sandstone until no spaces are left between them. Silica, the main ingredient in quartz, will replace the calcite as the cement holding the rock together. The rock's texture will change from gritty to smooth. After millions of years, the sandstone will have changed into the metamorphic rock quartzite.

What will happen next? You could wait tens of millions of years to find out how the quartzite completes the rock cycle. Or you can trace alternative pathways in *Exploring the Rock Cycle.*

Sharpen your Skills

Classifying

ACTIVITY

Some metamorphic rocks form out of igneous rocks, and other metamorphic rocks form out of sedimentary rocks.

1. If you find a fine-grained metamorphic rock with thin, flaky layers, from which group of rocks did it probably form? Explain.
2. If you find a metamorphic rock with distinct grains of different colors and sizes arranged in parallel bands, from which group of rocks did it probably form? Explain.

EXPLORING the Rock Cycle

Earth's constructive and destructive forces build up and wear down the crust. Igneous, sedimentary, and metamorphic rocks change continuously through the rock cycle. Rocks can follow many different pathways. The outer circle shows a complete cycle. The arrows within the circle show alternate pathways.

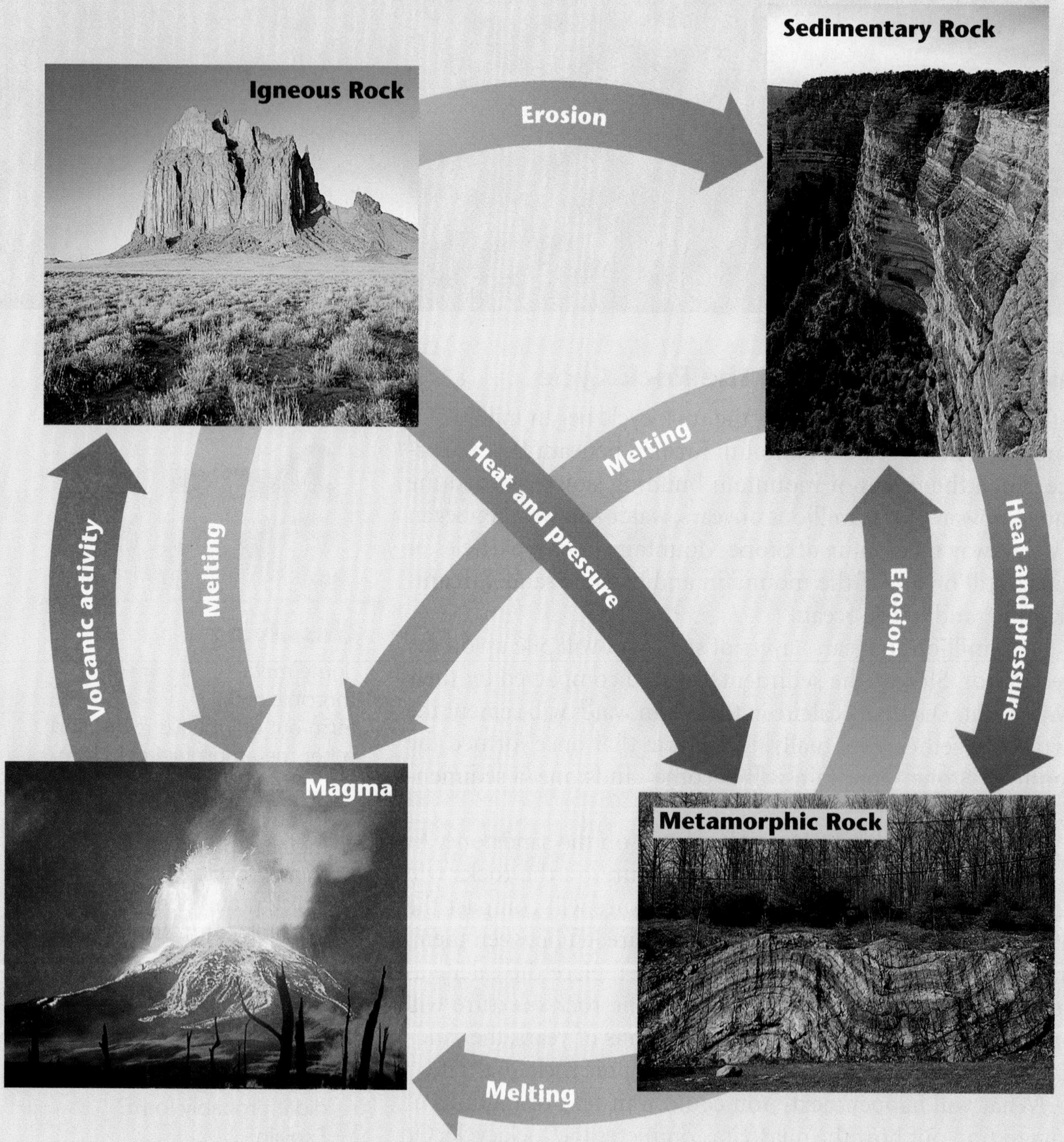
Igneous Rock
Erosion
Sedimentary Rock
Melting
Heat and pressure
Volcanic activity
Melting
Erosion
Heat and pressure
Magma
Metamorphic Rock
Melting

The Rock Cycle and Plate Tectonics

The changes of the rock cycle are closely related to plate tectonics. Recall that plate tectonics causes the movement of sections of Earth's lithosphere called plates. **Plate movements drive the rock cycle by pushing rocks back into the mantle, where they melt and become magma again. Plate movements also cause the folding, faulting, and uplift of the crust that move rocks through the rock cycle.** At least two types of plate movement advance the rock cycle. One type is a collision between subducting oceanic plates. The other type is a collision between continental plates.

Figure 21 This fossil trilobite lived on an ocean floor about 500 million years ago. As plate tectonics moved pieces of Earth's crust, the rock containing this fossil became part of a mountain.

Subducting Oceanic Plates Consider what could happen to the sand grains that once were part of Stone Mountain. The sand may become sandstone attached to oceanic crust. On this pathway through the rock cycle, the oceanic crust carrying the sandstone drifts toward a deep-ocean trench. At the trench, subduction returns some of the sandstone to the mantle. There, it melts and forms magma, which eventually becomes igneous rock.

Colliding Continental Plates Collisions between continental plates can also change a rock's path through the rock cycle. Such a collision can squeeze some sandstone from the ocean floor. As a result, the sandstone will change to quartzite. Eventually, the collision could form a mountain range or plateau. Then, as the mountains or plateaus containing quartzite are worn away, the rock cycle continues.

Section 6 Review

1. What process gradually changes rocks from one form to another?
2. How can plate movements move rocks through the rock cycle?
3. What rock comes before quartzite in the rock cycle? What rock or rocks could come just after quartzite in the rock cycle? Explain your answer.
4. **Thinking Critically Applying Concepts** Begin with a grain of sand on a beach. Describe what happens as you follow the grain through the rock cycle until it returns to a beach as a grain of sand again.
5. **Thinking Critically Making Judgments** In your opinion, at what point does the rock cycle really begin? Give reasons for your answer.

CHAPTER PROJECT

Check Your Progress

Now that you have collected, described, tested, and recorded your rocks, classify them as igneous, sedimentary, or metamorphic. Are any of your rocks foliated? Try to identify specific types of rock. Compare your rock samples with pictures of rocks in a field guide or other library reference sources.

Real-World Lab

You, the Consumer

TESTING ROCK FLOORING

You are building your own house. For the kitchen floor, you want to use some building stones such as granite, marble, or limestone. You need to know which material is easiest to maintain and keep clean.

Problem

What kind of building stone makes the best flooring?

Skills Focus

designing experiments,
forming operational definitions
drawing conclusions

Suggested Materials

steel nail
wire brush
water
plastic dropper
hand lens
samples of igneous, sedimentary, and metamorphic rocks with flat surfaces
materials that form stains, such as ink and paints
greasy materials such as butter and crayons

Procedure

1. Brainstorm with your partner the qualities of good flooring. For example, good flooring should resist stains, scratches, and grease marks, and be safe to walk on when wet.
2. Predict what you think is the best building stone for a kitchen floor. Why?
3. Write the steps you plan to follow to answer the problem question. As you design your plan, consider the following factors:
   - What igneous, sedimentary, and metamorphic rocks will you test? (Pick at least one rock from each group.)
   - What materials or equipment will you need to acquire, and in what amounts?
   - What tests will you perform on the samples?
   - How will you control the variables in each test?
   - How will you measure each sample's resistance to staining, grease, and scratches?
   - How will you measure slipperiness?
4. Review your plan. Will it lead to an answer to the problem question?
5. Check your procedure and safety plan with your teacher.
6. Create a data table that includes a column in which you predict how each material will perform in each test.

Analyze and Conclude

1. Which material performed the best on each test? Which performed the worst on each test?
2. Which material is best for the kitchen flooring? Which material would you least want to use?
3. Do your answers support your initial prediction? Why or why not?
4. The person installing the floor might want stone that is easy to cut to the correct size or shape. What other qualities would matter to the flooring installer?
5. **Apply** Based on your results for flooring, what materials would you use for kitchen counters? How might the qualities needed for countertops differ from those for flooring?

More to Explore

Find out the cost per square meter of some materials used to build kitchen floors in your community. How does cost influence your decision on which material to use? What other factors can influence the choice of materials?

Section 1 Classifying Rocks

Key Ideas

- A rock is a hard piece of Earth's crust.
- Geologists classify rocks according to their color, texture, mineral composition, and origin.
- The three kinds of rocks are igneous, sedimentary, and metamorphic.

Key Terms

texture
grain
igneous rock
sedimentary rock
metamorphic rock

Section 2 Igneous Rocks

Key Ideas

- Igneous rocks form when hot, liquid magma or lava cools and hardens.
- Igneous rocks are classified according to their origin, texture, and composition.

Key Terms

extrusive rock
intrusive rock
porphyritic texture

Section 3 Sedimentary Rocks

Key Ideas

- Most sedimentary rocks are formed from sediments that are compacted and cemented together.
- Sedimentary rocks are classified according to the origin of the materials from which the rocks are made.
- The three types of sedimentary rocks are clastic rocks, organic rocks, and chemical rocks.

Key Terms

sediment
erosion
deposition
compaction
cementation
clastic rock
organic rock
chemical rock

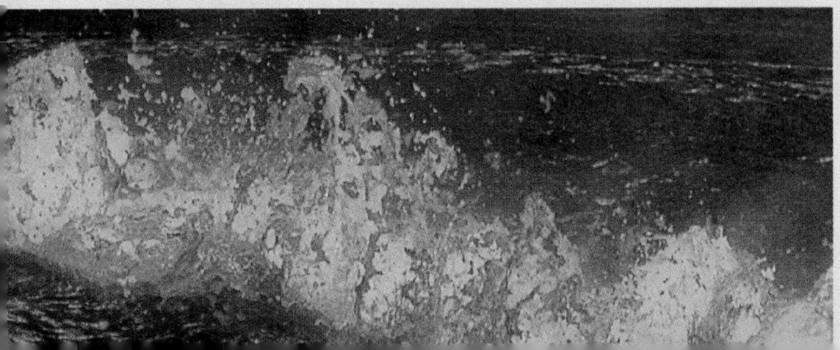

Section 4 Rocks From Reefs

INTEGRATING LIFE SCIENCE

Key Ideas

- When coral animals die, their skeletons remain and more corals grow on top of them, eventually forming a coral reef.
- Over millions of years, the movement of Earth's crust can bring to the surface deposits of limestone formed by ancient coral reefs.

Key Terms

coral reef
atoll

Section 5 Metamorphic Rocks

Key Ideas

- In a process that takes place deep beneath the surface, heat and pressure can change any type of rock into metamorphic rock.
- Geologists classify metamorphic rock according to whether the rock is foliated or nonfoliated.

Key Term

foliated

Section 6 The Rock Cycle

Key Ideas

- The series of processes on and beneath Earth's surface that change rocks from one type of rock to another is called the rock cycle.
- Plate movements drive the rock cycle by pushing rocks back into the mantle, where they melt and become magma again. Plate movements also advance the rock cycle by causing folding, faulting, and uplifting of the crust.

Key Term

rock cycle

ACTIVITY

USING THE INTERNET

www.phschool.com/state_focus/california/

CHAPTER 5 ASSESSMENT

California Test Prep: Reviewing Content

Multiple Choice

Choose the letter of the best answer.

1. Which of the following sedimentary rocks is a chemical rock?
a. shale
b. sandstone
c. halite
d. breccia

2. Metamorphic rocks can be formed from
a. igneous rocks.
b. sedimentary rocks.
c. metamorphic rocks.
d. all rock groups.

3. The rock formed when granite changes to a metamorphic rock is
a. marble. **b.** basalt.
c. gneiss. **d.** pumice.

4. Which of the following helps create both metamorphic and sedimentary rocks?
a. cementation **b.** pressure
c. evaporation **d.** heat

5. Millions of years ago, a deposit of organic limestone was probably
a. a swampy forest. **b.** a lava flow.
c. a coral reef. **d.** an intrusive rock.

True or False

If the statement is true, write true. If it is false, change the underlined word or words to make the statement true.

6. Igneous rocks are classified by how they formed and by their color, texture, and shape.

7. Granite is a fine-grained igneous rock.

8. Sedimentary rocks that form when minerals come out of solution are classified as porphyritic.

9. A barrier reef is a ring-shaped coral island found in the open ocean.

10. The series of processes that slowly change rocks from one kind to another is called the rock cycle.

Checking Concepts

11. What is the relationship between an igneous rock's texture and where it was formed?

12. Why can water pass easily through sandstone but not through shale?

13. Describe how a rock can form by evaporation. What type of rock is it?

14. How do the properties of a rock change when the rock changes to metamorphic?

15. What are the sources of the heat that helps metamorphic rocks to form?

16. Writing to Learn You are a camp counselor taking your campers on a mountain hike. One of your campers cracks open a rock and finds a fossil fish inside. The camper wants to know how a fish fossil from the sea floor ended up on the side of a mountain. What explanation would you give the camper?

Thinking Visually

17. Cycle Diagram Copy the cycle diagram of the rock cycle onto a sheet of paper. To complete the diagram, match each of the following with the correct letter: sediments build up, igneous rock wears away, sedimentary rock forms, igneous rock forms, lava erupts. Add a title. (For more on cycle diagrams, see the Skills Handbook).

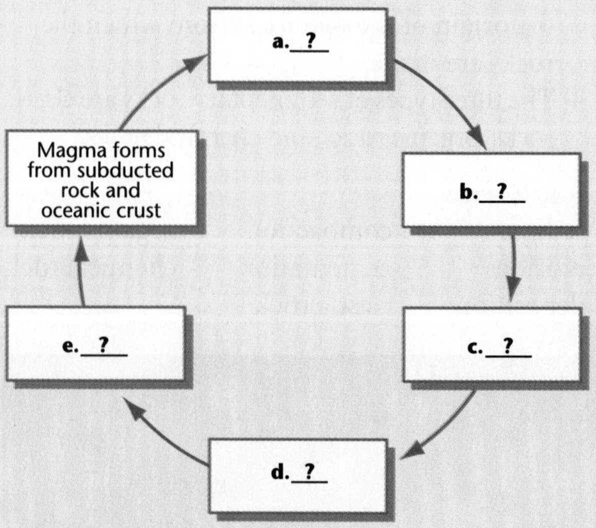
a. ?
b. ?
c. ?
d. ?
e. ?
Magma forms from subducted rock and oceanic crust

Test Prep: Skills

Answer Questions 18–20 using the photos of three rocks.

18. Observing How would you describe the texture of each rock?

19. Classifying Which of the three rocks would you classify as a metamorphic rock? Explain your answer.

20. Inferring A rock's texture gives clues about how the rock formed. What can you infer about the process by which rock B formed?

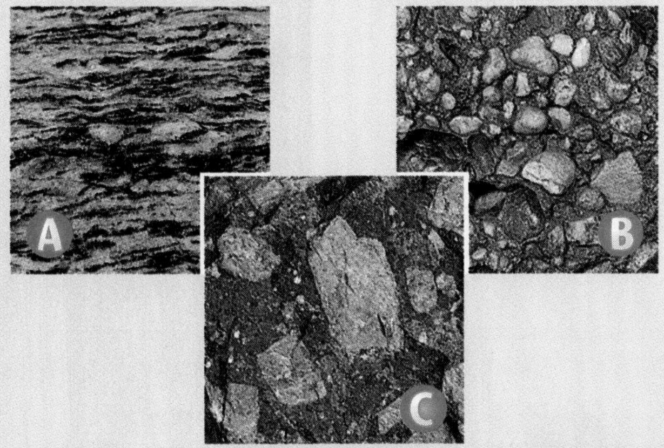
A
B
C

Thinking Critically

21. Applying Concepts The sedimentary rocks limestone and sandstone are used as building materials. However, they wear away more rapidly than marble and quartzite, the metamorphic rocks that are formed from them. Why do you think this is so?

22. Inferring As a geologist exploring for rock and mineral deposits, you come across an area where the rocks are layers of coal and shale. What kind of environment probably existed in this area millions of years ago when these rocks formed?

23. Comparing and Contrasting How are clastic rocks and organic rocks similar? How are they different?

24. Relating Cause and Effect In the rock cycle, igneous, metamorphic, and sedimentary rocks can all become magma again. What step in the rock cycle causes this to happen? Explain your answer.

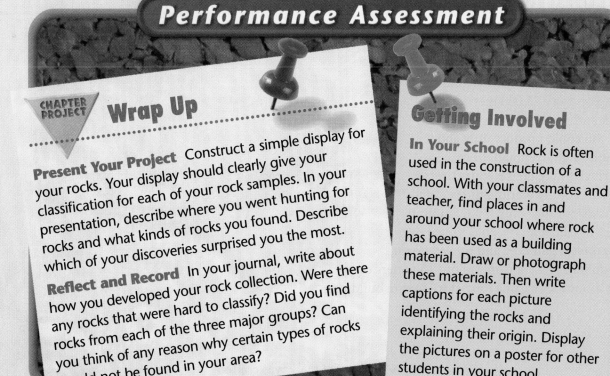

Performance Assessment

CHAPTER PROJECT Wrap Up

Present Your Project Construct a simple display for your rocks. Your display should clearly give your classification for each of your rock samples. In your presentation, describe where you went hunting for rocks and what kinds of rocks you found. Describe which of your discoveries surprised you the most.

Reflect and Record In your journal, write about how you developed your rock collection. Were there any rocks that were hard to classify? Did you find rocks from each of the three major groups? Can you think of any reason why certain types of rocks would not be found in your area?

Getting Involved

In Your School Rock is often used in the construction of a school. With your classmates and teacher, find places in and around your school where rock has been used as a building material. Draw or photograph these materials. Then write captions for each picture identifying the rocks and explaining their origin. Display the pictures on a poster for other students in your school.

The Noble Metal

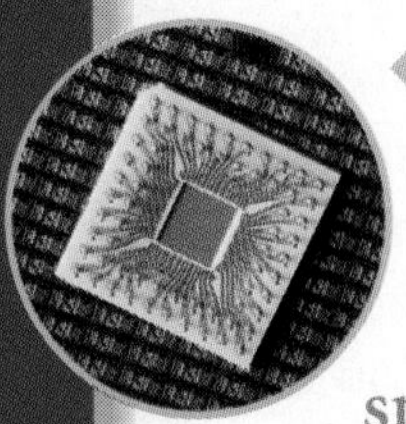

You can find it . . .

◆ on people's wrists and on their ears ◆ in your computer ◆ around the edge of some dinner plates ◆ in outer space—on satellites and in spacesuits ◆

What is this mysterious substance? It's the rare, beautiful—and very useful—metal called *Gold*

Because it is both rare and beautiful, people have prized gold since ancient times. Gold was so valuable that it was used to make crowns for rulers and coins for trade. In some cultures, people wore gold bracelets and necklaces to show their wealth.

In spite of its many uses, gold is scarce. For every 23,000 metric tons of rock and minerals from the Earth's crust, you could produce only about 14 grams of gold, enough to make a small ring. Today, gold is found in many parts of the world. But even rich gold fields produce only small amounts of gold. In fact, if all the gold mined over the years were gathered and melted down, you would have a cube only about 15 meters on a side—about the size of a four-story square building.

This gold burial mask was crafted around 1550 B.C. by the Mycenaeans, people who lived in the eastern Mediterranean.

Properties of Gold

Gold reflects heat and, when combined with other materials, filters sunlight. For this reason, gold is used in spacesuits and face visors. This astronaut wears a face visor coated with gold. The window glass in some skyscrapers is tinted with gold to keep out heat and protect people's eyes.

Why is gold used for everything from bracelets to space helmets to medicine? You'll find the answers in this precious metal's unusual chemical and physical properties. Gold is deep yellow in color and so shiny, or lustrous, that its Latin name, *aurum,* means "glowing dawn." Gold's chemical symbol—*Au*—comes from that Latin word.

Gold is very stable. Unlike iron, gold doesn't rust. It also doesn't tarnish in air as silver does, so its luster can last forever. Ancient chemists thought that gold was superior to other metals. They classified it as one of the "noble" metals.

Gold is very soft and malleable. That is, it's easy to bend or hammer into shapes without breaking. It can be pounded into very thin sheets called gold leaf. In fact, you can pound 30 grams of gold into a sheet that's large enough to cover the floor of a small room. Gold is also the most ductile metal. You can draw out 30 grams of gold into a fine thread as long as 8 kilometers without breaking it.

Ancient people of Egypt, Greece, and China found ways to dig gold from mines. But most of the gold that people have used in the last 6,000 years has come from Earth's surface, often from streams and riverbanks. Gold is very heavy—one of the densest metals. Over centuries, mountain streams have washed away dirt and pebbles from veins of gold-bearing rocks and minerals and left the heavy gold in the streambeds.

Science Activity

Many of the gold hunters who flocked to California during the Gold Rush of 1849 were searching for gold in streams and rivers. Although they had very simple equipment, their technique worked because gold is so dense. Using pans, miners washed gold-bearing gravel in running water. Try your own gold panning.

Procedure:
Set up your own model of gold panning, using a large pan, a gravel mixture, and a very dense material as a substitute for gold. Use a sink trap. Under running water, shake and swirl the pan until the lighter materials wash away. What's left is your "gold."

- Why is "gold" left in the pan while other materials are washed away?

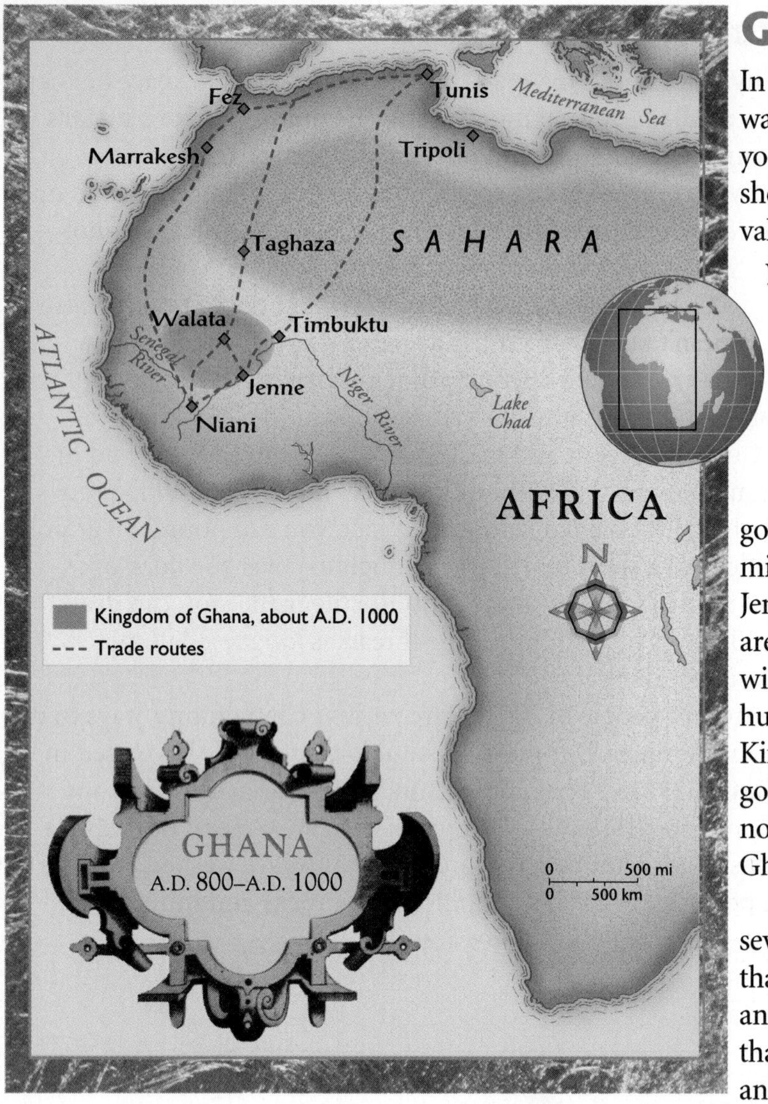
Fez
Tunis
Mediterranean Sea
Marrakesh
Tripoli
Taghaza
SAHARA
Walata
Timbuktu
Senegal River
Jenne
Niger River
Niani
Lake Chad
ATLANTIC OCEAN
AFRICA
N
Kingdom of Ghana, about A.D. 1000
Trade routes
GHANA
A.D. 800–A.D. 1000
0 500 mi
0 500 km

Golden Trade Routes

In West Africa nearly 1,000 years ago, salt was said to be worth its weight in gold. If you get your salt from the supermarket shelf, it may be hard to imagine how valuable this mineral was to people. But if you lived in a very hot, dry climate, you would need salt. It would be as valuable to you as gold. In West Africa, salt and gold were the most important goods traded in a busy north-south trade.

Camel caravans crossed the desert going south, carrying slabs of salt from mines in the desert. Trade centers, such as Jenne and Timbuktu, flourished. In the area around Taghaza, people built houses with walls of salt slabs. But several hundred kilometers south in the Kingdom of Ghana, salt was scarce and gold was plentiful. Salt traders from the north traveled deep into the forests of Ghana to trade salt for gold.

African gold became the basis for several rich cultures and trading empires that grew up in West Africa between 800 and 1400. At that time, most of the gold that Europeans used for crowns, coins, and jewelry was carried north from Africa.

Around 1100, Arab travelers in Africa wrote about the fabulous wealth of the Kingdom of Ghana. The most popular tale was that the salt traders and gold miners never met, as a way of keeping secret the location of gold mines. Traders from the north left slabs of salt in an agreed-upon trading place, pounded their drums to indicate a trade, and then withdrew. Miners from the south arrived, left an amount of gold that seemed fair, and withdrew. The salt traders returned. If they thought the trade was fair, they took the gold and left. If they were not satisfied, the silent trade continued.

Social Studies Activity

How would you succeed as a gold or salt trader? Find out by carrying out your own silent trade. Work in teams of Salt Traders and Gold Miners. Before trading, each team should decide how much a bag of gold or a block of salt is worth. Then, for each silent trade, make up a situation that would change the value of gold or salt, such as, "Demand for gold in Europe increases."

- Suppose you are selling a product today. How would the supply of the product affect the value or sale price of the product?

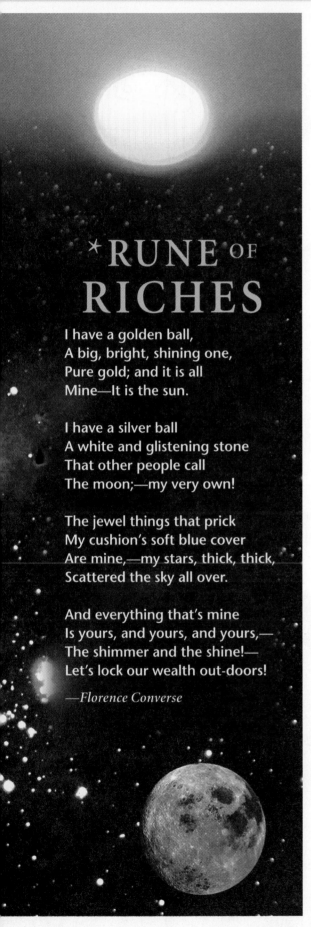

*RUNE OF RICHES

I have a golden ball,
A big, bright, shining one,
Pure gold; and it is all
Mine—It is the sun.

I have a silver ball
A white and glistening stone
That other people call
The moon;—my very own!

The jewel things that prick
My cushion's soft blue cover
Are mine,—my stars, thick, thick,
Scattered the sky all over.

And everything that's mine
Is yours, and yours, and yours,—
The shimmer and the shine!—
Let's lock our wealth out-doors!

—Florence Converse

Go for the gold

What do these sayings have in common?

- It's worth its weight in gold.
- Speech is silver, silence is golden.
- All that glitters is not gold.
- Go for the gold!

All of these sayings use gold as a symbol of perfection and value. Because gold has always been beautiful and scarce, it has for centuries been a symbol of excellence and richness—things that people want and search for. When writers use *gold* or *golden,* they are referring to something desirable, of value or worth. These words may also represent the beauty of gold.

In literature, writers and poets often use *gold* to make a comparison in a simile or metaphor. Similes and metaphors are figures of speech.

- A simile makes a comparison between two things, using *like* or *as* in the comparison. Here's an example: "An honest person's promise is as good as gold."
- A metaphor is a comparison without the use of like or as, such as, "When you're in trouble, true friends are golden."

Look for similes and metaphors in the poem by Florence Converse.

- What similes or metaphors has Converse made?
- What would this poem be like without the comparisons?

**A rune is a song or poem.*

Language Arts Activity

What does gold symbolize for you? Think of some comparisons of your own in which you use gold in a simile or metaphor. After jotting down all of your ideas, choose one (or more) and decide what comparison you will make. Write a short saying, a proverb, or a short poem that includes your own simile or metaphor.

- How does your comparison make your saying or poem more interesting?

Mathematics

Measuring Gold

People often say that something is "worth its weight in gold." But how do you measure the weight of gold? Most gold that's mined today is used to make jewelry. But modern-day jewelry is seldom made of pure gold. Because gold is so soft, it is usually mixed with another metal to form an alloy—a mixture of two or more metals.

Most commonly the other metal in a gold alloy is copper, although alloys of gold can also contain silver, zinc, or other metals. A gold alloy keeps most of the properties of gold but is harder and resists denting and scratching. The other metals affect the color. More copper produces "red gold," while "white gold" may contain gold and copper along with nickel, palladium, or silver.

14K Gold
18K Gold

Suppose you are shopping for a gold ring. You see two rings that look the same and are exactly the same size. How do you decide which one to buy? If you look carefully at the gold jewelry, you'll probably see small letters that read "18 K," "20 K," "14 K," or "12 K." The "K" here stands for karat. That's the measure of how pure an alloy of gold is. Pure gold—used very rarely—is 24 karat. Gold that is 50 percent pure is $\frac{12}{24}$ gold, or 12 karat. The greater the amount of gold in a piece of jewelry, the higher the value.

24K
20K
18K
14K
12K

Look at the display of rings above. The 18-karat ring has copper in it. What percent of the 18 K gold ring is gold? What percent is copper?

Analyze. You know that pure gold is $\frac{24}{24}$ gold. In order to find out what percent of an 18 K ring is gold, you need to write a proportion.

Write the proportion.

$$\frac{\text{number of gold parts}}{\text{number of parts in the whole}} \begin{matrix} \rightarrow \\ \rightarrow \end{matrix} \frac{18}{24}$$

Simplify and solve.

$$\frac{18}{24} = \frac{3}{4} = 75\%$$

Think about it. If 75% of the ring is gold, then 25% of the ring must be copper.

Math Activity

Look at the other gold rings to determine what percent of each is gold.

- What percent of the 14 K gold ring is gold? What percent is another metal? Round decimals to the nearest hundredth.
- What percent of the 12 K ring is gold? What percent of the 20 K ring is gold?
- Which ring would you like to own—the 12 K or the 20 K? Why?
- Which ring in the display would probably be the most expensive?

Tie It Together

Gold Producers

1. South Africa
2. United States
3. Australia
4. Canada
5. Russia
6. China

A Treasure Hunt

Work in small groups to make a World Treasure Map of one of the countries where gold is mined today. Use the information above to get you started. Then use the library to learn about these gold-producing countries.

On a large map of the world, use push pins to mark the location of the gold sites. In the United States and Canada, mark the states and provinces that are the largest producers. Make up fact sheets with information that will answer questions such as the following:

- Where are gold sites located in each country?
- When was gold first discovered there?
- Did a gold rush influence the history of that area?

If possible, collect photographs to illustrate gold products in each country. Post your pictures and fact sheets at the side of the World Treasure Map.

CHAPTER

6 Mapping Earth's Surface

The following California Science Content Standards are addressed in this chapter:

1. **Plate tectonics explains important features of the Earth's surface and major geologic events.**
   - b. The solid Earth is layered with cold, brittle lithosphere; hot, convecting mantle; and dense, metallic core.
2. **Topography is reshaped by weathering of rock and soil and by the transportation and deposition of sediment.**
   - a. Water running downhill is the dominant process in shaping the landscape, including California's landscape.
   - b. Rivers and streams are dynamic systems that erode and transport sediment, change course, and flood their banks in natural and recurring patterns.
7. **Scientific progress is made by asking meaningful questions and conducting careful investigations.**
   - d. Communicate the steps and results from an investigation in written reports and verbal presentations.
   - f. Read a topographic map and a geologic map for evidence provided on the maps, and construct and interpret a simple scale map.

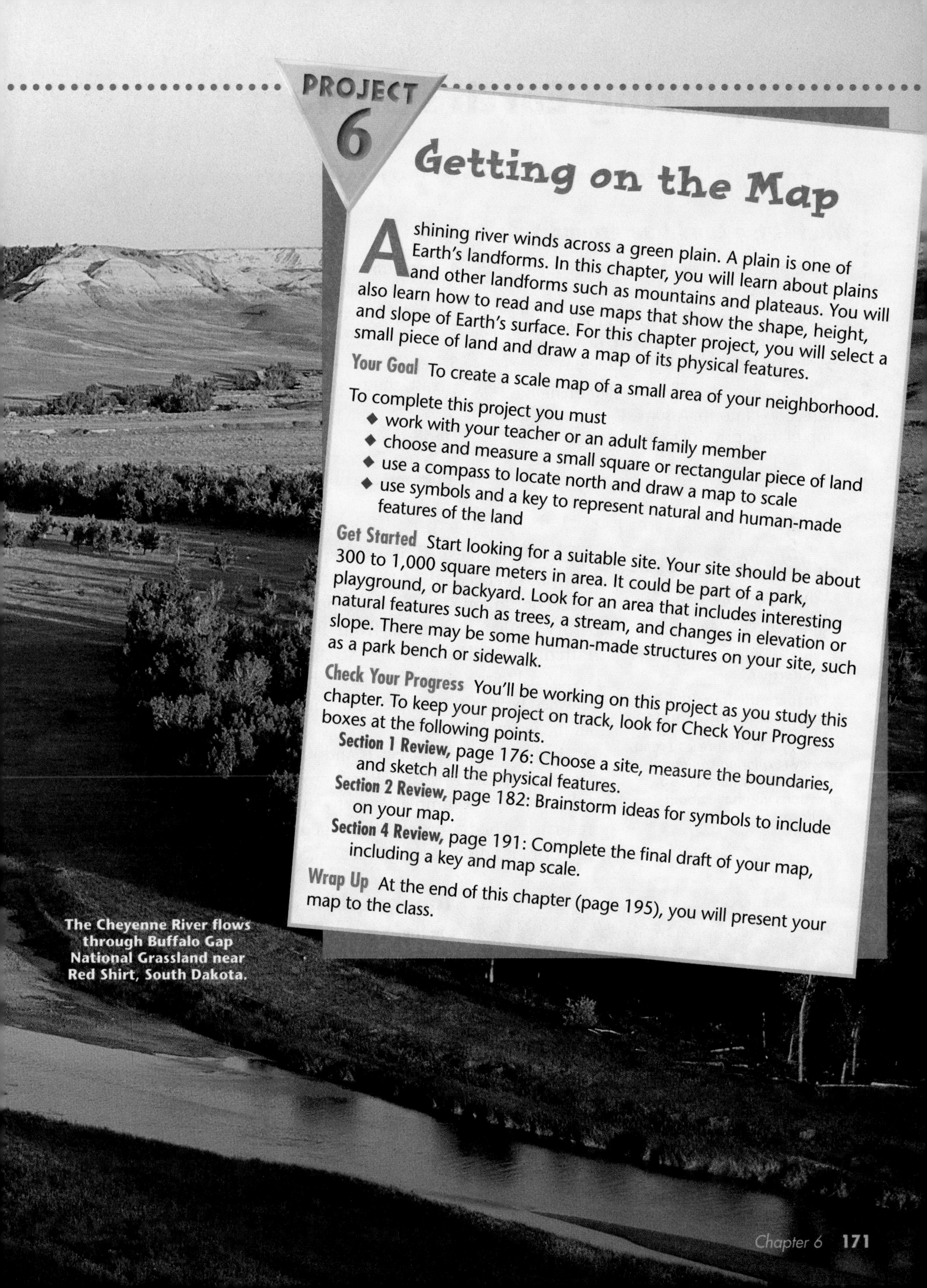

The Cheyenne River flows through Buffalo Gap National Grassland near Red Shirt, South Dakota.

PROJECT 6

Getting on the Map

A shining river winds across a green plain. A plain is one of Earth's landforms. In this chapter, you will learn about plains and other landforms such as mountains and plateaus. You will also learn how to read and use maps that show the shape, height, and slope of Earth's surface. For this chapter project, you will select a small piece of land and draw a map of its physical features.

Your Goal To create a scale map of a small area of your neighborhood.

To complete this project you must

- work with your teacher or an adult family member
- choose and measure a small square or rectangular piece of land
- use a compass to locate north and draw a map to scale
- use symbols and a key to represent natural and human-made features of the land

Get Started Start looking for a suitable site. Your site should be about 300 to 1,000 square meters in area. It could be part of a park, playground, or backyard. Look for an area that includes interesting natural features such as trees, a stream, and changes in elevation or slope. There may be some human-made structures on your site, such as a park bench or sidewalk.

Check Your Progress You'll be working on this project as you study this chapter. To keep your project on track, look for Check Your Progress boxes at the following points.

Section 1 Review, page 176: Choose a site, measure the boundaries, and sketch all the physical features.

Section 2 Review, page 182: Brainstorm ideas for symbols to include on your map.

Section 4 Review, page 191: Complete the final draft of your map, including a key and map scale.

Wrap Up At the end of this chapter (page 195), you will present your map to the class.

Section 1 Exploring Earth's Surface

Discover Activity

What Is the Land Like Around Your School?

1. On a piece of paper, draw a small square to represent your school.
2. Choose a word that describes the type of land near your school, such as flat, hilly, or rolling. Write the word next to the square.
3. Use a magnetic compass to determine the direction of north. Assume that north is at the top of your piece of paper.
4. If you travel due north 1 kilometer from your school, what type of land do you find? Choose a word to describe the land in this area. Write that word to the north of the square.
5. Repeat Step 4 for areas located 1 kilometer east, south, and west of your school.

Think It Over

Forming Operational Definitions What phrase could you use to describe the land in your area?

GUIDE FOR READING

- **What determines the topography of Earth's surface?**
- **What are the main types of landforms?**
- **What are the four "spheres" that make up Earth's surface?**

Reading Tip **Before you read, preview *Exploring Landforms* on page 175. Make a list of questions you have about landforms.**

In 1804, an expedition set out from St. Louis to explore the land between the Mississippi River and the Pacific Ocean. The United States had just purchased a part of this vast territory, called Louisiana, from France. Before the Louisiana Purchase, the United States stretched from the Atlantic coast westward to the Mississippi River. Few United States citizens had traveled west of the Mississippi. None had ever traveled over land all the way to the Pacific.

Led by Meriwether Lewis and William Clark, the expedition traveled up the Missouri River, crossed the Rocky Mountains, followed the Columbia River to the Pacific Ocean—and then returned. The purpose of the expedition was to map America's interior and discover resources.

Figure 1 While traveling down the Columbia River, the Lewis and Clark expedition meets the Chinook people.

Topography

On the journey to the Pacific, the Lewis and Clark expedition traveled more than 5,000 kilometers across the continent of North America. As they traveled, Lewis and Clark observed many changes in topography. **Topography** is the shape of the land. An area's topography may be flat, sloping, hilly, or mountainous.

The topography of an area is determined by the area's elevation, relief, and landforms. The desktop where you do homework probably has piles of books, papers, and other objects of different sizes and shapes. Your desktop has both elevation and relief!

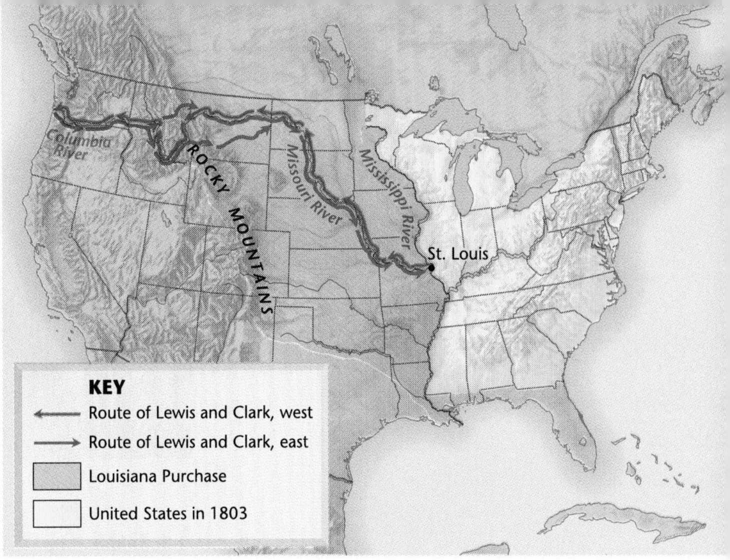

Columbia River
ROCKY MOUNTAINS
Missouri River
Mississippi River
St. Louis
KEY
Route of Lewis and Clark, west
Route of Lewis and Clark, east
Louisiana Purchase
United States in 1803

Figure 2 The Lewis and Clark expedition followed major rivers, except when crossing the Rocky Mountains.

Elevation The height above sea level of a point on Earth's surface is its **elevation.** When Lewis and Clark started in St. Louis, they were about 140 meters above sea level. By the time they reached Lemhi Pass in the Rocky Mountains, they were more than 2,200 meters above sea level.

Relief The difference in elevation between the highest and lowest parts of an area is its **relief.** As the Lewis and Clark expedition entered the Rocky Mountains, the relief of the land changed from flat or rolling land with low relief to huge mountains with high relief.

Landforms If you followed the route of the Lewis and Clark expedition across the western part of North America, you would see many different landforms. A **landform** is a feature of topography formed by the processes that shape Earth's surface. All landforms have elevation and relief. A large area of land where the topography is similar is called a **landform region.** Figure 3 shows the landform regions of the United States.

✓ *Checkpoint* ***What is the difference between elevation and relief?***

Figure 3 The United States has many different landform regions. *Interpreting Maps In what regions are Charleston, Topeka, Santa Fe, and Walla Walla located?*

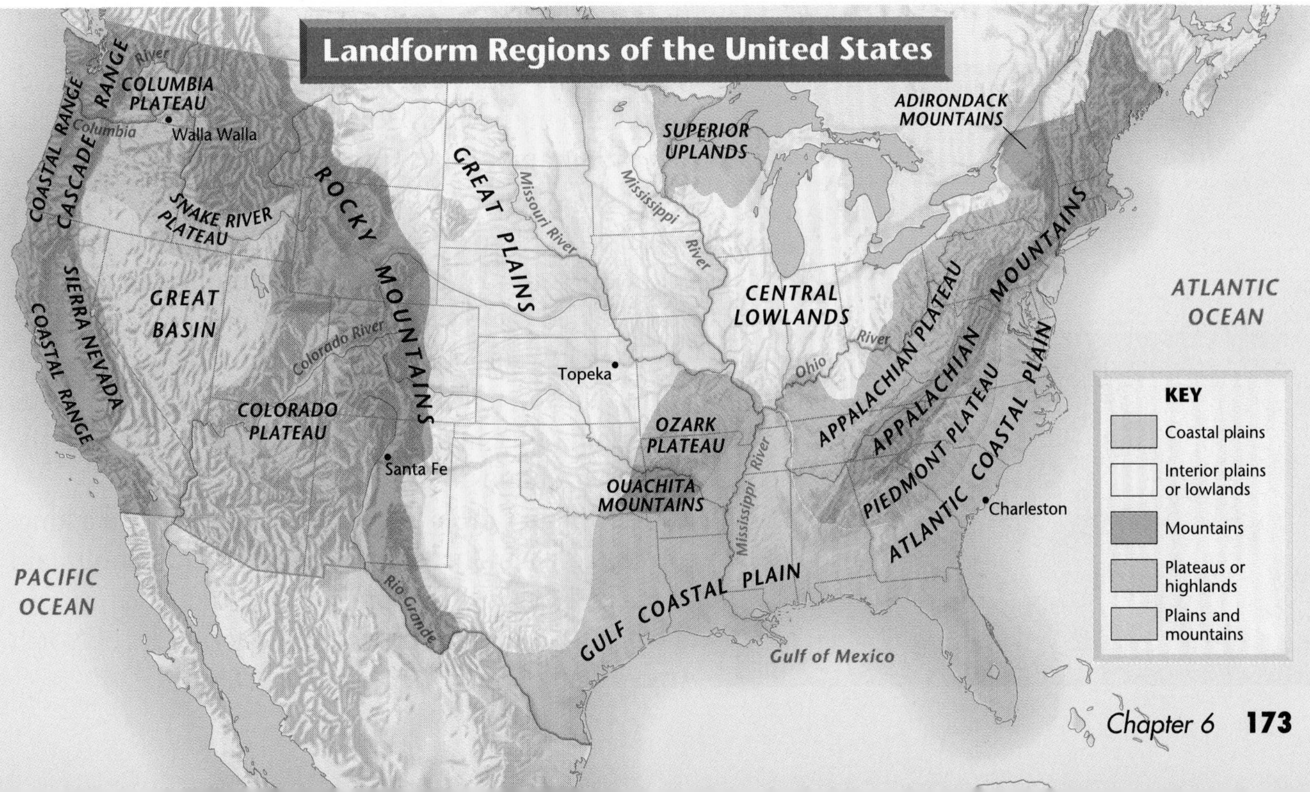

Landform Regions of the United States
COASTAL RANGE
CASCADE RANGE
COLUMBIA PLATEAU
Columbia River
Walla Walla
SNAKE RIVER PLATEAU
ROCKY MOUNTAINS
GREAT PLAINS
Missouri River
SUPERIOR UPLANDS
Mississippi River
ADIRONDACK MOUNTAINS
SIERRA NEVADA
COASTAL RANGE
GREAT BASIN
Colorado River
COLORADO PLATEAU
Santa Fe
Topeka
CENTRAL LOWLANDS
Ohio River
APPALACHIAN PLATEAU
APPALACHIAN MOUNTAINS
PIEDMONT PLATEAU
ATLANTIC COASTAL PLAIN
Charleston
OZARK PLATEAU
OUACHITA MOUNTAINS
Rio Grande
GULF COASTAL PLAIN
Gulf of Mexico
PACIFIC OCEAN
ATLANTIC OCEAN
KEY
Coastal plains
Interior plains or lowlands
Mountains
Plateaus or highlands
Plains and mountains

Figure 4 The Great Plains of western North America include a vast area of flat or rolling land. The Great Plains are interior plains. *Predicting What do you think would be some differences between interior plains and coastal plains?*

Types of Landforms

Landforms can vary greatly in size and shape—from level plains extending as far as the eye can see, to low, rounded hills that you could climb on foot, to jagged mountains that would take you days to walk around. **There are three main types of landforms: plains, mountains, and plateaus.**

Plains A **plain** is a landform made up of flat or gently rolling land with low relief. A plain that lies along a seacoast is called a coastal plain. In North America, a coastal plain wraps like an apron around the continent's eastern and southeastern shores. Coastal plains have both low elevation and low relief.

A plain that lies away from the coast is called an interior plain. Although interior plains have low relief, their elevation can vary. The broad interior plain of North America is called the Great Plains.

The Great Plains extend from Texas north into Canada. From their eastern border in the states of North and South Dakota, Nebraska, Kansas, Oklahoma, and Texas, the Great Plains stretch west to the Rocky Mountains. At the time of the Lewis and Clark expedition, the Great Plains were a vast grassland.

Figure 5 The Bitterroot Mountains in Idaho are part of the Rocky Mountains system.

Mountains A **mountain** is a landform with high elevation and high relief. Mountains usually occur as part of a mountain range. A **mountain range** is a group of mountains that are closely related in shape, structure, and age. After crossing the Great Plains, the Lewis and Clark expedition crossed a rugged mountain range in Idaho called the Bitterroot Mountains.

The different mountain ranges in a region make up a mountain system. The Bitterroot Mountains are one mountain range in the mountain system known as the Rocky Mountains.

Mountain ranges and mountain systems in a long, connected chain form a larger unit called a mountain belt. The Rocky Mountains are part of a great mountain belt that stretches down the western sides of North America and South America.

Plateaus A landform that has high elevation and a more or less level surface is called a **plateau**. A plateau is rarely perfectly smooth on top. Streams and rivers may cut into the plateau's surface. The Columbia Plateau in Washington State is an example. The Columbia River, which the Lewis and Clark expedition followed, slices through this plateau. The many layers of rock that make up the Columbia Plateau are about 1,500 meters thick.

☑ *Checkpoint* ***What types of landforms have low relief?***

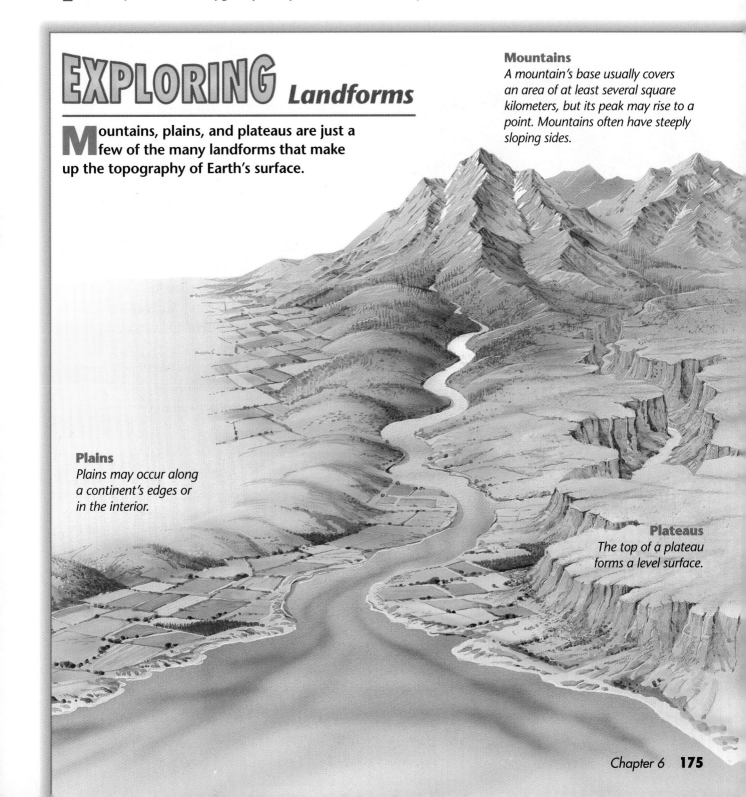

EXPLORING Landforms

Mountains, plains, and plateaus are just a few of the many landforms that make up the topography of Earth's surface.

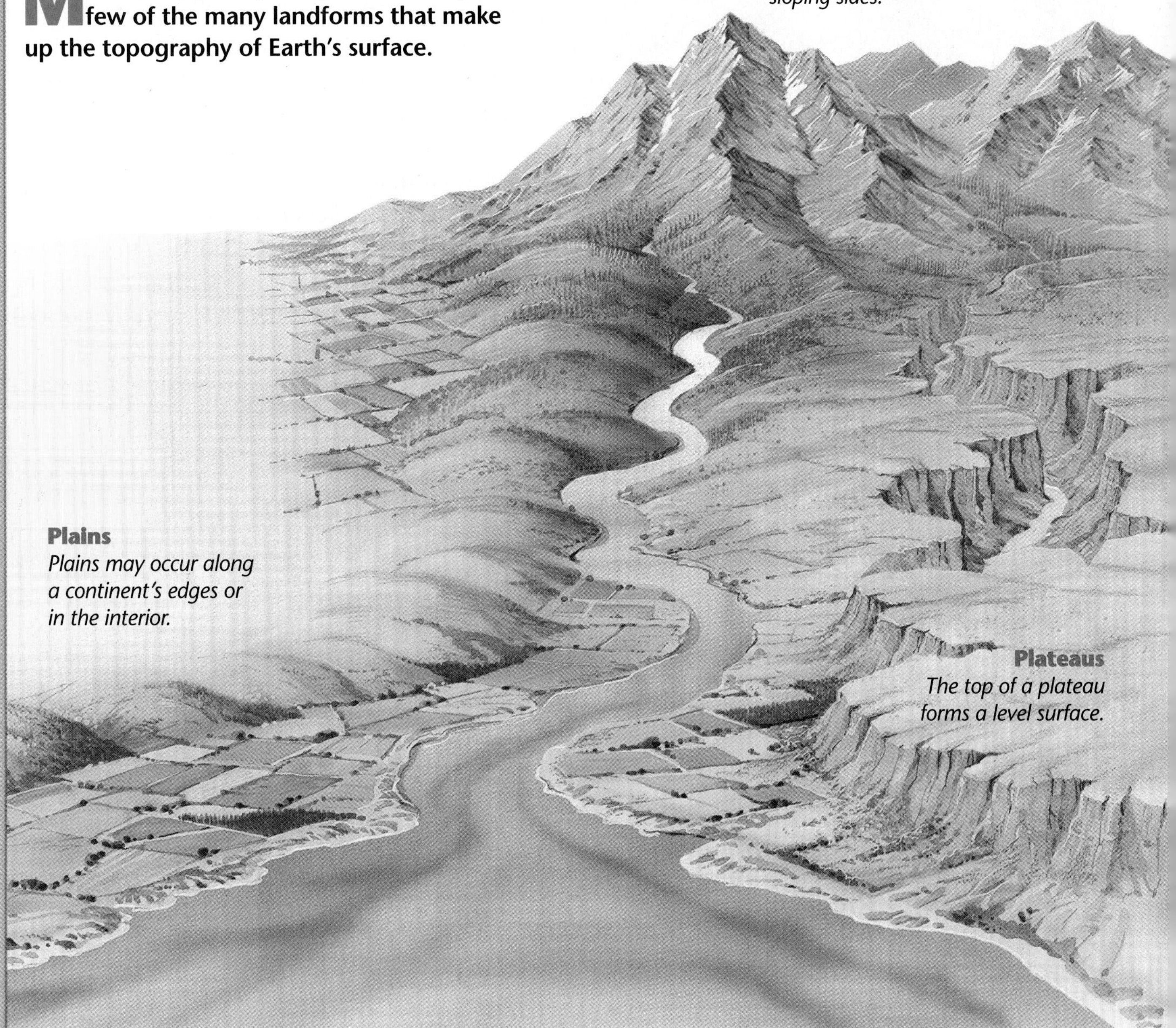

Mountains
A mountain's base usually covers an area of at least several square kilometers, but its peak may rise to a point. Mountains often have steeply sloping sides.

Plains
Plains may occur along a continent's edges or in the interior.

Plateaus
The top of a plateau forms a level surface.

Earth's Four Spheres

Lewis and Clark's two-year journey took them across western North America. Along the way, they observed the land, water, air, and living things. Together, these four things make up everything that is on and around planet Earth. **Scientists divide Earth into four spheres: the lithosphere, hydrosphere, atmosphere, and biosphere.** In this book, you will learn mainly about the lithosphere and how it is affected by each of the other spheres.

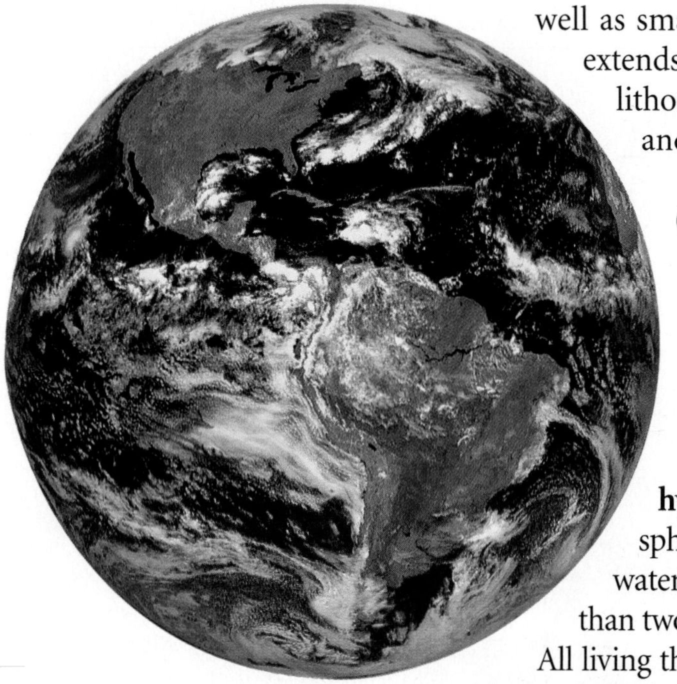

Figure 6 A view from space shows all four of Earth's spheres—the atmosphere, hydrosphere, biosphere, and lithosphere. *Observing What evidence of each of the spheres can you see in the photograph?*

Earth's solid, rocky outer layer is called the **lithosphere** (LITH uh sfeer). The lithosphere is made up of the continents as well as smaller landmasses called islands. The lithosphere extends under the entire ocean floor. The surface of the lithosphere varies from smooth plains to wrinkled hills and valleys to jagged mountain peaks.

The outermost sphere is the **atmosphere** (AT muh sfeer), the mixture of gases that surrounds the planet. By far the most abundant gases are nitrogen and oxygen, but the atmosphere also contains water vapor, carbon dioxide, and other gases. When water vapor condenses, it forms the droplets that make up clouds.

Earth's oceans, lakes, rivers, and ice form the **hydrosphere** (HY druh sfeer). Most of the hydrosphere consists of the salt water in the oceans, but fresh water is also part of the hydrosphere. Oceans cover more than two thirds of Earth.

All living things—whether in the air, in the oceans, or on and beneath the land surface—make up the **biosphere** (BY uh sfeer). The biosphere extends into each of the other spheres.

Section 1 Review

1. What three factors determine the topography of a region?
2. What are the most common types of landforms?
3. Which is larger, a mountain belt or a mountain system?
4. In which of Earth's spheres would you find a cloud? A mountain? A lake? A tree?
5. **Thinking Critically Comparing and Contrasting** How are mountains and plateaus similar? How are they different?

CHAPTER PROJECT

Check Your Progress

Choose a site that is as square or rectangular as possible. **CAUTION:** *Make sure to obtain permission from the property owner before you begin.* To start mapping your site, mark the four corners with stakes, stones, or other markers. Measure the boundaries and record the distances on a rough sketch. Your sketch should show your site's topography, plus natural and human-made features. Include a north arrow on your sketch. How can you determine which direction is north?

SECTION 2 Models of Earth

DISCOVER ACTIVITY

How Can You Flatten the Curved Earth?

1. Using a felt-tip pen, make a rough sketch of the outlines of the continents on the surface of an orange or grapefruit.
2. Using a plastic knife, carefully peel the orange. If possible, keep the peel in one large piece so that the continents remain intact.
3. Try to lay the pieces of orange peel flat on a table.

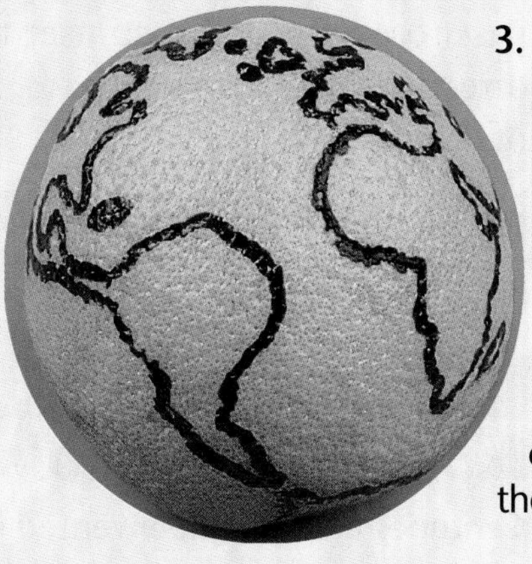

Think It Over

Observing What happens to the continents when you try to flatten the pieces? What adjustments would you need to make to the shapes of the continents to get them to match their shape and position on a sphere?

You want to invite relatives from out of town to a sports event at your school. You could use words to explain how to find the school: Take the third exit off the highway, turn left at the first traffic light, and so on. But verbal directions can be hard to follow. Instead, you might sketch a map of the best route to your school. Maps use a picture instead of words to tell where things are.

GUIDE FOR READING

- **How do maps and globes represent Earth's surface?**
- **How are latitude and longitude used to locate points on Earth's surface?**

Reading Tip **Before you read, rewrite the headings in the section as *how, why,* or *what* questions. As you read, look for answers to these questions.**

Maps and Globes

Maps and globes show the shape, size, and position of Earth's surface features. A **map** is a model on a flat surface of all or part of Earth's surface as seen from above. A **globe** is a sphere that represents Earth's entire surface. A globe correctly shows the relative size and shape of landmasses and bodies of water, much as if you were viewing Earth from space.

Maps and globes are drawn to scale and use symbols to represent topography and other features on Earth's surface. A map's **scale** relates distance on a map to a distance on Earth's surface. Scale is often given as a ratio. For example, one unit on the map equals 25,000 units on the ground. So one centimeter on the map represents 0.25 kilometers. This scale, "one to twenty-five thousand," would be written "1 : 25,000." Figure 7 shows three ways of giving a map's scale.

Figure 7 Here are three ways to show scale on a map.

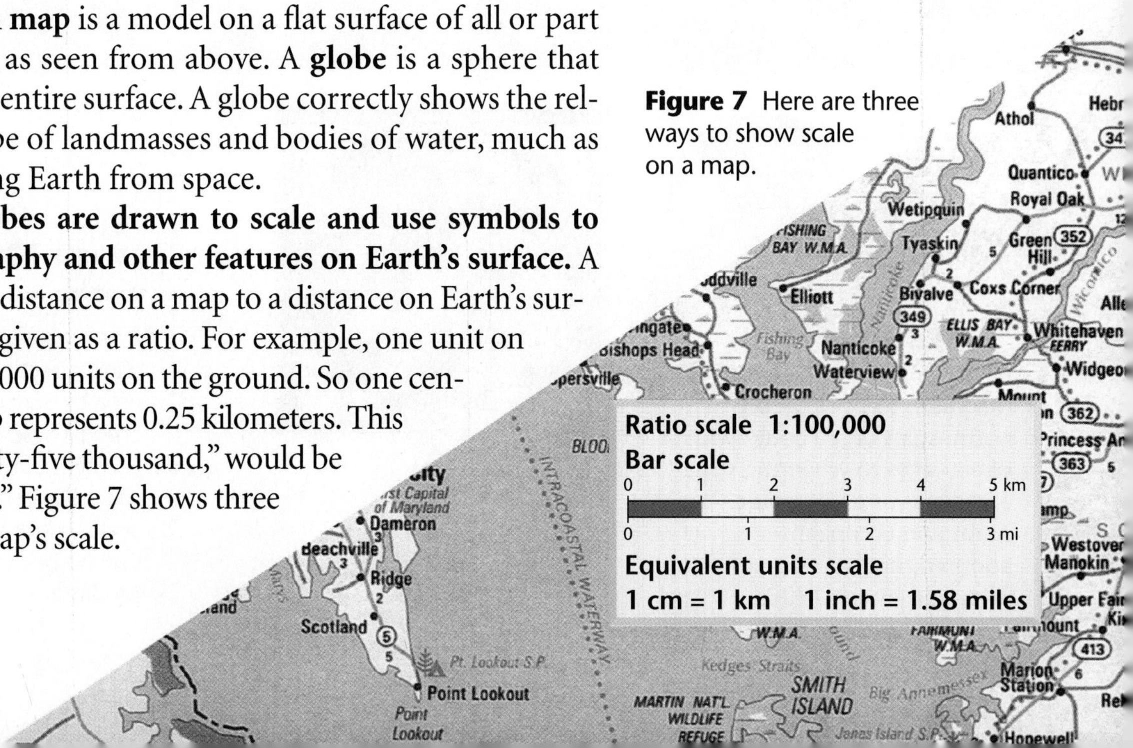

Ratio scale 1:100,000
Bar scale
0 1 2 3 4 5 km
0 1 2 3 mi
Equivalent units scale
1 cm = 1 km 1 inch = 1.58 miles
Athol
Quantico
Royal Oak
Wetipquin
Tyaskin
Elliott
Bivalve
Coxs Corner
Nanticoke
Waterview
Crocheron
Whitehaven
Dameron
Ridge
Scotland
Point Lookout
SMITH ISLAND
INTRACOASTAL WATERWAY

Mapmakers use pictures called **symbols** to stand for features on Earth's surface. A symbol can represent a physical feature, such as a river, lake, mountain, or plain. A symbol also can stand for a human-made feature, such as a highway, a city, or an airport. A map's **key,** or legend, is a list of all the symbols used on the map with an explanation of their meaning.

Maps also include a compass rose or north arrow. The compass rose helps the map user to relate directions on the map to directions on Earth's surface. North usually is located at the top of the map.

☑ *Checkpoint* *Where can you find the meaning of the symbols on a map?*

SCIENCE & History

Maps and Technology

Centuries ago, people invented instruments for determining compass direction, latitude, and longitude. Mapmakers developed techniques to show Earth's surface accurately.

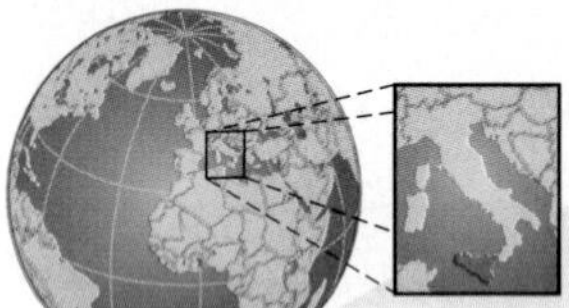

1154 Sicily

The Arab mapmaker Al-Idrisi made several world maps for King Roger of Sicily. Idrisi's maps marked a great advance over other maps of that time. They showed the Arabs' grasp of scientific mapmaking and geography. But unlike modern maps, these maps placed south at the top!

1100 | 1200 | 1300 | 1400

AROUND 1100 China

Because the needle of a magnetic compass points north, ships at sea could tell direction even when the sun and stars were not visible. Arabs and Europeans adopted this Chinese invention by the 1200s.

AROUND 1300 Spain

Lines representing wind directions criss-crossed a type of map called a portolan chart. These charts also showed coastlines and harbors. A sea captain would use a portolan chart and a compass when sailing from one harbor to another in the Mediterranean Sea.

An Earth Reference System

When you play chess or checkers, the grid of squares helps you to keep track of where each piece should be. To find a point on Earth's surface, you need a reference system like the grid of squares on a checkerboard. Of course, Earth itself does not have grid lines, but most maps and globes show a grid. The grid is based on two imaginary lines: the equator and the prime meridian.

The Equator Halfway between the North and South poles, the **equator** forms an imaginary line that circles Earth. The equator divides Earth into the Northern and Southern hemispheres. A **hemisphere** (HEH mih sfeer) is one half of the sphere that makes up Earth's surface.

In Your Journal

Choose one period on the time line to learn more about. Use the library to find information about maps in that time. Who used maps? Why were they important? Share what you learn in the form of a letter written by a traveler or explorer who is using a map of that period.

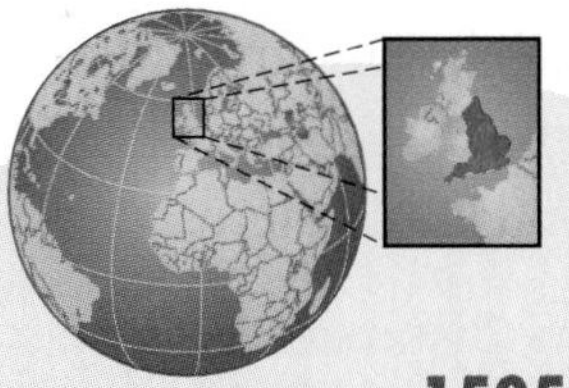

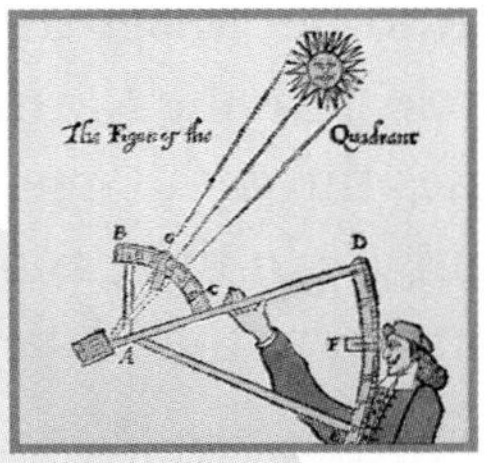

1595 England

To find latitude, sailors used a variety of instruments, including the backstaff. The navigator sighted along the backstaff's straight edge to measure the angle of the sun or North star above the horizon. Later improvements led to modern instruments for navigation.

1684 France

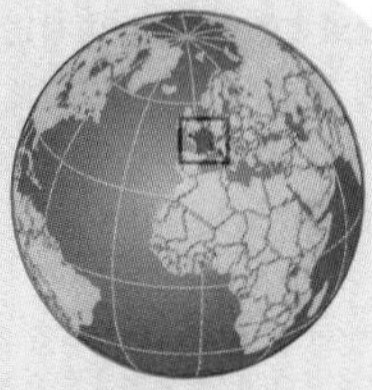

On land, mapmakers developed new ways of measuring land areas accurately. Philippe de La Hire's map of France proved that the country was actually smaller than people had thought. The king of France said that he lost more land because of this map than he would have lost through losing a war.

1500 **1600** **1700** **1800**

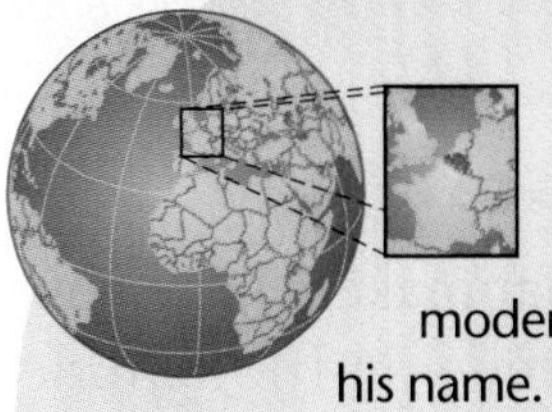

1569 Belgium

Flemish mapmaker Gerardus Mercator invented the first modern map projection, which bears his name. Mercator and his son, Rumold, also made an atlas and maps of the world such as the one shown below.

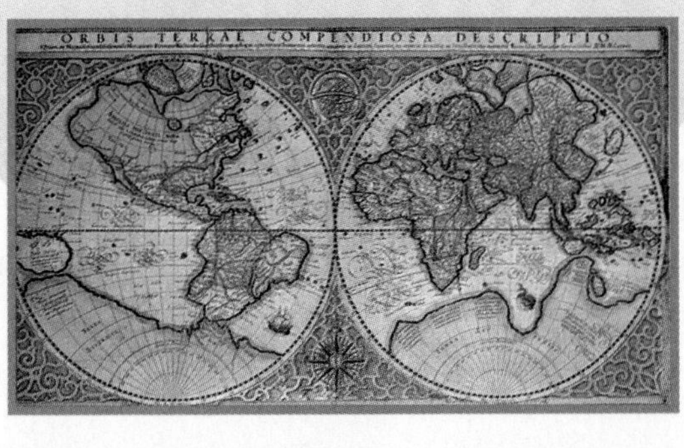
ORBIS TERRAE COMPENDIOSA DESCRIPTIO

1763 England

John Harrison, a carpenter and mechanic, won a prize from the British navy for building a highly accurate clock called a chronometer. Harrison's invention made finding longitudes quicker and easier. With exact longitudes, mapmakers could greatly improve the accuracy of their maps.

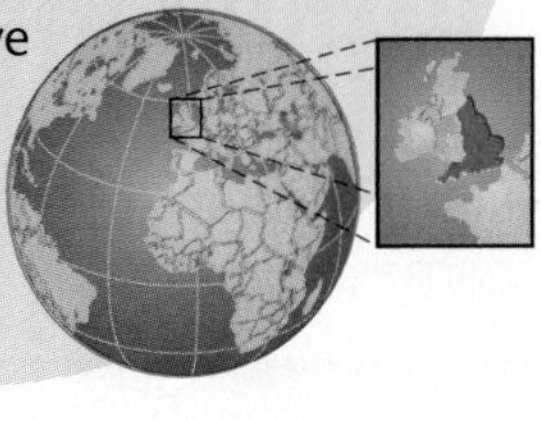

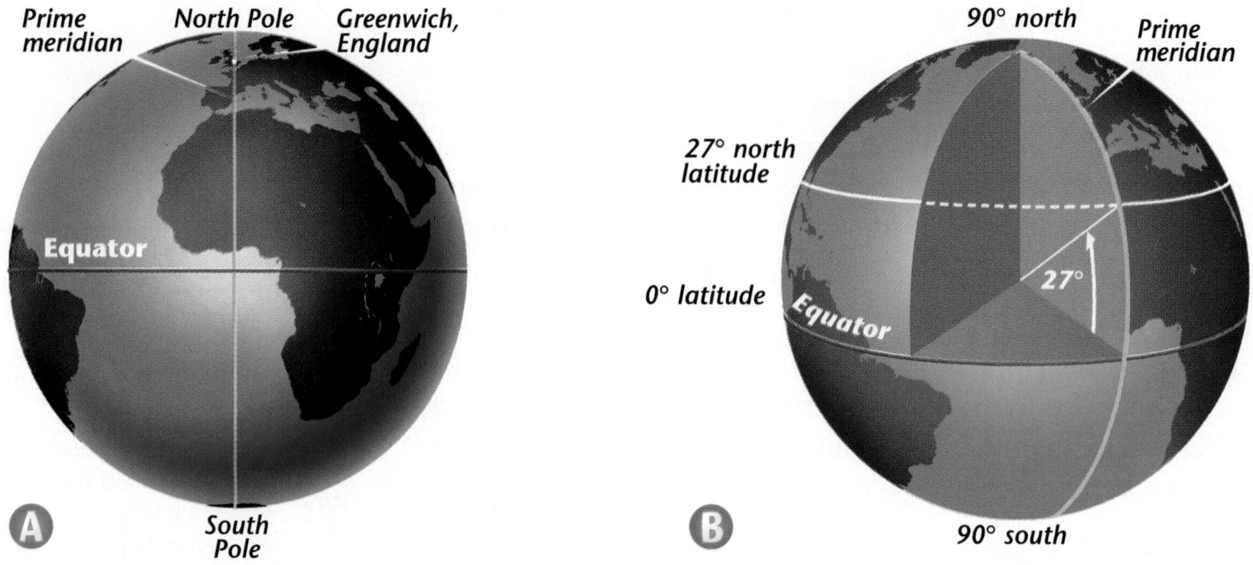
Prime meridian
North Pole
Greenwich, England
Equator
South Pole
A
90° north
Prime meridian
27° north latitude
0° latitude
Equator
27°
B
90° south

Figure 8 A. The equator and the prime meridian divide Earth's surface into hemispheres. B. Latitude measures distances north or south of the equator. C. Longitude measures distances east or west of the prime meridian. D. Cairo, Egypt, is located where the latitude line 30° N crosses the longitude line 31° E.

The Prime Meridian Another imaginary line, called the **prime meridian,** makes a half circle from the North Pole to the South Pole. The prime meridian passes through Greenwich, England. Places east of the prime meridian are in the Eastern Hemisphere. Places west of the prime meridian are in the Western Hemisphere.

Measurements on a Sphere To measure distances around a circle, scientists use units called degrees. A **degree** (°) is $\frac{1}{360}$ of the way around a full circle. As you can see in Figure 8, each degree is a measure of the angle formed by lines drawn from the center of Earth to points on the surface. If you started at the prime meridian and traveled west along the equator, you would travel through 360 degrees before returning to your starting point. If you started at the equator and traveled to one of the poles, you would travel 90 degrees—one quarter of the distance in a full circle.

☑ *Checkpoint* *In what two hemispheres is the United States located?*

Locating Points on Earth's Surface

Using the equator and prime meridian, mapmakers have constructed a grid made up of lines of latitude and longitude. **You can use lines of latitude and longitude to find locations anywhere on Earth.**

Latitude The equator is the starting line for measuring **latitude,** or distance in degrees north or south of the equator. Between the equator and both poles are evenly spaced lines called lines of latitude. All lines of latitude are parallel to the equator. Latitude is measured from the equator, which is at 0°. The latitude of each pole is 90° north or 90° south.

TRY THIS

Where in the World?

ACTIVITY

Using a globe, determine what city is found at each of the following points:

2° S 79° W
38° N 9° W
34° N 135° E
34° S 58° W
55° N 3° W
1° N 103° E

What word is spelled by the first letters of these city names?

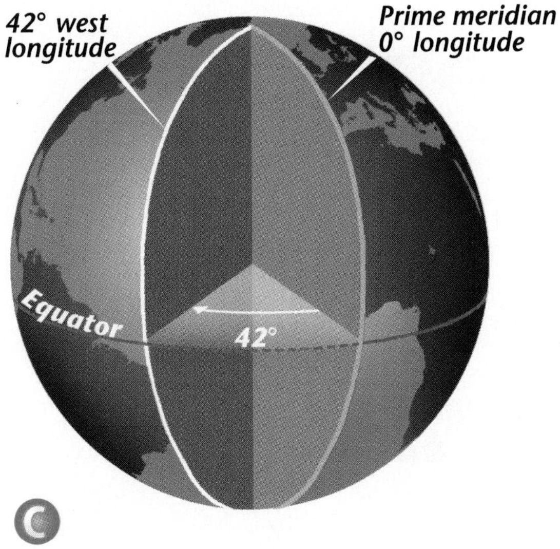
42° west longitude
Prime meridian 0° longitude
Equator
42°
C

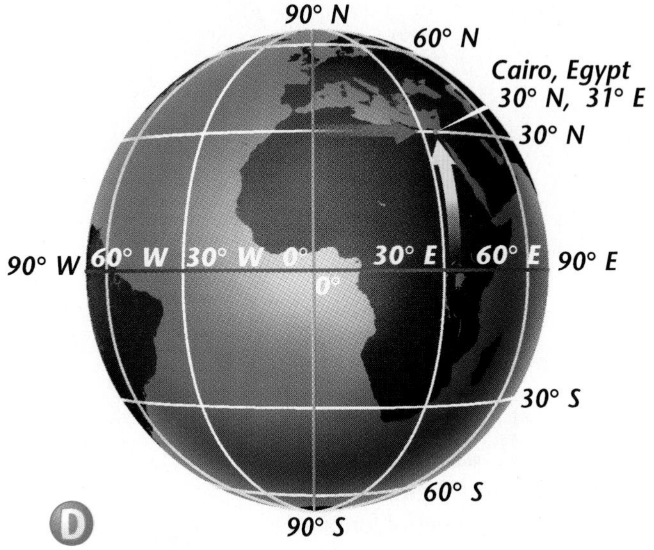
90° N
60° N
Cairo, Egypt 30° N, 31° E
30° N
90° W
60° W
30° W
0°
30° E
60° E
90° E
0°
30° S
60° S
90° S
D

Longitude The distance in degrees east or west of the prime meridian is called **longitude.** There are 360 lines of longitude that run from north to south, meeting at the poles. Each line represents one degree of longitude. The prime meridian, which is the starting line for measuring longitude, is at 0°. Each longitude line crosses the latitude lines, including the equator, at a right angle.

As Figure 9 shows, the longitude lines in each hemisphere are numbered up to 180 degrees. This is one half the total number of degrees in a circle. At 180 degrees east or 180 degrees west lies a single longitude line directly opposite the prime meridian.

Figure 9 Every point on Earth's surface has a particular latitude and longitude. ***Interpreting Maps*** *What are the latitude and longitude of New Orleans? Of Sydney?*

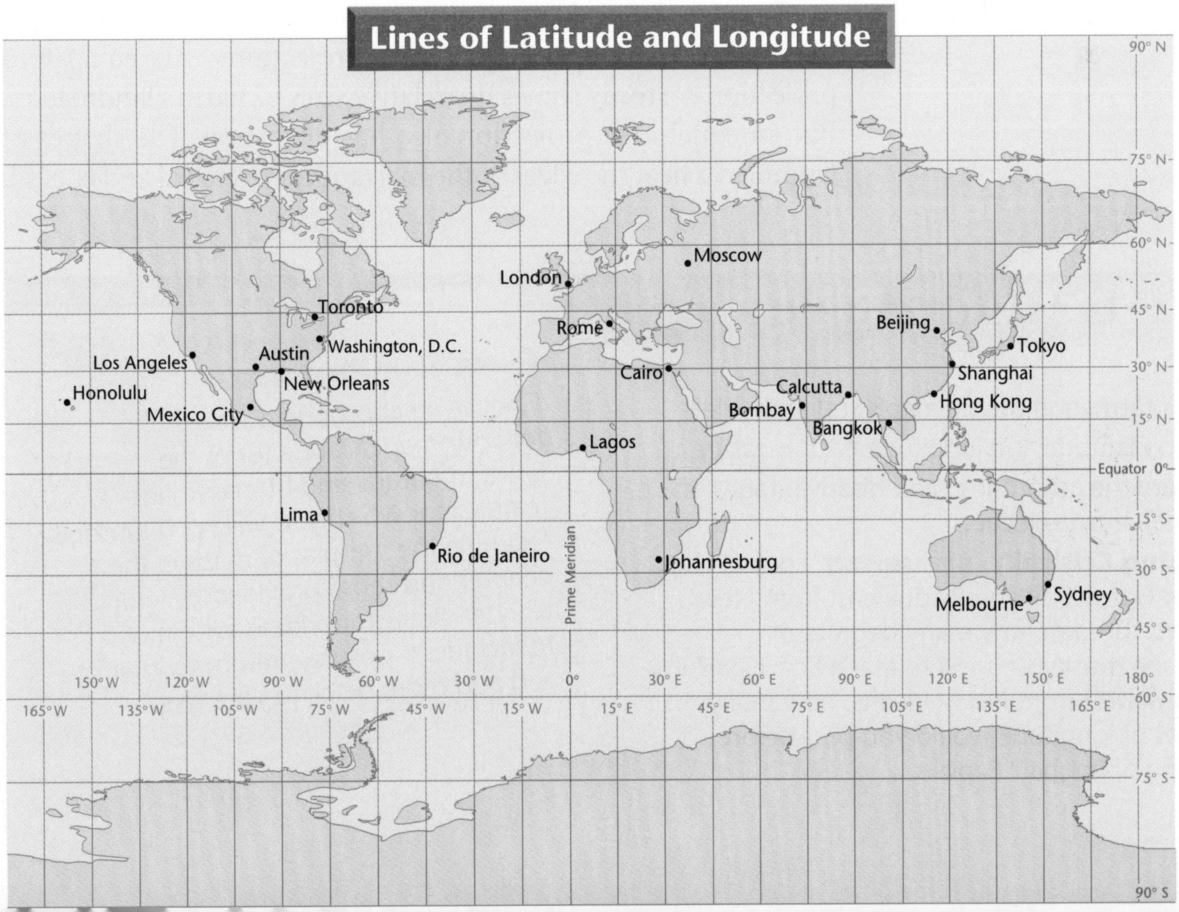
Lines of Latitude and Longitude
90° N
75° N
60° N
45° N
30° N
15° N
Equator 0°
15° S
30° S
45° S
60° S
75° S
90° S
Moscow
London
Toronto
Rome
Beijing
Tokyo
Washington, D.C.
Austin
Los Angeles
Cairo
Shanghai
New Orleans
Honolulu
Calcutta
Hong Kong
Mexico City
Bombay
Bangkok
Lagos
Lima
Rio de Janeiro
Johannesburg
Prime Meridian
Sydney
Melbourne
150° W
120° W
90° W
60° W
30° W
0°
30° E
60° E
90° E
120° E
150° E
180°
165° W
135° W
105° W
75° W
45° W
15° W
15° E
45° E
75° E
105° E
135° E
165° E

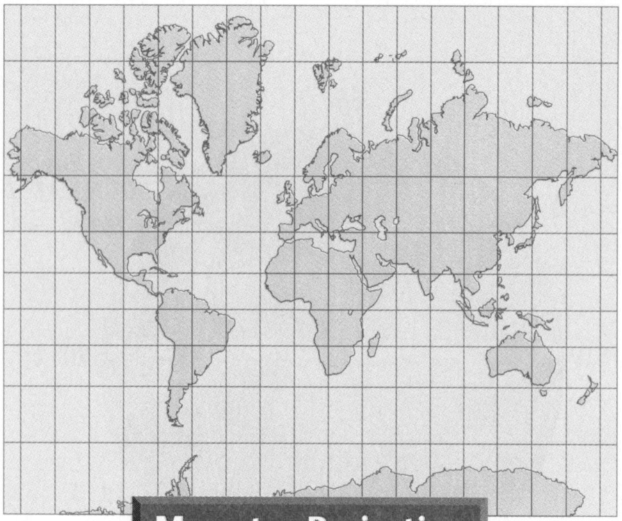
Mercator Projection

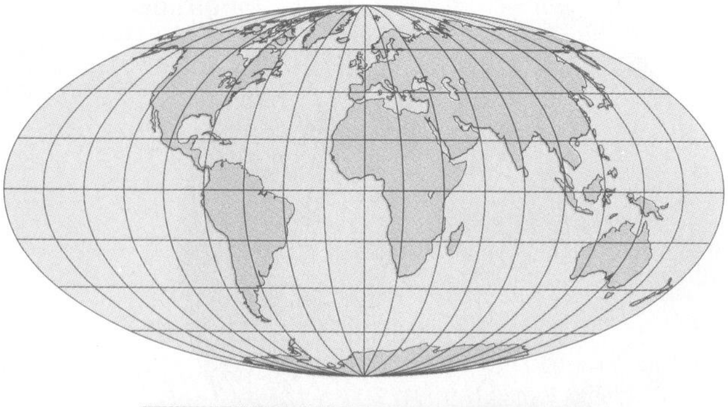
Equal-Area Projection

Figure 10 On a Mercator projection (left), lines of longitude are parallel, so shapes near the poles are distorted. An equal-area projection (right) shows areas correctly, but distorts some shapes around its edges.
Comparing and Contrasting *Why does Greenland appear larger on the Mercator projection than on the equal-area projection?*

Map Projections

To show Earth's curved surface on a flat map, mapmakers use map projections. A **map projection** is a framework of lines that helps to show landmasses on a flat surface.

On a Mercator projection, the lines of latitude and longitude all appear as straight, parallel lines that form a rectangle. On a Mercator projection, the size and shape of landmasses near the equator are distorted only a little. But as you go toward the poles, size and shape become more and more distorted. The reason for this distortion is that the lines of longitude do not come together at the poles as they do on a globe. As you can see in Figure 10, this projection also changes the relative sizes of landmasses.

To solve the problem of distortion on Mercator projections, mapmakers developed equal-area projections. An equal-area projection correctly shows the relative sizes of Earth's landmasses. But an equal-area projection also has distortion. The shapes of landmasses near the edges of the map appear stretched and curved.

Section 2 Review

1. What information does a map's scale provide?
2. What do latitude and longitude each measure?
3. What are the advantages and disadvantages of an equal-area projection?
4. **Thinking Critically** **Measuring** Look at the map in Figure 9. If you fly due east from New Orleans, through how many degrees of longitude must you travel to reach Shanghai? If you flew west from New Orleans, how many degrees of longitude would you pass before reaching Shanghai? Explain.

Check Your Progress

CHAPTER PROJECT

Choose an appropriate scale for your map. Make a list of the types of natural and human-made features for which you will need symbols. Examine the samples of maps in the chapter and those provided by your teacher. Brainstorm ideas for symbols to include. If possible, return to your site and add more detail to your map.

A Borderline Case

You may have wondered how people first decided where to locate the borders between states.

Problem

Which was more important in locating state borders: lines of latitude and longitude or physical features?

Skills Focus

drawing conclusions, observing, inferring

Materials

United States map with latitude, longitude, and state borders

tracing paper   paper clips   colored pencils

Procedure

1. Lay a sheet of tracing paper on top of a map of the United States.
2. Trace over the Pacific and Atlantic coasts of the United States with a blue pencil.
3. Using the blue pencil, trace all Great Lakes shorelines that reach nearby states.
4. Trace all state borders that go exactly north-south with a red pencil. (*Hint:* Some straight-line borders that appear to run north-south, such as the western border of Maine, do not follow lines of longitude.)
5. Use a green pencil to trace all state borders or sections of state borders that go exactly east-west. (*Hint:* Straight-line borders that are slanted, such as the southern border of Nevada, do not follow lines of latitude.)
6. Now use a blue pencil to trace the borders that follow rivers.
7. Use a brown pencil to trace any borders that are not straight lines or rivers.

Analyze and Conclude

1. How many state boundaries are completely defined by longitude and latitude? How many are partially defined by longitude and latitude?
2. What feature is used to define a state border when longitude and latitude are not used? Give examples of specific states.
3. Study the physical map of the United States in Appendix B. What other physical features are used to define borders? Which state borders are defined by these features?
4. Which was used more often in locating state borders: longitude or latitude?
5. How many states do not use longitude and latitude for the location of their borders?
6. **Apply** In which region of the country were lines of latitude and longitude most important in determining state borders? What do you think is the reason for this?

More to Explore

Research the history of your state to find out when and how its borders were established. Are your state's borders based on longitude and latitude, landforms and topography, or both?

Review a map of your county or state. Are any features, other than the state's border, related to longitude and latitude? Which features seem to follow landforms and topography?

SECTION 3

Maps in the Computer Age

DISCOVER ACTIVITY

Can You Make a Pixel Picture?

1. With a pencil, draw a square grid of lines spaced 1 centimeter apart. The grid should have 6 squares on each side.
2. On the grid, draw the outline of a simple object, such as an apple.
3. Using a different color pencil, fill in all squares that are completely inside the apple. If a square is mostly inside the apple, fill it in completely. If it is mostly outside, leave it blank.
4. Each square on your grid represents one pixel, or bit of information, about your picture. Looking at your pixel picture, can you recognize the shape you started with?

Think It Over

Predicting How would the pixel picture change if you drew the object smaller? How would the pixel picture look if you used graph paper with squares that are smaller than your grid?

GUIDE FOR READING

- **How are satellites and computers used in mapmaking?**

Reading Tip **Before you read, preview Figures 12 and 13. Predict how computers have affected mapmaking.**

For centuries, mapmakers slowly gathered data and then drew maps by hand. Explorers made maps by sketching coastlines as seen from their ships. Mapmakers sometimes drew the land based on reports from people who had traveled there. More accurate maps were made by locating points on the surface in a process called surveying.

During the twentieth century, people learned to make highly accurate maps using photographs taken from airplanes. These photographs are called aerial photographs. Aerial photographs are still important in many types of mapmaking.

Since the 1970s, information gathered by satellites has revolutionized mapmaking. Powerful computers use the satellite data to make maps quickly and accurately.

Figure 11 A satellite image is made up of many pixels. This enlargement of a satellite image shows Tampa Bay and St. Petersburg, Florida.

Satellite Mapping

Beginning in 1972, the United States launched a series of Landsat satellites designed to observe Earth's surface. Landsat uses electronic devices to collect information about the land surface in the form of computer data. **Satellite images** are pictures of the surface based on these data. As Landsat orbits Earth, it collects and stores information about a strip of the surface that is

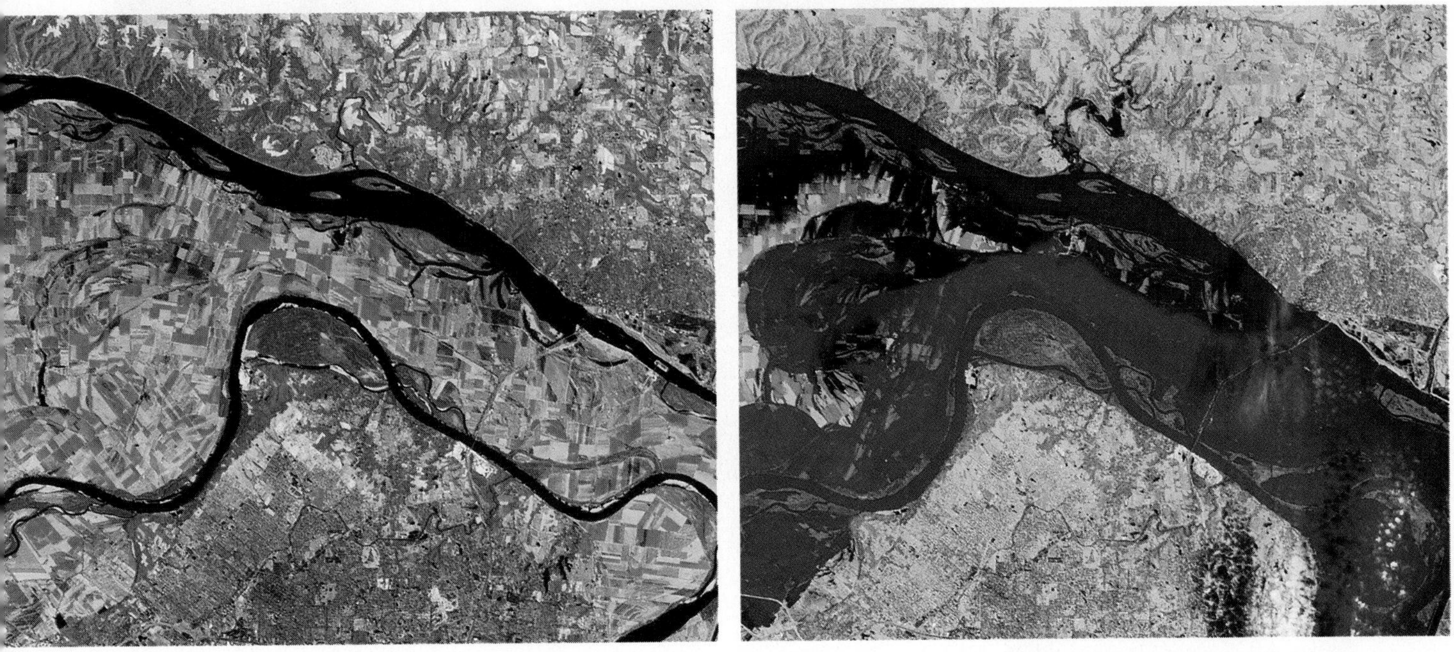

Figure 12 Landsat made these images of part of the Mississippi and Missouri rivers. They show an area just north of St. Louis, before (left) and during (right) a flood in 1993. The Mississippi is the wider river in each image. In both images, north is at the top.
Inferring What can you infer about the relief of the land between the Mississippi and Missouri rivers?

185 kilometers wide. The satellite relays the data back to a station on Earth, where computers create images of the surface.

Pictures made by Landsat show what covers the land surface—plants, soil, sand, rock, water, or snow and ice. Large human-made features, such as cities, are also visible.

Printing Satellite Images Unlike a photograph, a satellite image is made up of thousands of tiny dots called **pixels.** A painting made of pixels would have many separate dots of color. Each pixel in a satellite image contains information on the color and brightness of a small part of Earth's surface. This information is stored on a computer as a series of 0's and 1's. When the satellite image is printed, the computer translates these numbers into colors.

Interpreting Satellite Images Scientists learn to identify specific features by the "signature," or combination of colors and shapes, that the feature makes on a satellite image. In a satellite image, areas covered by grass, trees, or crops are often shown as red, water as black or blue, and cities as bluish gray. Landsat images may show features such as grasslands, forests, and agricultural crops, as well as desert areas, mountains, or cities. By comparing one image with another made at an earlier time, scientists can see changes due to drought, forest fires, or floods. Figure 12 shows satellite images taken before and during a flood in the Mississippi River valley.

INTEGRATING ENVIRONMENTAL SCIENCE

☑ *Checkpoint* ***What information does a pixel in a satellite image contain?***

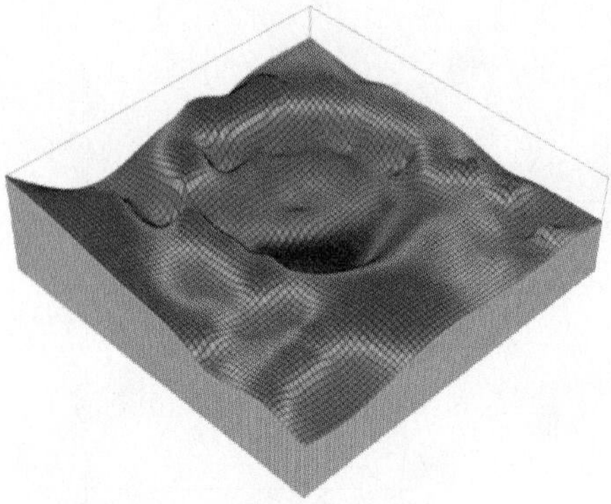

Figure 13 Today computers are an essential tool in making accurate maps. A computer produced the digital model shown above.

Computer Mapping

With computers, mapmakers have new ways of storing and displaying map data. Computer mapmakers use up-to-the-minute data to produce maps quickly and easily.

All of the data used in computer mapping must be in numbers, just like the pixels in a satellite image. The process by which mapmakers convert the location of map points to numbers is called **digitizing.** Once the map data have been digitized, they can be displayed on a computer screen, modified, and printed out in map form.

Computers can automatically create three-dimensional views that might take a person hundreds of hours to draw by hand. The computer image in Figure 13, for example, was made to help geologists search for oil.

Section 3 Review

1. Describe how Landsat collects data about Earth's surface.
2. What are the two ways in which computers are useful in making maps?
3. How are the data for a map put in a form that a computer can use?
4. **Thinking Critically Making Generalizations** In your own words, describe how computers and satellites have improved the accuracy of maps.

Science at Home

Most of the maps that you see today in newspapers and magazines are made using computers. With family members look through newspapers and news magazines. How many different types of maps can you find? Explain to your family the map's scale, symbols, and key. After you have studied the map, try to state the main point of the information shown on the map.

SECTION 4 Topographic Maps

DISCOVER ACTIVITY

Can a Map Show Relief?

1. Carefully cut the corners off 8 pieces of cardboard so that they look rounded. Each piece should be at least 1 centimeter smaller than the one before.

2. Trim the long sides of the two largest pieces so that the long sides appear wavy. Don't cut any more than one-half centimeter into the cardboard.
3. Trace the largest cardboard piece on a sheet of paper.
4. Trace the next largest piece inside the tracing of the first. Don't let any lines cross.
5. Trace the other cardboard pieces, from largest to smallest, one inside the other, on the same paper.
6. Stack the cardboard pieces in the same order they were traced beside the paper. Compare the stack of cardboard pieces with your drawing. How are they alike? How are they different?

Think It Over

Making Models If the cardboard pieces are a model of a landform, what do the lines on the paper represent?

You are an engineer planning a route for a highway over a mountain pass. You need to consider many different factors. To design a safe highway, you need a route that avoids the steepest slopes. To protect the area's water supply, the highway must stay a certain distance from rivers and lakes. You also want to find a route that avoids houses and other buildings. How would you find the best route? You could start by studying a topographic map.

GUIDE FOR READING

- **What is a topographic map?**
- **How do mapmakers represent elevation, relief, and slope?**
- **What is the Global Positioning System?**

Reading Tip **As you read, make a list of main ideas and supporting details about topographic maps.**

Mapping Earth's Topography

A **topographic map** is a map showing the surface features of an area. Topographic maps use symbols to portray the land as if you were looking down on it from above. **Topographic maps provide highly accurate information on the elevation, relief, and slope of the ground surface.**

Figure 14 Topographic maps provide the data necessary for the planning of highways, bridges, and other large construction projects.

Math Toolbox

Scale and Ratios

A ratio compares two numbers by division. For example, the scale of a map given as a ratio is 1 : 250,000. At this scale, the distance between two points on the map measures 23.5 cm. How would you find the actual distance? Begin by writing the scale as a fraction.

$$\frac{1}{250{,}000}$$

Next, write a proportion. Let d represent the actual distance between the two points.

$$\frac{1}{250{,}000} = \frac{23.5 \text{ cm}}{d}$$

Then write the cross products.

$$1 \times d = 250{,}000 \times 23.5 \text{ cm}$$
$$d = 5{,}875{,}000 \text{ cm}$$

(*Hint:* To convert cm to km, divide d by 100,000.)

Uses of Topographic Maps People find many uses for topographic maps. Businesses use them to help decide where to build new stores, housing, or factories. Cities and towns use them to decide where to build new schools. Topographic maps have recreational uses, too. If you were planning a bicycle trip, you could use a topographic map to see whether your trip would be flat or hilly.

Scale Topographic maps usually are large-scale maps. A large-scale map is one that shows a close-up view of part of Earth's surface. In the United States, most topographic maps are at a scale of 1 : 24,000, or 1 centimeter equals 0.24 kilometers. At this scale, a map can show the details of elevation and features such as rivers and coastlines. Large buildings, airports, and major highways appear as outlines at the correct scale. Symbols are used to show houses and other small features.

Coverage Most nations have a government agency that is responsible for making topographic maps. In the United States, that agency is the U. S. Geological Survey, or USGS. The USGS has produced about 57,000 topographic maps at scales of either 1 : 24,000 or 1 : 25,000. The maps cover all of the United States, except for parts of Alaska. Each map covers an area of roughly 145 square kilometers.

Symbols Mapmakers use a great variety of symbols on topographic maps. If you were drawing a map, what symbols would you use to represent woods, a campground, an orchard, a swamp, or a school? Look at Figure 15 to see the symbols that the USGS uses for these and other features.

☑ *Checkpoint* ***In the United States, what agency is responsible for producing topographic maps?***

Figure 15 Maps made by the U. S. Geological Survey use more than 150 symbols.

Commonly Used Map Symbols

Contour line: elevation	Primary highway	River
Contour line: depression	Secondary highway	Stream
Building	Divided highway	Waterfall or rapids
School; church	Railroad tracks	Marsh or swamp
Built-up area	Airport	Rock or coral reef
Campground; picnic area	Woods	Breakwater; wharf
Cemetery [Cem]	Orchard	Exposed wreck

Figure 16 The contour lines on a topographic map represent elevation and relief. ***Comparing and Contrasting*** *What information does the topographic map provide that the photograph does not?*

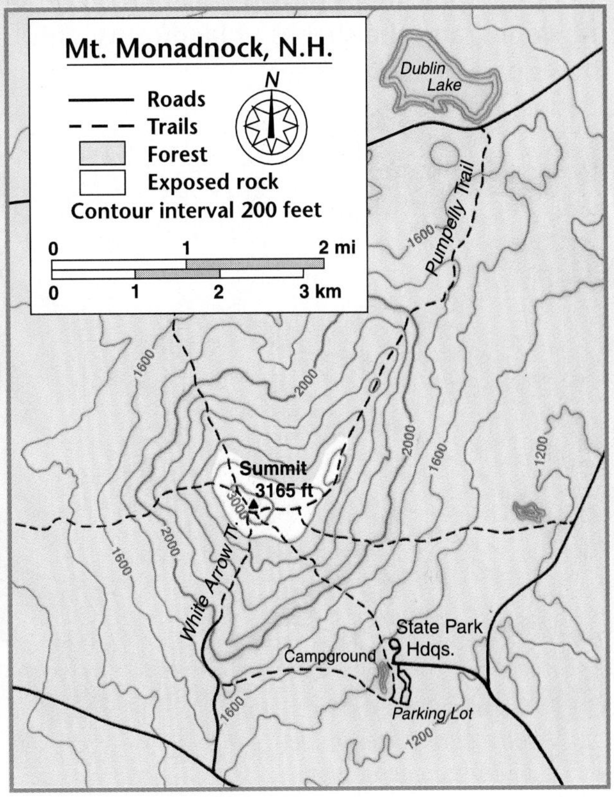

Mt. Monadnock, N.H.
N
Roads
Trails
Forest
Exposed rock
Contour interval 200 feet
0
1
2 mi
0
1
2
3 km
Dublin Lake
Pumpelly Trail
1600
2000
1200
Summit 3165 ft
3000
White Arrow Tr.
State Park Hdqs.
Campground
Parking Lot

Showing Relief on Topographic Maps

To represent elevation, relief, and slope on topographic maps, mapmakers use contour lines. On a topographic map, a **contour line** connects points of equal elevation.

The change in elevation from contour line to contour line is called the **contour interval.** The contour interval for a given map is always the same. For example, the map in Figure 16 has a contour interval of 200 feet. If you start at one contour line and count up 10 contour lines, you have reached an elevation 2,000 feet above where you started. Usually, every fifth contour line is darker and heavier than the others. These lines are labeled with the elevation in round units, such as 1,600 or 2,000 feet above sea level. Most USGS maps give contour intervals in feet rather than meters.

Looking at a topographic map with many squiggly contour lines, you may feel as if you are gazing into a bowl of spaghetti. But if you follow the rules listed in *Exploring Topographic Maps* on the following page, you can learn to read contour lines. Reading contour lines is the first step toward "seeing" an area's topography by looking at a topographic map.

Sharpen your Skills

Interpreting Data

ACTIVITY

You are planning to hike up Mt. Monadnock. Use the topographic map in Figure 16 to determine which route is steeper: the White Arrow Trail or the Pumpelly Trail. What is the difference in elevation between the park headquarters and the summit?

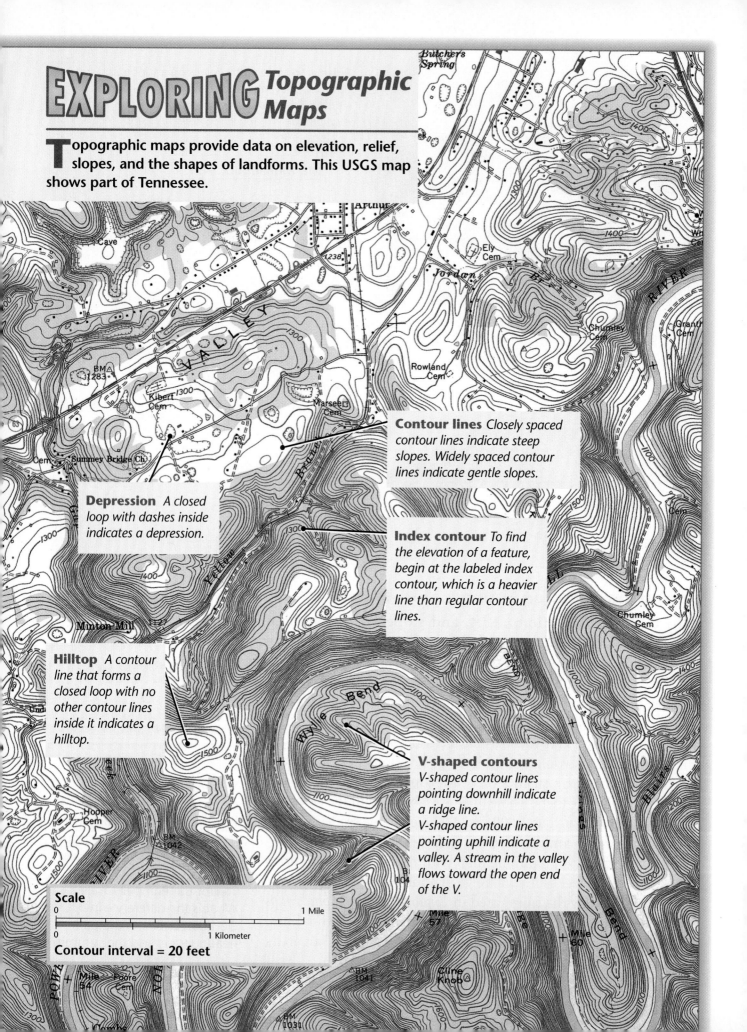

EXPLORING Topographic Maps

Topographic maps provide data on elevation, relief, slopes, and the shapes of landforms. This USGS map shows part of Tennessee.

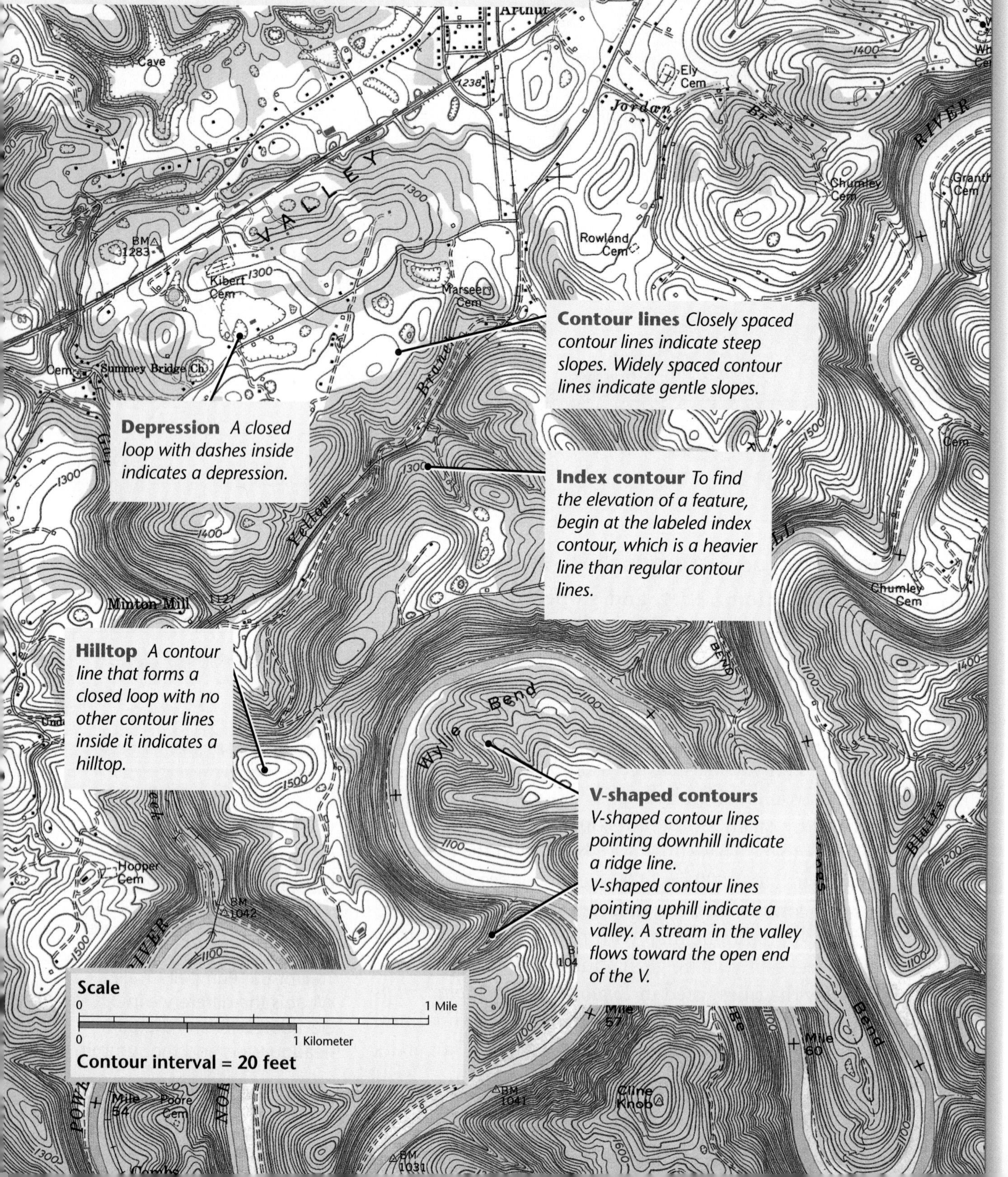
Contour lines *Closely spaced contour lines indicate steep slopes. Widely spaced contour lines indicate gentle slopes.*
Depression *A closed loop with dashes inside indicates a depression.*
Index contour *To find the elevation of a feature, begin at the labeled index contour, which is a heavier line than regular contour lines.*
Hilltop *A contour line that forms a closed loop with no other contour lines inside it indicates a hilltop.*
V-shaped contours *V-shaped contour lines pointing downhill indicate a ridge line. V-shaped contour lines pointing uphill indicate a valley. A stream in the valley flows toward the open end of the V.*
Scale
0
1 Mile
0
1 Kilometer
Contour interval = 20 feet

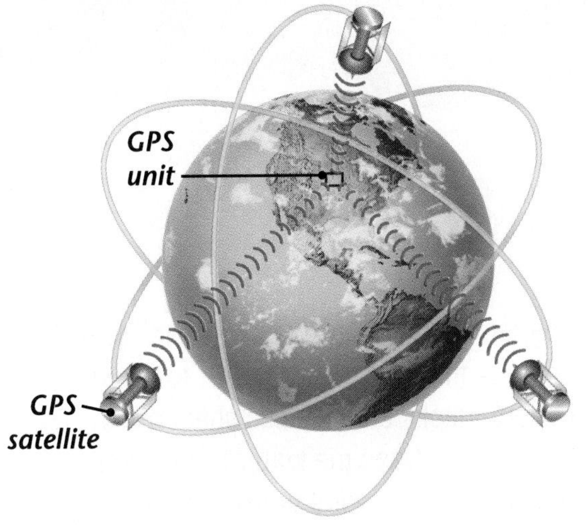
GPS
unit
GPS
satellite

Figure 17 The GPS network includes 24 satellites. Three satellites (left) must be above the horizon to pinpoint the location of the user (right). The user's latitude and longitude appear on the screen of a portable GPS unit like the one in the photograph.

Global Positioning System

Integrating Technology Today, surveyors, pilots, and mapmakers around the world rely on the **Global Positioning System,** or GPS, to determine locations precisely. **The Global Positioning System is a method of finding latitude, longitude, and elevation of points on Earth's surface using a network of satellites.** At any given moment, there are between five and eight GPS satellites above the horizon in a given area. A hand-held unit the size of a cellular phone picks up signals broadcast by these satellites. A computer inside the GPS unit then calculates the user's location and elevation.

Engineers can use GPS to locate points on the ground for a construction project. Airplanes, ships, and hikers can use GPS to navigate. Some cars now contain both a GPS unit and a digital road map stored in a computer. Using GPS, the computer determines the car's location and suggests a route to your destination.

Section 4 Review

1. What kind of information does a topographic map provide about landforms?
2. How do topographic maps represent elevation and relief?
3. What would the highest and lowest points in an area look like on a topographic map?
4. What is the role of satellites in the Global Positioning System?
5. **Thinking Critically Interpreting Maps** Look at the map on page 190. Where is the highest elevation? Where do you find the steepest slopes? The gentlest slopes?

Chapter Project

Check Your Progress

On a large piece of paper, draw your map to scale. Locate all natural and human-made features on the map using the measurements you recorded on your rough sketch and the symbols you brainstormed earlier. Include a north arrow, a legend, and scale on your map. Show the topography of the land by using contour lines or other symbols that show how the land slopes.

Skills Lab

Making Models

A Map in a Pan

A topographic map is a two-dimensional model of three-dimensional landforms.

Problem

How can you make a topographic map?

Materials

deep-sided pan	1 L water
marking pencil	rigid cardboard
clear, hard sheet of plastic	modeling clay
sheet of unlined white paper	metric ruler

Procedure

1. Cut a piece of cardboard to fit the bottom of a deep-sided pan.
2. On the cardboard, shape some clay into a model of a hill.
3. Place the model in the pan. Pour colored water into the pan to a depth of 1 centimeter to represent sea level.
4. Place a sheet of hard, clear plastic over the container.
5. Trace the outline of the pan on the plastic sheet with a marking pencil. Then, looking straight down into the pan, trace the outline the water makes around the edges of the clay model. Remove the plastic sheet from the pan.

6. Add another centimeter of water to the pan, bringing the depth of the water to 2 centimeters. Replace the plastic sheet exactly as before, then trace the water level again.
7. Repeat Step 6 several times. Stop when the next addition of water would completely cover your model.
8. Remove the plastic sheet. Trace the outlines that you drew on the plastic sheet onto a sheet of paper.

Analyze and Conclude

1. Looking at your topographic map, how can you tell which parts of your model hill have a steep slope? A gentle slope?
2. How can you tell from the map which point on the hill is the highest?
3. Where on your map would you be likely to find a stream? Explain.
4. Is there any depression on your map where water would collect after it rained? What symbol should you use to identify this depression?
5. **Think About It** Compare your map with the clay landform. How are they alike? How are they different? How could you improve your map as a model of the landform?

More to Explore

Obtain a topographic map that includes an interesting landform such as a mountain, canyon, river valley, or coastline. After studying the contour lines on the map, make a sketch of what you think the landform looks like. Then build a scale model of the landform using clay or layers of cardboard or foamboard. How does your model landform compare with your sketch?

SECTION 1 Exploring Earth's Surface

Key Ideas

- Earth's topography is made up of landforms that have elevation and relief.
- Three common types of landforms are plains, mountains, and plateaus.
- The atmosphere, hydrosphere, and biosphere surround Earth's rocky outer layer, the lithosphere.

Key Terms

topography	plain	lithosphere
elevation	mountain	atmosphere
relief	mountain range	hydrosphere
landform	plateau	biosphere
landform region		

SECTION 2 Models of Earth

Key Ideas

- Maps and globes are drawn to scale and use symbols to show features on Earth's surface as seen from above.
- The grid of latitude and longitude lines can be used to locate points on Earth's surface.
- Map projections enable mapmakers to show Earth's curved surface on a flat map.

Key Terms

map	key	degree
globe	equator	latitude
scale	hemisphere	longitude
symbols	prime meridian	map projection

SECTION 3 Maps in the Computer Age

INTEGRATING TECHNOLOGY

Key Ideas

- Instruments carried aboard satellites in orbit around Earth make pictures of the surface called satellite images.
- Satellite images contain information about Earth's surface in a form that can be stored on computers as a series of 0's and 1's.
- Computers are used to store and display the information used in making maps.

Key Terms

satellite image	digitizing
pixel	

SECTION 4 Topographic Maps

Key Ideas

- Topographic maps portray the elevation, relief, and slope of the landforms in an area.
- Contour lines are the symbols used on a topographic map to show elevation and relief.
- The contour interval of a topographic map is the amount that elevation changes between contour lines.
- In addition to showing elevation and relief, topographic maps use symbols to show a wide variety of other natural and human-made features.
- The Global Positioning System is a network of satellites and ground-based units that can be used to pinpoint locations on Earth's surface.

Key Terms

topographic map	contour interval
contour line	Global Positioning System

ACTIVITY

USING THE INTERNET

www.phschool.com/state_focus/california/

CHAPTER 6 ASSESSMENT

California Test Prep: Reviewing Content

Multiple Choice

Choose the letter of the best answer.

1. A landform that has high elevation and a mostly flat surface is a
   a. coastal plain. b. mountain.
   c. mountain belt. d. plateau.
2. Of Earth's four "spheres," the one that extends into all the others is the
   a. lithosphere. b. hydrosphere.
   c. biosphere. d. atmosphere.
3. Latitude is a measurement of distance north or south of the
   a. hemispheres. b. equator.
   c. axis. d. prime meridian.
4. To show the continents without distorting their relative sizes and shapes, a map-maker would choose a
   a. Mercator projection.
   b. globe.
   c. equal-area projection.
   d. topographic map.
5. On a topographic map, the contour lines form a V at a
   a. hilltop. b. level area.
   c. depression. d. valley.

True or False

If the statement is true, write true. If it is false, change the underlined word or words to make the statement true.

6. Relief measures a landform's height above sea level.
7. Going north or south from the prime meridian, the distance to one of the poles is 90 degrees.
8. Computers use data about Earth's surface that has been digitized, or put in the form of numbers.
9. If contour lines on a slope are spaced wide apart, then the slope is very steep.
10. Contour lines that form a closed loop marked with dashes indicate a depression.

Checking Concepts

11. What do geologists call an area where there is mostly one kind of topography?
12. What is a mountain range?
13. Compare the elevation of a coastal plain to that of an interior plain.
14. The South Island of New Zealand lies at about 170° E. What hemisphere is it in?
15. Could contour lines on a map ever cross? Explain.
16. Which would be more likely to show a shallow, 1.5-meter-deep depression in the ground: a 1-meter contour interval or a 5-meter contour interval? Explain.
17. **Writing to Learn** With your family, you make a car trip across the United States along the latitude line 35° N. Write a series of postcards to friends describing the landforms that you see on your trip. Use Appendix D to determine what the land is like along your route.

Thinking Visually

18. **Concept Map** Copy the concept map about landforms onto a separate piece of paper. Then complete it and add a title. (For more on concept maps, see the Skills Handbook.)

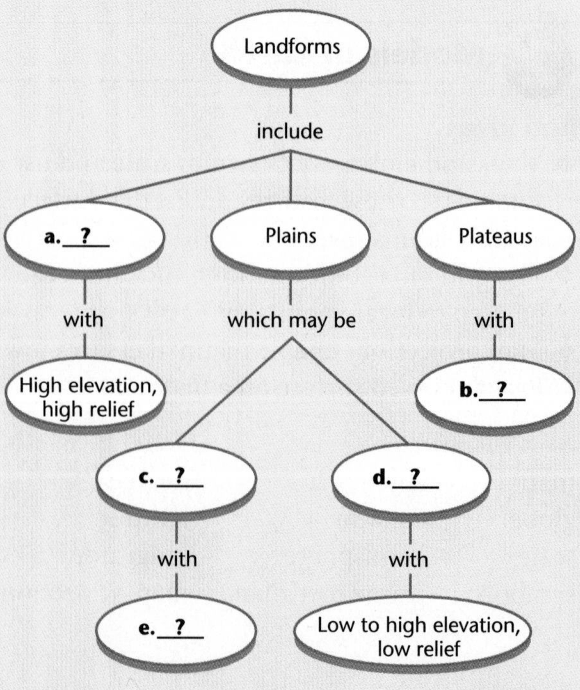

Landforms
include
a. ?
Plains
Plateaus
with
which may be
with
High elevation, high relief
b. ?
c. ?
d. ?
with
with
e. ?
Low to high elevation, low relief

Test Prep: Skills

This map shows part of Acadia National Park in Maine. The contour interval is 20 feet. Use the map to answer Questions 19–21.

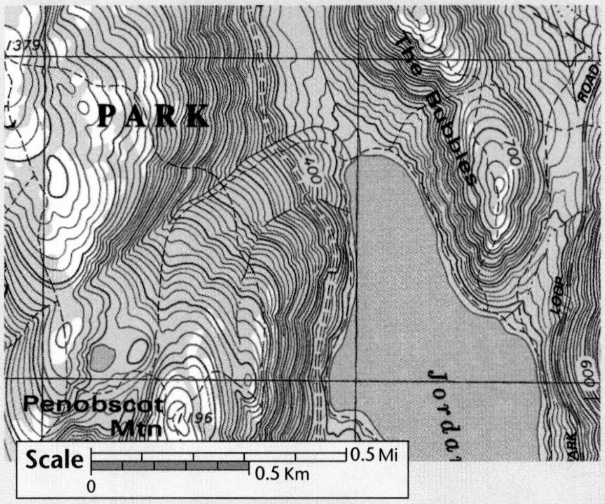
PARK
The Bubbles
ROAD
700
400
Penobscot Mtn
Jorda
Scale
0
0.5 Mi
0.5 Km

19. **Interpreting Maps**
    A. What is the elevation of the large lake?
    B. Which of the two Bubbles is higher?
20. **Calculating** Use the map scale to calculate the distance from the top of Penobscot Mountain to the large lake.
21. **Inferring** How can you tell whether the streams flow into or out of the large lake?

Thinking Critically

22. **Applying Concepts** Earth's diameter is about 13,000 kilometers. If a globe has a diameter of 0.5 meter, write the globe's scale as a ratio. What distance on Earth would 1 centimeter on the globe represent?
23. **Inferring** An airplane flies directly west at 1,000 kilometers per hour. Without changing direction, the plane returns to its starting point in just one hour. What can you infer about the plane's route with regard to lines of latitude and longitude? Explain.
24. **Observing** Using an atlas, determine the latitude and longitude of San Francisco, California; Wichita, Kansas; and Richmond, Virginia. What do these three cities have in common?
25. **Comparing and Contrasting** How is mapmaking with computers different from earlier mapmaking techniques?
26. **Problem Solving** Your community has decided to build a zoo for animals from many regions of Earth. How could you use topographic maps of your area to help decide on the best location for the zoo?

Performance Assessment

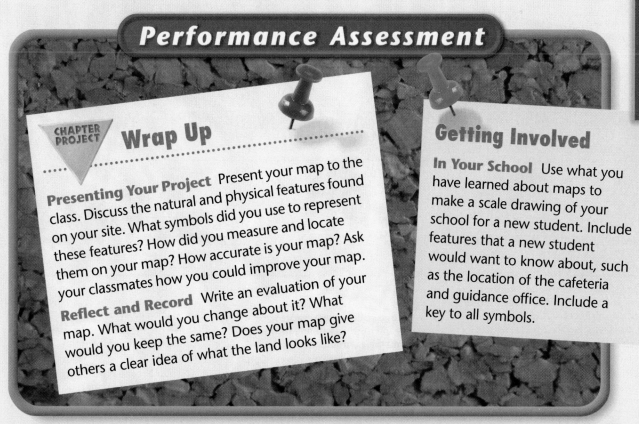

CHAPTER PROJECT Wrap Up

Presenting Your Project Present your map to the class. Discuss the natural and physical features found on your site. What symbols did you use to represent these features? How did you measure and locate them on your map? How accurate is your map? Ask your classmates how you could improve your map.

Reflect and Record Write an evaluation of your map. What would you change about it? What would you keep the same? Does your map give others a clear idea of what the land looks like?

Getting Involved

In Your School Use what you have learned about maps to make a scale drawing of your school for a new student. Include features that a new student would want to know about, such as the location of the cafeteria and guidance office. Include a key to all symbols.

CHAPTER 7

Weathering and Soil Formation

These stone gargoyles on the cathedral of Notre Dame in Paris, France, are wearing away because of weathering.

The following California Science Content Standards are addressed in this chapter:

2. Topography is reshaped by weathering of rock and soil and by the transportation and deposition of sediment.

a. Water running downhill is the dominant process in shaping the landscape, including California's landscape.

b. Rivers and streams are dynamic systems that erode and transport sediment, change course, and flood their banks in natural and recurring patterns.

5. Organisms in ecosystems exchange energy and nutrients among themselves and with the environment.

b. Over time, matter is transferred from one organism to others in the food web, and between organisms and the physical environment.

c. Populations of organisms can be categorized by the functions they serve in an ecosystem.

d. Different kinds of organisms may play similar ecological roles in similar biomes.

e. The number and types of organisms an ecosystem can support depends on the resources available and abiotic

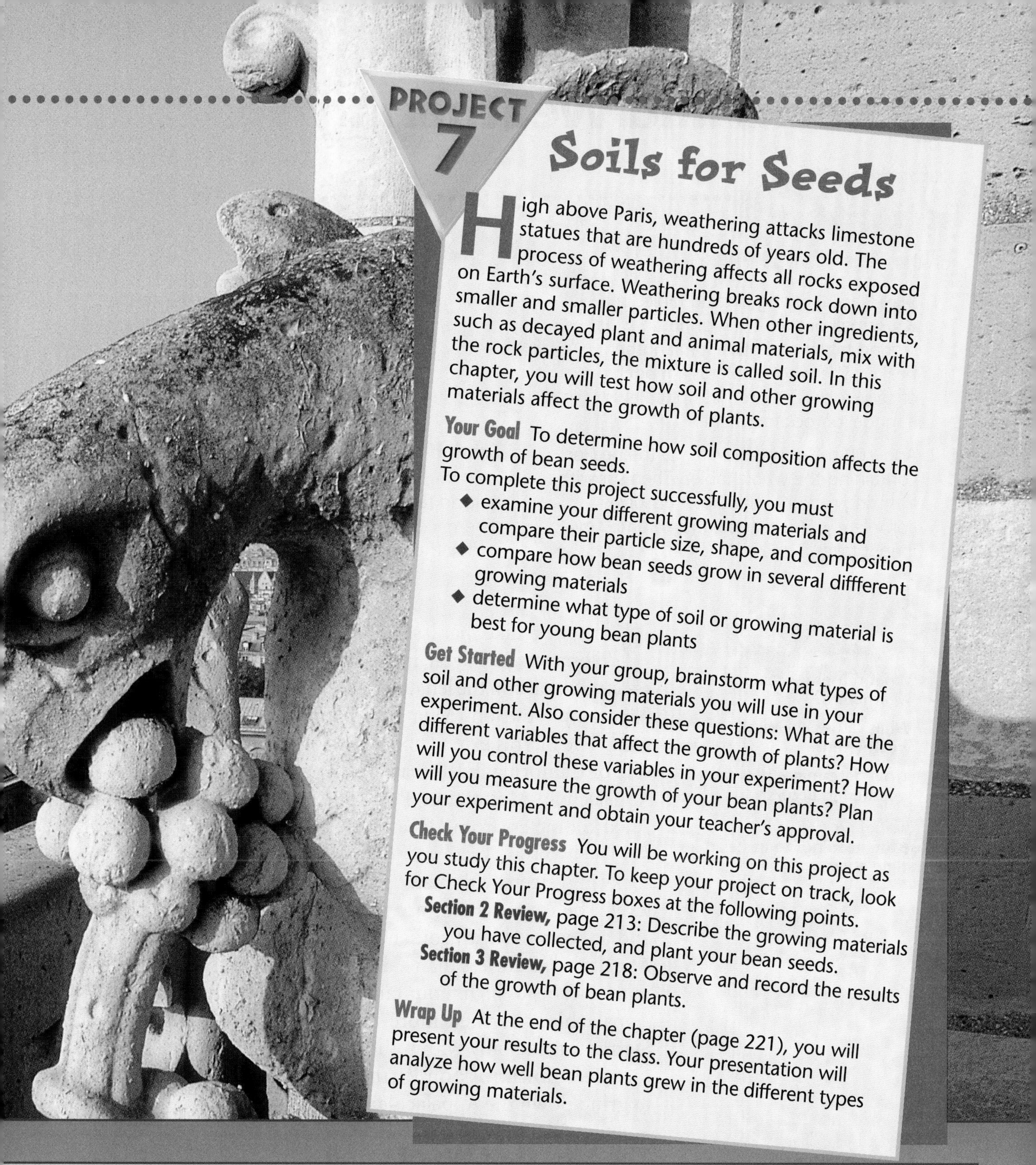

PROJECT 7

Soils for Seeds

High above Paris, weathering attacks limestone statues that are hundreds of years old. The process of weathering affects all rocks exposed on Earth's surface. Weathering breaks rock down into smaller and smaller particles. When other ingredients, such as decayed plant and animal materials, mix with the rock particles, the mixture is called soil. In this chapter, you will test how soil and other growing materials affect the growth of plants.

Your Goal To determine how soil composition affects the growth of bean seeds.

To complete this project successfully, you must

- examine your different growing materials and compare their particle size, shape, and composition
- compare how bean seeds grow in several diffferent growing materials
- determine what type of soil or growing material is best for young bean plants

Get Started With your group, brainstorm what types of soil and other growing materials you will use in your experiment. Also consider these questions: What are the different variables that affect the growth of plants? How will you control these variables in your experiment? How will you measure the growth of your bean plants? Plan your experiment and obtain your teacher's approval.

Check Your Progress You will be working on this project as you study this chapter. To keep your project on track, look for Check Your Progress boxes at the following points.

Section 2 Review, page 213: Describe the growing materials you have collected, and plant your bean seeds.

Section 3 Review, page 218: Observe and record the results of the growth of bean plants.

Wrap Up At the end of the chapter (page 221), you will present your results to the class. Your presentation will analyze how well bean plants grew in the different types of growing materials.

factors, such as quantity of light and water, range of temperatures, and soil composition.

6. **Sources of energy and materials differ in amounts, distribution, usefulness, and the time required for their formation.**
   b. Different natural energy and material resources, including air, soil, rocks, minerals, petroleum, fresh water, wildlife, and forests, and classify them as renewable or nonrenewable.

7. **Scientific progress is made by asking meaningful questions and conducting careful investigations.**
   a. Develop a hypothesis.
   b. Select and use appropriate tools and technology (including calculators, computers, balances, spring scales, microscopes, and binoculars) to perform tests, collect data, and display data.
   f. Read a topographic map and a geologic map for evidence provided on the maps, and construct and interpret a simple scale map.

SECTION 1

Rocks and Weathering

DISCOVER

ACTIVITY

How Fast Can It Fizz?

1. Place a fizzing antacid tablet in a small beaker. Then grind up a second tablet and place it in another beaker. The whole tablet is a model of solid rock. The ground-up tablet is a model of rock fragments.
2. Add 100 mL of warm water to the beaker containing the whole tablet. Then stir with a stirring rod until the tablet dissolves completely. Use a stopwatch to time how long it takes.

3. Add 100 mL of warm water to the beaker containing the ground-up tablet. Then stir until all of the ground-up tablet dissolves. Time how long it takes.

Think It Over

Inferring Which dissolved faster, the whole antacid tablet or the ground-up tablet? What difference between the two affected how long it took them to dissolve?

GUIDE FOR READING

- **What causes mechanical weathering?**
- **What causes chemical weathering?**
- **What determines how fast weathering occurs?**

Reading Tip **As you read, use the headings to make an outline about weathering.**

Imagine a hike that lasts for months and covers hundreds of kilometers. Each year, many hikers go on such treks. They hike trails that run the length of America's great mountain ranges. For example, the John Muir Trail follows the Sierra Nevada mountains. The Sierras extend about 640 kilometers along the eastern side of California. In the east, the Appalachian Trail follows the Appalachian Mountains. The Appalachians stretch more than 2,000 kilometers from Alabama to Maine.

The two trails cross very different landscapes. The Sierras are rocky and steep, with many peaks rising 3,000 meters above sea level. The Appalachians are more rounded and gently sloping, and are covered with soil and plants. The highest peaks in the Appalachians are less than half the elevation of the highest peaks in the Sierras. Which mountain range do you think is older? The Appalachians formed more than 250 million years ago. The Sierras formed only within the last 10 million years. The forces that wear down rock on Earth's surface have had much longer to grind down the Appalachians.

The Effects of Weathering

The process of mountain building thrusts rock up to the Earth's surface. There, the rock becomes exposed to weathering. **Weathering** is the process that breaks down rock and other substances at Earth's surface. Heat, cold, water, and ice all contribute to weathering. So do the oxygen and carbon dioxide in the atmosphere. Repeated freezing

Figure 1 The jagged, rocky peaks of the Sierra Nevadas (left) show that the mountains are young. The more gently sloping Appalachians (right) have been exposed to weathering for 250 million years.

and thawing, for example, can crack rock apart into smaller pieces. Rainwater can dissolve minerals that bind rock together. You don't need to go to the mountains to see examples of weathering. The forces that wear down mountains also cause bicycles to rust, paint to peel, sidewalks to crack, and potholes to form.

The forces of weathering break rocks into smaller and smaller pieces. Then the forces of erosion carry the pieces away. **Erosion** (ee ROH zhun) is the movement of rock particles by wind, water, ice, or gravity. Weathering and erosion work together continuously to wear down and carry away the rocks at Earth's surface.

There are two kinds of weathering: mechanical weathering and chemical weathering. Both types of weathering act slowly, but over time they break down even the biggest, hardest rocks.

☑ *Checkpoint* ***What is the difference between weathering and erosion?***

Mechanical Weathering

If you hit a rock hard enough with a hammer, the rock will break into pieces. Some forces of weathering can also break rock into pieces. The type of weathering in which rock is physically broken into smaller pieces is called **mechanical weathering.** These smaller pieces of rock have the same composition as the rock they came from. If you have seen rocks that are cracked or peeling in layers, then you have seen rocks that are undergoing mechanical weathering.

Mechanical weathering breaks rock into pieces by freezing and thawing, release of pressure, growth of plants, actions of animals, and abrasion. The term **abrasion** (uh BRAY zhun) refers to the grinding away of rock by rock particles carried by water, ice, wind, or gravity. Mechanical weathering works slowly. But over very long periods of time, it does more than wear down rocks. Mechanical weathering eventually wears away whole mountains.

INTEGRATING PHYSICS In cool climates, the most important force of mechanical weathering is freezing and thawing of water. Water seeps into cracks in rocks and then freezes when the temperature drops. Water expands when it freezes. Ice therefore acts like a wedge, a simple machine that forces things apart. Wedges of ice in rocks widen and deepen cracks. This process is called **ice wedging.** When the ice melts, the water seeps deeper into the cracks. With repeated freezing and thawing, the cracks slowly expand until pieces of rock break off. *Exploring the Forces of Mechanical Weathering* shows how this process weathers rock.

✓ *Checkpoint* ***How does ice wedging weather rock?***

EXPLORING *the Forces of Mechanical Weathering*

Mechanical weathering affects all the rock on Earth's surface. Given enough time, mechanical weathering can break down a massive mountain into tiny particles of sand.

Release of Pressure
As erosion removes material from the surface of a mass of rock, pressure on the rock below is reduced. This release of pressure causes the outside of the rock to crack and flake off like the layers of an onion.

Freezing and Thawing
When water freezes in a crack in a rock, it expands and makes the crack bigger. The process of ice wedging also widens cracks in sidewalks and causes potholes in streets.

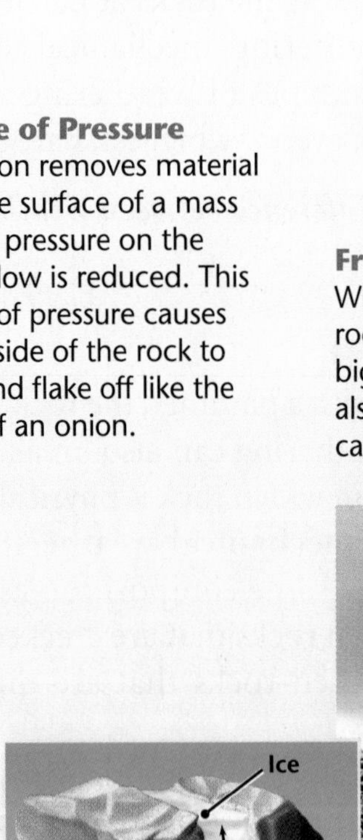
Ice

Chemical Weathering

In addition to mechanical weathering, another type of weathering attacks rock. **Chemical weathering** is the process that breaks down rock through chemical changes. **The agents of chemical weathering include water, oxygen, carbon dioxide, living organisms, and acid rain.**

Chemical weathering produces rock particles that have a different mineral makeup from the rock they came from. Each rock is made up of one or more minerals. For example, granite is made up of several minerals, including feldspar, quartz, and mica. But chemical weathering of granite eventually changes the feldspar minerals to clay minerals.

Plant Growth
Roots of trees and other plants enter cracks in rocks. As the roots grow, they force the cracks farther apart. Over time, the roots of even small plants can pry apart cracked rocks.

Abrasion
Sand and other rock particles that are carried by wind, water, or ice can wear away exposed rock surfaces like sandpaper on wood. Wind-driven sand helped shape the rocks shown here.

Animal Actions
Animals that burrow in the ground—including moles, gophers, prairie dogs, and some insects—loosen and break apart rocks in the soil.

Figure 2 As weathering breaks apart rock, the surface area exposed to further weathering increases.

Chemical weathering creates holes or soft spots in rock, so the rock breaks apart more easily. Chemical and mechanical weathering often work together. As mechanical weathering breaks rock into pieces, more surface area becomes exposed to chemical weathering. The Discover activity in this section shows how increasing the surface area increases the rate of a chemical reaction.

Water Water is the most important agent of chemical weathering. Water weathers rock by dissolving it. When a rock or other substance dissolves in water, it mixes uniformly throughout the water to make a solution. Over time, many rocks will dissolve in water.

Oxygen The oxygen gas in air is an important cause of chemical weathering. If you have ever left a bicycle or metal tool outside in the rain, then you have seen how oxygen can weather iron. Iron combines with oxygen in the presence of water in a process called oxidation. The product of oxidation is rust. Rock that contains iron also oxidizes, or rusts. Rust makes rock soft and crumbly and gives it a red or brown color.

Carbon Dioxide Another gas found in air, carbon dioxide, also causes chemical weathering. Carbon dioxide becomes dissolved in rainwater and in water that sinks through air pockets in the soil. The result is a weak acid called carbonic acid. Carbonic acid easily weathers marble and limestone.

Living Organisms Imagine a seed landing on a rock face. As it sprouts, its roots push into cracks in the rock. As the plant's roots grow, they produce weak acids that slowly dissolve rock around the roots. Lichens—plantlike organisms that grow on rocks—also produce weak acids that chemically weather rock.

Acid Rain Over the past 150 years, people have been burning large amounts of coal, oil, and gas for energy. Burning these fuels can pollute the air with sulfur, carbon, and nitrogen compounds. Such compounds react chemically with the water vapor in clouds, forming acids. These acids mix with raindrops and fall as acid rain. Acid rain causes very rapid chemical weathering.

INTEGRATING ENVIRONMENTAL SCIENCE

TRY THIS

Rusting Away

ACTIVITY

Here's how you can observe weathering.

1. Moisten some steel wool and place it in a closed container so it will not dry out.
2. Observe the steel wool after a few days. What has happened to the steel wool?
3. Take a new piece of steel wool and squeeze it between your fingers. Remove the steel wool from the container and squeeze it between your fingers. What happens? Wash your hands when you have finished.

Predicting If you kept the steel wool moist for a longer time, what would eventually happen to it? How is the weathering of steel wool like the weathering of a rock?

Rate of Weathering

Visitors to New England's historic cemeteries may notice a surprising fact. Slate tombstones from the 1700s are less weathered and easier to read than marble gravestones from the 1800s. Why is this so? **The most important factors that determine the rate at which weathering occurs are type of rock and climate.**

Type of Rock Some kinds of rocks weather more rapidly than others. The minerals that make up the rock determine how fast it weathers. Rock made of minerals that do not dissolve easily in water weathers slowly. Rock made of minerals that dissolve easily in water weathers faster.

Some rock weathers easily because it is permeable. **Permeable** (PUR mee uh bul) means that a material is full of tiny, connected air spaces that allow water to seep through it. Permeable rock weathers chemically at a fast rate. Why? As water seeps through the spaces in the rock, it removes dissolved material formed by weathering.

Climate Climate refers to the average weather conditions in an area. Both chemical and mechanical weathering occur faster in wet climates. Rainfall provides the water needed for chemical changes as well as for freezing and thawing.

Chemical reactions occur faster at higher temperatures. That is why chemical weathering occurs more quickly where the climate is both hot and wet. Granite, for example, is a very hard rock that forms when molten material cools inside Earth. Granite weathers so slowly in cool climates that it is often used as a building stone. But in hot and wet climates, granite weathers faster and eventually crumbles apart.

Figure 3 The rate of weathering of these tombstones depends on the type of rock. Slate (top) resists weathering better than marble (bottom). ***Inferring*** *What type of weathering probably wore away the letters on the marble tombstone?*

Section 1 Review

1. What factors cause mechanical weathering?
2. Describe three causes of chemical weathering.
3. What factors affect the rate of weathering?
4. Explain why chemical weathering occurs faster in hot, wet climates than in cool, dry climates.
5. **Thinking Critically Predicting** Suppose you see a large boulder with several cracks in it. What would you expect to see if you could observe the boulder again in several hundred years? Explain.

Science at Home

Here's how to demonstrate one type of weathering for your family. Plug one end of a drinking straw with a small piece of clay. Fill the straw with water. Now plug the top of the straw with clay. Make sure that the clay plugs do not leak. Lay the straw flat in the freezer overnight. Remove the straw the next day. What happened to the clay plugs? What process produced this result? Be sure to dispose of the straw so that no one will use it for drinking.

Skills Lab

Controlling Variables

Rock Shake

Which do you think would weather faster, a rock attacked by plant acids or a rock in the rushing waters of a stream? Many factors affect the rate at which rock weathers. In this lab, you will compare the rates of weathering that take place under different conditions.

Problem

How will shaking and acid conditions affect the rate at which limestone weathers?

Materials

300 mL of water
balance
paper towels
masking tape
2 pieces of thin cloth
marking pen or pencil
300 mL of vinegar, an acid
plastic graduated cylinder, 250 mL
80 small pieces of water-soaked limestone
4 watertight plastic containers with screw-on caps, 500-mL

Procedure

Part 1— Day 1

1. Using masking tape, label the four 500-mL containers A, B, C, and D.
2. Separate the 80 pieces of limestone into four sets of 20.
3. Copy the data table in your notebook. Then place the first 20 pieces of limestone on the balance and record their mass in the data table. Place the rocks in Container A.
4. Repeat Step 3 for the other sets of rocks and place them in containers B, C, and D.
5. Pour 150 mL of water into container A and container B. Put caps on both containers.
6. Pour 150 mL of vinegar into container C and also into container D. Put caps on both containers.
7. Predict the effect of weathering on the mass of the limestone pieces. Which will weather more: the limestone in water or the limestone in vinegar? (*Hint:* Vinegar is an acid.) Also predict the effect of shaking on the limestone in containers B and D. Record your predictions in your notebook.
8. Allow the pieces to soak overnight.

Container	Total Mass Start	Total Mass Next Day	Change in Mass	Percent Change in Mass
A (water, no shaking)				
B (water, shaking)				
C (vinegar, no shaking)				
D (vinegar, shaking)				

Part 2—Day 2

9. Screw the caps tightly on containers B and D. Shake both containers for 10 to 15 minutes. Make sure that each container is shaken for exactly the same amount of time and at the same intensity. After shaking, set the containers aside. Do not shake containers A and C.
10. Open the top of container A. Place one piece of thin cloth over the opening of the container. Carefully pour all of the water out through the cloth into a waste container. Be careful not to let any of the pieces flow out with the water. Dry these pieces carefully and record their mass in your data table.
11. Next, determine how much limestone was lost through weathering in container A. (*Hint:* Subtract the mass of the limestone pieces remaining on Day 2 from the mass of the pieces on Day 1.)
12. Repeat Steps 10 and 11 for containers B, C, and D.

Analyze and Conclude

1. Calculate the percent change in mass of the 20 pieces for each container.

$$\% \text{ change} = \frac{\text{Change in mass} \times 100}{\text{Total mass start}}$$

   Record the results in the data table.
2. Do your data show a change in mass of the 20 pieces in each of the four containers?
3. Is there a greater change in total mass for the pieces in one container than for the pieces in another? Explain.
4. How correct were your predictions of how shaking and acid would affect the weathering of limestone? Explain.
5. If your data showed a greater change in the mass of the pieces in one of the containers, how might this change be explained?
6. **Think About It** Based on your data, which variable do you think was more responsible for breaking down the limestone: the vinegar or the shaking? Explain.

Design an Experiment

Would your results for this experiment change if you changed the variables? For example, you could soak or shake the pieces for a longer time, or test rocks other than limestone. You could also test whether adding more limestone pieces (30 rather than 20 in each set) would make a difference in the outcome. Design an experiment on the rate of weathering to test the effects of changing one of these variables. Have your teacher approve your plan before you begin.

D
C
B
A

SCIENCE AND SOCIETY

Preserving Stone Monuments

A statue with a human head and a lion's body crouches in the desert beside the pyramids of Egypt. This is the great Sphinx. It was carved out of limestone about 4,500 years ago. Thousands of years of weathering by water, wind, and sand have worn away much of the Sphinx's face. In the 1800s, sand that had protected the Sphinx's body was cleared away. Weathering attacked the newly exposed parts of the Sphinx. Flakes and even chunks of stone fell from the statue. Workers tried to repair the Sphinx with cement. But the repairs weakened the statue and changed its shape.

The Issues

Should Structures Be Restored?

Weathering threatens many ancient stone monuments throughout the world. Pollutants in air and rain make stone weather faster. But there are ways to slow the weathering of a monument without changing or damaging it. In 1998, workers in Egypt completed a new restoration of the Sphinx. They removed the added cement. They replaced the damaged stones with new, hand-cut limestone blocks of the same size and weight. The new stone will help protect what remains of the monument. Visitors to the Sphinx will now see only the original statue and repairs made with original materials. The new repairs preserve the statue's original shape.

Most people want the Sphinx and other monuments to be restored. But restoration is time-consuming and very expensive. And in some cases, repair work can damage or change the original structure.

Can New Technology Slow Weathering?

Advances in technology may provide some solutions. At the Sphinx, scientists measure wind direction, wind speed, and moisture in the air. This information helps scientists follow the weathering process and provides data that will help prevent more damage. Similar instruments are used at other monuments.

Other scientists are working on a way of coating stone with a chemical compound to strengthen and repair the surface. So far, they have found a compound that sticks well to sandstone, but not to marble or limestone.

What Else Can People Do? Repair and restoration are not the only options. Some say that ancient monuments should be buried again after being uncovered by archaeologists. Some people suggest that the Sphinx itself should be reburied in the sand that protected it for so many centuries. But scholars, archaeologists, and tourists disagree. Meanwhile, as people seek solutions, rain, wind, sun, and polluted air continue to take their toll.

You Decide

1. Identify the Problem

In your own words, explain the difficulties involved in preserving ancient monuments.

2. Analyze the Options

List methods for preserving ancient buildings and monuments. Note the advantages and disadvantages of repair work, technology, and other approaches.

3. Find a Solution

Make a plan to preserve a monument in your city. Write your recommendations in the form of a letter to a city mayor or town council.

Section 2 Soil Formation and Composition

Discover Activity

What Is Soil?

1. Use a toothpick to separate a sample of soil into individual particles. With a hand lens, try to identify the different types of particles in the sample. Wash your hands when you are finished.
2. Write a "recipe" for the sample of soil, naming each of the "ingredients" that you think the soil contains. Include what percentage of each ingredient would be needed to make up the soil.
3. Compare your recipe with those of your classmates.

Think It Over

Forming Operational Definitions Based on your observations, how would you define *soil*?

GUIDE FOR READING

- **How does soil form?**
- **What is soil made of?**
- **What is the role of plants and animals in soil formation?**

Reading Tip **Before you read, rewrite the headings as *how, what, where,* and *why* questions. Then look for answers as you read.**

A bare rock surface does not look like a spot where a plant could grow. But look more closely. In that hard surface is a small crack. Over many years, mechanical and chemical weathering will slowly enlarge the crack. Rain and wind will bring bits of weathered rock, dust, and dry leaves. The wind also may carry tiny seeds. With enough moisture, a seed will sprout and take root. Then, when the plant blossoms a few months later, the rock itself will seem to have burst into flower.

Soil Formation

The crack in the rock seems to have little in common with a flower garden containing thick, rich soil. But soil is what the weathered rock and other materials in the crack have started to become. **Soil** is the loose, weathered material on Earth's surface in which plants can grow. **Soil forms as rock is broken down by weathering and mixes with other materials on the surface.**

Soil is constantly being formed wherever bedrock is exposed. **Bedrock** is the solid layer of rock beneath the soil. Once exposed at the surface, bedrock gradually weathers into smaller and smaller particles that are the basic material of soil.

Figure 4 A crack between rocks holds just enough soil for this plant.

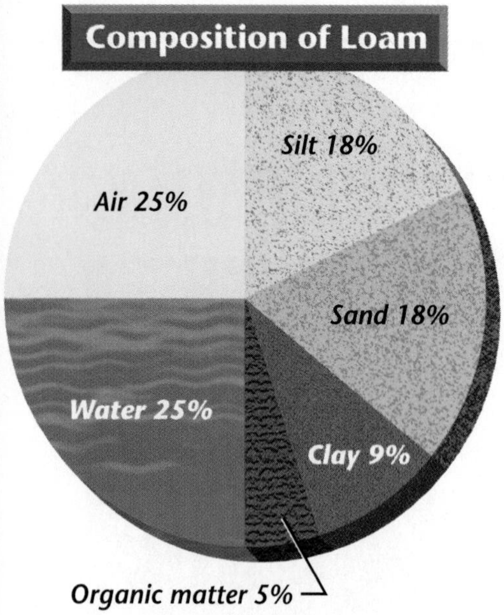

Composition of Loam
Silt 18%
Air 25%
Sand 18%
Water 25%
Clay 9%
Organic matter 5%

Figure 5 Loam, a type of soil, is made up of air, water, and organic matter as well as materials from weathered rock.
Interpreting Graphs What two materials make up the major portion of this soil?

Soil Composition

Soil is more than just particles of weathered bedrock. **Soil is a mixture of rock particles, minerals, decayed organic material, air, and water.**

The type of rock particles and minerals in any given soil depends on two factors: the bedrock that was weathered to form the soil and the type of weathering. Together, sand, silt, and clay make up the portion of soil that comes from weathered rock.

The decayed organic material in soil is humus. **Humus** (HYOO mus) is a dark-colored substance that forms as plant and animal remains decay. Humus helps create spaces in soil for the air and water that plants must have. Humus is also rich in the nitrogen, sulfur, phosphorus, and potassium that plants need to grow.

Soil Texture

Sand feels coarse and grainy, but clay feels smooth and silky. These differences are differences in texture. Soil texture depends on the size of individual soil particles.

The particles of rock in soil are classified by size. As you can see in Figure 6, the largest soil particles are gravel. Small pebbles and even large boulders are considered gravel. Next in size are particles of sand, followed by silt particles, which are smaller than sand. The smallest soil particles are clay. Clay particles are smaller than the period at the end of this sentence.

Soil texture is important for plant growth. Soil that is mostly clay has a dense, heavy texture. Some clay soils hold a lot of water, so plants grown in them may "drown" for lack of air. In contrast, sandy soil has a coarse texture. Water quickly drains through it, so plants may die for lack of water.

Soil that is made up of about equal parts of clay, sand, and silt is called **loam.** It has a crumbly texture that holds both air and water. Loam is best for growing most types of plants.

Gravel
2 mm and larger
Sand
less than 2 mm
Silt
less than 1/16 mm
Clay
less than 1/256 mm

Figure 6 Soil particles range in size from gravel to clay particles too small to be seen by the unaided eye. The sand, silt, and clay shown here have been enlarged.

Soil Horizons

Soil formation continues over a long period of time. Gradually, soil develops layers called horizons. A **soil horizon** is a layer of soil that differs in color and texture from the layers above or below it.

If you dug a hole in the ground about half a meter deep, you would see the different soil horizons. Figure 7 shows how soil scientists classify the soil into three horizons. The A horizon is made up of **topsoil,** a crumbly, dark brown soil that is a mixture of humus, clay, and other minerals. The B horizon, often called **subsoil,** usually consists of clay and other particles washed down from the A horizon, but little humus. The C horizon contains only partly weathered rock.

☑ *Checkpoint* *What are soil horizons?*

The Rate of Soil Formation

The rate at which soil forms depends on the climate and type of rock. Remember that weathering occurs most rapidly in areas with a warm, rainy climate. As a result, soil develops more quickly in these areas. In contrast, weathering and soil formation take place slowly in areas where the climate is cold and dry.

Some types of rock weather and form soil faster than others. For example, limestone weathers faster than granite. Thus, soil forms more quickly from limestone than from granite.

Sharpen your Skills

Predicting ACTIVITY

Gardeners often improve soil by adding materials to it. These added materials change the soil's composition. They make the soil more fertile or improve its ability to hold water. For example, a gardener might add compost (partly decayed leaves) to sandy soil. How would the compost change the sandy soil?

Figure 7 Soil horizons form in three steps.

1. The C horizon forms as bedrock weathers and rock breaks up into soil particles.

2. The A horizon develops from the C horizon when plant roots weather the rock mechanically and chemically. Plants also add organic material to the soil.

3. The B horizon develops as rainwater washes clay and minerals from the A horizon to the B horizon.

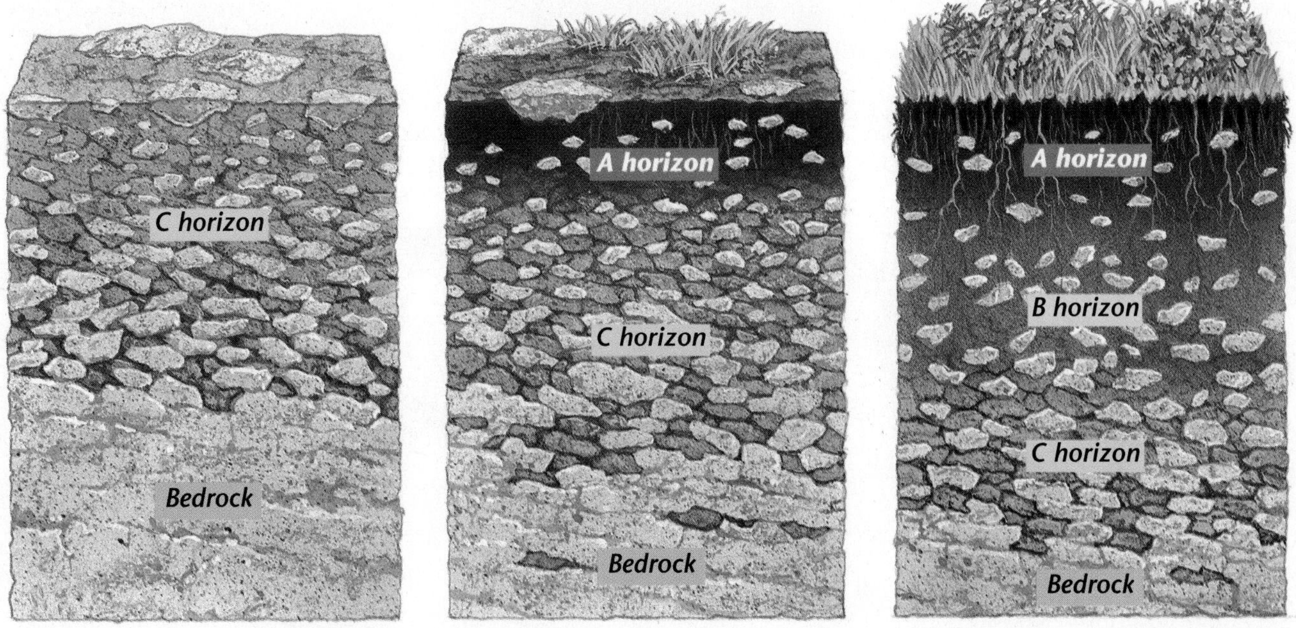
C horizon
Bedrock
A horizon
C horizon
Bedrock
A horizon
B horizon
C horizon
Bedrock

Life in Soil

INTEGRATING LIFE SCIENCE Soil is more than just bits of rock. If you look closely at some soil, you can see that it is teeming with living things. **Some soil organisms mix the soil and make spaces in it for air and water. Other soil organisms make humus, the material that makes soil fertile.** Fertile soil is rich in nutrients that plants need, such as nitrogen and phosphorus.

Plants contribute most of the organic remains that form humus. As plants shed leaves, they form a loose layer called **litter.**

EXPLORING *Living Organisms in Soil*

In every cubic meter of soil live billions of organisms. All organisms that live in soil enrich humus with their remains or wastes. Animals and plant roots break up the soil, opening spaces for air and water.

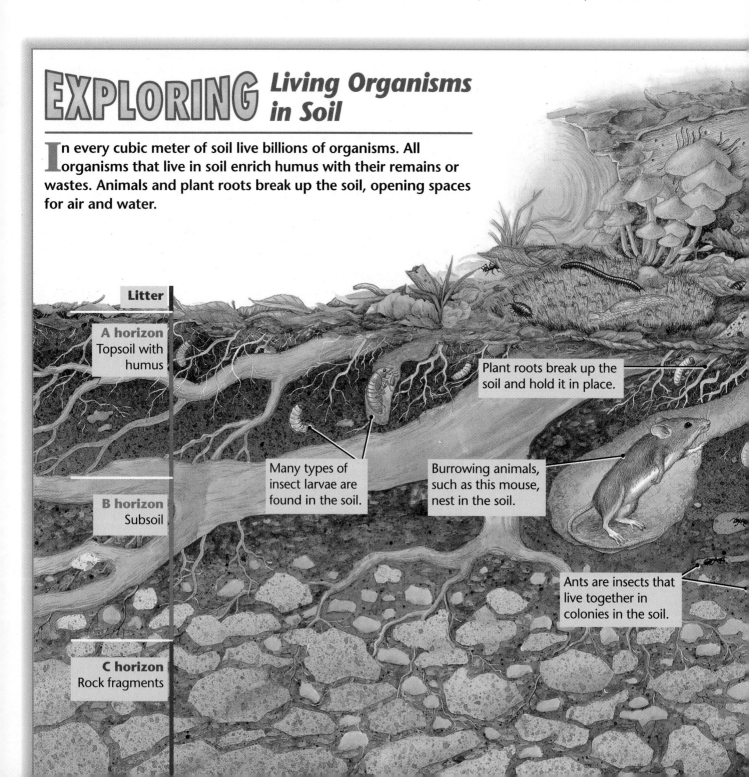

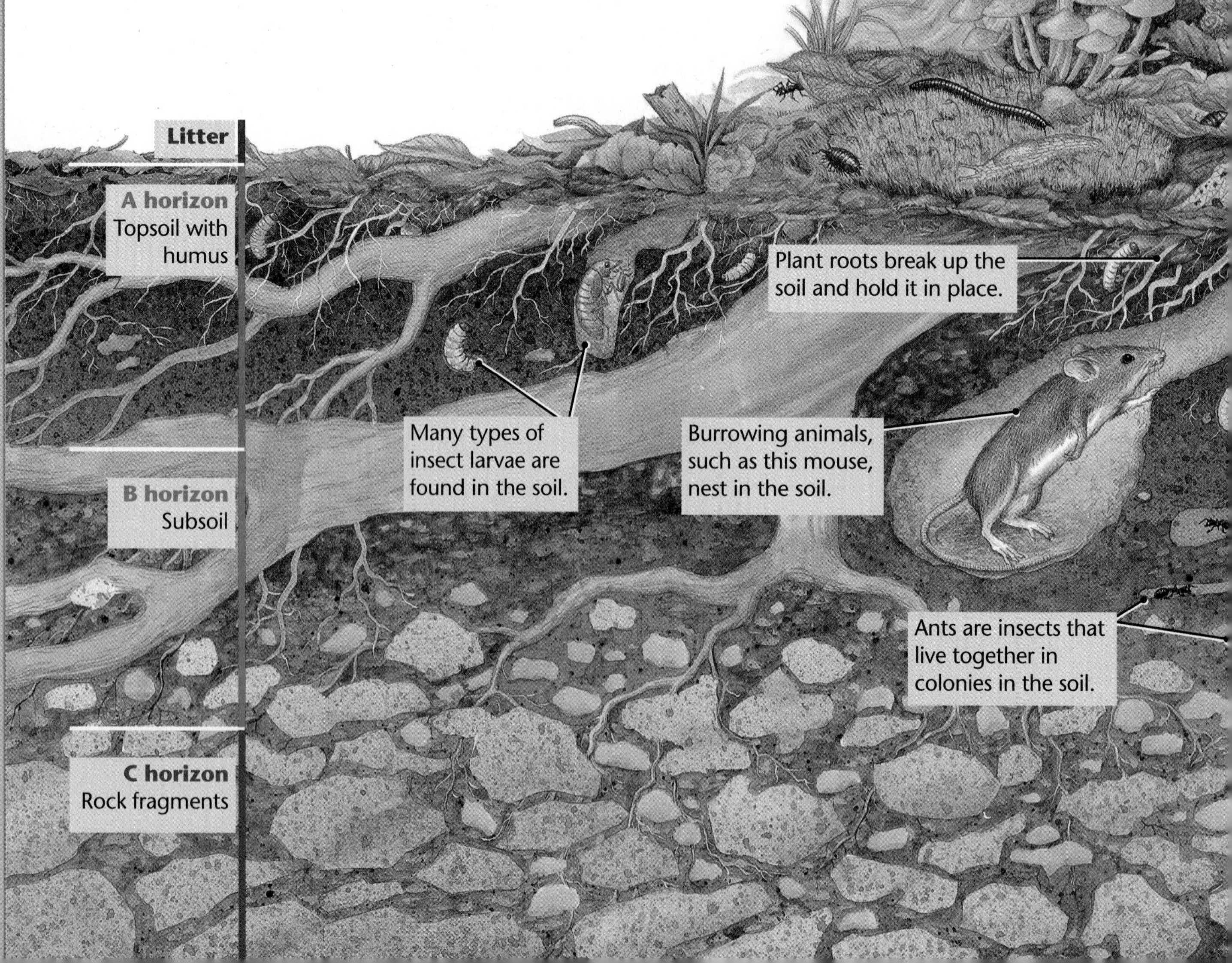
Litter
A horizon
Topsoil with humus
B horizon
Subsoil
C horizon
Rock fragments
Plant roots break up the soil and hold it in place.
Many types of insect larvae are found in the soil.
Burrowing animals, such as this mouse, nest in the soil.
Ants are insects that live together in colonies in the soil.

When plants die, their remains fall to the ground and become part of the litter. Plant roots also die and begin to decay underground. Although plant remains are full of stored nutrients, they are not yet humus.

Humus forms in a process called decomposition. As decomposition occurs, organisms that live in soil turn dead organic material into humus. These organisms are called decomposers. **Decomposers** are the organisms that break the remains of dead organisms into smaller pieces and digest them with chemicals.

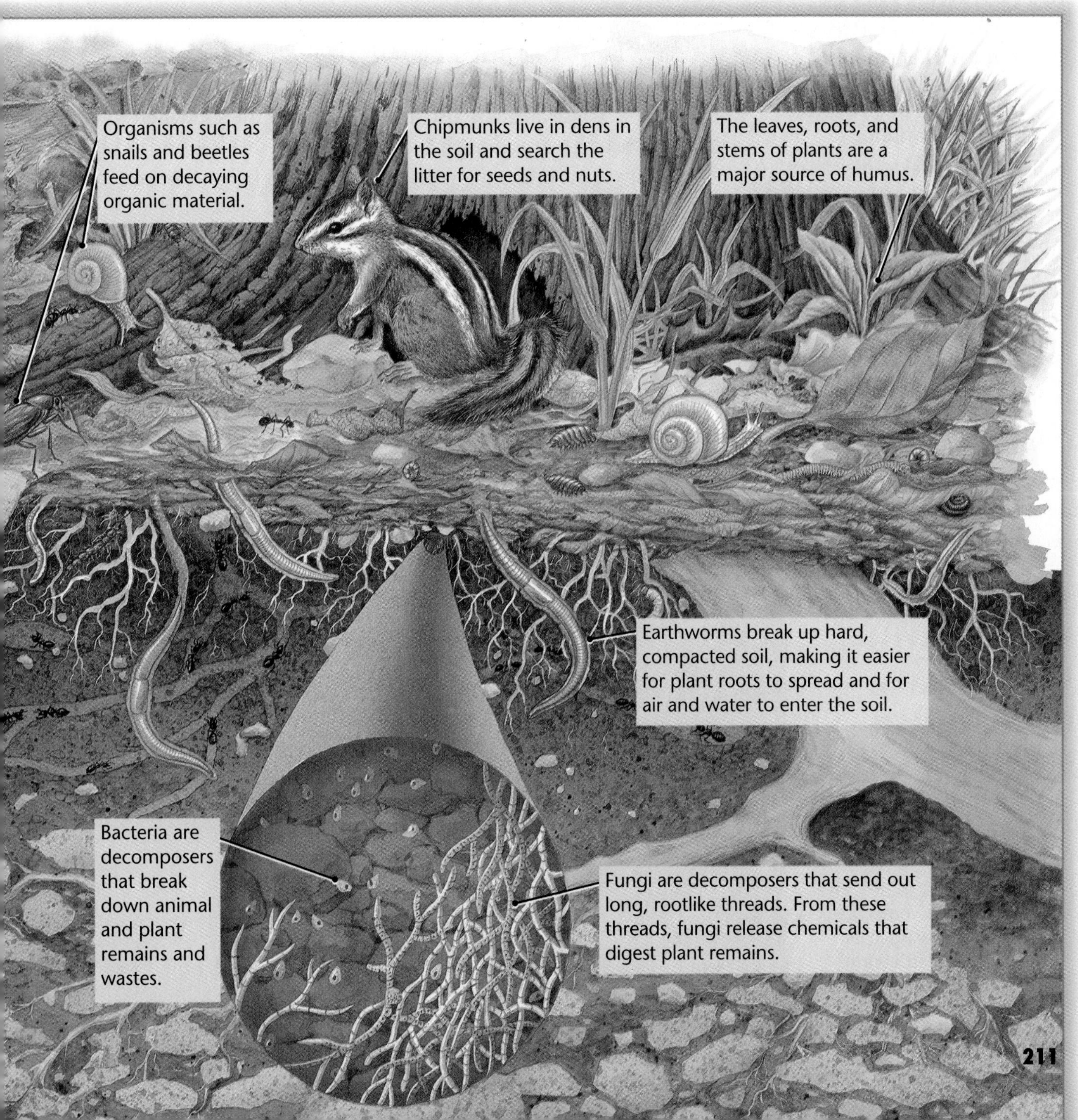
Organisms such as snails and beetles feed on decaying organic material.
Chipmunks live in dens in the soil and search the litter for seeds and nuts.
The leaves, roots, and stems of plants are a major source of humus.
Earthworms break up hard, compacted soil, making it easier for plant roots to spread and for air and water to enter the soil.
Bacteria are decomposers that break down animal and plant remains and wastes.
Fungi are decomposers that send out long, rootlike threads. From these threads, fungi release chemicals that digest plant remains.

TRY THIS

A Square Meter of Soil

ACTIVITY

1. Outdoors, measure an area of one square meter. Mark your square with string.
2. Observe the color and texture of the surface soil. Is it dry or moist? Does it contain sand, clay, or gravel? Are there plants, animals, or humus?
3. Use a trowel to dig down several centimeters into the soil. What is the soil's color and texture there?
4. When you finish, leave the soil as you found it. Wash your hands.

Drawing Conclusions What can you conclude about the soil's fertility? What evidence supports your conclusions?

Fungi, protists, bacteria, and worms are the main soil decomposers. Fungi are organisms such as molds and mushrooms. Fungi grow on, and digest, plant remains. Bacteria are microscopic decomposers that cause decay. Bacteria attack dead organisms and their wastes in soil. Other very small animals, such as mites and worms, also decompose dead organic material and mix it with the soil.

Earthworms do most of the work of mixing humus with other materials in soil. As earthworms eat their way through the soil, they carry humus down to the subsoil and subsoil up to the surface. Earthworms also pass out the soil they eat as waste. The waste soil is enriched with substances that plants need to grow, such as nitrogen.

Many burrowing mammals such as mice, moles, prairie dogs, and gophers break up hard, compacted soil and mix humus through it. These animals also add nitrogen to the soil when they excrete waste. They add organic material when they die and decay.

Earthworms and burrowing animals also help to aerate, or mix air into, the soil. Plant roots need the oxygen that this process adds to the soil.

Checkpoint ***How do decomposers contribute to the formation of soil?***

Soil Types in the United States

If you were traveling across the hills of north-central Georgia, you would see soils that seem to be made of red clay. In other parts of the country, soils can be black, brown, yellow, or gray. In the United States alone, differences in climate and local bedrock have led to the formation of thousands of different types of soil.

Figure 8 Earthworms break up the soil, allowing in air and water. An earthworm eats its own weight in soil every day.

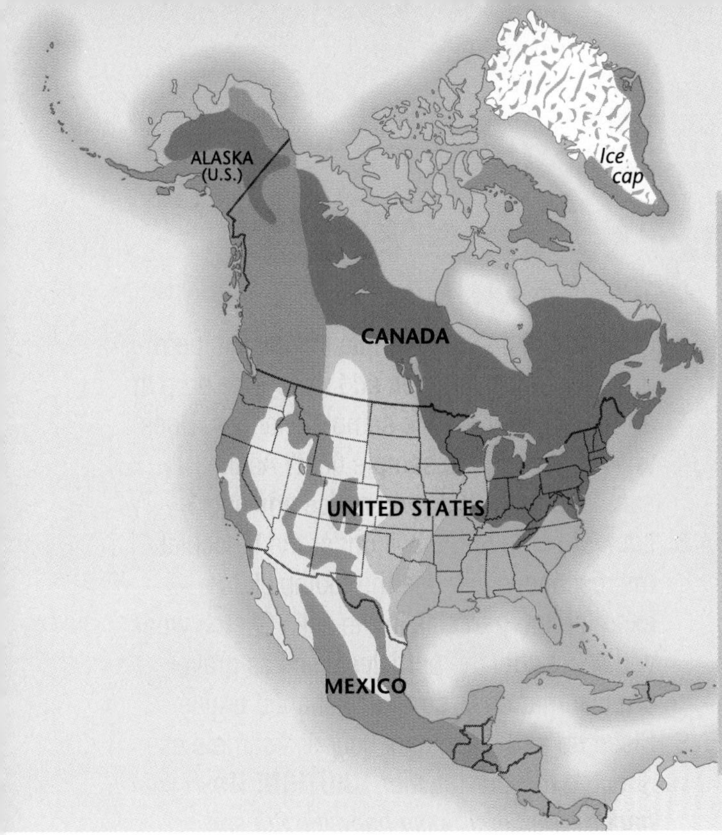
ALASKA (U.S.)
Ice cap
CANADA
UNITED STATES
MEXICO

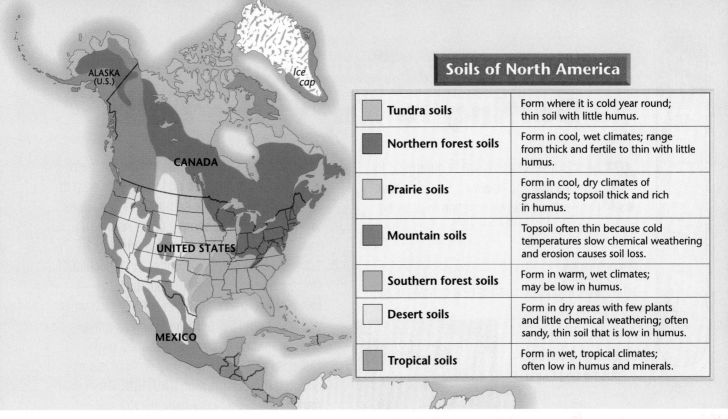

Soils of North America

Tundra soils	Form where it is cold year round; thin soil with little humus.
Northern forest soils	Form in cool, wet climates; range from thick and fertile to thin with little humus.
Prairie soils	Form in cool, dry climates of grasslands; topsoil thick and rich in humus.
Mountain soils	Topsoil often thin because cold temperatures slow chemical weathering and erosion causes soil loss.
Southern forest soils	Form in warm, wet climates; may be low in humus.
Desert soils	Form in dry areas with few plants and little chemical weathering; often sandy, thin soil that is low in humus.
Tropical soils	Form in wet, tropical climates; often low in humus and minerals.

Figure 9 An area's climate and plant life help to determine what type of soil forms from bedrock. ***Interpreting Maps*** *Recall that soil forms more rapidly in warm, wet areas than in cold, dry areas. Which types of soil on the map would you expect to form most slowly?*

Scientists classify the different types of soil into groups. These groups are based partly on the climate in a region. The most common plants found in a region are also used to help classify the soil. In addition, scientists classify soil by its composition—whether it is rocky, sandy, or rich in clay. Major soil types found in North America include forest, prairie, desert, mountain, tundra, and tropical soils. Look at Figure 9 to see where each of the major soil types is found. Which soil type is found in your part of the country?

Section 2 Review

1. What role does weathering play in the formation of soil?
2. What are the different materials that make up soil?
3. How do plants and animals affect the formation and composition of soil?
4. How do forest soils differ from prairie soils?
5. **Thinking Critically Relating Cause and Effect** Earthworms breathe by absorbing air in the soil through their skin. Why do you think earthworms crawl to the surface when it rains? Explain.

CHAPTER PROJECT

Check Your Progress

Obtain samples of the soil and growing materials you will use to grow your bean seeds. Choices include sand, vermiculite, gravel, potting soil, and local topsoil. **CAUTION:** *Avoid collecting soil near animal droppings. Wash your hands after handling the soil.* Make notes describing each sample. Predict which soil or mixture will be best for the growth of bean seeds. Design a method for recording the growth of your bean plants. Plant the bean seeds in the growing materials.

Careers in Science

Getting to Know the Soil

Soil scientists observe soil to determine its composition and how well it holds water. Farmers use this information in growing their crops.

Problem

What are the characteristics of a sample of soil?

Skills Focus

observing, inferring, posing questions

Materials

20–30 grams of soil
plastic spoon
plastic dropper
toothpick
water
binocular microscope
graph paper ruled with 1- or 2-mm spacing
plastic petri dish or jar lid

Procedure

1. Your teacher will give you a dry sample of soil. As you observe the sample, record your observations in your lab notebook.
2. Spread half of the sample on the graph paper. Spread the soil thinly so that you can see the lines on the paper through the soil. Using the graph paper as a background, estimate the sizes of the particles that make up the soil.
3. Place the rest of the sample in the palm of your hand, rub it between your fingers, and squeeze it. Is it soft or gritty? Does it clump together or crumble when you squeeze it?
4. Place about half the sample in a plastic petri dish. Using the dropper, add water one drop at a time. Watch how the sample changes. Does any material in the sample float? As the sample gets wet, do you notice any odor?
5. Look at some of the soil under the binocular microscope. (*Hint:* Use the toothpick to examine the particles in the soil.) Sketch what you see. Label the particles, such as gravel, organic matter, or strangely shaped grains.
6. Clean up and dispose of your soil sample as directed by your teacher. **CAUTION:** *Wash your hands when you finish handling the soil.*

Analyze and Conclude

1. What did you notice about the appearance of the soil sample when you first obtained it?
2. What can you infer about the composition of the soil from the different sizes of its particles? From your observations of its texture? From how the sample changed when water was added? What surprised you the most about the composition of your sample?
3. Based on the composition of your soil sample, can you determine the type of environment from which it was taken?
4. **Apply** List several questions that a soil scientist would need to answer to determine whether a soil sample was good for growing flowers or vegetables. Did your observations answer these questions for your soil sample?

More to Explore

Repeat the procedure using a soil sample from a different location. How does it compare with the first soil sample you tested?

SECTION 3 Soil Conservation

DISCOVER ACTIVITY

How Can You Keep Soil From Washing Away?

1. Pour about 500 mL of soil into a pie plate, forming a pile.
2. Devise a way to keep the soil from washing away when water is poured over it. To protect the pile of soil, you may use craft sticks, paper clips, pebbles, modeling clay, strips of paper, or other materials approved by your teacher.

3. After arranging your materials to protect the soil, hold a container containing 200 mL of water about 20 cm above the center of the soil. Slowly pour the water in a stream onto the pile of soil.
4. Compare your pan of soil with those of your classmates.

Think It Over

Observing Based on your observations, what do you think is the best way to prevent soil on a slope from washing away?

GUIDE FOR READING

- Why is soil one of Earth's most valuable resources?
- What caused the Dust Bowl?
- What are some ways that soil can be conserved?

Reading Tip As you read, make a list of human activities that can harm the soil and a list of activities that can help save the soil.

Suppose you were a settler traveling west in the early 1800s. Much of your journey would have been through vast, open grasslands called prairies. After the forests and mountains of the East, the prairies were an amazing sight. Grass taller than a person rippled and flowed in the wind like a sea of green.

The prairie soil was very fertile. It was rich with humus because of the tall grass. The **sod**—the thick mass of tough roots at the surface of the soil—kept the soil in place and held onto moisture.

The prairies covered a vast area. They included the eastern parts of Kansas, Nebraska, North and South Dakota, as well as Iowa and Illinois. Today, farms growing crops such as corn, soybeans, and wheat have replaced the prairies. But the prairie soils are still among the most fertile in the world.

The Value of Soil

Soil is one of Earth's most valuable resources because everything that lives on land depends directly or indirectly on soil. Plants depend directly on the soil to live and grow. Animals depend on plants—or on other animals that depend on plants—for food. Soil is a renewable resource that can be found wherever weathering occurs. But soil formation takes a long time. It can take hundreds of years for just a few centimeters of soil to form. The thick, fertile soil of the prairies took many thousands of years to develop.

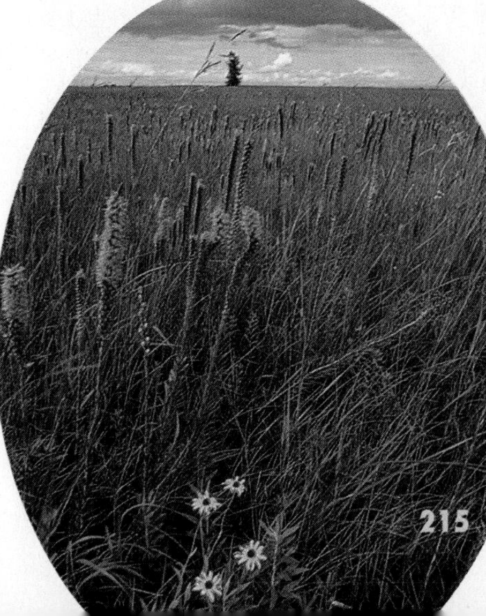

Prairie grasses and wildflowers ▶

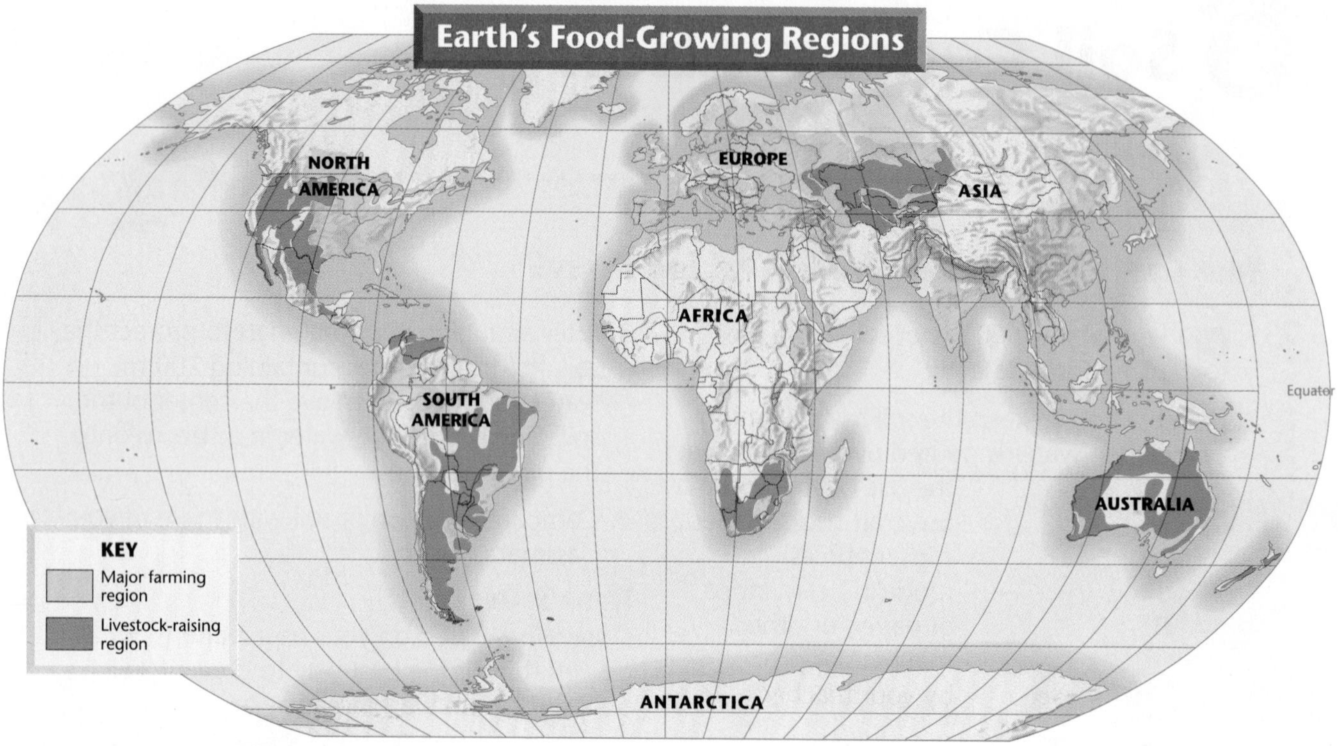
Earth's Food-Growing Regions
NORTH AMERICA
EUROPE
ASIA
AFRICA
SOUTH AMERICA
AUSTRALIA
ANTARCTICA
Equator
KEY
Major farming region
Livestock-raising region

Figure 10 The world's best soils for farming often are found in river valleys or interior and coastal plains. Areas too dry, too mountainous, or not fertile enough for farming may be used for grazing cattle, sheep, or other livestock.

Fertile soil is valuable because there is a limited supply. Less than one eighth of the land on Earth has soils that are well suited for farming. Figure 10 shows where these regions are located. In many areas, farming is difficult and little food is produced. The reasons for this include low soil fertility, lack of water, steep slopes, or a short growing season.

☑ *Checkpoint* *Why is soil valuable?*

Soil Damage and Loss

Soil is one of Earth's most important resources. But soil can be lost or damaged. For example, soil can become exhausted, or lose its fertility. This occurred in large parts of the South in the late 1800s. Soils in which only cotton had been grown were exhausted. Many farmers abandoned their farms. Early in the 1900s in Alabama, a scientist named George Washington Carver developed new crops and farming methods that helped to restore soil fertility in the South. Peanuts were one crop that helped make the soil fertile again.

Soil can be lost to erosion by water and wind. Water erosion can occur wherever soil is not protected by plant cover. Plants break the force of falling rain, and plant roots hold the soil together. Wind erosion is another cause of soil loss. Wind erosion, combined with farming methods that were not suited to dry conditions, caused the Dust Bowl on the Great Plains.

Figure 11 George Washington Carver (1864–1943) taught new methods of soil conservation to farmers in the South.

The Dust Bowl

Toward the end of the 1800s, farmers had settled most of the prairies. New settlers moved on to the Great Plains farther west. This region sweeps eastward from the base of the Rocky Mountains across the western parts of North and South Dakota, Nebraska, Kansas, Oklahoma, and Texas.

The soil of the Great Plains is fertile. But there is an important difference between the Great Plains and the prairie. Rainfall decreases steadily from east to west across the Great Plains. The tall grass gives way to shorter, thinner grass needing less moisture. **Plowing removed the grass from the Great Plains and exposed the soil. In times of drought, the topsoil quickly dried out, turned to dust, and blew away.**

By 1930, almost all of the Great Plains had been turned into farms or ranches. Then, several very dry years in a row turned the soil on parts of the Great Plains to dust. The wind blew the soil east in great, black clouds. The clouds turned the sky dark as far away as Chicago and even New York City. Eventually the soil blew out over the Atlantic Ocean, where it was lost forever.

The problem was most serious in the southern Plains states. There, the drought and topsoil loss lasted until 1938. This area, shown in Figure 12, was called the **Dust Bowl.** Many people in the Dust Bowl states abandoned their farms and moved away.

Language Arts CONNECTION

Woody Guthrie wrote and sang folk songs. Guthrie lived in Oklahoma and Texas at the time of the Dust Bowl and wrote a series of songs called "Dust Bowl Ballads." (A ballad is a song that tells a story.) One of the ballads describes how

We saw outside our window
Where wheat fields they had grown
Was now a rippling ocean
Of dust the wind had blown.

In Your Journal

Write the words for a ballad that tells the story of a problem in your community and how you think the problem should be solved.

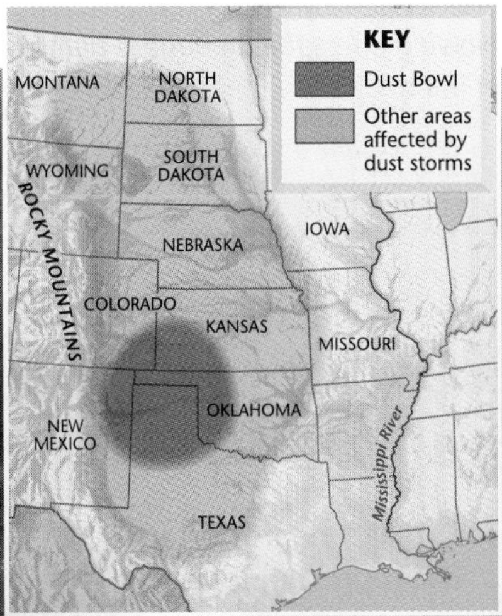

KEY
Dust Bowl
Other areas affected by dust storms
MONTANA
NORTH DAKOTA
WYOMING
SOUTH DAKOTA
ROCKY MOUNTAINS
NEBRASKA
IOWA
COLORADO
KANSAS
MISSOURI
OKLAHOMA
NEW MEXICO
TEXAS
Mississippi River

Figure 12 The Dust Bowl included western Oklahoma and parts of the surrounding states. Wind blew dry particles of soil into great clouds of dust that traveled thousands of kilometers.

Figure 13 Contour plowing (above) and conservation plowing (below) help prevent soil erosion. *Predicting How might conservation plowing affect the amount of humus in the soil?*

Soil Conservation

The Dust Bowl helped people appreciate the value of soil. In the 1930s, with government support, farmers in the Great Plains and throughout the country began to take better care of their land. They adopted methods of farming that helped save the soil. Some of the methods were new. Others had been practiced for hundreds of years.

Farmers in the United States adopted modern methods of soil conservation. **Soil conservation** is the management of soil to prevent its destruction. **Two ways that soil can be conserved include contour plowing and conservation plowing.**

Contour plowing is the practice of plowing fields along the curves of a slope. This helps slow the runoff of excess rainfall and prevents it from washing the soil away.

Conservation plowing disturbs the soil and its plant cover as little as possible. Dead weeds and stalks of the previous year's crop are left in the ground to help return soil nutrients, retain moisture, and hold soil in place. This method is also called low-till or no-till plowing.

In grasslands such as the Great Plains, grazing livestock is an important use of the land. But if too many cattle graze on the grass during dry periods, the grass cover protecting the soil may be damaged. This exposes the soil to both wind and water erosion. To prevent damage to the soil, ranchers must limit the size of their herds.

Section 3 Review

1. Explain the importance of soil as one of Earth's resources.
2. How did settlers on the Great Plains help create the Dust Bowl?
3. What are some techniques that farmers use to conserve soil?
4. **Thinking Critically Problem Solving** If you had to plant corn on a steep hillside, how would you do it so that rain would not wash the soil away?

CHAPTER PROJECT

Check Your Progress

Check your bean seeds daily and water them as needed. Count and record the number of seeds that sprout. You can also measure the height of each plant, count the number of leaves, and note the leaf color. After about 14 days, you should be able to make comparisons. What differences did you observe in the bean plants grown in the different materials? When did these differences appear? Based on your data, what conclusions can you draw about which material is best for growing bean plants?

Section 1 Rocks and Weathering

Key Ideas

- Rock weathers, or wears down, when it is exposed to air, water, weather, and living things at Earth's surface.
- Mechanical weathering breaks rock into smaller pieces. The agents of mechanical weathering include freezing and thawing, heating and cooling, growth of plants, actions of animals, and abrasion.
- Chemical weathering changes the mineral content of rock. The agents of chemical weathering are water, oxygen, carbon dioxide, living organisms, and acid rain.
- Climate and rock type determine how fast weathering occurs.

Key Terms

weathering
erosion
mechanical weathering
ice wedging
abrasion
chemical weathering
permeable

Section 2 Soil Formation and Composition

Key Ideas

- Soil is made of small particles of rock mixed with the decaying remains of organisms.
- Soil forms gradually in layers called horizons as bedrock weathers and organic materials build up.
- The three soil horizons are the A horizon, the B horizon, and the C horizon. The A horizon is made up of topsoil, which is rich in humus. The B horizon consists of clay and other particles washed down from the A horizon, but little humus. The C horizon is made up of partly weathered rock without clay or humus.
- Plants and animals break up and mix the soil, and also add the organic materials that form humus.

Key Terms

soil
bedrock
humus
loam
soil horizon
topsoil
subsoil
litter
decomposers

Section 3 Soil Conservation

INTEGRATING ENVIRONMENTAL SCIENCE

Key Ideas

- Soil is a valuable resource because life on land depends on it, yet it forms very slowly.
- Soil can be eroded away and its fertility can be decreased by improper farming practices.
- Plowing the Great Plains caused the Dust Bowl by removing the sod covering that kept the soil from blowing away during droughts.
- Soil can be conserved and its fertility can be maintained by using various methods of soil conservation.

Key Terms

sod
Dust Bowl
soil conservation
contour plowing
conservation plowing

ACTIVITY

USING THE INTERNET

www.phschool.com/state_focus/california/

California Test Prep: Reviewing Content

Multiple Choice

Choose the letter of the best answer.

1. The most important force of mechanical weathering in cool climates is
a. oxidation.
b. freezing and thawing.
c. animal activity.
d. abrasion.

2. Most chemical weathering is caused by
a. acid rain.
b. water.
c. oxygen.
d. carbon dioxide.

3. The B horizon consists of
a. subsoil.
b. topsoil.
c. rock particles.
d. bedrock.

4. One of the best types of soil for farming is
a. forest soil.
b. mountain soil.
c. tropical soil.
d. prairie soil.

5. Most of the work of mixing humus into the soil is done by
a. fungi.
b. bacteria.
c. earthworms.
d. mites.

True or False

If the statement is true, write true. If it is false, change the underlined word or words to make the statement true.

6. Mechanical weathering is the movement of rock particles by wind, water, or ice.

7. Weathering occurs faster in a wet climate.

8. The decayed organic material in soil is called loam.

9. Fungi produce chemicals that digest plant remains.

10. Scientists classify types of soil based partly on a region's climate.

Checking Concepts

11. Where is mechanical weathering likely to occur more quickly: where the winter temperature usually stays below freezing, or where it more often shifts back and forth around the freezing point? Explain.

12. Briefly describe how soil is formed.

13. Which contains more humus, topsoil or subsoil?

14. Explain how plants can act as agents of both mechanical and chemical weathering.

15. What role did grass play in conserving the soil of the prairies?

16. How does conservation plowing contribute to soil conservation?

17. Writing to Learn Write a description of your life as an earthworm. What would it be like to live in the soil? What would you see? What would you eat? How would you move through the soil? How would you change it?

Thinking Visually

18. Concept Map Copy the concept map about soil horizons onto a piece of paper. Then complete it and add a title. (For more on concept maps, see the Skills Handbook.)

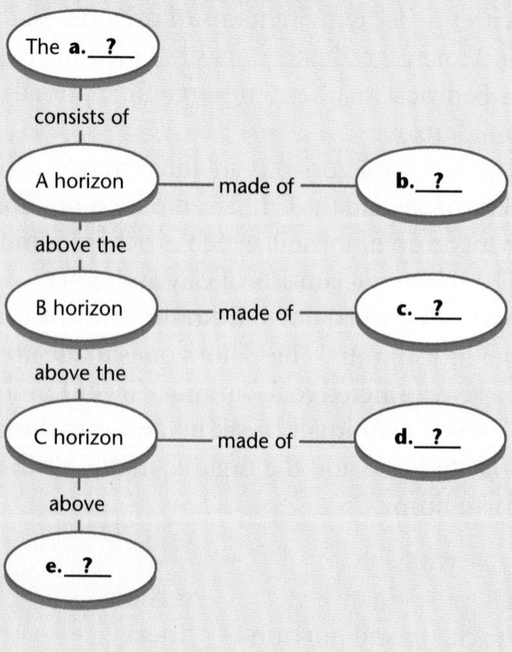
The a. ?
consists of
A horizon
made of
b. ?
above the
B horizon
made of
c. ?
above the
C horizon
made of
d. ?
above
e. ?

Test Prep: Skills

Use the following information to answer Questions 19–21. You have two samples of soil. One is mostly sand and one is mostly clay.

19. Developing Hypotheses Which soil sample do you think would lose water more quickly? Why?

20. Designing Experiments Design an experiment to test how quickly water passes through each soil sample.

21. Posing Questions Suppose you are a farmer who wants to grow soybeans in one of these two soils. What questions would you need to answer before choosing where to plant your soybeans?

Thinking Critically

22. Predicting Suppose mechanical weathering breaks a rock into pieces. How would this affect the rate at which the rock weathers chemically?

23. Classifying Classify the following examples as either mechanical weathering or chemical weathering:

A. Cracks appear in a sidewalk next to a large tree.

B. A piece of limestone develops holes like Swiss cheese.

C. A rock exposed at the surface slowly turns reddish brown.

24. Developing Hypotheses On the moon there is no air or water. Develop a hypothesis about how fast rocks would weather on the moon compared with their rate of weathering on Earth. Explain.

25. Relating Cause and Effect Two rocks, each in a different location, have been weathering for the same amount of time. Mature soil has formed from one rock but only immature soil from the other. What factors might have caused this difference in rate of soil formation?

26. Making Judgments What is the value of soil to human beings and other living things? Explain your answer.

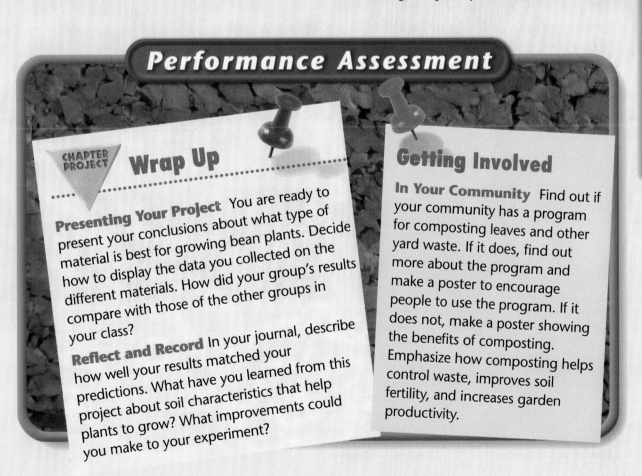

Performance Assessment

CHAPTER PROJECT Wrap Up

Presenting Your Project You are ready to present your conclusions about what type of material is best for growing bean plants. Decide how to display the data you collected on the different materials. How did your group's results compare with those of the other groups in your class?

Reflect and Record In your journal, describe how well your results matched your predictions. What have you learned from this project about soil characteristics that help plants to grow? What improvements could you make to your experiment?

Getting Involved

In Your Community Find out if your community has a program for composting leaves and other yard waste. If it does, find out more about the program and make a poster to encourage people to use the program. If it does not, make a poster showing the benefits of composting. Emphasize how composting helps control waste, improves soil fertility, and increases garden productivity.

CHAPTER

8 Erosion and Deposition

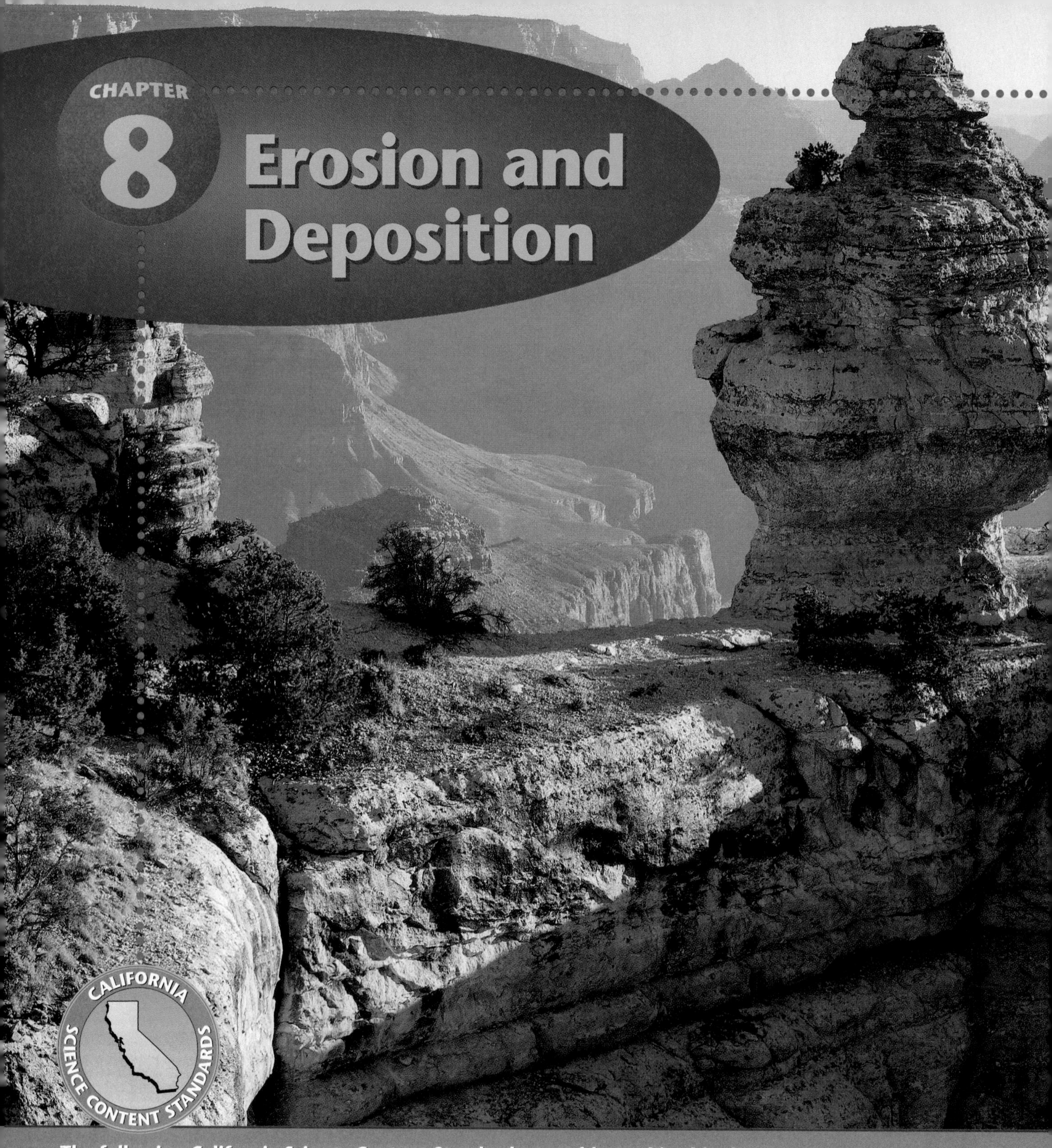
CALIFORNIA SCIENCE CONTENT STANDARDS

The following California Science Content Standards are addressed in this chapter:

2. Topography is reshaped by weathering of rock and soil and by the transportation and deposition of sediment.

- **a.** Water running downhill is the dominant process in shaping the landscape, including California's landscape.
- **b.** Rivers and streams are dynamic systems that erode and transport sediment, change course, and flood their banks in natural and recurring patterns.
- **c.** Beaches are dynamic systems in which sand is supplied by rivers and moved along the coast by wave action.
- **d.** Earthquakes, volcanic eruptions, landslides, and floods change human and wildlife habitats.

3. Heat moves in a predictable flow from warmer objects to cooler objects until all objects are at the same temperature.

- **a.** Energy can be carried from one place to another by heat flow, or by waves including water waves, light and sound, or by moving objects.

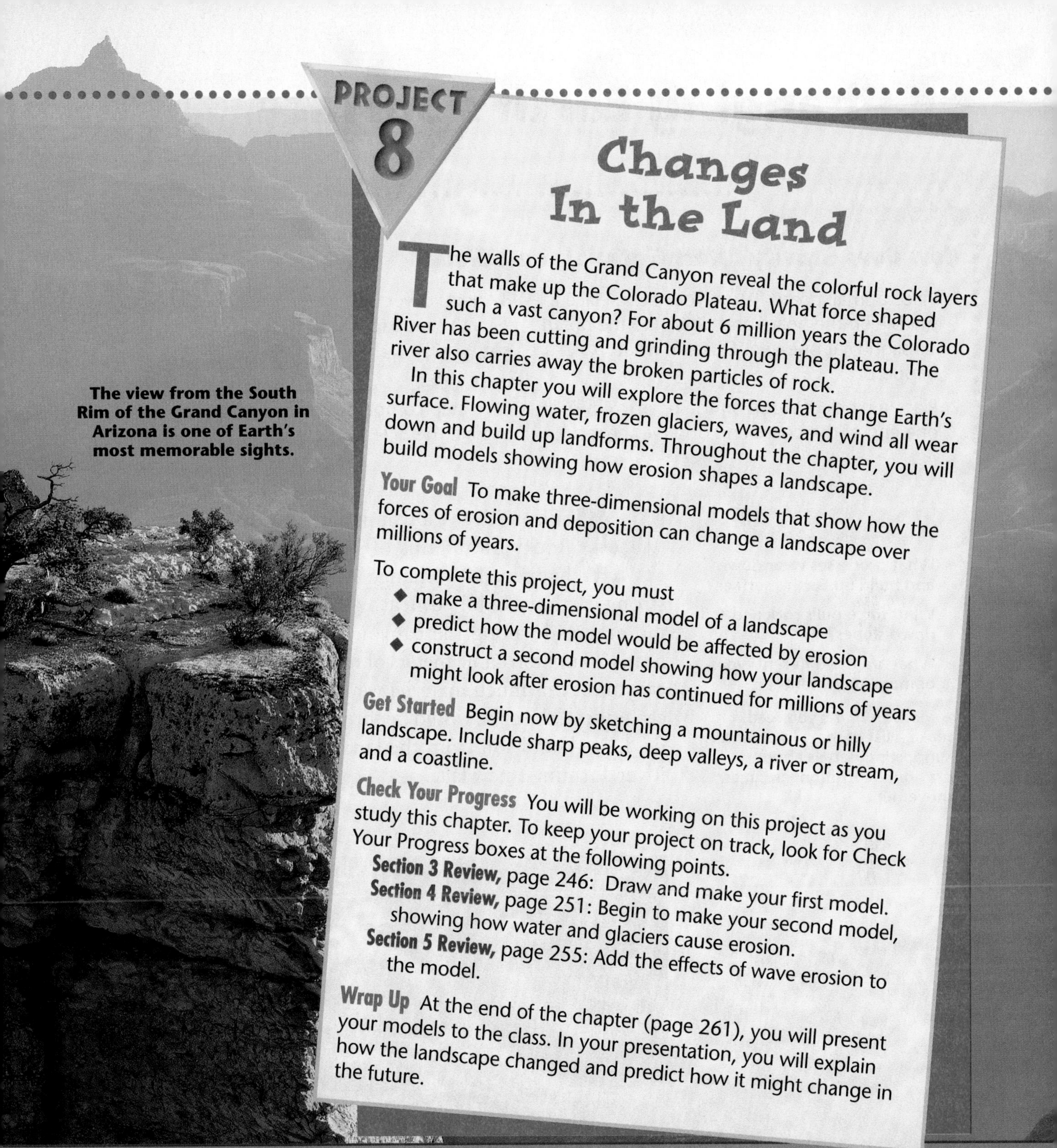

The view from the South Rim of the Grand Canyon in Arizona is one of Earth's most memorable sights.

PROJECT 8

Changes In the Land

The walls of the Grand Canyon reveal the colorful rock layers that make up the Colorado Plateau. What force shaped such a vast canyon? For about 6 million years the Colorado River has been cutting and grinding through the plateau. The river also carries away the broken particles of rock.

In this chapter you will explore the forces that change Earth's surface. Flowing water, frozen glaciers, waves, and wind all wear down and build up landforms. Throughout the chapter, you will build models showing how erosion shapes a landscape.

Your Goal To make three-dimensional models that show how the forces of erosion and deposition can change a landscape over millions of years.

To complete this project, you must

- make a three-dimensional model of a landscape
- predict how the model would be affected by erosion
- construct a second model showing how your landscape might look after erosion has continued for millions of years

Get Started Begin now by sketching a mountainous or hilly landscape. Include sharp peaks, deep valleys, a river or stream, and a coastline.

Check Your Progress You will be working on this project as you study this chapter. To keep your project on track, look for Check Your Progress boxes at the following points.

Section 3 Review, page 246: Draw and make your first model.
Section 4 Review, page 251: Begin to make your second model, showing how water and glaciers cause erosion.
Section 5 Review, page 255: Add the effects of wave erosion to the model.

Wrap Up At the end of the chapter (page 261), you will present your models to the class. In your presentation, you will explain how the landscape changed and predict how it might change in the future.

6. Sources of energy and materials differ in amounts, distribution, usefulness, and the time required for their formation.

b. Different natural energy and material resources, including air, soil, rocks, minerals, petroleum, fresh water, wildlife, and forests, and classify them as renewable or nonrenewable.

7. Scientific progress is made by asking meaningful questions and conducting careful investigations.

a. Develop a hypothesis.

e. Recognize whether evidence is consistent with a proposed explanation.

f. Read a topographic map and a geologic map for evidence provided on the maps, and construct and interpret a simple scale map.

1 Changing Earth's Surface

Discover Activity

How Does Gravity Affect Materials on a Slope?

1. Place a small board flat on your desk. Place a marble on the board and slowly tip the board up slightly at one end. Observe what happens.
2. Place a block of wood on the board. Slowly lift one end of the board and observe the result.
3. Next, cover the board and the wood block with sandpaper and repeat Step 2.

Think It Over

Developing Hypotheses How do the results of each step compare? Develop a hypothesis to explain the differences in your observations.

GUIDE FOR READING

- What processes wear down and build up Earth's surface?
- What force pulls rock and soil down slopes?
- What are the different types of mass movement?

Reading Tip **As you read, make a list of main ideas and supporting details about erosion, deposition, and mass movement.**

Madison River Canyon is a quiet wilderness area in the Rocky Mountains of Montana. In 1959, something happened to change the canyon forever. When a strong earthquake jolted nearby Yellowstone National Park, a mountainside along the canyon gave way. In a few seconds, nearly 30 million cubic meters of rock, soil, and trees slid into the canyon. If this much material were in the shape of a cube, then each side of the cube would be three times longer than a football field. Rock and soil from the landslide dammed the Madison River, forming a new lake.

Figure 1 During a landslide, loose rock and soil on the side of a mountain suddenly slide away from underlying bedrock. This landslide in Madison River Canyon, Montana, buried a highway and campground.

Wearing Down and Building Up

A landslide like the one in Madison River Canyon is a spectacular example of erosion. **Erosion** is the process by which natural forces move weathered rock and soil from one place to another. A landslide is a very rapid type of erosion. Other types of erosion move soil and rock more slowly. Gravity, running water, glaciers, waves, and wind can all cause erosion. You may have seen water carrying soil and gravel down a driveway after it rains. That's an example of erosion. Erosion also caused the damage to the road in Figure 2.

The material moved by erosion is **sediment.** Both weathering and erosion produce sediment. **Deposition** occurs where the agents of erosion lay down sediment. Deposition changes the shape of the land. You may have watched a playing child who picked up several toys and then carried them across a room and put them down. This child was acting something like an agent of erosion and deposition.

Figure 2 Heavy winter rains washed out this California highway. *Relating Cause and Effect What caused the erosion that you can see in the photograph?*

Weathering, erosion, and deposition act together in a cycle that wears down and builds up Earth's surface. Erosion and deposition are at work everywhere on Earth. Sometimes they work slowly. At other times, they work more quickly, such as during a thunderstorm. Then, heavy rain soaks into rock and soil. These water-soaked materials may then come loose suddenly and slide down a mountain. But as a mountain wears down in one place, new landforms build up in other places. Erosion and deposition are never-ending.

☑ *Checkpoint* ***What happens to sediment as a result of erosion and deposition?***

Mass Movement

Imagine that you are sitting on a bicycle at the top of a hill. With only a slight push, you can coast down the hill. If the slope of the hill is very steep, you will reach a high speed before reaching the bottom. The force that pulls you and your bicycle downward is gravity. Gravity pulls everything toward the center of Earth.

Gravity is the force that moves rock and other materials downhill. Gravity causes **mass movement,** any one of several processes that move sediment downhill. Mass movement can be rapid or slow. **The different types of mass movement include landslides, mudslides, slump, and creep.**

Figure 3 A mudflow caused by heavy rains raced through the streets of this town in Italy. *Relating Cause and Effect What characteristic of soil can contribute to a mudflow?*

Landslides The most destructive kind of mass movement is a landslide, which occurs when rock and soil slide quickly down a steep slope. Some landslides may contain huge masses of rock. But many landslides contain only a small amount of rock and soil. Such mass movement is common where road builders have cut highways through hills or mountains.

Mudflows A mudflow is the rapid downhill movement of a mixture of water, rock, and soil. The amount of water in a mudflow can be as high as 60 percent. Mudflows often occur after heavy rains in a normally dry area. In clay soils with a high water content, mudflows may occur even on very gentle slopes. Under certain conditions, clay soils suddenly turn to liquid and begin to flow. For example, an earthquake can trigger both mudflows and landslides. Mudflows like the one in Figure 3 can be very dangerous.

Slump If you slump your shoulders, the entire upper part of your body drops down. In the type of mass movement known as slump, a mass of rock and soil suddenly slips down a slope. Unlike a landslide, the material in slump moves down in one large mass. It looks as if someone pulled the bottom out from under part of the slope. Figure 4 shows an example of slump. Slump often occurs when water soaks the base of a mass of soil that is rich in clay.

Figure 4 Slump can look as if a giant spoon has started to scoop a mass of soil out from a hillside.

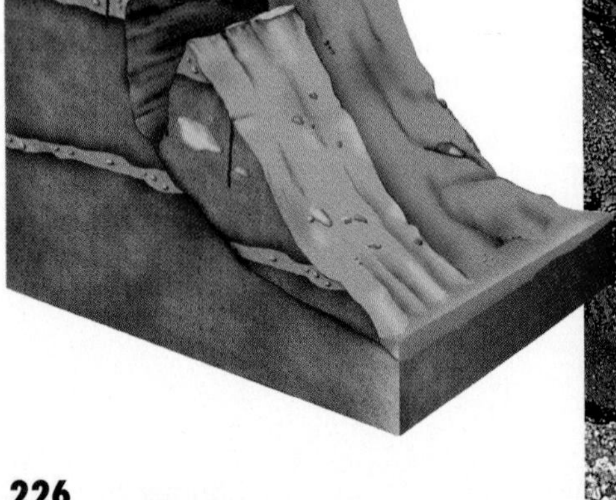

Creep Landscapes affected by creep may have the eerie, out-of-kilter look of a funhouse in an amusement park. Creep is the very slow downhill movement of rock and soil. It can even occur on gentle slopes. Like the movement of an hour hand on a clock, creep is so slow you can barely notice it. But you can see the effects of creep in objects such as telephone poles, gravestones, and fenceposts. Creep may tilt these objects at spooky angles. Creep often results from the freezing and thawing of water in cracked layers of rock beneath the soil. How have the trees in Figure 5 been affected by creep?

Sharpen your Skills

Observing

ACTIVITY

Compare the examples of mass movement in Figures 4 and 5. Based on your observations, construct a table comparing slump and creep. Include the Earth materials involved, the type of slope, and the speed for each type of mass movement.

Figure 5 Creep has slowly tilted these trees downhill, causing their trunks to grow in a curve. *Predicting If creep continues, how might it affect the road, the fence, and the electric power lines?*

Section 1 Review

1. Explain the difference between erosion and deposition.
2. What force causes erosion?
3. What are four types of mass movement?
4. **Thinking Critically Relating Cause and Effect** Why would a landslide be more likely on a steep mountain than on a gently sloping hill?

Science at Home

After a rainstorm, take a walk with an adult family member around your neighborhood. Look for evidence of erosion. Try to find areas where there is loose soil, sand, gravel, or rock. (**CAUTION:** *Stay away from any large pile of loose sand or soil—it may slide without warning.*) Which areas have the most erosion? The least erosion? How does the slope of the ground affect the amount of erosion? Sketch or take photographs of the areas showing evidence of erosion.

Skills Lab

Developing Hypotheses

Sand Hills

In this lab, you will develop and test a hypothesis about how mass movement affects the size and shape of a sand hill.

Problem

What is the relationship between the height and width of a sand hill?

Materials

Dry sand, 500 mL
Cardboard toilet paper tube
Tray (about 15 cm × 45 cm × 60 cm)
Wooden barbecue skewer
Masking tape
Spoon
Ruler
Pencil or crayon
Several sheets of white paper

Procedure

1. Begin by observing how gravity causes mass movement in sand. To start, place the cardboard tube vertically in the center of the tray.
2. Using the spoon, fill the cardboard tube with the dry sand. Take care not to spill the sand around the outside of the tube.

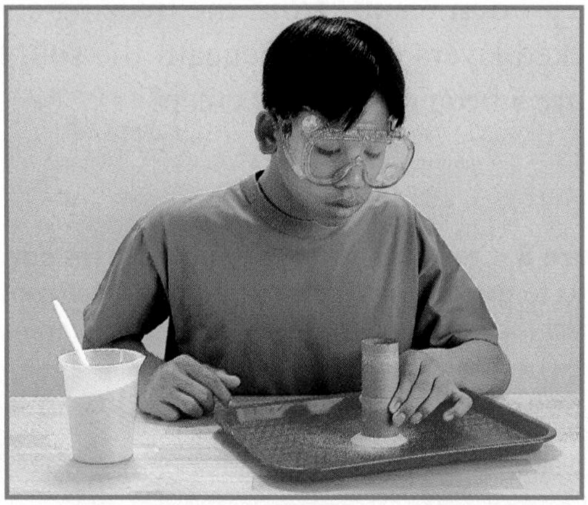

3. Carefully lift the sand-filled tube straight up so that all the sand flows out. As you lift the tube, observe the sand's movement.
4. Develop a hypothesis explaining how the width of a sand hill is related to the height for different amounts of sand.
5. Plan a method for testing your hypothesis. To test your hypothesis, you will need a method of measuring a sand hill (see instructions below).
6. Empty the sand in the tray back into a container. Then set up your system for measuring the sand hill.
7. Copy the data table into your lab notebook.

How to Measure a Sand Hill

1. Cover the bottom of the tray with unlined white paper and tape it firmly in place.
2. Mark off points 0.5 cm apart along one side of the paper in the tray.
3. Carefully draw the sand hill's outline on the paper. The line should go completely around the base of the hill.
4. Now measure the width of the hill against the marks you made along the edge of the paper.
5. Measure the sand hill's height by inserting a barbecue skewer through its center. Make a mark on the skewer at the top of the hill.
6. Remove the skewer and use the ruler to measure how much of the skewer was buried in the hill. Try not to disturb the sand.

DATA TABLE

Test	1	2	3	4	5
Height					
Width					

8. Following Steps 1 through 3, make a new sand hill.
9. Measure and record the sand hill's height and width for Test 1.
10. Now test what happens when you add more sand to the sand hill. Place your cardboard tube vertically at the center of the sand hill. Be careful not to push the tube down into the sand hill! Using the spoon, fill the tube with sand as before.
11. Carefully raise the tube and observe the results of the sand's movement.
12. Measure and record the sand hill's height and width for Test 2.
13. Repeat Steps 10 through 12 at least three more times. After each test, record your results. Be sure to number each test.

Analyze and Conclude

1. Make a graph showing how the sand hill's height and width changed with each test. (*Hint:* Use the *x*-axis of the graph for height. Use the *y*-axis of the graph for width.)
2. What does your graph show about the relationship between the sand hill's height and width?
3. Does your graph support your hypothesis about the sand hill's height and width? Why or why not?
4. How would you revise your original hypothesis after examining your data? Give reasons for your answer.
5. **Think About It** Predict what would happen if you continued the experiment for five more tests. Extend your graph with a dashed line to show your prediction. How could you test your prediction?

Design an Experiment

Do you think the use of different materials, such as wet sand or gravel, would produce different results from dry sand? Make a new hypothesis about the relationship between slope and width in hills made of materials other than dry sand. Design an experiment in which you test how these different materials form hills. Obtain your teacher's approval before you try the experiment.

SECTION 2

Water Erosion

DISCOVER ACTIVITY

How Does Moving Water Wear Away Rocks?

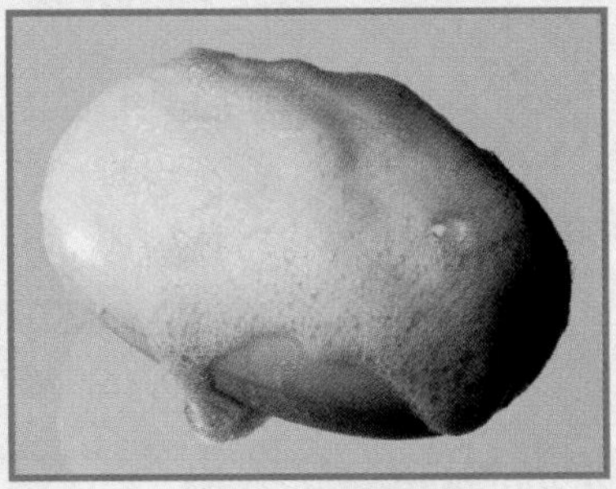

1. Obtain two bars of soap that are the same size and brand.
2. Open a faucet just enough to let the water drip out very slowly. How many drops of water does the faucet release per minute?
3. Place one bar of soap in a dry place. Place the other bar of soap under the faucet. Predict the effect of the dripping water droplets on the soap.
4. Let the faucet drip for 10 minutes.
5. Turn off the faucet and observe both bars of soap. What difference do you observe between them?

Think It Over

Predicting What would the bar of soap under the dripping faucet look like if you left it there for another 10 minutes? For an hour? How could you speed up the process? Slow it down?

GUIDE FOR READING

- **What process is mainly responsible for shaping Earth's land surface?**
- **What features are formed by water erosion?**
- **What features are formed when rivers and streams deposit sediment?**

Reading Tip **Before you read, use the headings to make an outline on water erosion and deposition.**

Walking in the woods in summer, you can hear the racing water of a stream before you see the stream itself. The water roars as it foams over rock ledges and boulders. When you reach the stream, you see water rushing by. Sand and pebbles tumble along the bottom of the stream. As it swirls downstream, it also carries twigs, leaves, and bits of soil. In sheltered pools, insects such as water striders silently skim the water's calm surface. Beneath the surface, you see a rainbow trout hovering in the clear water.

If you visit the stream at other times of year, it will be very different. In winter, the stream freezes. Chunks of ice scrape and grind away at the stream's bed and banks. In spring, the stream floods. Then the flow of water may be strong enough to move large rocks. But throughout the year, the stream continues to erode its small part of Earth's surface.

A woodland stream ▼

Gully
Side gully
Rills
Stream

Figure 6 A falling raindrop starts the process of erosion. Water flowing across the surface runs together in small rills. Rills combine to form larger gullies. *Predicting What will happen to the land between the gully and the side gully as the two gullies grow wider?*

Runoff and Erosion

Running water creates many landforms. **Moving water is the major agent of the erosion that has shaped Earth's land surface.**

Erosion by water begins with the splash of rain, as you can see in Figure 6. Some rainfall sinks into the ground. Some evaporates or is taken up by plants. The force of a falling raindrop can loosen and pick up soil particles. As water moves over the land, it carries these particles with it. This moving water is called runoff. **Runoff** is all the remaining water that moves over Earth's surface. When runoff flows in a thin layer over the land, it may cause a type of erosion called sheet erosion.

Rills and Gullies Because of gravity, runoff and the material it contains move downhill. As runoff travels, it forms tiny grooves in the soil called **rills.** As the rills flow into one another, they grow larger, forming gullies. A **gully** is a large groove, or channel, in the soil that carries runoff after a rainstorm. As water flows through gullies, it moves soil and rocks with it, thus enlarging the gullies through erosion. Gullies flow only after it rains.

Figure 7 As water erodes gullies, soil can be lost.

TRY THIS

Raindrops Falling

ACTIVITY

Find out how the force of falling raindrops affects soil.

1. Fill a petri dish with fine-textured soil to a depth of about 1 cm. Make sure the soil has a smooth flat surface, but do not pack it firmly in the dish.
2. Place the dish in the center of a newspaper.
3. Fill a dropper with water. Squeeze a large water drop from a height of 1 m onto the surface of the soil. Repeat 4 times.
4. Use a meter stick to measure the distance the soil splashed from the dish. Record your observations.
5. Repeat Steps 1 through 4, this time from a height of 2 m. Which traveled further, the splash from 1 m or the splash from 2 m?

Drawing Conclusions Which test produced the greater amount of erosion? Why?

Streams and Rivers Gullies join together to form a larger channel called a stream. A **stream** is a channel along which water is continually flowing down a slope. Unlike gullies, streams rarely dry up. Small streams are also called creeks or brooks. As streams flow together, they form larger and larger bodies of flowing water. A large stream is often called a **river.**

Amount of Runoff The amount of runoff in an area depends on five main factors. The first factor is the amount of rain an area receives. A second factor is vegetation. Grasses, shrubs, and trees reduce runoff by absorbing water and holding soil in place. A third factor is the type of soil. Some types of soils absorb more water than others. A fourth factor is the shape of the land. Land that is steeply sloped has more runoff than flatter land. Finally, a fifth factor is how people use the land. For instance, a paved parking lot absorbs no water, so all the rain that falls on it becomes runoff. Runoff also increases when a farmer cuts down crops, since this removes vegetation from the land.

Generally, more runoff means more erosion. In contrast, things that reduce runoff, such as plant leaves and roots, will reduce erosion. Even though deserts have little rainfall, they often have high runoff and erosion. This is because deserts usually have few plants. In wet areas, runoff and erosion may be low because there are more plants to protect the soil.

☑ *Checkpoint* *What factors affect the amount of runoff in a region?*

River Systems

A stream grows into a larger stream or river by receiving water from tributaries. A **tributary** is a stream that flows into a larger stream. A small creek that flows into a large river is a tributary to that river. So too is a large river that adds its water to another large river. For instance, the Missouri River becomes a tributary of the Mississippi River near the city of St. Louis, even though both rivers are about the same size there.

Look at Figure 8. Notice all the tributaries to the Sacramento River. Together, all these streams—from tiny rills to great rivers—form a system that drains the northern part of California's Central Valley. A **drainage basin** is the land area from which a river and its tributaries collect their water.

If you were to follow a river upstream all the way to its source, you would finally reach a divide. A **divide** is the high ground between two drainage basins. The most famous divide within the United States is the Continental Divide, which follows the high ground of the Rocky Mountains. The Continental Divide separates streams that flow into the Gulf of Mexico from streams that flow into the Great Basin or the Pacific Ocean.

Sacramento River Drainage Basin
OREGON
0 25 50 mi
0 25 50 km
Pit R.
CALIFORNIA
NEVADA
Sacramento R.
Middle Fk. Feather
Stony Cr.
Feather R.
Yuba R.
American R.
Cache Cr.
Lake Tahoe
N
W
E
S
PACIFIC OCEAN
Sacramento
Sacramento–San Joaquin Delta
KEY
Drainage basin
San Francisco Bay
San Joaquin R.

Figure 8 The drainage basin of the Sacramento River drains much of northern California. *Interpreting Maps What are some tributaries of the Sacramento River? Could a tributary come from outside the drainage basin?*

Erosion by Rivers

Scientists classify rivers by identifying certain features that form as a result of erosion. **Through erosion, a river creates valleys, waterfalls, flood plains, meanders, and oxbow lakes.**

Rivers often form on steep mountain slopes. Near its source, a river is often fast-flowing and generally follows a straight, narrow course. The steep slopes along the river erode rapidly. The result is a deep, V-shaped valley.

Waterfalls may occur where a river meets an area of rock that is very hard and erodes slowly. The river flows over this rock and then flows over softer rock downstream. The softer rock wears away faster than the harder rock. Eventually a waterfall develops where the softer rock was removed. This process formed Niagara Falls, shown in Figure 9. Areas of rough water called rapids also occur where a river tumbles over hard rock.

Figure 9 Niagara Falls formed on the Niagara River, which connects Lake Erie and Lake Ontario. A flat layer of tough rock lies over a layer of softer rock that erodes easily. When the softer rock erodes, pieces of the harder rock above break off, creating the waterfall's sharp drop.

Harder rock layer
Softer rock layers

Figure 10 The oxbow lake (above) was formerly a part of the channel of the Kasanak River in Alaska. These meanders (right) were formed by the Owens River in California and several of its tributaries.

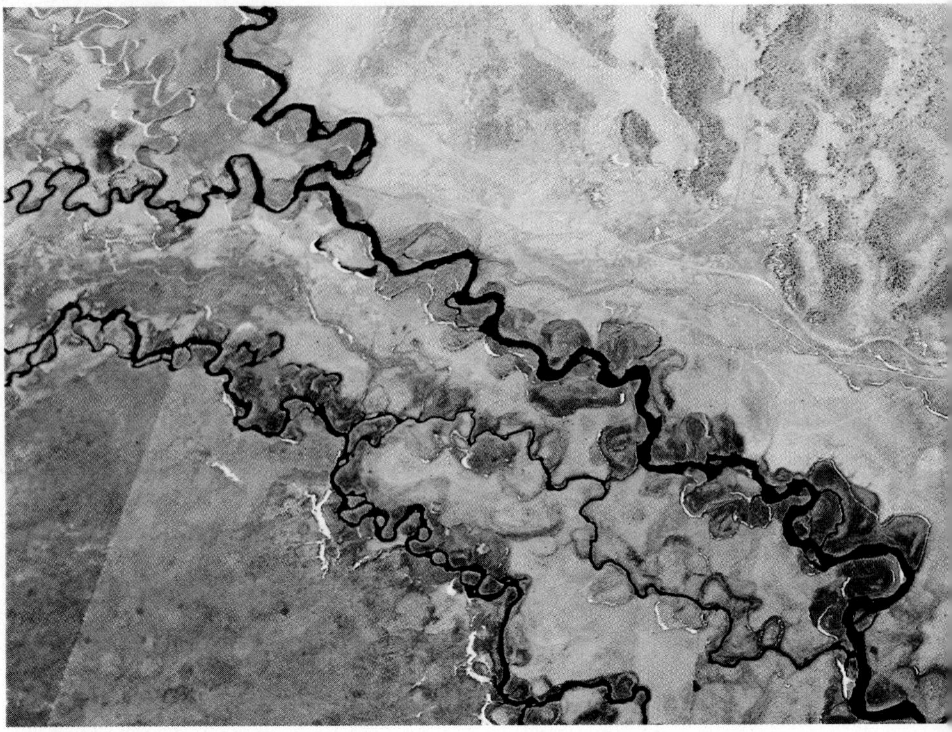

Lower down on its course, a river usually flows over more gently sloping land. The river spreads out and erodes the land, forming a wide river valley. The flat, wide area of land along a river is a **flood plain.** A river often covers its flood plain when it overflows its banks during floods. On a wide flood plain, the valley walls may be kilometers away from the river itself.

A river often develops meanders where it flows through easily eroded rock or sediment. A **meander** is a looplike bend in the course of a river. As the river widens from side to side, it tends to erode the outer bank and deposit sediment on the inner bank of a bend. Over time, the bend—or meander—becomes more and more curved.

When the gently sloping part of a river flows through an area of sediment or soft rock, it can erode a very wide flood plain. Along this part of a river's course, its channel is deep and wide. Meanders are common along this part of a river. The southern stretch of the Mississippi River is one example of a river that meanders on a wide, gently sloping flood plain.

Sometimes a meandering river forms a feature called an oxbow lake. An **oxbow lake** is a meander that has been cut off from the river. An oxbow lake may form when a river floods. During the flood, high water finds a straighter route downstream. As the flood waters fall, sediments dam up the ends of a meander. The meander has become an oxbow lake.

☑ *Checkpoint* *How does an oxbow lake form?*

Deposits by Rivers

As water moves, it carries sediments with it. Any time moving water slows down, it drops, or deposits, some of the sediment. As the water slows down, fine particles fall to the river's bed. Larger stones quit rolling and sliding. **Deposition creates landforms such as alluvial fans and deltas. It can also add soil to a river's flood plain.** In *Exploring the Course of a River* on pages 236–237, you can see these and other features shaped by rivers and streams.

Figure 11 This alluvial fan in Death Valley, California, was formed from deposits by streams from the mountains.

Alluvial Fans Where a stream flows out of a steep, narrow mountain valley, the stream suddenly becomes wider and shallower. The water slows down. Here sediments are deposited in an alluvial fan. An **alluvial fan** is a wide, sloping deposit of sediment formed where a stream leaves a mountain range. As its name suggests, this deposit is shaped like a fan.

Deltas A river ends its journey when it flows into a still body of water, such as an ocean or a lake. Because the river water is no longer flowing downhill, the water slows down. At this point, the sediment in the water drops to the bottom. Sediment deposited where a river flows into an ocean or lake builds up a landform called a **delta.** Deltas can be a variety of shapes: some are arc-shaped, others are triangle-shaped. The delta of the Mississippi River is an example of a type of delta called a "bird's foot" delta.

Soil on Flood Plains Deposition also occurs during floods. INTEGRATING LIFE SCIENCE Then heavy rains or melting snow cause a river to rise above its banks and spread out over its flood plain. When the flood water finally retreats, it deposits sediment as new soil. Deposition of new soil over a flood plain is what makes a river valley fertile. Dense forests can grow in the rich soil of a flood plain. The soil is also perfect for growing crops.

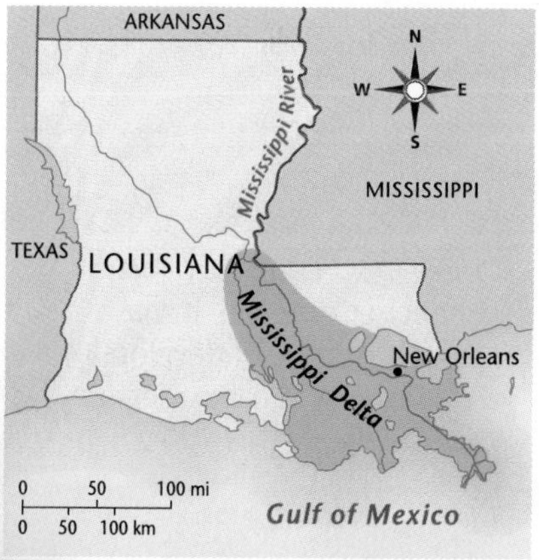
ARKANSAS
N
W
E
S
Mississippi River
MISSISSIPPI
TEXAS
LOUISIANA
Mississippi Delta
New Orleans
0 50 100 mi
0 50 100 km
Gulf of Mexico

Figure 12 This satellite image shows part of the Mississippi River delta, which is always growing and changing. *Observing What happens to the Mississippi River as it flows through its delta? Can you find the river's main channel?*

EXPLORING the Course of a River

The slope and size of a river, as well as the land through which it flows, determine how a river shapes the land.

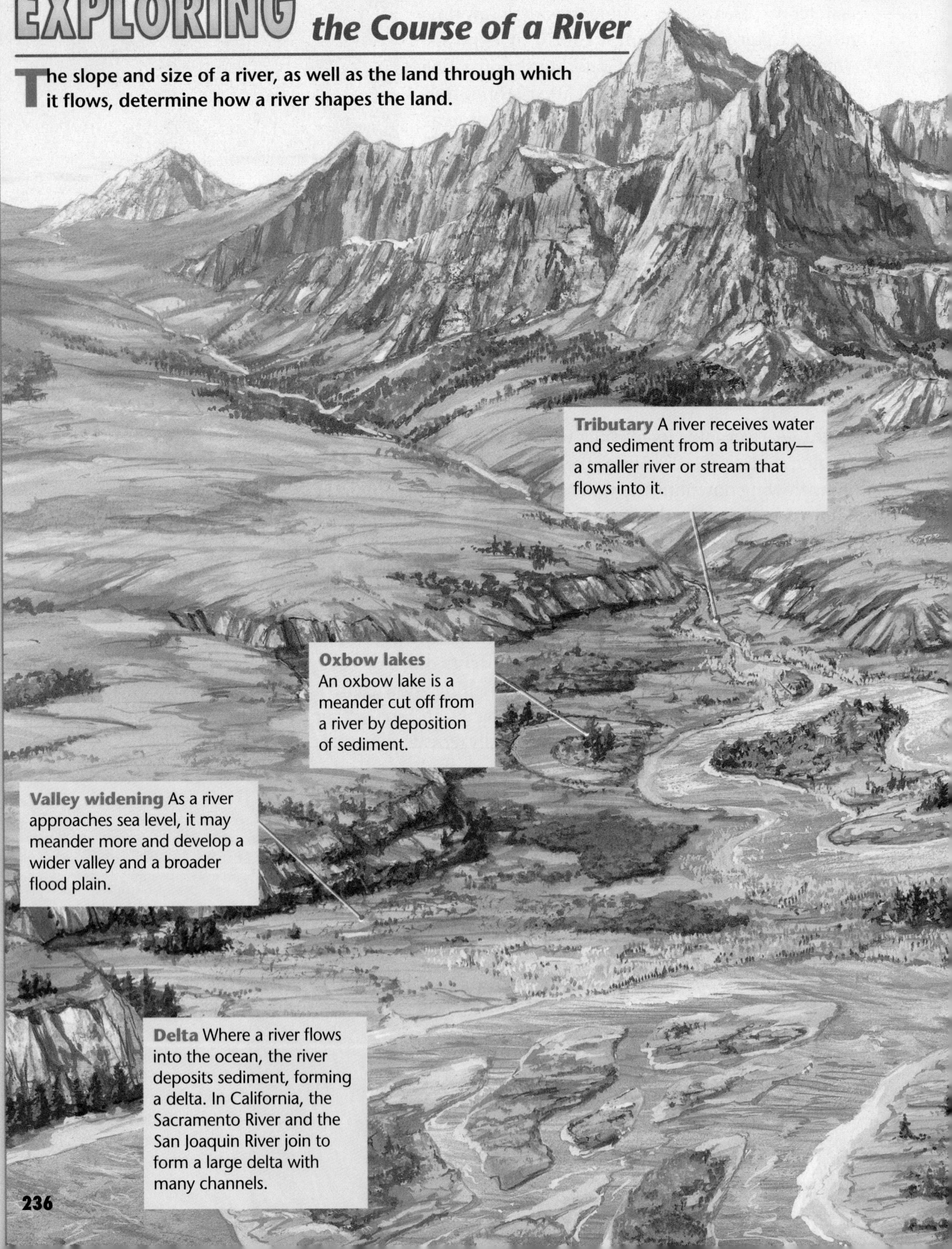
Tributary A river receives water and sediment from a tributary—a smaller river or stream that flows into it.
Oxbow lakes An oxbow lake is a meander cut off from a river by deposition of sediment.
Valley widening As a river approaches sea level, it may meander more and develop a wider valley and a broader flood plain.
Delta Where a river flows into the ocean, the river deposits sediment, forming a delta. In California, the Sacramento River and the San Joaquin River join to form a large delta with many channels.

Waterfalls and rapids Waterfalls and rapids are common where the river passes over harder rock. Many California rivers have waterfalls and rapids. The waterfalls in Yosemite National Park are world famous. Rapids are common on fast-flowing rivers like the Trinity and American rivers.
V-shaped valley Near its source, a river often flows through a deep, V-shaped valley. As the river flows, it cuts a deeper valley. Many California rivers in the Sierra Nevada have steep, V-shaped valleys, except where glaciers have carved the valley walls. Examples include the Merced and Tuolumne rivers.
Meanders Where a river flows across easily eroded sediment, its channel bends from side to side in a series of meanders. The Sacramento River has both meanders and oxbow lakes where it winds through California's Central Valley.
Oxbow lake
Flood plain A flood plain forms when a river's power of erosion widens its valley rather than deepening it. The San Joaquin and Sacramento rivers both have vast flood plans.
Beaches Sand carried downstream by rivers spreads along the coast to form beaches.

Groundwater Erosion and Deposition

When rain falls and snow melts, not all of the water evaporates or becomes runoff. Some water soaks into the ground. There it fills the openings in the soil and trickles into cracks and spaces in layers of rock. **Groundwater** is the term geologists use for this underground water. Like running water on the surface, groundwater affects the shape of the land.

INTEGRATING CHEMISTRY Groundwater can cause erosion through a process of chemical weathering. When water sinks into the ground, it combines with carbon dioxide to form a weak acid, called carbonic acid. Carbonic acid can break down limestone. Groundwater containing carbonic acid flows into cracks in the limestone. Then some of the limestone changes chemically and is carried away in a solution of water. This gradually hollows out pockets in the rock. Over time, these pockets develop into large holes underground, called caves or caverns. California has limestone caverns that formed in this way. Several of these caverns, such as Boyden Cavern in Kings Canyon National Park, are found along the western side of the Sierra Nevada.

The action of carbonic acid on limestone can also result in deposition. Inside limestone caves, deposits called stalactites and stalagmites often form. Water containing carbonic acid and calcium from limestone drips from a cave's roof. As the water

Figure 13 Over millions of years, chemical weathering of limestone and groundwater erosion created the beautiful shapes in Carlsbad Caverns in New Mexico. *Interpreting Photos What evidence of deposition do you see in the photo of Carlsbad Caverns?*

Figure 14 A sinkhole, such as this one in Florida, is a characteristic feature of karst topography. Sinkholes can pose a hazard for people who live in a karst region.

evaporates, a deposit of calcite forms. A deposit that hangs like an icicle from the roof of a cave is called a **stalactite** (stuh LAK tyt). Slow dripping builds up a cone-shaped **stalagmite** (stuh LAG myt) from the cave floor.

In rainy regions where there is a layer of limestone near the surface, groundwater erosion can significantly change the shape of the land. Streams are rare, because water sinks easily down into the weathered limestone. Deep valleys and caverns are common. If the roof of a cave collapses because of the erosion of the underlying limestone, the result is a depression called a sinkhole. This type of landscape is called **karst topography** after a region in Eastern Europe. In the United States, there are regions of karst topography in Florida, Kentucky, and Indiana.

Section 2 Review

1. What is the major cause of erosion on Earth's surface?
2. Briefly describe five features formed by rivers and streams as they erode the land.
3. What are the results of deposition along the course of a stream or river?
4. How can groundwater contribute to erosion?
5. **Thinking Critically** **Comparing and Contrasting** How is an alluvial fan similar to a delta? How is it different?

Science at Home

In a small dish, build a cube out of 27 small sugar cubes. Your cube should be three sugar cubes on a side. Fold a square piece of paper towel to fit the top of the cube. Wet the paper towel, place it on the cube, and let it stand for 15 or 20 minutes. Every few minutes, sprinkle a few drops of water on the paper towel to keep it wet. Then remove the paper towel. What happened to your cube? How is the effect of water on a sugar cube similar to groundwater eroding limestone? How is it different?

Streams in Action

Erosion can form gullies, wash away topsoil, and pollute rivers with sediment. You can observe the effects of erosion using a stream table.

Problem

How do rivers and streams erode the land?

Skills Focus

making models, observing, predicting

Materials

plastic tub at least 27 cm × 40 cm × 10 cm
diatomaceous earth
spray bottle
watch or clock
1 metal spoon
blue food coloring
scissors
plastic measuring cup
hand lens
water
plastic foam cup
liquid detergent
2 wood blocks about 2.5 cm thick
bucket to hold 2–3 L of water or a source of tap water
plastic stirrers, 10–12 cm long, with two small holes each
wire 13–15 cm long, 20 gauge

Procedure

Part A Creating Streams Over Time

1. Your teacher will give you a plastic tub containing diatomaceous earth that has been soaked with water. Place the tub on a level surface. **CAUTION:** *Dry diatomaceous earth produces dust that may be irritating if inhaled. To keep the diatomaceous earth from drying out, spray it lightly with water.*

Making the Dripper

1. Insert the wire into one of the two holes in a plastic stirrer. The ends of the wire should protrude from the stirrer.
2. Gently bend the stirrer into a U shape. Be careful not to make any sharp bends. This is the dripper.
3. With scissors, carefully cut two small notches on opposite sides of the top of the foam cup.
4. Fill the cup to just below the notches with water colored with two drops of blue food coloring. Add more food coloring later as you add more water to the cup.
5. Add one drop of detergent to keep air bubbles out of the dripper and increase flow.
6. To start the dripper, fill it with water. Then quickly tip it and place it in one of the notches in the cup, as shown above.
7. Adjust the flow rate of the dripper to about 2 drips per 1 second. (*Hint:* Bend the dripper into more of a U shape to increase flow. Lessen the curve to reduce flow.)

2. One end of the tub will contain more diatomaceous earth. Use the block of wood to raise this end of the tub 2.5 cm.
3. Place the cup at the upper end of the slope with the notches pointing to the left and right.
4. Press the cup firmly down into the earth to secure its position.
5. Start the dripper (see Step 6 in the box above). Allow the water to drip to the right onto the diatomaceous earth.

6. Allow the dripper to drip for 5 minutes. (*Hint:* When you need to add more water, be careful not to disturb the dripper.)
7. Observe the flow of water and the changes it makes. Use the hand lens to look closely at the stream bed.
8. After 5 minutes, remove the dripper.
9. In your lab notebook, draw a picture of the resulting stream and label it "5 minutes."
10. Now switch the dripper to the left side of the cup. Restart the dripper and allow it to drip for 10 minutes. Then remove the dripper.
11. Draw a picture and label it "10 minutes."

Part B Changing the Angle of Slope

1. Remove the cup from the stream table.
2. Save the stream bed on the right side of the tub. Using the bowl of the spoon, smooth out the diatomaceous earth on the left side.
3. To increase the angle of slope of your stream table, raise the end of the tub another 2.5 cm.
4. In your lab notebook, predict the effects of increasing the angle of slope.
5. Replace the cup and restart the dripper, placing it in the notch on the left side of the cup. Allow the dripper to drip for 5 minutes. Notice any changes in the new stream bed.
6. At the end of 5 minutes, remove the dripper.
7. Draw a picture of the new stream bed in your lab notebook. Label it "Increased Angle."
8. Follow your teacher's instructions for clean-up after this activity. Wash your hands when you have finished.

Analyze and Conclude

1. Compare the 5-minute stream with the 10-minute stream. How did the length of time that the water flowed affect erosion along the stream bed?
2. Were your predictions about the effects of increasing the angle of slope correct? Explain your answer.
3. What eventually happened to the eroded material that was carried downstream?
4. What other variables besides time and angle of slope might affect the way rivers and streams erode the land?
5. **Apply** Have you ever seen water flowing down a hillside or street after a heavy rain? If so, how much did the land slope in that area? Did you notice anything about the color of the water? Explain.

Design an Experiment

Design a stream table experiment to measure how the amount of sediment carried by a river changes as the volume of flow of the river increases. Obtain your teacher's approval before you try the experiment.

Protecting Homes in Flood Plains

MAIN ST.
MAPLE

At least ten million American households are located in flood plains. Living near a river is tempting. Riverside land is often flat and easy to build on. Because so many people now live in flood plains, the cost of flood damage has been growing. Communities along rivers want to limit the cost of flooding. They want to know how they can protect the people and buildings already in flood plains. They also want to know how to discourage more people from moving into flood plains.

The Issues

Should the Government Insure People Against Flood Damage? The United States government offers insurance to households in flood plains. The insurance pays part of the cost of repairs after a flood. Insurance helps people, but it is very expensive. Only 17 percent of people who live in flood plains buy the government insurance. Government flood insurance is available only in places that take steps to reduce flood damage. Cities must allow new building only on high ground. The insurance will not pay to rebuild homes that are badly damaged by floodwater. Instead, these people must use the money to find a home somewhere else.

Critics say that insurance just encourages people to move back into areas that flood. Supporters say it rewards towns and cities that make rules to control building on flood plains.

How Much of the Flood Plain Should Be Protected? Government flood insurance is available only in areas where scientists expect flooding about once in 100 years, or once in 500 years. Such figures are just estimates. Three floods occurred in only 12 years in a government flood-insurance area near Sacramento, California.

Should the Government Tell People Where They Can Live? Some programs of flood control forbid all new building. Other programs may also encourage people to move to safer areas. The 1997 flood on the Red River in Grand Forks, North Dakota, is one example. After the flood, the city of Grand Forks offered to buy all the damaged buildings near the river. The city wants to build high walls of earth to protect the rest of the town.

The Grand Forks plan might prevent future damage, but is it fair? Supporters say that since the government has to pay for flood damage, it has the right to make people leave flood plains. Critics of such plans say that people should be free to live where they want, even in risky areas.

Who should decide in which neighborhood no new houses can be built? Who decides which people should be asked to move away from a flood plain? Experts disagree over whether local, state, or United States government officials should decide which areas to include. Some believe scientists should make the decision.

You Decide

1. Identify the Problem
In your own words, describe the controversy surrounding flood plains and housing.

2. Analyze the Options
List several steps that could be taken to reduce the damage done to buildings in flood plains. For each step, include who would benefit from the step, and who would pay the costs.

3. Find a Solution
Your town has to decide what to do about a neighborhood damaged by the worst flood in 50 years. Write a speech that argues for your solution.

SECTION 3 The Force of Moving Water

DISCOVER ACTIVITY

How Are Sediments Deposited?

1. Put on your goggles.
2. Obtain a clear plastic jar or bottle with a top. Fill the jar about two-thirds full with water.
3. Fill a plastic beaker with 200 mL of fine and coarse sand, soil, clay, and small pebbles.
4. Pour the mixture into the jar of water. Screw on the top tightly and shake for two minutes. Be sure to hold onto the jar firmly.
5. Set the jar down and observe it for 10 to 15 minutes.

Think It Over

Inferring In what order are the sediments in the jar deposited? What do you think causes this pattern?

GUIDE FOR READING

- **What enables water to do work?**
- **How does sediment enter rivers and streams?**
- **What factors affect a river's ability to erode and carry sediment?**

Reading Tip **Before you read, rewrite the headings of the section as *how, why,* or *what* questions. As you read, look for answers to these questions.**

The Merrimack River in New Hampshire and Massachusetts is only 180 kilometers long. But the Merrimack does a great deal of work as it runs from the mountains to the sea. The river's waters fall 82 meters through many rapids and waterfalls. During the 1800s, people harnessed this falling water to run machines. These machines could spin thread and weave cloth very quickly and cheaply. Thanks to water power, the towns along the river grew quickly into cities.

Work and Energy

The waters of the Merrimack River could drive machines because a river's water has energy. **Energy** is the ability to do work or cause change. There are two kinds of energy. **Potential energy** is energy that is stored and waiting to be used later. The Merrimack's waters begin with potential energy due to their position above sea level. **Kinetic energy** is the energy an object has due to its motion. **As gravity pulls water down a slope, the water's potential energy changes to kinetic energy that can do work.**

Figure 15 Dams like this one on the Merrimack River in Lowell, Massachusetts, help to harness the power of flowing water.

Social Studies CONNECTION

The cotton mills in Lowell, Massachusetts, were built in the 1820s. The mills employed young women from the farms and small towns of New England. At that time, it was unusual for women to work outside the home. The hours of work at a mill were long and pay was low. But mill work helped these women to earn and save their own money. Most later returned to their home towns.

In Your Journal

Use library references to find out more about the daily life of the mill workers. Write a diary entry describing a worker's typical day.

When energy does work, the energy is transferred from one object to another. At the textile mills along the Merrimack River, the kinetic energy of the moving water was transferred to the spinning machines. It became mechanical energy harnessed for a human purpose—making cloth. But all along a river, kinetic energy does other work. A river is always moving sediment from the mountains to the sea. At the same time, a river is also eroding its banks and valley.

☑ *Checkpoint* *What are potential energy and kinetic energy?*

How Water Erodes and Carries Sediment

Gravity causes the movement of water across Earth's land surface. But how does water cause erosion? In the process of water erosion, water picks up and moves sediment. Sediment includes soil, rock, clay, and sand. Sediment can enter rivers and streams in a number of ways. **Most sediment washes or falls into the river as a result of mass movement and runoff. Other sediment erodes from the bottom or sides of the river.** Wind may also drop sediment into the water.

Abrasion is another process by which a river obtains sediment. **Abrasion** is the wearing away of rock by a grinding action. Abrasion occurs when particles of sediment in flowing water bump into the streambed again and again. Abrasion grinds down sediment particles. For example, boulders become smaller as they are moved down a streambed. Sediments also grind and chip away at the rock of the streambed, deepening and widening the stream's channel.

The amount of sediment that a river carries is its **load.** Gravity and the force of the moving water cause the sediment load to move downstream. Most large sediment falls to the bottom and moves by rolling and sliding. Fast-moving water actually lifts sand and other, smaller, sediment and carries it downstream. Water dissolves some sediment completely. The river carries these dissolved sediments in solution. If you look at Figure 16, you can observe the different ways in which water can carry sediment. Notice for example, how grains of sand or small stones can move by bouncing.

Figure 16 Rivers and streams carry sediment in several ways. *Predicting What will eventually happen to a boulder on the bottom of a river?*

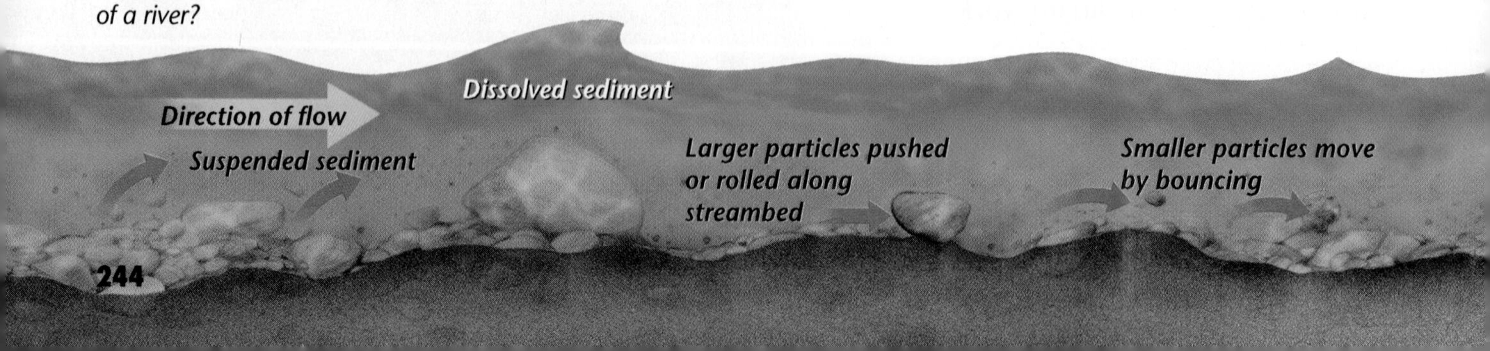
Dissolved sediment
Direction of flow
Suspended sediment
Larger particles pushed or rolled along streambed
Smaller particles move by bouncing

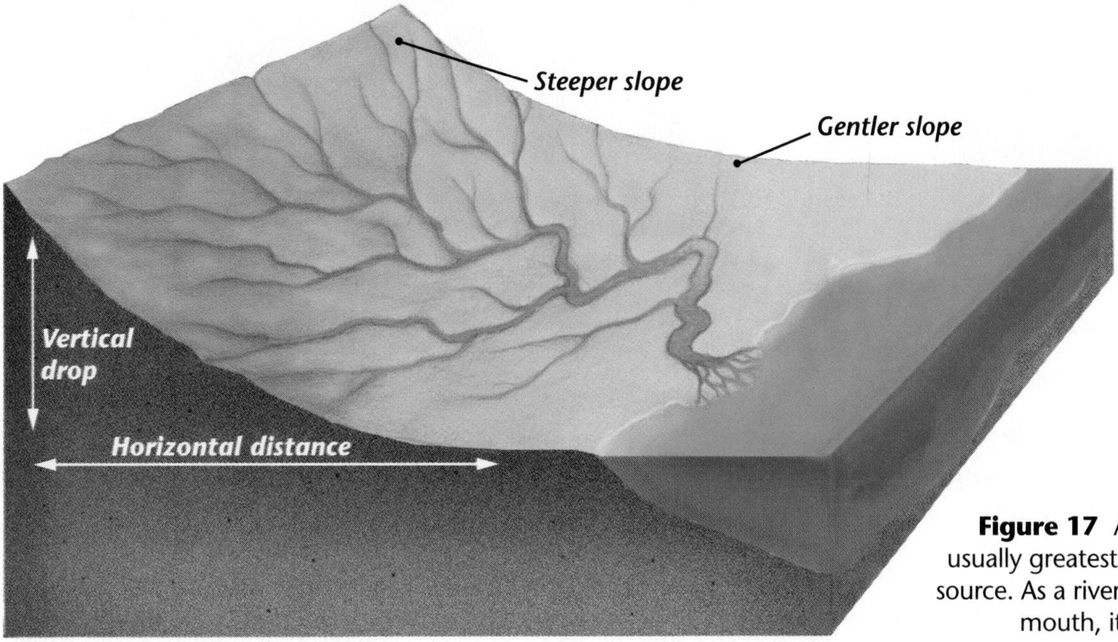
Steeper slope
Gentler slope
Vertical drop
Horizontal distance

Figure 17 A river's slope is usually greatest near the river's source. As a river approaches its mouth, its slope lessens.

Erosion and Sediment Load

The power of a river to cause erosion and carry sediment depends on several factors. **A river's slope, volume of flow, and the shape of its streambed all affect how fast the river flows and how much sediment it can erode.**

A fast-flowing river carries more and larger particles of sediment. When a river slows down, its sediment load is deposited. The larger particles of sediment are deposited first.

Slope Generally, if a river's slope increases, the water's speed also increases. A river's slope is the amount the river drops toward sea level over a given distance. If a river's speed increases, its sediment load and power to erode may increase. But other factors are also important in determining how much sediment the river erodes and carries.

Volume of Flow A river's flow is the volume of water that moves past a point on the river in a given time. As more water flows through a river, its speed increases. During a flood, the increased volume of water helps the river to cut more deeply into its banks and bed. A flooding river may have hundreds of times more eroding power than the river has at other times. A flooding river can carry huge amounts of sand, soil, and other sediments. It may move giant boulders as if they were pebbles.

Streambed Shape A streambed's shape affects the amount of friction between the water and the streambed. **Friction** is the force that opposes the motion of one surface as it moves across another surface. Friction, in turn, affects a river's speed. Where a river is deep, less water comes in contact with the streambed. This reduces

Sharpen your Skills

Developing Hypotheses

ACTIVITY

A geologist is comparing alluvial fans. One alluvial fan is composed of gravel and small boulders. The other fan is composed of sand and silt. Propose a hypothesis to explain the difference in the size of the particles in the two fans. (*Hint*: Think of the characteristics of the streams that formed each alluvial fan.)

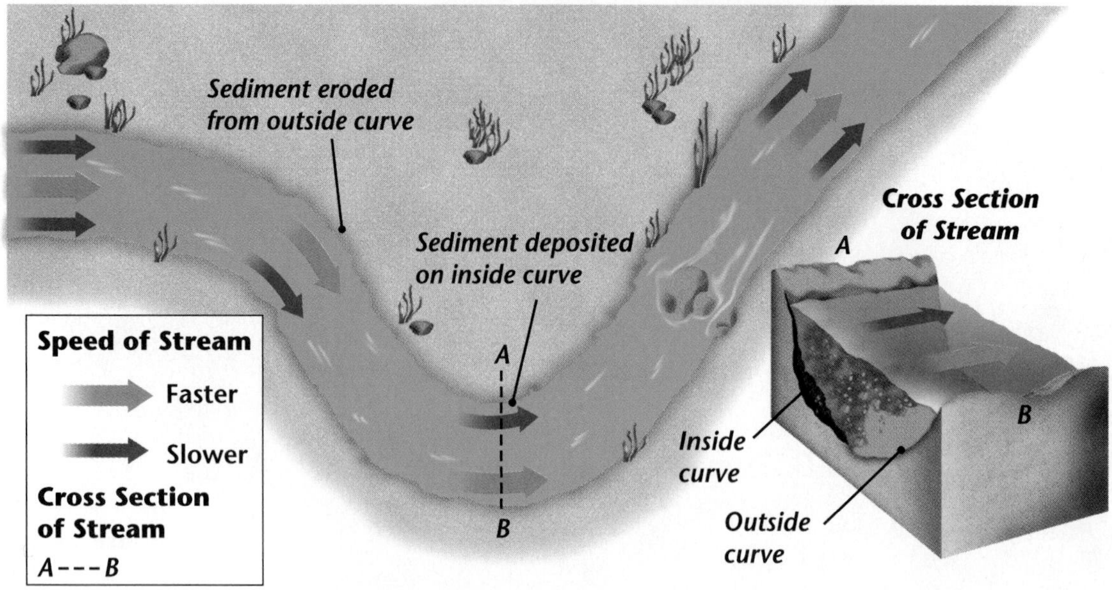
Sediment eroded from outside curve
Sediment deposited on inside curve
Speed of Stream
Faster
Slower
Cross Section of Stream
A---B
A
B
Cross Section of Stream
A
B
Inside curve
Outside curve

Figure 18 A river erodes sediment from its banks on the outside curve and deposits its sediment on the inside curve.
Relating Cause and Effect Why does a river deposit sediment on the inside of a curve?

friction and allows the river to flow faster. In a shallow river, much of the water comes in contact with the streambed. Therefore friction increases, reducing the river's speed.

A streambed is often full of boulders and other obstacles. This roughness prevents the water from flowing smoothly. Roughness thus increases friction and reduces the river's speed. Instead of moving downstream, the water moves every which way in a type of movement called **turbulence.** For example, a stream on a steep slope may flow at a lower speed than a large river on a gentle slope. Friction and turbulence slow the stream's flow. But a turbulent stream or river may have great power to erode.

The shape of a river affects the way it deposits sediment. Where a river flows in a straight line, the water flows faster near the center of the river than along its sides. Deposition occurs along the sides of the river, where the water moves more slowly.

If a river curves, the water moves fastest along the outside of the curve. There, the river tends to cut into its bank. Sediment is deposited on the inside curve, where the water speed is slowest. You can see this process in Figure 18.

Section 3 Review

1. How can moving water on Earth's surface do work?
2. How does a river collect sediment?
3. What are three factors that affect a river's sediment load?
4. Describe three ways that sediment moves in a river.
5. **Thinking Critically Relating Cause and Effect** What effect does increased slope have on a river's speed and sediment load? Explain.

CHAPTER PROJECT

Check Your Progress

Make a drawing of the landscape that you plan to model. This landscape will show the land before erosion. What kinds of landforms will you show in the model? Be sure to include a high mountain and a coastline. Make a list of materials that you will use to build your model. Once your teacher has approved your drawing and your list of materials, you may build your first model.

SECTION

4 Glaciers

DISCOVER ACTIVITY

How Do Glaciers Change the Land?

1. Put some sand in a small plastic container.
2. Fill the container with water and place the container in a freezer until the water turns to ice.
3. Remove the block of ice from the container.
4. Holding the ice with paper towels, rub the ice, sand side down, over a bar of soap. Observe what happens to the surface of the soap.

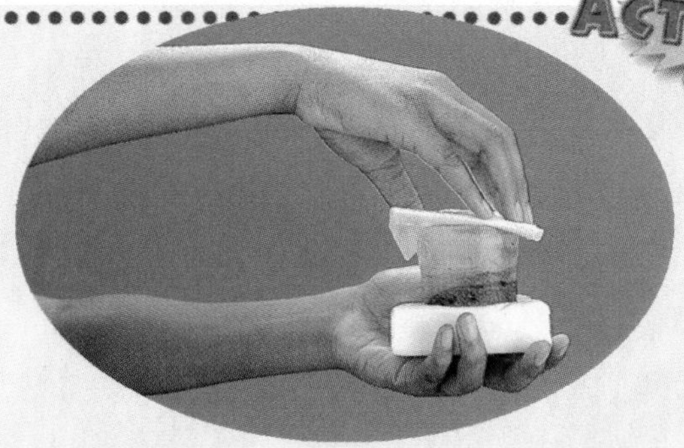

Think It Over

Inferring Based on your observations, how do you think moving ice could change the surface of the land?

GUIDE FOR READING

- **What are the two kinds of glaciers?**
- **How do glaciers cause erosion and deposition?**

Reading Tip **Before you read, preview the headings and key terms in the section. Predict some characteristics of glaciers.**

You are on a boat trip near the coast of Alaska. You sail by vast evergreen forests and snow-capped mountains. Then, as your boat rounds a point of land, you see an amazing sight. A great mass of ice winds like a river between rows of mountains. Suddenly you hear a noise like thunder. Where the ice meets the sea, a giant chunk of ice breaks off and plunges into the water. Carefully, you pilot your boat around the iceberg and toward the mass of ice. It towers over your boat. You see that it is made up of solid ice that is deep blue and green as well as white. What is this river of ice?

Kinds of Glaciers

Geologists define a **glacier** as any large mass of ice that moves slowly over land. **There are two kinds of glaciers—valley glaciers and continental glaciers.**

A **valley glacier** is a long, narrow glacier that forms when snow and ice build up high in a mountain valley. The sides of mountains keep these glaciers from spreading out in all directions. Instead, they usually move down valleys that have already been cut by rivers. Valley glaciers are found on many high mountains.

A **continental glacier** is a glacier that covers much of a continent or large island. Continental glaciers are much larger than

Figure 19 The Mendenhall Glacier in Alaska winds downhill between high mountains.

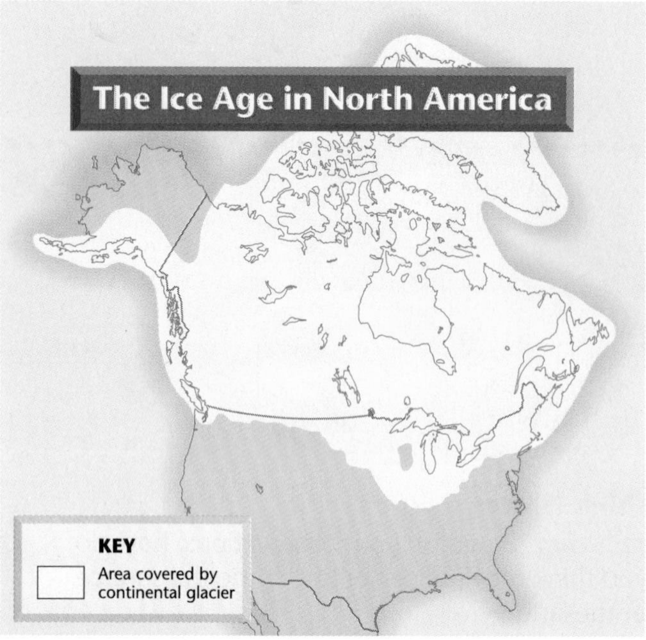
The Ice Age in North America
KEY
Area covered by continental glacier

Figure 20 The continental glacier of the last ice age covered most of Canada and Alaska as well as much of the northern United States. The ice age lasted about 70,000 years and ended about 10,000 years ago.

valley glaciers. They spread out over large areas of the land. Today, continental glaciers cover about 10 percent of Earth's land. They cover Antarctica and most of Greenland. The glacier covering Antarctica spreads out over 14 million square kilometers and is over 2 kilometers thick.

Ice Ages

Many times in the past, continental glaciers have covered large parts of Earth's surface. These times are known as **ice ages.** For example, about 9 million years ago, continental glaciers began to form in North America, Europe, and Asia. These glaciers slowly grew and advanced southward. By about 2.5 million years ago, they covered about a third of Earth's land. The glaciers advanced and retreated, or melted back, several times. Figure 20 shows how far south the glaciers came on the North American continent during the most recent ice age. They finally retreated about 10,000 years ago.

How Glaciers Form and Move

Glaciers can form only in an area where more snow falls than melts. High in mountain valleys, temperatures seldom rise above freezing. Snow builds up year after year. The pressure of the weight of more and more snow compacts the snow at the bottom into ice. Once the depth of snow and ice reaches more than 30 to 40 meters, gravity begins to pull the glacier downhill.

Valley glaciers flow at a rate of a few centimeters to a few meters per day. But sometimes a valley glacier slides down more quickly in what is called a surge. A surging glacier can flow as much as 6 kilometers a year. Unlike valley glaciers, continental glaciers can flow in all directions. Continental glaciers spread out much as pancake batter spreads out in a frying pan.

☑ *Checkpoint* *How do glaciers form?*

Glacial Erosion

The movement of a glacier changes the land beneath it. Although glaciers work slowly, they are a major force of erosion. **The two processes by which glaciers erode the land are plucking and abrasion.**

As a glacier flows over the land, it picks up rocks in a process called **plucking.** Beneath a glacier, the weight of the ice can break rocks apart. These rock fragments freeze to the bottom of the glacier. When the glacier moves, it carries the rocks with it. Figure 21 shows plucking by a glacier. Plucking can move even huge boulders.

Many rocks remain on the bottom of the glacier, and the glacier drags them across the land. This process, called abrasion, gouges and scratches the bedrock. You can see the results of erosion by glaciers in *Exploring Glacial Landforms* on pages 250–251.

Direction of ice flow
Ice in cracks
Bedrock

Figure 21 As a glacier moves downhill, the ice plucks pieces of bedrock from the ground. *Predicting What evidence of plucking might you find after a glacier melts?*

Glacial Deposition

A glacier gathers a huge amount of rock and soil as it erodes the land in its path. **When a glacier melts, it deposits the sediment it eroded from the land, creating various landforms.** These landforms remain for thousands of years after the glacier has melted.

The mixture of sediments that a glacier deposits directly on the surface is called **till.** Till is made up of particles of many different sizes. Clay, silt, sand, gravel, and boulders can all be found in till.

The till deposited at the edges of a glacier forms a ridge called a **moraine.** A terminal moraine is the ridge of till at the farthest point reached by a glacier. Long Island in New York is a terminal moraine from the continental glaciers of the last ice age.

INTEGRATING LIFE SCIENCE Other features left in glacial sediments are prairie potholes. These potholes are shallow depressions in till that were formed by flowing water as the continental glacier melted. Today, prairie potholes contain water for only part of the year. Each prairie pothole is a small oasis for living things. Grasses and moisture-loving plants grow thickly in and around the potholes. In the spring, the potholes brim with water from melting snow or rain. Thousands of migrating ducks and other birds stop off at the potholes to feed and rest on their way north. Some stay to build nests and raise their young.

Figure 22 This prairie pothole in Wisconsin is surrounded by farmland. Prairie potholes were left in till deposited by glaciers.

EXPLORING Glacial Landforms

As glaciers advance and retreat, they sculpt the landscape by erosion and deposition.

Horn When glaciers carve away the sides of a mountain, the result is a horn, a sharpened peak.
Cirque A cirque is a bowl-shaped hollow eroded by a glacier.
Arête An arête is a sharp ridge separating two cirques.
Fiord A fiord forms when the level of the sea rises, filling a valley once cut by a glacier in a coastal region.

Retreating glaciers also create features called kettles. A **kettle** is a small depression that forms when a chunk of ice is left in glacial till. When the ice melts, the kettle remains. The continental glacier of the last ice age left behind many kettles. Kettles often fill with water, forming small ponds or lakes called kettle lakes. Such lakes are common in areas that were covered with ice.

The continental glacier of the last ice age also formed the Great Lakes. Before the ice age, there were large river valleys in the area now occupied by the lakes. As the ice advanced over these valleys, it scooped out loose sediment and soft rock, forming broad, deep basins. The Great Lakes formed over thousands of years as the glaciers melted and these basins filled with water.

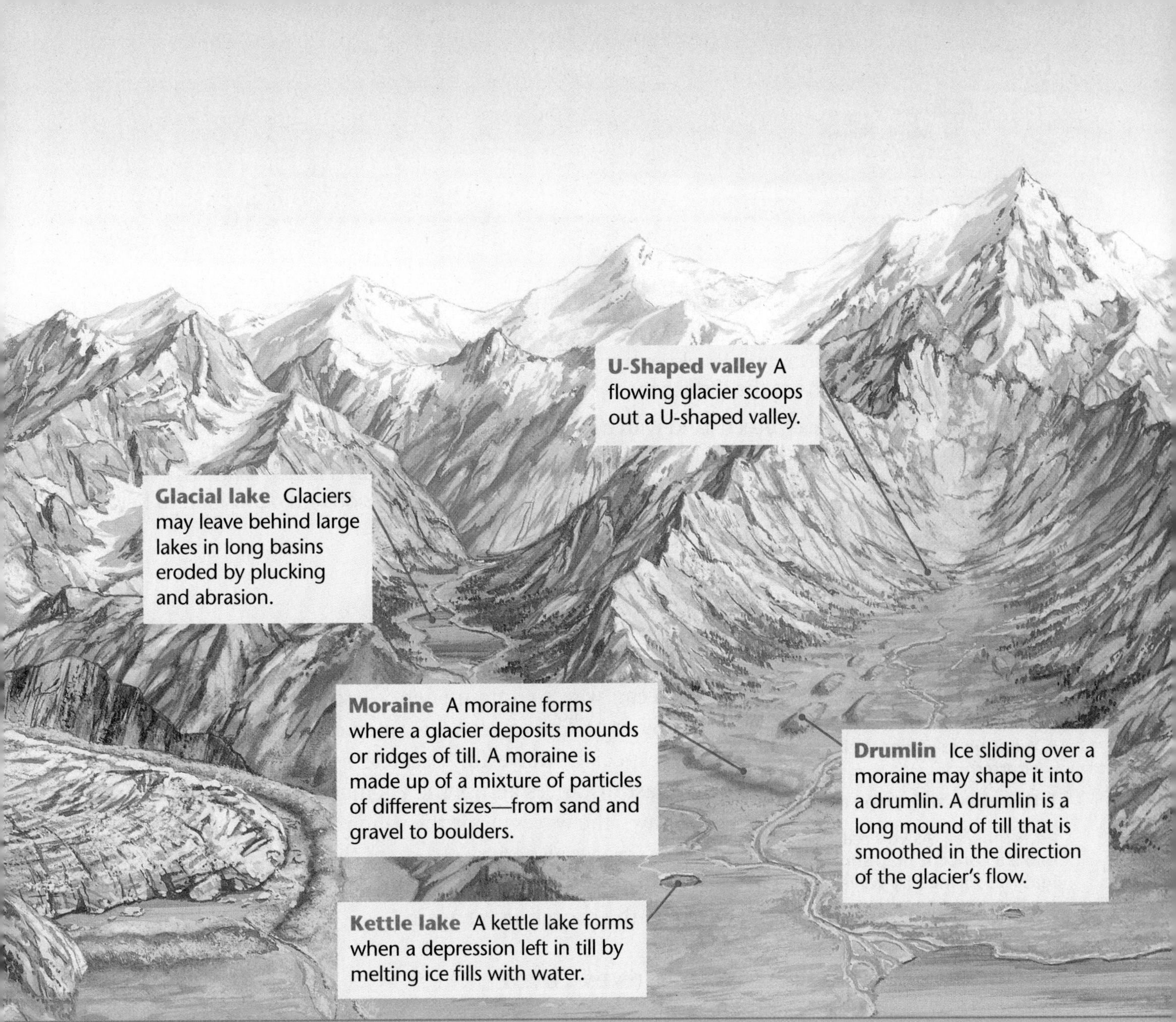
U-Shaped valley A flowing glacier scoops out a U-shaped valley.
Glacial lake Glaciers may leave behind large lakes in long basins eroded by plucking and abrasion.
Moraine A moraine forms where a glacier deposits mounds or ridges of till. A moraine is made up of a mixture of particles of different sizes—from sand and gravel to boulders.
Drumlin Ice sliding over a moraine may shape it into a drumlin. A drumlin is a long mound of till that is smoothed in the direction of the glacier's flow.
Kettle lake A kettle lake forms when a depression left in till by melting ice fills with water.

Section 4 Review

1. How are valley glaciers and continental glaciers different?
2. What are two types of glacial erosion?
3. Describe three features formed by glacial deposition.
4. **Thinking Critically Relating Cause and Effect** Driving through the countryside in Michigan, you and your family come upon a series of small, round lakes. Explain the process that formed these features.

CHAPTER PROJECT

Check Your Progress

Now you are ready to begin building your second model. Pattern the model after your drawing that predicts the effects of erosion and deposition. The model will show how gravity, water, and glaciers have changed your model landscape. Where on your model would glaciers be likely to form?

SECTION 5 Waves

DISCOVER — ACTIVITY

What Can Be Learned From Beach Sand?

1. Collect a spoonful of sand from each of two different beaches. The two samples also may come from different parts of the same beach.
2. Examine the first sample of beach sand with a hand lens.
3. Record the properties of the sand grains, for example, color and shape. Are the grains smooth and rounded or angular and rough? Are all the grains in the sample the same shape and color?
4. Examine the second sample and repeat Step 3. How do the two samples compare?

Think It Over

Posing Questions What questions do you need to answer to understand beach sand? Use what you know about erosion and deposition to help you think of questions.

GUIDE FOR READING

- **What gives waves their energy?**
- **How do waves shape a coast?**

Reading Tip **As you read, make a concept map showing features formed by wave erosion and deposition.**

Ocean waves contain energy—sometimes a great deal of energy. The waves that sweep onto the Pacific coast are especially powerful. Created by ocean winds, they carry energy vast distances across the Pacific Ocean. Acting like drills or buzzsaws, the waves erode the solid rock of the coast into cliffs and caves. Waves also carry sediment that forms features such as beaches. But these features do not last long. More waves follow to change the shoreline yet again.

How Waves Form

The energy in waves comes from wind that blows across the water's surface. As the wind makes contact with the water, some of its energy transfers to the water. Large ocean waves are the result of powerful storms far out at sea. But ordinary breezes can produce waves in lakes or small ponds.

The energy that water picks up from the wind causes water particles to move up and down as the wave goes by. But the water particles themselves don't move forward. Only the form of the wave moves. Have you ever watched a wave in a field of tall grass? Each blade of grass moves back and forth but doesn't move from its place. But the energy of the wave moves across the field.

Waves on the Oregon coast ▼

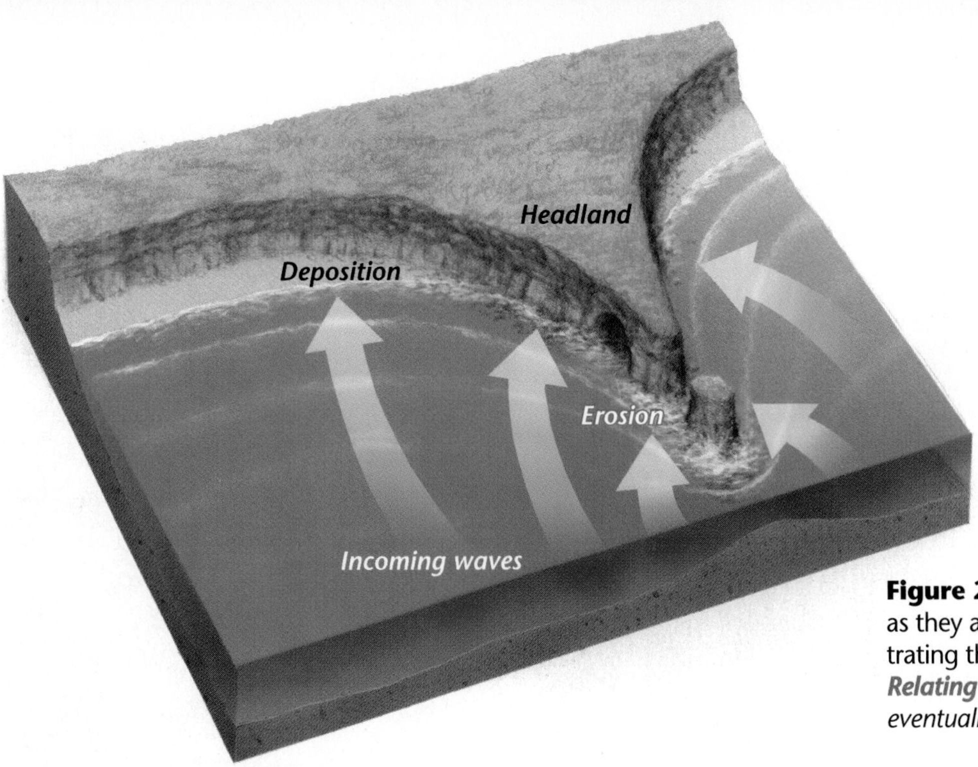
Headland
Deposition
Erosion
Incoming waves

Figure 23 Incoming waves bend as they approach the shore, concentrating their energy on headlands. ***Relating Cause and Effect*** *What will eventually happen to the headlands?*

A wave changes as it approaches land. In deep water, a wave only affects the water near the surface. But as the wave approaches shallow water, the wave begins to drag the bottom. The friction between the wave and the bottom causes the wave to slow down. Now the water actually does move forward with the wave. This forward-moving water provides the force that shapes the land along the shoreline.

Erosion by Waves

Waves are the major force of erosion along coasts. One way waves erode the land is by impact. Large waves can hit rocks along the shore with great force. This energy in waves can break apart rocks. Over time, waves can make small cracks larger. Eventually, the waves cause pieces of rock to break off.

Waves also erode land by abrasion. As a wave approaches shallow water, it picks up sediment, including sand and gravel. This sediment is carried forward by the wave. When the wave hits land, the sediment wears away rock like sandpaper wearing away wood.

Waves coming to shore gradually change direction. The change in direction occurs as different parts of a wave begin to drag on the bottom. Notice how the waves in Figure 23 change direction as they approach the shore. The energy of these waves is concentrated on headlands. A headland is a part of the shore that sticks out into the ocean. Headlands stand out from the coast because they are made of harder rock that resists the waves. But, over time, waves erode the headlands and even out the shoreline.

Checkpoint *What are two of the processes by which waves can cause erosion?*

Sharpen your Skills

Calculating ACTIVITY

A sandy coast erodes at a rate of 1.25 meters per year. But a severe storm can erode an additional 3.75 meters from the shore. If 12 severe storms occur during a 50-year period, how much will the coast erode? If you wish, you may use an electronic calculator to find the answer.

Figure 24 Waves cut these cliffs on the coast of Australia. The blocks of rock offshore are sea stacks. *Developing Hypotheses Develop a hypothesis to explain how these sea stacks formed.*

Landforms Created by Wave Erosion

When waves hit a steep, rocky coast, they strike the area again and again. Think of an ax striking the trunk of a tree. The cut gets bigger and deeper with each strike of the blade. Finally the tree falls. In a similar way, ocean waves erode the base of the land along a steep coast. Where the rock is softer, the waves erode the land faster. Over time the waves may erode a hollow area in the rock called a sea cave.

Eventually, waves may erode the base of a cliff so much that the rock above collapses. The result is a wave-cut cliff. You can see an example of such a cliff in Figure 24.

Another feature created by wave erosion is a sea arch. A sea arch forms when waves erode a layer of softer rock that underlies a layer of harder rock. If an arch collapses, the result might be a sea stack, a pillar of rock rising above the water.

☑ *Checkpoint* *How can waves produce a cliff on a rocky coast?*

Deposits by Waves

Waves not only erode the land, they also deposit sediment. **Waves shape the coast through both erosion and deposition.** Deposition occurs when waves slow down and the water drops its sediment. This process is similar to the deposition that occurs on a river delta when the river slows down and drops its sediment load.

As waves reach the shore, they drop the sediment they carry, forming a beach. A **beach** is an area of wave-washed sediment along a coast. The sediment deposited on beaches is usually sand. Most sand comes from rivers that carry eroded particles of rock into the ocean. But not all beaches are made of sand carried by rivers. Some beaches are made of small fragments of coral or sea shells piled up by wave action. Florida has many such beaches.

The sediment on a beach usually moves down the beach after it has been deposited. Waves usually hit the beach at an angle instead of straight on. These angled waves create a current that runs parallel to the coastline. As repeated waves hit the beach, some of the beach sediment moves down the beach with the current, in a process called **longshore drift.**

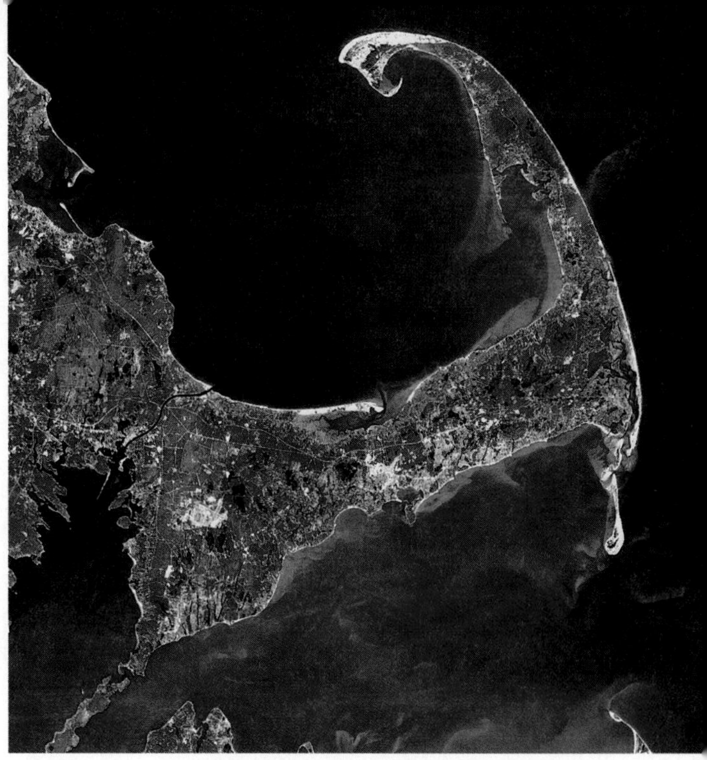

Figure 25 This satellite image of Cape Cod in Massachusetts shows how longshore drift can carry sand and deposit it to form a spit. *Observing How many spits can you find in this image?*

One result of longshore drift is the formation of a spit. A **spit** is a beach that projects like a finger out into the water. Spits form as a result of deposition by longshore drift. Spits occur where a headland or other obstacle interrupts longshore drift, or where the coast turns abruptly. Incoming waves carrying sand may build up sandbars, long ridges of sand parallel to the shore.

Integrating Environmental Science A barrier beach is similar to a sandbar, but a barrier beach forms when storm waves pile up sand above sea level. Barrier beaches are found in many places along the Atlantic coast of the United States, such as the Outer Banks of North Carolina. People have built homes on many of these barrier beaches. But the storm waves that build up the beaches can also wash them away. Barrier beach communities must be prepared for the damage that hurricanes and other storms can bring.

Section 5 Review

1. How do ocean waves form?
2. Describe two landforms created by wave erosion and two landforms created by wave deposition.
3. Why are headlands eroded faster than the land at the ends of inlets and bays?
4. **Thinking Critically Predicting** You visit a rocky headland by the ocean that has a sea arch and several sea stacks. How might this area change in the next 500 years?

Chapter Project

Check Your Progress

Now you are ready to add the effects of wave erosion to your model. What landforms will wave erosion produce along the coastline on your model? What materials will you use to model these landforms? When you have finished your second model, make labels for the landforms on your models.

SECTION 6 Wind

DISCOVER ACTIVITY

How Does Moving Air Affect Sediment?

1. Cover the bottom of a pan with a flat layer of cornmeal 1–2 centimeters deep.
2. Gently blow over the layer of cornmeal using a straw to direct your breath. Observe what happens.

CAUTION: *Do not blow the cornmeal in the direction of another student.*

Think It Over

Observing What changes did the wind you created make in the flat layer of cornmeal?

GUIDE FOR READING

- **How does wind cause erosion?**
- **What features result from deposition by wind?**

Reading Tip **Before you read, preview Figure 27. Predict some characteristics of wind erosion.**

Imagine a landscape made almost entirely of sand. One such place is the Namib Desert. The desert stretches for about 1,900 kilometers along the coast of Namibia in Africa. In the southern half of the Namib are long rows of giant sand dunes. A **sand dune** is a deposit of wind-blown sand. Some sand dunes in the Namib are more than 200 meters high and 15 kilometers long. Much of the sand in the dunes originally came from the nearby Orange River. Over thousands of years, wind has swept the sand across the desert, piling up huge, ever-changing dunes.

How Wind Causes Erosion

Wind by itself is the weakest agent of erosion. Water, waves, moving ice, and even mass movement have more effect on the land. Yet wind can be a powerful force in shaping the land in areas where there are few plants to hold the soil in place. As you might guess, wind is very effective in causing erosion in deserts. There few plants can grow, and wind can easily move the grains of dry, light sand.

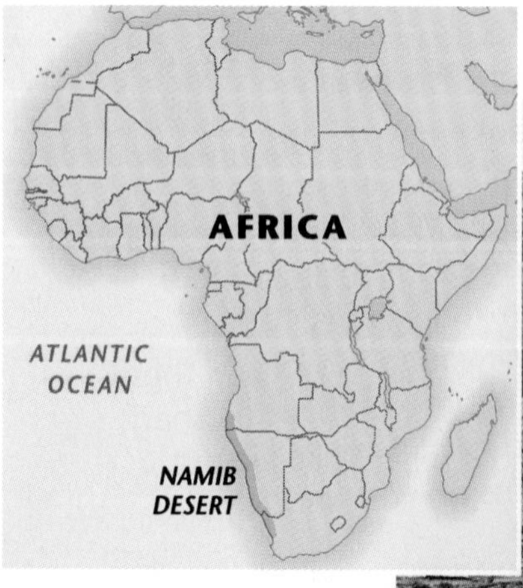
AFRICA
ATLANTIC OCEAN
NAMIB DESERT

Figure 26 Wind erosion continues to shape the giant sand dunes in the Namib Desert along Africa's southwestern coast.

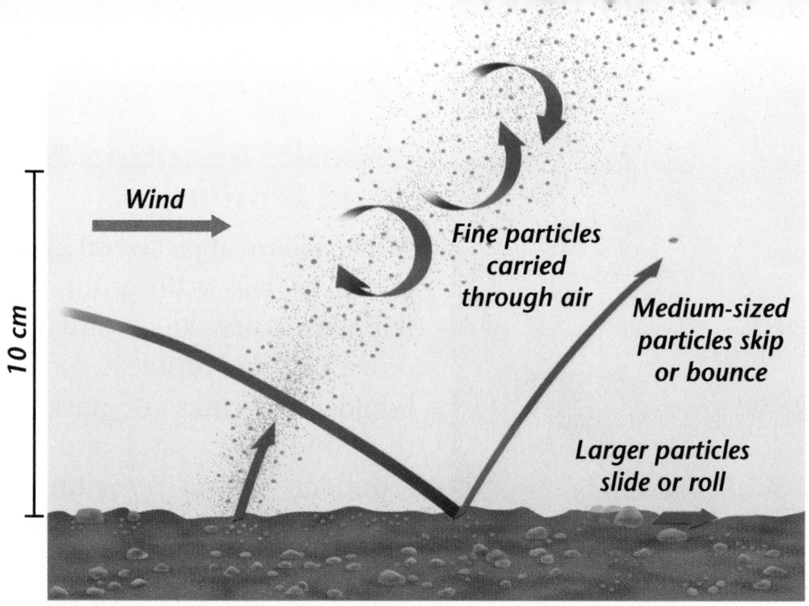
Wind
Fine particles carried through air
Medium-sized particles skip or bounce
Larger particles slide or roll
10 cm

Figure 27 Wind erosion moves sediment particles of different sizes in the three ways shown above. *Comparing and Contrasting* *Compare the movement of sediment by wind with the movement of sediment by water in Figure 16 on page 244. How are the processes similar? How are they different?*

The main way that wind causes erosion is by deflation. Geologists define **deflation** as the process by which wind removes surface materials. When wind blows over the land, it picks up the smallest particles of sediment. This sediment is made of bits of clay and silt. The stronger the wind, the larger the particles that it can pick up and move through the air. Slightly heavier particles, such as sand, might skip or bounce for a short distance. But sand soon falls back to the ground. Strong winds can even roll heavier sediment particles over the ground. Figure 27 shows how wind erodes by deflation.

Deflation does not usually have a great effect on the land. However, in parts of the Great Plains in the 1930s, deflation caused the loss of about 1 meter of topsoil in just a few years. In deserts, deflation can sometimes create an area of rock fragments called desert pavement. You can see an area of desert pavement in Figure 28. There, wind has blown away the smaller sediment. All that remains are rocky materials that are too large and heavy to be moved. Where there is already a slight depression in the ground, deflation can produce a bowl-shaped hollow called a blowout.

Figure 28 Wind erosion formed this desert pavement in the Arizona desert. Wind-driven sand may polish and shape individual stones.

Abrasion by wind-carried sand can polish rock, but it causes little erosion. At one time, geologists thought that the sediment carried by wind cut the stone shapes seen in deserts. But now evidence shows that most desert landforms are the result of weathering and water erosion.

☑ *Checkpoint* *Where would you be most likely to see evidence of wind erosion?*

LOESS BLUFF

Figure 29 Wind carrying fine particles of silt built up this loess deposit near Natchez, Mississippi.

Deposits Resulting From Wind Erosion

All the sediment picked up by wind eventually falls to the ground. This happens when the wind slows down or some obstacle, such as a boulder or a clump of grass, traps the windblown sand and other sediment. **Wind erosion and deposition may form sand dunes and loess deposits.** When the wind strikes an obstacle, the result is usually a sand dune. Sand dunes can be seen on beaches and in deserts where wind-blown sediment has built up.

Sand dunes come in many shapes and sizes. Some are long, with parallel ridges, while others are U-shaped. They can also be very small or very large—some sand dunes in China have grown to heights of 500 meters. Sand dunes move over time. Little by little, the sand shifts with the wind from one side of the dune to the other. Sometimes plants begin growing on a dune. Plant roots can help to anchor the dune in one place.

Sand dunes are most often made of the coarser sediments carried by wind. The finer sediments, including particles of clay and silt, are sometimes deposited in layers far from their source. This fine, wind-deposited sediment is **loess** (LES). Large loess deposits are found in central China and in such states as Nebraska, South Dakota, Iowa, Missouri, and Illinois. Loess helps to form fertile soil. Many areas with thick loess deposits are valuable farmlands.

Section 6 Review

1. Describe how wind erodes the land.
2. How do sand dunes and loess deposits form?
3. What is a blowout and what is the process that produces one?
4. **Thinking Critically Predicting** You visit a beach that has sand dunes covered with dune grass. But where people take a shortcut over one dune, the grass has been worn away. What may eventually happen to the dune if people keep taking this path?

Science at Home

Here's how to make a model of desert pavement. Put a few coins in a shallow pan about 1 centimeter deep. Sprinkle enough flour over the coins to bury them beneath a thin layer of flour. Then blow air gently through a straw across the surface of the flour. Be careful not to draw in any flour through the straw. Be certain the blown flour will not get in your or anyone else's eyes. Ask your family to predict what the surface of the pan would look like if the "wind" continued to blow for a long time.

Section 1 Changing Earth's Surface

Key Ideas

- Weathering, erosion, and deposition act to wear down and build up Earth's surface.
- Gravity pulls sediment downhill in the process of mass movement. There are four main types of mass movement: landslides, mudslides, slump, and creep.

Key Terms

erosion
sediment
deposition
mass movement

Section 2 Water Erosion

Key Ideas

- Moving water is the major force of erosion that has shaped Earth's land surface.
- A river may form V-shaped valleys, waterfalls, meanders, oxbow lakes, and flood plains.
- When a river slows down, it deposits some of the sediment load it carries, forming features such as alluvial fans and deltas.

Key Terms

runoff
rill
gully
stream
river
tributary
drainage basin
divide
flood plain
meander
oxbow lake
alluvial fan
delta
groundwater
stalactite
stalagmite
karst topography

Section 3 The Force of Moving Water

Integrating Physics

Key Ideas

- When gravity pulls water down a slope, water's potential energy changes to kinetic energy, and it does work.
- Most sediment washes or falls into streams, or is eroded from the streambed by abrasion.
- The greater a river's slope or volume of flow, the more sediment it can erode.

Key Terms

energy
potential energy
kinetic energy
abrasion
load
friction
turbulence

Section 4 Glaciers

Key Ideas

- The two kinds of glaciers are valley glaciers and continental glaciers.
- Glaciers erode the land through two processes, plucking and abrasion.
- Melting glaciers deposit sediment, dropping the rocks and soil that they have eroded.

Key Terms

glacier
valley glacier
continental glacier
ice age
plucking
till
moraine
kettle

Section 5 Waves

Key Ideas

- The energy of ocean waves comes from wind blowing across the water's surface and transferring energy to the water.
- Ocean waves hitting land cause erosion through impact and abrasion. Waves also move and deposit sediment along the shore.

Key Terms

beach
longshore drift
spit

Section 6 Wind

Key Ideas

- Wind causes erosion mainly through deflation, the blowing of surface materials.
- The major landforms created by wind deposition are sand dunes and loess deposits.

Key Terms

deflation
sand dune
loess

ACTIVITY — USING THE INTERNET

www.phschool.com/state_focus/california/

California Test Prep: Reviewing Content

For more review of key concepts, see the Interactive Student Tutorial CD-ROM.

Multiple Choice

Choose the answer that best completes the sentence.

1. The eroded materials carried by water or wind are called
   a. stalactites.
   b. desert pavement.
   c. sediment.
   d. moraines.
2. The downhill movement of eroded materials is known as
   a. mass movement.
   b. abrasion.
   c. deposition.
   d. deflation.
3. A mass of rock and soil deposited directly by a glacier is called
   a. load. b. till.
   c. loess. d. erosion.
4. When waves strike a shoreline, they concentrate their energy on
   a. beaches. b. cirques.
   c. sand dunes. d. headlands.
5. The erosion of sediments by wind is
   a. deposition. b. deflation.
   c. plucking. d. glaciation.

True or False

If the statement is true, write true. If it is false, change the underlined word or words to make the statement true.

6. The process by which sediment in water settles in new locations is mass movement.
7. An area of alluvial fans may be found where groundwater erodes limestone to form valleys, sinkholes, and caverns.
8. Because it is moving, flowing water has a type of energy called kinetic energy.
9. A looplike bend in the course of a river is a meander.
10. The sediment deposited at the edge of a glacier forms a ridge called a kettle.

Checking Concepts

11. What agents of erosion are in part caused by the force of gravity?
12. How do a river's slope and volume of flow affect the river's sediment load?
13. Describe how the speed of flowing water changes where a river bends. How does this affect a river's deposition of sediment?
14. Why does a delta develop when a river flows into a larger body of water?
15. What are ice ages?
16. **Writing to Learn** You go on a rafting journey that takes you down a river from the mountains to the sea. Write a letter to a friend describing the features created by erosion and deposition that you see as you travel down the river. Include features near the river's source, along the middle of its course, and where it reaches the ocean.

Thinking Visually

17. **Flowchart** The partially completed flowchart shows the process that begins when raindrops hit the ground. Copy the flowchart onto a separate piece of paper. Then complete it and add a title. (For more on flowcharts, see the Skills Handbook.)

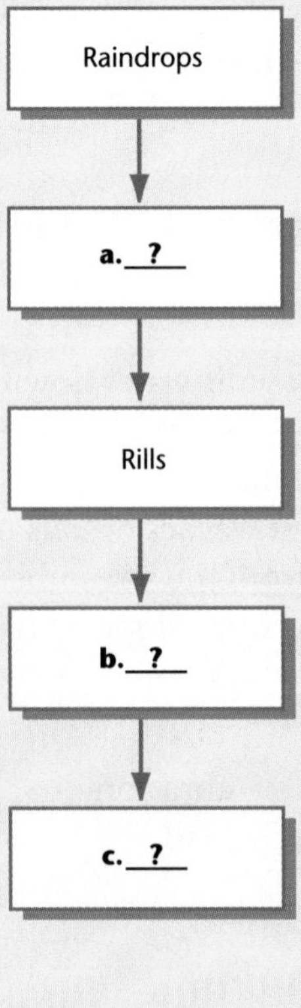
Raindrops
a. ?
Rills
b. ?
c. ?

Test Prep: Skills

The table below shows how a river's volume of flow and sediment load change over six months. Use the table to answer Questions 18–21.

Month	Volume of Flow (cubic meters/second)	Sediment Load (metric tons/day)
January	1.5	200
February	1.7	320
March	2.6	725
April	4.0	1600
May	3.2	1100
June	2.8	900

18. Graphing Make two graphs. For the first graph, put the month on the *x*-axis and the volume of flow on the *y*-axis. For the second graph, put the sediment load on the *y*-axis. Compare your two graphs. When were the river's volume of flow and load the greatest? When were they the lowest?

19. Developing Hypotheses Use your graphs to develop a hypothesis about the relationship between volume of flow and sediment load.

20. Relating Cause and Effect What may have occurred in the river's drainage basin in April to cause the changes in volume of flow and sediment load? Explain.

21. Predicting Rainfall is low in June where this river is located. What can you predict about sediment load for July? Explain.

Thinking Critically

22. Applying Concepts Under what conditions would you expect abrasion to cause the most erosion of a riverbed?

23. Relating Cause and Effect In a desert, you see an area that looks as if it were paved with rock fragments. Explain how this situation occurred naturally.

24. Problem Solving Suppose you are a geologist studying a valley glacier. What method could you use to tell if it is advancing or retreating?

25. Making Judgments A salesperson offers to sell your family a new house right on a riverbank for very little money. Why might your family hesitate to buy this house?

CHAPTER 8 REVIEW

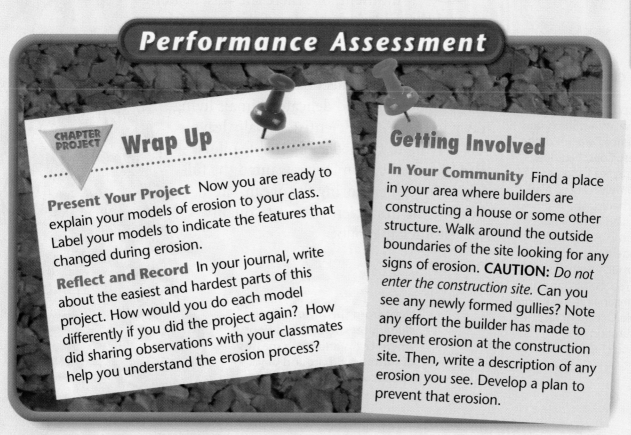

Performance Assessment

CHAPTER PROJECT Wrap Up

Present Your Project Now you are ready to explain your models of erosion to your class. Label your models to indicate the features that changed during erosion.

Reflect and Record In your journal, write about the easiest and hardest parts of this project. How would you do each model differently if you did the project again? How did sharing observations with your classmates help you understand the erosion process?

Getting Involved

In Your Community Find a place in your area where builders are constructing a house or some other structure. Walk around the outside boundaries of the site looking for any signs of erosion. **CAUTION:** *Do not enter the construction site.* Can you see any newly formed gullies? Note any effort the builder has made to prevent erosion at the construction site. Then, write a description of any erosion you see. Develop a plan to prevent that erosion.

Life in a Sunless World

Dr. Cindy Lee Van Dover was born and raised in Eatontown, New Jersey. She is now Science Director of the West Coast National Undersea Laboratory at the University of Alaska, Fairbanks. She first studied ocean-floor shrimp as a graduate student at the Massachusetts Institute of Technology and as a researcher at the Woods Hole Oceanographic Institution in Massachusetts.

Oceanographer Cindy Lee Van Dover never thought that her childhood curiosity would lead her to this moment. But there she was, heading toward the cold, dark depths of the ocean floor. She was piloting the famous *Alvin*, a tiny research submarine known as a submersible. The *Alvin* would collect data and gather samples of rocks and delicate animals living deep in the ocean. Scientists usually leave the driving to trained submersible pilots. But because Dr. Van Dover wanted the full experience of exploring the ocean, she became the first scientist ever to qualify as a submersible pilot.

Light from the *Alvin* illuminates the dark sea floor where crabs and huge masses of shrimp feed around black smoker vents. ▶

Life on the Ocean Floor

Slowly, the *Alvin* entered the sunless world far beneath the surface of the Atlantic Ocean — one of the strangest and most remote places on Earth. As the *Alvin* approached an underwater mountain range, Dr. Van Dover could see colonies of animals swarming around undersea hot springs called "black smokers."

The black clouds that give these areas their name are not smoke at all. Rather they are streams of very hot water packed with minerals flowing from openings in the sea floor. Some microorganisms are able to use the minerals as their food source. Dr. Van Dover's special interest was in some very unusual shrimp that feed on these microorganisms.

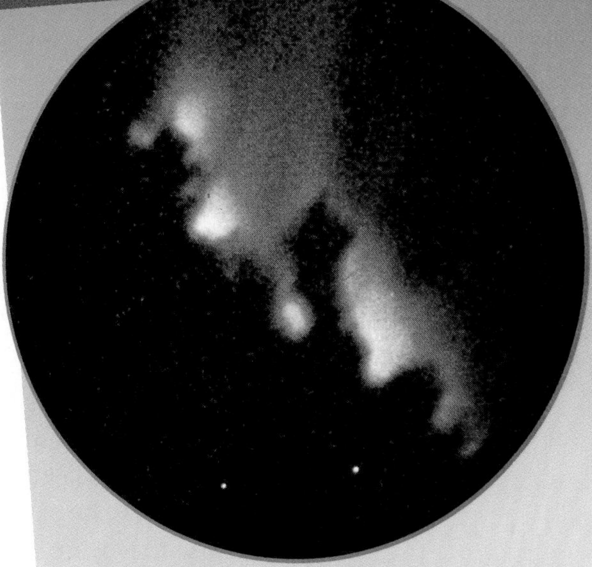

▲ Black smoker vents are hot enough to glow. Water as hot as 350°C pours up from these hot springs. When the hot water mixes with the cold sea water, it quickly cools.

Endless Questions

How did Dr. Van Dover reach this moment in her life? As a child she was full of questions about everything in nature. "I had my bug period; I had my frog-and-tadpole period; I had my flower period and tree period and bird period. But I settled pretty firmly and quickly on marine invertebrates, sea animals without backbones," she explains. "That's because they were so unusual. I just loved all the odd structures they had, each with a function. Why does a crustacean have ten legs — or whatever number it might have? What does it use them all for?"

Could These Shrimp Have Eyes?

As she steered the *Alvin,* Dr. Van Dover thought about the shrimp she planned to observe. She knew that these shrimp live in the dark depths of the ocean. They lack eyestalks and the black, beady eyes of their better known relatives. She also knew that eyeless animals are common at depths too far beneath the surface for sunlight to reach.

Dr. Van Dover had made an interesting discovery about the shrimp in the lab. Her discovery came after she noticed odd, shiny patches on their backs. She asked herself what the function of the patches might be. "I dissected a shrimp in the laboratory," she recounts. "I found this pair of organs and pulled it out. It was very recognizable, and to my surprise, it was attached to what I took to be the brain of the shrimp.

"Other people told me I was crazy. There's no light on the sea floor. Why do they need eyes?"

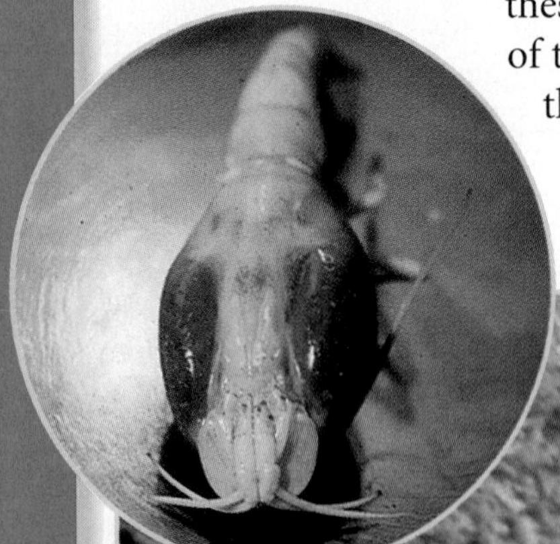

▲ Each shrimp has a pair of bright spots— "eyes"— on its back.

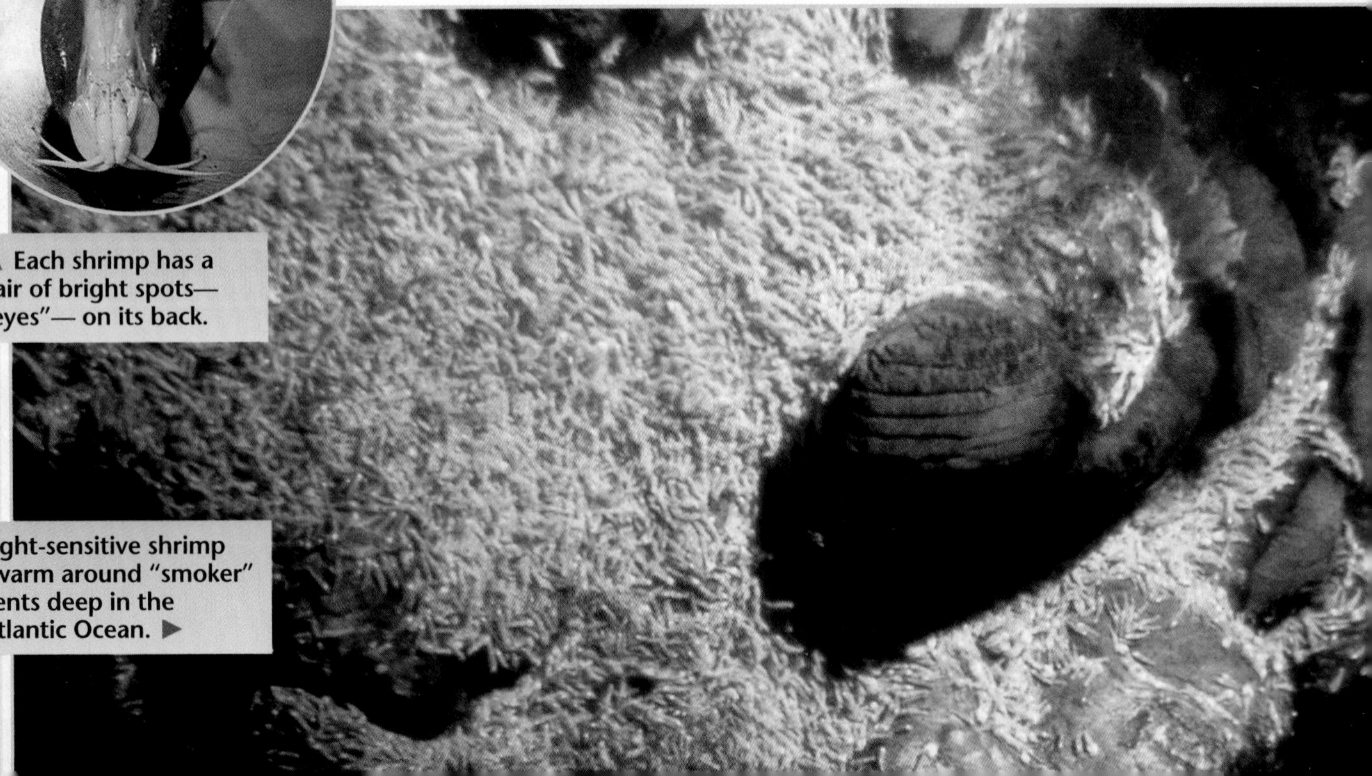

Light-sensitive shrimp swarm around "smoker" vents deep in the Atlantic Ocean. ▶

I looked at it and said, 'Looks like an eye!' Other people told me I was crazy. There's no light on the sea floor. Why do they need eyes?"

Dr. Van Dover kept an open mind and showed the structure to crustacean eye experts. They confirmed that it was not only an eye, but a very unusual one. It was able to detect very dim light. Immediately that raised another question: What could the shrimp be looking at?

"We thought about alternatives," Dr. Van Dover says. "The obvious thing is that these shrimp are only found around high-temperature black smokers. We all know that hot things glow. Did these vents glow?" The answer turned out to be yes. Those unusual eyes were just right for spotting undersea hot spots. Scientists hypothesize that the shrimp use these eyes to guide them toward the dim light in order to feed on the microorganisms. As the shrimp approach the vent, the light gets brighter. That signals the shrimp to keep a distance from the hottest water just emerging from the vent.

▲ **A surface ship lifts the *Alvin* from the ocean after a deep-sea expedition.**

Looking Ahead

From time to time now, Dr. Van Dover thinks about the submersible that scientists plan to send to watery Europa, a moon of Jupiter. Scientists in a control room will pilot a robot version of *Alvin* under the oceans of Europa. "I'm delighted that I'm young enough that I'm going to see that," she says. When asked if she would like to be one of those scientists, she doesn't hesitate.

"Wouldn't that be sweet!" she says — and smiles.

In Your Journal

Cindy Lee Van Dover's discoveries usually begin with her paying attention to details and then asking questions about what she finds. Think of a familiar place outdoors that you like to visit. Describe the place from memory. Jot down details. Then visit the place again to observe and record questions.

CHAPTER

9 Earth: The Water Planet

Hikers in California's Yosemite National Park are awed by its thundering waterfalls.

CALIFORNIA SCIENCE CONTENT STANDARDS

The following California Science Content Standards are addressed in this chapter:

2. Topography is reshaped by weathering of rock and soil and by the transportation and deposition of sediment.
   - **b.** Rivers and streams are dynamic systems that erode and transport sediment, change course, and flood their banks in natural and recurring patterns.
3. Heat moves in a predictable flow from warmer objects to cooler objects until all objects are at the same temperature.
   - **c.** Heat flows in solids by conduction (which involves no flow of matter) and in fluids by conduction and also by convection (which involves flow of matter).
4. Many phenomena on the Earth's surface are affected by the transfer of energy through radiation and convection currents.
   - **a.** The sun is the major source of energy for phenomena on the Earth's surface, powering winds, ocean currents, and the water cycle.
5. Organisms in ecosystems exchange energy and nutrients among themselves and with the environment.

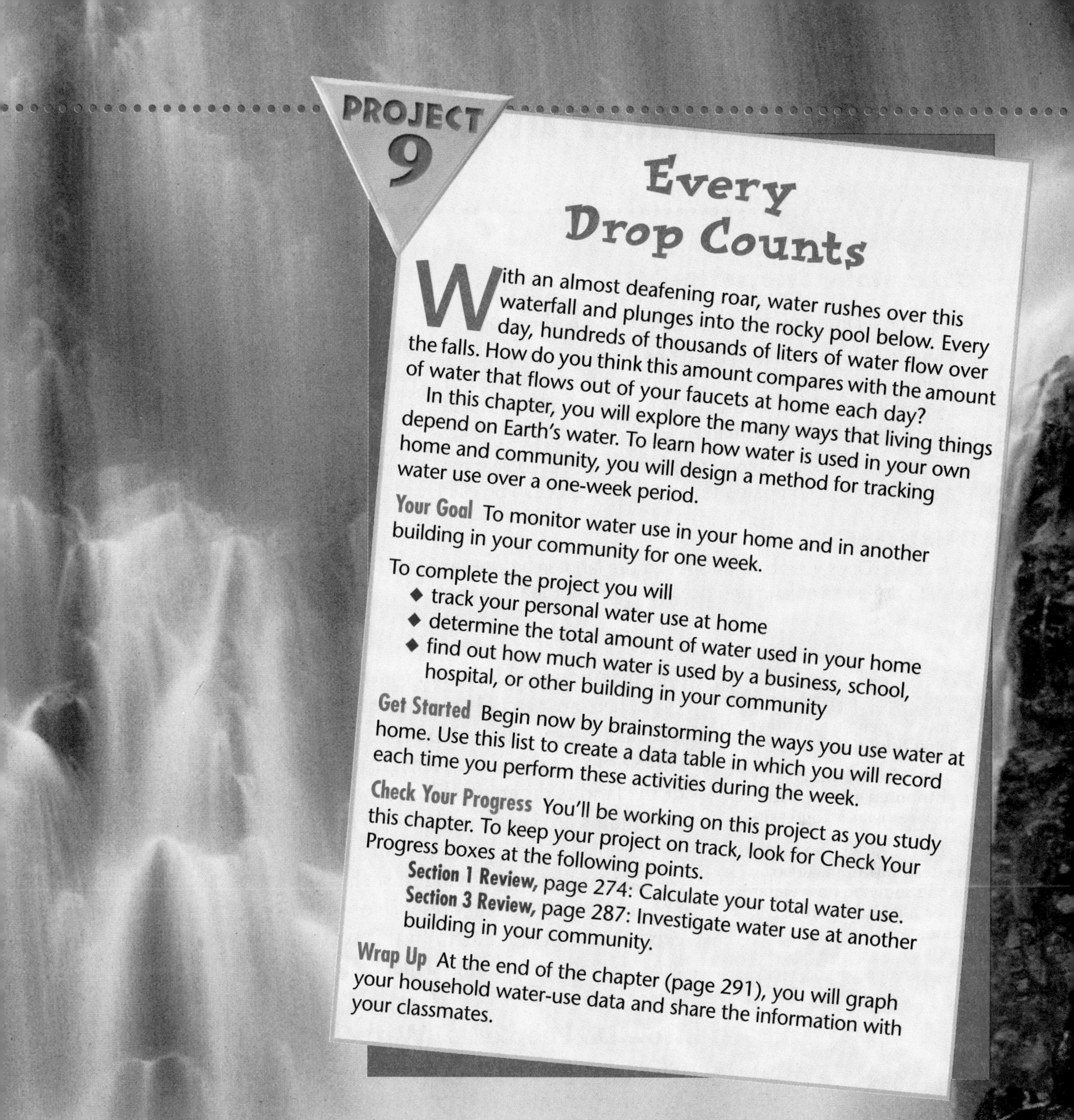

PROJECT 9

Every Drop Counts

With an almost deafening roar, water rushes over this waterfall and plunges into the rocky pool below. Every day, hundreds of thousands of liters of water flow over the falls. How do you think this amount compares with the amount of water that flows out of your faucets at home each day?

In this chapter, you will explore the many ways that living things depend on Earth's water. To learn how water is used in your own home and community, you will design a method for tracking water use over a one-week period.

Your Goal To monitor water use in your home and in another building in your community for one week.

To complete the project you will

- track your personal water use at home
- determine the total amount of water used in your home
- find out how much water is used by a business, school, hospital, or other building in your community

Get Started Begin now by brainstorming the ways you use water at home. Use this list to create a data table in which you will record each time you perform these activities during the week.

Check Your Progress You'll be working on this project as you study this chapter. To keep your project on track, look for Check Your Progress boxes at the following points.

Section 1 Review, page 274: Calculate your total water use.

Section 3 Review, page 287: Investigate water use at another building in your community.

Wrap Up At the end of the chapter (page 291), you will graph your household water-use data and share the information with your classmates.

a. Energy entering ecosystems as sunlight is transferred by producers into chemical energy through photosynthesis, and then from organism to organism in food webs.

e. The number and types of organisms an ecosystem can support depends on the resources available and abiotic factors, such as quantity of light and water, range of temperatures, and soil composition.

6. Sources of energy and materials differ in amounts, distribution, usefulness, and the time required for their formation.

b. Different natural energy and material resources, including air, soil, rocks, minerals, petroleum, fresh water, wildlife, and forests, and classify them as renewable or nonrenewable.

7. Scientific progress is made by asking meaningful questions and conducting careful investigations.

a. Develop a hypothesis.

c. Construct appropriate graphs from data and develop qualitative statements about the relationships between variables.

SECTION 1

How Is Water Important?

DISCOVER — ACTIVITY

Water, Water Everywhere?

1. Blow up a large, round balloon. Tie a knot at the end.
2. Pretend that your balloon is a globe. Using a permanent marker, draw the basic shapes of the continents at the size they would be if Earth were the size of your balloon. Shade the continents with the marker.
3. Now compare your balloon to an actual globe. Look at the amount of land compared to the amount of ocean on each.

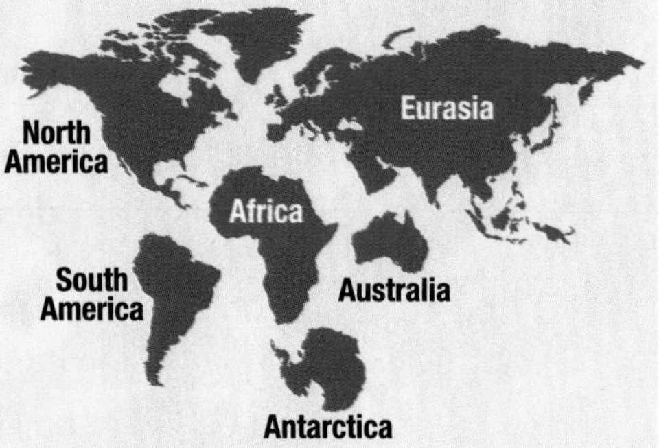
North America
Eurasia
Africa
South America
Australia
Antarctica

Think It Over

Observing Does your balloon show more land area or ocean area? How do the areas of land and ocean actually compare on Earth?

GUIDE FOR READING

- **How do people and other living things use water?**
- **How is Earth's water distributed among saltwater and freshwater sources?**

Reading Tip **As you read, use the headings to make an outline showing how water is important and where it is found.**

Imagine a world without water. The planet is a barren desert. There are no cool green forests or deep oceans. The world is silent — no rain falls on rooftops; no birds or other animals stir. No clouds shield the planet from the hot sun. Even the shape of the land is different. Without water to wear them down, the mountains are jagged and rough. There are no Great Lakes, no Niagara Falls, and no Grand Canyon.

Can you imagine living in such a world? In fact, you could not survive there. The presence of water is essential for life to exist on the planet Earth. In this section, you will explore the ways that all living things depend on water.

How Do People Use Water?

Take a minute to list all of the ways you used water this morning. You probably washed your face, brushed your teeth, and flushed the toilet. Perhaps you drank a glass of water or used water to make oatmeal. These are some common uses of water in the home. But the water people use at home is just a small percentage of all the water used in the United States. **In addition to household purposes, people use water for agriculture, industry, transportation, and recreation.**

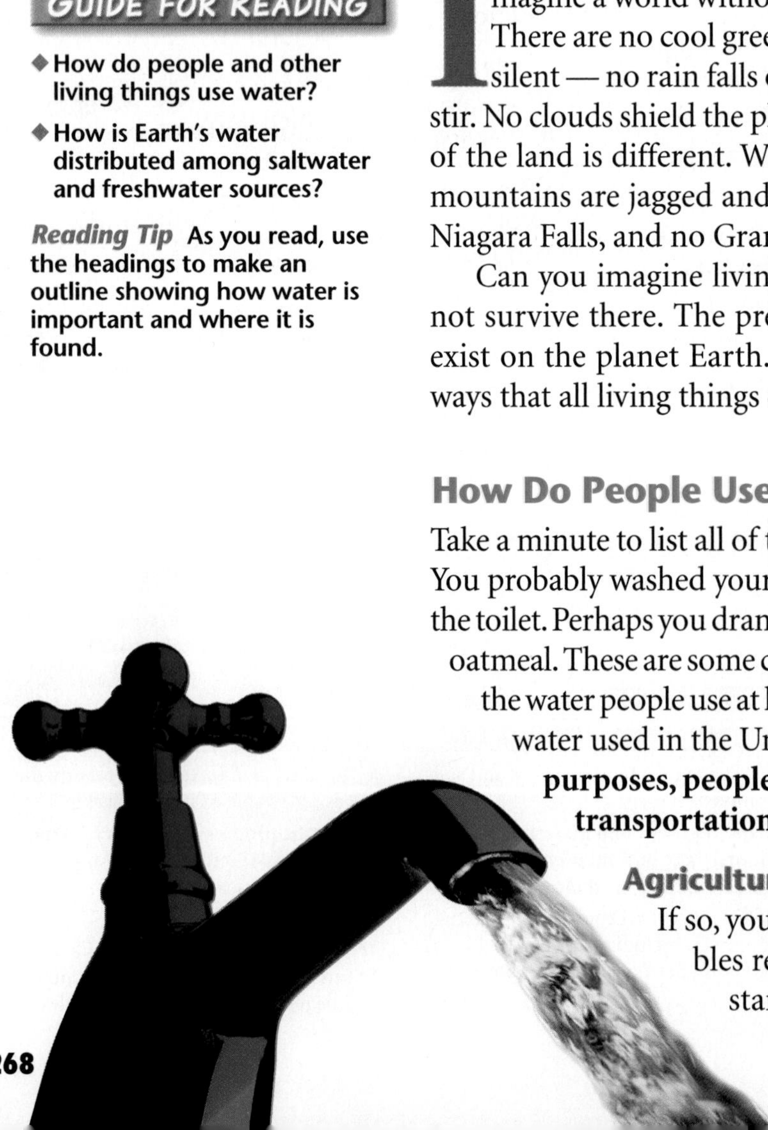

Agriculture Has your family ever had a garden? If so, you know that growing fruits and vegetables requires water. On a large farm, a constant supply of fresh water is essential.

Figure 1 The food processing industry requires large amounts of water. Before these juicy red tomatoes can be made into ketchup or spaghetti sauce, they must be washed.

Growing the wheat to make a single loaf of bread takes 435 liters of water, enough to fill 1,200 soft drink cans!

However, some parts of the United States don't receive enough regular rainfall for agriculture. For example, parts of California's Central Valley receive less than 26 centimeters of rain a year. Yet this area is one of the most productive farming regions in the country. How is it possible to farm in this dry place? The solution is irrigation. **Irrigation** is the process of supplying water to areas of land to make them suitable for growing crops. In the United States, more water is used for irrigating farmland than for any other single purpose.

Industry Think about the objects in a typical school locker. There's a jacket, some textbooks, a few pens without caps, and maybe a basketball or a flute for band practice. Did you know that water is needed to produce all these objects? Even though water is not part of the final products, it plays a role in the industrial processes that created them. For example, water is needed to make the paper in the textbooks. Wood chips are washed and then soaked in vats of water and chemicals to form pulp. The pulp is rinsed again, squeezed dry, and pressed into paper.

Industries use water in many other ways. For example, power plants and steel mills both need huge volumes of water to cool down hot machinery. Water that is used for cooling can often be recycled, or used again for another purpose.

Transportation If you live near a large waterway, you have probably seen barges carrying heavy loads of coal or iron. Oceans and rivers have been used for transporting people and goods since ancient times. If you look at a map of the United States, you will notice that many large cities are located on the coasts.

Water Used in the Home

Task	Water Used (liters)
Showering for 5 minutes	95
Brushing teeth	10
Washing hands	7.5
Flushing standard toilet	23
Flushing "low-flow" toilet	6
Washing one load of laundry	151
Running dishwasher	19
Washing dishes by hand	114

Figure 2 Many common household activities involve water. *Interpreting Data How much water would a person save per flush by replacing a standard toilet with a "low-flow" toilet?*

Ocean travel led to the growth of port cities such as Boston, New York, and San Francisco. In early America, rivers also served as natural highways. St. Louis, Memphis, and Baton Rouge are some cities that began as trading posts along the Mississippi River.

Recreation Do you like to swim in a neighborhood pool? Catch fish from a rowboat in the middle of a lake? Walk along a beach collecting seashells? Or maybe just sit on the edge of a dock and dangle your feet in the water? Then you know some ways water is used for recreation. And if you brave the winter cold to ski or skate, you are enjoying water in its frozen form.

☑ *Checkpoint* ***List an agricultural use, an industrial use, and a household use of water that you relied on today.***

SCIENCE & History

Water and Agriculture

Plants require a steady supply of water to grow. How have farmers throughout history provided their crops with water? This time line shows some methods developed in different parts of the world.

2000 B.C. Egypt

Egyptian farmers invented a way to raise water from the Nile River. The device, called a *shaduf,* acted as a lever to make lifting a bucket of water easier. The farmers then emptied the water into a network of canals to irrigate their fields. The *shaduf* is still in use in Egypt, India, and other countries.

3000 B.C. **2000 B.C.** **1000 B.C.**

3000 B.C. China

One of the oldest known methods of irrigation was developed for growing rice. Farmers built paddies, or artificial ponds with raised edges. The farmers flooded the paddies with water from a nearby stream. This ancient technique is still widely used throughout Southeast Asia.

700 B.C. Assyria

Sennacherib, king of the ancient nation Assyria, surrounded the capital city of Nineveh with fruit trees, cotton, and exotic plants. To help irrigate the plantations, he built a 10-kilometer canal and a stone aqueduct to transport water from the nearby hills.

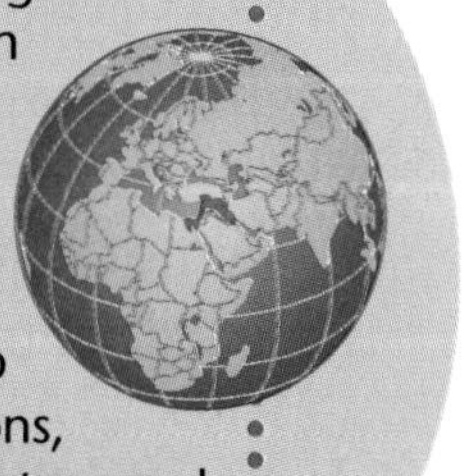

Water and Living Things

INTEGRATING LIFE SCIENCE Here's a riddle for you: What do you and an apple have in common? You both consist mostly of water! In fact, water is a large part of every living thing. Water makes up nearly two thirds of your body. That water is necessary to keep your body functioning.

Water is essential for living things to grow, reproduce, and carry out other important processes. For example, plants use water, plus carbon dioxide and energy from the sun, to make food in a process called **photosynthesis** (foh toh SIN thuh sis). Animals and many other living things depend on the food made by plants. They may eat the plants directly or eat other organisms that eat plants.

In Your Journal

Find out more about one of these agricultural techniques. Imagine that you are a farmer seeing the method in action for the first time. Write a letter to a friend describing the new technique. What problem will it solve? How will it improve your farming?

A.D. 1870 United States

When homesteaders arrived on the dry Great Plains of the central United States, they had to rely on water stored underground. Windmills provided the energy to pump the groundwater to the surface. The farmers dug ditches to carry the water to irrigate their fields.

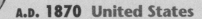

A.D. 1 **A.D. 1000** **A.D. 2000**

A.D. 500 Mexico

To grow crops in areas covered by swampy lakes, the Aztecs built raised plots of farmland called *chinampas.* They grew maize on fertile soil scooped from the lake bottom. A grid of canals kept the crops wet and allowed the farmers to navigate boats between the *chinampas.*

Present Israel

Irrigation is the key to survival in desert regions. Today, methods such as drip irrigation ensure that very little water is wasted when crops are watered. Holes in the pipe allow water to drip directly onto the soil around the roots of each plant.

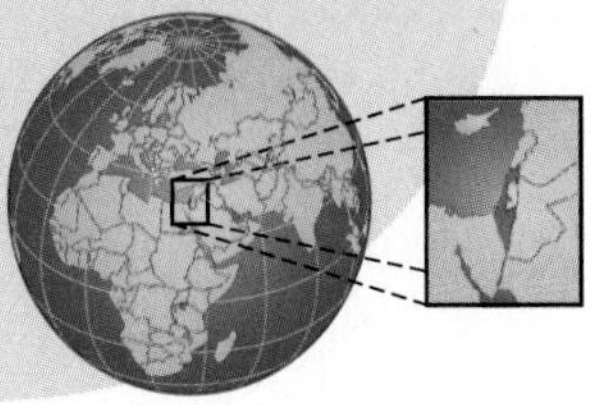

Sharpen your Skills

Calculating

This activity shows how Earth's water is distributed.

ACTIVITY

1. Fill a one-liter plastic bottle with water. This represents the total water on Earth.
2. First, measure 97 percent, or 970 milliliters (mL), of the water and pour it into a large bowl. This represents the salt water in Earth's oceans and salt lakes.
3. Next, you will demonstrate how the remaining fresh water is divided. Label five cups to match the fresh-water sources in Figure 3. Calculate how much of the remaining 30 mL of water you should pour into each cup to represent the percentage of Earth's fresh water found there.
4. Use a plastic graduated cylinder to measure out the amount of water for each cup. Use a plastic dropper to approximate amounts that are too small to measure accurately.

Which cups contain water that is available for humans to use? How does the amount of water in these cups compare to the original one liter?

Another way that living things use water is as a home. An organism's **habitat** is the place where it lives and that provides the things it needs to survive. Both fresh water and salt water provide habitats for many living things.

Water on Earth

Why do you think Earth is often called the "water planet"? Perhaps an astronaut suggested this name. From space, an astronaut can see that there is much more water than land on planet Earth. Oceans cover nearly 71 percent of Earth's surface.

Figure 3 shows how Earth's water is distributed. **Most of Earth's water — more than 97 percent — is salt water that is found in the oceans. Only 3 percent is fresh water.** Of that 3 percent, about three quarters is found in the huge masses of ice near the North and South Poles. A fraction more is found in the atmosphere. Most water in the atmosphere is invisible **water vapor,** the gaseous form of water. Less than 1 percent of the water on Earth is fresh water that is available for humans to use.

To explore where Earth's water is found, you can take an imaginary boat trip around the world. As you read, follow your route on the map in Figure 4.

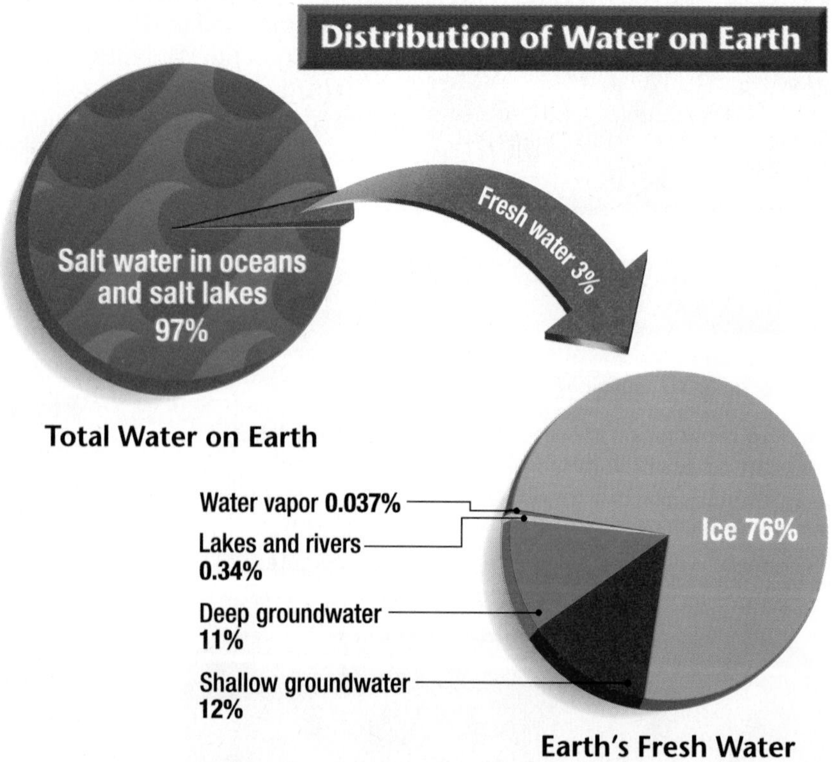

Distribution of Water on Earth
Salt water in oceans and salt lakes 97%
Fresh water 3%
Total Water on Earth
Water vapor 0.037%
Lakes and rivers 0.34%
Deep groundwater 11%
Shallow groundwater 12%
Ice 76%
Earth's Fresh Water

Figure 3 Most of Earth's water is salt water. Of the freshwater sources shown in the bottom circle graph, only the water in lakes, rivers, and shallow groundwater is available for human use.

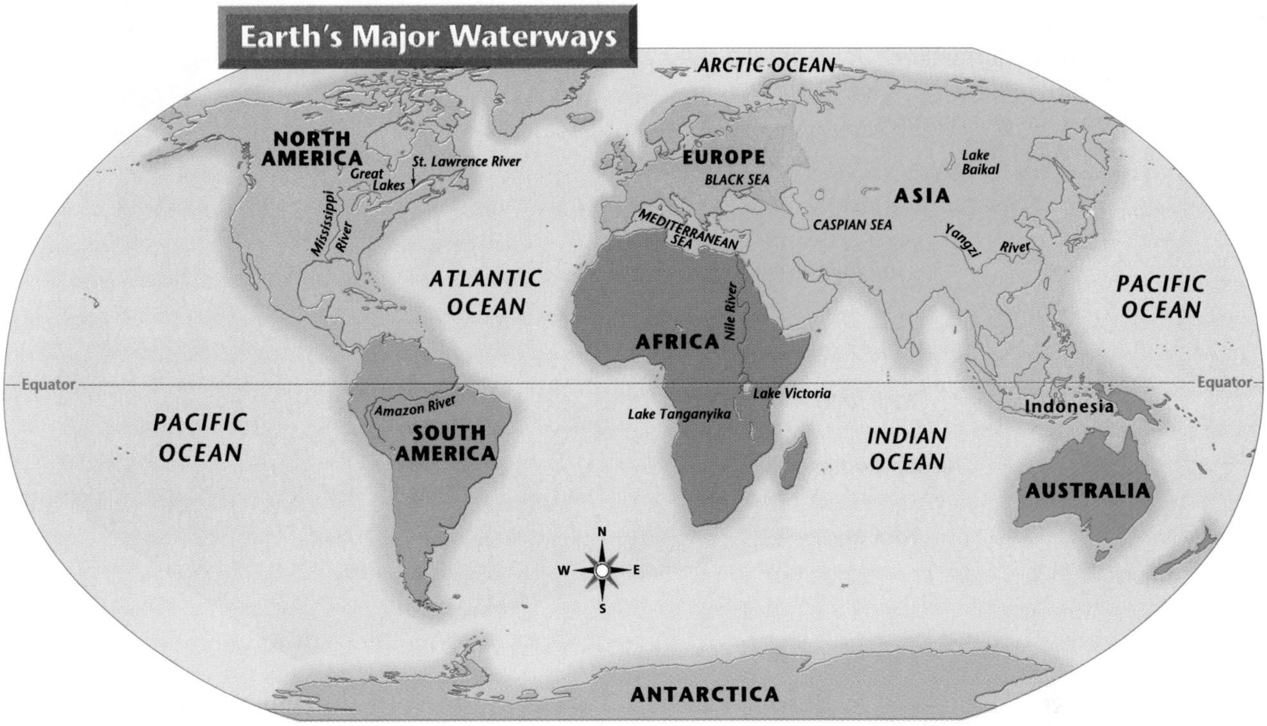
Earth's Major Waterways
ARCTIC OCEAN
NORTH AMERICA
Great Lakes
St. Lawrence River
Mississippi River
EUROPE
BLACK SEA
Lake Baikal
ASIA
MEDITERRANEAN SEA
CASPIAN SEA
Yangzi River
ATLANTIC OCEAN
Nile River
AFRICA
PACIFIC OCEAN
Equator
Lake Victoria
Lake Tanganyika
Amazon River
SOUTH AMERICA
PACIFIC OCEAN
INDIAN OCEAN
Indonesia
AUSTRALIA
N
W
E
S
ANTARCTICA

Figure 4 Earth's oceans are all connected, enabling a ship to sail all the way around the world. This map also shows some of the world's major rivers and lakes. *Interpreting Maps Which continents touch the Pacific Ocean? The Atlantic Ocean?*

Oceans Your journey starts in Miami, Florida. From here, you can sail completely around the world without ever going ashore. Although people have given names to regions of the ocean, these regions are all connected, forming a single world ocean.

First you sail southeast across the Atlantic Ocean toward Africa. Swinging around the continent's southern tip, you enter the smaller but deeper Indian Ocean. After zigzagging among the islands of Indonesia, you head east across the Pacific Ocean, the longest part of your trip. This vast ocean, dotted with islands, covers an area greater than all the land on Earth put together.

Ice How can you get back to Miami? If you're not in a hurry, you could sail all the way around South America. But watch out for icebergs! These floating chunks of ice are your first encounter with fresh water on your journey. Icebergs in the southern Pacific and Atlantic oceans have broken off the massive sheets of ice that cover most of Antarctica. You would also find icebergs in the Arctic Ocean around the North Pole.

Rivers and Lakes To see examples of fresh water in rivers and lakes, you'll have to make a side trip inland. Sail north past Nova Scotia, Canada, to the beginning of the St. Lawrence Seaway. Navigate through the series of locks along the St. Lawrence River. Suddenly the river widens and you enter Lake Ontario, one of North America's five Great Lakes. Together, the Great Lakes cover an area nearly twice the size of New York state. They contain nearly 20 percent of all the water in the world's freshwater lakes.

Figure 5 This diagram shows an earthworm's view of the formation of groundwater. *Interpreting Diagrams Why does the groundwater collect where you see it in this diagram?*

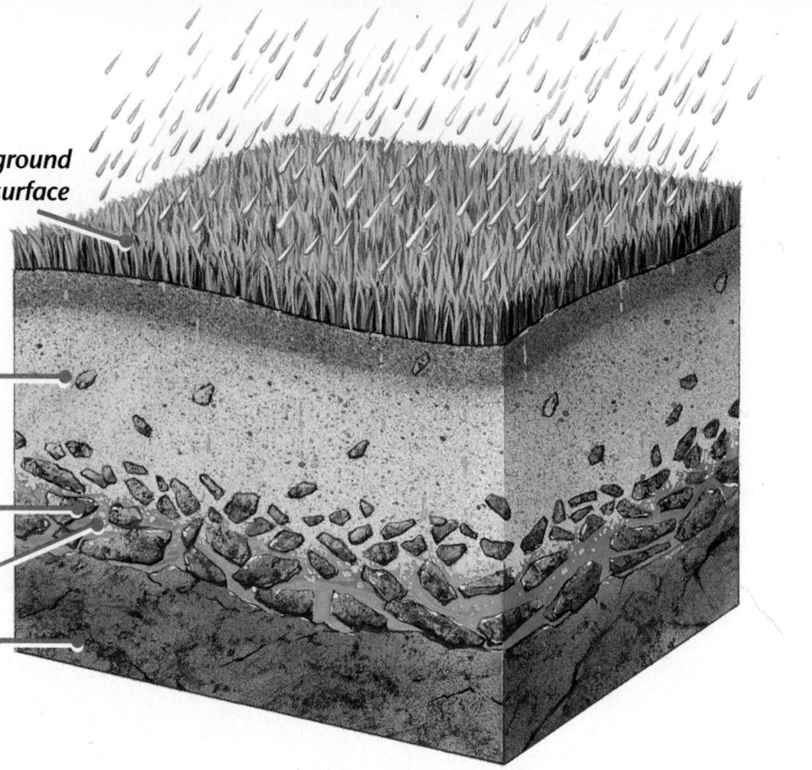
ground surface
soil layer
rock layer
groundwater
rock layer

Below Earth's Surface On your journey around the world, you would not see most of Earth's liquid fresh water. Far more fresh water is located underground than in all Earth's rivers and lakes. How did this water get underground?

As Figure 5 shows, when rain or snow falls some of the water soaks into the ground. The water trickles downward through spaces between the particles of soil and rock. Eventually the water reaches a layer that it cannot move through. Then the water begins to fill up the spaces above that layer. Water that fills the cracks and spaces in underground soil and rock layers is called **groundwater.** Chapter 10 explains more about groundwater, the source of much of the water used by humans.

Section 1 Review

1. What are five major ways that people in the United States use water?
2. Describe two ways that plants and other living things depend on water.
3. What percent of Earth's water is salt water? What percent is fresh water?
4. Where is most of the fresh water on Earth found?
5. **Thinking Critically Classifying** Classify the following as fresh water or salt water: groundwater, iceberg, ocean, and river.

CHAPTER PROJECT

Check Your Progress

Complete your water-use data table by calculating the total amount of water you used during the week. Use Figure 2 to estimate the water used for some common activities. Then determine how much water your family used during the week. You can do this by reading your water meter, estimating based on your personal water use, or having your family members record their usage. (*Hint:* Convert all amounts to liters.)

SECTION 2 The Properties of Water

DISCOVER ACTIVITY

What Are Some Properties of Water?

1. Pour a small amount of water into a plastic cup. Pour an equal amount of vegetable oil into a second cup.
2. Cut two strips of paper towel. Hold the strips so that the bottom of one strip is in the water and the other is in the oil.
3. After one minute, measure how high each substance climbed up the paper towel.
4. Using a plastic dropper, place a big drop of water onto a piece of wax paper.

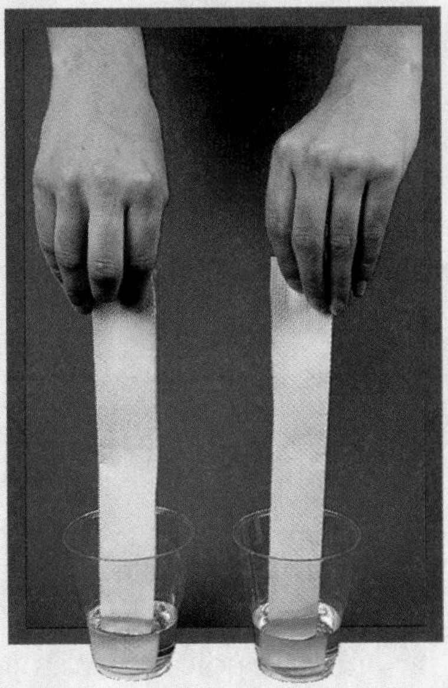

5. Using another dropper, place a drop of oil the same size as the water drop beside it on the wax paper.
6. Observe the shape of the two drops from the side.
7. Follow your teacher's instructions for disposing of the oil when you clean up after this activity.

Think It Over

Observing What differences do you notice between the water and the oil in each experiment?

How would you describe water to someone who had never seen it before? You might say that pure water has no color, no taste, and no odor. You might even say that water is a rather plain, ordinary substance. But if you asked a chemist to describe water, the response would be different. The chemist would say that water is very unusual. Its properties differ from those of most other familiar substances.

Are you and the chemist talking about the same substance? To understand the chemist's description of water, you need to know something about the chemical structure of water.

GUIDE FOR READING

- **How does the chemical structure of water molecules cause them to stick together?**
- **How does water dissolve other polar substances?**
- **What are the three states in which water exists on Earth?**

Reading Tip **As you read, make a list of water's properties. Write a sentence describing each property.**

Water's Unique Structure

Like all matter, water is made up of atoms. Just as the 26 letters of the alphabet combine in different ways to form all the words in the English language, about 100 types of atoms combine in different ways to form all types of matter. Atoms attach together, or bond, to form molecules. Two hydrogen atoms bonded to an oxygen atom form a water molecule. A short way of writing this is to use the chemical formula for water, H_2O.

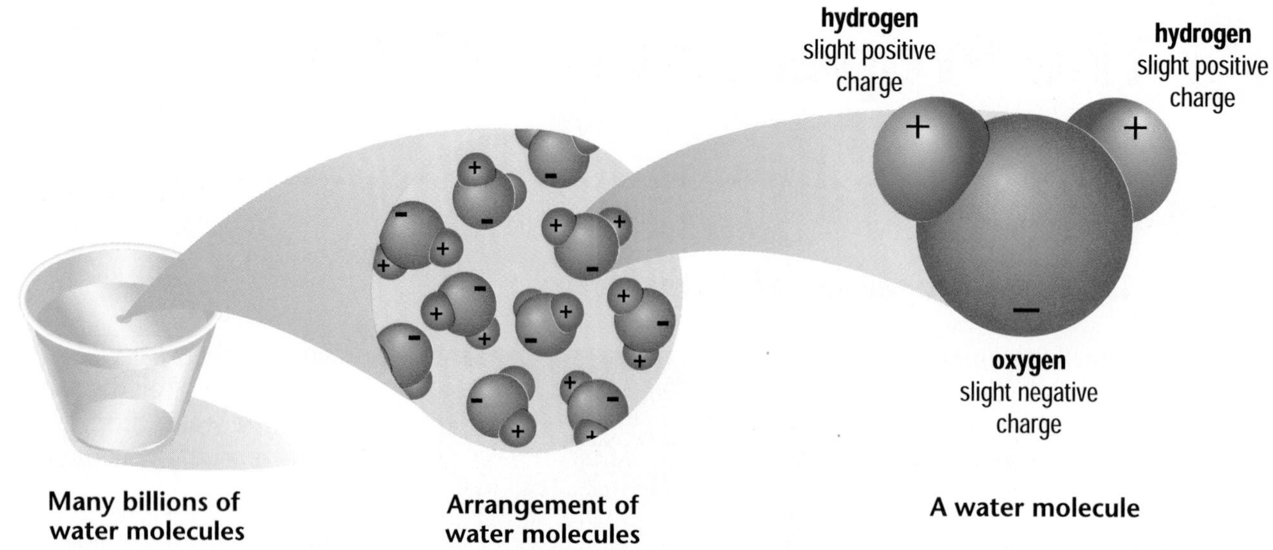
hydrogen
slight positive
charge
hydrogen
slight positive
charge
oxygen
slight negative
charge
Many billions of
water molecules
Arrangement of
water molecules
A water molecule

Figure 6 A glass of water contains many billions of water molecules. Notice how the water molecules are arranged in the center image. The positive ends of one molecule are attracted to the negative end of another molecule.

Figure 6 shows how the hydrogen and oxygen atoms are arranged in a water molecule. Each end of the molecule has a slight electric charge. The oxygen end has a slight negative charge. The hydrogen ends have a slight positive charge. A molecule that has electrically charged areas is called a **polar molecule.** Because water consists of polar molecules, it is called a polar substance.

Have you ever played with bar magnets? If so, you know that the opposite poles of two magnets attract each other. The same is true with polar molecules, except that an electric force rather than a magnetic force causes the attraction. **The positive hydrogen ends of one water molecule attract the negative oxygen ends of nearby water molecules. As a result, the water molecules tend to stick together.** Many of water's unusual properties occur because of this attraction among the polar water molecules.

Checkpoint *Describe the arrangement of the atoms in a water molecule. What makes it a polar molecule?*

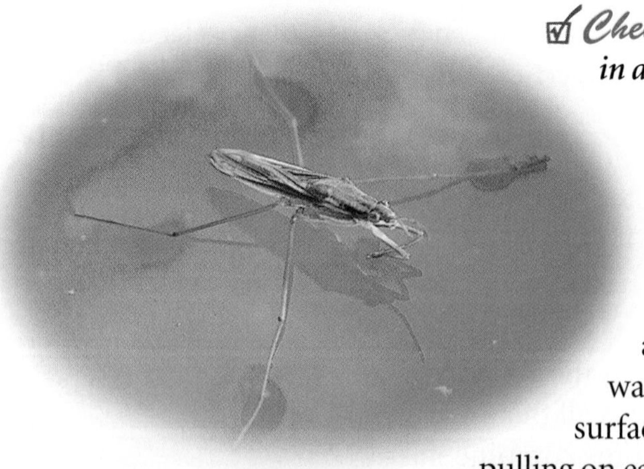

Figure 7 A water strider skips lightly across the surface of a pond. *Applying Concepts How do water's polar molecules keep the insect from falling into the water?*

Surface Tension

Have you ever watched a water strider like the one at the left? These insects can skate across the surface of a pond without sinking. They are supported by the surface tension of the water. **Surface tension** is the tightness across the surface of water that is caused by the polar molecules pulling on each other. The molecules at the surface are being pulled by the molecules next to them and below them. The pulling forces the surface of the water into a curved shape. Surface tension also causes raindrops to form round beads when they fall onto a car windshield.

Capillary Action

The next time you have a drink with a straw in it, look closely at the level of the liquid outside and inside the straw. You will see that the liquid rises higher inside the straw. Similarly, water will climb up into the pores of a brick or piece of wood. How does water move up against the force of gravity? Just as water molecules stick to each other, they also stick to the sides of a tube. As water molecules are attracted to the tube, they pull other water molecules up with them. The combined force of attraction among water molecules and with the molecules of surrounding materials is called **capillary action.** Capillary action allows water to move through materials with pores or narrow spaces inside.

Capillary action causes water molecules to cling to the fibers of materials like paper and cloth. You may have seen outdoor or athletic clothing that claims to "wick moisture away from the skin." The capillary action that occurs along the cloth's fibers pulls water away from your skin. By pulling the water away from your skin, the fibers keep you dry.

Water, the Universal Solvent

What happens when you make lemonade from a powdered mix? As you stir the powder into a pitcher of water, the powder seems to disappear. When you make lemonade, you are making a solution. A **solution** is a mixture that forms when one substance dissolves another. The substance that does the dissolving is called the **solvent.** In this example, the water is the solvent.

One reason that water is able to dissolve many substances is that it is polar. The charged ends of the water molecule attract the molecules of other polar substances. Sugar is a familiar polar substance. When you add a sugar cube to a cup of hot tea, the polar water molecules in the tea pull on the polar sugar molecules on the surfaces of the cube. As those sugar molecules

TRY THIS

Follow That String

ACTIVITY

You can use a string to pour water sideways! Try this activity over a sink or outdoors.

1. Cut a piece of string as long as your arm. Wet the string.
2. Fill a pitcher with water. Tie the string to the handle.
3. Drape the string across the spout and let the other end dangle into a plastic cup. Tape the end of the string to the inside of the cup.

4. Hold the cup below the pitcher so that the string is pulled tight. As your partner gently pours the water into the cup, slowly move the cup to the right of the spout, keeping the string tight.

Inferring How do water's polar molecules cause it to follow the string?

Figure 8 Water's ability to dissolve limestone created the spiky stalactites and stalagmites in this cave in Arkansas' Ozark Mountains. As the water evaporated, the rock formations were left behind.

TRY THIS

Comparing Solvents

ACTIVITY

In this activity you will compare how well water and oil dissolve several substances.

1. Label six small plastic cups A, B, C, D, E, and F.
2. Add water to cups A, B, and C until they are half full. Add the same amount of vegetable oil to cups D, E, and F.
3. Make a table like the one shown below to help organize your observations.

Cup	Contents	Result
A	Water	
	Salt	

4. Now stir a spoonful of salt into cups A and D. Record your observations.
5. Stir a spoonful of baking soda into cups B and E. Record your observations.
6. Add two drops of food coloring to cups C and F. Do not stir. Record your observations.

Drawing Conclusions In which solvent did each substance dissolve better? Propose an explanation for your results. (*Hint:* Think about the difference between polar and nonpolar molecules.)

dissolve, other sugar molecules are exposed to the water. Eventually the sugar cube dissolves into many individual molecules too small to see. The result is a solution of sweetened tea.

Water dissolves so many substances that it is often called the "universal solvent." It can dissolve solids, such as salt and soap, and liquids, such as bleach and rubbing alcohol. Water also dissolves many gases, including oxygen and carbon dioxide. These dissolved gases are important for organisms that live in the water.

However, some substances, such as oils and wax, do not dissolve in water. You have observed this if you have ever seen the oil separate from the vinegar and water in salad dressing. The molecules of oil are nonpolar molecules — they have no charged regions. Nonpolar molecules do not dissolve well in water.

☑ *Checkpoint* ***List a solid, a liquid, and a gas that dissolve in water.***

Changing State

It's a hot, humid summer day. To cool down, you put some ice cubes in a glass and add cold water. Is there anything unusual about this scene? Surprisingly, yes! You are interacting with water in three different **states,** or forms: solid, liquid, and gas. **The ice is a solid, the water is a liquid, and the water vapor in the air is a gas.** In terms of chemistry, this is a remarkable situation. Water is the only substance on Earth that commonly exists in all of its different states.

As you know if you have ever boiled water or made ice cubes, water can change from one state to another. Most other substances require extremes of hot or cold to change state. A steel car door doesn't melt in a July heat wave. In fact, steel would remain a solid even inside your kitchen oven. The air you breathe remains a gas whether the weather is hot or cold. Water, however, can change states within the range of Earth's normal temperatures.

Melting To understand how temperature is related to change of state, start by thinking about an ice cube. The ice is a solid. It has a regular shape because its molecules are arranged in a rigid structure. Suppose that the temperature of the ice is $-10°C$. What does the temperature tell you? Temperature is a measurement of the average speed of the molecules. Although you can't see them, all the molecules in a substance are constantly moving. At $-10°C$, the molecules in the ice cube are vibrating back and forth, but they are not moving fast enough to break free of their structure.

Now suppose that you put the ice cube in a pan on the stove. As heat energy is added, the molecules in the ice start moving faster. The temperature rises. When the temperature reaches 0°C, the solid ice melts and becomes liquid water.

Boiling and Evaporation As you know, liquid water looks very different from solid ice. The liquid flows and takes the shape of the pan. This is true because the molecules in liquid water have more energy than the molecules in ice. The molecules move more freely, bouncing off each other.

What happens if you continue to heat the water on the stove? As more energy is added to the liquid water, the speed of the molecules increases and the temperature rises. At 100°C, the water boils and another change of state occurs. The molecules have enough energy to escape the liquid and become invisible water vapor. The molecules in a gas move even more freely than those in a liquid. They spread out to fill their container — in this example, your whole kitchen!

Another way that liquid water can become a gas is through evaporation. **Evaporation** is the process by which molecules at the surface of a liquid absorb enough energy to change to the gaseous state. If you let your hair air-dry after going swimming, you are taking advantage of evaporation.

Condensation As water vapor cools down, it releases some of its energy to its surroundings. The molecules slow down and the temperature decreases. As the temperature of the gas reaches the boiling point, the water vapor begins to change back to the liquid state. The process by which a gas changes to a liquid is called **condensation.** When you fog up a window by breathing on it, you are seeing the effects of condensation. The invisible water vapor in your breath is cooled by the window and forms visible drops of liquid water.

Figure 9 Water exists on Earth in all three states: solid, liquid, and gas. **A.** The molecules in solid ice are close together and form a rigid structure. **B.** In liquid water, the molecules move more freely and the water takes the shape of its container. **C.** The molecules in gaseous water vapor move very freely and spread out to fill a space. *Comparing and Contrasting In which state do the molecules move the slowest? The fastest?*

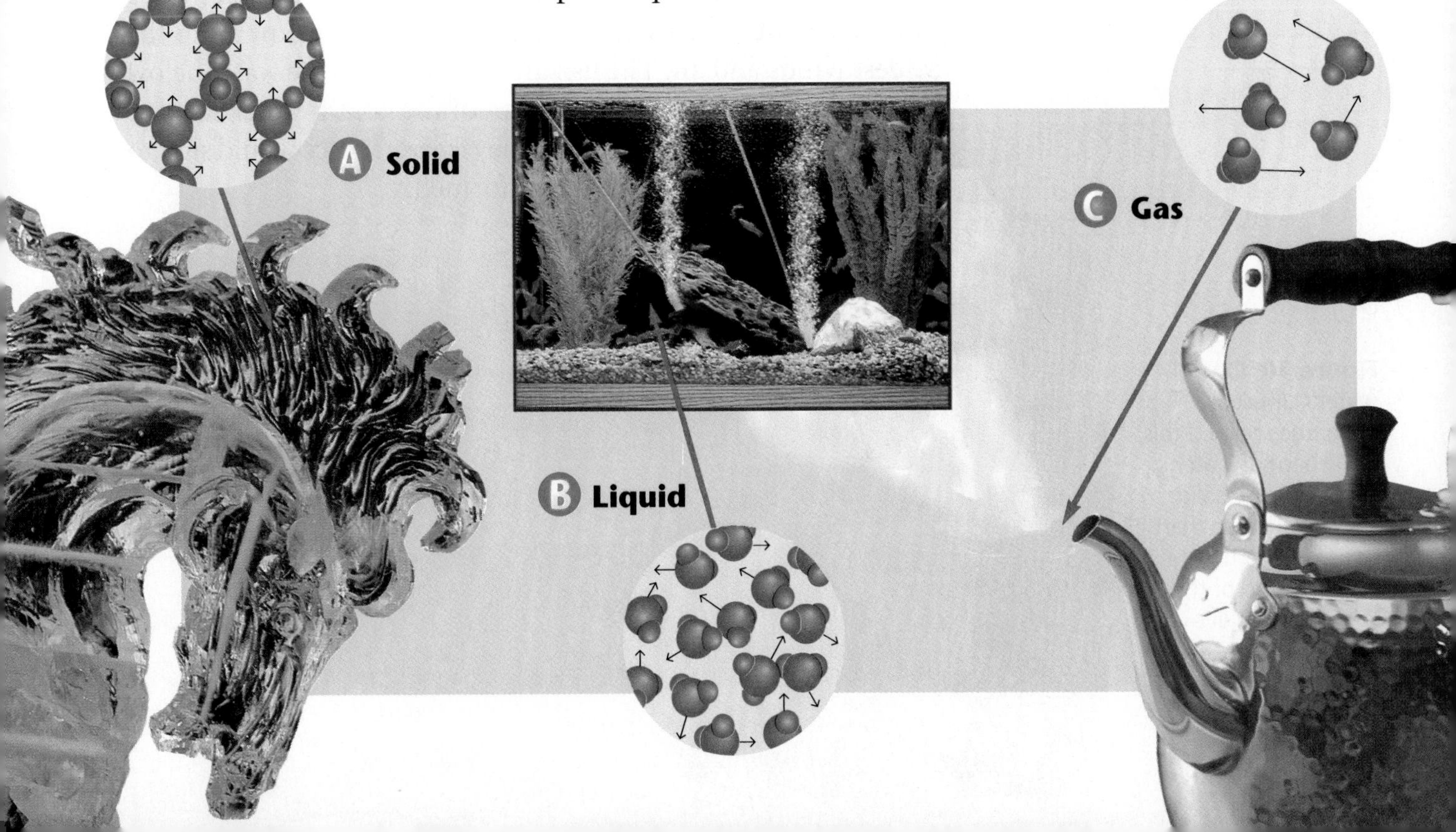
A Solid
B Liquid
C Gas

Language Arts CONNECTION

Imagine that you work at an advertising agency. Your agency has just been hired to design an advertising campaign for water. You know that water has many properties that make it unique. Your plan is to highlight one or more of these properties in an ad to show people what an unusual substance water is.

In Your Journal

Before you begin to write, decide which properties you will highlight in your ad. Write down some facts about each property that you think will interest people. Now you are ready to create the ad. Use humor, pictures, and everyday examples to make your point in an appealing way. Will your ad convince people that water is a unique substance?

Freezing If the liquid water continues to be cooled, the molecules continue to lose energy. They move more and more slowly. At 0°C, the liquid water freezes, changing back into solid ice. If you have ever observed an icicle forming from water dripping off a roof, you have seen this change of state in progress.

☑ *Checkpoint* ***In which state do water molecules have the most energy?***

Why Ice Floats

You know from experience that ice cubes in a glass float at the top of the water. If you combine the solid and liquid forms of most other substances, the solid sinks to the bottom. You have observed this if you have ever melted wax to make candles. The solid wax pieces sink to the bottom of the hot liquid wax.

As most liquids cool, their molecules slow down and move closer together until they reach their compact solid form. But surprisingly, something different happens to water. When water cools below about 4°C, the molecules begin to line up in a gridlike crystal structure. The molecules take up more space in this crystal structure than as a liquid. Frozen water in an ice cube tray contains the same amount of matter as when it was a liquid. However, the water takes up more space as ice than it did as a liquid. This means that ice is less dense than liquid water. Less dense substances, like the ice, float on more dense substances, like the liquid water.

INTEGRATING LIFE SCIENCE The fact that ice floats has important consequences for fish and other organisms that live in water. When lakes and ponds freeze in the winter, the ice stays at the top. The ice layer shelters the water below from the coldest winds and air. The fish are able to live in the water below the ice and find food on the bottom of the lake. If water acted as most substances do when they freeze, the ice would sink to the bottom of the lake as it formed.

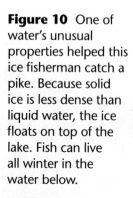

Figure 10 One of water's unusual properties helped this ice fisherman catch a pike. Because solid ice is less dense than liquid water, the ice floats on top of the lake. Fish can live all winter in the water below.

Specific Heat

Imagine a steamy July day. The air is hot, the sidewalk is hot, and the sandy beach is hot. You jump into a pool or the ocean, and the water is surprisingly cool! But if you go for an evening swim, the water is warm compared to the cool air.

You feel this difference in temperature because of water's unusually high specific heat. **Specific heat** is the amount of heat needed to increase the temperature of a certain mass of a substance by 1°C. Compared to other substances, water requires a lot of heat to increase its temperature.

Water's high specific heat is due to the many attractions among water molecules. Other substances, such as air and rocks, have fewer attractions between their molecules. Their temperature increases more quickly as they are heated than water that is heated the same amount.

One effect of water's high specific heat is that land areas located near large bodies of water experience less dramatic temperature changes than areas far inland. In the summer, the sun's heat warms the land more quickly than the water. The warm land heats the air above it to a higher temperature than the air over the ocean. As a result, the air is warmer inland than on the coast. Just the opposite effect occurs in the winter. The land loses heat to the air more quickly than the water. The water remains warm and keeps the air above it warmer than the air over the cold land.

Figure 11 What could be more refreshing than a swim on a hot summer day? This swimmer is taking advantage of water's high specific heat. ***Applying Concepts*** *How does this property of water help the swimmer cool off?*

Section 2 Review

1. What causes water molecules to be attracted to each other?
2. Why does sugar dissolve well in water?
3. Describe what is happening to the water molecules as ice melts.
4. What unusual fact about ice causes it to float in liquid water?
5. **Thinking Critically Predicting** If you place a cup of sand and a cup of water in the sun, which one will heat up faster? Explain your prediction in terms of a property of water.

Science at Home

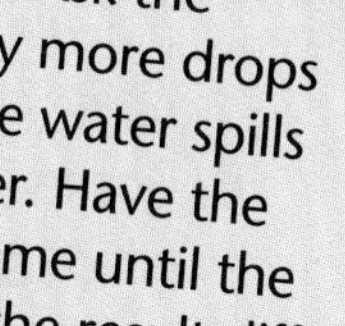

Put a penny on a piece of paper. With a plastic dropper or a toothpick, have a family member place a single drop of water on the penny. Ask the person to predict how many more drops he or she can add before the water spills off the penny onto the paper. Have the person add drops one at a time until the water overflows. How does the result differ from the prediction? Explain to your family member which property of water might account for this result.

Skills Lab

Developing Hypotheses

Speeding Up Evaporation

You have just learned that water changes from a liquid to a gas through evaporation. In this lab, you will develop hypotheses as you investigate this process.

Problem

What factors increase the rate at which water evaporates?

Materials

water
plastic dropper
2 plastic petri dishes
1 petri dish cover
3 index cards
paper towels
stopwatch
lamp

DATA TABLE

Part 1 Effect of Heat	
Hypothesis	
Result	
Part 2 Effect of a Cover	
Hypothesis	
Result	
Part 3 Effect of Wind	
Hypothesis	
Result	

Procedure

Part 1 Effect of Heat

1. Copy the data table into your notebook.
2. How does heating a water sample affect how fast it evaporates? Record your hypothesis in the data table.
3. Place each petri dish on an index card.
4. Add a single drop of water to each of the petri dishes. Try to make the two drops the same size.
5. Position the lamp over one of the dishes as a heat source. Turn on the light. Make sure the light does not shine on the other dish. **CAUTION:** *The light bulb will become very hot. Avoid touching the bulb or getting water on it.*
6. Observe the dishes every 3 minutes to see which sample evaporates faster. Record your result in the data table.

Part 2 Effect of a Cover

7. How does placing a cover over the water sample affect how fast it evaporates? Record your hypothesis in the data table.
8. Dry both petri dishes and place them side by side over the index cards. Add a drop of water to each dish as you did in Step 4.
9. Place a cover over one dish. Leave the other dish uncovered.
10. Observe the dishes after 10 minutes to see which sample evaporates faster. Record your result in the data table.

Part 3 Effect of Wind

11. How does fanning the water sample affect how fast it evaporates? Record your hypothesis in the data table.
12. Dry both petri dishes and place them over the index cards. Add a drop of water to each dish as you did in Step 4.

13. Use an index card to fan one of the dishes for 5 minutes. Be careful not to fan the other dish as well.
14. Observe the dishes to see which sample evaporates faster. Record your result in the data table.

Analyze and Conclude

1. In which cases were your hypotheses correct? In which cases were they incorrect?
2. For each part of the experiment, explain why the water evaporated faster in one dish than the other. (*Hint:* Think about what happened to the water molecules in each dish.)
3. Make a general statement about factors that increase the rate at which water evaporates.
4. Based on this experiment, predict what would happen in each of the following situations.
   a. Would a wet swimsuit dry faster in a plastic bag or out in the open? Explain.
   b. Would wet clothes on a clothesline dry faster on a windy day or on a calm day? Explain.
   c. Would wet clothes dry faster if they were hung on a clothesline located on the sunny side of a house or on the shady side? Explain.
5. **Think About It** What knowledge or everyday experiences helped you make your hypotheses at the beginning of the experiment?

More to Explore

Develop a hypothesis to explain how increasing the surface area of a water sample affects how fast the sample evaporates. Write your hypothesis and then design an experiment to test it. Be sure to check your plan with your teacher before carrying out your experiment.

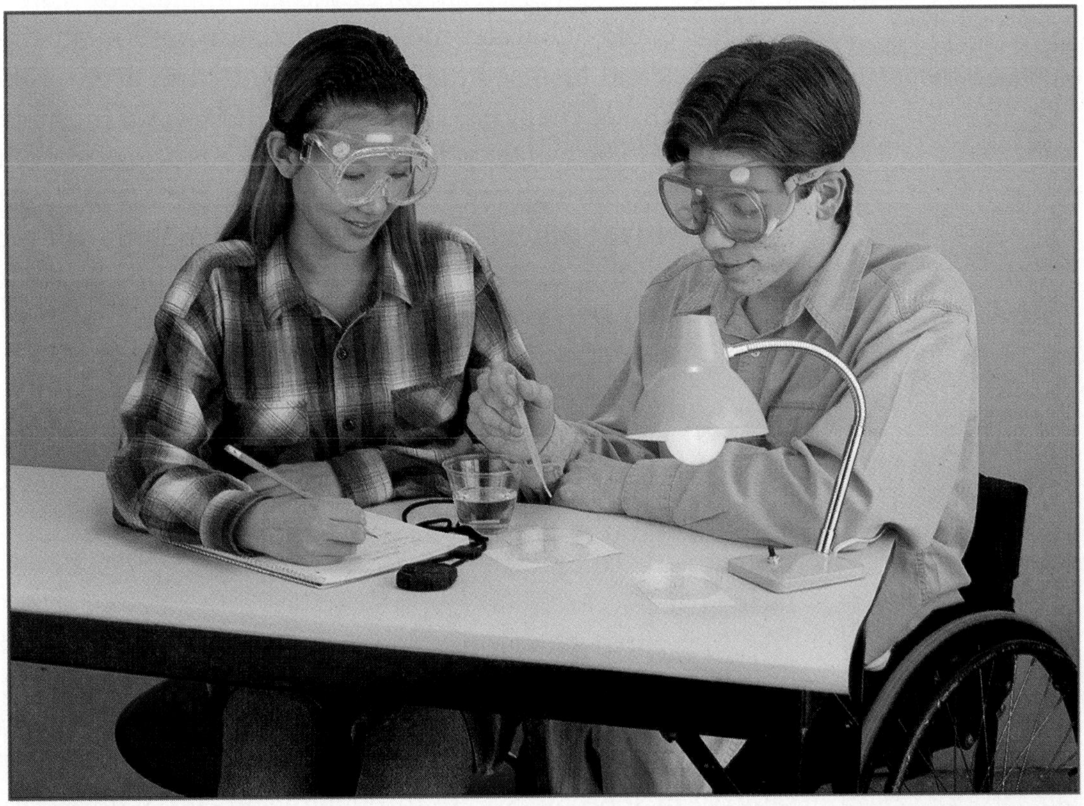

SECTION 3

The Water Cycle

DISCOVER

ACTIVITY

Where Does the Water Come From?

1. Fill a glass with ice cubes and water, being careful not to spill any water. Set the glass aside for 5 minutes.
2. Observe the outside of the glass and the surface it was sitting on.

Think It Over

Inferring Where did the water on the outside of the glass come from? How do you think it got there?

GUIDE FOR READING

- **How does Earth's water move through the water cycle?**
- **In what ways do living things depend on the water cycle?**

Reading Tip **Before you read, preview** ***Exploring the Water Cycle*** **on the facing page. Make a list of any unfamiliar words in the diagram.**

The next time it rains, cup your hand and catch some raindrops. Think about where a single water molecule in one of those raindrops may have traveled. Most recently, it was part of the gray cloud overhead. Last year, it may have tumbled over a waterfall or floated down the Nile River. Perhaps it spent years as part of the Pacific Ocean. The same water molecule may even have fallen as rain on a dinosaur millions of years ago.

How could one water molecule reappear in so many different places and forms? In fact, all the water on Earth has been through similar changes. Water is naturally recycled through the water cycle. The **water cycle** is the continuous process by which water moves through the living and nonliving parts of the environment. **In the water cycle, water moves from bodies of water, land, and living things on Earth's surface to the atmosphere and back to Earth's surface.** The sun is the source of energy that drives the water cycle.

Water Evaporates

Water moves continuously through the water cycle. The cycle has no real beginning or end. You can follow a water molecule through one complete cycle in *Exploring the Water Cycle* on the facing page.

Think about a molecule of water floating near the surface of an ocean. The sun is shining and the air is warm. Soon, the molecule has absorbed enough heat energy to change state. It evaporates and becomes water vapor. Although the water comes from the salty ocean, it becomes fresh through the process of evaporation. The salt remains in the ocean.

Large amounts of water evaporate constantly from the surfaces of oceans and large lakes. In addition, small amounts evaporate from the soil, puddles, and even from your skin.

A significant amount of water is given off by plants. Plants draw in water from the soil through their roots. Eventually the water is given off through the leaves as water vapor in a process called **transpiration.** You may be surprised to learn how much water plants release to the atmosphere through transpiration.

EXPLORING *the Water Cycle*

The water cycle is the continuous process by which water moves through the environment. The sun is the source of energy that drives the water cycle.

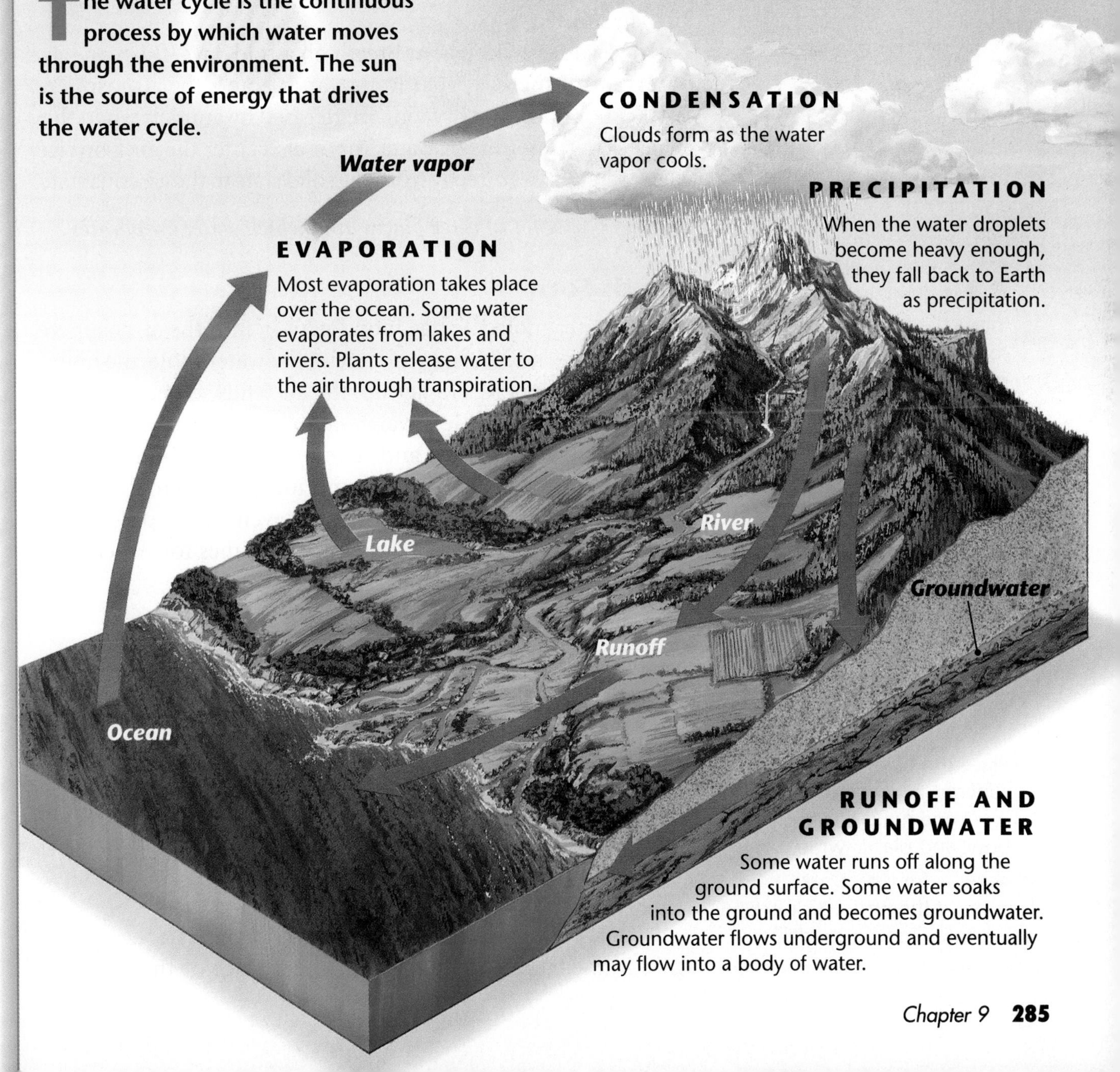
CONDENSATION
Clouds form as the water vapor cools.
Water vapor
PRECIPITATION
When the water droplets become heavy enough, they fall back to Earth as precipitation.
EVAPORATION
Most evaporation takes place over the ocean. Some water evaporates from lakes and rivers. Plants release water to the air through transpiration.
River
Lake
Groundwater
Runoff
Ocean
RUNOFF AND GROUNDWATER
Some water runs off along the ground surface. Some water soaks into the ground and becomes groundwater. Groundwater flows underground and eventually may flow into a body of water.

Figure 12 Clouds and mist blanket this lush rain forest in Costa Rica. ***Relating Cause and Effect*** *Describe how the processes of evaporation and condensation can cause clouds to form.*

The thousands of leaves on a single birch tree, for example, may give off 260 liters of water in one day — enough to fill nine kitchen sinks!

Have you ever seen your breath on a cold day? If so, you have observed another way that water vapor enters the atmosphere. Small amounts of water vapor are released by animals when they exhale. Tiny amounts of water vapor also enter the air from ice, when water passes directly from the solid state to the gaseous state.

☑ *Checkpoint* ***List three places from which water evaporates.***

Clouds Form

Once a water molecule has found its way into the atmosphere, what happens next? Warm air carries the water molecule higher into the atmosphere. Higher up, the air tends to become much colder. Cold air holds less water vapor than warm air. Some of the water vapor cools and condenses into liquid water. Condensed droplets of water clump together around tiny dust particles in the air, forming clouds. In even colder parts of the upper atmosphere, the water vapor sometimes forms ice crystals rather than water droplets.

Water Falls As Precipitation

As more water vapor condenses, the water droplets in a cloud grow larger and larger. Eventually, the drops become so heavy that they fall back to Earth. Water that falls to Earth as rain, snow, hail, or sleet is called **precipitation.** Most water molecules probably spend only about 10 days in the atmosphere before falling back to Earth. Most precipitation falls directly into the oceans. Water in the ocean may stay there for many years before evaporating, thus continuing the cycle.

When precipitation falls on land, some of the water evaporates again immediately. Some runs off the surface of the land into

TRY THIS

Tabletop Water Cycle

ACTIVITY

In this activity you will build a model of the water cycle.

1. Put on your goggles. Pour enough water into a flat-bottomed bowl to cover the bottom. Fill a small jar with sand and place it in the bowl.
2. Loosely cover the top of the bowl with plastic wrap. Secure with a rubber band.
3. Place a rock on top of the plastic, directly over the jar.

4. Place the bowl in direct sunlight or under a lamp. After one hour, observe the bowl and plastic wrap.

Making a Model What features of the water cycle are represented in your model?

rivers and lakes. From there, it may eventually evaporate or flow back into the ocean. Some water trickles down into the ground and forms groundwater. Groundwater may move underground until it reaches a river, lake, or ocean. Once groundwater reaches the surface, it can continue through the cycle by evaporating again.

Before returning to the atmosphere, some water passes through living things. Animals drink the water and eventually release it back to the environment as a waste product. Plants use the water to grow and to produce food. When these living things die, their bodies are broken down slowly, and the water returns to the environment.

Figure 13 These thirsty zebras are a part of the water cycle. The water they drink passes through their bodies and is released in their wastes.

A Global Process

Precipitation is the source of all fresh water on and below Earth's surface. The water cycle renews the usable supply of fresh water on Earth. For millions of years, the total amount of water on Earth has remained fairly constant. The worldwide amounts of evaporation and precipitation balance each other. This may not seem believable if you live in an area where there is either a lot of precipitation or very little. It is possible for parts of India to receive as much as 1,000 centimeters of precipitation in a year, while the Sahara, a desert in Africa, may get only 5 centimeters. But in the world as a whole, the rates of evaporation and precipitation are balanced.

Section 3 Review

1. Describe the general path of water as it moves through the water cycle.
2. How does the water cycle renew Earth's supply of fresh water?
3. What is the source of the energy that drives the water cycle?
4. **Thinking Critically Relating Cause and Effect** How might cutting down trees affect the amount of evaporation in an area?

CHAPTER PROJECT

Check Your Progress

By now you should have chosen a building in your community to monitor. How will you determine the amount and type of water usage there? Be sure to check with your teacher before contacting anyone at the site. (*Hint:* A building manager or facilities manager often has information about water use. You may find it helpful to write down your questions before you interview the person.)

You and Your Environment

Water From Trees

Trees play many important roles in the environment—they keep the soil from washing away, remove carbon dioxide from the air, and produce oxygen. Trees are also a vital part of the water cycle. In this lab you will discover how trees help to keep water moving through the cycle.

Problem

How much water do the leaves on a tree give off in a 24-hour period?

Skills Focus

observing, calculating, inferring

Materials

3 plastic sandwich bags
3 small pebbles
balance
3 twist ties

Procedure

1. Copy the data table into your notebook.
2. Place the sandwich bags, twist ties, and pebbles on a balance. Determine their total mass to the nearest tenth of a gram.
3. Select an outdoor tree or shrub with leaves that are within your reach.
4. Put one pebble into a sandwich bag and place the bag over one of the tree's leaves as shown. Fasten the twist tie around the bag, forming a tight seal around the stem of the leaf.
5. Repeat Step 4 with the other plastic bags on two more leaves. Leave the bags in place on the leaves for 24 hours.

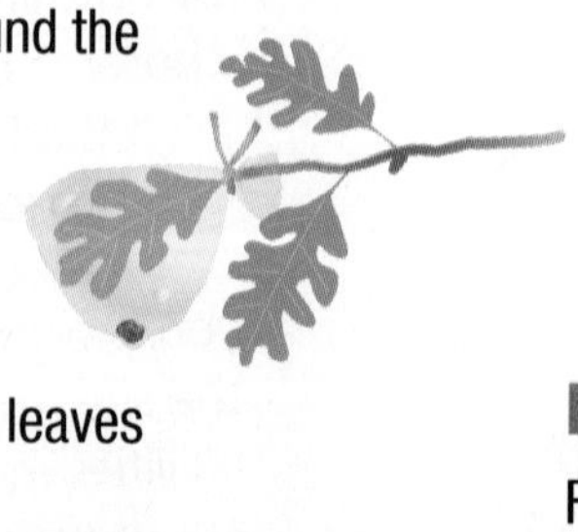

6. The following day, examine the bags and record your observations in your notebook.

DATA TABLE

Starting mass of bags, ties, and pebbles	
Mass of bags, ties, and pebbles after 24 hours	
Difference in mass	

7. Carefully remove the bags from the leaves and refasten each twist tie around its bag so that the bag is closed tightly.
8. Place the three bags, including pebbles and twist ties, on the balance. Determine their total mass to the nearest tenth of a gram.
9. Subtract the original mass of the bags, ties, and pebbles that you found in Step 2 from the mass you found in Step 8.

Analyze and Conclude

1. Based on your observations, how can you account for the difference in mass?
2. What is the name of the process that caused the results you observed? Explain the role of that process in the water cycle.
3. A single birch tree may transpire as much as 260 liters of water in a day. How much water would a grove of 1,000 birch trees return to the atmosphere in a year?
4. **Apply** Based on what you learned from this investigation, what is one reason that people may be concerned about the destruction of forests around the world?

More to Explore

Find another type of tree and repeat this experiment. What might account for any differences in the amount of water the two trees transpire?

Section 1 How Is Water Important?

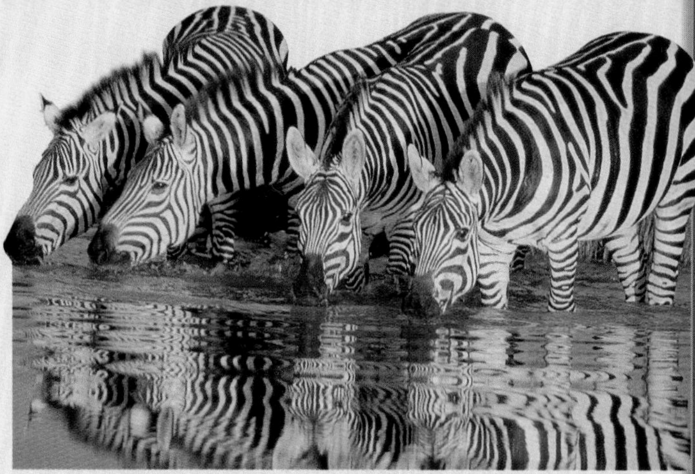

Key Ideas

- People use water for many purposes, including household use, industry, agriculture, transportation, and recreation.
- All living things need water to carry out their life processes.
- About 97 percent of Earth's water is salt water stored in the oceans. Less than 1 percent is usable fresh water.

Key Terms

irrigation	photosynthesis	habitat
water vapor	groundwater	

Section 2 The Properties of Water

Integrating Chemistry

Key Ideas

- A water molecule consists of two hydrogen atoms bonded to an oxygen atom. The hydrogen ends of the molecule have a slight positive charge. The oxygen end of the molecule has a slight negative charge.
- The charged ends of water's polar molecules attract the charged ends of other water molecules. Water molecules are also attracted to other charged particles.
- Some properties caused by the attractions among water molecules are surface tension, capillary action, and high specific heat.
- Water dissolves so many substances that it is sometimes called the "universal solvent."
- Water on Earth exists in three states: liquid water; ice, a solid; and water vapor, a gas.
- Energy must be added or released for water molecules to change state.
- Unlike most other substances, the solid form of water is less dense than the liquid form.

Key Terms

polar molecule	surface tension	capillary action
solution	solvent	state
evaporation	condensation	specific heat

Section 3 The Water Cycle

Key Ideas

- In the water cycle, water evaporates from Earth's surface into the atmosphere. The water forms clouds, then falls back to Earth as precipitation. The sun's energy drives the water cycle.
- The water cycle renews Earth's supply of fresh water. In the world as a whole, the rates of evaporation and precipitation balance each other.

Key Terms

water cycle	transpiration	precipitation

+
-
+
-
+
-
+
-
+
-
+
-
+
-
+
-
+
-

ACTIVITY

USING THE INTERNET

www.phschool.com/state_focus/california/

California Test Prep: Reviewing Content

Multiple Choice

Choose the letter of the best answer.

1. The process of supplying land areas with water to make them suitable for farming is
   a. transpiration. b. irrigation.
   c. condensation. d. capillary action.
2. More than 97 percent of Earth's total water supply is found in
   a. ice sheets.
   b. the atmosphere.
   c. the oceans.
   d. groundwater.
3. A molecule with electrically charged parts is a
   a. nonpolar molecule.
   b. solution.
   c. polar molecule.
   d. gas.
4. When you stir salt into water, you are making a
   a. solution. b. solvent.
   c. solid. d. molecule.
5. The energy that drives the water cycle comes from the
   a. Earth. b. sun.
   c. rain. d. ocean.

True or False

If the statement is true, write true. If it is false, change the underlined word or words to make the statement true.

6. The process in which plants use water, light, and carbon dioxide to make food is called photosynthesis.
7. Most of Earth's liquid fresh water is found in the form of lakes.
8. The property of surface tension allows insects to walk on water.
9. In the water cycle, precipitation returns salt water to Earth.
10. The process by which the leaves of plants give off water into the atmosphere is condensation.

Checking Concepts

11. How is the water supplied to plants important for many other living things on Earth?
12. Explain why Earth is called the "water planet."
13. Explain why so little of Earth's water is available for human use.
14. Draw a diagram of a water molecule that shows how it is polar. Be sure to include labels in your diagram.
15. Give examples of two properties of water that are caused by the attractions between water molecules.
16. Describe two changes of state that occur during the water cycle.
17. **Writing to Learn** As the information officer aboard a starship, you are assigned to write a handbook describing Earth's waters to visitors from other galaxies. Write a description in which you explain how water is important to living things on Earth.

Thinking Visually

18. **Cycle Diagram** Copy the cycle diagram onto a sheet of paper and complete it to show one possible path for a water molecule. Add a title. (For more on cycle diagrams, see the Skills Handbook.)

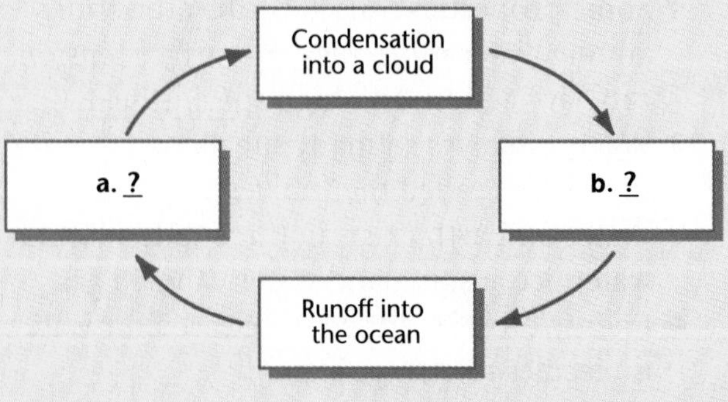
Condensation into a cloud
b. ?
Runoff into the ocean
a. ?

Test Prep: Skills

Use this circle graph to answer questions 19–21.

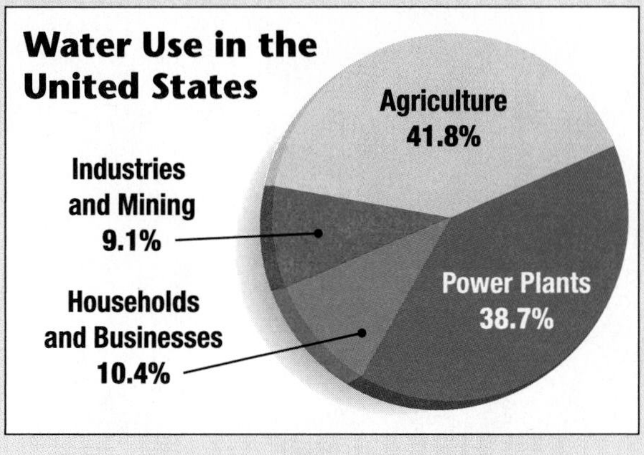
Water Use in the United States
Agriculture 41.8%
Industries and Mining 9.1%
Power Plants 38.7%
Households and Businesses 10.4%

19. Interpreting Data Which category represents the largest use of water in the United States? Which is the smallest?

20. Calculating If the total daily usage of water in the United States is 1,280 billion liters, how many liters are used each day by power plants?

21. Predicting How would an increase in the amount of irrigation affect this graph?

Thinking Critically

22. Making Generalizations Explain why towns and cities are often located along bodies of water.

23. Comparing and Contrasting Compare the three states of water in terms of the speed and arrangement of their molecules.

24. Applying Concepts You may have heard the saying, "Oil and water don't mix." Explain this statement in terms of the chemistry of water.

25. Predicting The city of Charleston, South Carolina, is located on the Atlantic coast. The city of Macon, Georgia, is located about 340 kilometers inland to the west. Predict which city is likely to be cooler in the summer. Explain your answer.

26. Relating Cause and Effect A molecule of water is likely to evaporate more quickly from the Caribbean Sea near the equator than from the Arctic Ocean. Explain why this statement is true.

Performance Assessment

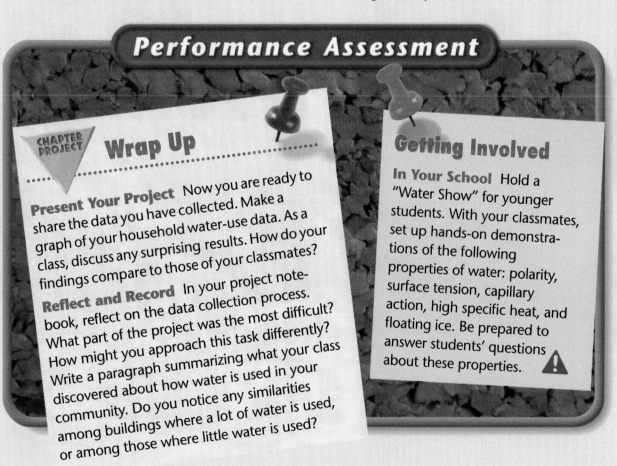

CHAPTER PROJECT Wrap Up

Present Your Project Now you are ready to share the data you have collected. Make a graph of your household water-use data. As a class, discuss any surprising results. How do your findings compare to those of your classmates?

Reflect and Record In your project notebook, reflect on the data collection process. What part of the project was the most difficult? How might you approach this task differently? Write a paragraph summarizing what your class discovered about how water is used in your community. Do you notice any similarities among buildings where a lot of water is used, or among those where little water is used?

Getting Involved

In Your School Hold a "Water Show" for younger students. With your classmates, set up hands-on demonstrations of the following properties of water: polarity, surface tension, capillary action, high specific heat, and floating ice. Be prepared to answer students' questions about these properties.

CHAPTER 10 Fresh Water

The following California Science Content Standards are addressed in this chapter:

2. Topography is reshaped by weathering of rock and soil and by the transportation and deposition of sediment.
   - **a.** Water running downhill is the dominant process in shaping the landscape, including California's landscape.
   - **b.** Rivers and streams are dynamic systems that erode and transport sediment, change course, and flood their banks in natural and recurring patterns.
   - **d.** Earthquakes, volcanic eruptions, landslides, and floods change human and wildlife habitats.
5. Organisms in ecosystems exchange energy and nutrients among themselves and with the environment.
   - **a.** Energy entering ecosystems as sunlight is transferred by producers into chemical energy through photosynthesis, and then from organism to organism in food webs.
   - **e.** The number and types of organisms an ecosystem can support depends on the resources available and abiotic factors, such as quantity of light and

A bull moose shakes himself off following a dip in an Alaskan stream.

PROJECT 10

Build a Watershed

The bull moose plunges into the stream, sending shimmering drops of water flying in all directions. In addition to a refreshing dip, the stream provides the moose with drinking water and a place to find food.

A stream is one place you can find fresh water on Earth. In this chapter you will explore fresh water as it moves and changes the land, as it collects in lakes and ponds and provides a home for living things, and as it flows underground. Throughout the chapter, you will be making a model showing how water moves over the land.

Your Goal To design and build a three-dimensional model of a watershed and river system.

Your model should

- include a main river and at least two tributaries
- show at least one example of a body of standing water
- be constructed of materials that allow water to run over it
- be built following the safety guidelines in Appendix A

Get Started Begin by previewing Section 1 to see some parts of a river system. Look at the shape of the land surrounding different parts of rivers. Start thinking about materials you could use to make your landscape.

Check Your Progress You'll be working on this project as you study this chapter. To keep your project on track, look for Check Your Progress boxes at the following points.

Section 1 Review, page 304: Sketch a design for your watershed.

Section 3 Review, page 316: Revise your design to include all features.

Section 5 Review, page 326: Build your model watershed.

Wrap Up At the end of the chapter (page 329), you will use a spray bottle to demonstrate your watershed in action!

water, range of temperatures, and soil composition.

6. **Sources of energy and materials differ in amounts, distribution, usefulness, and the time required for their formation.**
   b. Different natural energy and material resources, including air, soil, rocks, minerals, petroleum, fresh water, wildlife, and forests, and classify them as renewable or nonrenewable.

7. **Scientific progress is made by asking meaningful questions and conducting careful investigations.**
   b. Select and use appropriate tools and technology to perform tests, collect data, and display data.
   c. Construct appropriate graphs from data and develop qualitative statements about the relationships between variables.
   e. Recognize whether evidence is consistent with a proposed explanation.
   f. Read a topographic map and a geologic map for evidence provided on the maps, and construct and interpret a simple scale map.

SECTION 1

Streams and Rivers

DISCOVER ACTIVITY

What Affects How Water Moves?

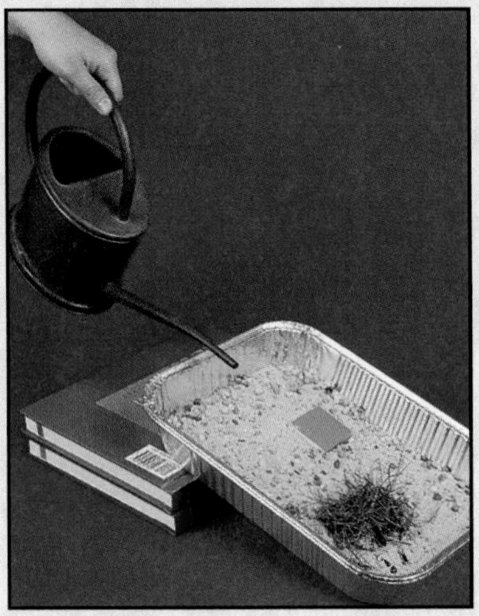

1. Cover the bottom of a pan with a mixture of sand and pebbles.
2. Press a small piece of porcelain tile onto the sand mixture to represent pavement. In another area of the pan, press a clump of soil and grass into the sand.
3. Prop up one end of the pan so it slopes gently.
4. Using a watering can, sprinkle "rain" onto the pan's contents.
5. Observe how the water moves when it falls on the sand mixture, on the tile, and on the grass.
6. Wash your hands when you are finished with this activity.

Think It Over

Predicting How would the movement of the water change if you poured the water all at once? If you tilted the pan more steeply?

GUIDE FOR READING

- **What is a river system?**
- **How does a river change the land around it?**
- **What conditions can cause a flood?**

Reading Tip **Before you read, use the section headings to make an outline. Leave space to take notes as you read.**

Standing on a bridge in Albuquerque, New Mexico, you look through your binoculars at the waters of the Rio Grande—the "Big River." The name fits this broad, deep stretch of water. But 700 kilometers upstream, the Rio Grande looks very different. The river begins as trickles of melting snow high in the San Juan Mountains in Colorado. As more water joins the river, it carves deep, narrow canyons out of the rock.

By the time it reaches Albuquerque the river has grown wider. It continues into Texas, winding back and forth across the dusty desert valley. In places, the river is so shallow that it may even dry up during the summer. When the Rio Grande finally empties its water into the Gulf of Mexico, it is sluggish and heavy with mud.

Spanish explorers once gave different names to three parts of the Rio Grande. They thought they had seen three different rivers! In this section, you will discover how rivers change, and how they change the land around them.

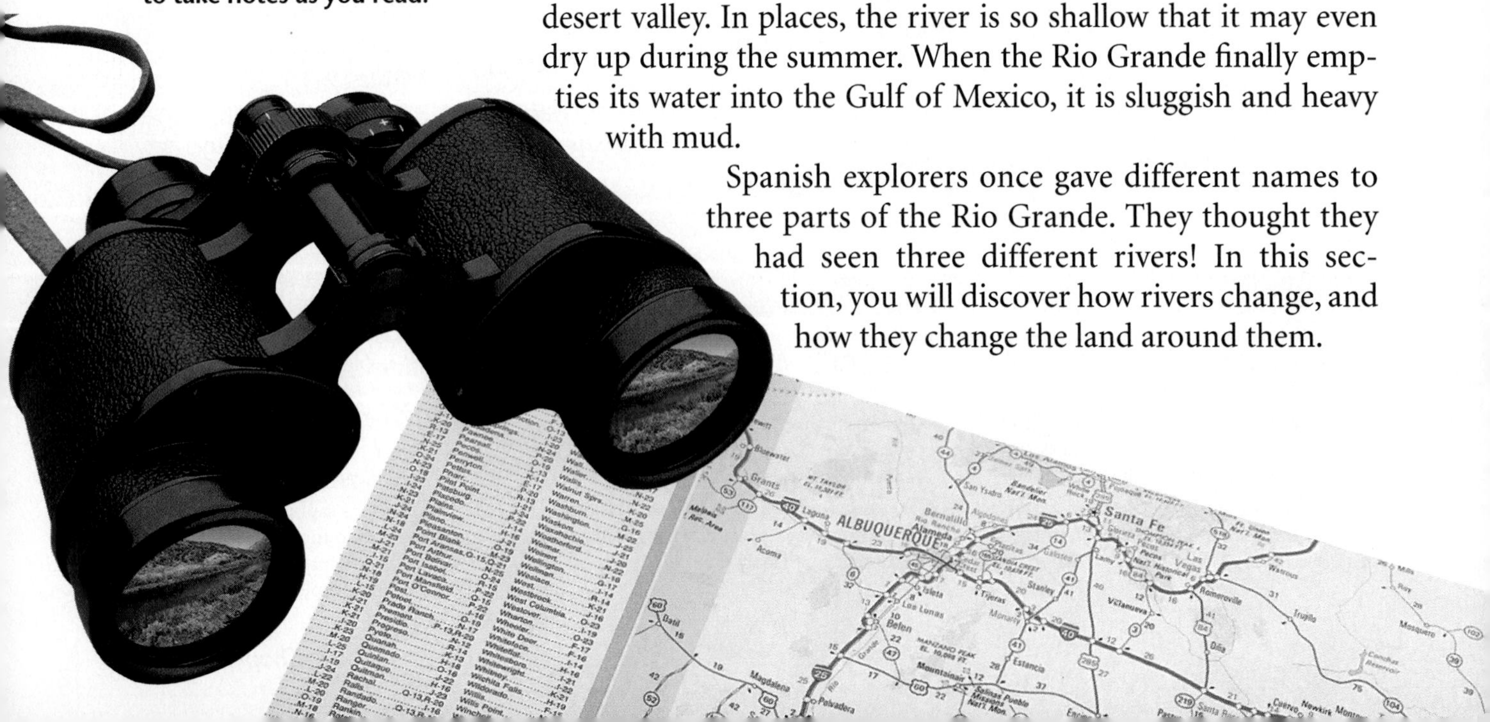
ALBUQUERQUE
Santa Fe
Grants
Belen
Los Lunas
Estancia
Magdalena
Acoma

How Do Rivers Begin?

Have you ever helped out at a car wash for your school or youth group? Think about what happened to the water that sloshed onto the pavement. First the water ran in little trickles, which then joined together into a larger stream. The water followed the slope of the pavement down to the street or into a storm drain. A river begins in much the same way—trickles of water run over the ground and join together in larger streams.

When rain falls, some of the water evaporates immediately. Some soaks into the soil. The remaining water that flows over the ground surface is called **runoff.** Runoff also comes from melting ice and snow, like the runoff that forms the beginnings of the Rio Grande.

Figure 1 In addition to washing a car, these teens are demonstrating how ground surface affects the formation of runoff. *Applying Concepts What happens to the water that lands on the pavement? The grass?*

Factors That Affect Runoff

What determines whether water soaks into the ground or flows over it as runoff? One factor is the nature of the ground surface. Water soaks into some types of ground covering more easily than others. How much water soaks in depends on the amount of space between the particles that make up the ground cover. For example, there is more space between the particles of soil than between the particles of pavement. As a result, water soaks into soil more easily than into pavement. Since plant roots also absorb water, ground that is covered with grass or trees absorbs water more easily than bare soil.

The rate of rainfall is a second factor that affects the amount of runoff. During a heavy downpour, so much rain falls in a short time that it can't all soak into the ground. Instead some becomes runoff.

A third factor is whether the land is flat or hilly. The force of gravity pulls water downhill, just as it pulls you downhill on a sled or skateboard. Water flows faster down a steep slope than over flat ground. Because the water is moving so quickly, it runs off instead of soaking in. As runoff flows along a trench, or channel, it forms a stream. This is the beginning of the process that forms a river.

☑ *Checkpoint* ***List three factors that affect the amount of runoff.***

River Systems

If you were hiking in the San Juan Mountains, you could observe the path of the runoff from melting snow. As you followed one small stream downhill, you would notice that the stream reached a larger stream and joined it. You could then continue along this stream until it flowed into a small river. Eventually this path would lead you to the Rio Grande itself.

Tributaries are the smaller streams and rivers that feed into a main river. **A river and all its tributaries together make up a river system.** The tributaries flow toward the main river following a downhill path due to the pull of gravity. Even a land area that appears flat can have small differences in height that affect how water flows.

Watersheds Just as all the water in a bathtub flows toward the drain, all the water in a river system drains into the main river. The land area that supplies water to a river system is called a **watershed.** Watersheds are also called drainage basins.

A river can flow into another, larger river. When rivers join another river system, the areas they drain become part of the largest river's watershed. You can identify a river's watershed on a map by drawing an imaginary line around the region drained by all its tributaries. Some watersheds are very small. The watershed of a stream that flows down a hill into a river is just that hillside—maybe a square kilometer or two. By contrast, the watershed of the Mississippi River covers more than 3 million

Figure 2 This map shows the watersheds of several large rivers in the United States. Each river's watershed consists of the region drained by the river and all its tributaries. ***Interpreting Maps*** *Name four tributaries of the Mississippi River. Which tributary has the largest watershed?*

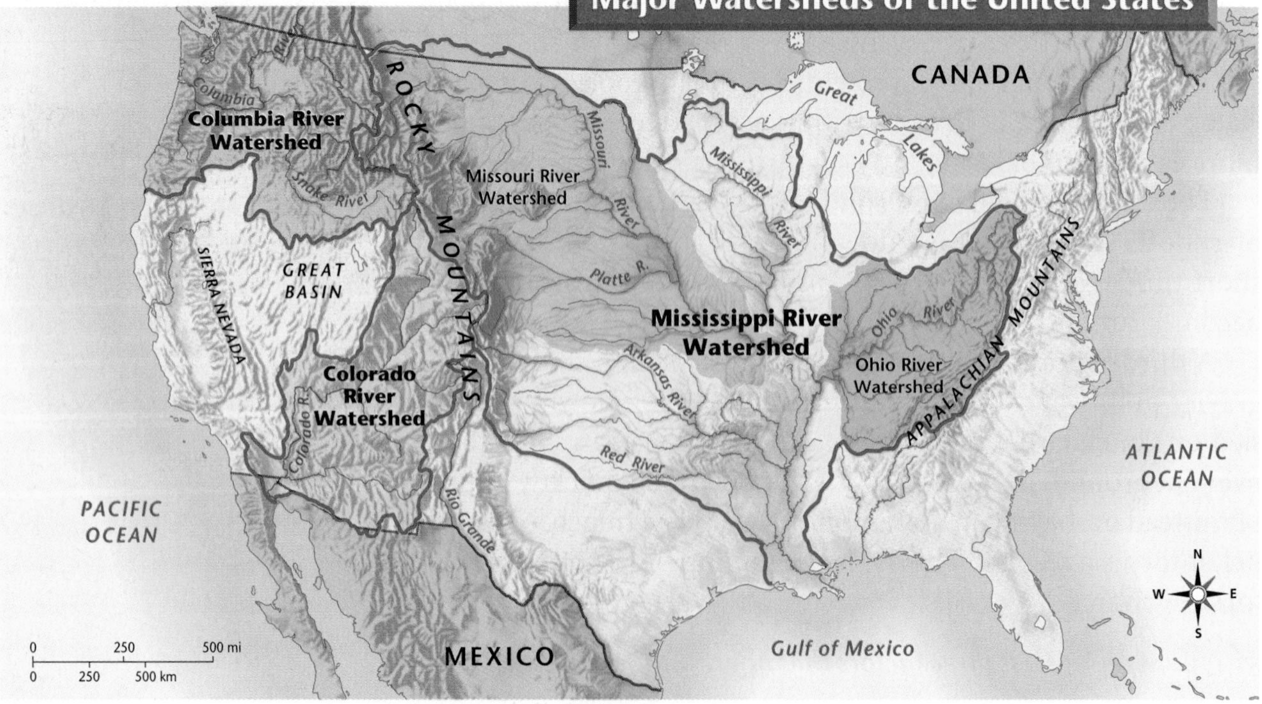
Major Watersheds of the United States
CANADA
Columbia
Columbia River Watershed
Snake River
ROCKY MOUNTAINS
Missouri River Watershed
Missouri River
Great Lakes
Mississippi River
SIERRA NEVADA
GREAT BASIN
Platte R.
Mississippi River Watershed
Ohio River
Ohio River Watershed
APPALACHIAN MOUNTAINS
Arkansas River
Colorado River Watershed
Colorado R.
Red River
Rio Grande
ATLANTIC OCEAN
PACIFIC OCEAN
MEXICO
Gulf of Mexico
N
W
E
S
0
250
500 mi
0
250
500 km

square kilometers! With your finger, trace the boundary of the Mississippi's watershed on Figure 2. Notice that it includes the watersheds of the Ohio River and the Missouri River, its two largest tributaries.

Divides One watershed is separated from another by a ridge of land called a **divide.** Streams on each side of the divide flow in different directions. The Continental Divide, the longest divide in North America, follows the line of the Rocky Mountains. Locate the Rocky Mountains on Figure 2. West of the Continental Divide, water either flows toward the Pacific Ocean or into the dry Great Basin, where the water usually evaporates. Between the Rocky Mountains and the Appalachian Mountains, water flows toward the Mississippi River or directly into the Gulf of Mexico.

☑ *Checkpoint* ***Into what ocean do rivers east of the Appalachian Mountains flow?***

TRY THIS

The Knuckle Divide

ACTIVITY

Make your hand into a fist and put it on a paper towel, knuckles facing up. With your other hand, dribble water from a spoon so that it falls onto your knuckles. Observe how the water flows over your hand.

Making a Model How are your knuckles similar to a mountain range on land? What parts of your hand represent a watershed?

Rivers Shape the Land

The next time it rains, watch the rainwater flow along the side of a road. Notice how the water picks up leaves and twigs and carries them away. Bits of paper and small pebbles bounce and swirl along in the flow. Even a tiny stream has the power to move objects.

Picture a stream ten times larger, and you will start to get an idea of how running water can cause erosion. **Erosion** is the process by which fragments of soil and rock are broken off from the ground surface and carried away. These fragments are carried along by the moving water until they are eventually dropped, or deposited, in a new location. **Deposition** is the process by which soil and rock are left behind. **Rivers wear away landforms through erosion and build new landforms through deposition.** The particles of rock and soil that are picked up and moved by erosion and deposition are called **sediments.**

A river's speed affects its ability to wear away, or erode, the land. The faster the water flows, the more energy it has. A river traveling at a speed of 1 kilometer an hour

Figure 3 A hiker carefully avoids the collapsed edge of this dirt road, evidence of moving water's power to erode soil.

has enough energy to move pebbles along. At 18 kilometers an hour it can move a boulder the size of an armchair! When a river slows down, its energy decreases. It can no longer move heavy objects. The river deposits heavier sediment particles first, then lighter ones.

One factor that affects how fast a river flows is the steepness of its slope. Water flows faster down a mountainside than over a flat plain. A second factor that affects a river's speed is the volume of water in the river. An increase in the amount of water in a river

Skills Lab

Interpreting Data

How Fast Does a Stream Flow?

In this lab, you will interpret data to see how different factors affect stream flow. First, you will build a model called a stream trough.

Problem

How do the slope of a stream and the volume of water it contains affect its speed?

Materials

meterstick
pencil with eraser
several wooden blocks
water
stopwatch
plastic tub
2 100-mL beakers with pour spouts
rain gutter section, 120 cm or longer
food coloring in squeeze-top bottle

Procedure

1. Copy the data table into your notebook. Label it "Experiment number 1."
2. Use the pencil to mark an "S" at one end of the gutter. This represents the stream's source. Mark an "M" at the other end of the gutter. This represents the stream's mouth.
3. About 10 cm from the source end, draw a dark line across the inside of the gutter.

DATA TABLE

Experiment number: ______

Number of blocks: ______

Number of beakers: ______

Trial Number	Time (seconds)
Trial 1	
Trial 2	
Trial 3	

Average time: ______

Average stream speed: ______

4. Measure 100 cm toward the mouth end from the first line. Draw a second line across the gutter.
5. Place the plastic tub under the mouth end of the gutter to collect the water.
6. Place enough blocks under the source end to raise it 5 cm above the tub. Record the number of blocks in the data table.
7. Write "1" after "Number of beakers" in the data table.

causes the river to flow faster. A third factor is the shape of the channel through which the river flows. As the water in the river rubs against the sides and bottom of its channel, it creates friction. This friction slows the water's movement. In a shallow, narrow channel, almost all the water is in contact with the sides or bottom, and it moves slowly. In a broad, deep channel, however, most of the water can flow without any friction, so the river flows faster.

8. One person should slowly pour water from one beaker into the source end of the gutter, trying not to spill any water out the back end. A second person should add one drop of food coloring at the source end, above the "S" line. A third person should begin timing when the food coloring first reaches the "S" line. Stop timing when the food coloring reaches the "M" line. Record the time on your data table. Be sure the water is collecting in the tub at the mouth end.
9. Repeat Step 8 twice, pouring the water at the same rate each time. Record your results.
10. Copy the data table again, labeling it "Experiment number 2." Repeat Steps 8 and 9 with an increased water volume in the stream. Increase the water volume by pouring water into the stream from two beakers at the same time. Try to pour both at the same rate.
11. Now increase the slope of the stream, adding blocks to raise the source end 5 cm higher.
12. Copy the data table two more times for Experiment numbers 3 and 4. For Experiment 3, repeat Steps 8 and 9 at this steeper slope. For Experiment 4, repeat Step 10.

Analyze and Conclude

1. Average the three trials for each experiment. Record the average times on your data table.
2. Calculate the average stream speed for each experiment using the following formula:

$$\text{Speed of stream (cm/s)} = \frac{\text{distance (100 cm)}}{\text{average time (s)}}$$

3. How did the speed of the stream change when you increased the volume of water?
4. How did the speed of the stream change when you increased the slope?
5. **Think About It** What errors might have affected your data? How could they be reduced?

More to Explore

The volume of sediments picked up and carried by a stream indicates how much erosion is occurring. How could you modify this experiment to test how the amount of erosion is affected by a stream's speed? Obtain your teacher's permission to try the experiment.

Profile of a River

Imagine taking a rafting trip along the entire length of a river to observe how it changes firsthand. You can follow the journey in *Exploring a River.*

The Headwaters Your trip starts near the river's beginning, or source, in the mountains. The many small streams that come together at the source of the river are called the **headwaters.** Your ride through the headwaters is quite bumpy as your raft bounces through rapids, dropping suddenly over a small waterfall. You notice how the fast-flowing water breaks off clumps of soil from

EXPLORING *a River*

As you follow this river from its headwaters to its mouth, notice how its speed, volume, and shape change. Each part of the river forms a different habitat for living things.

A Headwaters

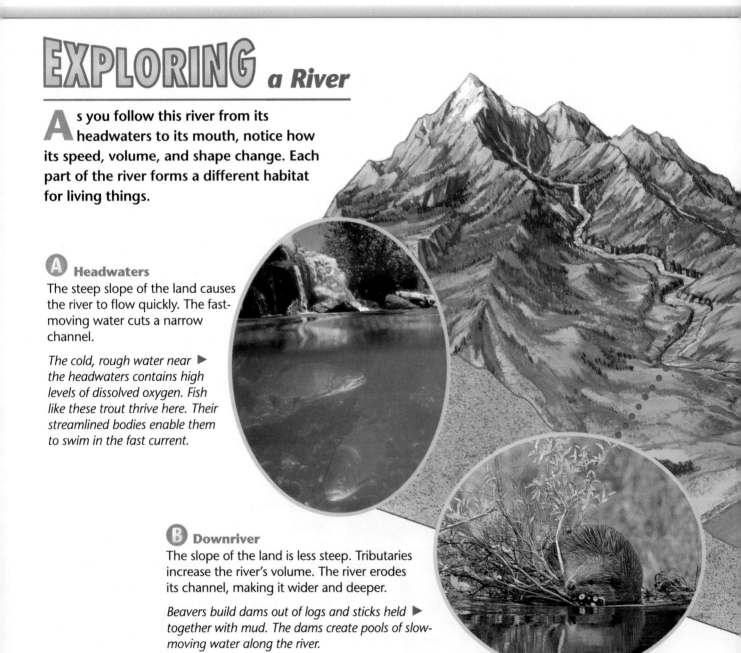

The steep slope of the land causes the river to flow quickly. The fast-moving water cuts a narrow channel.

The cold, rough water near the headwaters contains high levels of dissolved oxygen. Fish like these trout thrive here. Their streamlined bodies enable them to swim in the fast current. ▶

B Downriver

The slope of the land is less steep. Tributaries increase the river's volume. The river erodes its channel, making it wider and deeper.

Beavers build dams out of logs and sticks held together with mud. The dams create pools of slow-moving water along the river. ▶

the riverbanks and carries them along. As the river continues this erosion, it wears away the sides and cuts into the bottom of its channel. The channel gradually becomes wider and deeper.

Downriver As you continue downriver, your ride becomes smoother. The land around the river is less steep than it was near the headwaters. Some smaller streams have joined the river, increasing the volume of water. Since less of the water is in contact with the channel, there is less friction slowing it down. As a result, although the slope is less steep, the river continues to flow fairly swiftly.

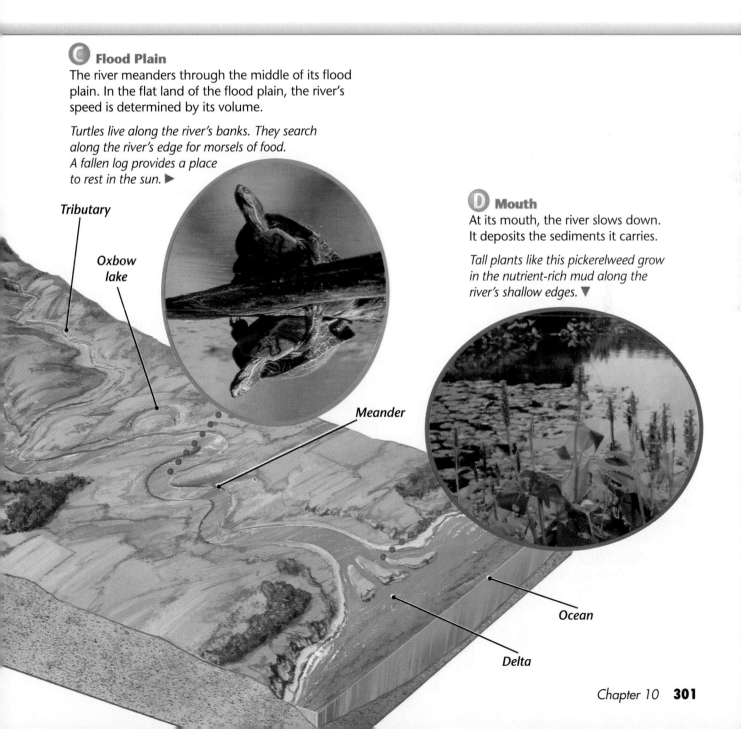

C Flood Plain
The river meanders through the middle of its flood plain. In the flat land of the flood plain, the river's speed is determined by its volume.

Turtles live along the river's banks. They search along the river's edge for morsels of food. A fallen log provides a place to rest in the sun. ▶

D Mouth
At its mouth, the river slows down. It deposits the sediments it carries.

Tall plants like this pickerelweed grow in the nutrient-rich mud along the river's shallow edges. ▼

Tributary
Oxbow lake
Meander
Ocean
Delta

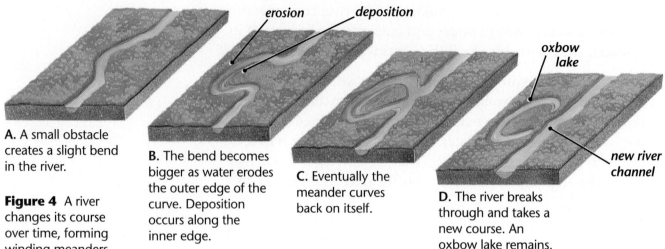

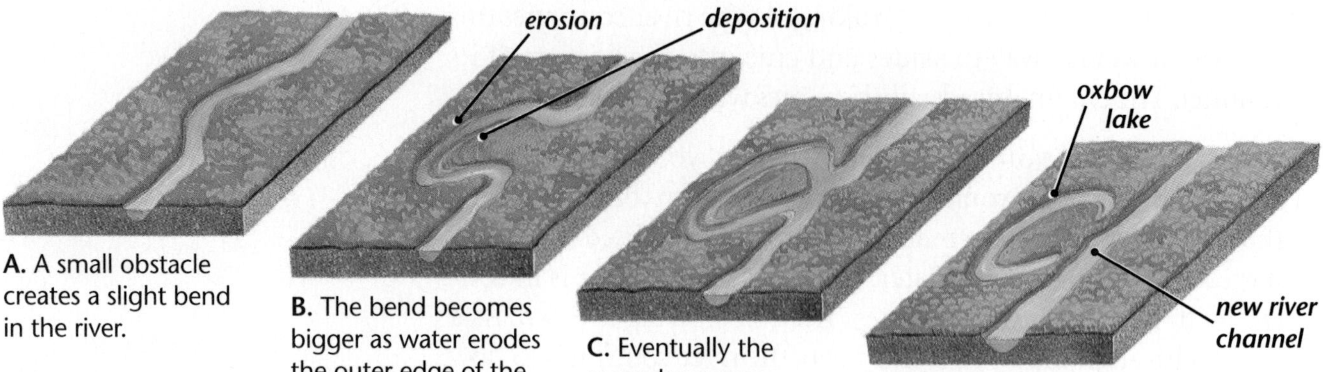
erosion
deposition
oxbow lake
new river channel

A. A small obstacle creates a slight bend in the river.

B. The bend becomes bigger as water erodes the outer edge of the curve. Deposition occurs along the inner edge.

C. Eventually the meander curves back on itself.

D. The river breaks through and takes a new course. An oxbow lake remains.

Figure 4 A river changes its course over time, forming winding meanders.

The Flood Plain Next your raft travels through the middle of a wide valley. The river created this valley over time by eroding the land along its banks. The broad, flat valley through which the river flows is called the **flood plain.**

In places, small obstacles in the river's channel cause the water to flow slightly to one side or the other. This movement creates a bend in the river. As Figure 4 shows, the water erodes the outer edge of the curve, where it flows faster. The river deposits sediments along the inner edge, where it flows slower. This process gradually forms looping curves in the river called **meanders.** Eventually the river may break through the ends of the meander, carving a new channel. The crescent-shaped, cutoff body of water that remains is called an **oxbow lake.**

The Mouth Your raft trip is nearly over as you approach the river's mouth. The **mouth** is the point where a river flows into another body of water—a larger river, a lake, or an ocean. When the fast-moving waters of a river hit the slower waters of a lake or ocean, the river suddenly slows down. As it slows, the river deposits most of its sediment. These deposits at the river's mouth build up, forming an area called a **delta.** The sediment deposits are rich in nutrients and minerals. As a result, the soil in delta areas is very fertile for farming.

Habitats Along a River Recall that an organism's habitat

INTEGRATING LIFE SCIENCE

provides the things that the organism needs to live. As you saw in *Exploring a River,* a river provides habitats for many living things. Some organisms live in the river and obtain nutrients and dissolved gases from the water. Others find shelter and food along its banks.

☑ *Checkpoint* ***How does a river's volume change between its headwaters and mouth?***

Sharpen your Skills

Inferring

ACTIVITY

Many of the world's rivers flow from north to south. However, the Nile River in Egypt flows from south to north. What can you infer about the slope of the land through which the Nile flows? (*Hint:* Think about the factors that determine how a river system forms.)

Rivers and Floods

Spring floods occur frequently on rivers in the Midwest, but the floods of 1997 were far worse than usual. The residents of Fargo, North Dakota, had already used a million sandbags, and the Red River of the North was still rising! As the flood waters rose, people piled the sandbags higher around their houses, hoping no water would break through. People moved their belongings to their attics, then watched as water flowed through their homes.

The Red River floods went on for weeks, fed by rain and melting snow. A spring blizzard added more snow. Other nearby rivers also flooded. Parts of North Dakota, South Dakota, and Minnesota were declared a disaster area. Weary residents just waited for the waters to recede so they could start to repair the damage.

What caused the Red River to flood so badly? **A flood occurs when the volume of water in a river increases so much that the river overflows its channel.** As rain and melting snow added more and more water, the river gained in speed and strength. Recall that as the speed of a river increases, so does the amount of energy it has. A flooding river can uproot trees and pluck boulders from the ground. As it overflows onto its floodplain, the powerful water can even wash away bridges and houses.

Throughout history, people have both feared and welcomed floods. Ancient Egyptians, for instance, called their fertile cropland "the gift of the Nile." Deposition from regular floods left a layer of rich soil on each side of the river, creating a green strip of good land in the middle of the desert. But floods can also destroy farms, towns, and crops. In the United States, 20 million people live in places where flooding is likely. Even in the last century, floods have killed millions of people around the world, many of them in the heavily populated flood plains of China, Bangladesh, and India.

Figure 5 A flood can be disastrous for nearby residents, such as the owners of this house. ***Making Generalizations*** *Explain how floods can be both harmful and helpful to people.*

SPEED
LIMIT
55

Can Floods Be Controlled?

INTEGRATING TECHNOLOGY As long as people have lived on flood plains, they have tried to control floods. Building dams is one method of flood control. A dam is a barrier across a river that may redirect the flow of a river to other channels or store the water in an artificial lake. Engineers can open the dam's floodgates to release water in dry seasons. Dams work fairly well to control small floods. During severe floods, however, powerful flood waters can wash over the top of a dam or break through it.

Sediment deposits actually build a natural defense against floods. As a river overflows onto its flood plain, it slows down, depositing the heavier sediments alongside the channel. Over time, these deposits build up into long ridges called **levees.** These natural levees help keep the river inside its banks. People sometimes build up the natural levees with sandbags or stone and concrete to provide further protection against floods.

But building up levees can sometimes backfire. These walls prevent the natural channel-widening process that rivers normally undergo as their volume increases. As a result, during a flood, the water has nowhere to go except downstream. Although built-up levees can work well to prevent small floods, they often make heavy flooding worse for areas farther downstream. The full power of the surge of flood water is passed on to flood the downstream areas.

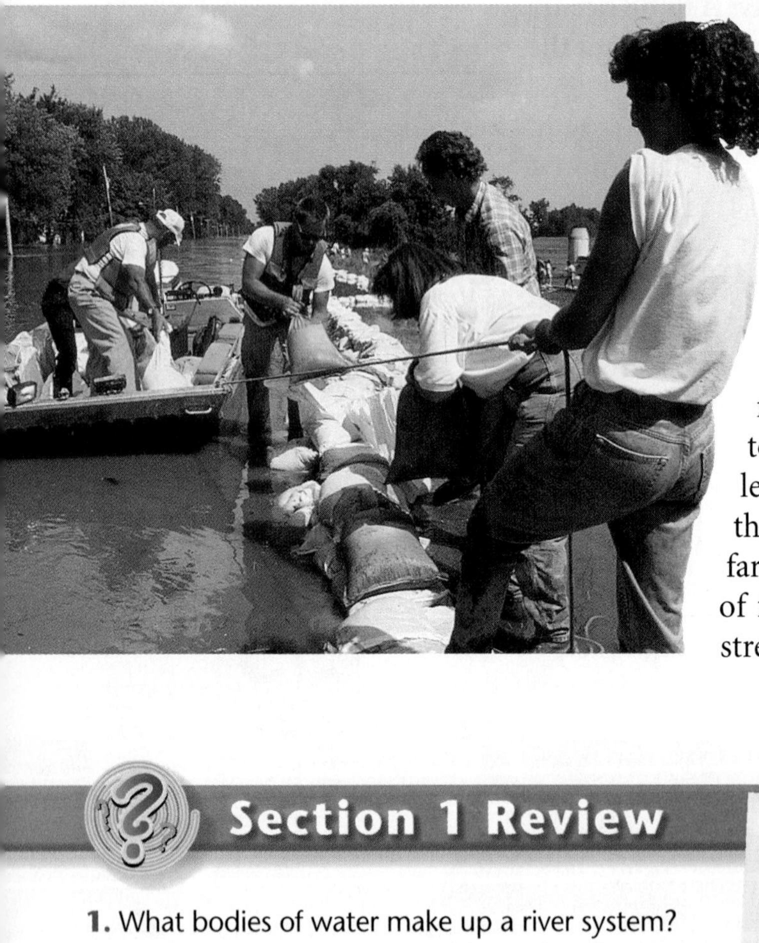

Figure 6 These people are working together to protect their community during a flood. *Applying Concepts How do sandbags help control flooding?*

Section 1 Review

1. What bodies of water make up a river system?
2. Name and describe the two major processes by which a river changes the land.
3. How might a period of very heavy rain cause a flood to occur?
4. Describe one method of controlling floods.
5. **Thinking Critically Applying Concepts** Is a river more likely to erode the land around its headwaters or at its mouth? Why?

CHAPTER PROJECT

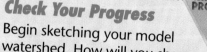

Check Your Progress

Begin sketching your model watershed. How will you shape the land to form the main river and tributary? What materials would be easy to shape and allow runoff to occur? Use the sketch to help estimate amounts of materials you will need. (*Hint:* Decide what to use as a base for your model. Draw your sketch on a piece of paper the same size as the base.)

SECTION 2 Ponds and Lakes

DISCOVER ACTIVITY

What's in Pond Water?

1. Using a hand lens, observe a sample of pond water.

2. Make a list of everything you see in the water. If you don't know the name of something, write a short description or draw a picture.
3. Your teacher has set up a microscope with a slide of pond water. Observe the slide and add any new items to your list. Wash your hands with soap when you are done.

Think It Over

Classifying Use one of these systems to divide the items on your list into two groups: moving/still, living/nonliving, or microscopic/visible without a microscope. What does your classification system tell you about pond water?

What do a glass of water, a canoe, and a snowstorm have in common? They're three things that could connect you to a nearby lake. Lake Michigan, for example, is a source of drinking water; a place to go boating and swimming; and the source of winter snowstorms on its shores.

While water in streams and rivers is always on the move, the water in lakes and ponds is still, or standing, water. Although there is no definite rule to determine whether a body of water is called a pond or a lake, ponds are generally smaller and shallower than lakes. Sunlight usually reaches to the bottom of all parts of a pond. Most lakes have parts where the water is too deep for sunlight to reach all the way to the bottom.

Ponds and lakes form when water collects in hollows and low-lying areas of land. Rainfall, melting snow and ice, and runoff supply water to ponds and lakes. Others are fed by rivers or groundwater. Eventually, water may flow out of a pond or lake into a river, or evaporate from its surface.

GUIDE FOR READING

- **How do ponds and lakes form?**
- **What is the result of lake turnover?**

Reading Tip **Before you read, predict one way in which ponds and lakes are similar and one way in which they are different. As you read, add to your explanation.**

EXPLORING a Pond

Many organisms live in the different habitats within a pond. From the shallow edges to the muddy bottom, conditions in each habitat vary in important ways.

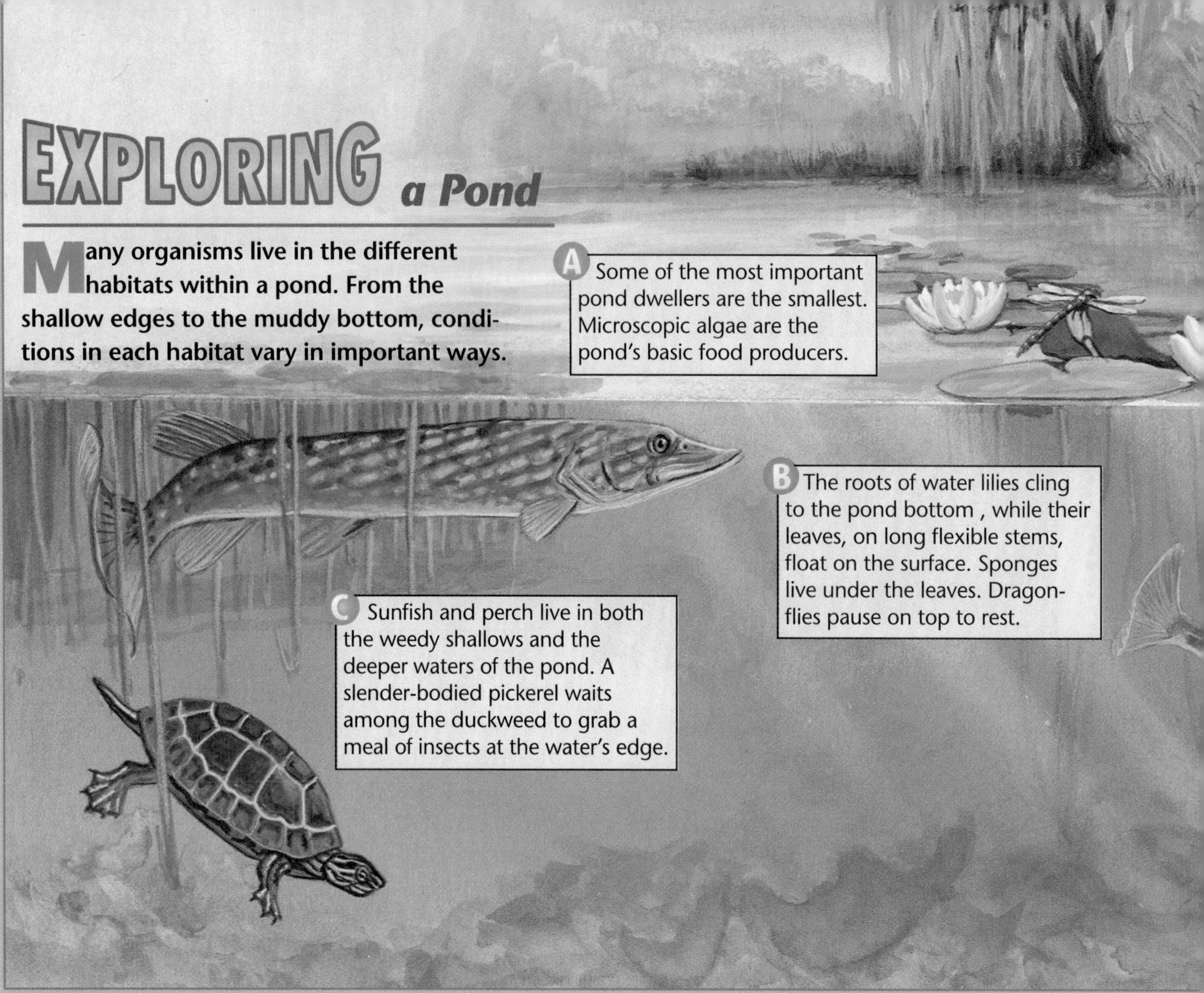
A Some of the most important pond dwellers are the smallest. Microscopic algae are the pond's basic food producers.
B The roots of water lilies cling to the pond bottom , while their leaves, on long flexible stems, float on the surface. Sponges live under the leaves. Dragonflies pause on top to rest.
C Sunfish and perch live in both the weedy shallows and the deeper waters of the pond. A slender-bodied pickerel waits among the duckweed to grab a meal of insects at the water's edge.

Ponds

INTEGRATING LIFE SCIENCE Compared to a tumbling mountain stream, a pond seems still and peaceful at first glance. Silvery minnows glide smoothly below the surface. A dragonfly touches the water, then whirs away. Lily pads with broad, green leaves and waxy, white blossoms float on the surface. This quiet pond is actually a thriving habitat, supporting a wide diversity of living things.

If you have ever waded in a pond, you know that the muddy bottom is often covered with weeds. Because the water is shallow enough for sunlight to reach the bottom, plants grow throughout a pond. Plantlike organisms called algae also live in the pond. As the plants and algae use sunlight to make food through photosynthesis, they also produce oxygen. Animals in the pond use the oxygen and food provided by plants and algae. You can see some common pond organisms in *Exploring a Pond.*

D The shore is edged with grasses and trees that require a lot of water, such as willows and maples. These plants provide shelter and nesting places for redwing blackbirds and other birds.
E Frogs lay eggs in the shallow water near shore. They hatch in the water as tadpoles and move to the land as adults.
F Snails find food on the soft bottom of the pond. Crayfish lie buried in the mud, waiting for bits of food to drift down.

Not all ponds exist year-round. For example, some ponds in the northern and western United States appear only in the spring, when runoff from spring rains and melting snow collects in low areas. The ponds dry up by midsummer as the shallow water quickly evaporates in the heat.

Ponds in colder climates often freeze over during the winter. As you learned in Chapter 9, ice floats because it is less dense than liquid water. As a result, ice forms on the surface of the pond, while the living things survive in the liquid water below.

☑ *Checkpoint* ***Why can plants grow throughout a pond?***

Lakes

Suppose you suddenly found yourself on a sandy beach. Waves break on the shore. The water stretches as far as your eye can see. Gulls screech overhead. Where are you? Although you might think you're at the ocean, this immense body of water could

A
B

Figure 7 Standing water is found in lakes and ponds. **A.** The cold waters of Crater Lake in Oregon fill the hollow of an ancient volcano. **B.** Water lilies float in a Colorado pond. ***Interpreting Photographs*** *In which of these bodies of water does sunlight reach the bottom? Give evidence to support your answer.*

actually be a lake! You could be on a beach in Indiana, on the shore of Lake Michigan.

Although most lakes are not as large as Lake Michigan, they are generally bigger and deeper than ponds. Most lakes are deep enough that sunlight does not reach all the way to the bottom. A lake bottom may consist of sand, pebbles, or rock. The bottom of a pond is usually covered with mud and algae.

Lake Formation Lakes form in many ways. As you read in Section 1, a cut-off river meander may become an oxbow lake. Ice sheets that melted at the end of the Ice Age created depressions that became lakes. Some lakes were created by movements of Earth's crust. Such movements created the deep valleys in central Africa that lie below Lake Tanganyika and Lake Victoria. Other lakes are the result of volcanoes. An erupting volcano can cause a flow of lava or mud that blocks a river and forms a lake. Some lakes, like the one in Figure 7, form in the empty craters of volcanoes.

People can also create a lake by building a dam across a river. The lake may be used for supplying drinking water, for irrigating fields, and for boating and fishing. A lake that stores water for human use is called a **reservoir.** One of the largest reservoirs in the United States is Lake Mead in Nevada, behind Hoover Dam on the Colorado River.

Lake Habitats Like a pond, a lake provides habitats for many

Integrating Life Science

organisms. In the shallow water near shore, the wildlife is similar to that in a pond. Water beetles scurry over the slippery, moss-covered rocks.

Loons and kingfishers pluck fish from the open water. But unlike a pond, sunlight does not reach the bottom at the center of a lake. Without sunlight, plants cannot live in the deep water. As a result, fewer other organisms live in the chilly, dark depths of the lake. A few worms and mollusks do live on the bottom. They feed on food particles that drift down from the surface. The deep waters of lakes are also the home of large, bony fish such as pike and sturgeon. These fish eat the tiny bottom dwellers. They also swim to the surface to feed on fish and even small birds.

☑ *Checkpoint* *List four possible ways a lake might form.*

Changes in a Lake

Particularly in cool, northern areas of North America, many lakes undergo changes with the seasons. In the summer, the sun warms the upper layer of water in the lake. The warm water floats on top of the cooler, denser lower layer. But in the fall, the top layer cools off, too. As the water cools, it becomes denser and sinks. This causes the lake waters to mix together. **As the water mixes, minerals, plant matter, and other nutrients rise from the lake bottom to the surface. Called lake turnover, this seasonal change refreshes the supply of nutrients throughout the lake.**

A second type of change that occurs in a lake happens over a long period of time. The organisms in a lake constantly release waste products into the water. The wastes and the remains of dead organisms contain nutrients such as nitrates and phosphates. Algae feed on these nutrients. Over many years, the nutrients build up in the lake in a process called **eutrophication** (you troh fih KAY shuhn). As eutrophication causes more algae to grow, a thick, green scum forms on the

Lake Titicaca

Figure 8 This island floating on Lake Titicaca is woven from totora reeds.

Social Studies CONNECTION

Imagine living on a floating island in the middle of a deep, cold lake. The island is a mat made of thick reeds you have woven tightly together. During a storm, you must anchor your island or it could be swept away. If you were a member of a group of Native Americans who live on Lake Titicaca in South America, such an island might be your home.

Lake Titicaca lies high in the Andes Mountains. Around the edges of the lake grows a hollow reed called totora. The people weave totora reeds together to form "islands" that are strong enough to hold homes and livestock. They also make ropes, boats, tea, and even medicine from the totora reeds.

In Your Journal

How would living on a totora reed island on Lake Titicaca affect your daily routine? Write a journal entry describing what a typical day might be like if you lived on a floating island.

A. The process begins as algae and other organisms add nutrients to the lake. These nutrients support more plant growth.

B. Soil, fallen leaves, and decaying matter pile up on the lake bottom. The lake becomes shallower and marshy.

C. Eventually, the plants completely fill the lake, creating a grassy meadow.

Figure 9 A lake environment gradually changes over time. *Predicting Would you expect the water temperature in the lake to be higher in A or B?*

surface of the water. Have you ever forgotten to clean a fish tank for a few weeks? You may have observed the process of eutrophication as algae began to grow on the sides of the tank.

When the algae layer becomes so thick that it begins to block out the sunlight, plants in the lake cannot carry out photosynthesis. They stop producing food and oxygen and die. As dead organisms in the lake decay, the amount of oxygen in the water decreases. The lake environment changes. Many of the fish and other animals no longer have enough oxygen to live. Material from decaying plants and animals piles up on the bottom, and the lake becomes more shallow. The sun warms the water to a higher temperature. Now many plants take root in the rich mud on the lake bottom. Eventually, the lake becomes completely filled with plants. The remaining water evaporates, and a grassy meadow takes the place of the former lake.

Section 2 Review

1. Explain how ponds and lakes form.
2. How does lake turnover renew the supply of nutrients in the water?
3. Give three examples of typical pond organisms. Describe where in a pond each is found.
4. What are two uses of reservoirs?
5. **Thinking Critically Relating Cause and Effect** How is the depth of the water in the middle of a lake related to the variety of living things there?

Science at Home

Ask a family member to crumple up a piece of waxed paper. Straighten out the paper to model a landscape with hills and valleys. Have the person use a permanent marker to draw lines along the highest divides of the landscape. Then have the person draw circles where lakes and ponds will form on the landscape. After placing the waxed paper in a sink to catch any overflow, tell the person to sprinkle water over the landscape to simulate rain. Point out where the water collects. Which would you classify as ponds and which as lakes?

SECTION 3 Wetland Environments

DISCOVER ACTIVITY

Wet or Dry?

1. Hold a kitchen sponge under water until it is soaked. Then squeeze out the water until the sponge is just damp.
2. Place the damp sponge next to a dry sponge in a pan. The sponges represent areas of wet and dry land.
3. Pour water into two paper cups until each is half full.
4. Hold one cup in each hand so that the cups are about 10 centimeters above the pan. Pour the water onto both sponges at the same time.

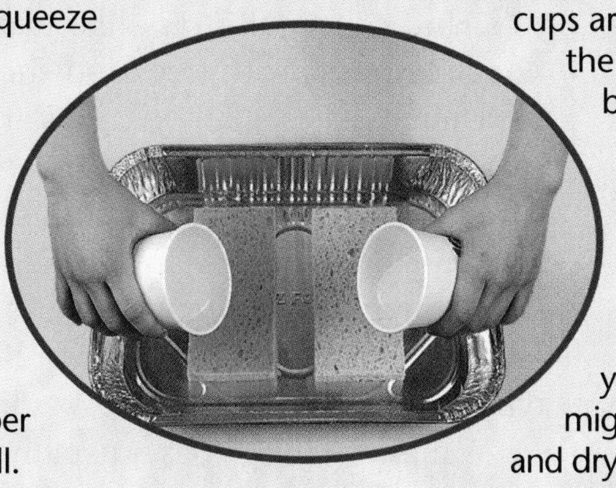

Think It Over

Observing Which of the two sponges absorbs water faster? How would you relate your observations to what might happen in areas of wet and dry land?

GUIDE FOR READING

- **What features of wetlands make them good habitats for living things?**
- **How do wetlands help control flooding?**

Reading Tip **Before you read, write a short description of what you think a wetland is. As you read, add details and examples to your description.**

Your canoe slips quietly through the brown-tinged waters of the marsh in South Dakota's Lacreek National Wildlife Refuge. Paddling among the thick clumps of velvety golden cattails, you scan for birds' nests. A spot of red catches your eye, and you realize you are only centimeters away from a black-and-white grebe sitting still atop a nest of dry rushes. Suddenly, a loud honking sound breaks the silence, as a huge flock of Canada geese flies by. You gasp as some of the black and brown birds land on a grassy mound nearby. Their outspread wings must be almost as long as your canoe!

The waters of this marsh serve as an important stopover for thousands of geese, swans, and other migrating birds. Birds stop to feed on grass and seeds as they fly south to their winter homes. Like other wetlands, the Lacreek marsh is a vital habitat for birds and many other living things.

▼ *Western grebe*

What Is a Wetland?

What image does the word *wetland* bring to mind? As the photographs on the next page show, not all wetlands are dark, smelly swamps oozing with mud. A **wetland** is an area of land that is covered with a shallow layer of water during some or all of the year. Wetlands form in places where water is trapped in low areas or where groundwater seeps onto the surface of the land. They can range in size from a water-filled roadside ditch to an area covering thousands of square kilometers. Some wetlands fill up during spring rains and dry up over the summer. Others, like the Lacreek marsh, are covered with water year-round.

Marshes, swamps, and bogs are three common types of freshwater wetlands. Marshes generally are grassy areas covered by a shallow layer or stream of water. They contain cattails, rushes, tule, and other tall grass-like plants. Swamps look more like flooded forests, with trees and shrubs growing in the water. In the United States, many swamps are located in the South, where trees grow quickly in the warm, humid climate. The cypress swamps of Mississippi and Louisiana are examples of wooded swamps. Bogs, which are more common in cooler northern states, often form in depressions left by melting ice sheets thousands of years ago. The water in bogs tends to be acidic. Many types of mosses thrive in the conditions found in bogs.

Wetlands along coasts usually contain both fresh and salt water. Coastal wetlands include salt marshes and mangrove forests. Salt marshes are found along both coasts of the United States. They often contain tall, strong grasses growing in a rich, muddy bottom. Mangrove forests, which are found along the central and southern coasts of Florida, consist of short trees with a thick tangle

Figure 10 Freshwater wetlands come in many forms. **A.** In Montana, colorful flowers dot a bed of velvety moss in an alpine bog. **B.** Water flows slowly through a marsh in Oregon's Willamette Valley. **C.** Curtains of Spanish moss hang from cypress trees in a Louisiana swamp. *Comparing and Contrasting How are these three environments similar? How are they different?*

A

B

of roots. The tough roots anchor the mangroves against tropical winds and storms.

☑ *Checkpoint* *Name three types of freshwater wetlands.*

Wetland Habitats

If you've ever enjoyed tart cranberry sauce or crunchy wild rice, you've eaten plants that grow in wetlands. The layer of water covering a wetland can range from several centimeters to a few meters deep. Dead leaves and other plant and animal material serve as natural fertilizer, adding nitrogen, phosphates, and other nutrients to the water and soil. **Because of their sheltered waters and rich supply of nutrients, wetlands provide habitats for many living things.**

Many year-round residents of wetlands are similar to those in other freshwater habitats. As in a pond, frogs, salamanders, turtles, raccoons, muskrats, and many types of insects find food and shelter among the wetland plants. Birds nest in and around the wetlands, feeding on the plants and insects there.

Wetlands also have many temporary residents. Many ducks, geese, and other waterfowl travel from Alaska and Canada to their winter homes in the South along a "flyway." For example, birds traveling along the Central Flyway through Montana, Minnesota, the Dakotas, Nebraska, and Iowa depend on the millions of small, shallow marshes called prairie potholes along their route. Like the geese at Lacreek Refuge, birds stop there to rest, feed, and mate. In the spring, thousands of birds build their nests in the prairie pothole region.

C

TRY THIS

A Natural Filter

ACTIVITY

This activity demonstrates one important role wetlands play in the environment.

1. Cover your work surface with newspaper. In one end of a loaf pan, build a sloping hill of damp soil.
2. Add water to the other end of the pan to form a lake.
3. Use a watering can to sprinkle rain onto the hill. Observe what happens to the hill and the lake.
4. Empty the water out of the pan and rebuild the hill.
5. Now push a sponge into the soil across the bottom of the hill to model a wetland.

6. Repeat Steps 2 through 4. Follow your teacher's instructions for cleaning up.

Observing What happened to the soil with and without the wetland? How did the lake look in each case?

The Importance of Wetlands

Imagine coming home from a long trip, only to find that your house is gone and in its place is a parking lot! That happened to thousands of migrating birds before people began to understand the importance of wetlands. Farmers and builders once considered the soggy soil of wetlands to be "wasteland." This land could not be used unless it was drained and filled in. Thousands of square kilometers of wetlands were developed for farmland or for building homes and businesses. Beginning in the 1970s, however, the government enacted laws to protect wetland habitats.

Wetlands serve important functions for people as well as for wildlife. For example, wetlands provide natural water filtration. As water moves slowly through a wetland, waste materials settle out. The thick network of plant roots traps silt and mud. **Wetlands also help control floods by absorbing extra runoff from heavy rains.** They act like giant sponges, storing water and gradually releasing it as it drains or evaporates. When wetlands are drained or paved over, the water cannot be absorbed. Instead, it runs off the land quickly and can cause floods.

Roseate spoonbills
Great egret
Snowy egret
Little blue heron
Sawgrass
Anhinga
Florida panther

Figure 11 Many unusual species live in the freshwater wetland habitats of the Everglades.

The Everglades: A Unique Environment

Walking down a path in Florida's Everglades National Park, you would feel the ground squish under your feet. Water is the key to the Everglades, a unique region of wetlands. A shallow layer of water moves slowly over the gently sloping land from Lake Okeechobee south to Florida Bay. Tall, sharp-edged blades of sawgrass grow in the water. The thick growth of sawgrass gave this region its Native American name, *Pa-hay-okee*, which means "river of grass." Low islands called hammocks are scattered throughout the sawgrass marsh. Trees like gumbo limbos and palms grow on the hammocks.

Everglades Wildlife As in other wetlands, water means life for many Everglades creatures. Fish and snakes gobble up tiny organisms in the warm, muddy water. Wading birds in a rainbow of colors—pink flamingoes, white egrets, and purple gallinules—stand on skinny legs in the water. A raccoon digs for alligator eggs, unaware of the alligator lying low in the sawgrass nearby.

The Everglades provide habitats for many rare or endangered species. The endangered Florida panther lives deep in the wilderness portions of the Everglades. Many species of birds, such as the wood

The Everglades
N
W
E
S
Lake Okeechobee
FLORIDA
THE EVERGLADES
Big Cypress Swamp
Naples
Boca Raton
Fort Lauderdale
Miami
Gulf of Mexico
ATLANTIC OCEAN
0
25 mi
0
25 km
Florida Bay
Key Largo
Florida Keys
Mangrove forests
Everglades National Park
Rivers and canals

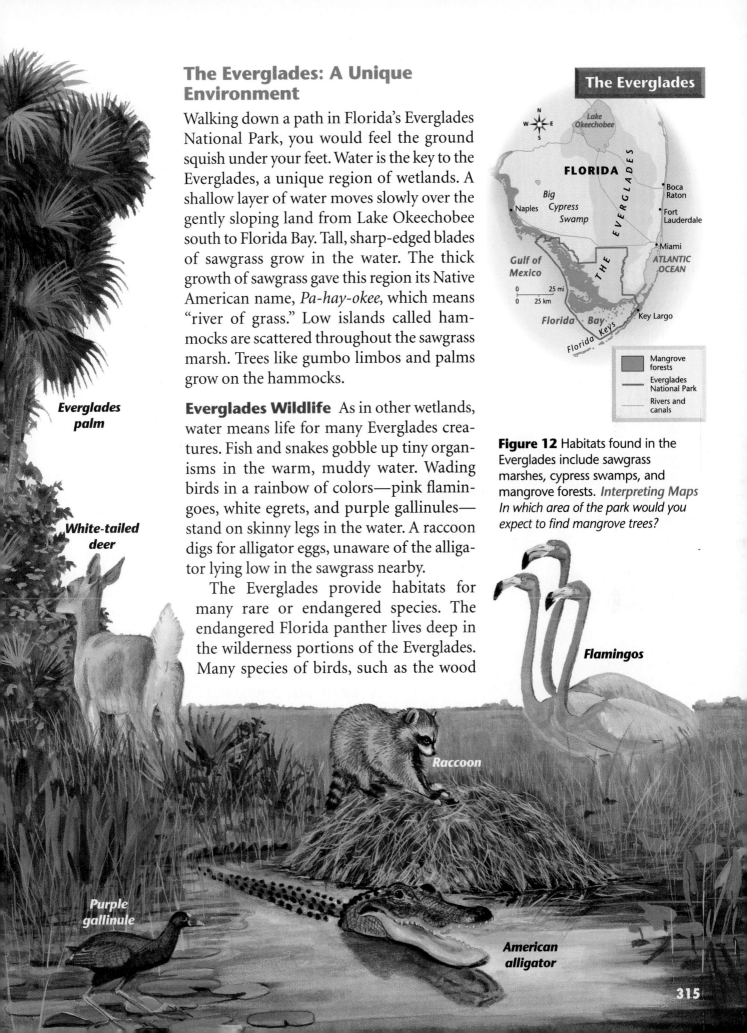

Figure 12 Habitats found in the Everglades include sawgrass marshes, cypress swamps, and mangrove forests. ***Interpreting Maps*** *In which area of the park would you expect to find mangrove trees?*

Everglades palm
White-tailed deer

Flamingos

Raccoon
Purple gallinule
American alligator

stork and the roseate spoonbill (named for the unusual shape of its beak), depend on the Everglades as a nesting area. The awkward-looking manatee, or sea cow, lives in the mangrove forests along the coast, grazing on water hyacinths. Because manatees swim so slowly, they are easily injured by the propellers of powerboats. They have become an endangered species as a result of increased boating in Florida Bay.

Threats to the Everglades The Everglades are a fragile environment. Nearby farming has introduced new chemicals into the slow-moving water of the marsh, upsetting the balance of nutrients. Outside the protected limits of the national park, developers have filled in areas of wetland to build new homes and roads. New organisms brought into the area accidentally or for pest control compete with other organisms for space and food.

Figure 13 A manatee floats in the warm waters of Florida Bay. This species is threatened by the increased use of coastal waters around the Everglades.

Water that once flowed into the Everglades from Lake Okeechobee has been diverted for farming. New canals and levees built to provide drinking water for nearby communities and to control flooding have changed the flow of water into and out of the Everglades. Some areas are drying up, while others are flooded.

Preserving the Everglades Scientists and government officials have been trying for many years to develop a plan to preserve the Everglades and save its endangered wildlife. One plan involves building an elaborate system of pipes and canals to refill some drained areas with fresh water. The National Park Service, the State of Florida, and the U.S. Army Corps of Engineers are working together to manage the supply of water to areas around and within the Everglades.

Section 3 Review

1. How are wetlands important to wildlife?
2. Explain how wetlands help control floods.
3. How are the Everglades unusual?
4. **Thinking Critically Making Judgments** Some of the plans to restore the Everglades will require millions of dollars and will negatively affect local farmers. What information would you want to have to help decide what plan of action to take to save the Everglades?

CHAPTER PROJECT

Check Your Progress

At this point, add the body of standing water to your watershed sketch. If your model will include any wetland areas, what materials will you use to model them? (*Hint:* Be sure to consider how water will enter and leave the body of water.)

SECTION 4 Glaciers and Icebergs

DISCOVER ACTIVITY

How Can Ice Change the Land?

1. Your teacher will give you two ice cubes, one of which has some sand and gravel frozen into its bottom side.
2. Rub each ice cube slowly along a piece of cardboard, pressing down slightly.
3. Observe the piece of cardboard. Wash your hands when you are finished with this activity.

Think It Over

Inferring How might a large, moving block of ice and rocks affect the surface of the land?

GUIDE FOR READING

- **How does a glacier form?**
- **Why are icebergs dangerous to ships?**

Reading Tip **As you read, make a list of main ideas and supporting details about glaciers and icebergs.**

Standing on a mountaintop more than 4,800 meters above sea level, sparkling ice and snow surround you in every direction. The temperature is −29°C, and the wind whistles around your ears. Where is this chilly spot? It's Vinson Massif, the highest point on the continent of Antarctica.

Recall that more than two thirds of the fresh water on Earth exists in the form of ice. About 85 percent of that ice is part of the massive ice sheet that covers Antarctica. This ice sheet is larger than the United States and Europe put together! The rest of the ice on Earth is found in other ice sheets and in icebergs.

Glaciers

The ice sheet that covers Antarctica is one form of a glacier. A **glacier** (GLAY shur) is a huge mass of ice and snow that moves slowly over the land.

Glaciers form in cold places where more snow falls each year than melts. Layers of snow pile on top of more layers of snow. **Over time, the weight of the layers presses the particles of snow so tightly together that they form a solid block of ice.** If you have ever squeezed a handful of fluffy snow until it became an icy ball, you have modeled the way a glacier forms.

Ice sheets that spread over a large area of land are called continental glaciers. Today, continental glaciers are

▲ *Gentoo penguins in Antarctica*

Figure 14 The massive Beloit Glacier towers above Prince William Sound in Alaska. *Classifying Which type of glacier is the Beloit Glacier? Explain your answer.*

found only in Antarctica and Greenland. The Antarctic glacier covers high mountain ranges and even active volcanoes. In some spots it is 3,000 meters thick. That's higher than six Empire State Buildings stacked on top of each other.

Most present-day glaciers are valley glaciers. These glaciers form in the mountains. They look like thick rivers of ice sliding down into the valley. As a valley glacier descends into warmer regions, it gradually melts. Valley glaciers are found mainly in high, cold mountain ranges such as the Alps in Europe, the Rockies in the United States, and the Himalayas in Asia.

Like moving water, moving ice can cause erosion. As a glacier forms, rocks, gravel, and other debris are frozen into the ice. Like a giant piece of sandpaper, the glacier scrapes against the ground as it moves. Over time, glaciers grind away rock and change the surface of the land.

☑ *Checkpoint* ***How does a glacier change the shape of the land?***

Icebergs

It was a dark night in the spring of 1912. The gleaming new ocean liner *Titanic* sailed through the North Atlantic on its first voyage, from Southampton, England, to New York City. Suddenly a huge white wall loomed out of the darkness in front of the ship! It was an iceberg, the terror of ships at sea. Underwater, the jagged ice tore a series of cuts in the *Titanic's* side. As the ship sank to the bottom of the ocean, nearly 1,500 people died.

Icebergs like the one that sank the *Titanic* form when a glacier reaches the seacoast. With a loud roar, large chunks

TITANIC
DISASTER
GREAT LOSS
OF LIFE
EVENING NEWS

Figure 15 The *Titanic* sank on its first voyage when it hit an iceberg in the North Atlantic Ocean.

break off, or calve, and float away. Although icebergs are found in the salty ocean, remember that they consist of fresh water.

In the North Atlantic and Arctic oceans, about 10,000 new icebergs form every year. Many of these icebergs calve from Greenland's continental glacier. As they drift south, the icebergs break into chunks as big as houses. They begin to melt in the warmer water.

The ocean around Antarctica is filled with even larger icebergs. Flat-topped pieces calve from the edges of the glaciers along the coast. In 1995, a giant iceberg broke off Antarctica's Larsen Ice Shelf. Scientists flying over the new iceberg reported that it was about 70 kilometers long and 25 kilometers wide — more than half the size of the state of Rhode Island!

The thought of a chunk of floating ice that big is scary enough, but it's more frightening to realize that only about 10 percent of an iceberg is visible above the water. **About 90 percent of an iceberg lies below the surface. The underwater part is a hazard to ships because it is often much wider than the visible part of the iceberg.** Icebergs are also a threat to floating platforms that support rigs for drilling oil from the ocean floor.

After the *Titanic* disaster, countries involved in Atlantic shipping set up the International Ice Patrol. The Patrol, which is managed by the United States Coast Guard, uses ships, planes, and satellites to track icebergs. The Patrol's warnings have saved many people aboard ships and floating oil rigs from disasters like the *Titanic.*

Figure 16 If you could see an entire iceberg at once, how would it look? An artist created this composite photograph to reveal the hidden part of the iceberg. *Applying Concepts What percentage of the ice is underwater?*

Section 4 Review

1. Describe the process by which a glacier forms.
2. Why is it hard to determine the size of an iceberg from the deck of a ship?
3. How do icebergs form?
4. Name the two types of glaciers. Where is each type of glacier found?
5. **Thinking Critically Making Judgments** How might the fact that glaciers and icebergs consist of fresh water make them useful to people?

Science at Home

With a family member, make a model iceberg. Fill the cut-off bottom of a milk or juice carton with water and freeze. When the water has frozen, peel the carton away from the iceberg. Add salt to a large bowl of water to create an "ocean." Float the iceberg in the bowl. Help your family member use a ruler to measure how much of the iceberg's thickness is above the surface of the water and how much is below. Use these measurements to explain why icebergs can be dangerous to ships.

SECTION 5

Water Underground

DISCOVER — ACTIVITY

Where Does the Water Go?

1. Add pebbles to a jar to form a layer about 5 centimeters deep. Cover the pebbles with a layer of dry sand about 3 centimeters thick. Pour the sand in slowly to avoid moving the pebbles. These materials represent underground soil layers.
2. Sprinkle water onto the sand to simulate rainfall.
3. Looking through the side of the jar, observe the path of the water as it soaks through the layers. Wash your hands when you are finished with this activity.

Think It Over

Observing Describe what happens when the water reaches the bottom of the jar.

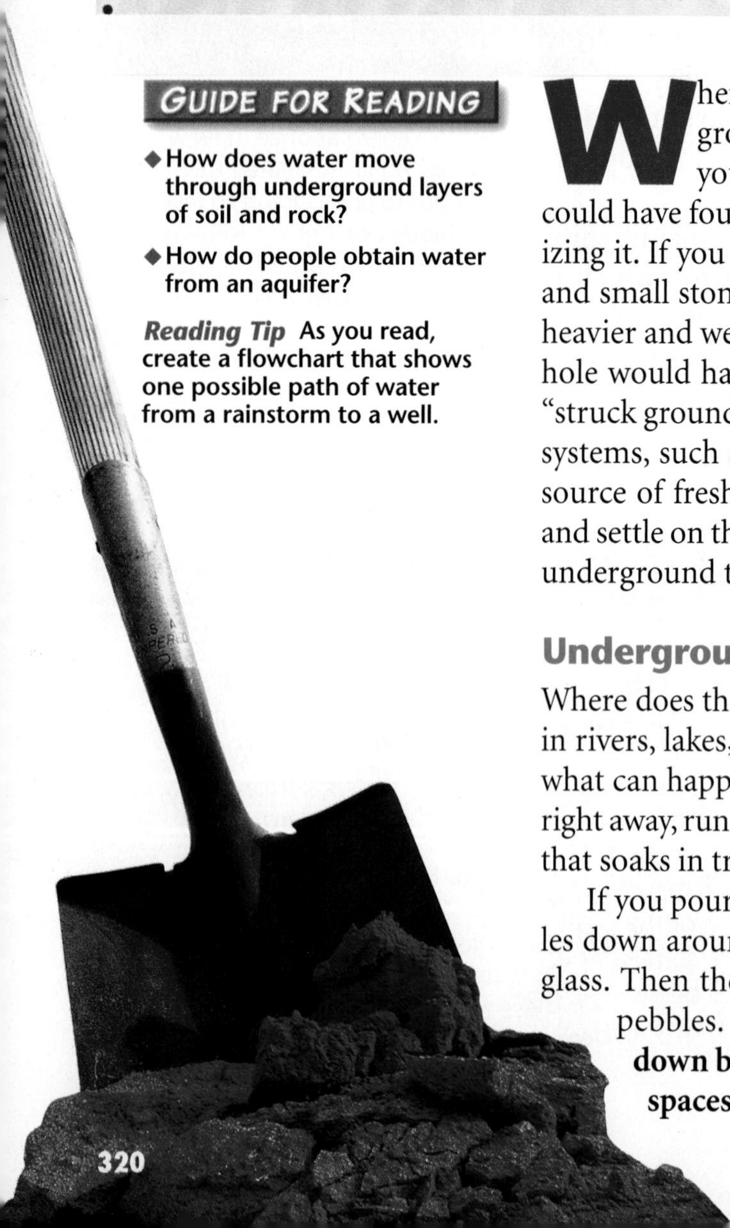

GUIDE FOR READING

- **How does water move through underground layers of soil and rock?**
- **How do people obtain water from an aquifer?**

Reading Tip **As you read, create a flowchart that shows one possible path of water from a rainstorm to a well.**

When you were younger, did you ever dig a hole in the ground hoping to find a buried treasure? Though you probably never found a trunk full of gold, you could have found a different kind of treasure without even realizing it. If you continued to dig deeper, past tangled grass roots and small stones, you would have noticed the soil begin to feel heavier and wetter. If you dug deep enough, the bottom of your hole would have started to fill up with water. You would have "struck groundwater!" In the days before pipes and public water systems, such a discovery was like finding a treasure. A usable source of fresh water enabled people to build a house or farm and settle on that land. Today, many people still rely on the water underground to meet their water needs.

Underground Layers

Where does this underground water come from? Like the water in rivers, lakes, and glaciers, it comes from precipitation. Recall what can happen to precipitation when it falls. It can evaporate right away, run off the surface, or soak into the ground. The water that soaks in trickles downward, following the pull of gravity.

If you pour water into a glass full of pebbles, the water trickles down around the pebbles until it reaches the bottom of the glass. Then the water begins to fill up the spaces between the pebbles. **In the same way, water underground trickles down between particles of soil and through cracks and spaces in layers of rock.**

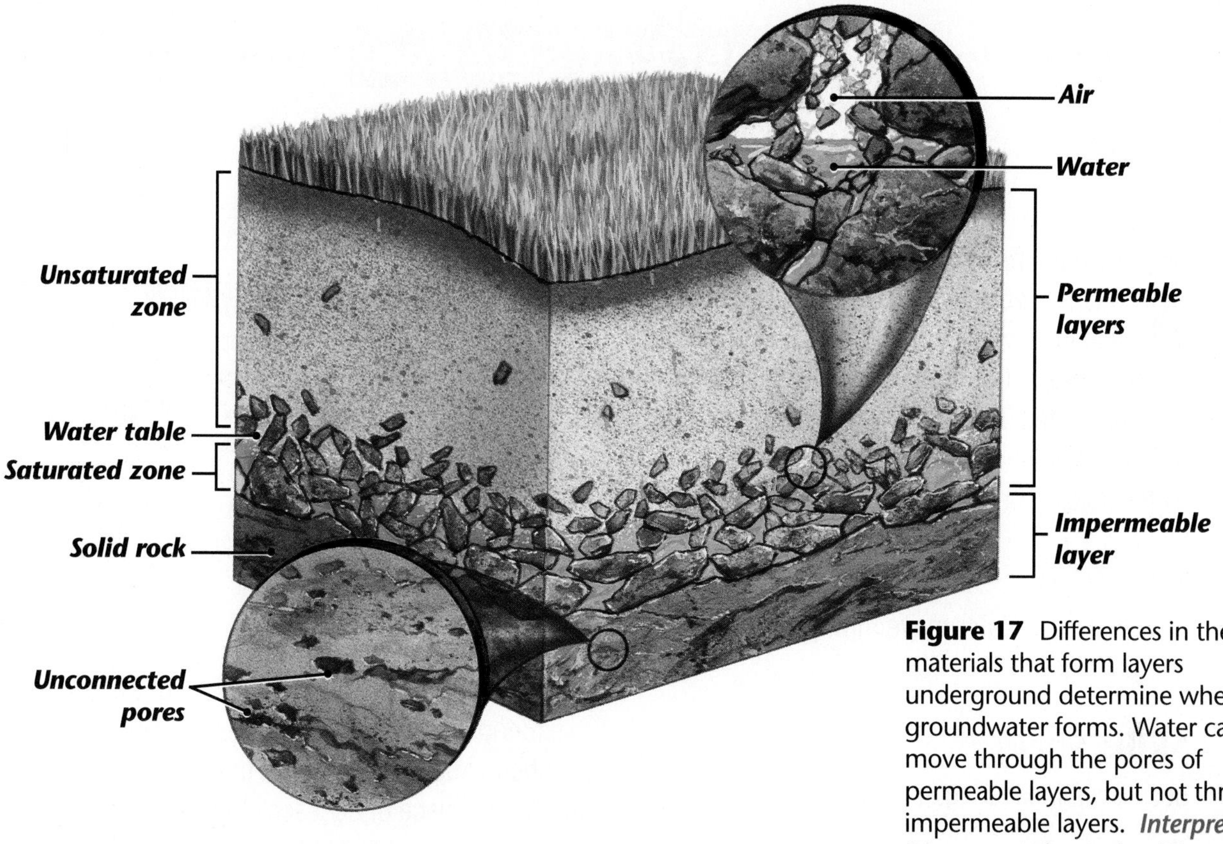
Air
Water
Unsaturated zone
Permeable layers
Water table
Saturated zone
Solid rock
Impermeable layer
Unconnected pores

Figure 17 Differences in the materials that form layers underground determine where groundwater forms. Water can move through the pores of permeable layers, but not through impermeable layers. ***Interpreting Diagrams*** *What is the difference between the saturated and unsaturated zone?*

Different types of rock and soil have different-sized spaces, or **pores,** between their particles. How easily water moves through the material depends not only on the size of the pores, but also on whether the pores are connected to each other. Materials that allow water to easily pass through, or permeate, are called **permeable.** Sand and gravel are permeable materials.

As water soaks down through permeable rock, it eventually reaches layers of material that it cannot pass through. These materials have few or no pores or cracks for the water to flow through. Materials that water cannot pass through easily are called **impermeable.** Clay and granite are impermeable materials.

Once water reaches an impermeable layer, it is trapped. It can't soak any deeper. Instead, the water begins to fill up the spaces above the impermeable material. The area of permeable rock or soil that is totally filled, or saturated, with water is called the **saturated zone.** The top of the saturated zone is the **water table.** Knowing the depth of the water table in an area tells you how deep you must dig to reach groundwater.

Soil and rock layers above the water table contain some moisture, too. But here the pores contain air as well as water. They are not saturated with water. Therefore, the layer of rocks and soil above the water table is called the **unsaturated zone.**

☑ *Checkpoint* *Give an example of a permeable material other than sand or gravel.*

Sharpen your Skills

Drawing Conclusions

ACTIVITY

You have just bought some land and need to dig a well. By drilling a number of holes on your property, you learn that there is a layer of impermeable granite rock located approximately 12 meters underground. If the saturated zone is 3 meters thick, how deep should you dig your well? (*Hint:* Drawing a diagram may be helpful.)

Careers in Science

SOIL TESTING

In what type of soil is it best to site a well? This is a question that hydrologists, scientists who study groundwater, need to answer before new houses or other buildings can be constructed. In this lab, you will compare different soil types to learn more about their water-holding properties.

HELP WANTED

Hydrologists to conduct soil tests for new housing development. Homes will have private wells. Engineers must test soil permeability to select best locations. Please send resumé and references to

Problem

How fast does water move through sand, clay, and pebbles?

Skills Focus

observing, measuring, drawing conclusions

Materials (per group)

hand lens	3 100-mL beakers
sand, 100 mL	water, 300 mL
stopwatch	pebbles, 100 mL

3 rubber bands
powdered potter's clay, 100 mL
3 squares of cheesecloth
3 large funnels or cut-off plastic soda bottle tops

Procedure

1. Copy the data table into your notebook.
2. Use a hand lens to observe each of the three material samples closely. Record your observations in your data table.
3. Place a piece of cheesecloth over the bottom of each funnel or bottle top and secure it with a rubber band.
4. Place the sand in one funnel, the pebbles in another, and the clay in another. Be sure that there is at least 5 cm of space above the material in each funnel.
5. Place each funnel on top of a beaker.
6. Slowly pour 100 mL of water into the funnel containing the sand. Do not let the water overflow the funnel.
7. Start the stopwatch when the water begins to flow or drip out of the bottom of the funnel.

DATA TABLE

Material	Observations	Time for Water to Stop Dripping
Sand		
Clay		
Pebbles		

8. Stop the stopwatch when the water stops dripping out of the funnel or after 5 minutes. Record the time to the nearest second in your data table.
9. Repeat Steps 6 through 8 with the pebbles and then with the clay. When you are finished with this activity, dispose of your materials according to your teacher's instructions. Wash your hands thoroughly with soap.

Analyze and Conclude

1. Through which material did water move the fastest? The slowest?
2. What can you conclude about the permeability of the three materials?
3. Based on your observations of each sample, suggest an explanation for the differences in their permeability.
4. Based on the results of this lab, would you expect to get more water from a well dug in sand, pebbles, or clay? Explain.
5. **Apply** Why might gardeners and landscapers need to know about the permeability of different soil types?

More to Explore

Which of the soil samples that you tested do you think the soil of the grounds at your school most resembles? Design an experiment to test your idea. With your teacher's permission, carry out your experiment.

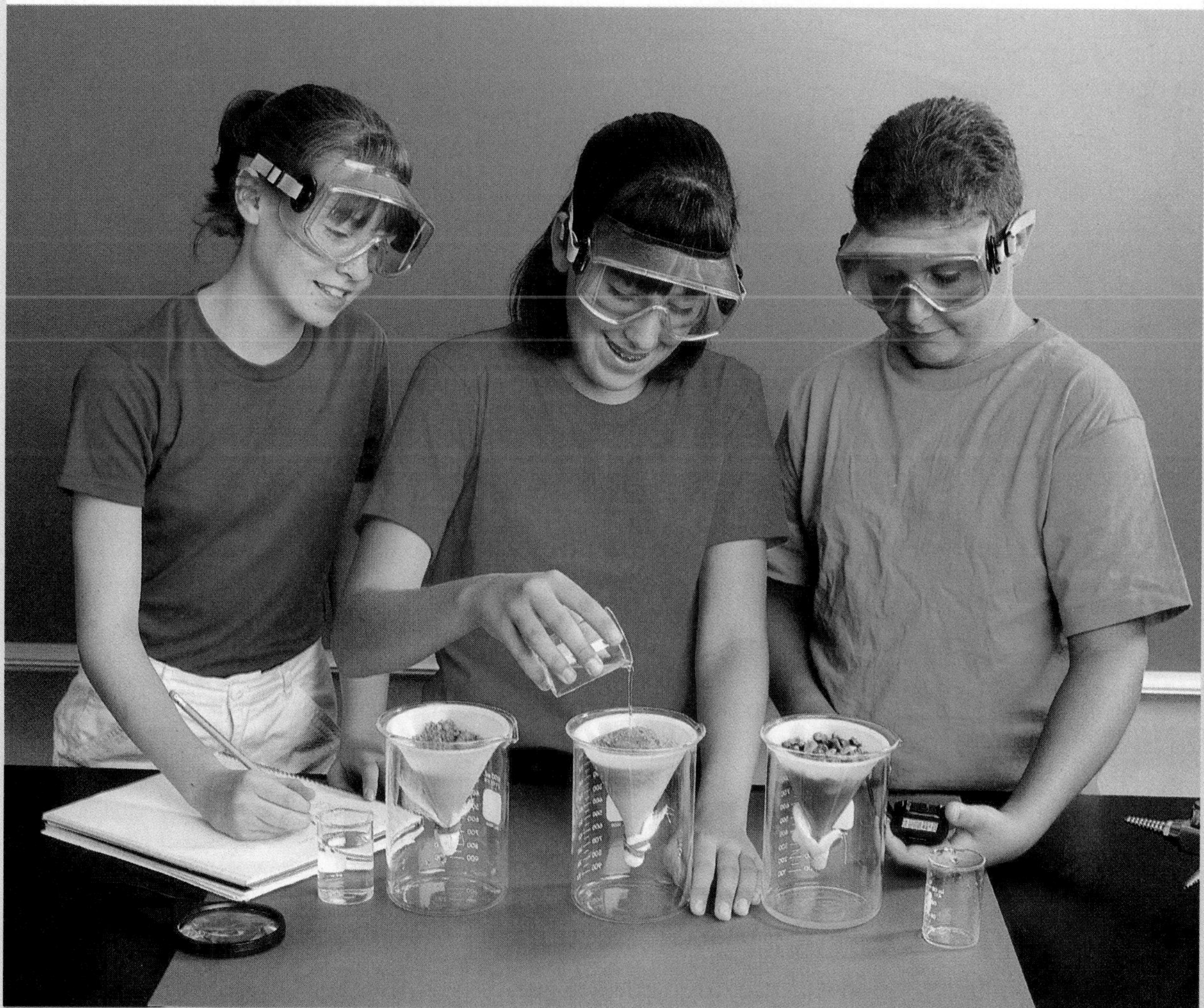

TRY THIS

An Artesian Well

ACTIVITY

In this activity you will build a model of an artesian well. Before you start, cover your desk or table with newspaper.

1. Cover the bottom of a loaf pan with clay. Pile the clay higher at one end.
2. Cover the clay with about 4 cm of moist sand.
3. Cover the sand with a thin sheet of clay. Seal the edges of the clay tightly against the sides of the pan.
4. Push a funnel into the high end so that the bottom of the funnel is in the sand.

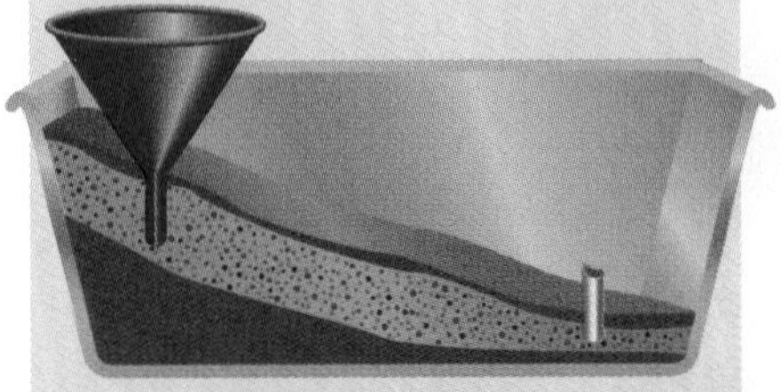

5. Insert a short piece of plastic straw through the clay and into the sand layer at the low end. Remove the straw, discard it, and then insert a new piece of straw in the same hole.
6. Slowly pour water into the funnel. Do not let the water overflow the funnel.
7. Observe the level of water in the straw. Wash your hands after this activity.

Making a Model What real-world feature does each part of your model represent? How is your model like a real artesian well? How is it different?

Aquifers

Any underground layer of rock or sediment that holds water is called an **aquifer.** Aquifers can range in size from a small underground patch of permeable material to an area the size of several states. The huge Ogallala aquifer lies beneath the plains of the midwest, stretching from South Dakota to Texas. Millions of people obtain their drinking water from this underground storehouse. The Ogallala aquifer also provides water for crops and livestock.

Maybe you picture groundwater as a large, still pool beneath Earth's surface. In fact, the water is actually in motion, seeping through the layers of rock. How fast it moves depends largely on how steeply the aquifer slopes and how permeable the rocks are. Groundwater in some aquifers moves only a few centimeters a day. At that rate, the water moves about 10 meters a year—less than the length of a typical classroom. Groundwater may travel hundreds of kilometers and stay in an aquifer for thousands of years before coming to the surface again.

☑ *Checkpoint* ***What factors affect how fast water moves in an aquifer?***

Bringing Groundwater to the Surface

Look at Figure 18 and notice how the level of the water table generally follows the shape of the underground rock layers. The depth of the water table can vary greatly even over a small area of land. Heavy rain or lots of melting snow raise the level of the water table. The level falls in dry weather.

In places where the water table meets the ground surface, groundwater seeps onto the surface. The groundwater may feed a stream or pond, or form a wetland. People can also bring groundwater to the surface.

Wells Since ancient times, people have brought groundwater to the surface for drinking and other everyday uses. **People can obtain groundwater from an aquifer by drilling a well below the water table.** Locate the well near the center of Figure 18. Because the bottom of the well is in the saturated zone, the well contains water. Notice the level of the bottom of the dry well in the diagram. Because this well does not reach below the water table, water cannot be obtained from it.

Long ago, people dug wells by hand. They lined the sides of the well with brick or stone to keep the walls from collapsing. To bring up water, they lowered and raised a bucket. Today, most wells are dug with well-drilling equipment. Pumps bring up the groundwater.

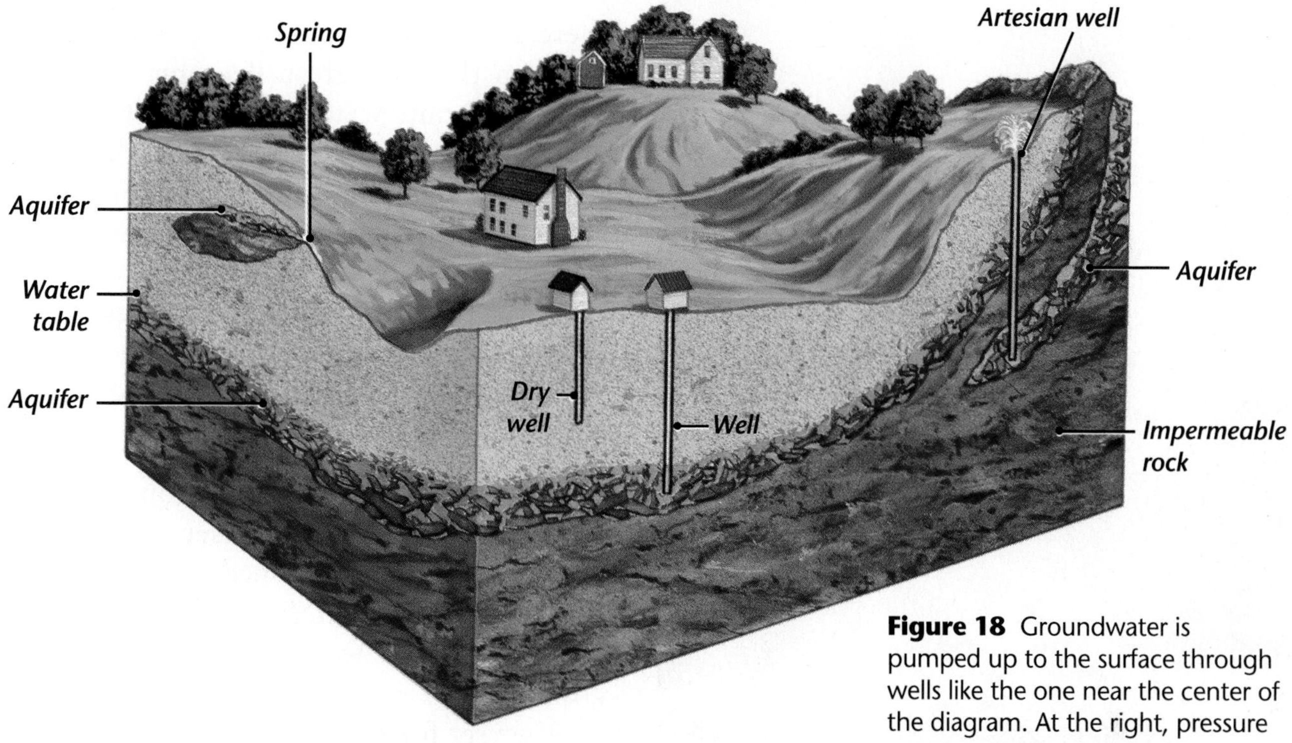
Spring
Artesian well
Aquifer
Water table
Aquifer
Dry well
Well
Aquifer
Impermeable rock

Figure 18 Groundwater is pumped up to the surface through wells like the one near the center of the diagram. At the right, pressure causes water to spurt from an artesian well. Where an aquifer meets the ground surface, at the left, a spring may form.
Interpreting Diagrams Why does the dry well not contain any water?

Pumping water out of an aquifer lowers the water level near the well. If too much water is pumped out too fast, the well may run dry. It will be necessary either to dig deeper to reach the lowered water table, or to wait for rainfall to refill the aquifer. New water that enters the aquifer from the surface is called **recharge.**

Artesian Wells In some aquifers, groundwater is trapped between two layers of impermeable rock or sediment. This water is under great pressure from the weight of the water above it. If the top layer of rock is punctured, the pressure sends water spurting up through the hole. Water flows without pumping from a well dug in such an aquifer. A well in which water rises because of pressure within the aquifer is called an **artesian well** (ahr TEEZH uhn well).

Springs and Geysers

Imagine that you are walking through a strange-looking land full of bubbling mud pools and mineral-filled ponds. With a loud roar, a column of boiling hot water and white steam suddenly erupts from the ground in front of you. The towering fountain soars high into the air as the hot steam blows around you. Although you might think you've landed on another planet, these are common sights in Wyoming's Yellowstone National Park.

Springs In Yellowstone, groundwater seeps, flows, and erupts onto the surface in very dramatic ways. But in most other places, groundwater comes to the surface more quietly. Places

Figure 19 A crowd of tourists is amazed by Yellowstone's most famous geyser, Old Faithful. The geyser's regular eruptions can reach as high as an eight-story building.

where groundwater bubbles or flows out of cracks in the rock are called **springs.** Most springs contain water at normal temperatures, but some springs, like those in Yellowstone, contain water that is warmed by the hot rocks deep below the surface. The heated water bubbles to the surface in hot springs. Not surprisingly, two places in the United States where such springs occur are Warm Springs, Georgia, and Hot Springs, Arkansas!

Geysers The fountain in Yellowstone that shot into the air is a geyser. A **geyser** (GY zur) is a type of hot spring from which the water bursts periodically into the air. The word *geyser* comes from an Icelandic word, *geysir,* which means "gusher."

A geyser forms when very hot water that has been circulating deep underground begins to rise through narrow passages in the rock. Heated gases and bubbles of steam are forced up these passages by the pressure of the hot water boiling below. Just as pressure builds up in a partly blocked water pipe, the pressure within these narrow openings in the rock increases. Finally the gases, steam, and hot water erupt high into the air. Outside the United States, many dramatic geysers are found in Iceland, New Zealand, Kenya, and Indonesia.

Section 5 Review

1. Describe what happens to water that soaks into the ground.
2. Why is it important to know the depth of an aquifer before drilling a well?
3. Draw a cross section of the ground that includes the following labeled features: permeable layer, saturated zone, unsaturated zone, impermeable layer, and water table.
4. What force causes a geyser to erupt?
5. **Thinking Critically Inferring** During the winter, a small spring flows on your property. Every summer, the spring dries up. What might be the reason for the change?

CHAPTER PROJECT

Check Your Progress

Now you are ready to build your model watershed. Be sure to follow the plan you have drawn. When your model is finished, do a practice run of your demonstration. (*Hint:* Some materials need to be worked with quickly before they harden. Others need time to dry before you can pour water over them. Be sure to leave yourself enough time to build your model and let it dry before your presentation.)

SECTION 1 Streams and Rivers

Key Ideas

- Runoff from precipitation forms streams, which flow together to form rivers. The area drained by a river system is its watershed.
- Rivers wear away landforms through erosion and build new ones through deposition.
- As a river flows from its headwaters to its mouth, the slope, speed, and volume change.
- Floods occur when a river overflows its channel and spreads out over its floodplain.

Key Terms

runoff	tributary	watershed
divide	erosion	deposition
sediment	headwaters	flood plain
meander	oxbow lake	mouth
delta	levee	

SECTION 2 Ponds and Lakes

Key Ideas

- Ponds and lakes are bodies of standing water that form when fresh water collects in depressions in the land.
- Because sunlight reaches the bottom of a pond, plants can grow throughout the pond.
- Lake turnover is a seasonal mixing that refreshes the nutrient supply in the lake.

Key Terms

reservoir eutrophication

SECTION 3 Wetland Environments

INTEGRATING LIFE SCIENCE

Key Ideas

- Wetlands are covered with a shallow layer of water for all or part of the year.
- Wetlands provide nesting and feeding areas for birds and other wildlife.Wetlands also filter water and help control floods.

Key Term

wetland

SECTION 4 Glaciers and Icebergs

Key Ideas

- Glaciers form when layers of snow pile up. The pressure from the mass of the layers packs the snow into ice.
- Icebergs form when the edges of glaciers reach the ocean and break off. About 90 percent of an iceberg is located underwater.

Key Term

glacier

SECTION 5 Water Underground

Key Ideas

- As water soaks into the ground, it moves through the pores between particles of soil and rock. Water moves easily through permeable materials, but does not move easily through impermeable materials.
- People dig wells to obtain groundwater from aquifers. To supply water, a well must reach below the level of the water table.
- Water pressure brings groundwater to the surface naturally in artesian wells, springs, and geysers.

Key Terms

pore	permeable	impermeable
saturated zone	unsaturated zone	
water table	aquifer	recharge
artesian well	spring	geyser

ACTIVITY

USING THE INTERNET

www.phschool.com/state_focus/california/

California Test Prep: Reviewing Content

Multiple Choice

Choose the letter of the best answer.

1. Rain that falls on a steep, paved street during a thunderstorm will most likely become
a. groundwater. **b.** runoff.
c. a spring. **d.** a reservoir.

2. Which of the following features is most typical of the headwaters of a river?
a. broad flat valley
b. waterfalls and rapids
c. winding meanders
d. muddy, slow-moving water

3. Lakes that store water for human use are called
a. reservoirs. **b.** aquifers.
c. oxbow lakes. **d.** wetlands.

4. More than two thirds of Earth's fresh water is found in
a. rivers and streams.
b. ponds and lakes.
c. wetlands.
d. glaciers and icebergs.

5. Groundwater is stored in
a. wetlands. **b.** water tables.
c. aquifers. **d.** impermeable layers.

True or False

If the statement is true, write true. If it is false, change the underlined word or words to make the statement true.

6. In the process of erosion, moving water breaks off rocks and soil and carries them downstream.

7. Dams are ridges that build up naturally alongside rivers that frequently flood.

8. Continental glaciers move like rivers of ice down mountain slopes.

9. Water moves easily through permeable rock layers.

10. To supply water, the bottom of a well must be located in the saturated zone.

Checking Concepts

11. What are two factors that affect amount of runoff?

12. Explain how a meander forms in a river.

13. Describe how temperature changes in the fall and spring can help distribute nutrients throughout a lake.

14. Explain how wetlands are important to migrating birds.

15. Describe one way that groundwater can come to the surface naturally.

16. Writing to Learn Imagine that you are on summer vacation in one of three different places: a river valley, a pond, or a lake. Write a letter to a friend describing the kinds of wildlife you see and the sports and other activities you are enjoying at the spot you chose.

Thinking Visually

17. Concept Map Copy the concept map about wetlands onto a sheet of paper. Complete it and add a title. (For more on concept maps, see the Skills Handbook).

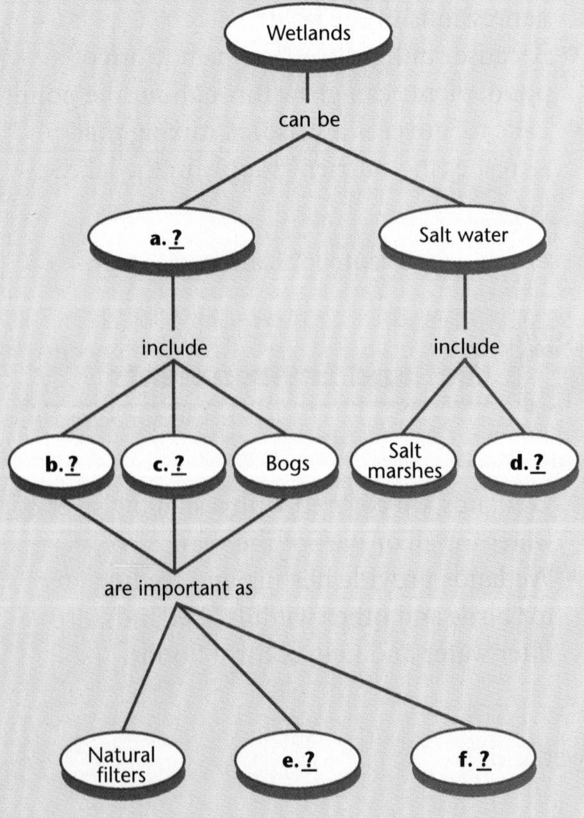
Wetlands
can be
a. ?
Salt water
include
include
b. ?
c. ?
Bogs
Salt marshes
d. ?
are important as
Natural filters
e. ?
f. ?

Test Prep: Skills

Use the diagram of underground layers to answer Questions 18–20.

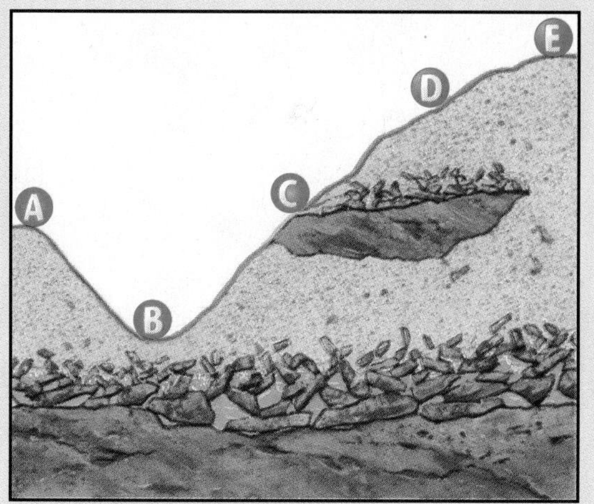
A
B
C
D
E

18. **Drawing Conclusions** Would point D or point E be a better location to dig a well? Explain your reasoning.
19. **Inferring** At which location could you obtain groundwater without having to pump it up? What is such a place called?
20. **Predicting** Draw a simple diagram showing how this area might look during a very rainy season.

Thinking Critically

21. **Comparing and Contrasting** How is the variety of organisms you would find in the center of a pond different from those you would find in deep water at the center of a lake?
22. **Classifying** Which of the following materials are permeable? Which of the materials are impermeable? Aluminum foil, cotton, plastic wrap, glass, paper towel, and bread.
23. **Problem Solving** Suppose that the water table in your area is located 8 meters below the ground surface in the spring. By the end of the summer, the level of groundwater drops 2 meters. How deep should you dig a well to be sure that it does not run dry?

Performance Assessment

CHAPTER PROJECT Wrap Up

Present Your Project Before presentation day, show your watershed model to a classmate. Ask your classmate to predict how the water will flow over the model. Can your classmate identify the features of the watershed? If you need to make any final adjustments to your model, do so now. On presentation day, use a spray bottle to spray rain onto your model.

Reflect and Record In your notebook, explain what you would change about your model now that you have demonstrated it. What aspect of freshwater flow was most difficult to model? What other watershed features might you add?

Getting Involved

In Your Community Obtain permission from your teacher and family to conduct a survey of lakes, ponds, and wetlands in your community. Choose one location and, with an adult family member, take an inventory of the wildlife you find there. If possible, sketch or photograph plants, birds, small mammals, frogs, and other wildlife. Prepare an exhibit for your local library that highlights the natural features of this water environment.

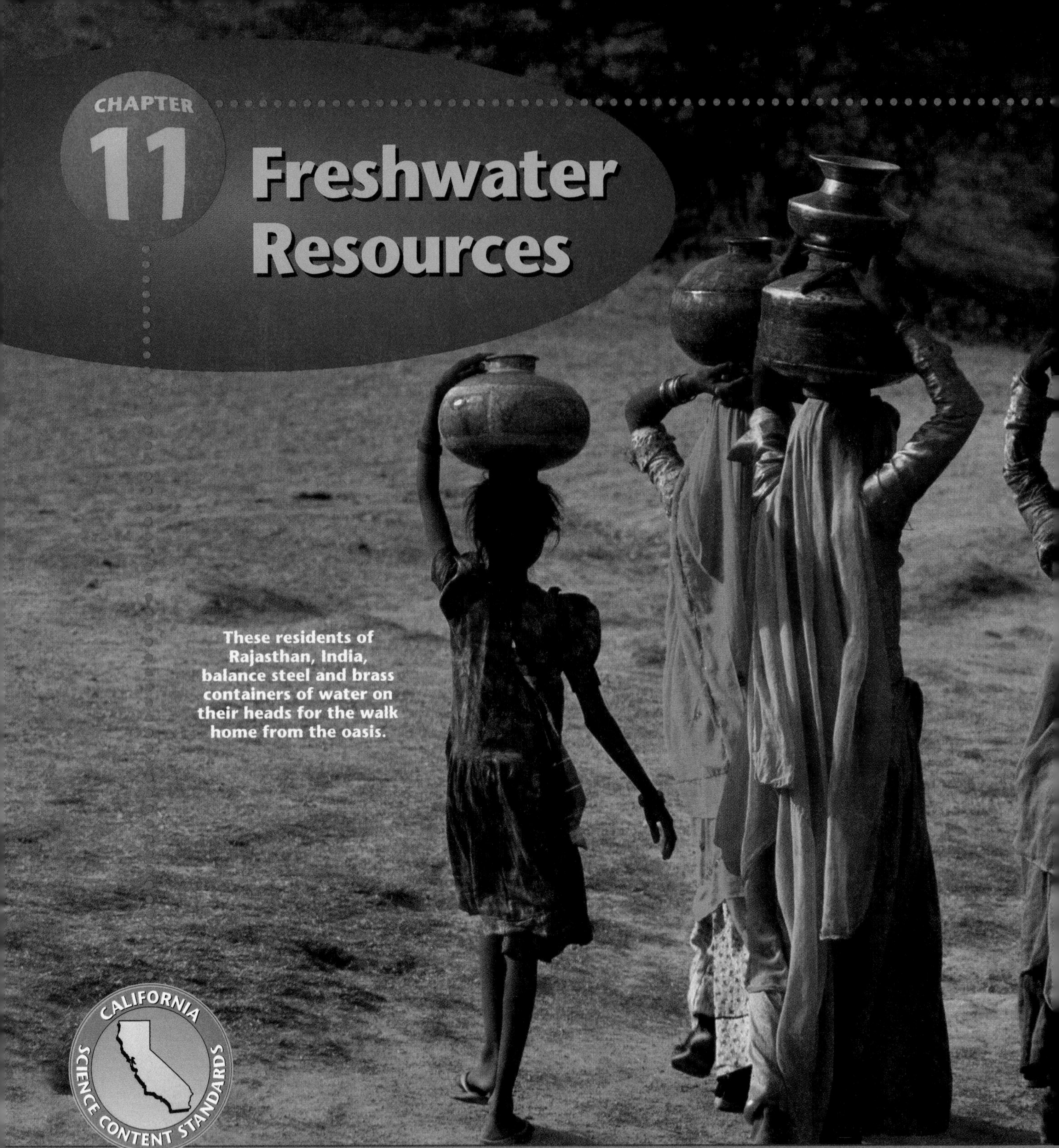

Chapter 11 Freshwater Resources

These residents of Rajasthan, India, balance steel and brass containers of water on their heads for the walk home from the oasis.

CALIFORNIA SCIENCE CONTENT STANDARDS

The following California Science Content Standards are addressed in this chapter:

2. Topography is reshaped by weathering of rock and soil and by the transportation and deposition of sediment.
   - **d.** Earthquakes, volcanic eruptions, landslides, and floods change human and wildlife habitats.
3. Heat moves in a predictable flow from warmer objects to cooler objects until all objects are at the same temperature.
   - **a.** Energy can be carried from one place to another by heat flow, or by waves including water waves, light and sound, or by moving objects.
5. Organisms in ecosystems exchange energy and nutrients among themselves and with the physical environment.
   - **b.** Over time, matter is transferred from one organism to others in the food web, and between organisms and the physical environment.
   - **e.** The number and types of organisms an ecosystem can support depends on the resources available and abiotic factors, such as quantity of light and water, range of temperatures, and soil composition.

PROJECT 11

A Precious Resource

If you lived in Rajasthan, India, you might walk two kilometers every morning to collect a heavy bucket of water from a spring-fed oasis. Your family would use this water for breakfast, washing dishes, and laundry. When you came home from school, you would fetch more water for the evening meal and bathing.

In this chapter, you will explore water as a resource. You will discover what happens when water is scarce, and how water can become polluted. You will also learn how people can use freshwater resources more wisely, and how water pollution can be prevented or cleaned up. Throughout the chapter, you will be building your own model water treatment system.

Your Goal To design and build a water treatment system to clean one liter of dirty water.

Your treatment system should

- consist of at least two treatment steps
- be made from materials that have been approved by your teacher
- recover as much of one liter of clean water as possible
- be built following the safety guidelines in Appendix A

Get Started Your teacher will give you a sample of dirty water. Begin now by using your senses to observe your sample. Make a list of all your observations. Think about what types of substances might be present in this water. **CAUTION:** *Never taste or drink the water samples before or after treatment.*

Check Your Progress You'll be working on this project as you study this chapter. To keep your project on track, look for Check Your Progress boxes at the following points.

Section 1 Review, page 341: Plan the steps of your system.
Section 3 Review, page 356: Assemble your treatment system.
Section 4 Review, page 360: Test and modify your system.

Wrap Up At the end of the chapter (page 363), you will demonstrate how well your system cleans up the dirty water sample.

6. Sources of energy and materials differ in amounts, distribution, usefulness, and the time required for their formation.

a. The utility of energy sources is determined by factors that are involved in converting these sources to useful forms and the consequences of the conversion process.

b. Different natural energy and material resources, including air, soil, rocks, minerals, petroleum, fresh water, wildlife, and forests, and classify them as renewable or nonrenewable.

7. Scientific progress is made by asking meaningful questions and conducting careful investigations.

b. Select and use appropriate tools and technology (including calculators, computers, balances, spring scales, microscopes, and binoculars) to perform tests, collect data, and display data.

d. Communicate the steps and results from an investigation in written reports and verbal presentations.

SECTION 1

Water to Drink

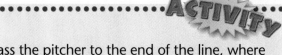

DISCOVER — ACTIVITY

How Hard Is It to Move Water?

1. Line two large trash barrels with heavy plastic bags. Fill one barrel with about 100 liters of water. This is about how much water a person uses during a five-minute shower.
2. Form a line of students between the barrels. Your goal is to transfer all the water from the first barrel to the second barrel. Avoid spilling the water. Be careful of slippery floors if you are doing this activity indoors.
3. The first person in line should fill a large plastic pitcher with water, put the cover on, and hand it to the next person.
4. Pass the pitcher to the end of the line, where the last person should empty it into the second barrel. Hand the empty pitcher back down the line to the first person.
5. Repeat Steps 3 and 4 until all the water has been transferred to the second barrel. How many times did you pass the pitcher down the line?

Think It Over

Calculating Suppose a person uses an average of 250 liters of water a day. How many times would you have to pass the pitcher to move the amount of water this person would use in a day? In a year?

GUIDE FOR READING

- **What is the goal of drinking-water treatment?**
- **What happens to wastewater in most large communities?**

Reading Tip **Before you read, rewrite the section headings as how, why, or what questions. As you read, find answers to these questions.**

At first, doctors in Milwaukee, Wisconsin, thought that 1993 was just a bad year for the flu. Patient after patient complained of nausea, fever, and other flulike symptoms. Within just a few weeks, about 400,000 people came down with symptoms of the disease. Public health officials began looking for another explanation for the epidemic.

The investigators discovered that all the victims had drunk water from the same water treatment plant. Tests revealed that the water contained a tiny parasite, a protist called *Cryptosporidium.* One sip of water could contain enough *Cryptosporidium* to make a person ill! This parasite had not been killed by the chemicals used to treat water at the plant. The scientists hypothesized that the *Cryptosporidium* might have come from runoff from fields where cows grazed. Although most of the victims recovered after a few weeks, about 100 deaths were blamed on the contamination.

Figure 1 An aqueduct carries water from one place to another. This aqueduct, the Pont du Gard in France, was built by the Romans more than 2,000 years ago. *Inferring Why do you think the Romans found it necessary to construct aqueducts?*

Milwaukee's experience was a reminder of the importance of a safe, clean water supply. In this section, you will follow drinking water on its journey to and from homes, schools, and businesses.

Sources of Drinking Water

Where does the water in your kitchen faucet come from? The first step in tracing the path of your water supply is to identify its source. Recall that Earth's liquid fresh water is found on the surface in rivers, lakes, and reservoirs, and underground in rock layers called aquifers. Most people in the United States get their drinking water from one of these sources.

If you live near a large lake or river, your water may come from that source. A distant lake or reservoir could also supply your drinking water. For instance, the city of Los Angeles draws much of its water from the Sierra Nevada Mountains, halfway across California. Or you may rely on groundwater as a source of drinking water. About half the people in the United States, including most people in rural areas, pump drinking water from aquifers.

Your drinking water comes from either a public or private water supply. Most large communities maintain public water supplies. These communities collect, treat, and distribute water to residents. In smaller communities and rural areas, people rely on private wells that supply water for individual families.

☑ *Checkpoint* *List three possible sources of drinking water.*

Treating Drinking Water

After you have identified the source of your drinking water, what is the next step in its journey to your faucet? **Water from both public and private supplies often needs some treatment to ensure that the water is safe and appealing to drink.** Treatment can range from a simple filter on a household well to complex processes at public treatment plants.

Appearance and Taste Picture a glass of water. What observations would affect whether or not you were willing to take a sip? What if the water were cloudy, or had a funny smell? What if the water were rust-colored? Cloudiness, odor, and color are three factors that affect water quality. **Water quality** is a measurement of the substances in water besides water molecules. Some substances, such as iron, can affect the taste or color of water but are harmless unless present at very high levels. Other

Real-World Lab

You, the Consumer

Testing the Waters

How does the bottled water sold in supermarkets differ from the water that comes out of your kitchen faucet? In this lab, you will discover some differences among various types of water.

evian
volvic

Problem

How do distilled water, spring water, and mineral water differ from tap water?

Skills Focus

observing, inferring, drawing conclusions

Materials

hot plate
liquid soap
ruler
wax pencil
tap water, 200 mL
distilled water, 200 mL
spring water, 200 mL
mineral water, 200 mL
4 200-mL beakers
4 test tubes and stoppers
4 pieces of pH paper
pH indicator chart
25-mL graduated cylinder
4 paper cups per person

Procedure

1. Copy the data table into your notebook.
2. Label the beakers A, B, C, and D. Pour 100 mL of tap water into beaker A. Pour 100 mL of the other water samples into the correct beaker (refer to the data table).
3. Heat each water sample on a hot plate until about 20 mL remains. Do not allow the water to boil completely away. **CAUTION:** *Do not touch the hot plate or beakers.*
4. After the water samples have cooled, look for solids that make the water cloudy. Rank the samples from 1 to 4, where 1 has the fewest visible solids and 4 has the most visible solids. Record your rankings in the data table.
5. Label the test tubes A, B, C, and D. Pour 10 mL of each water sample from the source bottle into the correct test tube.
6. Dip a piece of pH paper into test tube A to measure its acidity. Match the color of the pH paper to a number on the pH indicator chart. Record the pH (0–14) in your data table.

substances, such as certain chemicals and microorganisms, can be harmful to your health.

Acidity The **pH** of water is a measurement of how acidic or basic it is, on a scale of 0 to 14. Pure water is neutral, meaning it is neither an acid or a base, and has a pH of 7. The lower the pH, the more acidic the water. Acidic water can cause problems by dissolving lead or other metals from the pipes it passes through. The higher the pH, the more basic the water.

DATA TABLE

Water Sample	Visible Solids (1–4)	pH (0–14)	Soapsud Height (cm)	Taste
A - Tap water				
B - Distilled water				
C - Spring water				
D - Mineral water				

7. Repeat Step 6 for the other samples.
8. Add 0.5 mL of liquid soap to test tube A. Put a stopper in the test tube and shake it 30 times. With the ruler, measure the height of the soapsuds in the test tube. Record the measurement in your data table.
9. Repeat Step 8 for the other samples.
10. Label the four cups A, B, C, and D. Write your name on each cup.
11. Pour a little tap water into cup A directly from the original source bottle. Taste the tap water. In your data table, describe the taste using one or more of these words: salty, flat, bitter, metallic, refreshing, tasteless. **CAUTION:** *Do not conduct the taste test in a lab room. Use a clean cup for each sample and discard it after use.*
12. Repeat Step 11 with the other samples.

Analyze and Conclude

1. Review your data table. Compare each of the bottled water samples to the tap water sample. What similarities and differences did you detect?
2. Rank the samples from the one with the fewest soapsuds to the one with the most. Compare this ranking to the one for visible solids. What pattern do you see? What do both of these tests have to do with the hardness of water?
3. What other information about the water samples might you need before deciding which one to drink regularly? Explain.
4. **Apply** Based on your results, which sample would you most want to use for (a) drinking, (b) boiling in a kettle, and (c) washing laundry? Which sample would you least want to use for each purpose? Explain.

Getting Involved

Conduct a survey to find out what percentage of people buy bottled mineral water, distilled water, and spring water. Why do they buy each type of water and how do they use it in their homes?

Math TOOLBOX

Parts per . . .

Concentrations are often measured in parts per million (ppm) or parts per billion (ppb). What do these units mean? If you own one compact disc by your favorite band, and the disc sells one million copies, your disc is one of the one million sold, or one part per million. When you see a concentration written in this form, you can rewrite it as a fraction:

1. Suppose the concentration of iron in a water sample is 500 parts per million.
2. Write this concentration as a fraction by putting the number of parts on top, and the "whole" on the bottom:

$$500 \text{ parts per million} = \frac{500}{1{,}000{,}000}$$

Hardness The level of two minerals—calcium and magnesium—in water is referred to as **hardness.** Hard water contains high levels of these minerals. The minerals come from rocks such as limestone that water flows through. For most people, the main drawback of hard water is that it does not form suds well when mixed with soap. That means that it takes more soap or detergent to get laundry clean in hard water. The minerals in hard water also form deposits that can clog pipes and machinery. Soft water, on the other hand, contains lower levels of calcium and magnesium. Soft water leaves fewer deposits and forms better soapsuds than hard water.

Disease-Causing Organisms Another factor affecting water quality is the presence of disease-causing organisms. The coliform count measures the number of *Escherichia coli* bacteria. Since these bacteria are found in human and animal wastes, their presence in the water shows that it contains waste material. A high coliform count is an indicator, or sign, that the water may also contain other disease-causing organisms.

Standards of Quality The Environmental Protection Agency (EPA), which is responsible for protecting the quality of water and other natural resources in the United States, has developed water-quality standards for drinking water. These standards set concentration limits for certain chemicals, minerals, and bacteria in drinking water. A **concentration** is the amount of one substance in a certain volume of another substance. For example, the concentration of letters in alphabet soup might be written as the number of letters per liter of soup. Figure 2 shows the standards for some different substances.

☑ ***Checkpoint*** *List five factors that affect water quality.*

Selected Water-Quality Standards

Substance	Limit
Arsenic	0.05 parts per million (ppm)
Carbon tetrachloride	0.005 ppm
Copper	1.3 ppm
Cyanide	0.2 ppm
Lead	0.015 ppm
Coliform count	No more than 5% of samples taken in a month can be positive.
pH	6.5–8.5

Source: U.S. Environmental Protection Agency, National Primary and Secondary Drinking-Water Standards.

Figure 2 The EPA has set standards for the amounts of various substances in drinking water. ***Interpreting Data*** *Based on this table, is a concentration of 0.09 ppm of arsenic in drinking water acceptable? Is a concentration of 0.05 ppm of cyanide acceptable?*

A Typical Treatment Plant

Follow the water from river to faucet in *Exploring Drinking-Water Treatment* to see what happens in a typical water treatment plant.

The first step in treating water from a lake or river is usually filtration. **Filtration** is the process of passing water through a series of screens that allows the water through, but not larger solid particles. During this first step, trash, leaves, branches, and other large objects are removed from the water.

In the second step, a chemical such as alum is added to cause sticky globs, called **flocs,** to form. Other particles in the water stick to the flocs, a process called **coagulation.** The heavy clumps sink to the bottom in the settling basins. The water is then filtered again.

EXPLORING *Drinking-Water Treatment*

A typical water treatment process includes several steps to remove unwanted substances from water.

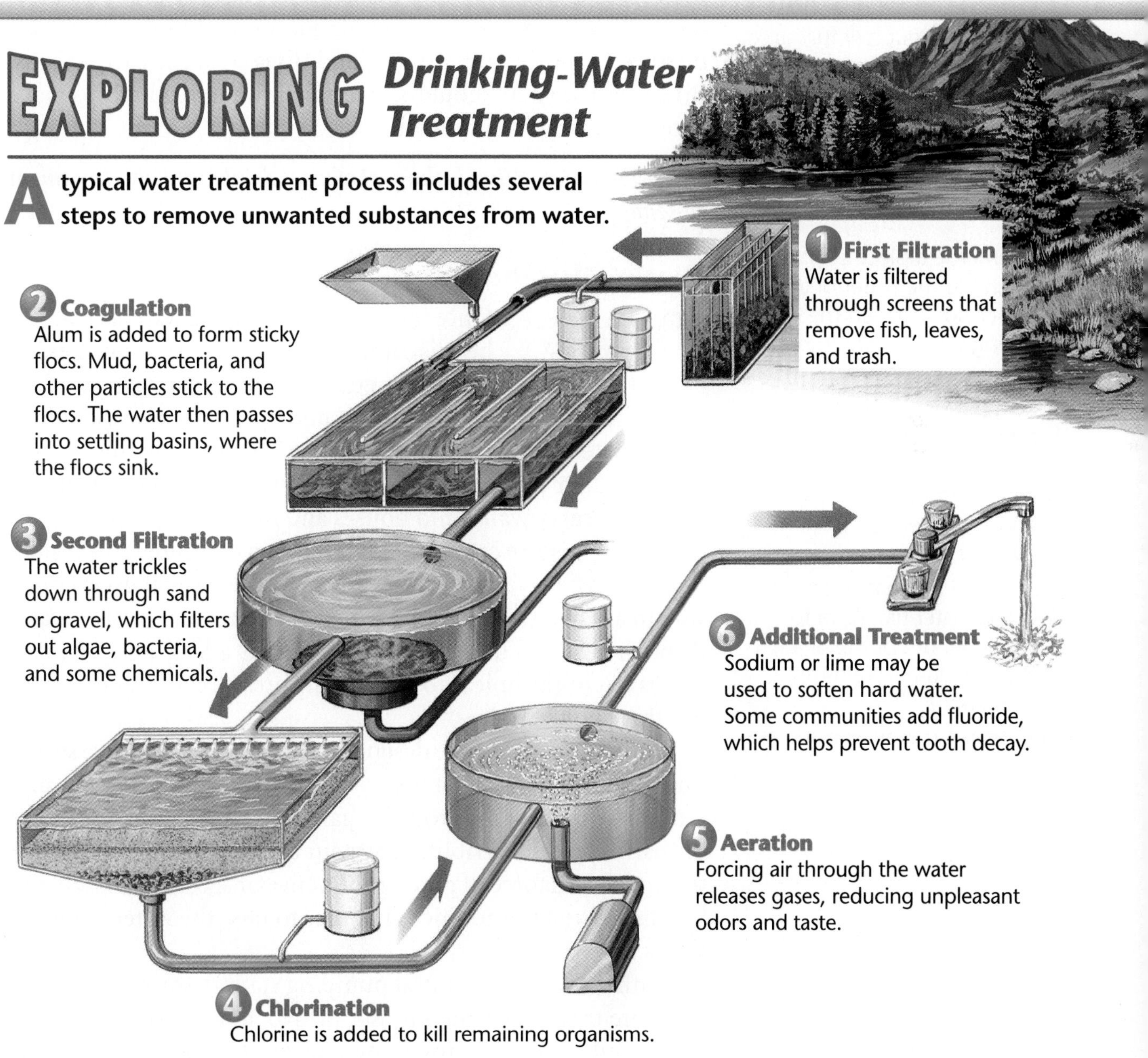

1 First Filtration
Water is filtered through screens that remove fish, leaves, and trash.
2 Coagulation
Alum is added to form sticky flocs. Mud, bacteria, and other particles stick to the flocs. The water then passes into settling basins, where the flocs sink.
3 Second Filtration
The water trickles down through sand or gravel, which filters out algae, bacteria, and some chemicals.
4 Chlorination
Chlorine is added to kill remaining organisms.
5 Aeration
Forcing air through the water releases gases, reducing unpleasant odors and taste.
6 Additional Treatment
Sodium or lime may be used to soften hard water. Some communities add fluoride, which helps prevent tooth decay.

TRY THIS

Moving Water Uphill

ACTIVITY

In this activity you will see how a device called a siphon can be used to move water.

1. Pile a stack of books on a table. Place one bowl on top of the books and another bowl on the table. Pour water into the higher bowl until it is about half full.

2. Submerge a piece of plastic tubing in the water in the upper bowl. When the tubing is full of water, put a finger over each end.
3. Keeping one end of the tubing underwater, place the other end in the lower, empty bowl. Release both fingers and watch what happens.

Observing In what direction does the water first have to travel to get out of the higher bowl? Can you explain this movement?

The next step is to chlorinate the water. If you have ever been to a public swimming pool, you are familiar with the smell of chlorine. Chlorine is added to drinking water for the same reason it is added to swimming pools—to kill disease-causing microorganisms. At this point, the water is usually ready to be distributed to homes. Sometimes other chemicals are added to kill specific organisms, such as the *Cryptosporidium* you read about earlier.

Water from an aquifer may require less treatment than water from a lake or river. Flowing through the rocks or sand naturally filters and purifies the water. However, most public water supplies that use a groundwater source still add chlorine to kill disease-causing organisms.

Public health officials regularly test samples from water treatment plants to assess water quality. They test for the substances covered by the drinking-water standards, including chemicals, dissolved solids, pH, hardness, and disease-causing organisms. Private well owners should also test their water regularly to make sure no treatment is needed.

☑ *Checkpoint* ***What is the goal of most drinking-water treatment systems?***

Water Distribution

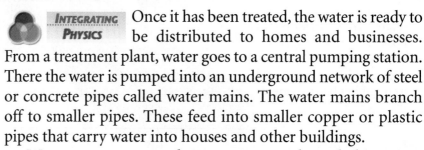

INTEGRATING PHYSICS Once it has been treated, the water is ready to be distributed to homes and businesses. From a treatment plant, water goes to a central pumping station. There the water is pumped into an underground network of steel or concrete pipes called water mains. The water mains branch off to smaller pipes. These feed into smaller copper or plastic pipes that carry water into houses and other buildings.

Water pressure causes the water to move through this system of pipes. Whenever water is in an enclosed space, it exerts pressure in all directions. For example, water pressure pushes water through a garden hose. If the hose springs a leak, a jet of water sprays out of the hole into the air. The pressure pushes the water out through the hole.

Pumping stations are designed to keep water pressure steady throughout the system. If there is a leak in one of the pipes, water escapes—just as it did from the garden hose—and the pressure drops. A typical distribution system can push water up against the downward force of gravity about five or six stories. High-rise buildings must use additional pumps to raise the water to higher floors.

Rather than use a central pumping station, some communities store their water high in the air! No, not as clouds or water vapor, but in a water tower or tank on top of a hill. Treated

Figure 3 These firefighters rely on water pressure to force streams of water through the air. *Predicting If the diameter of the firehose were larger, would the spray be more powerful or less powerful?*

water is pumped up into the water tower. When the water is released, the weight of the water supplies additional pressure that sends the water rushing downward, filling the town's water mains and pipes.

Treating Wastewater

Finally, after a long journey, the water reaches your house. You take a shower, flush the toilet, or wash a load of laundry. What happens now to the used water that goes down the drain? That wastewater and the different kinds of wastes in it are called **sewage.** You might be surprised to learn that this water could someday return as part of your drinking water! No need to worry, however. The wastewater goes through many changes to make this possible.

In many communities, a network of pipes called sanitary sewers carries sewage away from homes. Sanitary sewers are separated from storm sewers, which drain rainwater and runoff from sidewalks, lawns, and parking lots.

Cities and towns have had sanitary sewer systems for only about the last 200 years. Before then, wastewater was often dumped into open gutters and allowed to run directly back into rivers or oceans. Although people eventually realized that this practice helped spread disease, it still occurs in some places, both in the United States and the rest of the world. Coastal cities, in particular, sometimes still pump untreated sewage into the oceans.

Most communities treat their wastewater to make it safe to return to the environment. Different communities may use different treatment processes.

SEWER

Figure 4 If your community has a sanitary sewer system, you may have seen a sewer cover like this one in the street. Sanitary sewers carry wastewater away from homes and businesses.

You can follow one typical wastewater treatment process, called a trickling filter system, in *Exploring Wastewater Treatment.*

During primary treatment, deposits of fine solids called **sludge** settle out from the wastewater. Despite its unappetizing name, sludge is a useful material. It can be treated with heat and chemicals and used as fertilizer. Sludge can also be reused in secondary treatment. In one method, bacteria are added to the sludge to create "activated sludge." The activated sludge is mixed into the wastewater. The bacteria then break down the remaining sewage in the water.

If necessary, additional treatment may remove other substances from the water, such as metals and industrial chemicals. Once wastewater has gone through an effective treatment process, it is safe to return to the environment. It may be released

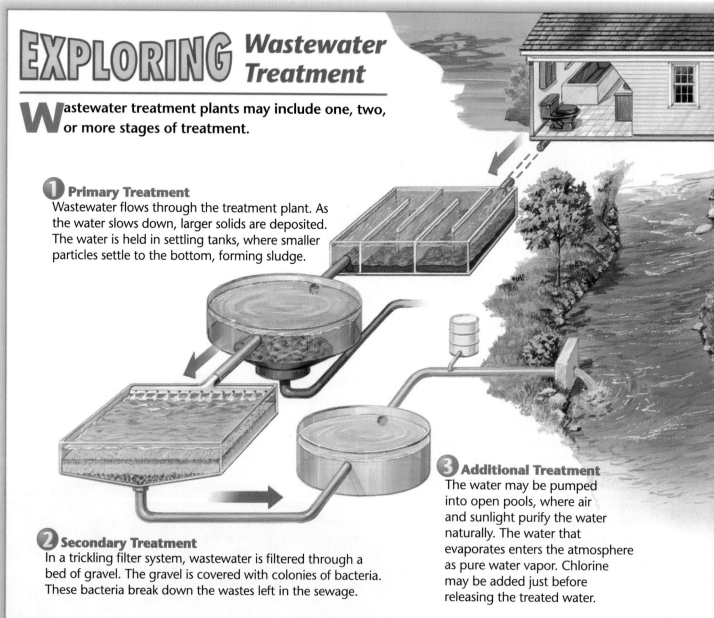

EXPLORING *Wastewater Treatment*

Wastewater treatment plants may include one, two, or more stages of treatment.

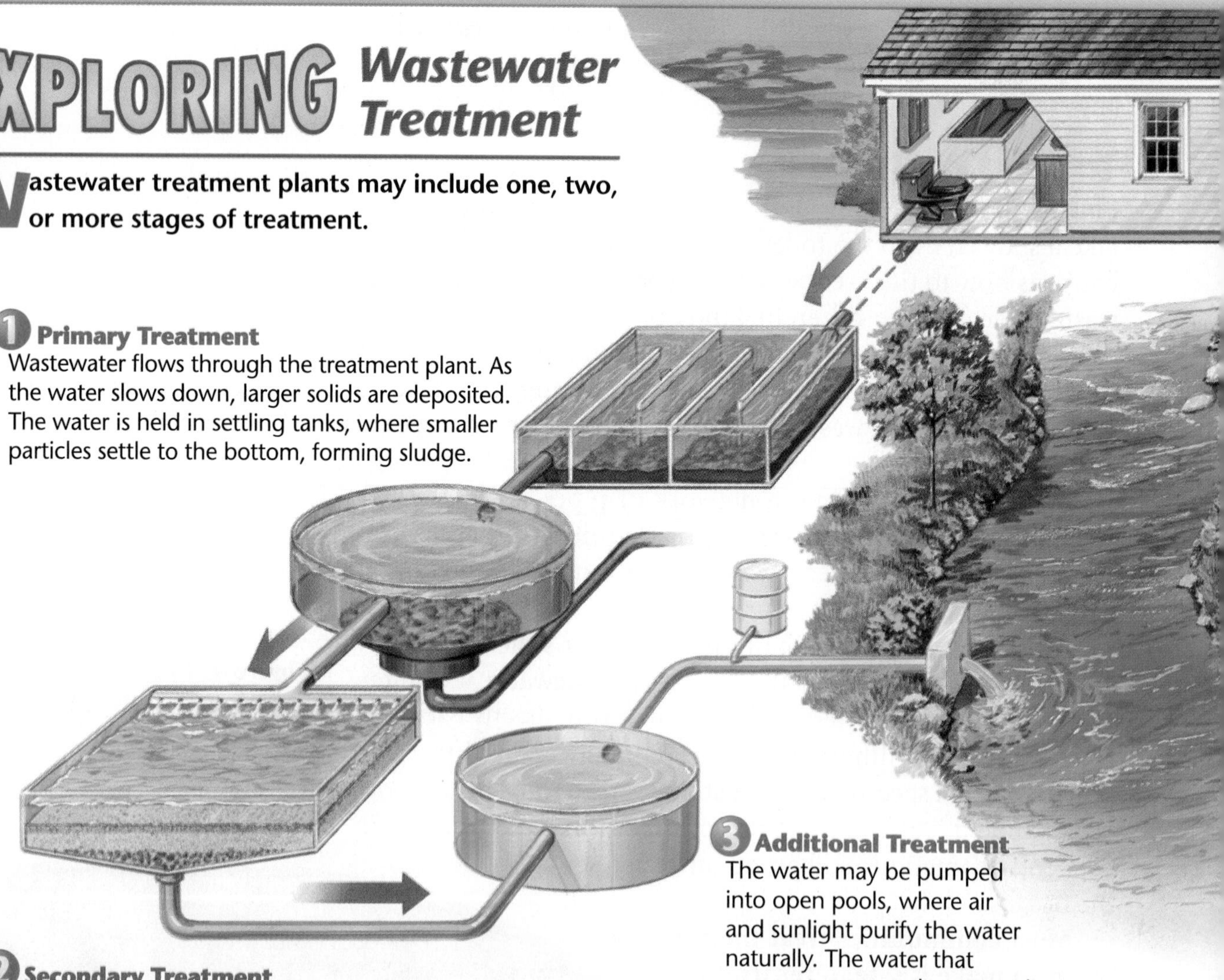

1 Primary Treatment
Wastewater flows through the treatment plant. As the water slows down, larger solids are deposited. The water is held in settling tanks, where smaller particles settle to the bottom, forming sludge.

2 Secondary Treatment
In a trickling filter system, wastewater is filtered through a bed of gravel. The gravel is covered with colonies of bacteria. These bacteria break down the wastes left in the sewage.

3 Additional Treatment
The water may be pumped into open pools, where air and sunlight purify the water naturally. The water that evaporates enters the atmosphere as pure water vapor. Chlorine may be added just before releasing the treated water.

back into lakes, rivers, and oceans or pumped back into the ground. The water rejoins the water cycle. Eventually, it could return to the same reservoir or aquifer that is the source of your water supply.

Treated wastewater that is not quite clean enough for drinking can still be used in other ways. For instance, some communities use this "gray water" to water the grass on golf courses or public parks. Gray water can also be used for irrigation or as cooling water in factories.

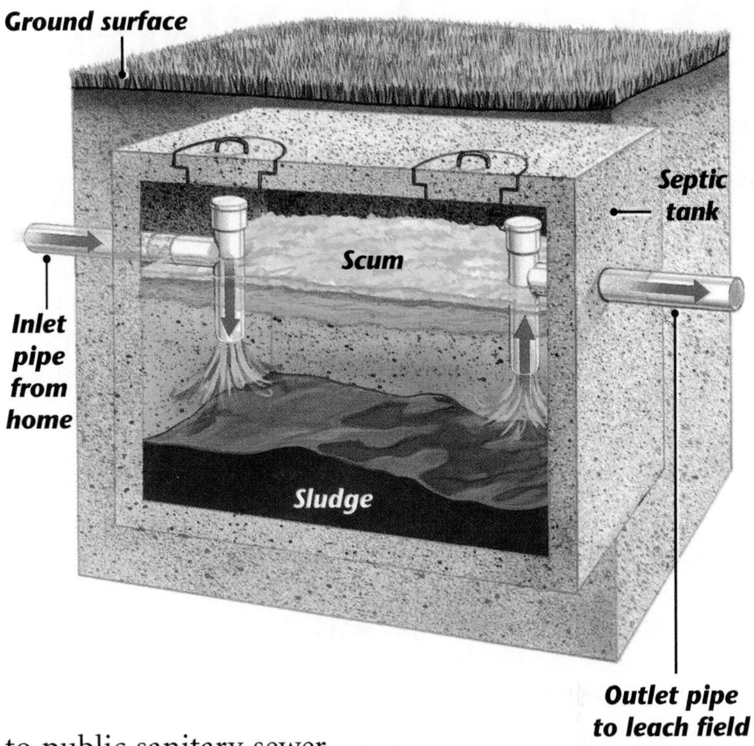

Ground surface
Septic tank
Scum
Inlet pipe from home
Sludge
Outlet pipe to leach field

Figure 5 Sewage flows into a septic tank, where bacteria break down the waste material. Cleaner water leaves the tank and flows into a leach field. There, the water slowly releases the remaining dissolved minerals into the soil.

Septic Systems

Just as some people rely on private wells rather than public water supplies, many people are not connected to public sanitary sewer systems. They use other methods to dispose of sewage, such as a septic system. A septic system like the one in Figure 5 includes a **septic tank,** an underground tank containing bacteria that treat wastewater as it passes through. Sludge settles to the bottom of the tank and must be cleaned out regularly so it does not fill up the tank. The remaining water filters out through holes in the septic tank into the ground around it. The area around the septic tank that the water filters through is called a **leach field.** Over time, the remaining wastes break down naturally in the soil of the leach field.

Section 1 Review

1. How does drinking-water treatment improve water quality?
2. What is the goal of wastewater treatment?
3. List the main sources of drinking water. Classify each source as surface water or groundwater.
4. Describe how drinking water is delivered to homes and businesses in a community.
5. **Thinking Critically** **Inferring** Explain why it is important to know the depth and location of drinking-water wells before deciding where to build a septic tank.

CHAPTER PROJECT

Check Your Progress

Now you are ready to plan the steps of your water treatment system. What will each step accomplish? What materials will you use to perform each step? Draw a diagram of your system and a flowchart showing how it will work. Check your plans with your teacher. *(Hint:* Be sure to consider how your treatment unit will be constructed. How will you hold the pieces in place?)

SECTION 2 Balancing Water Needs

DISCOVER ACTIVITY

Can You Reach a Balance?

1. Fill a large measuring cup with water to represent a reservoir. Record the level of the water. One partner, the water supplier, should have a plastic dropper and a small bowl of water. The other partner, the water user, should have a spoon and an empty bowl.
2. Start a stopwatch. For two minutes, the water supplier should add water to the measuring cup one dropperful at a time. Each time the water supplier adds a dropperful of water, the water user should remove one spoonful of water from the reservoir.
3. At the end of two minutes, record the level of water in the cup.
4. Now increase the rate of water use by removing two spoonfuls of water for every dropperful added.

5. After another two minutes, record the level of water in the cup again.

Think It Over

Predicting What changes will you need to make so that the water level in the reservoir stays constant?

GUIDE FOR READING

- **What conditions can result in a water shortage?**
- **What are some ways industries can conserve water?**

Reading Tip **Before you read, write an explanation of what you think water conservation means. As you read, add to your explanation.**

Has this ever happened to you? You're eating dinner with your family and you ask someone to pass the rolls. As the basket makes its way around the table, each person takes a roll. By the time it gets to you, there's nothing left in the basket but crumbs!

This scenario is an example of a limited resource, the rolls, being used by many people. The same thing can happen to a river! For example, the Colorado River holds a resource that is precious in the Southwest—water. In this desert region there is little precipitation to provide water for people's needs. As the river flows through five states and into Mexico, it is tapped again and again to provide water for drinking, irrigation, and other uses. The river's mouth at the Gulf of California is now often only a dry riverbed.

Figure 6 Cracks appear in the dry soil of an empty riverbed.

Water Supply and Demand

States along a river such as the Colorado have to decide how much water each one can take from the river. The deserts of Nevada and Arizona are home to some of the fastest-growing cities in the country. As more people move to Las Vegas, Phoenix, and Tucson, these cities need more water. They increase their demand on already scarce water supplies. Meanwhile, farmers claim a large share to irrigate their fields. Mining companies use water to cool down machinery and flush out the mines they dig. The cities, farms, and mines compete for water rights—the legal right to take water from a particular source.

The Southwest is just one of many places in the world where there doesn't seem to be enough water to go around. As you know, the water cycle ensures that water is a renewable resource. However, the water supply in a specific area is only renewed when there is enough time for rainfall to replace what has been used. **A water shortage occurs when there is too little water or too great a demand in an area—or both.**

Figure 7 Farmers require large amounts of water to irrigate crops in the dry desert. *Relating Cause and Effect What are two factors that might result in a shortage of water available for irrigation?*

Drought Places that normally get enough precipitation may experience a few years of scarce rainfall, a condition known as a **drought.** A drought affects the supply of groundwater as well as surface water. Without precipitation to recharge the aquifer, the amount of groundwater in the aquifer decreases. What happens to a well as the level of the water table falls? Imagine trying to drink from a tall glass of milk through a straw the length of a toothpick. When the level of the milk falls below the bottom of the straw, you can no longer reach it to drink. In the same way, when the water table falls below the bottom of a well, the well runs dry.

Aquifer Overuse Even without droughts, the demands of growing populations can result in overuse of aquifers. When water is used up faster than the aquifer can be recharged, the aquifer is depleted, or emptied.

INTEGRATING TECHNOLOGY

When too much water is pumped out of an aquifer, the ground above the aquifer can sink or collapse. The ground is no longer supported by the pressure of the water inside it. To prevent collapse, engineers can artificially recharge an aquifer. One method is to pump water from wastewater treatment plants or industrial cooling water into shallow ponds that feed the aquifer. Another method is to inject water down wells directly into the saturated zone. However, because these techniques require expensive equipment and additional water, it is a better solution not to overuse the aquifer.

☑ *Checkpoint* *How can a drought cause a well to run dry?*

Conserving Water

During a water shortage, people often pay more attention to how they use water. They look for ways to avoid wasting water both at home and at work. Using a resource wisely so that it will not be used up is called **conservation.**

In the Home Most people in the United States have access to as much clean, safe water as they want. As a result, it is often easy to use more water than needed without thinking much about it. But as Figure 8 shows, there are some simple things you can do to help conserve water around your home.

Can these suggestions really make a difference? Figure it out. How long do you stand under the shower? For every minute, you use about 18 liters of water. If you stand under the shower for 10 minutes, that's about 180 liters. But if you showered for 5 minutes instead, you would use only 90 liters. And if each student in a class of 25 showered for 5 minutes instead of 10, they would save a total of 2,250 liters of water—enough to fill 22 trash barrels! As you can see, small efforts by many individuals can add up to a lot of water savings.

In Agriculture As you learned in Chapter 9, the biggest use of water in the United States is for agriculture. In the last few decades, farmers have found new ways to use less water. When water is carried into fields in open canals or ditches, much of it is lost through evaporation. Using pipes to carry water reduces the time that water is exposed to the air. Two such methods are sprinkler irrigation and drip irrigation. Sprinkler irrigation sprays water onto crops from overhead pipes. Drip irrigation distributes water through pipes with tiny holes. The water drips directly onto the soil near the plants' roots so that very little is wasted.

In Industry Paper mills, oil refineries, chemical factories, and other industries have made changes in manufacturing processes to use less water. For example, in the 1950s it took about 227,000 liters of water to make 1,000 kilograms of

Social Studies CONNECTION

Laws regarding the use of water are a very old concept. Nearly 4,000 years ago in ancient Mesopotamia, now modern-day Iraq, a ruler named Hammurabi wrote in his code of laws:

"If a man neglects the canal so that water floods a neighboring field, he shall repay the loss with his own grain."

In Your Journal

A river carries 10,000 liters of water a day through your village. Imagine that you are a member of the village council. Propose a fair way to assign water rights to the following people. (*Hint:* Think about which uses will return water to the river and which will not.)

- Grain farmer, wants 4,000 liters a day for watering crops
- Livestock owner, wants 600 liters a day for washing animals and 500 liters a day for animals to drink
- Fisherman, needs to keep the river at least half full for the fish to survive
- Miller, needs 3,500 liters a day to turn waterwheel

writing paper. By the 1980s, paper mills needed only half that much water to produce the same amount of paper.

New water-saving techniques help industries save money in water costs and meet the requirements of environmental laws. **Reducing water use, recycling water, and reusing water are three major forms of water conservation by industries.** These approaches conserve water while also reducing the amount of wastewater that plants release. For example, some factories that use water to cool machinery are building lagoons on their property. The heated water cools off in the lagoons and then can be used again. Other factories are replacing water-cooling systems with cooling systems that use air. Another change is to use high-pressure water sprays to clean products and equipment instead of dipping the objects in large tanks of water.

Fresh Water for the Future

As the number of people in the world increases, so does the need for water. Where can people find new sources of water for the future? One obvious place would seem to be the other 97 percent of water on Earth—the salt water in the oceans. For thousands

Sharpen your Skills

Predicting

ACTIVITY

Find a leaking faucet in your school or home, or turn on a faucet just enough to produce a very slow drip. How much water do you think will drip from the faucet in half an hour? Write down your prediction. Place a large measuring cup under the faucet. After half an hour, check the cup. How does the result compare with your prediction? How much water would you save per day if you fixed the leaking faucet?

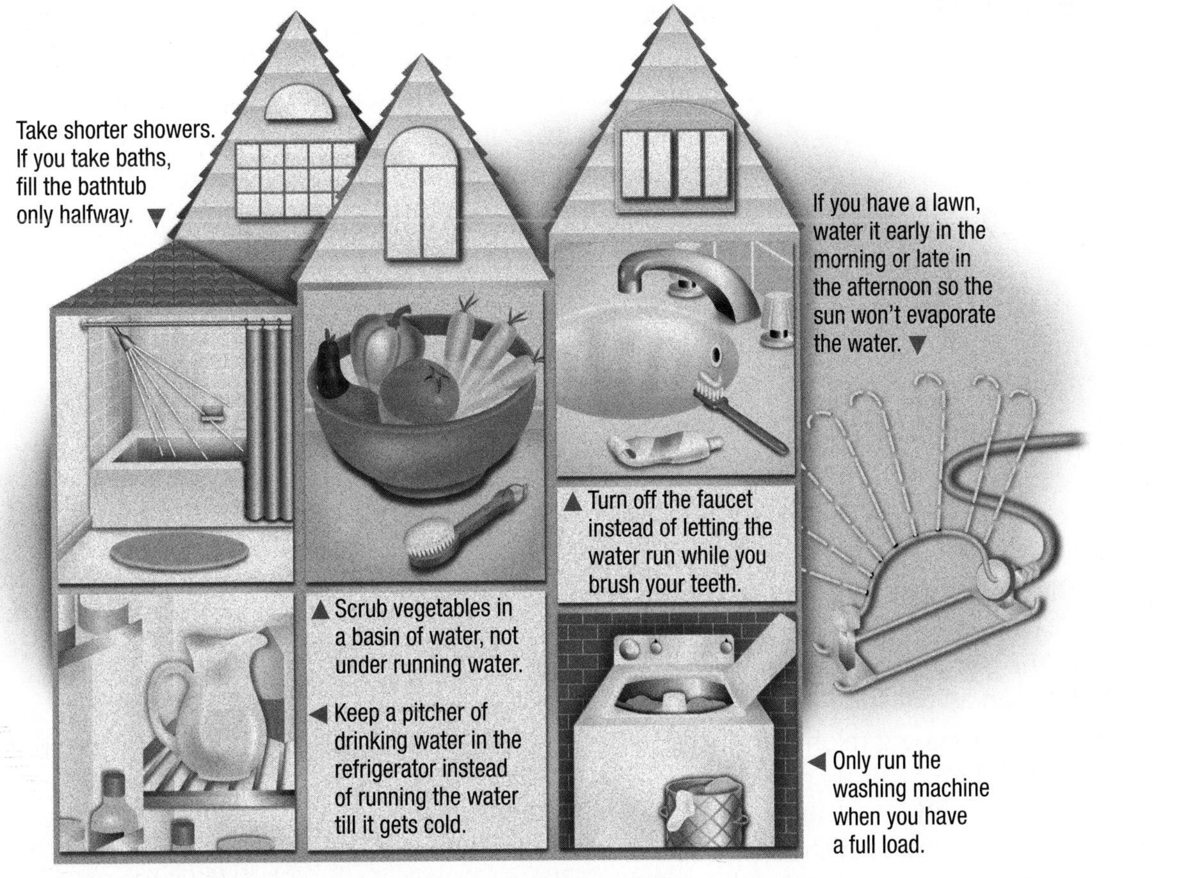
Take shorter showers. If you take baths, fill the bathtub only halfway.
If you have a lawn, water it early in the morning or late in the afternoon so the sun won't evaporate the water.
Turn off the faucet instead of letting the water run while you brush your teeth.
Scrub vegetables in a basin of water, not under running water.
Keep a pitcher of drinking water in the refrigerator instead of running the water till it gets cold.
Only run the washing machine when you have a full load.

Figure 8 There are many simple ways to conserve water around the home. *Predicting Which of these ideas do you think would save the most water per day in your home? How could you test your prediction?*

Figure 9 The ocean is one possible source of drinking water for the future. *Applying Concepts How can ocean water be made suitable for drinking?*

of years, people have tried different methods to make salty ocean water drinkable.

Desalination The process of obtaining fresh water from salt water is called **desalination.** One method of desalination, called distillation, is to boil water so that it evaporates, leaving the salt behind. The water vapor is then condensed to produce liquid fresh water. Another method involves freezing the water, which also leaves the salt behind. Still another method is to pump water at high pressure through a very fine filter. The filter separates out pure water and returns saltier water to the ocean.

Integrating Chemistry

Desalination is very expensive because of the energy and equipment it requires. In spite of the cost, however, Saudi Arabia, Kuwait, Israel, and other nations in the dry Middle East depend on this technology. A few cities in the United States, such as Santa Barbara, California, have also built desalination plants.

Icebergs Some people think that icebergs are another possible source of fresh water for dry regions. Tugboats could tow a wrapped iceberg from Antarctica to a coastal area of Africa or South America. An iceberg would provide millions of liters of pure water that could be piped to shore as the iceberg melted. However, such plans raise environmental questions: How would a huge mass of ice offshore affect local weather? What would happen to living things as the ice cooled the water around it? These questions need to be answered before icebergs can be seen as a solution to Earth's future water needs.

Section 2 Review

1. Describe a situation that could lead to a water shortage in a community.
2. Name three ways that industries can conserve water.
3. Describe the possible effects overpumping might have on an aquifer.
4. Explain how an iceberg might provide drinking water in the future.
5. **Thinking Critically Making Judgments** Do you think communities should be able to limit how often people water their lawns or wash their cars? Why or why not?

Science at Home

Place a stopper over the drain in a sink. Ask a family member to brush his or her teeth over the sink, allowing the water to run until he or she is done. Mark the level of the water in the sink with a small piece of tape. Remove the stopper and let the water drain. Replace the stopper and have the person repeat the brushing, this time turning the water on only when needed. Mark the water level with another piece of tape. Point out the difference in the amount of water used in each case.

Making Models

Getting the Salt Out

Desalination plants use many methods to produce fresh water from ocean water. In this lab, you will make a model of a desalination plant using the method of distillation.

Problem

How can distillation be used to obtain fresh water from salt water?

Materials

hot plate	aluminum foil	250-mL beaker
plastic spoon	water, 100 mL	shallow pan
ice	plastic tube	500-mL flask
stirring rod	rubber stopper	salt
rubber tubing, 50 cm		

Procedure

1. Pour 100 mL of water into the flask.
2. Add one spoonful of salt to the water in the flask and stir until dissolved. The solution should not be cloudy.
3. Gently insert the plastic tube through the hole of the rubber stopper. Do not force the tube into the hole; ask your teacher for help if you are having difficulty.
4. Insert one end of the plastic tube into the rubber tubing.
5. Put the rubber stopper in the flask. The bottom of the plastic tube should be above the surface of the solution.
6. Cover the beaker with aluminum foil. Press the edges of the foil against the beaker.
7. Push the free end of the rubber tubing through the center of the aluminum foil covering the top of the beaker.
8. Place the beaker in the pan, surrounded by ice.
9. Put the flask on the hot plate, keeping it away from the pan of ice. Turn the hot plate on. Bring the solution to a boil. **CAUTION:** *Do not touch the hot plate or flask. Do not allow the solution to boil completely away.*
10. Observe what happens in the flask and the beaker. Continue heating the solution until a liquid has accumulated in the beaker.
11. Turn off the hot plate and allow the flask and the beaker to cool. What is left behind in the flask? Record your observations.

Analyze and Conclude

1. What happened to the water in the flask during the boiling process? What happened inside the beaker?
2. How does the liquid collected in the beaker differ from the liquid in the flask?
3. What is the purpose of the ice in this activity?
4. **Think About It** Imagine building a desalination plant that uses the method of distillation to produce water for a city. What difficulties might you encounter in using this process on such a large scale?

More to Explore

How could you change the setup and procedure to recover fresh water from salt water without using the hot plate? Design an experiment to accomplish this goal. Obtain your teacher's permission before carrying out your experiment.

Skills Lab

SCIENCE AND SOCIETY

The Ogallala Aquifer

The Ogallala Aquifer lies beneath eight states of the Great Plains. It contains about 4 quadrillion liters of groundwater—about the amount of water in Lake Huron. Rainfall is scarce on the Great Plains. But by pumping water out of the aquifer, farmers can grow cotton, wheat, sorghum, and corn to feed cattle. More than one third of the nation's livestock are raised in this area.

Water in the Ogallala was trapped there during the last Ice Age, about 12,000 years ago. Now, due to the demands of irrigation, water levels are dropping much faster than the aquifer can recharge. In certain parts of the aquifer, water levels have fallen as much as 12 meters since 1980. Farmers recognize that the Ogallala cannot withstand this heavy use for long. However, not all agree on what should be done.

South Dakota
Wyoming
Nebraska
Colorado
OGALLALA AQUIFER
Kansas
New Mexico
Oklahoma
Texas

The Issues

Should Water Use Be Regulated? One way to reduce water use might be to charge people for water. But who owns the water and who would determine the cost? In most of the Great Plains, water has been free to anyone who dug a well on their land. To charge for water, local governments would need to construct a public water system as in most cities. This would be a very complex and costly task. Both farmers and consumers would be affected by the charge. Higher costs for growing crops would result in higher supermarket prices for grains and meat.

Should Farmers Change Their Practices? Farmers could switch to crops such as sunflowers and grains that need less water. These crops, however, are less valuable than others for producing food and for feeding livestock. As a result, they would be less profitable than traditional crops. Farmers could use water-saving methods of irrigation. Such methods are expensive to install but eventually save both water and money.

Another possibility is "dryland farming," a method that was used by pioneer farmers. This method involves keeping the soil moist using only rainwater. Because dryland farming depends on the amount of rainfall, it is unpredictable. It may not produce large harvests.

Should Current Use Continue? Many residents of the Great Plains depend on the aquifer for a living. Some people feel that farmers there must continue their present water use in order to compete with farmers elsewhere in the nation and around the world. They feel that people today should not have to suffer in order to preserve the aquifer for future generations. New sources of water may be discovered, or better methods of transporting water to the Great Plains may be developed. Better irrigation techniques that use less water may also be invented. But other people feel that since these possibilities are not certain, water use must be greatly reduced now to save the aquifer.

You Decide

1. Identify the Problem
In your own words, explain the problem facing the farmers on the Great Plains.

2. Analyze the Options
Make a chart of the solutions mentioned. List advantages and drawbacks of each. Who would benefit from each solution? Who would suffer?

3. Find a Solution
As a resident of the Great Plains, write a letter to the newspaper proposing a solution to the Ogallala problem.

Section 3 Freshwater Pollution

Discover Activity

Will the Pollution Reach Your Wells?

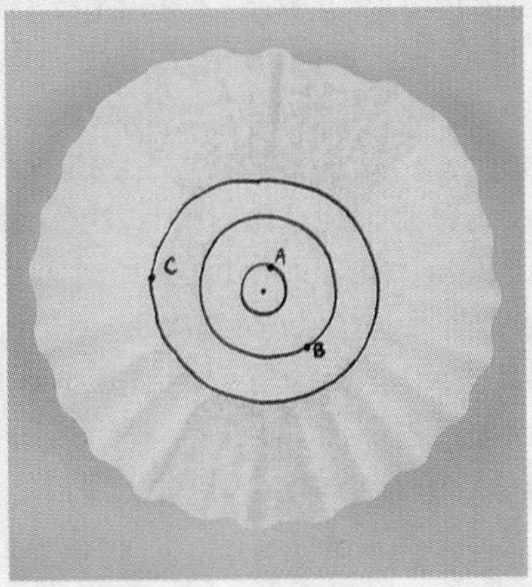

C
A
B

1. With a permanent marker, draw three rings on a coffee filter as shown in the picture. Draw three dots and label them A, B, and C as shown. These dots represent the locations of drinking-water supply wells.
2. Place the coffee filter on a paper plate. Moisten the coffee filter with a wet sponge. The damp coffee filter represents an aquifer.
3. Squirt five drops of food coloring onto the center of the damp coffee filter. Observe how the "pollution" travels.

Think It Over

Observing Which wells are affected by the pollution? Describe the pattern the pollution forms.

The newspaper headlines told an amazing story: "River in Flames!" "Bridges Burn As River Catches Fire!" This really happened to the Cuyahoga River in Cleveland, Ohio, in the summer of 1969. Are you wondering how a river could catch fire? What was in the Cuyahoga that allowed it to burn?

The Cuyahoga flows through a large industrial region on its way to Lake Erie. Factories along its banks used to dump their wastes into the river. Freighters spilled oil and gasoline into the water. Over time, the river became so full of chemicals and sewage that the pollution floating in it could actually burn.

Alarmed by the fire and the destruction it caused, people in Ohio began a massive campaign to clean up the Cuyahoga. Today it is safe to use for boating and fishing. The Cuyahoga River is a dramatic example of how serious water pollution can become—and of how people can work together to undo its damage.

Guide for Reading

- **What are some sources of water pollution?**
- **How does agricultural runoff affect ponds and streams?**
- **How can living things help clean up polluted water?**

Reading Tip **As you read, make a list of sources of freshwater pollution. Write one sentence about each source.**

WARNING
Fish Contaminated
DO NOT EAT

What Is Pollution?

If you turned on your faucet and a stream of bright green water came out, you'd be fairly sure that the water contained something it shouldn't. But many things that can make water unsafe to drink don't change its color, taste, or smell. The addition of any substance that has a negative effect on water or the living things that depend on the water is called **water pollution.** Water pollution can affect surface water, groundwater, and even rain. It can result from both natural causes and human activities.

The substances that cause water pollution are called pollutants. Disease-causing organisms such as the *Cryptosporidium* you read about in Section 1 are one form of pollutant. As Figure 10 shows, other types of pollutants include toxic, or poisonous, chemicals and metals, as well as radioactive substances.

INTEGRATING LIFE SCIENCE Some types of pollutants can build up in the bodies of living things. Trace the path of one such pollutant in Figure 11. The pesticide DDT dissolves in water and is absorbed by microscopic algae. The algae, which contain only low levels of the chemical, are eaten by small water animals. When frogs or fish eat these smaller animals, they also consume the chemicals from the algae these animals had eaten. The frogs and fish are in turn eaten by birds or other animals. Each larger organism consumes a greater number of the smaller organisms, and therefore more of the DDT.

When humans eat the fish from such a pond, the toxic chemicals build up in their bodies in the same way. Over a long time, even tiny amounts of certain pollutants can build up to levels that can cause birth defects or illnesses such as cancer. Drinking impure water or eating contaminated fish are not the only ways that pollutants can affect humans. Bathing or swimming in polluted water can irritate the skin or cause more serious problems.

Point and Nonpoint Sources

To clean up a polluted body of water like the Cuyahoga River, people first need to identify the source of the pollution to prevent further damage. **The major sources of water pollution are human wastes, industrial wastes, agricultural chemicals, and runoff from roads.**

Freshwater Pollutants

Kind of Pollutant	Examples	Sources
Disease-causing organisms	*Giardia, Cryptosporidium,* bacteria	Human wastes, runoff from livestock pens
Pesticides and fertilizers	DDT, nitrates, phosphates	Runoff from farm fields, golf courses
Industrial chemicals	PCBs, carbon tetrachloride, dioxin	Factories, industrial waste disposal sites
Metals	Lead, mercury, copper	Factories, waste disposal sites
Radioactive wastes	Uranium, carbon-14	Medical and scientific disposal sites, nuclear power plants
Petroleum products	Oil, gasoline	Road runoff, leaking underground storage tanks

Figure 10 This table lists some examples of the different types of freshwater pollutants. *Relating Cause and Effect Why might it be helpful to know the source of a particular pollutant detected in a body of water?*

20.0
2.0
0.2
0.4
0.000003
Increasing DDT concentration (parts per million)

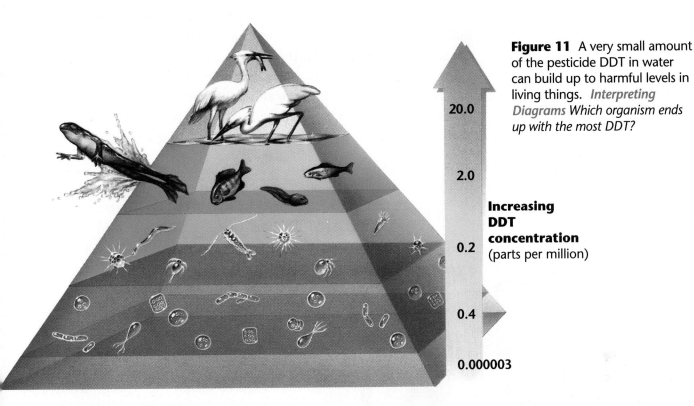

Figure 11 A very small amount of the pesticide DDT in water can build up to harmful levels in living things. *Interpreting Diagrams* *Which organism ends up with the most DDT?*

Each of these sources of pollution can be a point source or a nonpoint source, depending on how the pollution enters a body of water. For example, suppose you notice a pipe gushing white sudsy water into a river. The pipe is a **point source,** a specific source of pollution that can be identified. More often, though, the source of pollution is less obvious. Pollutants may be carried along in runoff from a farm field, a street, or a construction site. The chemicals, sewage, or radioactive materials eventually flow into a lake or river or seep into groundwater and are carried far away. It's hard to trace the exact source of this pollution. A widely spread source of pollution that can't be tied to a specific point of origin is called a **nonpoint source.**

☑ *Checkpoint* *Why are nonpoint sources difficult to identify?*

Human Wastes

Today it seems obvious that dumping human wastes into drinking water can spread disease. But scientists have only understood this connection for the last 150 years.

Dr. Snow's Discovery Cholera is a disease caused by bacteria

INTEGRATING HEALTH

that live in human wastes. Cholera causes people to become very dehydrated and can be fatal. In 1854, an English doctor named John Snow discovered the cause of a cholera outbreak in London. In the poorer

Sharpen your Skills

Classifying

ACTIVITY

Classify the following as point sources or nonpoint sources of water pollution:

- salt used on icy roads
- an open drain in a sink at a paint factory
- a sanitary sewer pipe with a leak
- fertilizer sprayed onto an orchard

Give a reason why you classified each source as you did.

sections of the city, people carried water home in buckets from public wells. After 500 people in one neighborhood died in just ten days, Dr. Snow traced the cholera to a well near a pipe carrying sewage. He ended the epidemic by removing the pump handle so no one could get water from that source. Dr. Snow's work showed the danger of releasing untreated sewage into bodies of water that might be used for drinking water.

Sewage in Cities As you know, today wastewater is usually treated before being released to the environment. However, while water treatment usually kills bacteria, some viruses and parasites are able to resist chlorine and other water treatment processes. Most of these organisms come from human or animal wastes that get into the water supply.

During heavy rains and floods, sanitary sewers sometimes overflow and run into storm sewers. Since the storm sewers generally lead directly into surface water, the sewage from the sanitary sewers can pollute the water. For this reason, people are often told to boil water for drinking and cooking after a flood. The boiling kills many disease-causing organisms.

Figure 12 This engraving from the late 1800s shows people in Hamburg, Germany, getting water from a cart during a cholera epidemic. The city wells were closed, and water was brought in from the countryside.

Sewage in Rural Areas Disposing of human waste is not just a problem in big cities. In rural areas, people must be careful where they locate septic tanks. If a tank is too near a stream or on a hill, wastewater can leak into the stream or flow into the area of a well downhill.

Wastes from cattle, pigs, and chickens can also be a problem in rural areas. They contribute disease-causing bacteria and other kinds of pollution to water that runs off from pastures and barnyards.

☑ *Checkpoint* ***Why should drinking water and sewage be kept separate?***

Industrial Wastes

Most cities and towns in the United States have wastewater treatment systems that handle sewage effectively. For this reason, water pollution by factories and mines is a more serious problem than sewage in most areas of the country. Chemicals, smoke, and heated water are three types of industrial pollutants.

Chemicals Many factory processes, especially those for making dyes and plastics or treating metals, involve toxic chemicals and strong acids. Other toxic wastes are produced as by-products, or side effects, of manufacturing and mining. Although laws now limit and control chemical pollution, some factories still release toxic chemicals directly into nearby rivers and lakes.

Another problem is leftover wastes. In the past, many industries stored toxic wastes in barrels or other containers buried underground. Over the years, however, many of these containers rusted or broke. The chemicals leaked out, polluting both the soil and the groundwater.

Figure 13 Many lakes and rivers have been polluted by wastes from nearby industries. These environmental scientists are collecting water samples from a pond for testing.

Smoke and Exhaust Many power plants and factories burn coal or oil to fuel their processes. The engines of millions of cars, trucks, and buses burn gasoline. Every day, smoke and exhaust from these sources pour into the air, especially around large cities. When coal, oil, and gasoline are burned, molecules of the gases sulfur dioxide and nitrogen oxide are released into the atmosphere. There the sulfur and nitrogen react with water, forming sulfuric and nitric acids. The result is rain or other forms of precipitation that are more acidic than normal, called **acid rain.** When acid rain falls on lakes and ponds, the water can become so acidic that fish and other wildlife cannot survive. Acid rain also eats away the stone of buildings and statues.

INTEGRATING CHEMISTRY

Heat Pollution Think about how hot a metal slide gets on a sunny day. Imagine borrowing enough water from a swimming pool to cool the slide, and then returning the water to the pool. How would this change the swimming pool? Would you still want to jump in to cool off? The warm water would probably not be very refreshing.

Figure 14 A noisy jumble of taxis, cars, and buses crowds a city street. *Relating Cause and Effect How are these vehicles related to water pollution?*

TRY THIS

How Do Your Algae Grow?

ACTIVITY

In this activity you will observe how fertilizers affect the growth of algae in pond water.

1. Label two jars A and B. Pour tap water into each jar until it is half full.
2. Add water from a pond or aquarium to each jar until it is three-quarters full.

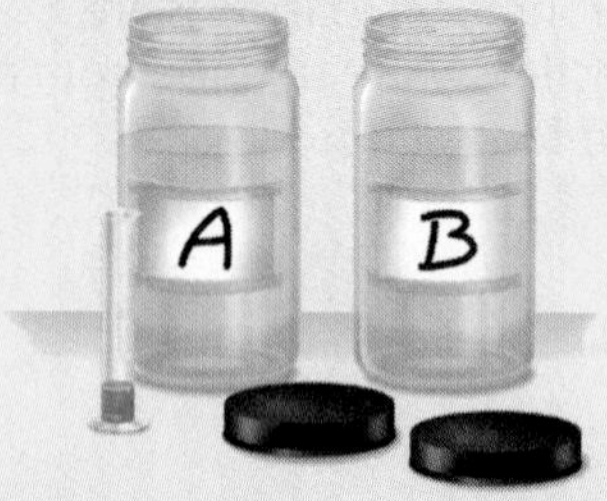

A
B

3. Add 5 mL of liquid fertilizer to jar A only.
4. Cover both jars tightly and place them on a windowsill in the sunlight. Wash your hands with soap.
5. Observe the jars every day for a week.

Drawing Conclusions How did the fertilizer affect the growth of the algae in jar A? What was the purpose of jar B in this experiment?

Much of the water in factories is used to cool machinery or metal objects. Even if it contains no chemicals, the warm water alone can act as a pollutant. Many water organisms can live in only a narrow range of temperatures. Warm water released by a factory into a nearby river or pond raises the temperature of the water, sometimes enough to harm the living things there.

Agricultural Chemicals

INTEGRATING LIFE SCIENCE Have you ever "fed" a houseplant with fertilizer to make it grow? On a larger scale, farmers spread or spray fertilizer on their fields to produce better crops. When rain falls on the fields, it washes some of the chemicals away as runoff. Water used for irrigation also creates runoff. The fertilizers in the runoff are a nonpoint source of pollution.

The rich supply of nutrients from fertilizers encourages the growth of plants and algae in and around nearby bodies of water. As you learned in Chapter 10, ponds and lakes naturally change over time due to the process of eutrophication. As more plants grow in the water, dead plant material piles up on the bottom, making the water shallower and warmer. As the plant matter decays, the amount of oxygen in the water decreases. With the addition of fertilizers, this natural process speeds up. A thick, soupy scum of algae forms on top of the water. The scum blocks the sunlight and chokes the flow of water, changing the living conditions for other organisms.

Runoff and irrigation water also carry away other pollutants from farm fields. **Pesticides** are chemicals intended to kill insects and other organisms that damage crops. Pesticides may be sprayed on crops and then run off. Sometimes they are sprayed directly on ponds to kill mosquitoes. But at the same time, these chemicals can harm other insects or the animals that eat them.

☑ ***Checkpoint*** *How can chemicals used in agriculture reach streams, ponds, and lakes?*

Runoff from Roads

Have you ever noticed an oily sheen on a puddle in a parking lot after a rain shower? The sheen was probably caused by gasoline and motor oil that leaked from cars. When it rains, these oily substances are washed off along with the runoff. During cold winter weather, runoff also picks up the salt that is sprinkled on roads and sidewalks to melt ice. This runoff is a nonpoint source of pollution. Gasoline, oil, and salt pollute rivers and lakes that the runoff enters. These substances can also seep down into groundwater and pollute wells or even an entire aquifer.

Figure 15 A thick layer of red algae tints a pond the color of tomato soup. *Inferring What might be the cause of the algae growth in this pond?*

Cleaning Up Polluted Water

Many pollutants are eventually removed from freshwater bodies through natural cleaning processes. **Living things in lakes, streams, and wetlands filter out and break down waste materials.** For example, plant roots filter larger particles from the water. Some plants, such as water hyacinths and duckweed, can absorb metals and chemicals. And just as certain bacteria are used in purifying wastewater, some are also useful in cleaning up toxic chemicals. Bacteria that consume oil have been used to help clean up oil spills. Waste-eating bacteria may also prove to be useful in breaking down toxic chemicals in rivers and lakes.

Pollution clean-up programs can be based on such natural treatment processes. For example, both natural and artificial wetlands are being used to clean up water pollution. Wetlands have been built near coal mines to treat acidic mining runoff before it returns to the environment.

Not only living things can help clean up polluted water. Passing through the sand or rock of an aquifer naturally filters and purifies groundwater. But natural filtering cannot remove or destroy many pollutants, such as metals or manufactured chemicals. Cleaning up this kind of pollution in groundwater is very difficult. One method involves pumping polluted groundwater to the surface, sending it through a treatment plant, and returning it to a nearby lake.

Figure 16 These purple water hyacinths can be an attractive part of a cleanup program. The plants absorb certain metals and chemicals from polluted water.

Preventing Pollution

Despite the successes in cleaning up some water pollution, most pollutants are very difficult to remove. It is often easier to avoid causing the pollution in the first place. In the late 1960s, as

DO NOT DUMP!
DRAINS TO CATAWBA RIVER

Figure 17 One way you can help prevent water pollution is to educate others about its causes. This student is stenciling a storm drain to remind people of its connection to a nearby river.

people became more aware of the problems of pollution, they urged the government to create laws to control pollution. The goals of those laws include the cleanup of polluted lakes and rivers, better wastewater treatment, and limits on releasing pollutants to the environment. The government also established water-quality standards and programs to clean up waste disposal sites.

Industry and Agriculture Many recycling techniques that help conserve water also help to lessen pollution. For example, factories cool water and reuse it instead of returning it to a river, reducing heat pollution. Industries also look for ways to replace toxic materials with less harmful ones. Printing inks, for instance, can be made with water instead of chemical solvents.

Farmers are trying to reduce the problem of runoff from pastures and barnyards. Some collect and reuse this water for irrigation. Other farmers plant fields of coarse grasses that filter out pollutants before the water reaches a river or pond.

What Can You Do? You can also help keep pollutants from entering the environment. Dispose of toxic substances carefully. For example, chemicals like paint and motor oil should never be poured down the drain, but instead be taken to sites that collect hazardous waste. Avoid overfertilizing lawns or gardens. Form a group of students to educate others in your community about the causes and effects of freshwater pollution. Because many kinds of water pollution are so difficult to clean up, the most important place to stop pollution is at its source.

Section 3 Review

1. List four sources of water pollution.
2. How can fertilizers cause water pollution?
3. Explain why people are often instructed to boil drinking water after a flood.
4. **Thinking Critically Making Judgments** To prevent water pollution, a factory proposes pumping its wastes into the ground instead of into a river. Would you support this change? Why or why not?

CHAPTER PROJECT

Check Your Progress

At this point, you should be ready to assemble your model treatment system. Does the system include at least two treatment steps? Be sure to ask an adult to help you cut materials or assemble them if necessary. (*Hint:* Test your treatment setup for leaks using clean tap water.)

Section 4 Water As an Energy Resource

DISCOVER — ACTIVITY

Can Water Do Work?

1. Spread out a large plastic trash bag on the ground. On top of the bag, place several cylindrical objects such as corks, spools, marbles, balls, and empty cans.

2. Fill a plant sprayer with water. Then turn the nozzle to produce a fine mist of water. Try to move the objects with the spray of water. **CAUTION:** *Be careful of slippery wet floors if you are doing this activity indoors.*
3. Now turn the sprayer nozzle to produce a narrower stream of water. Try again to move the objects. Be sure to wipe up any spilled water when you are done.

Think It Over

Observing How does changing the nozzle opening affect the stream of water? At which setting did the objects move more easily? Why?

GUIDE FOR READING

- **How does moving water produce electricity?**
- **In what ways is hydroelectric power a good source of energy?**

Reading Tip **Before you read the section, preview *Exploring a Hydroelectric Power Plant.* Write a list of questions you have about hydroelectric power.**

Picture a curving wall of concrete swooping up nearly 170 meters—taller than a 40-story building. On one side of the wall is a deep reservoir. On the other side, only a narrow river trickles between rocky canyon walls. This is Grand Coulee Dam on the Columbia River in Washington. Completed in 1942, it is still one of the largest dams in the world. Behind Grand Coulee, the water in the reservoir pushes on the concrete dam. The dam's floodgates control that awesome energy. When the gates open to release the water, the water's energy is transformed into enough electricity to light thousands of homes and businesses.

For centuries, people have used the energy of moving water to turn water wheels and run machinery. Today that energy is also a source of electrical power in many parts of the world.

Power from Moving Water

Have you ever seen a fast-moving river propel a kayaker along? If so, you know how much energy moving water can have. It can move boats, carve out canyons, and sweep away cars in a flood. The energy that sends the kayak through the rapids is kinetic

TRY THIS

Making a Water Wheel

ACTIVITY

In this activity you will see how the kinetic energy of water can do work.

1. Put on your goggles.
2. Cut an aluminum pie plate into four squares about 5 cm on a side. **CAUTION:** *Be careful not to cut yourself on the sharp edges of the pie plate.*
3. Push the sides of the aluminum squares into a foam ball as shown. Insert two toothpicks into the sides of the ball.

4. Rest the toothpicks on top of your fingers and place the blades under a stream of slowly running water.

Developing Hypotheses
Develop a hypothesis to explain how the volume of water and the speed of the water wheel are related. Test your hypothesis. Describe what happens to the speed of the water wheel.

energy. **Kinetic energy** is the form of energy that an object has when it is moving.

Energy can change from one form to another. If the water's movement is stopped, all of its energy becomes potential energy. **Potential energy** is energy that is stored and waiting to be used. To think about potential energy in another way, imagine that you're holding a baseball bat at the top of your swing. The bat at that point has potential energy. As you swing at a ball, the bat's energy becomes kinetic energy. If you hit the ball, the energy is transferred again, becoming the kinetic energy of the ball.

Hydroelectric power is electricity produced by the kinetic energy of water moving over a waterfall or a dam. To generate hydroelectric power (or "hydropower"), engineers build a dam across a river. Water backs up behind the dam, floods the valley, and creates a reservoir. Water stored behind a dam has potential energy, which is changed to kinetic energy when the water is released. **Hydroelectric power plants capture the kinetic energy of moving water and change it into electrical energy.**

How is the kinetic energy of moving water changed into the energy that lights your house and runs your computer? Follow the path of the water in *Exploring a Hydroelectric Power Plant* on the next page to see how these energy changes take place.

☑ *Checkpoint* *What type of energy does a diver have while standing at the edge of a diving board?*

The Impact of Dams

In some ways, hydroelectric power seems like an ideal way to produce electricity. **Hydroelectric power is clean, safe, and efficient. Although building a dam is expensive, the water is free and is naturally renewed by the water cycle.** Unlike power plants that burn coal or oil, hydroelectric plants do not contribute to air pollution. In the United States, hydroelectric power accounts for about 8 or 9 percent of electricity produced, while worldwide it generates about 20 percent. Some countries, such as Norway and Brazil, produce almost all their electrical energy through hydropower.

Hydroelectric plants do have limitations, however. Only certain locations are suitable for building a dam. A fast-moving river is necessary, as is an area that can be flooded to create a reservoir.

Dams and the Environment Dams affect all living things in the area around them. Flooding the land behind a dam can destroy wildlife habitats as well as farms and towns. What was once a fast-moving river becomes the still, deep waters of a reservoir. Some organisms

INTEGRATING LIFE SCIENCE

EXPLORING a Hydroelectric Power Plant

Hydroelectric power is generated by changing energy from one form to another.

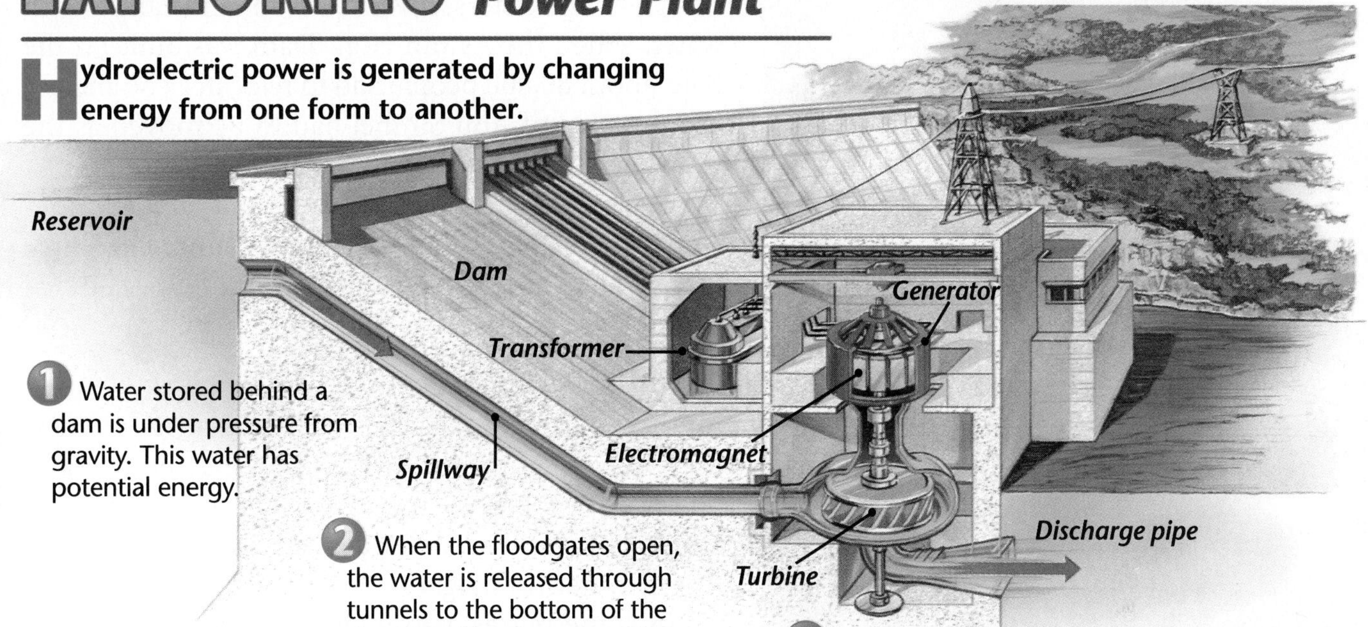

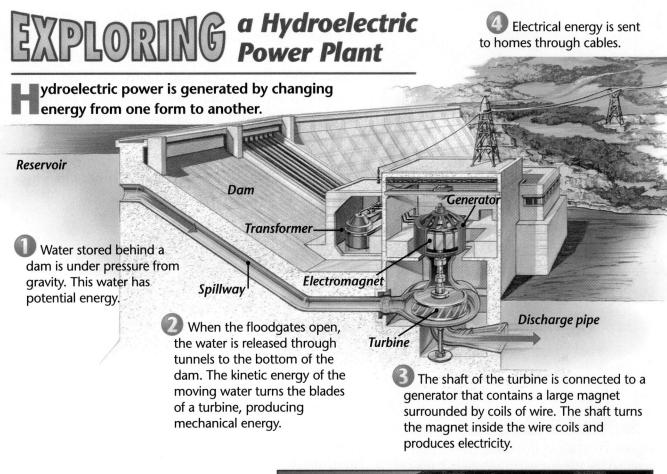

Reservoir
Dam
Transformer
Generator
Electromagnet
Spillway
Turbine
Discharge pipe
1 Water stored behind a dam is under pressure from gravity. This water has potential energy.
2 When the floodgates open, the water is released through tunnels to the bottom of the dam. The kinetic energy of the moving water turns the blades of a turbine, producing mechanical energy.
3 The shaft of the turbine is connected to a generator that contains a large magnet surrounded by coils of wire. The shaft turns the magnet inside the wire coils and produces electricity.
4 Electrical energy is sent to homes through cables.

Figure 18 This photograph shows the Theodore Roosevelt Dam in Arizona. ***Interpreting Photographs*** *What natural feature of the river made this a good location to build a dam?*

cannot survive the change. In addition, the dam is a barrier across the river. It may prevent fish from traveling to the parts of a river where they usually lay their eggs and young fish are hatched. Dams like Grand Coulee on the Columbia River, for instance, have greatly reduced the population of salmon in the river.

As a river slows down, it deposits some of the sediments it carries. These deposits can build up behind a dam instead of being carried downstream to enrich the flood plain near the river's mouth. Since the Aswan Dam was built in Egypt, for example, farmlands near the mouth of the Nile River no longer receive the rich load of nutrients the river once brought.

Displaced by a Dam How would you feel if you discovered that your riverside home would soon be dozens of meters under the water of a lake? People whose homes or farms are located

Figure 19 Building the Aswan Dam meant flooding the valley that housed these statues of ancient Egyptian rulers. Piece by piece, workers carefully dismantled the great monuments and moved them to higher ground.

where a dam's reservoir is planned have had to face this issue. Large dams flood hundreds or thousands of square kilometers, covering towns and valleys with water. When the Aswan High Dam was built on the Nile, about 80,000 people had to relocate. The ancient monuments of Abu Simbel had to be moved as the water in Lake Nasser rose higher and higher.

One of the largest dams ever built is now under construction on the Yangzi River in China. The Three Gorges Dam, due to be completed in 2009, could displace more than 1.5 million people.

Benefits of Dams For countries that want to build up their industries, hydroelectric power often seems the best way to provide the electricity they need. Water power is the least expensive and least polluting large-scale energy source. Besides electricity, dams can supply water for irrigation and help in flood control.

In some places, people have suggested building small dams to supply power to a local area. Smaller dams uproot fewer people and do less harm to the environment, while still providing energy for a region to grow. However, since dams are expensive to build, small dams may not produce enough power to be worthwhile. Large dams, on the other hand, produce great amounts of power, but they also have a major effect on the land around them.

Section 4 Review

1. How does a hydroelectric plant use moving water to generate electric power?
2. Name two advantages of hydroelectric power.
3. Give one positive example and one negative example of how building a dam could affect wildlife in the area.
4. **Thinking Critically Problem Solving** Suppose you were assigned to choose a site to build a new hydroelectric plant. What features would you look for to find a good site? Be sure to consider the impact on living things as well as the physical characteristics of the site.

CHAPTER PROJECT

Check Your Progress

Now you are ready to test your model system, using the dirty water sample your teacher has provided. Does your treatment unit clean up the water? Measure how much of the original one liter of water is recovered. Based on your results, decide whether you need to redesign any part of your treatment system. (*Hint:* To modify your system, consider changing materials as well as adding more steps.)

Section 1 Water to Drink

Key Ideas

- Sources of drinking water include rivers, lakes, reservoirs, and groundwater.
- Many communities maintain public water supplies to collect, treat, and distribute water to residents. Some homes have private wells.
- Most drinking water is treated to ensure that it is safe and appealing to drink.
- Pumps and gravity are used to increase water pressure and move water through a system of pipes.
- Wastewater and sewage are treated to prevent contamination of drinking water.

Key Terms

water quality	pH	hardness
concentration	filtration	flocs
coagulation	sewage	sludge
septic tank	leach field	

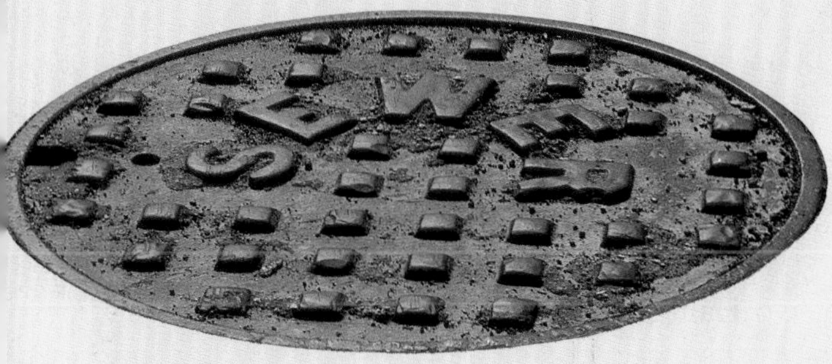
SEWER

Section 2 Balancing Water Needs

Key Ideas

- Water is scarce in many places, leading to competition for limited supplies.
- Water shortage can occur when there is too little water or too much demand in an area.
- Industries can conserve water by reducing water use, recycling water, and reusing water.
- Desalination of ocean water and icebergs are two possible future sources of fresh water.

Key Terms

drought conservation desalination

Section 3 Freshwater Pollution

Key Ideas

- Sources of water pollution include human and animal wastes, industrial and agricultural chemicals, and runoff from roads.
- Acid rain is caused by sulfur and nitrogen from smokestacks and car exhausts.
- Runoff of fertilizers into bodies of water can cause plants to grow too rapidly, changing the conditions for living things there.
- Living organisms help to naturally remove many pollutants from water, but other pollutants are difficult to remove.

Key Terms

water pollution	point source
nonpoint source	acid rain
pesticide	

Section 4 Water As an Energy Resource

INTEGRATING PHYSICS

Key Ideas

- Hydroelectric power plants capture the kinetic energy of moving water and change it into electrical energy.
- Hydroelectric power is a clean, renewable energy source, but dams are expensive to build and change the land around them.

Key Terms

kinetic energy	potential energy
hydroelectric power	

ACTIVITY

USING THE INTERNET

www.phschool.com/state_focus/california/

CALIFORNIA SCIENCE CONTENT STANDARDS

California Test Prep: Reviewing Content

Multiple Choice

Choose the letter of the best answer.

1. Chlorine is added during water treatment in order to
   a. make particles form flocs.
   b. kill disease-causing organisms.
   c. improve the taste of the water.
   d. remove objects such as fish and trash.
2. Primary treatment of wastewater typically involves
   a. adding chlorine.
   b. filtering out solids.
   c. adding sludge.
   d. adding waste-eating bacteria.
3. One process used to obtain fresh water from salt water is
   a. coagulation. b. filtration.
   c. recharge. d. desalination.
4. The main source of acid precipitation is
   a. smoke from coal-burning factories.
   b. pesticides sprayed in the air.
   c. runoff from farm fields.
   d. toxic chemicals buried underground.
5. Water flowing swiftly possesses
   a. mechanical energy. b. electrical energy.
   c. potential energy. d. kinetic energy.

True or False

If the statement is true, write true. If it is false, change the underlined word or words to make the statement true.

6. The pH of water is a measurement of the amount of calcium and magnesium.
7. Sludge is produced during the treatment of drinking water.
8. A drought can cause wells to dry up if the level of the water table falls.
9. Oily runoff from highways is an example of a point source of pollution.
10. Agricultural runoff containing pesticides often results in increased plant growth in nearby ponds and streams.

Checking Concepts

11. Describe one possible path of drinking water from its source to a home.
12. Explain how a septic system works.
13. Why are water rights an important issue in dry areas?
14. Describe one way that farmers can reduce the amount of water lost during irrigation.
15. Explain how low levels of a pollutant in a stream can have harmful effects on wildlife in and around the stream.
16. How might building a dam affect people living nearby?
17. **Writing to Learn** You have been hired as a public relations specialist for the city water department. Your first assignment is to prepare a brief fact sheet for city residents about the importance of conserving water. The fact sheet should also include some simple suggestions of ways to conserve water at home.

Thinking Visually

18. **Concept Map** Copy the concept map about freshwater pollution onto a separate sheet of paper. Complete it and add a title. (For more on concept maps, see the Skills Handbook.)

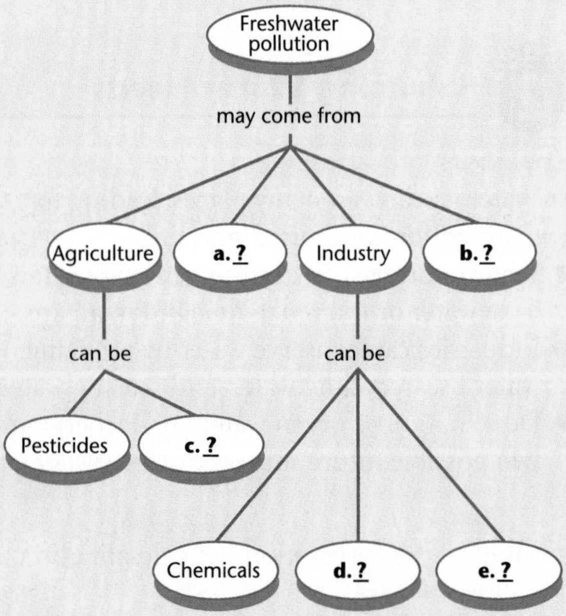
Freshwater pollution
may come from
Agriculture
a. ?
Industry
b. ?
can be
can be
Pesticides
c. ?
Chemicals
d. ?
e. ?

Test Prep: Skills

A family had their drinking-water well tested to check the water quality. The test results are shown in the table below. Use the data in the table to answer Questions 19–22.

Drinking Water Sample Test Results

Lead	0.2 parts per million
Copper	0.006 parts per million
pH	5.0
Coliform count	5 out of 5 samples positive

19. Inferring The homeowners suspect that their septic tank is polluting the well. What evidence exists to support this conclusion?

20. Designing Experiments What might be the source of the lead in the water? How could you test your answer?

21. Developing Hypotheses How might the low pH of the water be related to the lead contamination?

22. Predicting The homeowners have noticed that their water does not form suds well when mixed with soap. Predict what other substances may be present in high levels in the water.

Thinking Critically

23. Relating Cause and Effect How can increased demand for water cause the ground above an aquifer to collapse?

24. Comparing and Contrasting How is the process of desalination similar to the water cycle? How is it different?

25. Making Judgments Do you think that the benefits of hydroelectric power outweigh the disadvantages? Give reasons to support your answer.

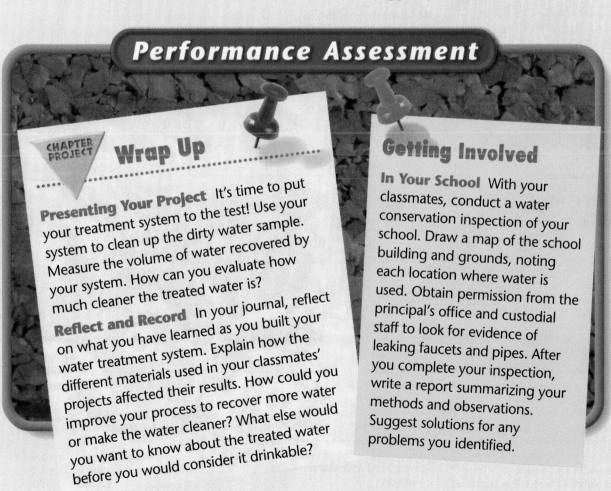

Performance Assessment

CHAPTER PROJECT

Wrap Up

Presenting Your Project It's time to put your treatment system to the test! Use your system to clean up the dirty water sample. Measure the volume of water recovered by your system. How can you evaluate how much cleaner the treated water is?

Reflect and Record In your journal, reflect on what you have learned as you built your water treatment system. Explain how the different materials used in your classmates' projects affected their results. How could you improve your process to recover more water or make the water cleaner? What else would you want to know about the treated water before you would consider it drinkable?

Getting Involved

In Your School With your classmates, conduct a water conservation inspection of your school. Draw a map of the school building and grounds, noting each location where water is used. Obtain permission from the principal's office and custodial staff to look for evidence of leaking faucets and pipes. After you complete your inspection, write a report summarizing your methods and observations. Suggest solutions for any problems you identified.

CHAPTER

12 Ocean Motions

Waves crash against the rocky Maine coast. Sweeping its beacon of light across the water, the Portland Head Lighthouse warns ships of the treacherous rocks.

The following California Science Content Standards are addressed in this chapter:

2. Topography is reshaped by weathering of rock and soil and by the transportation and deposition of sediment.

- **c.** Beaches are dynamic systems in which sand is supplied by rivers and moved along the coast by wave action.

3. Heat moves in a predictable flow from warmer objects to cooler objects until all objects are at the same temperature.

- **a.** Energy can be carried from one place to another by heat flow, or by waves including water waves, light and sound, or by moving objects.

4. Many phenomena on the Earth's surface are affected by the transfer of energy through radiation and convection currents.

- **d.** Convection currents distribute heat in the atmosphere and oceans.

5. Organisms in ecosystems exchange energy and nutrients among themselves and with the environment.

- **e.** The number and types of organisms an ecosystem can support depends on the resources available and abiotic

PROJECT 12

Protecting a Shoreline

The world's oceans are always in motion. Waves, tides, and currents each move Earth's waters in different ways. In this chapter you will study these movements and their power to change the land. You will build your own model of a shoreline with a lighthouse and use the model to demonstrate how some ocean motions can affect the land along the coast.

Your Goal To design and build a model ocean beach and test possible methods for preventing shoreline erosion.

To complete this project successfully, you must

- build a model beach and use it to demonstrate the effects of wave erosion
- test methods of protecting the lighthouse from damage
- follow the safety guidelines outlined in Appendix A

Get Started Begin now by previewing Figure 4 on page 370. Start thinking about how you will build a model of an ocean beach like the one in the diagram. Brainstorm a list of materials that you could use to build your model.

Check Your Progress You'll be working on this project as you study this chapter. To keep your project on track, look for Check Your Progress boxes at the following points.

Section 1 Review, page 373: Design your model beach.
Section 2 Review, page 378: Construct your model and test it.
Section 4 Review, page 392: Improve your model and test it again.

Wrap Up At the end of the chapter (page 395), you will show how well your design keeps the lighthouse from toppling into the surf.

factors, such as quantity of light and water, range of temperatures, and soil composition.

6. Sources of energy and materials differ in amounts, distribution, usefulness, and the time required for their formation.

a. The utility of energy sources is determined by factors that are involved in converting these sources to useful forms and the consequences of the conversion process.

b. Different natural energy and material resources, including air, soil, rocks, minerals, petroleum, fresh water, wildlife, and forests, and classify them as renewable or nonrenewable.

7. Scientific progress is made by asking meaningful questions and conducting careful investigations.

c. Construct appropriate graphs from data and develop qualitative statements about the relationships between variables.

e. Recognize whether evidence is consistent with a proposed explanation.

SECTION 1

Wave Action

DISCOVER ACTIVITY

How Do Waves Change a Beach?

1. In one end of an aluminum pan, build a "beach" of sand and pebbles. Put a book under that end of the pan to raise it about 5 centimeters.

2. Pour water slowly into the other end of the pan until it covers the edge of the sand, just as water touches the edge of a beach.
3. Place a wooden tongue depressor in the water. Move it back and forth gently in a regular rhythm to make waves in the pan. Continue for about 2 minutes.
4. Once the water has stopped moving, observe what has happened to the beach. Wash your hands when you are finished with this activity.

Think It Over

Observing How has the motion of the water changed the edge of the beach?

GUIDE FOR READING

- **How does a wave form?**
- **How do waves change near the shore?**
- **How do waves affect beaches and coastlines?**

Reading Tip **Before you read, preview the diagrams and photographs in the section to see different types of wave action. Make a list of questions you have about wave motion.**

Stretched flat on his surfboard, the surfer paddles out into the clear turquoise water. The surfboard bobs up and down as he awaits the perfect surfing wave. After a few minutes, he spots the telltale signs in an approaching wave. At the last possible minute before the wave crashes over him, the surfer jumps into a standing position. He balances skillfully as the energy of the wave sends the surfboard skimming down the smooth front of the curling wave.

If you've ever seen a video of surfers "catching a wave" along a Pacific beach, you know that they make this difficult sport look almost easy. But even experienced surfers can seldom predict when the next good wave will roll into shore. As you will read in this section, many different forces influence the size, shape, and timing of waves.

How Waves Form

When you watch the surfer's wave crash onto the beach, you are seeing the last step in the process of the wave's development. The process begins with wind. Without the energy of wind, the surface of the ocean would be as smooth as a mirror. **Most waves form when winds blowing across the water's surface transmit their energy to the water.** A **wave** is the movement of energy through a body of water.

Waves start in the open ocean. The size of the wave depends on the strength of the wind and on the length of time it blows. A gentle breeze creates small ripples on the surface of the water. Stronger winds create larger waves.

The size of the wave also depends on the distance over which the wind blows. Winds blowing across longer distances build up bigger waves. In the wide Pacific Ocean, a wave might travel a third of the way around the world before reaching the California coast.

Although waves may appear to carry water toward shore, the water does not actually move forward in deep water. If it did, ocean water would eventually pile up on the coasts of every continent! The energy of the wave moves toward shore, but the water itself remains where it was. You can test this for yourself by floating a piece of wood or a cork in a bowl of water. Use a spoon to make a wave in the bowl. As the wave passes, the object lurches forward a little, then bobs backward. It ends up in almost the same spot where it started.

Figure 1 A surfer cruises along the smooth front of this cresting wave. The wave's energy moves along, but the water mostly stays where it is. *Applying Concepts In which direction is the energy of this wave moving?*

TRY THIS

Wave Motion

ACTIVITY

This activity shows how waves formed at the surface affect deeper water.

1. Fill an aquarium about three-quarters full of water.
2. Tie enough metal washers to a cork so that the cork floats about 3 cm from the bottom of the tank.
3. Repeat Step 2 with more corks so that they float 9 cm from the bottom, 15 cm from the bottom, and so on until the last cork floats on the surface.

4. Make small, steady waves in the tank by moving your hand up and down in the water. Note what happens to each cork.
5. Repeat Step 4, increasing the height of the waves by moving your hand faster.

Observing How does increasing the wave height affect the motion of each cork?

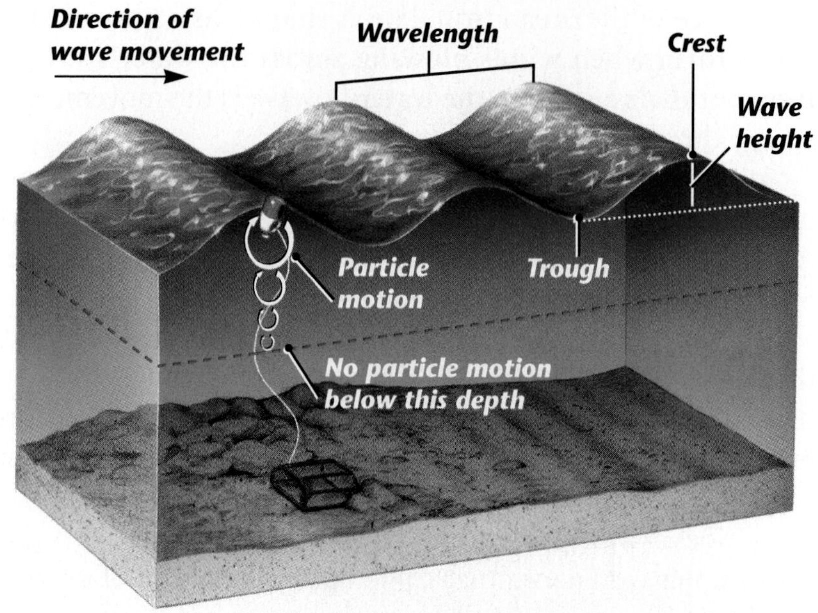
Direction of wave movement
Wavelength
Crest
Wave height
Particle motion
Trough
No particle motion below this depth

Figure 2 As a wave passes by, the water particles move in a circular motion. The buoy on the surface swings down into the trough of one wave, then back up to the crest of the next wave. Below the surface, the water particles move in smaller circles. At a depth equal to about one half the wavelength, the water particles are not affected by the surface wave.

Figure 2 shows what happens to the water as a wave travels along. As the wave passes, water particles move in a circular path. They swing forward and down with the energy of the wave, then back up to their original position.

Notice that the deeper water particles in Figure 2 move in smaller circles than those near the surface. The wind affects the water at the surface more than the deep water. Below a certain depth, the water does not move at all as the wave passes. If you were inside a submarine in deep water, you would not be able to tell whether the water above you was rough or smooth.

Describing Waves

If you ask a sailor to describe a wave, you might hear some unfamiliar terms. To a sailor, "a following sea" refers to waves traveling in the same direction as the boat. "Combers" are large, cresting waves. And "spindrift" is ocean spray torn by the wind from the surface of the waves.

Scientists have their own vocabulary of terms to describe the size and strength of waves. The name for the highest part of a wave is the **crest**. The horizontal distance between crests is the **wavelength**. Long, rolling waves with lots of space between crests have long wavelengths. Short, choppy waves have shorter wavelengths. Waves are also measured by their **frequency**, the number of waves that pass a point in a certain amount of time.

The name for the lowest part of a wave is the **trough**. The vertical distance from the crest to the trough is the **wave height**. The energy and strength of a wave depend mainly on its wave height. In the open ocean, most waves are between 2 and 5 meters high. During storms, the waves can grow much higher and more powerful.

☑ *Checkpoint* *Do waves that are close together have a longer or shorter wavelength than waves that are far apart?*

How Waves Change Near Shore

In deep water, waves usually travel as long, low waves called swells. As the waves approach the shore, the water becomes shallower. Follow the waves in Figure 3 as they enter the shallow water. The bottoms of the waves begin to touch the sloping ocean floor. Friction between the ocean floor and the water causes the waves to slow down. As the speed of the waves decrease, their shapes change. **Near shore, the wave height increases and the wavelength decreases.** When the wave reaches a certain height, the crest of the wave topples. The wave breaks onto the shore, forming surf.

At first, the energy of the breaking wave, or breaker, causes the water to surge up the beach. But the force of gravity pulling down on the rising water soon causes it to lose its energy. The water that moves up the beach flows back into the sea. Have you ever stood at the water's edge and felt the pull of the water rushing back out to the ocean? This pull, often called an undertow, carries shells, seaweed, and sand away from the beach. A strong undertow can be dangerous to swimmers.

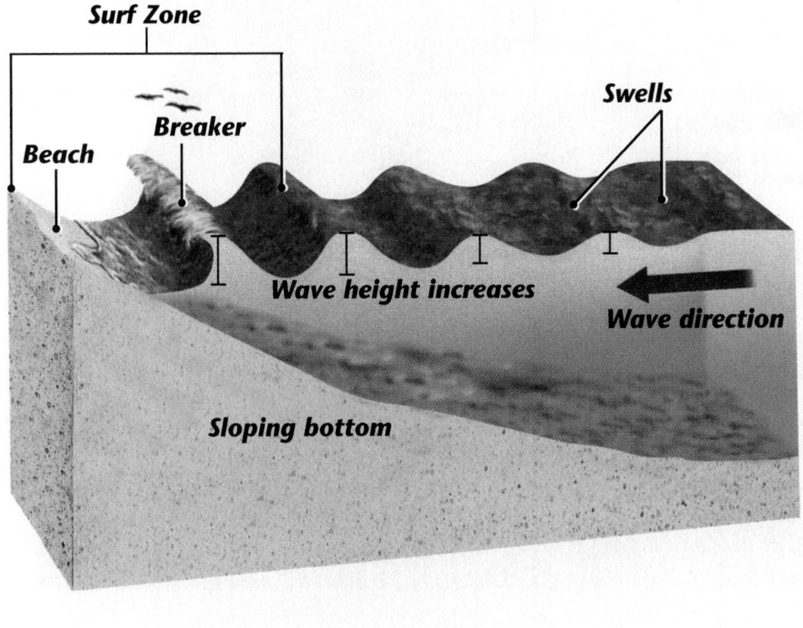
Surf Zone
Swells
Breaker
Beach
Wave height increases
Wave direction
Sloping bottom

Figure 3 Friction with the ocean floor causes waves to slow down in the shallow water near shore. The wave height increases until the waves break, forming surf. *Interpreting Diagrams What happens to the wavelength as the waves approach shore?*

How Waves Affect the Shore

What happens on shore as waves pound the beach? The diagram in Figure 4 shows some of their effects. Since wave direction at sea is determined by the wind, waves usually roll toward shore at an angle. But as they touch bottom, the shallower water slows the shoreward side of the wave first. The rows of waves gradually turn and become more nearly parallel to the shore.

Longshore Drift As the waves come into shore, water washes up the beach at an angle, carrying sand grains with it. The water and sand then run straight back down the beach. This movement of sand along the beach is called **longshore drift**. As the waves slow down, they deposit the sand they are carrying on the shallow, underwater slope in a long ridge called a **sandbar**.

Rip Currents As a sandbar grows, it can trap the water flowing along the shore. In some places, water breaks through the sandbar and begins to flow back down the sloping ocean bottom. This process creates a **rip current**, a rush of water that flows rapidly back to sea through a narrow opening. Rip currents can carry a swimmer out into deep water. Because rip currents are narrow, a strong swimmer can usually escape by swimming across the current, parallel to the beach.

✓ *Checkpoint* *In what direction does a rip current pull a swimmer?*

Figure 4 Waves approach the shore at an angle. This results in a gradual movement of sand along the beach. *Interpreting Diagrams In which direction is longshore drift moving the sand along this beach?*

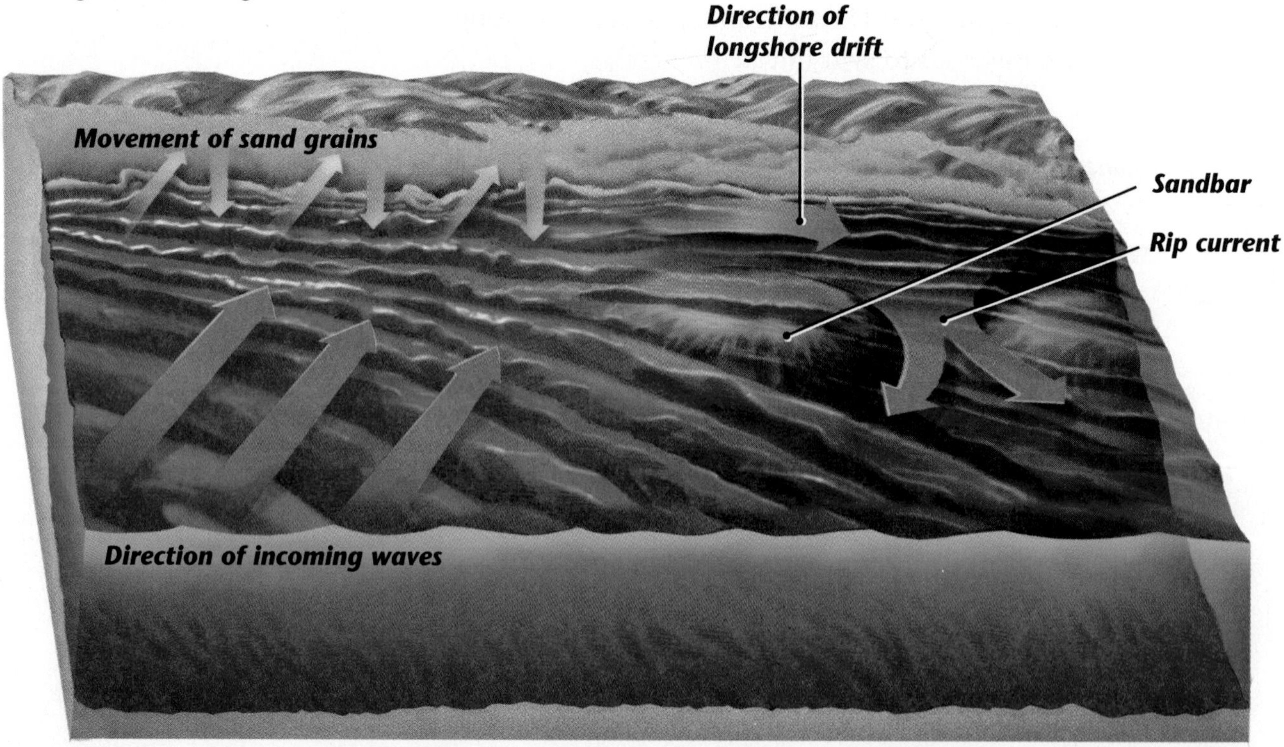
Direction of longshore drift
Movement of sand grains
Sandbar
Rip current
Direction of incoming waves

Figure 5 "The Breaking Wave off Kanagawa" is a wood-block print by the Japanese artist Hokusai.

Waves and Beach Erosion

The boundary between land and ocean is always changing shape. If you walk on the same beach every day, you might not notice that it is changing. From day to day, waves remove sand and bring new sand at about the same rate. But if you visit a beach just once each year, you might be startled by what you see. **Waves shape a beach by eroding the shore in some places and building it up in others.**

As you learned in Chapter 10, erosion is the process of breaking up rock and carrying it away. At first, waves striking a rocky shoreline carve the rocks into tall cliffs and arches. Over many thousands of years, waves break the rocks into pebbles and grains of sand. A wide, sandy beach forms. Then the waves begin to eat away at the exposed beach. The shoreline slowly moves farther inland. Longshore drift carries the sand along the coast and deposits it elsewhere.

Reducing Erosion

Many people like to live near the ocean. But over time, erosion can wear away the beach. This threatens the homes and other buildings. To avoid losing their property, people look for ways to reduce the effect of erosion.

Groins One method of reducing erosion along a stretch of beach is to build a wall of rocks or concrete, called a **groin,** outward from the beach. The sand carried by the water piles up

Visual Arts CONNECTION

The Japanese artist Hokusai (1760–1849) is well known for his land and ocean scenes. His print at the left shows a cresting wave with the snow-capped Mt. Fuji in the background.

As a teenager, Hokusai was apprenticed to a wood-block engraver. A wood-block print is made by engraving a separate block of wood for each color ink used in the picture. How many blocks do you think Hokusai needed for this print?

In Your Journal

Imagine you are writing a catalog for a museum exhibit of ocean scenes. Write a brief description of Hokusai's print for the catalog.

Figure 6 Sand piles up against a series of groins people have built along the North Carolina coast. Building groins to stop longshore drift is one way to reduce beach erosion.

against the groins instead of moving along the shore. Figure 6 shows how groins interrupt the movement of water. However, the groins increase the amount of erosion farther down the beach.

Dunes Some natural landforms protect beaches and reduce erosion, although they can't completely stop the movement of sand. Dunes, hills of wind-blown sand covered with plants, make a beach more stable and protect the shore from erosion. The strong roots of dune plants, such as beach grass and sea oats, hold the sand in place. These plants help to slow erosion by both wind and water. But the dunes and plants can be easily destroyed by cars, bicycles, or even by many people walking over them. Without the plants to hold the sand in place, the dunes can be easily washed away by wave action.

Barrier Beaches Another natural landform that protects shorelines from wave action occurs along low-lying beaches. Long sand deposits called barrier beaches form parallel to the shore. The beaches are separated from the mainland by a shallow lagoon. Waves break against the barrier beach instead of against the land inside. For this reason, people are working to preserve natural barrier beaches like those off Cape Cod, the New Jersey shore, and the Georgia and Carolina coasts.

Figure 7 Sand dunes are a natural form of beach protection. These yellow-flowered sea oats and beach grasses anchor a dune on Cape Cod, Massachusetts.

Tsunamis

So far you have been reading about waves that are caused by the wind. Another kind of wave forms far below the ocean surface. This type of wave, called a **tsunami**, is usually caused by an earthquake on the ocean floor. The abrupt movement of the ocean floor sends pulses of energy through the water above it. When tsunamis reach the coast, they can be as devastating as an earthquake on land, smashing buildings and bridges.

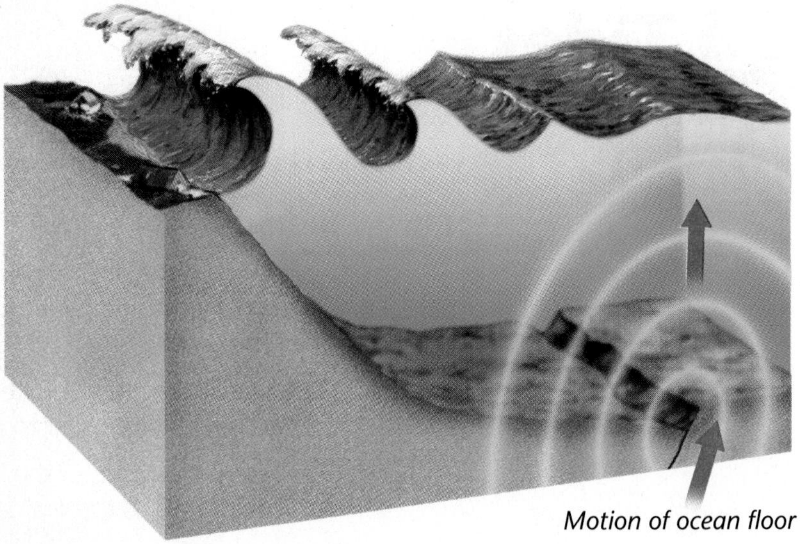
Motion of ocean floor

Figure 8 At sea, a tsunami travels as a long, low wave. Near shore, the wave height increases suddenly. The wall of water smashes onto the land, tossing ships onto the shore and destroying buildings. *Interpreting Diagrams What is the source of a tsunami's energy?*

Despite the tremendous amount of energy a tsunami carries, people on a ship at sea may not even realize a tsunami is passing. How is this possible? A tsunami in deep water may have a wavelength of 200 kilometers or more, but have a wave height of less than a meter. But when the tsunami reaches shallow water near the coast, friction with the ocean floor causes the long wavelength to decrease suddenly. The wave height increases as the water "piles up." The tsunami becomes a towering wall of water. Some tsunamis have reached heights of 20 meters—taller than a five-story building!

Tsunamis are most common in the Pacific Ocean, often striking Alaska, Hawaii, and Japan. In 1998, tsunamis in Papua New Guinea killed more than 2,000 people. Nations are searching for ways to avoid such devastation. Some Japanese cities have built barriers designed to break up the waves. Scientists also monitor the ocean floor for warnings of earthquakes that may produce tsunamis.

Section 1 Review

1. Describe how ocean waves form.
2. How do wavelength and wave height change as a wave enters shallow water?
3. How does wave action cause changes in a coastline?
4. How do water particles move within a wave?
5. **Thinking Critically Relating Cause and Effect** Explain how building a groin affects the beach on each side of the groin.

CHAPTER PROJECT

Check Your Progress

You are ready to design your model ocean beach. Sketch your design. Be sure to consider what materials you will use for your shoreline and lighthouse. How will you make waves? When your design is finished, you are ready to gather your materials and construct your model. (*Hint:* Design your model, including the lighthouse, to scale.)

SECTION 2

Tides

DISCOVER ACTIVITY

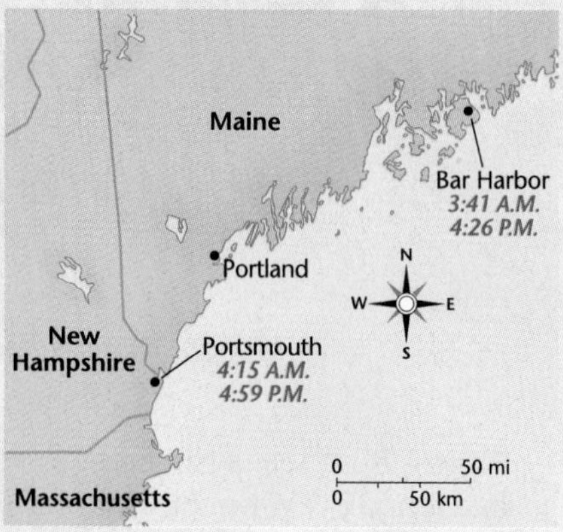
Maine
Bar Harbor
3:41 A.M.
4:26 P.M.
Portland
N
W
E
S
New Hampshire
Portsmouth
4:15 A.M.
4:59 P.M.
0
50 mi
0
50 km
Massachusetts

When Is High Tide?

Twice a day, the ocean rises and falls on the New England coast. These daily changes in water level are called tides. The map shows the times of the two high tides in each city on a particular day.

1. Calculate the length of time between the two high tides for each city. Remember to consider both hours and minutes.
2. Look at the times of the high tides in Bar Harbor and in Portsmouth. Is there a pattern in the times of the high tides?

Think It Over

Predicting Notice that the high tides for Portland are not shown. Based on the times of the other high tides on the map, predict when the high tides will occur in Portland.

GUIDE FOR READING

- **What causes tides?**
- **How are tides a source of energy?**

Reading Tip **As you read, use the headings to make an outline about tides.**

You're standing on a riverbank in the town of Saint John, Canada. In the distance there's a loud roaring sound, like a train approaching. Suddenly a wall of water twice your height thunders past. The surge of water rushes up the river channel so fast that it almost looks as if the river is flowing backward!

This thundering wall of water is an everyday event at Saint John. The town is located where the Saint John River enters the Bay of Fundy, an arm of the Atlantic Ocean. The Bay of Fundy is famous for its dramatic daily tides. When the tide comes in, fishing boats float on the water near the piers. But once the tide goes out, so much water flows back to sea that the boats are stranded on the muddy harbor bottom.

A

Figure 9 The Bay of Fundy in Canada is noted for its great differences in water level at high and low tide. **A.** Near the mouth of the bay, boats float in the Saint John River at high tide. **B.** At low tide, the boats are grounded.

What Causes Tides?

The daily rise and fall of Earth's waters on its coastlines are called **tides.** As the tide comes in, the level of the water on the beach rises gradually. When the water reaches its highest point, it is high tide. Then the tide goes out, flowing back toward the sea. When the water reaches its lowest point, it is low tide. Unlike the surface waves you read about in Section 1, tides happen regularly no matter how the wind blows. Tides occur in all bodies of water, but they are most noticeable in the ocean and large lakes.

Tides are caused by the interaction of Earth, the moon, and the sun. How can distant objects like the moon and sun influence water on Earth? The answer is gravity. Gravity is the force exerted by an object that pulls other objects toward it. Gravity keeps you and everything around you on Earth's surface. As the distance between objects increases, however, gravity's pull grows weaker.

Figure 10 shows the effect of the moon's gravity on the water on Earth's surface. The moon pulls on the water on the side closest to it (point A) more strongly than it pulls on the center of the Earth. This pull creates a bulge of water, called a tidal bulge, on the side of Earth facing the moon. The water at point C is pulled toward the moon less strongly than is Earth as a whole. This water is "left behind," forming a second bulge.

In the places in Figure 10 where there are tidal bulges (points A and C), high tide is occurring along the coastlines. In the places between the bulges (points B and D), low tide is occurring. As Earth rotates, different places on the planet's surface pass through the areas of the tidal bulges and experience the change in water levels.

Checkpoint *What force causes the tides to occur on Earth's surface?*

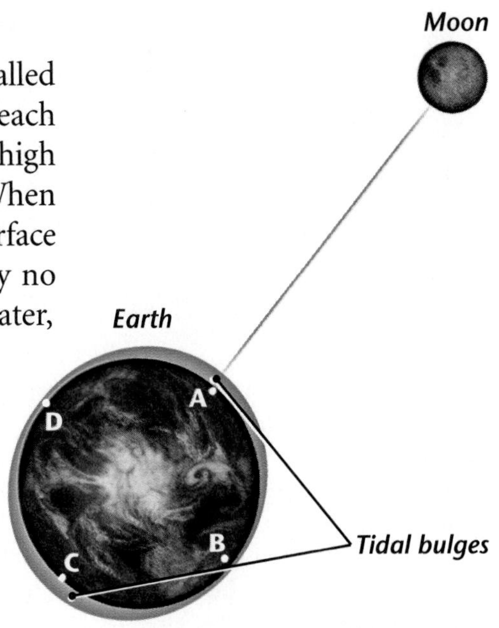
Moon
Earth
A
B
C
D
Tidal bulges

Figure 10 The moon's pull on Earth's water causes tidal bulges to form on the side closest to the moon and the side farthest from the moon. **Comparing and Contrasting** *Where is the level of the water higher, at point C or point D?*

B

Sharpen your Skills

Graphing

ACTIVITY

This table lists the highest high tides and lowest low tides at the mouth of the Savannah River at the Atlantic Ocean in Georgia for one week. Use the data to make a graph.

Day	Highest High Tide (m)	Lowest Low Tide (m)
1	1.9	0.2
2	2.1	0.1
3	2.3	0.0
4	2.4	−0.2
5	2.5	−0.2
6	2.6	−0.3
7	1.9	0.3

1. On the horizontal axis, mark the days.
2. On the vertical axis, mark tide heights ranging from 3.0 to –1.0 meters. (*Hint:* Mark the negative numbers below the horizontal axis.)
3. Plot the tide heights for each day on the graph. Connect the high tide points with one line and the low tide points with another line.

How do the high and low tides change during the week? What type of tide might be occurring on Day 6? Explain.

The Daily Tide Cycle

As Earth turns completely around once each day, people on or near the shore observe the rise and fall of the tides as they reach the area of each tidal bulge. The high tides occur about 12 hours and 25 minutes apart in each location. As Earth rotates, easternmost points pass through the area of the tidal bulge before points farther to the west. Therefore, high tide occurs later the farther west you go along a coastline.

In some places, the two high tides and two low tides are easy to observe each day. But in other places, the range between the water levels is less dramatic. One set of tides may even be so minimal that there appears to be only one high tide and one low tide per day. This situation is common along the coasts of Texas and western Florida, due to the gradual slope of the ocean floor in the Gulf of Mexico.

Several factors affect the height of the tide in any particular location. For example, high tide on a certain day in southern California is not necessarily the same height as high tide farther up the Pacific coast in Oregon. Landforms such as capes, peninsulas, and islands interrupt the water's movements. A basin at the mouth of a river can also increase the range of tides. As you read in Chapter 10, the speed and depth of moving water increases when it flows into a narrower channel. That is what causes the dramatic tides in the mouth of the Saint John River you read about earlier.

☑ ***Checkpoint*** ***Describe one factor that affects the height of the tides in a particular area.***

The Monthly Tide Cycle

Even though the sun is 150 million kilometers from Earth, it is so massive that its gravity also affects the tides. The sun pulls the water on Earth's surface toward it. In Figure 11 on the facing page, you can follow the positions of the Earth, moon, and sun at different times during a month. Notice that sometimes the moon and sun pull together on Earth's waters. At other times, they pull in different directions. Changes in the positions of Earth, the moon, and the sun affect the height of the tides during a month.

Spring Tides Twice a month, at the new moon and the full moon, the sun and moon are lined up. Their combined gravitational pull produces the greatest range between high and low tide, called a **spring tide.** These tides get their name not because they occur during the season spring, but from an Old English word, *springen,* which means "to jump."

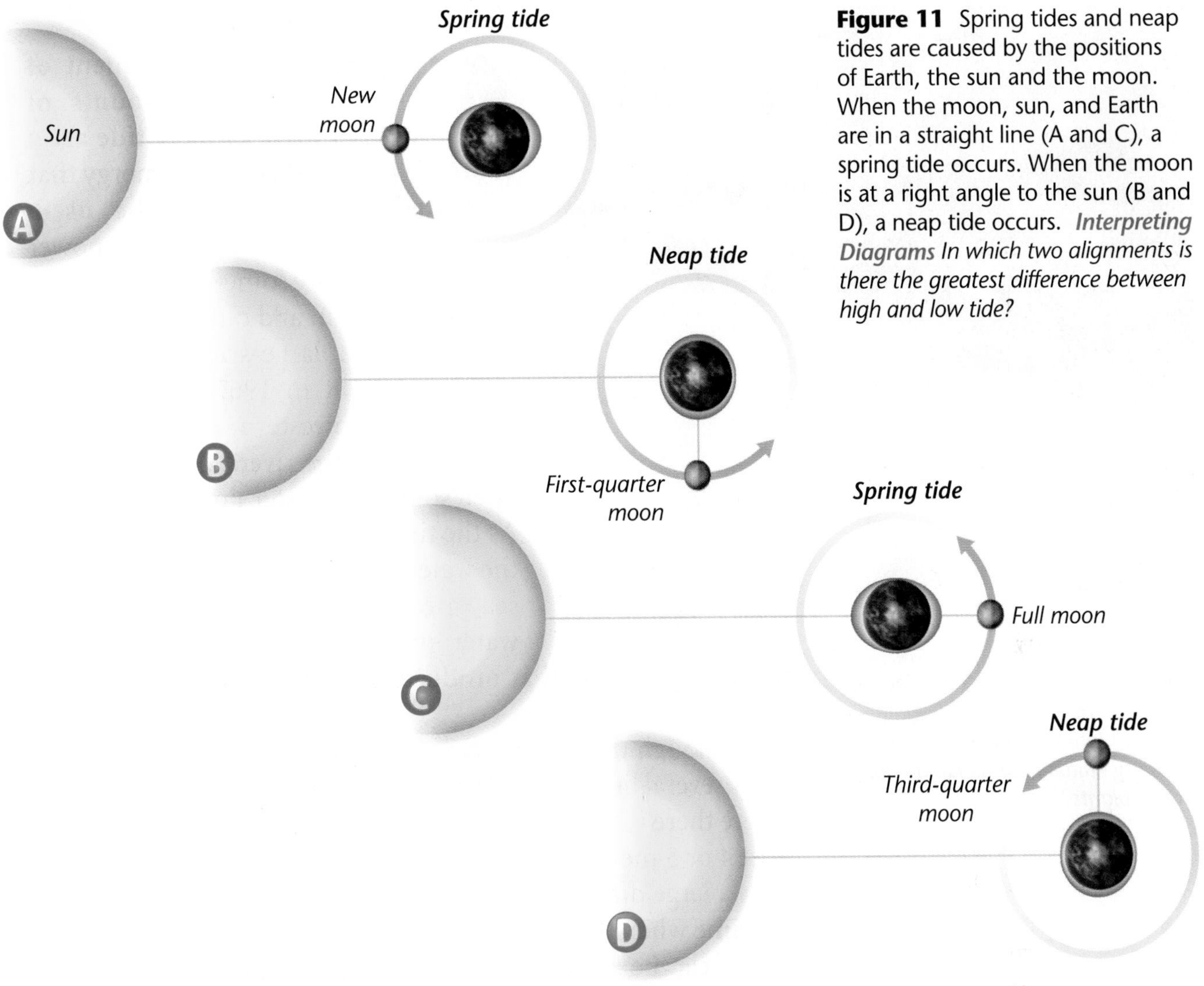
Spring tide
Sun
New
moon
A
Neap tide
B
First-quarter
moon
Spring tide
C
Full moon
Neap tide
Third-quarter
moon
D

Figure 11 Spring tides and neap tides are caused by the positions of Earth, the sun and the moon. When the moon, sun, and Earth are in a straight line (A and C), a spring tide occurs. When the moon is at a right angle to the sun (B and D), a neap tide occurs. ***Interpreting Diagrams*** *In which two alignments is there the greatest difference between high and low tide?*

Neap Tides In between spring tides, at the first and third quarters of the moon, the sun and moon pull at right angles to each other. This line-up produces a **neap tide**, a tide with the least difference between low and high tide. During a neap tide, the sun's gravity pulls some of the water away from the tidal bulge facing the moon. This acts to "even out" the water level over Earth's surface, reducing the difference between high and low tides.

Monthly Tide Tables Despite the complex factors affecting the tides, scientists can predict tides quite accurately for various locations. They combine knowledge of the movements of the moon and Earth with information about the shape of the coastline and other local conditions. If you live near the coast, your local newspaper probably publishes a tide table. Knowing the times and heights of tides is important to sailors, marine scientists, people who fish, and others who live along a coast.

Figure 12 Pulled by the tide, water rushes through this tidal power plant in France. *Making Generalizations Why are very few locations suitable for building tidal power plants?*

Energy From Tides

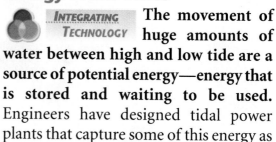

INTEGRATING TECHNOLOGY **The movement of huge amounts of water between high and low tide are a source of potential energy—energy that is stored and waiting to be used.** Engineers have designed tidal power plants that capture some of this energy as the tide moves in and out.

The first large-scale tidal power plant was built in 1967 on the Rance River in northwestern France. As high tide swirls up the river, the plant's gates open so that the water flows into a basin. As the tide retreats, the gates shut to trap the water. Gravity pulls the water back to sea through tunnels. The energy of the water moving through the tunnels powers generators that produce electricity, just as in a hydroelectric dam on a river.

Although tidal energy is a clean, renewable source of energy, it has several limitations. Harnessing tidal power is practical only where there is a large difference between high and low tides—at least 4 or 5 meters. There are very few places in the world where such a large difference occurs. Daily tides also may not occur at the time when there is a demand for electricity. However, tidal power can be a useful part of an overall plan to generate electricity that also includes other power sources between tides.

Section 2 Review

1. Explain how the moon causes a tidal bulge to form on the side of Earth closest to it.
2. How can tides be used to generate electricity?
3. Describe the positions of the sun and the moon in relation to Earth when spring tides occur.
4. **Thinking Critically Applying Concepts** Imagine that you are the captain of a fishing boat. Why would it be helpful to know the times of the tides?

Check Your Progress

CHAPTER PROJECT

Now that you have built your model, plan an experiment to observe the effects of wave erosion on the shoreline. How will you measure the amount of wave action needed to topple the lighthouse? Once you have observed how waves cause shoreline erosion, repair the beach and design a way to reduce the erosion. Test your method by sending more waves against the shore. (*Hint:* For both tests, place toothpicks at regular intervals on the beach to measure erosion.)

SECTION 3 Ocean Water Chemistry

DISCOVER ACTIVITY

Will the Eggs Sink or Float?

1. Fill two beakers or jars with tap water.
2. Add three teaspoons of salt to one beaker. Stir until it dissolves.
3. Place a whole, uncooked egg in each jar. Handle the eggs gently to avoid breakage. Observe what happens to each egg.
4. Wash your hands when you are finished with this activity.

Think It Over

Observing Compare what happens to the two eggs. What does this tell you about the difference between salt water and fresh water?

GUIDE FOR READING

- **How salty is ocean water?**
- **How do conditions in the ocean change with depth?**

Reading Tip **Before you read, preview the headings in the section. Then predict some characteristics of ocean water.**

If you've ever been swimming in the ocean and swallowed some water, you know that it is salty. Why? According to an old Swedish legend, it's all because of a magic mill. This mill could grind out anything its owner wanted, such as herring, porridge, or even gold. A greedy sea captain once stole the mill and took it away on his ship, but without finding out how to use it. He asked the mill to grind some salt but then could not stop it. The mill ground more and more salt, until the captain's ship sank from its weight. According to the tale, the mill is still at the bottom of the sea, grinding out salt!

Probably no one ever took this tale seriously, even when it was first told. The scientific explanation for the ocean's saltiness begins with the early stages of Earth's history, when the ocean covered much of the surface of the planet. Undersea volcanoes erupted, spewing chemicals into the water. Gradually, the lava from these volcanic eruptions built up areas of land. Rain fell on the bare land, washing more chemicals from the rocks into the ocean. Over time, these dissolved substances built up to the levels present in the ocean today.

The Salty Ocean

Just how salty is the ocean? If you boiled a kilogram of seawater in a pot until the water was all gone, there would be about 35 grams of salts left in the bottom of the pot. **On average, one kilogram of ocean water contains about 35 grams of salts—that is, 35 parts per thousand.** The total amount of dissolved salts in water is called **salinity**.

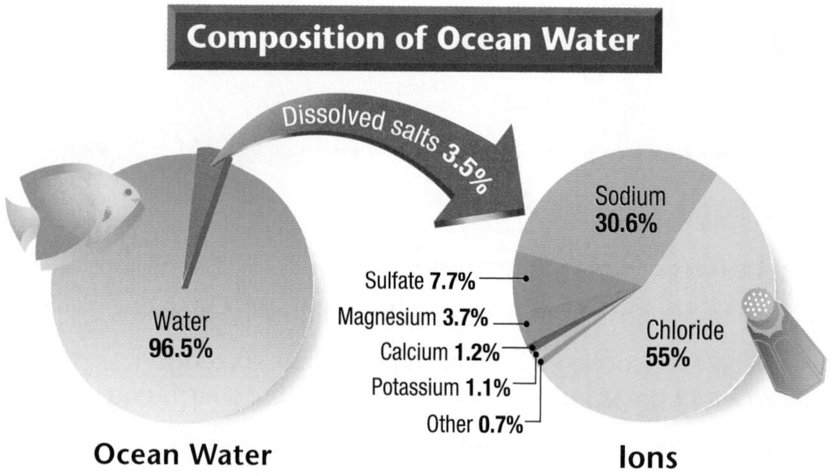
Composition of Ocean Water
Dissolved salts 3.5%
Water
96.5%
Ocean Water
Sodium
30.6%
Sulfate 7.7%
Magnesium 3.7%
Calcium 1.2%
Potassium 1.1%
Other 0.7%
Chloride
55%
Ions

Figure 13 Ocean water contains many different dissolved salts. When salts dissolve, they separate into particles called ions. *Interpreting Graphs Which ion is most common in ocean water?*

The substance you know as table salt—sodium chloride—is the salt present in the greatest amount in ocean water. When sodium chloride dissolves in water, it separates into sodium and chloride particles called ions. Other salts, such as magnesium chloride, form ions in water in the same way. Together, chloride and sodium make up almost 86 percent of the ions dissolved in ocean water, as shown in Figure 13. Ocean water also contains smaller amounts of about a dozen other ions, including magnesium and calcium, and other substances that organisms need, such as nitrogen and phosphorus.

Variations in Salinity In most parts of the ocean, the salinity is between 34 and 37 parts per thousand. But near the surface, rain, snow, and melting ice add fresh water to the ocean, lowering the salinity there. Salinity is also lower near the mouths of large rivers such as the Amazon or Mississippi. These rivers empty great amounts of fresh water into the ocean. Evaporation, on the other hand, increases salinity, since the salt is left behind as the water evaporates. For example, in the Red Sea, where the climate is hot and dry, the salinity can be as high as 41 parts per thousand. Salinity can also be higher near the poles. As the surface water freezes into ice, the salt is left behind in the remaining water.

Figure 14 These people are relaxing with the paper while floating in the water! The Dead Sea between Israel and Jordan is so salty that people float easily on its surface. *Relating Cause and Effect How is the area's hot, dry climate related to the Dead Sea's high salinity?*

Effects of Salinity Salinity affects several properties of ocean

INTEGRATING CHEMISTRY

water. For instance, ocean water does not freeze until the temperature drops to about $-1.9°C$. The salt acts as a kind of antifreeze by interfering with the formation of ice crystals. Salt water also has a higher density than fresh water. That means that the mass of one liter of salt water is greater than the mass of one liter of fresh water. Because its density is greater, seawater has greater buoyancy. It lifts, or buoys up, less dense objects floating in it. This is why an egg floats higher in salt water than in fresh water.

Gases in Ocean Water

Just as land organisms use oxygen and other gases in the air, marine organisms use gases dissolved in ocean water. Two gases found in ocean water that are necessary for living things are oxygen and carbon dioxide.

Oxygen in seawater comes from the atmosphere and from algae in the ocean. Algae use sunlight to carry out photosynthesis, releasing oxygen into the water in the process. Oxygen is scarcer in seawater than in air and is most plentiful near the surface. Carbon dioxide, on the other hand, is about 60 times as plentiful in the oceans as in the atmosphere. Algae need carbon dioxide for photosynthesis. Animals such as corals also use carbon dioxide, which provides the carbon to build their hard skeletons.

☑ *Checkpoint* *What are two sources of the oxygen in ocean water?*

The Temperature of Ocean Water

In New England, the news reports on New Year's Day often feature the shivering members of a "Polar Bear Club" taking a dip in the icy Atlantic Ocean. Yet on the same day, people enjoy the warm waters of a Puerto Rico beach. Like temperatures on land, temperatures at the surface of the ocean vary with location and the seasons.

The broad surface of the ocean absorbs energy from the sun. Because warm water is less dense than cold water, this warm water stays as a layer on the surface. Near the equator, surface temperatures often reach 25°C, about room temperature. The temperature drops as you travel away from the equator.

The temperature of water affects the amount of dissolved oxygen it can hold. The cold waters in the polar regions contain more dissolved oxygen than warm, tropical waters. But there is still enough oxygen in tropical seas to support a variety of organisms, such as those shown in Figure 15.

Math Toolbox

Calculating Density

To calculate the density of a substance, divide the mass of the substance by its volume.

$$\text{density} = \frac{\text{mass}}{\text{volume}}$$

For example, one liter (L) of ocean water has a mass of 1.03 kilograms (kg). Therefore, its density is

$$\frac{1.03 \text{ kg}}{1.00 \text{ L}} = 1.03 \text{ kg/L}$$

Five liters of one type of crude oil has a mass of 4.10 kg. What is its density?

$$\frac{4.10 \text{ kg}}{5.00 \text{ L}} = 0.82 \text{ kg/L}$$

If this oil spilled on the ocean's surface, would it sink or float? Explain your answer in terms of density.

Figure 15 Both this neon-pink basslet and the lacy green sponge depend on the dissolved gases in ocean water.

EXPLORING the Water Column

Conditions change as you descend from the surface to the ocean floor.

▼ A scuba diver can descend to about 40 meters.

DEPTH
0.5 km
1.0 km
1.5 km
2.0 km
2.5 km
3.0 km
3.5 km
4.0 km
PRESSURE INCREASES
3.8 km
Average ocean depth

Surface Zone
Extends from surface to about 200 meters. Average temperature worldwide is 17.5°C.

Transition Zone
Extends from bottom of surface zone to about 1 kilometer. Temperature rapidly drops to 4°C.

Deep Zone
Extends from about 1 kilometer to ocean floor. Average temperature is 3.5°C.

The submersible *Alvin* can descend to about 4 kilometers. ▼

▼ In 1960, the submersible *Trieste* dived to a record depth of 11 kilometers.

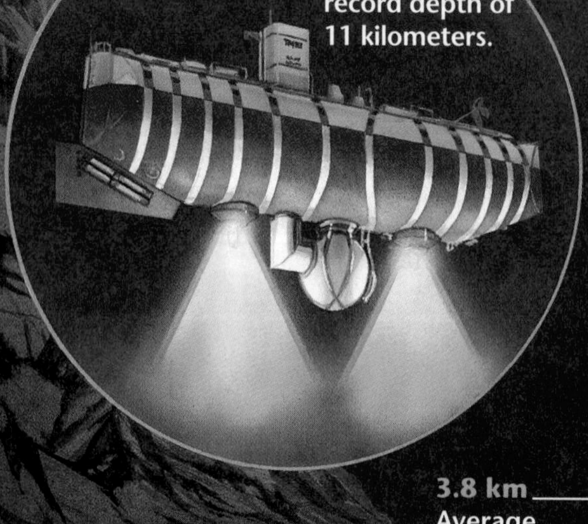

Color and Light
Sunlight penetrates the surface of the ocean. It appears first yellowish, then blue-green, as the water absorbs the red light. No light reaches below about 200 meters.

Temperature
Near the surface, temperature is affected by the weather above. In the transition zone, the temperature drops rapidly. In the deep zone, the water is always extremely cold.

Salinity
Rainfall decreases salinity near the surface, while evaporation increases salinity in warm, dry areas. Below the surface zone, salinity remains fairly constant throughout the water column.

Density
The density of seawater depends on temperature and salinity. The ocean is generally least dense in the surface zone, where it is warmest. However, higher salinity also increases density. The most dense water is found in the cold deep zone.

Pressure
Pressure increases at the rate of 10 times the air pressure at sea level per 100 meters of depth.

Changes with Depth

Gazing down into the blue-green water from the deck of a ship, you might think that the vast volume of water beneath you is all the same. But in fact, conditions change dramatically from the surface to the depths. If you could descend from the surface to the ocean floor, you would pass through a vertical section of the ocean referred to as the water column. *Exploring the Water Column* shows some of the changes you would observe.

Temperature Decreases If you took temperature readings at different depths, you would observe a pattern. **Temperature decreases as you descend through the water column.** There are three temperature zones in the water column. The first zone, the surface zone, typically extends from the surface to between 100 and 500 meters. Next is the transition zone, which extends from the bottom of the surface zone to about one kilometer. The temperature drops very quickly in the transition zone, to about 4°C. Below the transition zone is the deep zone. The temperature in the deep zone is a constant 3.5°C or colder in most of the ocean.

Pressure Increases Pressure is the force exerted by the weight of water above pressing down. **Pressure increases continuously from the surface to the deepest part of the ocean.** The average depth of the ocean floor is 3.8 kilometers. There the pressure is about 400 times greater than air pressure at Earth's surface.

INTEGRATING TECHNOLOGY Pressure is one obstacle facing scientists who want to study the ocean. A diver can descend safely only to about 40 meters. To survive in deeper water, scientists must use a submersible. A **submersible** is an underwater vehicle built of strong materials to resist pressure. In a submersible, scientists can directly observe the ocean floor, collect samples, and study deep ocean water chemistry.

Section 3 Review

1. What is the salinity of ocean water?
2. How do temperature and pressure change as you descend from the surface to the ocean floor?
3. Describe one factor that increases the salinity of seawater and one factor that decreases salinity.
4. **Thinking Critically** **Inferring** Would you expect the seawater just below the floating ice in the Arctic Ocean to be higher or lower in salinity than the water in the deep zone there? Explain.

Nutrition Facts
Grade A
FAT FREE MILK

Science at Home

Use a ball-point pen to poke two holes in a milk carton—one about one-third of the way from the bottom and one two-thirds of the way from the bottom. Cover the holes with tape and fill the carton with water. Holding the carton a meter above a sink, remove the tape and observe the streams of water. Explain that increased pressure causes the water to flow out of the bottom hole more quickly. How does this model conditions in the ocean?

Skills Lab

Controlling Variables

Investigating Changes in Density

In this lab, you will practice the skill of controlling variables as you learn more about density.

Problem

How do various factors affect the density of ocean water?

Materials

thumbtacks	beaker, 250 mL	water
thermometer	ice	hot plate
table salt	balance	spoon
metric ruler	sharpened pencil	

unsharpened pencil with eraser
graduated cylinders, 100 mL and 250 mL

Procedure

1. Work with your group to brainstorm a list of variables that affect the density of ocean water. Some variables to consider are water temperature and salinity. As a group, choose one variable to test in this investigation.
2. One way to measure density is with a tool called a *hydrometer.* To make a hydrometer, follow the instructions on the facing page.
3. Design an experimental plan to determine how the variable you chose affects density. For example, if you have chosen temperature as your variable, you might choose to start with salt water at 0°C, then heat it to 10°C, 20°C, and 30°C. If salinity is your variable, you might start with 100 mL of tap (fresh) water and add 10 g of salt, then add another 10 g to make 20 g, then add 10 g more to make 30 g. Write out your experimental plan.

DATA TABLE

Manipulated Variable: ______________

Condition Tested	Hydrometer Reading

4. List all the variables you will need to keep constant during your experiment. Revise your experimental plan and add steps to ensure that all other variables remain constant.
5. Review your plan. Make sure it includes the materials you will use and their amounts. Also make sure you have addressed all safety issues. Then check the plan with your teacher.
6. Copy the data table into your notebook.
7. Perform your experiment using the pencil hydrometer.

Analyze and Conclude

1. In your experimental plan, which variable was the manipulated variable, and which was the responding variable? Explain. (Refer to the Skills Handbook if you need more information about these types of variables.)
2. Make a graph of the data you collected in the experiment. Graph the manipulated variable on the horizontal axis. Graph the responding variable on the vertical axis.
3. How do changes in the hydrometer reading relate to density?

Making a Hydrometer

A. Begin with an unsharpened pencil. Starting 1 cm from the unsharpened end, use a second, sharpened pencil to make marks every 0.5 cm along the side of the pencil. Continue making marks until you reach the 4-cm mark.

B. Label each mark, starting at the unsharpened end of the pencil with the label 0.5.

C. Insert 3 thumbtacks as weights into the eraser end of the pencil. **CAUTION:** *Be careful not to cut yourself on the sharp points of the thumbtacks.*

D. Fill the 250-mL graduated cylinder with water at room temperature. Place the pencil in the water, eraser down.

E. Add or remove thumbtacks and adjust their placement in the eraser until the pencil floats upright, with about 2 cm sticking up above the surface of the water.

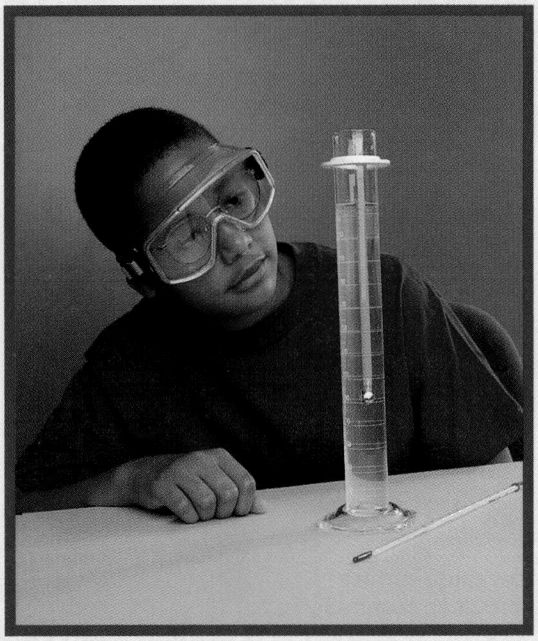

F. In your notebook, record the number next to the mark that is closest to the point where the pencil hydrometer projects from the water. As the density of the water increases, the hydrometer will float above the point you have just marked. If the water becomes less dense, the hydrometer will float below that point.

4. Use the graph to describe the relationship between the manipulated variable you tested and density.
5. Where in Earth's oceans would you find conditions like the ones that you tested?
6. **Think About It** Why is it important to make sure that all conditions other than the manipulated variable are kept constant in an experiment? How well were you able to keep the other variables constant?

More To Explore

In this experiment you observed how manipulating a particular variable affects the density of ocean water. Now conduct a second experiment, this time manipulating a different variable. As you design this experiment, make sure to control all variables except the one you are testing. Be sure to check your experimental plan with your teacher before you begin.

SECTION 4 Currents and Climate

DISCOVER ACTIVITY

Which Is More Dense?

1. Fill a plastic container three-quarters full with warm water. Wait for the water to stop moving.
2. Add several drops of food coloring to a cup of ice water and stir.

3. Gently dribble colored water down the inside of the container. Observe.

Think It Over

Inferring Describe what happened to the cold water. Which is more dense, warm water or cold water? Explain.

GUIDE FOR READING

- What forces cause surface currents and deep currents?
- How do surface currents affect climate on land?

Reading Tip **As you read, make a list of the kinds of ocean currents. Write a sentence describing the causes of each.**

People strolling along a Washington beach one May day in 1990 could hardly believe their eyes. Hundreds of sneakers, in all colors and sizes, were washing ashore from the Pacific Ocean. Puzzled, people gathered up the soggy shoes and took them home, wondering where the sneakers had come from. Eventually, the sneaker spill was traced to a cargo ship from South Korea. Containers had washed overboard in a storm and broken open, spilling thousands of shoes into the water.

The sneakers were a ready-made experiment for oceanographers, scientists who study the oceans. From the shoes' drifting, oceanographers could infer both the path and the speed of water movements in the Pacific. Using what they already knew about these movements, scientists made a computer model predicting when and where more sneakers would come ashore. Right on schedule, sneakers washed up in Oregon and British Columbia, Canada. The model also predicted that the shoes would turn back westward across the Pacific. Again it was correct, as some sneakers arrived in Hawaii. The shoes that did not sink could have traveled all the way back to South Korea!

Earlier in this chapter you learned how the oceans move as a result of wave action and tides. A third type of water movement is currents. A **current** is a large stream of moving water that flows through the oceans. Unlike waves, which do not actually transport water from one place to another, currents carry water great distances. Some currents move water at the surface of the ocean, while other currents move the deep water. Both surface currents and deep currents result from unequal heating of Earth's oceans and atmosphere by the sun's rays. Areas near the equator receive more solar energy, while areas near the poles receive less.

Surface Currents

Figure 16 shows the major surface currents in Earth's oceans. **Surface currents, which affect water to a depth of several hundred meters, are driven mainly by winds.** Following the major wind patterns of the globe, surface currents move in circular patterns in the five major ocean basins. Trace these currents on the map. Notice that most of the currents flow east or west, then double back to complete the circle.

Why do the currents move in these circular patterns? If Earth were standing still, winds and currents would flow in straight lines between the poles and the equator. But as Earth rotates, the paths of the winds and currents curve in relation to Earth's surface. This effect of Earth's rotation on the direction of winds and currents is called the **Coriolis effect** (kawr ee OH lis effect). In the Northern Hemisphere, the Coriolis effect causes the currents to curve to the right. In the Southern Hemisphere, the Coriolis effect causes the currents to curve to the left.

Figure 16 Large surface currents generally move in circular patterns in Earth's oceans. ***Interpreting Maps*** *Name four currents that flow along the coasts of North America. State whether each current is warm or cold.*

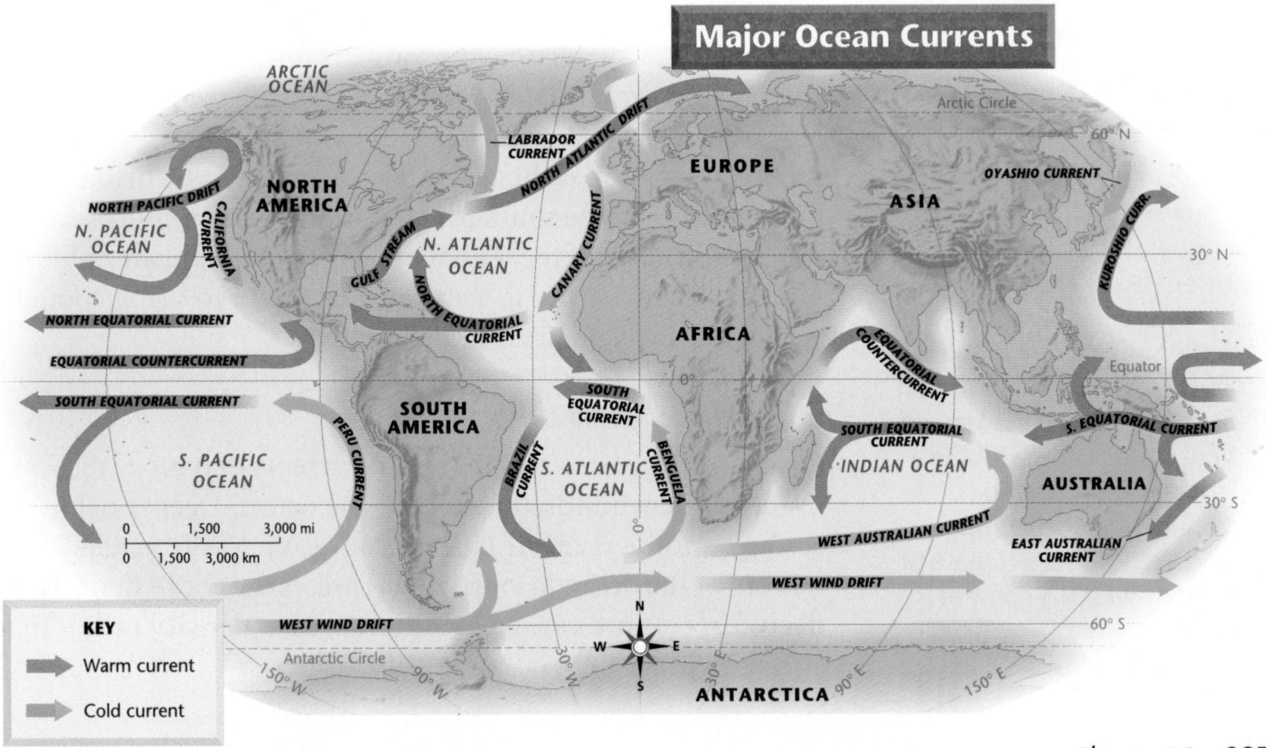
Major Ocean Currents
ARCTIC OCEAN
Arctic Circle
60° N
30° N
Equator
30° S
60° S
LABRADOR CURRENT
NORTH ATLANTIC DRIFT
EUROPE
ASIA
OYASHIO CURRENT
NORTH AMERICA
NORTH PACIFIC DRIFT
CALIFORNIA CURRENT
N. PACIFIC OCEAN
KUROSHIO CURR.
GULF STREAM
N. ATLANTIC OCEAN
CANARY CURRENT
NORTH EQUATORIAL CURRENT
EQUATORIAL COUNTERCURRENT
SOUTH EQUATORIAL CURRENT
AFRICA
EQUATORIAL COUNTERCURRENT
SOUTH AMERICA
PERU CURRENT
SOUTH EQUATORIAL CURRENT
S. PACIFIC OCEAN
BRAZIL CURRENT
S. ATLANTIC OCEAN
BENGUELA CURRENT
INDIAN OCEAN
S. EQUATORIAL CURRENT
AUSTRALIA
WEST AUSTRALIAN CURRENT
EAST AUSTRALIAN CURRENT
WEST WIND DRIFT
0 1,500 3,000 mi
0 1,500 3,000 km
KEY
Warm current
Cold current
Antarctic Circle
ANTARCTICA
N
S
W
E
150° W
90° W
30° W
0°
30° E
90° E
150° E

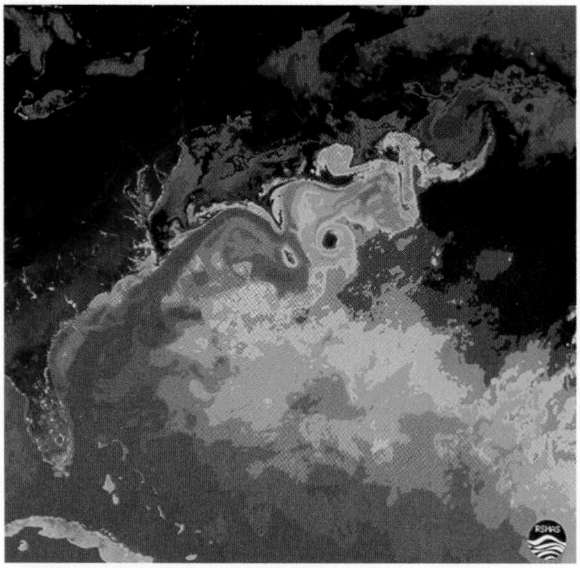

Figure 17 This satellite image of the Atlantic Ocean has been enhanced with colors that show water temperature. Red and orange indicate warmer water, while green and blue indicate colder water. The warm Gulf Stream flows around Florida, as you can see in the lower left corner of the image.

The largest and most powerful surface current in the North Atlantic Ocean, the Gulf Stream, is caused by strong winds from the west. The Gulf Stream resembles a fast-moving, deep-blue river within the ocean. It is more than 30 kilometers wide and 300 meters deep, and it carries a volume of water 100 times greater than the Mississippi River. The Gulf Stream carries warm water from the Gulf of Mexico to the Caribbean Sea, then northward along the coast of the United States. Near Cape Hatteras, North Carolina, it curves eastward across the Atlantic, as a result of the Coriolis effect.

☑ *Checkpoint* ***Why doesn't the Gulf Stream travel in a straight line?***

How Surface Currents Affect Climate

The Gulf Stream and North Atlantic Drift are very important to people in the city of Trondheim, Norway. Trondheim is located along Norway's western coast. Although it is very close to the Arctic Circle, winter there is fairly mild. Snow melts soon after it falls. And fortunately for the fishing boats, the local harbors are free of ice most of the winter. The two warm currents bring this area of Norway its mild climate. **Climate** is the pattern of temperature and precipitation typical of an area over a long period of time.

Currents affect climate by moving cold and warm water around the globe. In general, currents carry warm water from the tropics toward the poles and bring cold water back toward the equator. **A surface current warms or cools the air above it, influencing the climate of the land near the coast.**

Winds pick up moisture as they blow across warm-water currents. For example, the warm Kuroshio Current brings mild, rainy weather to the southern islands of Japan. In contrast, cold-water currents cool the air above them. Since cold air holds less moisture than warm air, these currents tend to bring cool, dry weather to the land areas in their path.

Sharpen your Skills

Drawing Conclusions

ACTIVITY

Locate the Benguela Current on Figure 16 on the previous page. Near the southern tip of Africa, the winds blow from west to east. Using what you have learned about surface currents and climate, what can you conclude about the impact of this current on the climate of the southwestern coast of Africa?

Deep Currents

So far you have been reading about currents that move the water in the top few hundred meters of the ocean. Deeper below the surface, another type of current causes the chilly waters at the bottom of the ocean to creep slowly across the ocean floor. **These deep currents are caused by differences in density rather than surface winds.**

As you read in Section 3, the density of water depends on its temperature and its salinity. When a warm-water surface current moves from the equator toward the poles, its water gradually cools off. As ice forms near the poles, the salinity of the water increases from the salt left behind during freezing. As its temperature decreases and salinity increases, the water becomes denser and sinks. Then, the cold water flows back along the ocean floor as a deep current. Deep currents follow the hills and valleys of the ocean floor. Deep ocean currents are also affected by the Coriolis effect, which causes them to curve.

Deep ocean currents move and mix water around the world. They carry cold water from the poles back toward the equator. Deep ocean currents flow much more slowly than surface currents. They may take as long as 1,000 years to make the round trip from the pole to the equator and back again!

Upwelling

In most parts of the ocean, the surface waters do not usually mix with the deep ocean waters. However, some mixing does occur in the polar regions when the surface waters cool, sink, and form deep currents. Mixing also occurs when winds cause upwelling. **Upwelling** is the upward movement of cold water from the ocean depths. As winds blow away the warm surface water, cold water rises to replace it, as shown in Figure 18.

Upwelling brings up tiny ocean organisms, minerals, and other nutrients from the deeper layers of the water. Without this

Wind
Warm
surface water
Upwelling

Figure 18 As cold water rises from the deep ocean, it brings a new supply of nutrients to the surface. The nutrients feed enormous schools of fish such as these anchovies. ***Relating Cause and Effect*** *What causes cold water to rise during upwelling?*

motion, the surface waters of the open ocean would be very scarce in nutrients. Because of the increased supply of nutrients, zones of upwelling are usually home to enormous schools of fish.

One major area of upwelling lies in the Pacific Ocean off the west coast of South America. Here, upwelling occurs when strong winds from the Andes Mountains sweep across the ocean. Huge schools of silvery anchovies thrive on the nutrients that are brought to the surface. This rich fishing area is important to millions of people who depend on it for food and jobs.

Real-World Lab

How Things Work

Modeling Ocean Currents

Why is the climate in Dublin, Ireland, so different from the climate in St. John's in Newfoundland, Canada? Since both cities are located at the same latitude, you might expect similar climate conditions in the two locations. But when it's 8°C in Dublin in January, it's usually below 0°C in St. John's. This investigation will help you understand why.

Problem

How can you model the movement of ocean water due to surface currents?

Skills Focus

making models, observing, inferring

Materials

rectangular baking tray
chalk
modeling clay, 3 sticks
ruler
permanent marker
hole puncher
newspaper
construction paper, blue and red
jointed drinking straws, one per student
light-reflecting rheoscopic fluid, 400 mL (or water and food coloring)

Procedure

1. Cover your work area with newspaper. Place the baking tray on top of the newspaper.
2. Using the map on the facing page as a guide, draw a chalk outline of the eastern coast of North and South America on the left side of the tray. Draw the outline of the west coast of Europe and Africa on the right side of the tray.
3. Use modeling clay to create the continents, roughly following the chalk outlines you have drawn. Build the continents to a depth of about 3 cm. Press the clay tightly to the pan to form a watertight seal.
4. Fill the ocean area of your model with rheoscopic fluid (or water and food coloring) to a depth of 1 cm.
5. Place 10 blue paper punches in the ocean area marked with a blue X on the map. Place 10 red paper punches in the area marked with a red X.
6. Select a drinking straw and bend it at the joint. Write your initials on the short end of the straw with the marker.

El Niño

Changes in winds and currents can greatly impact the oceans and the neighboring land. One example is **El Niño,** an abnormal climate event that occurs every 2 to 7 years in the Pacific Ocean. El Niño begins when an unusual pattern of winds forms over the western Pacific. This causes a vast sheet of warm water to move eastward toward the South American coast. El Niño conditions can last for one to two years before the usual winds and currents return.

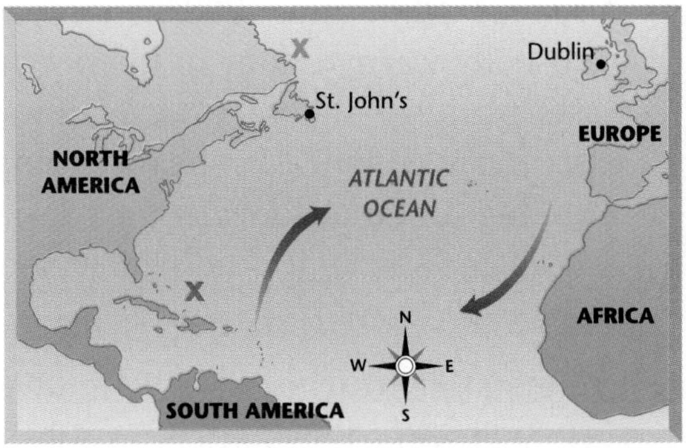
Dublin
St. John's
EUROPE
NORTH AMERICA
ATLANTIC OCEAN
AFRICA
SOUTH AMERICA
N
W
E
S
X
X

7. With a partner, simulate the pattern of winds that blow in this region of the world. One partner should position his or her straw across the westernmost bulge of Africa and blow toward the west (see arrow on map). The other partner should position his or her straw across the northern end of South America and blow toward the northeast (see arrow on map). Make sure that the straws are bent and that the short ends are parallel to the ocean surface. Both partners should begin blowing gently through the straws at the same time. Try to blow as continuously as possible for one to two minutes.
8. Observe the motion of the fluid and paper punches over the surface of the ocean. Notice what happens when the fluid and punches flow around landmasses.

Analyze and Conclude

1. Draw a map that shows the pattern of ocean currents that was produced in your model. Use red arrows to show the flow of warm water moving north from the equator. Use blue arrows to show the flow of cold water southward from the polar regions.
2. Use Figure 16 to add names to the currents you drew on your map. Which currents are warm-water currents? Which are cold-water currents?
3. Use your model to describe the relationship between winds and surface currents in the ocean.
4. Use your knowledge of ocean currents to explain why the climate in St. John's is different than the climate in Dublin.
5. **Apply** Suppose you wanted to sail to Europe from the east coast of the United States. What two natural factors could help speed up your trip? Explain your answer.

More to Explore

Use your model to simulate an upwelling off the coast of Africa. What conditions cause upwellings to occur? What are the results?

Figure 19 Heavy rains caused by El Niño washed out this road in La Honda, California, forcing homes to be evacuated. El Niño can result in severe weather all around the world.

El Niño's Impact El Niño can have disastrous consequences. For example, the arrival of El Niño's warm surface water prevents upwelling off the western coast of South America. Without the nutrients brought by upwelling, fish die or go elsewhere to find food, ruining the fishing catch that season. Seabirds, with no fish to eat, also must leave the area or starve.

El Niño has serious effects on land, too. It causes shifts in weather patterns around the world, bringing unusual and often severe conditions to different areas. For example, El Niño of 1997 and 1998 caused an unusually warm winter in the northeastern United States. However, it was also responsible for heavy rains, flooding, and mudslides in California, as well as a string of deadly tornadoes in Florida.

Forecasting El Niño Although scientists do not fully understand the conditions that create El Niño, they have been able to predict its occurrence using computer models of world climate. Knowing when El Niño will occur can reduce its impact. Scientists and public officials can plan emergency procedures and make changes to protect people and wildlife.

Section 4 Review

1. Describe how surface currents form and travel in the ocean.
2. How is heat transferred from Earth's oceans to land areas?
3. Explain how deep currents form and move in the ocean.
4. **Thinking Critically Comparing and Contrasting** Describe the similarities and differences in the movement of surface currents in the Northern Hemisphere and Southern Hemisphere.

CHAPTER PROJECT

Check Your Progress

This is the time to make final changes to your method of shoreline protection to further decrease erosion. Test your improved method. How much additional wave action does the lighthouse withstand? (*Hint:* Try using a combination of methods to protect the shoreline and lighthouse.)

Section 1 Wave Action

Key Ideas

- Most waves are caused by winds blowing across the surface of the water.
- When waves enter shallow water, the wavelength shortens and wave height increases. The wave becomes unstable and breaks on the shore.
- Waves erode shorelines, carving cliffs and breaking up rocks into pebbles and sand.
- An earthquake on the ocean floor can cause a very powerful wave called a tsunami.

Key Terms

wave	crest	wavelength
frequency	trough	wave height
longshore drift	sandbar	rip current
groin	tsunami	

Section 2 Tides

INTEGRATING SPACE SCIENCE

Key Ideas

- Tides are caused by the interaction of Earth, the moon, and the sun.
- There are two high tides and two low tides each day in most places.
- The height of tides during a month varies with changes in the positions of Earth, the moon, and the sun.

Key Terms

tide spring tide neap tide

Section 3 Ocean Water Chemistry

Key Ideas

- Chloride and sodium are the most abundant ions in ocean water.
- Salinity varies throughout the ocean, depending on the amount of evaporation or freezing, as well as the addition of fresh water from rivers or precipitation.
- Below the ocean surface, the water is divided into layers by temperature, with uniformly cold temperatures in deep water.
- Pressure increases greatly with increasing depth in the ocean.

Key Terms

salinity submersible

Section 4 Currents and Climate

Key Ideas

- Currents are formed by Earth's rotation, winds, and differences in water temperature.
- The movement of warm-water and cold-water surface currents carries water around the world and influences coastal climates.
- Density differences between warm and cold water cause many deep-water currents in the ocean.
- El Niño changes the pattern of winds and currents and affects Earth's weather.

Key Terms

current	Coriolis effect	climate
upwelling	El Niño	

ACTIVITY

USING THE INTERNET

www.phschool.com/state_focus/california/

CHAPTER 12 ASSESSMENT

California Test Prep: Reviewing Content

Multiple Choice

Choose the letter of the best answer.

1. Rolling waves with a large distance between crests have a long
   a. wave height. **b.** wavelength.
   c. frequency. **d.** trough.
2. Groins are built to reduce the effect of
   a. tsunamis. **b.** longshore drift.
   c. rip currents. **d.** deep currents.
3. At the full moon, the combined gravitational pulls of the sun and moon produce the biggest difference between low and high tide, called a
   a. surface current. **b.** neap tide.
   c. spring tide. **d.** rip current.
4. Ocean water is more dense than fresh water at the same temperature because of
   a. pressure.
   b. the Coriolis effect.
   c. upwelling.
   d. salinity.
5. Winds and currents move in curved paths because of
   a. the Coriolis effect.
   b. longshore drift.
   c. wave height.
   d. tides.

True or False

If the statement is true, write true. If it is false, change the underlined word or words to make the statement true.

6. Sand is gradually carried down the beach by upwelling.
7. The most common ions dissolved in ocean water are sodium and potassium.
8. Two gases dissolved in ocean water that are important to living things are oxygen and carbon dioxide.
9. As you descend deeper into the ocean, the water gets colder and pressure decreases.
10. Currents carry cold and warm ocean water around the world.

Checking Concepts

11. Explain how a rip current forms.
12. Explain how a tsunami forms and moves. Why are tsunamis so destructive?
13. Why are there two high tides a day in most places?
14. How do warm-water currents affect climate?
15. Describe the causes and result of upwelling.
16. **Writing to Learn** Imagine a beach or seashore that you have visited or would like to visit. Using what you know about wave action, write a description of the shape of the beach, sand drift, cliffs, dunes, and other features.

Thinking Visually

17. **Flowchart** Copy the flowchart about the movement of a wave onto a sheet of paper. Complete the flowchart by putting the following five steps in the correct sequence: *wave travels as low swell; wind creates ripple on ocean surface; wave breaks on shore; wavelength decreases and wave height increases; wave touches bottom in shallow water.* Add a title. (For more on flowcharts, see the Skills Handbook.)

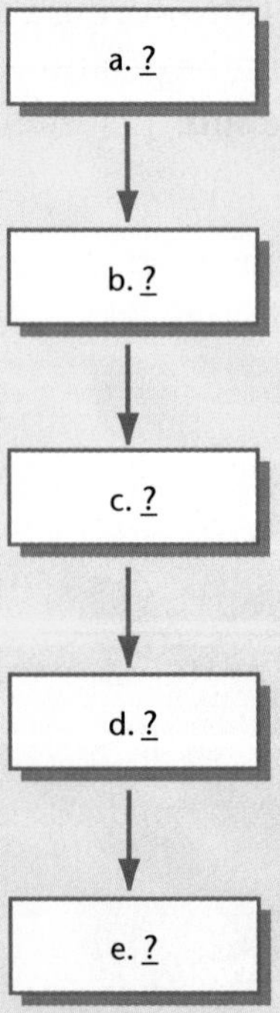
a. ?
b. ?
c. ?
d. ?
e. ?

Test Prep: Skills

The temperature readings in the table were obtained in the Atlantic Ocean near Bermuda. Use the data to answer Questions 18–20.

Depth (m)	Temp. (°C)	Depth (m)	Temp. (°C)
0	19	1,000	9
200	18	1,200	5
400	18	1,400	5
600	16	1,600	4
800	12	1,800	4

18. **Graphing** Construct a line graph using the data in the table. Plot depth readings on the horizontal axis and temperature readings on the vertical axis.
19. **Drawing Conclusions** Use your graph to identify the temperature range in the transition zone.
20. **Predicting** Predict how the ocean temperature at depths of 0 meters and at 1,400 meters would change with the seasons in this location. Explain your reasoning.

Thinking Critically

21. **Classifying** Classify these different movements of ocean water by whether each is caused by winds or not caused by winds: waves, tsunamis, tides, surface currents, deep currents, upwelling.
22. **Applying Concepts** Would you expect salinity to be high or low in a rainy ocean region near the mouth of a river? Why?
23. **Comparing and Contrasting** In what ways is the ocean at 1,000 meters deep different from the ocean at the surface in the same location?
24. **Relating Cause and Effect** How does the movement of ocean currents explain the fact that much of western Europe has a mild, wet climate?

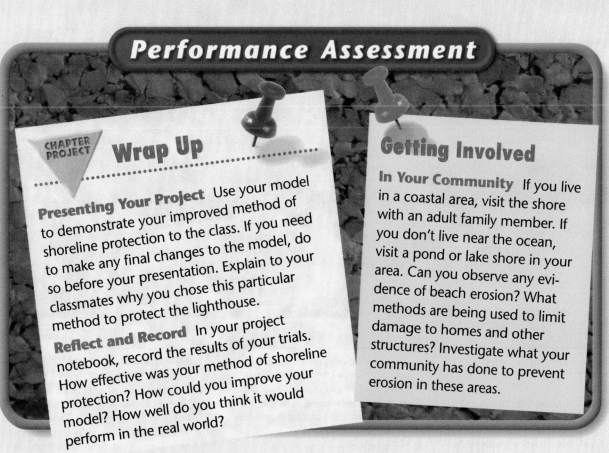

Performance Assessment

CHAPTER PROJECT Wrap Up

Presenting Your Project Use your model to demonstrate your improved method of shoreline protection to the class. If you need to make any final changes to the model, do so before your presentation. Explain to your classmates why you chose this particular method to protect the lighthouse.

Reflect and Record In your project notebook, record the results of your trials. How effective was your method of shoreline protection? How could you improve your model? How well do you think it would perform in the real world?

Getting Involved

In Your Community If you live in a coastal area, visit the shore with an adult family member. If you don't live near the ocean, visit a pond or lake shore in your area. Can you observe any evidence of beach erosion? What methods are being used to limit damage to homes and other structures? Investigate what your community has done to prevent erosion in these areas.

CHAPTER 13

Ocean Zones

The many residents of this New Guinea coral reef include golden fairy basslets, a red gorgonian sea fan, and a vibrant blue sea star.

The following California Science Content Standards are addressed in this chapter:

1. **Plate tectonics explains important features of the Earth's surface and major geologic events.**
   - **a.** The fit of the continents, location of earthquakes, volcanoes, and midocean ridges, and the distribution of fossils, rock types, and ancient climatic zones provide evidence for plate tectonics.
   - **e.** Major geologic events, such as earthquakes, volcanic eruptions, and mountain building result from plate motions.

5. **Organisms in ecosystems exchange energy and nutrients among themselves and with the environment.**
   - **a.** Energy entering ecosystems as sunlight is transferred by producers into chemical energy through photosynthesis, and then from organism to organism in food webs.
   - **d.** Different kinds of organisms may play similar ecological roles in similar biomes.
   - **e.** The number and types of organisms an ecosystem can support depends on the resources available and abiotic factors, such as quantity of light and

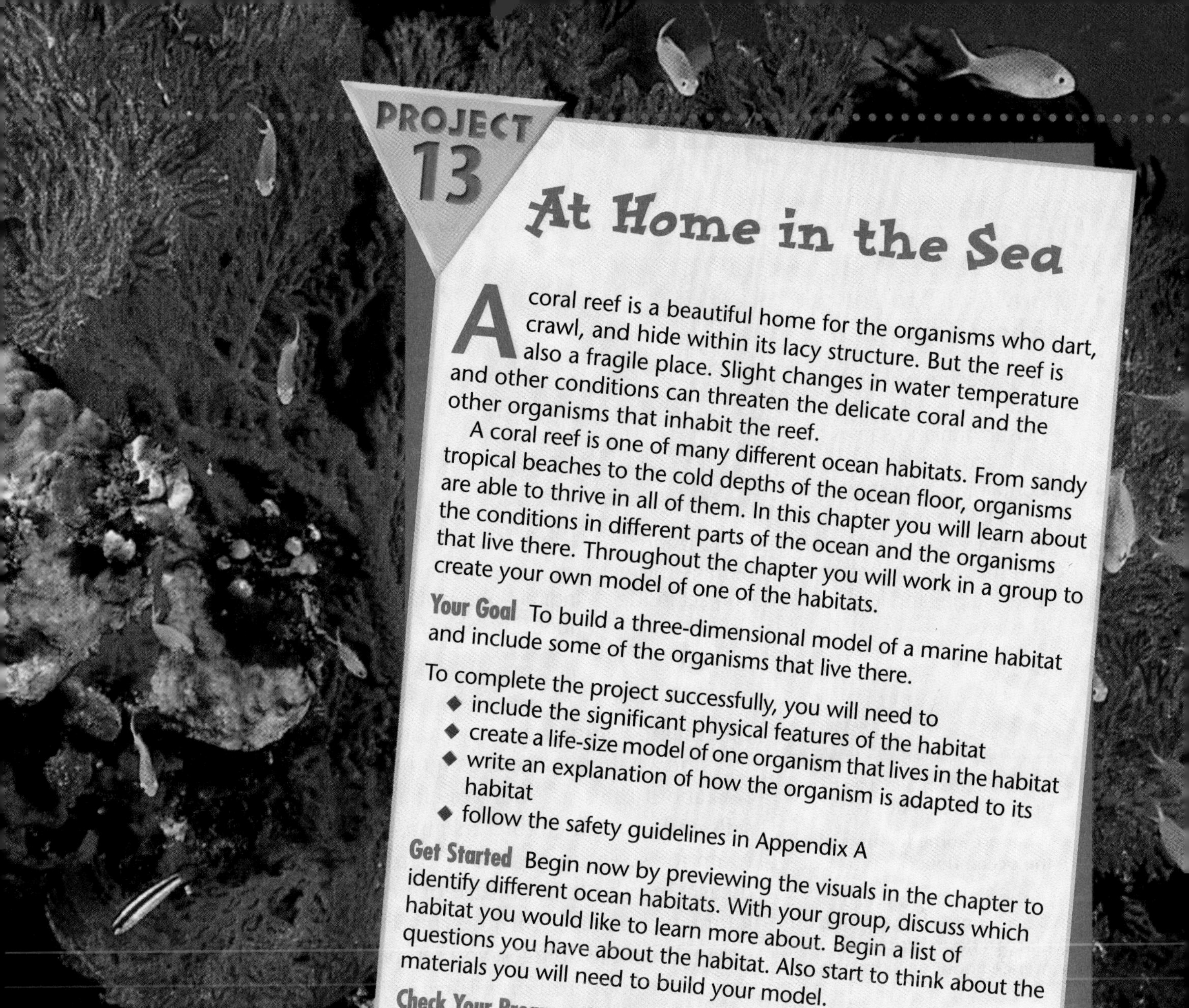

PROJECT 13

At Home in the Sea

A coral reef is a beautiful home for the organisms who dart, crawl, and hide within its lacy structure. But the reef is also a fragile place. Slight changes in water temperature and other conditions can threaten the delicate coral and the other organisms that inhabit the reef.

A coral reef is one of many different ocean habitats. From sandy tropical beaches to the cold depths of the ocean floor, organisms are able to thrive in all of them. In this chapter you will learn about the conditions in different parts of the ocean and the organisms that live there. Throughout the chapter you will work in a group to create your own model of one of the habitats.

Your Goal To build a three-dimensional model of a marine habitat and include some of the organisms that live there.

To complete the project successfully, you will need to

- include the significant physical features of the habitat
- create a life-size model of one organism that lives in the habitat
- write an explanation of how the organism is adapted to its habitat
- follow the safety guidelines in Appendix A

Get Started Begin now by previewing the visuals in the chapter to identify different ocean habitats. With your group, discuss which habitat you would like to learn more about. Begin a list of questions you have about the habitat. Also start to think about the materials you will need to build your model.

Check Your Progress You'll be working on this project as you study this chapter. To keep your project on track, look for Check Your Progress boxes at the following points.

Section 2 Review, page 413: Draw a scale diagram of your model.

Section 3 Review, page 420: Research your organism and build your model.

Wrap Up At the end of the chapter (page 431), you will display your model organism in its habitat.

water, range of temperatures, and soil composition.

6. Sources of energy and materials differ in amounts, distribution, usefulness, and the time required for their formation.

a. The utility of energy sources is determined by factors that are involved in converting these sources to useful forms and the consequences of the conversion process.

b. Different natural energy and material resources, including air, soil, rocks, minerals, petroleum, fresh water, wildlife, and forests, and classify them as renewable or nonrenewable.

c. Natural origin of the materials used to make common objects.

7. Scientific progress is made by asking meaningful questions and conducting careful investigations.

c. Construct appropriate graphs from data and develop qualitative statements about the relationships between variables.

e. Recognize whether evidence is consistent with a proposed explanation.

SECTION 1 Exploring the Ocean

DISCOVER ACTIVITY

What Can You Learn Without Seeing?

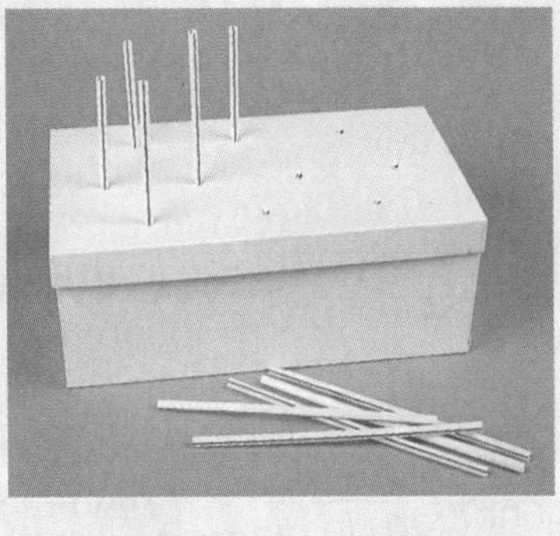

1. Your teacher will provide your group with ten plastic drinking straws and a covered box containing a mystery object. The top of the box has several holes punched in it. Using the straws as probes, try to determine the size, shape, and location of the object inside the box.
2. Based on the information you gathered, describe your object. What can you say about its length, shape, and position? Write down your hypothesis about the identity of the object.
3. Remove the box top to reveal the object.

Think It Over

Inferring Explain how you used the method of indirect observation in this activity to learn about the object.

GUIDE FOR READING

- **What factors make ocean-floor research difficult?**
- **What are some features of the ocean floor?**

Reading Tip **As you read, make a list of features found on the ocean floor. Write one sentence about each feature.**

Imagine going on a voyage around the world lasting three and a half years. Your assignment: to investigate "everything about the sea." Your vessel: a former warship, powered by sails and a steam engine. Its guns have been removed to make room for scientific gear. On board there are thermometers for measuring the temperature of ocean water and hundreds of kilometers of cable for lowering dredges to the bottom of the ocean. With the dredges, you scrape sand, muck, and rock from the ocean floor. You drag trawl nets behind the ship to collect ocean organisms.

The crew of a British ship, HMS *Challenger*, began such a voyage in 1872. By the end of the journey, the scientists had gathered enough data to fill 50 volumes and had collected more than 4,000 new organisms! It took 23 years to publish all the information they learned about oceanwater chemistry, currents, ocean life, and the shape of the ocean floor. The voyage of the *Challenger* was so successful that it became the model for many later ocean expeditions.

Figure 1 This engraving shows HMS *Challenger* in the Indian Ocean in 1874, two years into its journey around the world.

Voyages of Discovery

For thousands of years before the *Challenger* expedition, people explored the ocean. Knowledge of the ocean has always been important to the people living along its coasts. The ocean has provided food and served as a route for trade and travel to new settlements.

The Phoenicians, who lived along the Mediterranean Sea, were one of the earliest cultures to explore the oceans. By 1200 B.C., they had established sea routes for trade with the other nations around the Mediterranean. After the Phoenicians, people of many European, African, and Asian cultures sailed along the coasts to trade with distant lands.

In the Pacific Ocean around 2,000 years ago, the Polynesians left the safety of the coastline and boldly sailed into the open ocean. Their knowledge of winds and currents enabled the Polynesians to settle the scattered islands of Hawaii, Tahiti, and New Zealand.

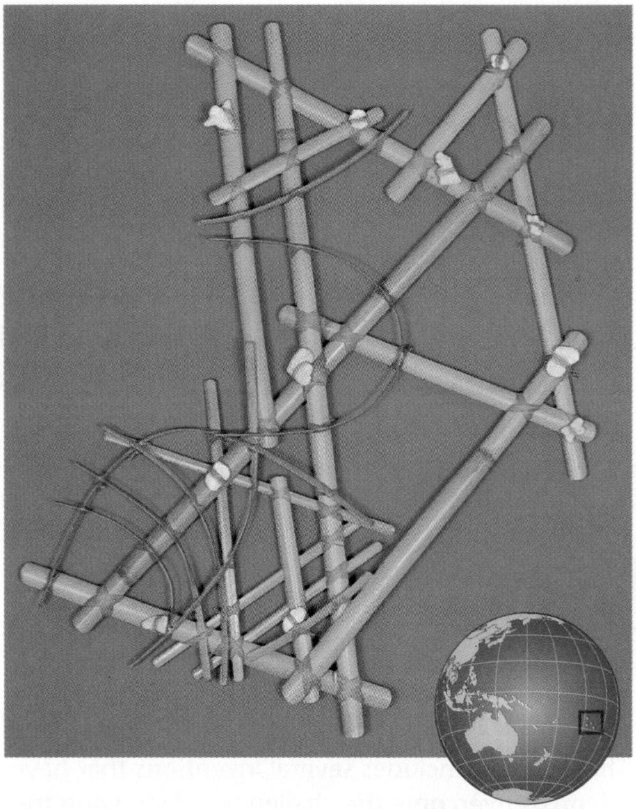

Figure 2 Polynesian sailors used stick charts to navigate the Pacific Ocean. The curved sticks represent currents and winds. The pieces of coral might represent rocks or small islands. *Interpreting Maps Use the map to explain why navigation tools were important to the Polynesians.*

As modern science developed and trade increased, ocean exploration changed. Nations needed accurate maps of the oceans and lands bordering them. Governments also wanted their countries to be known for new scientific discoveries. For example, in the late 1700s, the British government hired Captain James Cook to lead three voyages of exploration. Cook's crew included scientists who studied the stars and collected new species of plants and animals.

Within a century of Cook's voyages, almost all of Earth's coastlines had been mapped. Scientists then turned to the study of the ocean's waters and invented methods to explore its unknown depths. The *Challenger* expedition marked the beginning of the modern science of oceanography.

☑ *Checkpoint* ***What are two reasons why people have explored the oceans?***

Exploring the Ocean Floor

INTEGRATING TECHNOLOGY Following the *Challenger's* example, governments and universities sponsored many other major ocean research expeditions. Until recently, however, the ocean floor was unexplored, and much of the life in the oceans was unknown. Why did it take so long to reach this part of the ocean? Studying the ocean floor is difficult because the ocean is so deep—3.8 kilometers deep on average, more than twice as deep as the Grand Canyon. As you learned in Chapter 4, conditions are very harsh at such depths. First, because sunlight does not penetrate far below the surface, the deep ocean is in total darkness. Second, the water is very cold—only a few degrees above freezing. Finally, there is tremendous pressure due to the mass of water pushing down from above.

Because of the darkness, cold, and extreme pressure, scientists have had to develop technology to enable them to study the deep ocean floor. Since humans cannot survive these conditions, many of the inventions have involved indirect methods of gathering information. One of the simplest methods, used by the *Challenger's* crew, was to lower a weight on a long line into the water until the weight touched the bottom. The length of line

SCIENCE & History

Technology and Ocean Exploration

The time line includes several inventions that have helped scientists overcome the challenges of studying the ocean world.

1943 SCUBA

Jacques Cousteau and Emile Gagnan invented SCUBA, which stands for "**s**elf-**c**ontained **u**nderwater **b**reathing **a**pparatus." A tank containing compressed air is strapped to the diver's back and connected by a tube to a mouthpiece. SCUBA enables divers to explore to a depth of 40 meters.

1915 1930 1945 1960

1925 Sonar

Scientists aboard the German ship *Meteor* used sonar to map the ocean floor. They used a device called an echo sounder to produce pulses of sound. The ship's crew then timed the return of the echoes.

1960 Submersibles

Vehicles with very thick metal hulls protect explorers from extreme pressure and temperature, while enabling them to directly observe the ocean depths.

that got wet was approximately equal to the water's depth at that location. This method was slow and often inaccurate, as the line would descend at an angle. Nevertheless, these depth readings produced the first rough maps of the floor of the North Atlantic.

A major advance in ocean-floor mapping was sonar, a technology invented during World War I to detect submarines. **Sonar**, which stands for **so**und **na**vigation and **r**anging, is a system that uses sound waves to calculate the distance to an object. The sonar equipment on a ship sends out pulses of sound that bounce off the ocean floor. The equipment then measures how quickly the sound waves return to the ship. Sound waves return quickly if the ocean floor is close. Sound waves take longer to return if the ocean floor is farther away.

☑ *Checkpoint* *How is sonar an indirect way of gathering data?*

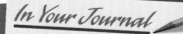

In Your Journal

Each of the inventions shown on these two pages helped solve a problem of ocean exploration. Find out more about one of these inventions. Write a short newspaper article telling the story of its development. Include details about the people who invented it and how it added to people's knowledge of the oceans.

1986

Remote Underwater Manipulator

The Remote Underwater Manipulator, or RUM III, is about the size of a small car. It is controlled by a computer aboard a ship at the surface. Without a crew, the RUM III can collect samples, take photographs, and map the ocean floor.

1975 **1990** **2005** **2020**

1978 Satellites

Seasat A was the first satellite in Earth's orbit to study the oceans. Since satellites make millions of observations a day, they provide data on rapidly changing and widespread ocean conditions. Such data include temperatures, algae growth patterns, and even the movement of large schools of fish.

1995

Gravity Mapping

The United States Navy used advanced satellite data to create a new map of the ocean floor. The satellite detected slight changes in gravity related to the shape of the ocean floor, providing accurate measurements within a few centimeters.

Features of the Ocean Floor

Once scientists were able to map the ocean floor, they discovered something surprising. The bottom of the ocean was not a flat, sandy plain. The deep waters hid mountain ranges bigger than any on Earth's surface, as well as deep canyons reaching into Earth's interior. If you could take a submarine voyage along the ocean floor, what would you see? Trace your journey from the edge of one continent to another in *Exploring the Ocean Floor.*

As you leave the harbor, your submarine first passes over the **continental shelf**, a gently sloping, shallow area of the ocean floor that extends outward from the edge of a continent. At a depth of about 130 meters, the ocean floor begins to slope more steeply. This incline at the edge of the continental shelf is called the **continental slope**. The continental slope marks the true edge of a continent, where the rock that makes up the continent stops and the rock of the ocean floor begins.

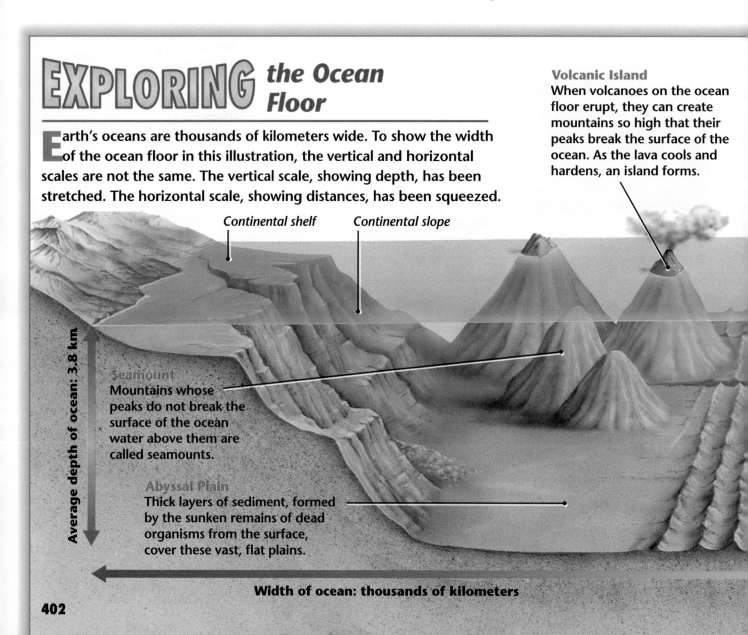

EXPLORING *the Ocean Floor*

Earth's oceans are thousands of kilometers wide. To show the width of the ocean floor in this illustration, the vertical and horizontal scales are not the same. The vertical scale, showing depth, has been stretched. The horizontal scale, showing distances, has been squeezed.

Volcanic Island
When volcanoes on the ocean floor erupt, they can create mountains so high that their peaks break the surface of the ocean. As the lava cools and hardens, an island forms.

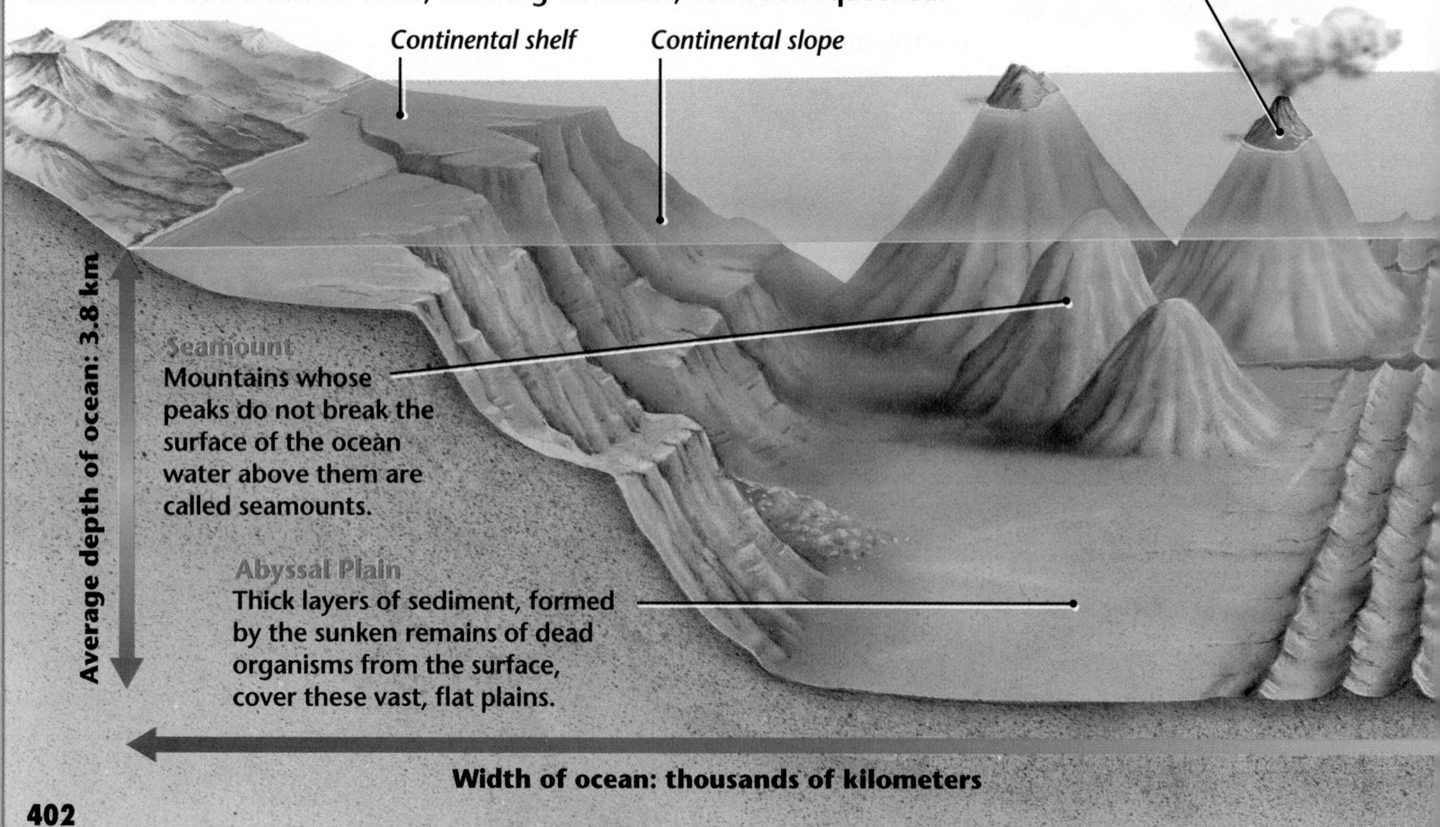
Continental shelf
Continental slope
Average depth of ocean: 3.8 km
Seamount
Mountains whose peaks do not break the surface of the ocean water above them are called seamounts.
Abyssal Plain
Thick layers of sediment, formed by the sunken remains of dead organisms from the surface, cover these vast, flat plains.
Width of ocean: thousands of kilometers

Your submarine descends more gradually now, following the ocean floor as it slopes toward the deep ocean. After some distance, you encounter a group of mountains. Some are tall enough to break the ocean's surface, forming islands. Others, called **seamounts**, are mountains that are completely underwater. Some seamounts have flat tops because their peaks have eroded away.

Next you cross a broad area covered with thick layers of mud and silt. This smooth, nearly flat region of the ocean floor is called the **abyssal plain** (uh BIHS uhl plain). After gliding over the abyssal plain for many kilometers, you need to steer the submarine sharply upward to avoid a mountain range ahead. The **mid-ocean ridge** is a continuous range of mountains that winds around Earth, much as the line of stitches winds around a baseball. The mid-ocean ridge passes through all of Earth's oceans. Nearly 80,000 kilometers long, it is the longest mountain range on Earth.

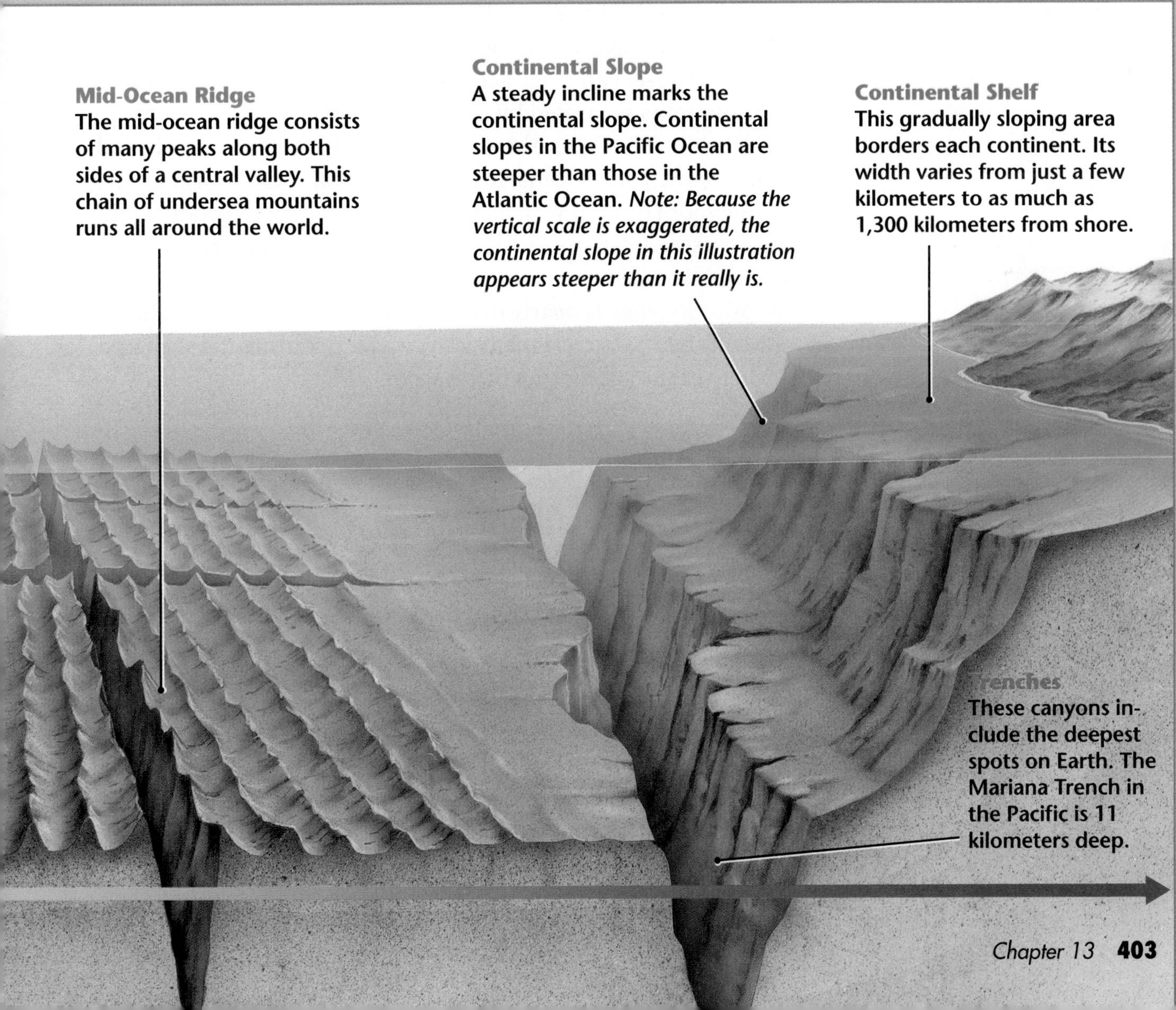
Mid-Ocean Ridge
The mid-ocean ridge consists of many peaks along both sides of a central valley. This chain of undersea mountains runs all around the world.
Continental Slope
A steady incline marks the continental slope. Continental slopes in the Pacific Ocean are steeper than those in the Atlantic Ocean. *Note: Because the vertical scale is exaggerated, the continental slope in this illustration appears steeper than it really is.*
Continental Shelf
This gradually sloping area borders each continent. Its width varies from just a few kilometers to as much as 1,300 kilometers from shore.
renches
These canyons include the deepest spots on Earth. The Mariana Trench in the Pacific is 11 kilometers deep.

Sharpen your Skills

Interpreting Data

ACTIVITY

What is Earth's largest mountain? Use the following data to answer the question. Mauna Kea projects about 4,200 meters above sea level. Its base is on the floor of the Pacific Ocean, approximately 5,550 meters below sea level. Mt. Everest rises 8,850 meters above sea level. Its base is located on land. (*Hint:* Drawing a diagram may be helpful. Start with a line that represents sea level.)

Figure 3 When an undersea volcano reaches above the surface of the water, it forms an island. This peak is Mauna Kea in Hawaii.

At the top of the mid-ocean ridge, your submarine is about two kilometers above the abyssal plain, but you are still at least one kilometer below the surface. From this vantage you can see that the mid-ocean ridge actually consists of two parallel chains of mountains separated by a central valley.

You descend from the mid-ocean ridge to another abyssal plain. Soon your submarine's lights reveal a dark gash in the ocean floor ahead of you. As you pass over it, you look down into a steep-sided canyon in the ocean floor called a **trench**. The trench is so deep you cannot see the bottom.

Your journey is nearly over as your submarine slowly climbs the continental slope. Finally you cross the continental shelf and maneuver the submarine into harbor.

☑ *Checkpoint* ***Which ocean floor feature makes up the deepest parts of the ocean?***

Movements of the Ocean Floor

As oceanographers mapped the ocean floor, their measurements told them about the features you saw on your imaginary journey between the continents. To learn more about the floor of the deep ocean, scientists aboard a drilling ship named *Glomar Challenger*, in honor of the original *Challenger*, collected samples of the rock. They drilled the rock samples from both sides of the mid-ocean ridge in the Atlantic Ocean. Tests on the samples showed that the rock closest to the ridge had formed much more recently than the rock farther away from the ridge. This information helped explain how the ocean floor formed. To understand how, you first need to know something about Earth's structure.

Layers Inside Earth Earth consists of layers that cover the planet's center, or core. The thin, rocky, outer layer of Earth is called the crust. The thick layer between the crust and the core is the mantle. The high temperature and pressure inside Earth cause some of the material in the mantle to form a hot liquid called **magma.** Magma flows very slowly. It can escape upward through cracks in the crust and erupting volcanoes. Magma that reaches the surface is called lava. As lava cools, it forms new crust.

A Cracked Crust Earth's crust is solid rock that is broken into irregularly shaped pieces like the shell of a cracked, hard-boiled egg. The pieces of Earth's crust, along with parts of the upper mantle, are called **plates.** Such plates move slowly on the underlying portion of the mantle. About 14 major plates make up Earth's crust, as shown in Figure 4. They lie beneath the continents as well as the oceans. The plates move at an average speed of several centimeters per year—barely faster than your fingernails grow! Where two plates come together or spread apart, they create different landforms. Plate movements have shaped many of the most dramatic features of the Earth, both on land and under the ocean. **The mountain ranges of the mid-ocean ridge, trenches, and underwater volcanoes are all formed by the interactions of Earth's plates.**

Diverging Plates The mid-ocean ridge is located along the boundaries between plates that are diverging, or moving apart. Along the ridge, magma squeezes up through the cracks between

Figure 4 Earth's crust is divided into 14 major plates. ***Interpreting Maps*** *Name the plates that lie beneath parts of the continent of North America.*

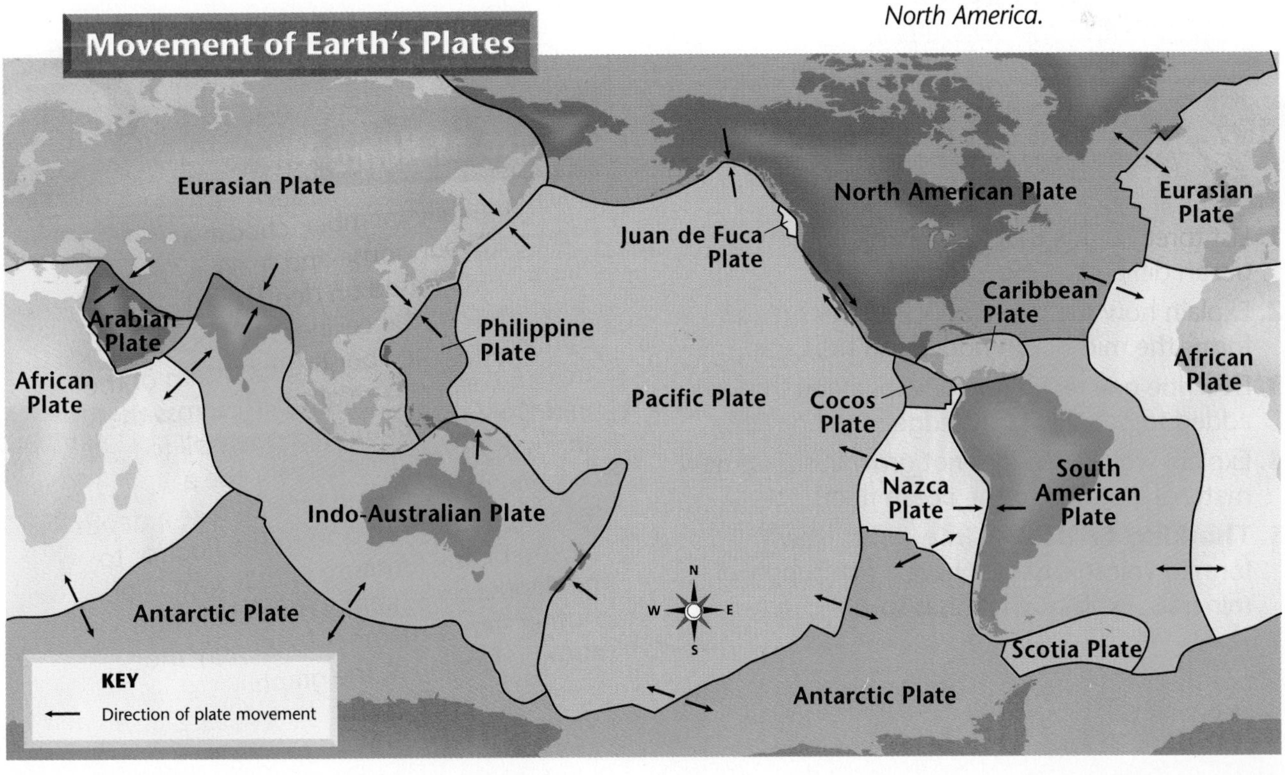
Movement of Earth's Plates
Eurasian Plate
North American Plate
Eurasian Plate
Juan de Fuca Plate
Arabian Plate
Philippine Plate
Caribbean Plate
African Plate
African Plate
Pacific Plate
Cocos Plate
Nazca Plate
South American Plate
Indo-Australian Plate
Antarctic Plate
Scotia Plate
Antarctic Plate
N
W
E
S
KEY
Direction of plate movement

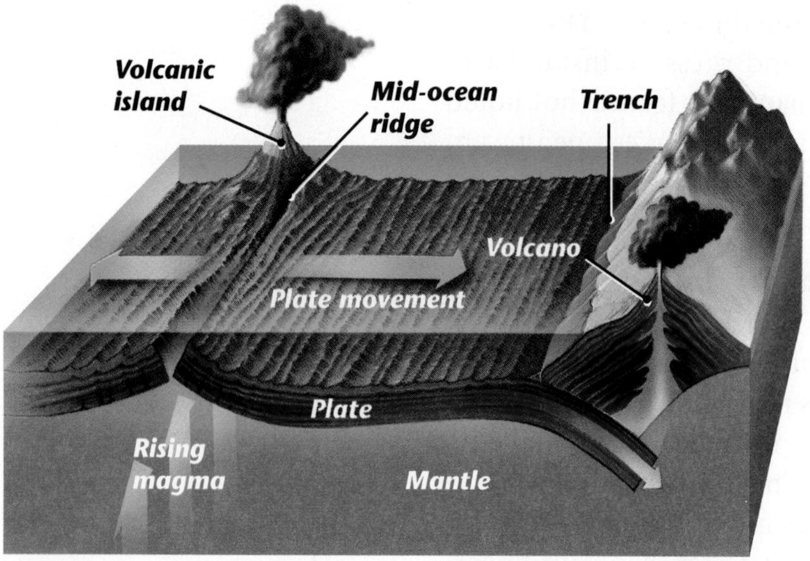
Volcanic island
Mid-ocean ridge
Trench
Volcano
Plate movement
Plate
Rising magma
Mantle

Figure 5 Where two plates diverge, magma from Earth's mantle rises up through the crack. Where two plates converge at a trench, one plate sinks under the other. *Interpreting Diagrams What happens when magma rises to Earth's surface?*

the diverging plates. As the magma hardens along the ridge, it adds a new strip of rock to the ocean floor. Each new eruption along the ridge gradually pushes the older rock away from the center of the ridge. Over many millions of years, this process, called **sea-floor spreading**, produced the ocean floor. The rock samples collected by the *Glomar Challenger* helped confirm the theory of sea-floor spreading by showing that the rocks closer to the ridge had been produced more recently than those farther away.

Converging Plates When the new ocean floor grows along the mid-ocean ridge, where does the old ocean floor farther away from the ridge go? Why doesn't Earth keep getting bigger? The answers to these questions lie in the deep ocean trenches you read about earlier. Where plates come together, or converge, one plate sinks under the other. As new rock is added at the edges of the plates along the mid-ocean ridge, old rock farther away from the mid-ocean ridge sinks into the trenches and back into Earth's interior. This process allows the ocean floor to spread while Earth itself remains the same size.

Section 1 Review

1. List three factors that make exploring the deep ocean difficult.
2. Explain how the movement of Earth's plates forms the mid-ocean ridges and trenches.
3. Describe one technique or expedition that has added to people's knowledge of the oceans.
4. Explain why Earth does not grow in size as new material is added to the ocean floor.
5. **Thinking Critically Inferring** Newly formed volcanic islands have a rich supply of minerals. Explain why this is so.

Science at Home

With a family member, choose a room in your house and make a "room-floor" map based on depth readings. Imagine that the ceiling is the ocean surface and the floor is the bottom of the ocean. Follow a straight path across the middle of the room from one wall to another. At regular intervals, use a carpenter's measuring tape to take a depth reading from the ceiling to the floor or to the top of any furniture in that spot. Plot the depths on a graph. Then challenge another family member to identify the room by looking at the graph.

Interpreting Data

THE SHAPE OF THE OCEAN FLOOR

Skills Lab

Imagine you are an oceanographer traveling across the Atlantic along the 45° N latitude line marked on the map. You and your crew are using sonar to gather data on the depth of the ocean between Nova Scotia, Canada, and the town of Soulac on the coast of France. In this lab, you will interpret the data to create a profile of the ocean floor.

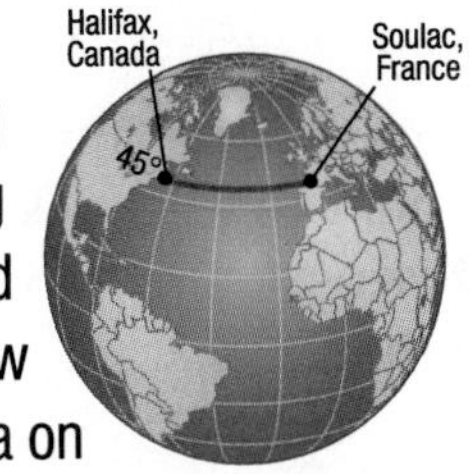
Halifax, Canada
Soulac, France
45°

Problem

How can you use data about ocean depths to determine the shape of the ocean floor?

Materials

pencil   graph paper

Procedure

1. Draw the axes of a graph. Label the horizontal axis Longitude. Mark from 65° W to 0° from left to right. Label the vertical axis Ocean Depth. Mark 0 meters at the top of the vertical axis to represent sea level. Mark –5000 meters at the bottom to represent the depth of 5000 meters below sea level. Mark depths at equal intervals along the vertical axis.
2. Examine the data in the table. The numbers in the Longitude column give the ship's location at 19 points in the Atlantic Ocean. Location 1 is Nova Scotia, and Location 19 is Soulac. The numbers in the Ocean Depth column give the depth measurements recorded at each location. Plot each measurement on your graph. Remember that the depths are represented on your graph as numbers below 0, or sea level.
3. Connect the points you have plotted with a line to create a profile of the ocean floor.

Analyze and Conclude

1. On your graph, identify and label the continental shelf and continental slope.
2. Label the abyssal plain on your graph. How would you expect the ocean floor to look there?
3. Label the mid-ocean ridge on your graph. Describe the process that is occurring there.
4. What might the feature at 10° W be? Explain.
5. **Think About It** How is it helpful to organize data into a data table or graph?

More to Explore

Use the depth measurements in the table to calculate the average depth of the Atlantic Ocean between Nova Scotia and France.

Ocean Depth Sonar Data

Longitude	Ocean Depth (m)
1. 64° W	0
2. 60° W	91
3. 55° W	132
4. 50° W	73
5. 48° W	3512
6. 45° W	4024
7. 40° W	3805
8. 35° W	4171
9. 33° W	3439
10. 30° W	3073
11. 28° W	1756
12. 27° W	2195
13. 25° W	3146
14. 20° W	4244
15. 15° W	4610
16. 10° W	4976
17. 05° W	4317
18. 04° W	146
19. 01° W	0

SECTION 2 Life at the Ocean's Edge

DISCOVER ACTIVITY

Can Your Animal Hold On?

1. Your teacher will give you a ping-pong ball, a rock, and a box containing some materials. The ping-pong ball represents an ocean animal. Use some of the materials to design a way for the animal to cling to the rock.
2. Attach the ping-pong ball to the rock.
3. Place the rock in a sink or deep pan. Run water over the rock from a faucet or pitcher. Observe how well your animal stays in place on the rock.

Think It Over

Inferring How might the ability to "hold on" be important to an animal that lives on the shore?

GUIDE FOR READING

- **What factors affect where ocean organisms live?**
- **What conditions must organisms in the rocky intertidal zone overcome?**
- **What are the major types of coastal wetlands?**

Reading Tip **As you read, make a list of the habitats described in this section. Write a sentence or two describing each habitat.**

At first glance, a sandy ocean beach may seem lifeless. As you walk along the water's edge in the soft, wet sand, you may notice some dark, tangled seaweed that has washed up on the shore. A crab scuttles away from the pile as you walk by. Seagulls screech and swoop overhead. But for the most part, the beach appears deserted.

If you look more closely at the wet sand, you will see evidence of living things right beneath your feet. Tiny, round holes are signs of burrowing clams. These clams dig down into the sand for protection and to prevent being washed away in the waves. If you wade into the water, you may be able to spot a sand crab taking advantage of the surf to feed. The bottom half of its body buried in the sand, the crab waits for the waves to carry in a fresh supply of food for its next meal.

The organisms on this beach are well suited to the conditions there. In this section, you will learn how marine organisms have adapted to other areas where the land and ocean meet.

Living Conditions

A sandy beach is one type of marine, or ocean, habitat. Remember that an organism's habitat provides the things the organism needs to survive. An organism also must be suited to the physical conditions of the environment it lives in. **Some physical factors that determine where marine organisms can live include salinity, water temperature, light, dissolved gases, nutrients, and wave action.**

As you learned in Chapter 4, these conditions vary in different parts of the ocean. For example, salinity is lower where rivers flow into the ocean, bringing a stream of fresh water. Salinity is higher in shallow, warm seas, where more evaporation takes place. Because cold water holds more dissolved gas than warm water, cold ocean waters contain more oxygen than tropical waters. Different organisms are suited to live in these different conditions. As a result, the same organisms do not live in every part of the ocean.

On land, most organisms live on or near the surface. The ocean, on the other hand, is a three-dimensional environment. It is inhabited by organisms at every depth. Scientists classify marine organisms according to where they live and how they move.

Plankton are tiny algae and animals that float in the water and are carried by waves and currents. Algae plankton include geometrically-shaped diatoms like those shown in Figure 6. Animal plankton include microscopic crustaceans and fish larvae. **Nekton** are free-swimming animals that can move throughout the water column. Octopus and squid, most fishes, and marine mammals such as whales and dolphins are nekton. **Benthos** are organisms that inhabit the ocean floor. Some benthos, like crabs, sea stars, and lobsters, move from place to place. Others, like sponges and sea anemones, stay in one location.

Plankton, nekton, and benthos are all found in most marine habitats. Many plankton and benthos are algae which, like plants, use sunlight to produce their own food through photosynthesis. Other plankton and benthos, as well as all nekton, are consumers. They eat either the algae or other consumers. Finally, some organisms, including many benthos, are decomposers. They break down wastes and remains of other organisms. These feeding relationships in a habitat make up a **food web**.

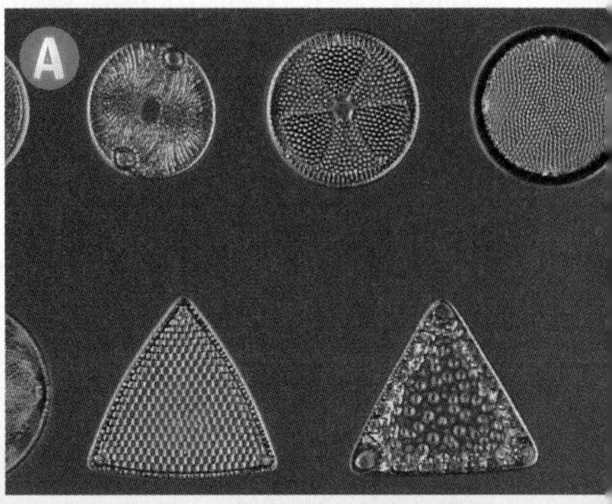
A

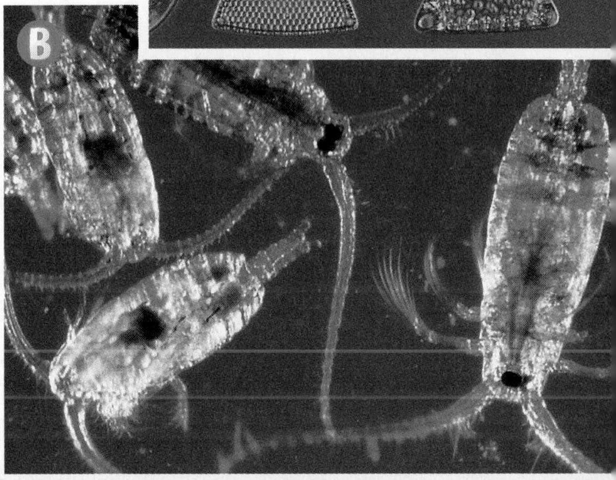
B

C

D

Figure 6 Marine organisms can be classified as plankton, nekton, or benthos. **A.** Intricate diatoms, one type of algae plankton, float on the ocean surface. **B.** These microscopic crustaceans, called copepods, are animal plankton. **C.** Free-swimming animals, such as this school of sweetlip fish, are nekton. **D.** Benthos live on the ocean floor. The sea stars and sea anemones in this colorful array are benthos.

Language Arts CONNECTION

About 350 years ago, a form of poetry called *haiku* grew popular in Japan. Here is an example of a haiku about a beach.

Shining air bubbles
pushing up the hardpacked sand:
a shy clam revealed.

This poem may appear simple, but it follows a strict structure. A haiku is a 17-syllable poem written in 3 lines. There are 5 syllables in the first line, 7 syllables in the second line, and 5 syllables in the third line. A haiku should capture a moment in nature and suggest a mood or feeling.

In Your Journal

Prepare to write your own haiku about the edge of the ocean. Work with a partner to think of what you might see, hear, and feel. Review the habitats in this section for ideas. Then choose one simple, specific subject to write about. Write a draft and exchange it with your partner. After making revisions, illustrate your poem.

The first group of ocean habitats you will learn about are those found at the very edge of the ocean. The sandy beach you read about earlier is one example. Two habitats with a richer variety of life are rocky shores and salt marshes. As you read, think about how conditions in these habitats are similar, and how they are different.

☑ *Checkpoint* ***Are sharks plankton, nekton, or benthos? Why?***

Rocky Shores

Imagine if your home had no walls or roof. Twice a day, a huge storm passes through, bringing a drenching downpour and winds so strong you can hardly keep your balance. At other times, the hot sun beats down, leaving you parched and dry. This is what life is like for organisms that live on rocky shores in the intertidal zone. The **intertidal zone** stretches from the highest high-tide line on land out to the point on the continental shelf exposed by the lowest low tide.

Organisms that live in the rocky intertidal zone must be able to tolerate the pounding of the waves and changes in salinity and temperature. They must also withstand periods of being underwater and periods of being exposed to the air. They must avoid drying out, hide from predators, and find food in this harsh setting. How are organisms able to survive?

Along the Rocks Rocky shores are found along much of both coasts of the United States. Figure 7 shows some of the colorful organisms that typically live along the rocky California coast.

The highest rocks, above the highest high-tide line, make up the spray zone. The spray zone is never completely covered with water, but it gets wet as the waves break against the rocks. A stripe of black algae indicates the highest high-tide line. The rocks below this level are encrusted with barnacles. Barnacles can close up their hard shells, trapping a drop of water inside to carry

Sea urchin
Sea lettuce
Sea anemones
Abalone
Brittle star

them through the dry period until the next high tide. Lower down, clumps of blue and black mussels stick out amidst the algae. The mussels produce sticky threads that harden on contact with the water, attaching the mussels to the rock. The threads are so strong that scientists are studying them as a model for new glues. The rocks are also home to flat mollusks called limpets. Limpets have a large, muscular foot to hold on tightly. They secrete drops of mucus around the edges of their shells to form a tight seal.

Algae that live in the intertidal zone are also adapted to withstand the physical conditions. Rootlike structures anchor the strands of algae firmly to the rocks. Some algae are covered with a thick layer of slime. The slime keeps the algae from drying out during low tide.

In Tide Pools When the tide goes out, some water remains in depressions among the rocks called tide pools. As the water in a tide pool is warmed by the sun, it begins to evaporate. The remaining water becomes saltier. If it rains, however, the salinity quickly decreases. Organisms in the tide pool must be able to withstand these changes in temperature and salinity, as well as the force of the waves when the tide comes in again.

Sea stars cling to the rocks with rows of tiny suction cups on their undersides. Spiny purple sea urchins crawl slowly along the bottom of the tide pool. If the bottom is sandy, sea urchins can use their spines to dig a hole in which to bury themselves during heavy surf. Under shady rock ledges, sponges and sea anemones wait for the incoming tide to bring a fresh supply of plankton and other food particles. A sea anemone may look delicate, but some can survive out of water for over two weeks. When out of the water, the anemone pulls its tentacles inside. It folds up into a round blob, resembling a rolled-up sock.

Figure 7 The constantly changing water level in the intertidal zone creates different habitats along a rocky coast. *Comparing and Contrasting How are conditions different for organisms near the top of the rocks compared to organisms at the bottom?*

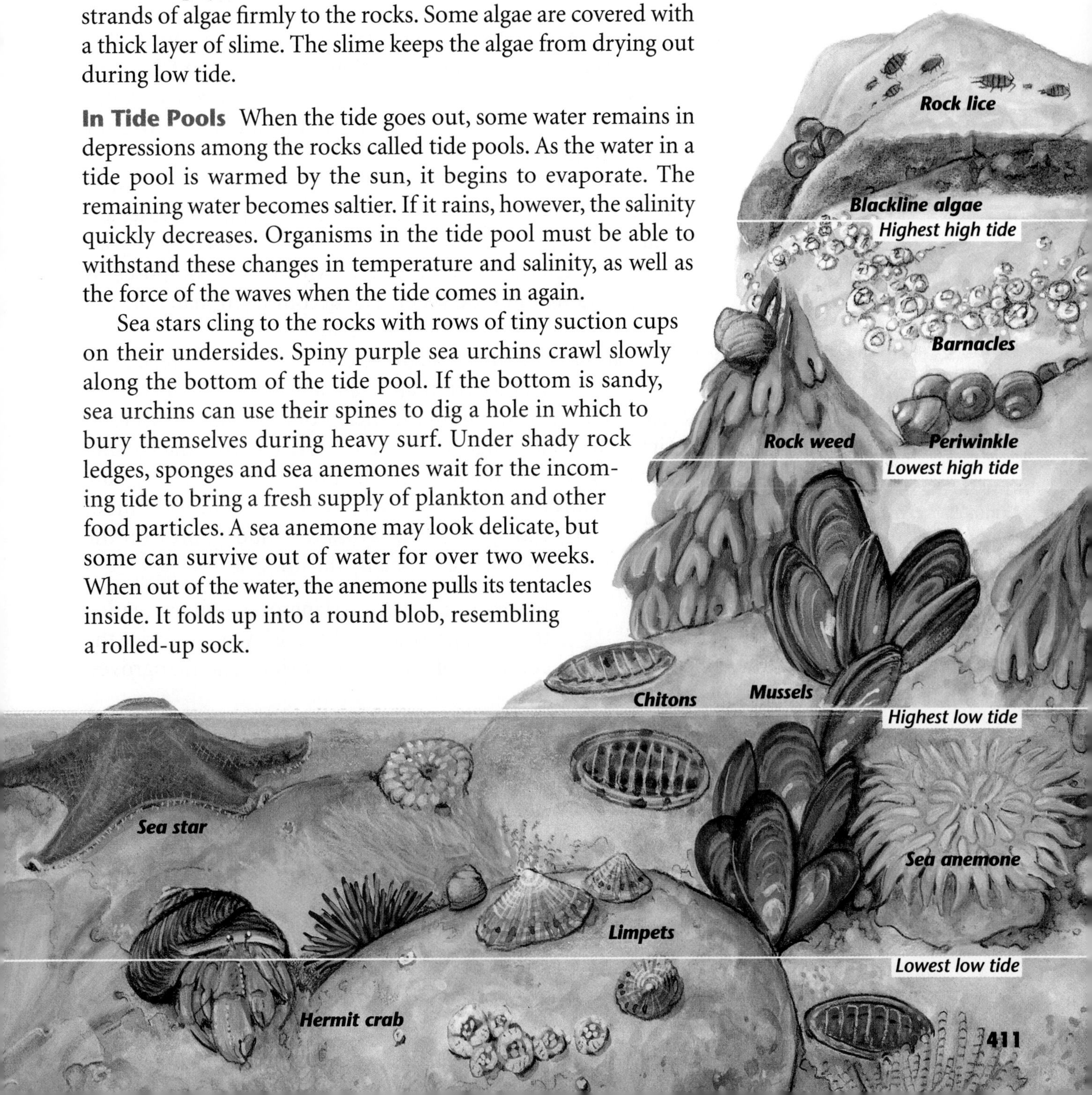
Rock lice
Blackline algae
Highest high tide
Barnacles
Rock weed
Periwinkle
Lowest high tide
Chitons
Mussels
Highest low tide
Sea star
Sea anemone
Limpets
Lowest low tide
Hermit crab

Where River Meets Ocean

Other important environments along the ocean's edge are estuaries. **Estuaries** are coastal inlets or bays where fresh water from rivers mixes with the salty ocean water. Water that is partly salty and partly fresh is **brackish.**

Coastal wetlands are habitats found in and around estuaries. **Along the United States coasts, most coastal wetlands are either salt marshes or mangrove forests.** Salt marshes are especially abundant along the east coast from Massachusetts to Florida. Mangrove forests are found in the tropical waters along the southern coast of Florida and the Gulf of Mexico.

Salt Marshes A salt marsh oozes with smelly mud. Mosquitoes swarm over the water as it flows slowly through the tall, green grasses. The fresh water and tides contribute sediments, animal and plant matter, and other nutrients to the salt marsh, forming a soft, rich mud bottom.

A single plant, cordgrass, dominates the marsh. Unlike most plants, cordgrass can survive in salt water. The plant releases salt through small openings in its long, narrow leaves. The cordgrass that is not eaten by animals breaks down and is decomposed by bacteria and fungi in the water. The decomposed material supplies nutrients to organisms in the marsh.

Tidal channels run through the cordgrass. Waves break up as they enter the channels, so that organisms in the marsh are protected from the surf. Within the shelter of the marsh, fish, crabs, shrimp, and oysters hatch and feed before entering the harsher ocean environment offshore. As the tide retreats, mud flats are exposed. Hordes of crabs search for food in the rich mud. Herons, stilts, and egrets stalk across the mud to prey on the crabs and other benthos exposed by the low tide.

Figure 8 Salt marshes and mangrove forests are two types of coastal wetlands. **A.** Salt water flows through tidal channels in a salt marsh. **B.** Arching prop roots anchor these black mangrove trees firmly in the soft, sandy soil around Florida Bay. ***Making Generalizations*** *How does the plant life in each of these habitats provide shelter for marine organisms?*

A

B

Mangrove Forests Mangroves—short, gnarled trees that grow well in brackish water—fringe the coastline of southern Florida. The mangroves' prop roots anchor the trees to the land. Mangroves can withstand all but the strongest hurricane winds. Without the mangroves to break the action of winds and waves, the coastline would change dramatically each hurricane season. The prop roots also trap sediment from the land. They create a protected nursery rich in nutrients for many young animals.

Protecting Estuaries The rivers that flow into estuaries can carry harmful substances as well as nutrients. When pollutants such as pesticides, sewage, and industrial waste get into the river water, they end up in the estuary. The pollutants change the water quality in the estuary. In turn, organisms that live in the estuary are affected. It can take many years for ocean tides to flush a heavy load of pollutants out of an estuary.

For example, Chesapeake Bay is a huge estuary located on the mid-Atlantic coast. It has been a rich source of oysters, clams, and blue crabs. However, pollutants from inland sources accumulated in the bay for many years. Their effect was to greatly reduce the number and kinds of organisms in the Chesapeake. When people realized the threat to the estuary, they took action. The water quality of rivers that empty into Chesapeake Bay is now regulated by law. Cleanup efforts have reduced much of the pollution in the bay. Today, organisms like the blue crab are making a comeback.

Figure 9 A crabber in Chesapeake Bay pulls up the last trap of the day. As the health of the estuary improves, the blue crab population is growing again.

Section 2 Review

1. Name five physical factors that affect organisms in marine habitats.
2. Describe conditions in the rocky intertidal zone.
3. List two ways that salt marshes and mangrove forests are alike and two ways they are different.
4. **Thinking Critically Making Judgments** A builder has proposed filling in a salt marsh to create a seaside resort. What positive and negative impacts might this proposal have on wildlife, local residents, and tourists? Would you support the proposal? Why or why not?

CHAPTER PROJECT

Check Your Progress

Your group should now select the marine environment you will create. Measure the space where you will build your model. Make a list of the physical features you will need to represent. Draw a scale diagram of your model and show it to your teacher. Label the different features and note the materials you will use. (*Hint:* Draw your sketch on graph paper to plan its size to fit the space.)

SECTION 3 The Neritic Zone and Open Ocean

DISCOVER ACTIVITY

How Deep Can You See?

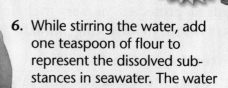

1. With a permanent marker, divide a white plastic lid into four quarters. Shade in two quarters as shown.
2. Use a pair of scissors to carefully poke a small hole in the center of the lid.
3. Tie a piece of string to a paper clip. Place the clip underneath the lid and thread the string up through the hole.
4. Tape the string tightly to a meterstick so that the lid presses against the bottom of the meterstick.
5. Fill a large, deep bucket with tap water.
6. While stirring the water, add one teaspoon of flour to represent the dissolved substances in seawater. The water should be slightly cloudy.
7. Lower the lid into the water so that it is 5 cm below the surface. Note whether the lid is still visible in the water.
8. Lower the lid 10 cm below the surface, then 15 cm, and so on until the lid is no longer visible.

Think It Over

Observing At what depth could you no longer see the lid? Based on your results, how do you think visibility changes with depth in the ocean?

GUIDE FOR READING

- **What conditions in the neritic zone support organisms?**
- **Where do algae live in the open ocean?**
- **How do hydrothermal vents support organisms?**

Reading Tip **Before you read, preview Figure 10 on the facing page. Predict how the neritic zone and open ocean are similar and how they are different.**

Floating mats of golden-brown, leaflike fronds on the ocean surface mark the location of a kelp forest. Diving below the surface, you find yourself surrounded by tall, swaying stalks of giant kelp. Sunlight filters through the water, producing a greenish light. As you pull yourself hand over hand down one of the kelp strands, you notice small bulbs at the base of each frond. You pinch one of the bulbs, and a bubble of gas escapes. These bulbs keep the heavy kelp fronds upright in the water.

The kelp forest is full of life. Bright-orange sheephead fish dart past you. Young sea lions chase each other around the kelp stalks. A sea otter, surrounded by a stream of bubbles, dives past you, down to the rocky bottom. When it rises, the otter is clutching a sea star between its paws. On the surface again, you watch the sea otter as it rolls onto its back among the kelp. The otter deftly uses its paws to scoop out the meat from the soft underside of the sea star.

◀ Sea otter eating a sea star

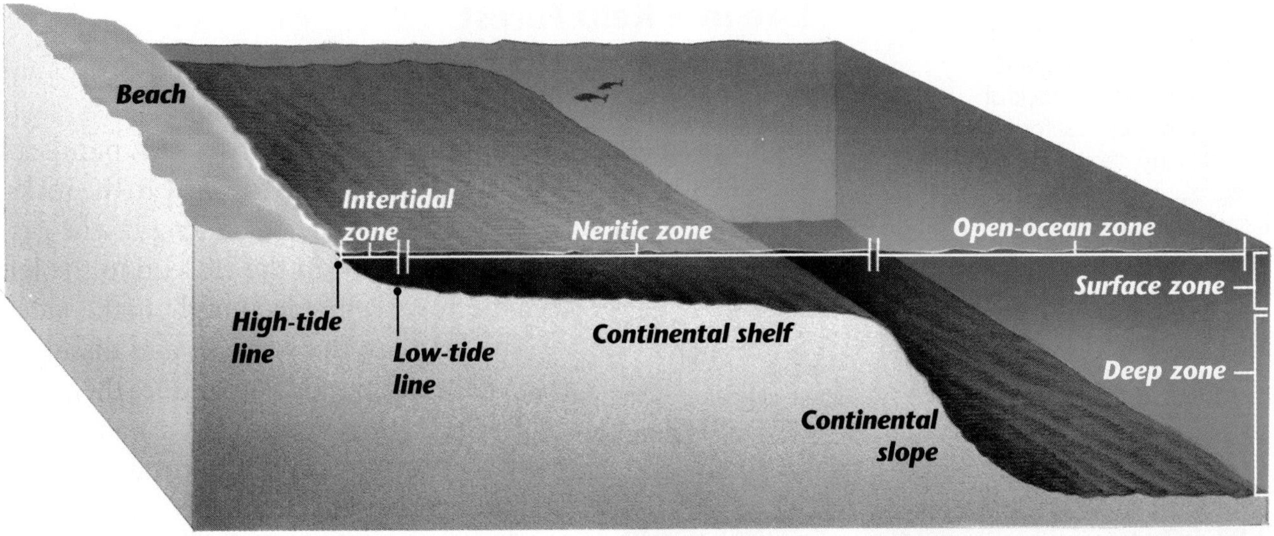
Beach
Intertidal zone
Neritic zone
Open-ocean zone
Surface zone
High-tide line
Low-tide line
Continental shelf
Deep zone
Continental slope

Figure 10 The ocean zone closest to land is the intertidal zone, which is bounded by the high-tide and low-tide lines. Next is the neritic zone, followed by the open-ocean zone, which makes up most of the world's oceans. The open ocean is divided by depth into the surface zone and the deep zone.
Interpreting Diagrams Which zones lie over the continental shelf?

A kelp forest is one habitat found in the neritic zone. The **neritic zone** is the part of the ocean that extends from the low-tide line out to the edge of the continental shelf. Beyond the edge of the continental shelf lies the **open-ocean zone.** Locate the neritic and open-ocean zones in Figure 10. In this section you will learn how organisms are adapted to the conditions in these zones, from the sunlit surface waters to the coldest depths.

Conditions in the Neritic Zone

A huge variety of organisms are found in the neritic zone, more than in any other area of the ocean. Most of the world's major fishing grounds are found in this zone. What makes the neritic zone home to so many living things? The answer has to do with its location over the continental shelf. **The shallow water over the continental shelf receives sunlight and a steady supply of nutrients washed from the land into the ocean.** The light and nutrients enable large plantlike algae, such as the giant kelp, to grow. These algae serve as a food source and shelter for other organisms.

In many parts of the neritic zone, upwelling currents bring additional nutrients from the bottom to the surface. These nutrients support large numbers of plankton, which form the base of ocean food webs. Schools of fish such as sardines and anchovies feed on the plankton. Major fisheries in upwelling areas include Monterey Canyon off the California coast, Newfoundland's Grand Banks, and Georges Bank off the New England coast.

Two diverse habitats typically found within the neritic zone are kelp forests and coral reefs. As you read about each, think about how they are similar and how they are different.

☑ *Checkpoint What are two ways that nutrients may be supplied to the neritic zone?*

Figure 11 Light streams through a forest of giant kelp and shadowy rockfish near Monterey, California. The closeup shows the gas-filled bulbs that keep the kelp upright in the water.

Life in a Kelp Forest

Kelp forests grow in cold neritic waters, such as those along the Pacific coast from Alaska to Mexico. These large, heavy algae require a solid, rocky bottom to anchor their stalks. A bundle of rootlike strands called a **holdfast** attaches the algae to the rocks. A stalk of giant kelp can grow to 30 meters in length. The gas-filled bulbs shown in the closeup to the left keep the heavy kelp stalk upright in the water.

The kelp use the sunlight and dissolved gases in the neritic zone to produce their own food. The kelp also provide a habitat for many other organisms. The curtains of kelp hide young gray whales from predators while their mothers are feeding. Sea slugs and snails live amid the tangle of the holdfasts.

Sea otters play a particularly important role in the kelp forest. In addition to eating abalone, sea otters feed on sea urchins, which eat the kelp. In areas where sea otters have disappeared, armies of sea urchins have devoured the kelp. The once-thriving forest has become a barren rocky zone.

Coral Reefs

Although a coral reef may look as if it is made of rock, it is actually made of living things. Coral reefs are created by colonies of tiny coral animals, each of which is not much larger than a pencil eraser. The coral animals produce a hard structure that surrounds their soft bodies. After the coral dies, the empty structure remains. New coral animals attach and grow on top of it. Over many years, a reef is built. Most of the coral reefs that exist today were begun about 5,000 to 10,000 years ago.

Microscopic algae live within the bodies of the coral animals and provide food for them. Because the algae require warm temperatures and sunlight, coral reefs can only form in shallow, tropical ocean waters. The reefs grow above continental shelves or around volcanic islands, where the water is shallow.

In areas where the seafloor is sinking, a reef may develop over time into an atoll. An **atoll** is a ring-shaped reef surrounding a shallow lagoon. Figure 12 shows the development of an atoll. It begins as a fringing reef that closely surrounds the edges of the island. As the reef grows upward, the island sinks, and a barrier reef forms. Water separates the top of the barrier reef from the land. The island continues to sink until it is eventually underwater, forming the atoll.

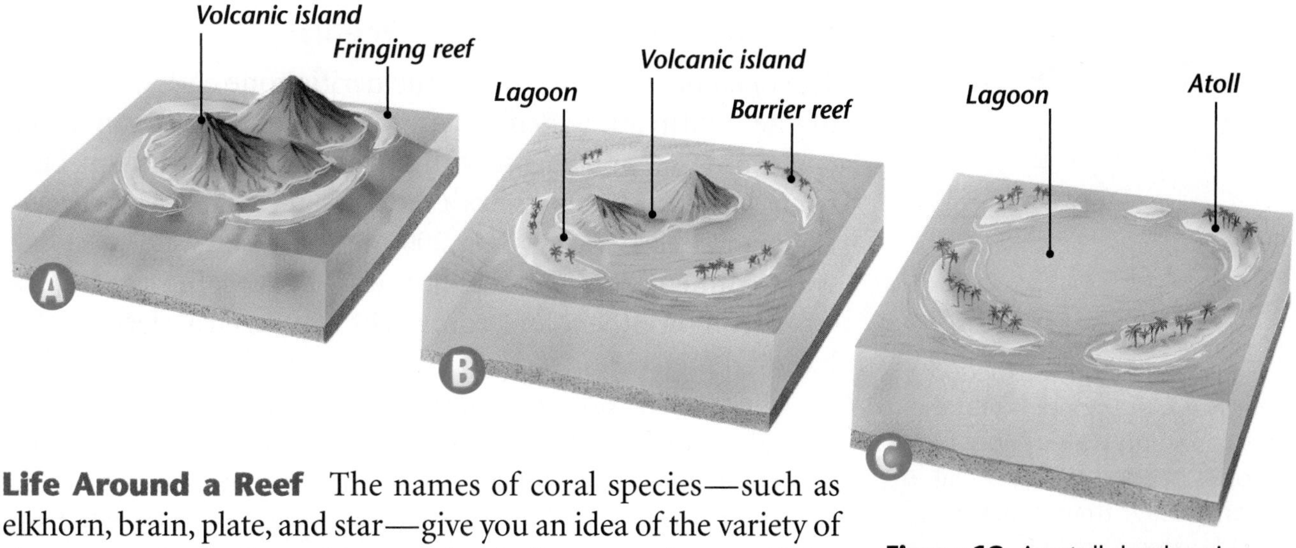
Volcanic island
Fringing reef
A
Lagoon
Volcanic island
Barrier reef
B
Lagoon
Atoll
C

Life Around a Reef The names of coral species—such as elkhorn, brain, plate, and star—give you an idea of the variety of shapes coral can form. Many animals live in and around the crevices of the reef, including octopuses, spiny lobsters, shrimp, toothy moray eels, and fish in all colors and sizes. Parrotfish like the one in Figure 13 scrape coral off the reef to eat. The parrotfish grind up the broken coral inside their bodies, producing the fine, soft sand commonly found around the reef.

Figure 12 An atoll develops in stages. **A.** A fringing reef closely surrounds an island. **B.** As the island sinks, a lagoon forms inside the barrier reef. **C.** Finally, the island sinks below the surface, leaving a ring-shaped atoll. ***Interpreting Diagrams*** *In which stage is the reef the youngest?*

Coral Reefs and Humans Coral reefs are natural aquarium exhibits, displaying a colorful diversity of life to be enjoyed and studied. Reefs also protect coastlines during violent storms. The reefs break up the surf, preventing waves from severely eroding the land. However, human activities can harm the fragile reefs. Boat anchors dragging across a reef can damage it. Divers can accidentally break off pieces of the reef. Even brushing against the reef can harm some of the coral animals. Because coral only grows a few millimeters a year, a reef cannot quickly recover.

Changes in water temperature and clarity also affect coral reefs. For example, if the water becomes too warm, the corals release the algae that live inside them. Cloudy water endangers the algae by reducing the amount of light that reaches them. If sediments produced by storms or human activities bury a reef, the algae in the living coral cannot survive. Without the algae, the coral animals do not grow well and eventually die.

Today many people understand the importance of coral reefs and try to protect them. Many reef areas have been designated as marine sanctuaries, which limits the amount of diving and other activity allowed near the reef. Scientists worldwide are also studying the effects of temperature change and pollution on the reefs to better protect them.

☑ *Checkpoint* *How can human activities impact a coral reef?*

Figure 13 A parrotfish delicately nibbles away at a coral reef in the Red Sea. Reefs provide a habitat for many fish and other marine organisms.

Sharpen your Skills

Inferring

ACTIVITY

To keep from sinking, many plankton rely on the friction between their bodies and the surrounding water. More friction is needed to stay afloat in warm water than in denser cold water. One of the copepods below is found in tropical ocean waters, while the other is found near the poles. Which do you think is which? Explain your reasoning. (*Hint:* More streamlined shapes create less friction with their surroundings.)

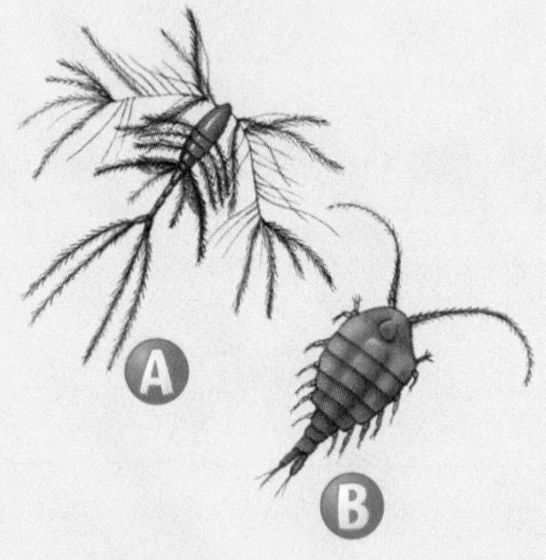
A
B

Conditions in the Open Ocean

The open ocean begins where the neritic zone ends, at the edge of the continental shelf. Diving into the open ocean is like descending a long staircase with a light only at the very top. Light from the sun only penetrates a short distance into the water, typically to a depth of less than 200 meters. If the water is cloudy with sediment, sunlight does not reach as deep. In clear tropical waters, on the other hand, some light may reach as deep as a few hundred meters.

The fact that only a small portion of the open ocean receives sunlight is one way it differs from the neritic zone. Another difference is the amount of dissolved nutrients in the water. While the neritic zone receives a constant supply of nutrients from shore, dissolved nutrients are less abundant in the open ocean. As a result, the open ocean zone supports fewer organisms.

The Surface Zone The surface zone extends as far as sunlight reaches below the surface. **The surface zone is the only part of the open ocean that receives enough sunlight to support the growth of algae.** These microscopic algae are the base of open-ocean food webs. Animal plankton that feed on algae include tiny crustaceans called copepods, shrimp-like krill, and the young of many ocean animals such as crabs, mollusks, and fishes.

Figure 15 on the facing page shows an Arctic food web. Each organism in this food web depends either directly or indirectly on the plankton. Throughout the ocean, plankton are a source of food for other organisms of all sizes. If you think of sharks as sharp-toothed, meat-eating hunters, you might be surprised to learn that the biggest sharks of all feed entirely on tiny plankton! Whale sharks, which can grow to more than 10 meters long, strain plankton from the water. Many whales feed only on plankton as well, including Earth's largest animal, the blue whale.

The Deep Zone When you explored the water column in Chapter 12, you observed that the ocean became darker and colder as you descended. Because of its harsh conditions, the deep ocean is often compared to a desert. Compared to other land and ocean environments, few organisms live in the deep zone. But unlike a desert baking under the bright sun, the deep ocean is cold, dark, and wet.

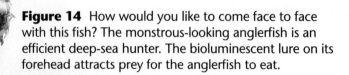

Figure 14 How would you like to come face to face with this fish? The monstrous-looking anglerfish is an efficient deep-sea hunter. The bioluminescent lure on its forehead attracts prey for the anglerfish to eat.

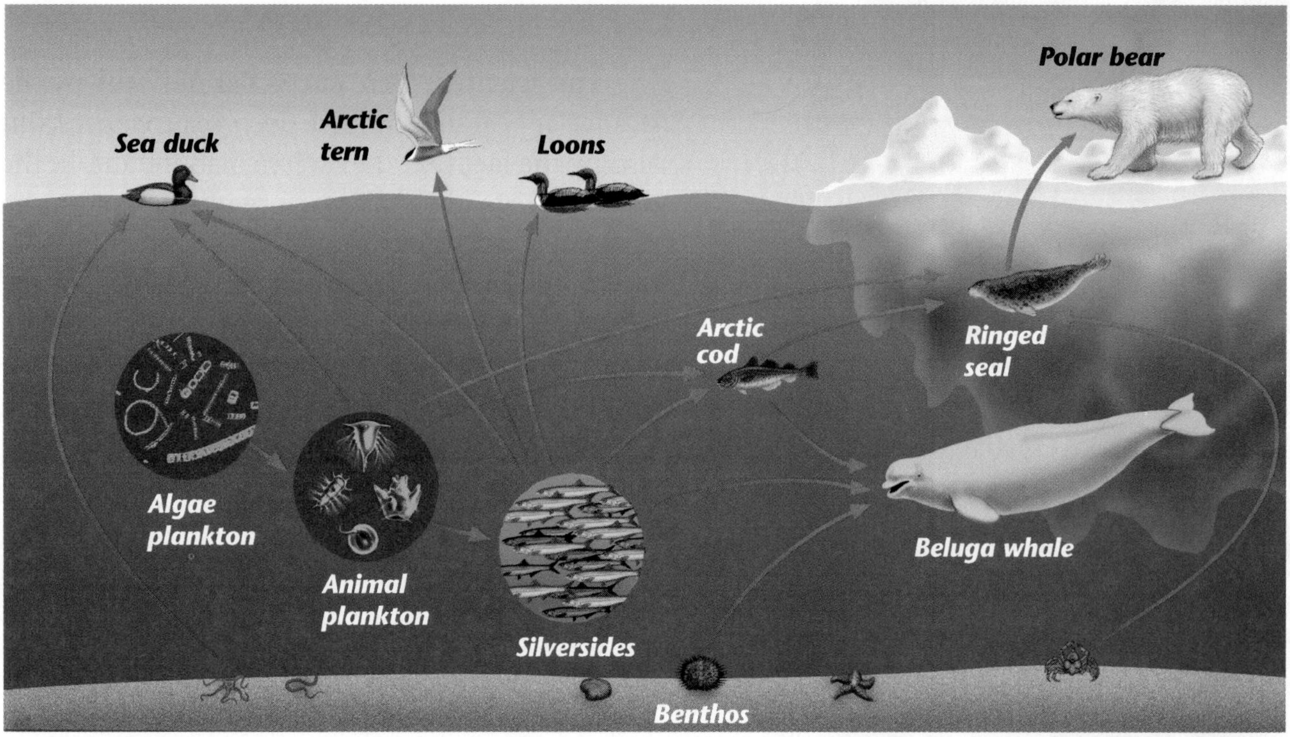
Polar bear
Sea duck
Arctic tern
Loons
Arctic cod
Ringed seal
Algae plankton
Animal plankton
Silversides
Beluga whale
Benthos

Figure 15 This marine food web includes typical organisms found in the Arctic Ocean. The arrows indicate what each organism eats. *Interpreting Diagrams Which organisms feed directly on the Arctic cod? Which organisms depend indirectly on the cod?*

Finding food in the darkness is a challenge. Many deep-sea fishes produce their own light. The production of light by living things is called **bioluminescence.** Some fishes use chemical reactions to produce their own light, like fireflies on land. Other fishes have colonies of bioluminescent bacteria living in pockets on their bodies. Still others have light-producing organs. The anglerfish, for example, has a light organ on its head. The fish lurks in the shadows below the pool of light. Shrimp and fishes that are attracted to the light become the anglerfish's prey.

Because the food supply in most of the deep ocean is much more limited than in shallower water, animals in this zone must be good hunters to survive. The gaping mouths of many deep-sea fishes are filled with fang-like teeth. Rows of sharp teeth stick out at angles, ensuring that any animal it bites cannot escape.

☑ *Checkpoint* ***Why do very few organisms live in the deep zone?***

Hydrothermal Vents

As the submersible *Alvin* descended to a depth of 2,500 meters into the Galápagos Rift in the Pacific Ocean one day in 1977, the scientists aboard could hardly believe their eyes. Outside the submersible, the headlights revealed a bizarre scene. Clouds of black water billowed up from chimney-shaped structures on the ocean floor. Meter-long tubes with gaping, lipstick-red ends swayed in the water. White crabs scuttled over the rocks, crawling around clams as big as dinner plates.

Figure 16 Giant tube worms cluster around a hydrothermal vent on the deep ocean floor.

The scientists were surprised not only by the strange appearance of these deep-sea creatures, but also by the fact that they were so abundant. In the deepest parts of the ocean, organisms tend to be very small and slow-moving because food is so rare. The number, size, and variety of organisms were unusually large for such a deep part of the ocean. What could these organisms find to eat so far from sunlight?

The strange community the scientists in *Alvin* observed was located around a hydrothermal vent. A **hydrothermal vent** is an area where ocean water sinks through cracks in the ocean floor, is heated by the underlying magma, and rises again through the cracks. These vents are located along ocean ridges, where the plates are moving apart and new ocean floor is forming.

The heated water coming from a vent carries gases and minerals from Earth's interior. **The chemical nutrients in the heated water support the unique group of organisms that are found around hydrothermal vents.** Bacteria feed directly on the chemical nutrients that are spewed out of the vents. Like the algae in the surface zone that use sunlight to produce food, these bacteria use the chemicals to produce food. They form the base of the food web at a hydrothermal vent.

Other organisms, like the giant clams, feed on the bacteria. The red-tipped tube worms are supplied with food by bacteria living within their tissues. Meanwhile, the scuttling crabs feed on the remains of the other inhabitants in their unusual habitat.

Section 3 Review

1. Describe the physical conditions in the neritic zone.
2. What factor limits where algae are found in the open ocean?
3. What is the source of nutrients for organisms around a hydrothermal vent?
4. Explain how bioluminescence is important to some fish that live in the deep ocean.
5. **Thinking Critically Relating Cause and Effect** When forests on a tropical island are cut down, the soil is more easily eroded. Explain how this could affect a coral reef near the island.

CHAPTER PROJECT

Check Your Progress

By now you should have selected an organism to model. Research your organism to determine its size and other physical characteristics. How does the organism survive in its marine habitat? Check your plan for constructing the organism with your teacher. Your group should also begin building your model habitat. Make sure you have collected all the necessary materials before you begin building.

Section 4 Resources From the Ocean

Discover Activity

Is It From the Ocean?

1. Your teacher will give you some labels from common household products. Read the ingredient information on each label.
2. Divide the products into two piles—those you think include substances that come from the ocean and those that do not.

Think It Over

Classifying For each product that you classified as coming from the ocean, name the item from the ocean that is used to produce it. In what ocean zone is it found?

When European explorers began sailing to North America, they were astounded by the huge number of codfish that lived off its eastern coast. One traveler reported that this area was so "swarming with fish that they could be taken not only with a net but in baskets let down and weighted with a stone." Others reported sailing through schools of cod so thick they slowed the boats down!

This cod fishery stretched from Newfoundland to a hook of land appropriately named Cape Cod. For more than 400 years, the seemingly endless supply of "King Cod" supported a thriving fishing industry. But beginning in the early 1900s, fishing crews had to work harder to catch the same amount of cod. As the fishing grew more difficult each year, it became clear that the cod were disappearing. With the price of cod rising, there was more competition to catch the fewer fish available. In 1992, the Canadian government had to declare the fishery closed.

No one knows for sure how long it will take the cod population to fully recover. Scientists are studying cod and other fisheries to learn how to preserve them for future generations.

Guide for Reading

- How does the supply of fish in a fishery change from year to year?
- Who controls and protects ocean resources?

Reading Tip **Before you read, rewrite the headings in the section as how, why, or what questions. As you read, look for answers to those questions.**

Living Resources

Cod are just one example of a living resource from the ocean. How many other kinds of seafood

Figure 17 Big catches of cod like this one from Georges Bank, off the New England coast, have become less common since the early 1900s.

have you tasted: tuna, shrimp, flounder, lobster, clams, squid, oysters, seaweed, or mussels? These foods and the many others that come from the ocean make up about five percent of the world's total food supply.

Harvesting Fish Just six species make up the majority of fishes harvested for eating: herring, sardine, anchovy, cod, pollock, and mackerel. Locate the world's major fisheries in Figure 18. You can see that they are all located close to coasts. Nearly all fishes caught are harvested from coastal waters or areas of upwelling. These waters contain nutrients and plankton on which they feed.

If used wisely, fisheries naturally renew themselves each year. **New fish are born, replacing those that are caught, but only as long as the fishery is not overfished. Overfishing causes the supply of fish to decrease.** Overfishing has become a problem as better technology has enabled people to catch large numbers of fish very quickly. For example, some fishing fleets have electronic equipment that allows them to locate schools of fish precisely. They can be caught faster than they can reproduce. Once this occurs, it begins a cycle that leads to fewer and fewer fish each season. Eventually, the fishery may be depleted, like the cod fishery you read about earlier.

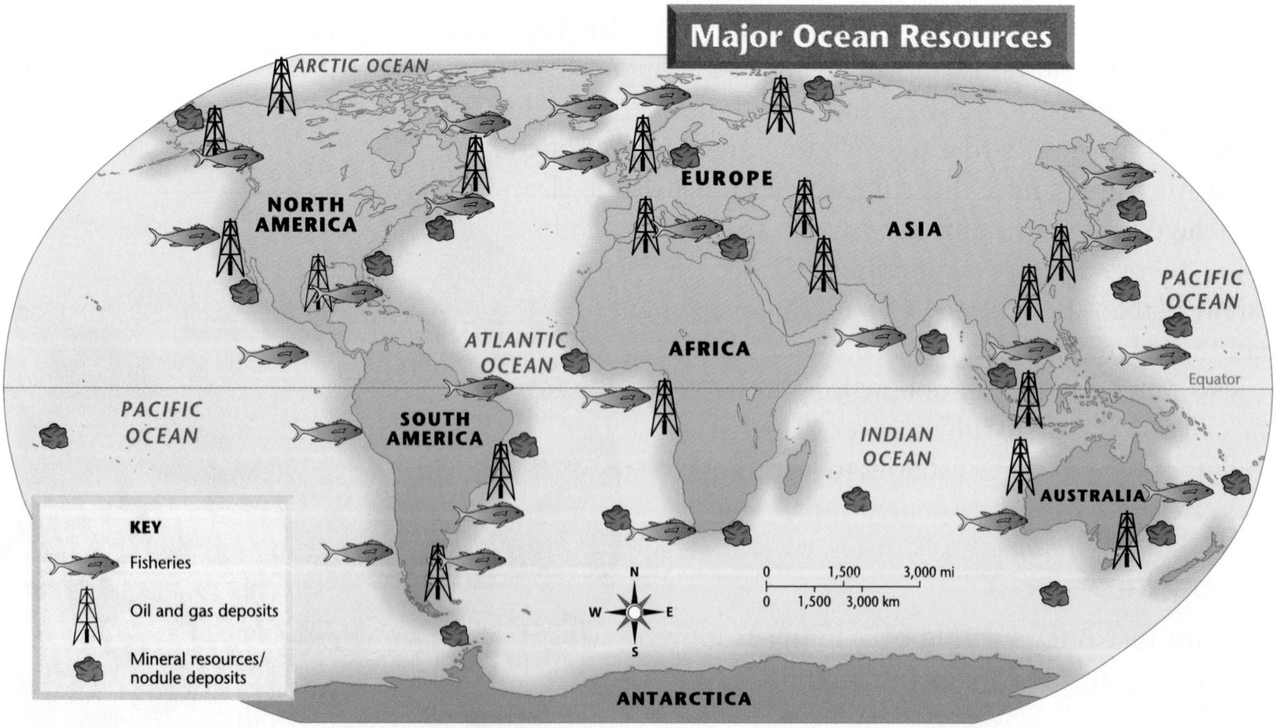
Major Ocean Resources
ARCTIC OCEAN
NORTH AMERICA
EUROPE
ASIA
PACIFIC OCEAN
ATLANTIC OCEAN
AFRICA
Equator
PACIFIC OCEAN
SOUTH AMERICA
INDIAN OCEAN
AUSTRALIA
KEY
Fisheries
Oil and gas deposits
Mineral resources/ nodule deposits
N
W
E
S
0 1,500 3,000 mi
0 1,500 3,000 km
ANTARCTICA

Figure 18 All over the world, the oceans are an important source of food, oil and gas, and minerals. *Interpreting Maps Where are Africa's major fisheries located?*

Aquaculture As fish stocks become depleted, **aquaculture,** the farming of saltwater and freshwater organisms, is likely to become more common. Aquaculture has been practiced in some Asian countries for centuries. This process involves creating an environment for the organisms and controlling nutrient levels, water temperature, light, and other factors to help them thrive. Oysters, abalone, and shrimp have successfully been farmed in artificial saltwater ponds and protected bays. Even landlocked regions can produce seafood using aquaculture. For example, salmon are now being raised in Nebraska fields that once were cattle ranches.

Integrating Technology

Other Ocean Products People harvest ocean organisms for many purposes besides food. For example, algae is an ingredient in many household products. Its gelatin-like texture makes it an ideal base for detergents, shampoos, cosmetics, paints, and even ice cream! Sediments containing the hard fragments of diatoms are used for abrasives and polishes. Many researchers believe that other marine organisms may be important sources of chemicals for medicines in the future.

☑ *Checkpoint* *How are fisheries naturally renewed each year?*

Mineral Resources

In addition to living organisms, the ocean contains valuable nonliving resources. Some of these are found within ocean water itself. Chapter 11 described how fresh water can be extracted from ocean water in the process of desalination. Desalination provides fresh water for many dry areas and islands. When the fresh water is removed from ocean water, the salts that are left behind are also a valuable resource. Over half of the world's supply of magnesium, a strong, light metal, is obtained from seawater in this way.

A second source of nonliving resources is the ocean floor. From the layer of sediments covering the continental shelves, gravel and sand are mined for use in building construction. In some areas of the world diamonds and gold are mined from sand deposits. Metals such as manganese also accumulate on the ocean floor. The metals concentrate around pieces of shell, forming black lumps called **nodules** (NAHJ oolz). Because they sometimes occur in waters as deep as 5,000 meters, recovering the nodules is a difficult process. The technology to gather them is still being developed.

Not all nations have agreed on who owns the rights to nodules and other resources on the deep ocean floor. Some feel the

TRY THIS

Seaweed Candy

ACTIVITY

Make this Asian dessert to discover one way to eat algae. Remember to prepare food only in a non-science classroom. Be sure to get permission before using a stove.

2 blocks of agar (one 0.5-ounce package)
1 cup sugar
4 cups guava juice or other fruit juice
food coloring

1. Rinse the agar, a substance obtained from algae.
2. Break agar into cubes and place them in a saucepan.
3. Put on your goggles. Add the sugar and juice to the pan. Bring the mixture to a boil. Turn down the heat and cook, stirring, until the agar dissolves.
4. Remove pan from heat and stir in a few drops of food coloring. Pour the mixture into a shallow pan. Let cool.
5. Refrigerate candy until firm.
6. Cut into blocks and serve.

Inferring What purpose does the agar serve in this recipe? What purposes do the sugar and juice serve?

Figure 19 Lit up like a city at night, this Norwegian oil-drilling platform rises above the icy waters of the North Sea. Hundreds of people may live and work aboard such an oil rig.

nations who find and recover the minerals should own them. Others feel that this is unfair to nations who cannot yet afford the technology to obtain a share of these resources.

Fuels From the Ocean Floor

Another type of nonliving resource forms from the remains of dead marine organisms. These remains sink to the bottom of the ocean, where they are buried by sediments. As more sediments accumulate, the buried remains decompose. Over hundreds of thousands of years, the heat and pressure from the overlying layers gradually transform the remains into oil and natural gas.

As you know, many organisms live in the part of the ocean above the continental shelf. The thick sediments on the continental shelves bury the remains of living things. As a result, the richest deposits of oil and gas are often located on the continental shelves.

Oil rigs like the one in Figure 19 drill the rocky ocean floor as much as 300 meters below the surface. Imagine trying to dig a hole in the concrete bottom of a swimming pool, while standing on a raft floating on the surface of the water. You can see why drilling the ocean floor is very difficult! Ocean drilling is made even harder by strong currents, winds, and violent storms.

☑ *Checkpoint* ***What is the source of the oil and gas deposits on the ocean floor?***

Ocean Pollution

It was once thought that the ocean was so vast that people could not damage it by throwing wastes into it. This is partially true—the ocean is a self-cleaning system that can absorb some wastes without permanent damage. But dumping large amounts of wastes into the ocean threatens many marine organisms.

Sharpen your Skills

Observing

ACTIVITY

Refer back to the map of ocean resources in Figure 18. Which resources are located close to land? Which are located throughout the ocean? Can you suggest an explanation for any patterns you observe?

Recall that water pollution is the addition of any substance that has a negative effect on the living things that depend on the water. Most ocean pollution comes from the land. Although some is the result of natural occurrences, most pollution is related to human activities.

Natural Sources Some pollution is the result of weather. For example, heavy rains wash fresh water into estuaries and out into the water offshore. This surge of fresh water pollutes the ocean by lowering its salinity. A sudden change in salinity may kill ocean animals that are unable to adjust to it.

Human Sources Pollutants related to human activities include sewage, chemicals, and trash dumped into coastal waters. Chemicals that run off fields and roads often end up in the ocean. These substances can harm ocean organisms directly. The pollutants can also build up in their bodies and poison other animals, including people, that feed on them. Trash can cause serious problems, too. Seals, otters, and other marine mammals that need to breathe air can get tangled in old fishing lines or nets and drown. Other animals are harmed when they swallow plastic bags that block their stomachs.

Oil Spills One major threat to ocean life is oil pollution. When an oil tanker or drilling platform is damaged, oil leaks into the surrounding ocean. Oil is harmful to many organisms. It coats the bodies of marine mammals and birds. This destroys their natural insulation and affects their ability to float. The oil is also harmful to animals that swallow it.

Figure 20 Removing oil from a beach is a difficult, messy chore. This cleanup worker is using absorbent mops to remove oil from the sand. In the closeup, two more workers try to clean oil from a bird's beak and feathers. *Inferring What might have caused this oil pollution?*

Figure 21 Flags fly outside the United Nations headquarters in New York City. The United Nations develops policies on the use of the oceans by countries. *Applying Concepts Why can't each nation make its own laws regarding ocean resources?*

Interestingly, there is a natural cleaning process that slowly takes place after oil spills. Certain bacteria that live in the ocean feed on the oil and multiply. It takes many years, but eventually an oil-covered beach can become clean again. This has happened even in the portions of the Prince William Sound in Alaska that were blanketed with oil from the 1989 wreck of the oil tanker *Exxon Valdez.*

Protecting Earth's Oceans

Who owns the ocean and its resources? Who has the responsibility of protecting them? These are questions that nations have been struggling to answer for hundreds of years. **Because the world ocean is a continuous body of water that has no boundaries, it is difficult to determine who, if anyone, should control portions of it. Nations must cooperate to manage and protect the oceans.**

The United Nations has established different boundaries in the oceans. According to one treaty, a nation now controls the first 22 kilometers out from its coasts. The nation also controls resources in the waters or on the continental shelf within 370 kilometers of shore. This treaty leaves approximately half of the ocean's surface waters as "high seas," owned by no nation. Ownership of the ocean floor beneath the high seas is still under debate.

Other international efforts have resulted in cooperation aimed at reducing ocean pollution. Examples include the establishment of marine refuges and regulations for building safer oil tankers.

Section 4 Review

1. How can overfishing affect a fishery?
2. Explain why international cooperation is necessary to solve many problems related to ocean resources.
3. Name a nonliving resource found in the ocean. Where is it located? How is it obtained and used?
4. **Thinking Critically Making Judgments** Should mineral resources on the ocean floor belong to whomever finds them, or to the closest nation? Consider each position and write a short paragraph stating your opinion.

Science at Home

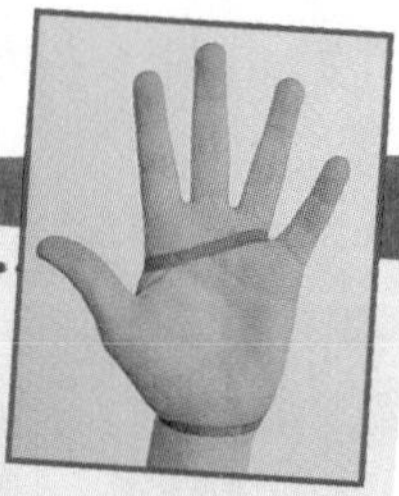

Have a family member hook one end of a rubber band around his or her wrist. Stretch the rubber band across the back of the hand and hook the free end over three fingers as shown. Now ask the person to try to remove the rubber band without using the other hand. Explain that this shows how difficult it is for seals or dolphins to free themselves from a plastic beverage ring or piece of net. Can you propose any ways to reduce this threat to marine mammals?

Shrimp Farms—At What Cost to the Environment?

About one quarter of the world's shrimp are raised on shrimp farms. Many shrimp farms are created by clearing trees from mangrove forests and digging shallow, fenced-in ponds. Farmers then fill the ponds with ocean water and shrimp larvae. After about six months, when the shrimp are big enough to sell, the farmers drain the pond water back into the ocean.

To grow healthy shrimp, farmers often add fertilizers, medicines, and pesticides to the ponds. When the pond water is released to the ocean, these chemicals can harm other animals. The United Nations has estimated that 25 percent of the world's mangrove forests have been destroyed as a result of shrimp farming. As awareness of the environmental impact of shrimp farms has grown, the industry has come under attack.

▲ Shrimp farmer in Malaysia

The Issues

How Important Is Shrimp Farming? For many people in the world, shrimp is more than luxury food: It is a staple of their diet and their main source of animal protein. The demand for shrimp currently is greater than the natural supply in Earth's oceans. To meet the demand, many countries, including the United States, have turned to shrimp farming. Shrimp farms provide needed food and jobs that some people believe are worth a certain amount of damage to the environment. They feel it is not possible to have shrimp farms that are both highly productive and environmentally safe.

Can the Pollution Be Reduced? Shrimp farmers are exploring ways to reduce the impact of their farms on the coastal environment. Better pond construction can help stop chemicals from leaking into the surrounding waters. Some governments recognize the importance of mangrove forests in providing a habitat for many species and in protecting the shoreline. These governments have passed laws regulating where shrimp farms may be built. Farmers must investigate the impact their ponds will have on nearby mangrove forests and get approval before choosing a location. These methods of reducing environmental damage, however, are expensive and time-consuming for the shrimp farmers.

Should Farmers Use Alternative Methods? In some parts of Asia, a less destructive method of shrimp farming has been practiced for centuries. Raising shrimp in ditches dug around clusters of mangroves provides the young shrimp with a natural nutrient supply that includes debris from the trees. A gate keeps the shrimp from escaping into the ocean and also allows the motion of the tides to replenish the water in the ditches. The disadvantage of this method is that it is much less profitable than the constructed shrimp ponds. Many shrimp farmers could not afford to switch to this method. If they did, the price of shrimp worldwide would rise.

You Decide

1. Identify the Problem

In your own words, summarize the problem facing shrimp farmers.

2. Analyze the Options

Make a list of the solutions mentioned. List the advantages and drawbacks of each. Who would benefit from each plan? Who might suffer?

3. Find a Solution

Write a brochure or pamphlet for shrimp farmers that states your proposed solution to their problem. After you have written the text, illustrate your brochure.

Cleaning Up an Oil Spill

Oil Spill in Bay

An oil tanker hit a reef yesterday, spilling thousands of barrels of crude oil into the water. Cleanup efforts will begin today. Workers must race against time to save birds and sea otters. With stormy weather forecasted, however, scientists expect considerable damage. Volunteers are needed to help clean up.

Imagine that you are a volunteer helping to clean up an oil spill. In this activity, you will use a variety of materials to remove as much oil as possible from the water and to keep oil from reaching the beach. You will also see how oil affects animals that are exposed to a spill.

Problem

How can an oil spill be cleaned up?

Skills Focus

making models, forming operational definitions

Materials

water	shallow pan	vegetable oil
feather	paper cup	plastic dropper
paper towels	cotton balls	wooden sticks
marking pen	graduated cylinder, 100 mL	

Procedure

1. Place a pan on a table or desk covered with newspaper. Label one end of the pan "Beach" and the other end "Open Ocean."
2. Pour water into the pan to a depth of 2 cm.
3. Gently pour 20 mL of vegetable oil into the center of the pan. Record your observations.
4. Dip a feather and your finger into the oil. Observe how each is affected by the oil.
5. Try to wipe oil off the feather and your finger using paper towels. Record whether any oil is left on the feather or your skin.
6. Now try to clean up the spill. Record your observations with each step. First, using the wooden sticks, try to keep the oil from reaching the "beach." Next, gently blow across the surface of the water from the "open ocean" side to simulate wind and waves. Then use the cotton balls, paper towels, and dropper to recover as much of the oil as possible.
7. When you are finished, dispose of the oil and used items in the paper cup. Wash your hands.

Analyze and Conclude

1. How successful were you in cleaning up the oil? Is the water as clean as it was at the start?
2. How well were you able to keep the oil from reaching the beach? Describe how useful the different materials were in cleaning up the oil.
3. Describe what happened when you cleaned the feather and your finger. What might happen to fish, birds, and other animals if they were coated with oil as a result of an oil spill?
4. Predict how storms with strong winds and waves would affect the cleanup of an oil spill.
5. **Apply** Look at the used cleanup materials in the paper cup. What additional problems for cleanup crews does this suggest?

Getting Involved

One way to reduce the threat of oil spills is to transport less oil across the oceans. To make that possible, people would need to use less oil in their daily lives. Oil is used to heat homes, to produce gasoline, and to make products such as plastics and textiles. List at least three ways to reduce the amount of oil you and your family use.

Section 1 Exploring the Ocean

Key Ideas

- Technology such as sonar enables scientists to study the deep ocean floor despite the darkness, cold, and extreme pressure there.
- The ocean floor has features similar to those found on the continents, including plains, mountain ranges, volcanoes, and trenches.

Key Terms

sonar, continental shelf, continental slope, seamount, abyssal plain, mid-ocean ridge, trench, magma

Section 2 Life at the Ocean's Edge

INTEGRATING LIFE SCIENCE

Key Ideas

- Physical factors that affect marine organisms include salinity, water temperature, light, dissolved gases, nutrients, and wave action.
- Organisms in the rocky intertidal zone must be able to tolerate the pounding of the waves, as well as being both underwater and exposed to the air for long periods of time.
- Coastal wetlands include salt marshes and mangrove forests.

Key Terms

plankton, nekton, benthos, food web, intertidal zone, estuary, brackish

Section 3 The Neritic Zone and Open Ocean

INTEGRATING LIFE SCIENCE

Key Ideas

- The neritic zone receives sunlight and nutrients washed from the land. Habitats in this zone include kelp forests and coral reefs.
- The thin layer of sunlit water at the surface is the only part of the open ocean that can support algae, which need the sunlight to produce food. Other marine organisms depend on the food made by algae.
- The chemical nutrients in the hot water around a hydrothermal vent support the organisms that live around the vent.

Key Terms

neritic zone, open-ocean zone, holdfast, atoll, bioluminescence, hydrothermal vent

Section 4 Resources From the Ocean

Key Ideas

- If used wisely, fisheries are a renewable resource. New fish will replace those that are caught, but only if overfishing does not reduce the population too severely.
- Nonliving resources from the ocean include dissolved substances in seawater and minerals and fuels from the ocean floor.
- Nations must cooperate to manage and protect the oceans.

Key Terms

aquaculture, nodules

ACTIVITY

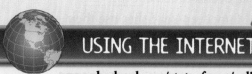

USING THE INTERNET

www.phschool.com/state_focus/california/

California Test Prep: Reviewing Content

Multiple Choice

Choose the letter of the best answer.

1. Earth's crust and upper mantle are made up of moving
   a. magma. b. plates.
   c. trenches. d. abyssal plains.
2. An area where rivers flow into the ocean and fresh water and salt water mix is a(n)
   a. tide pool.
   b. hydrothermal vent.
   c. estuary.
   d. kelp forest.
3. A tropical ocean community made by tiny animals that have algae growing in their tissues is a
   a. mangrove forest. b. salt marsh.
   c. intertidal zone. d. coral reef.
4. In the open-ocean zone, organisms depend directly or indirectly on food that is made by
   a. marine mammals.
   b. nekton in the water column.
   c. plants growing on the deep ocean floor.
   d. algae near the surface.
5. Most ocean pollutants come from
   a. marine organisms. b. the land.
   c. the atmosphere. d. Earth's core.

True or False

If the statement is true, write true. If it is false, change the underlined word or words to make the statement true.

6. The mid-ocean ridge is formed where two plates converge.
7. The area between the high and low tide lines is the neritic zone.
8. Water that is partly salty and partly fresh is brackish.
9. A ring-shaped coral reef surrounding a lagoon is called a seamount.
10. Many deep-sea fishes use their bioluminescence to attract prey.

Checking Concepts

11. Describe one method that has been used to study the ocean floor.
12. Describe three physical factors that organisms in the rocky intertidal zone must overcome.
13. Explain why estuaries are especially vulnerable to pollution.
14. Explain why scientists were surprised to discover the variety of organisms living around hydrothermal vents.
15. **Writing to Learn** Imagine that you are an "aquanaut" on a voyage of discovery across the ocean floor. Write a logbook entry that summarizes your observations as you travel from one continent to another. Include details about the shape of the ocean floor, as well as some organisms you encounter along your journey.

Thinking Visually

16. **Compare/Contrast Table** Copy the table about ocean habitats onto a separate sheet of paper. Then fill in the empty spaces and add a title. (See the Skills Handbook for more on compare/contrast tables.)

Habitat	Zone	Conditions	Organisms
Tide pool	Intertidal	a. ?	b. ?
Coral reef	c. ?	d. ?	Coral, fishes, shrimp, eels
Surface zone	Open ocean	e. ?	f. ?
Hydrothermal vent	g. ?	High pressure, dark, warm	h. ?

Test Prep: Skills

Use the diagram of a portion of the ocean floor to answer Questions 17–19.

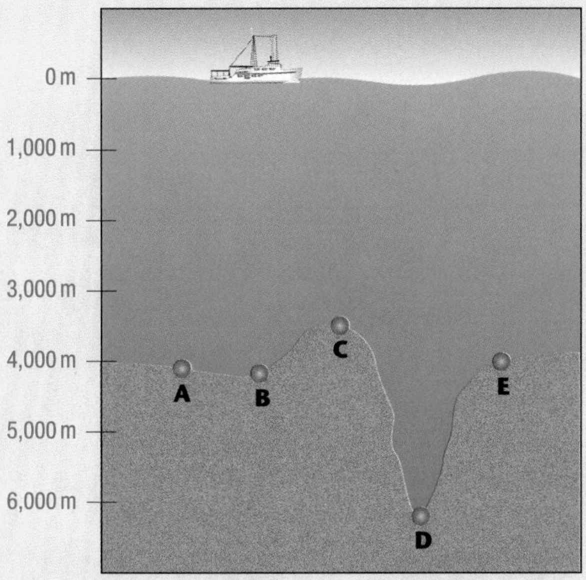

0 m
1,000 m
2,000 m
3,000 m
4,000 m
5,000 m
6,000 m
A
B
C
D
E

17. **Interpreting Diagrams** What is the approximate depth of the ocean floor at point A? At point C?
18. **Inferring** What might the feature between locations A and B be? The feature at point D?
19. **Posing Questions** What other information would help you determine whether point A or point E is closer to the mid-ocean ridge? Explain.

Thinking Critically

20. **Classifying** Classify each of the following organisms as plankton, nekton, or benthos: squid, sea stars, microscopic algae, whales, sea otters, anglerfish, and giant clams.
21. **Making Generalizations** Explain why many of the world's fisheries are located in the neritic zone.
22. **Predicting** Suppose the number of plankton in the ocean suddenly decreased to half their current number. Predict how this would affect other marine organisms.
23. **Relating Cause and Effect** How might fertilizers used on farmland result in ocean pollution near shore?

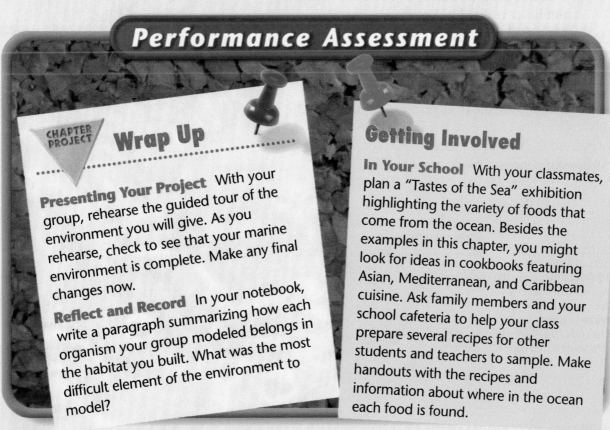

Performance Assessment

CHAPTER PROJECT

Wrap Up

Presenting Your Project With your group, rehearse the guided tour of the environment you will give. As you rehearse, check to see that your marine environment is complete. Make any final changes now.

Reflect and Record In your notebook, write a paragraph summarizing how each organism your group modeled belongs in the habitat you built. What was the most difficult element of the environment to model?

Getting Involved

In Your School With your classmates, plan a "Tastes of the Sea" exhibition highlighting the variety of foods that come from the ocean. Besides the examples in this chapter, you might look for ideas in cookbooks featuring Asian, Mediterranean, and Caribbean cuisine. Ask family members and your school cafeteria to help your class prepare several recipes for other students and teachers to sample. Make handouts with the recipes and information about where in the ocean each food is found.

THE MISSISSIPPI

What would you name a river that—

- *carries about 420 million metric tons of cargo a year,*
- *drains 31 states and 2 Canadian provinces,*
- *looks like a tree that has a thin top trunk and 2 strong branches,*
- *flows at about 18,100 cubic meters of water per second?*

Native Americans called the river *misi sipi*, an Algonquin name meaning "big water," or "father of waters."

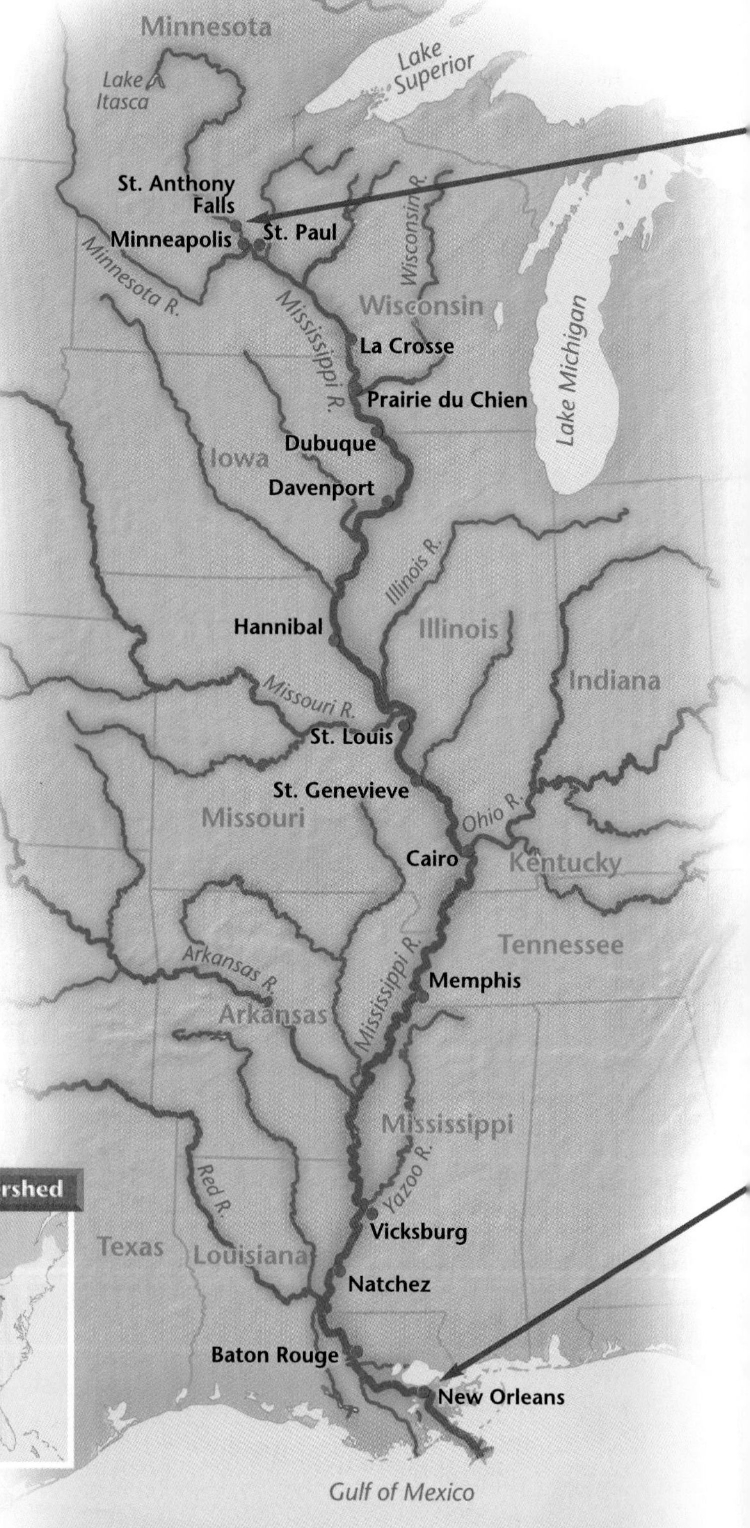
Minnesota
Lake Itasca
Lake Superior
St. Anthony Falls
Minneapolis
St. Paul
Minnesota R.
Wisconsin R.
Mississippi R.
Wisconsin
La Crosse
Prairie du Chien
Lake Michigan
Iowa
Dubuque
Davenport
Illinois R.
Hannibal
Illinois
Indiana
Missouri R.
St. Louis
St. Genevieve
Missouri
Ohio R.
Cairo
Kentucky
Tennessee
Arkansas R.
Memphis
Arkansas
Mississippi R.
Mississippi
Yazoo R.
Red R.
Vicksburg
Texas
Louisiana
Natchez
Baton Rouge
New Orleans
Gulf of Mexico

Have you ever traveled on a river or lake that feeds into the mighty Mississippi River? Perhaps you have but never realized it. The map below shows the watershed of this great river. From the west, the Missouri River — the "Big Muddy"— carries soft silt eroded from the Great Plains. The Missouri joins the Mississippi near St. Louis, turning the river's clear water to muddy brown. From the east, the Ohio River flows in from the rocky Appalachian plateau, nearly doubling the volume of water in the river. In all, the huge Mississippi watershed drains about 40 percent of the United States.

The Mississippi River starts at Lake Itasca and flows through 10 states to the Gulf of Mexico. The river is a drainage point for hundreds of tributaries in the vast Mississippi watershed. ▶

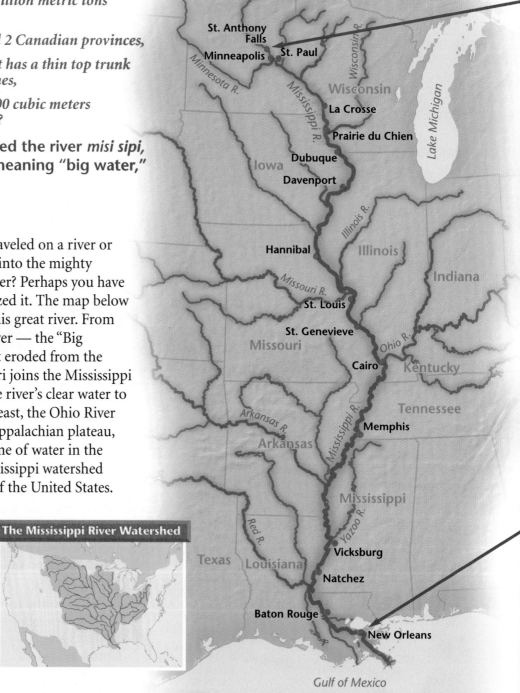

The Mississippi River Watershed

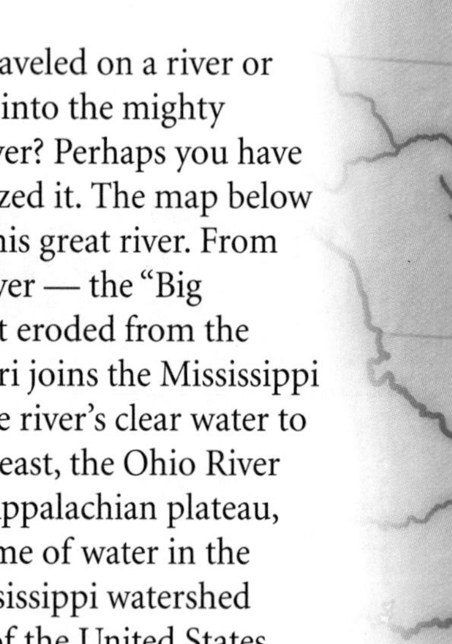

A National Trade Route

Since Native Americans settled in villages along the Mississippi around 1,200 years ago, the river has served as a water highway for trade and travel.

▲ St. Anthony Falls is the northernmost point of navigation on the Mississippi.

In the late 1600s, French explorers, fur traders, and soldiers arrived in the Mississippi Valley. They chose strategic sites for forts and fur-trading posts — Prairie du Chien, St. Louis, and St. Genevieve. At first, traders used canoes, rafts, and flatboats to carry goods downstream. But traveling up the river was difficult. Crews had to use long poles to push narrow keelboats upstream against the current.

▲ Crews in flatboats rode the river currents, steering with long oars.

In 1811, the arrival of *The New Orleans,* the first steamboat on the Mississippi River, changed the river forever. Within 40 years, there were hundreds more steamboats and many new river towns. On the upper Mississippi, the city of Minneapolis grew up around flour mills near the falls. Farther downstream, Memphis became a center for transporting cotton. Later, it was a stopping point for showboats and musicians. New Orleans quickly became a world port. It received cotton, tobacco, and sugar cane from southern plantations and exported corn, wheat and indigo to Europe. Imported luxury items, such as soap, coffee, shoes, and textiles, traveled upstream from the port of New Orleans. Up and down the river townspeople eagerly waited for the cry, "Steamboat comin'!"

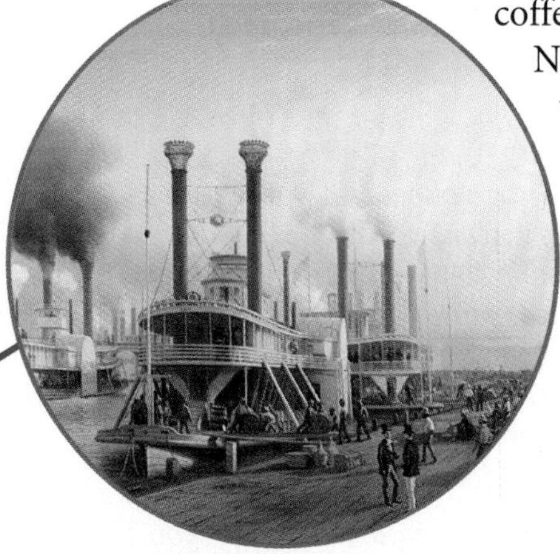

▲ New Orleans has been a major trading port since its founding in 1718.

Social Studies Activity

Use the map to choose a city on the Mississippi River to learn about. Imagine that you are an early settler in the city. Write a letter to convince relatives to move to your city. Before writing, learn about the history, founding, and trade of the city. Look for answers to the following questions:

- Who founded the city? When was the city founded? Why did settlers decide to move there? Where did they come from?
- What part did the Mississippi River play in the city's founding?
- What other physical features were important to the city?
- Where did the city's name come from?
- What products were grown, bought, or sold there?

Taming the River

Navigating the sandbars, shallow water, and rocky rapids on the upper Mississippi River was treacherous for captains of ships and barges in the 1800s. To make traveling easier, engineers in the early 1900s built a "water staircase," a series of 29 locks and dams between Minneapolis, Minnesota, and Alton, Illinois, above St. Louis. A lock is an enclosed basin, with gates at each end. Locks allow engineers to raise or lower the water level in a certain area of the river. Between the locks on the upper Mississippi, the river forms wide pools of quiet water, maintaining a channel deep enough for large boats.

1 The lock gate opens. Your boat moves in and you tie up to the wall.

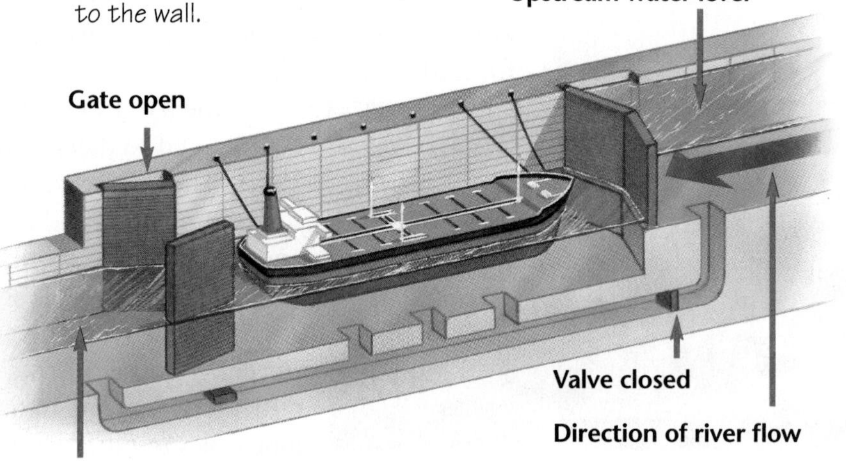
Upstream water level
Gate open
Valve closed
Direction of river flow
Downstream water level

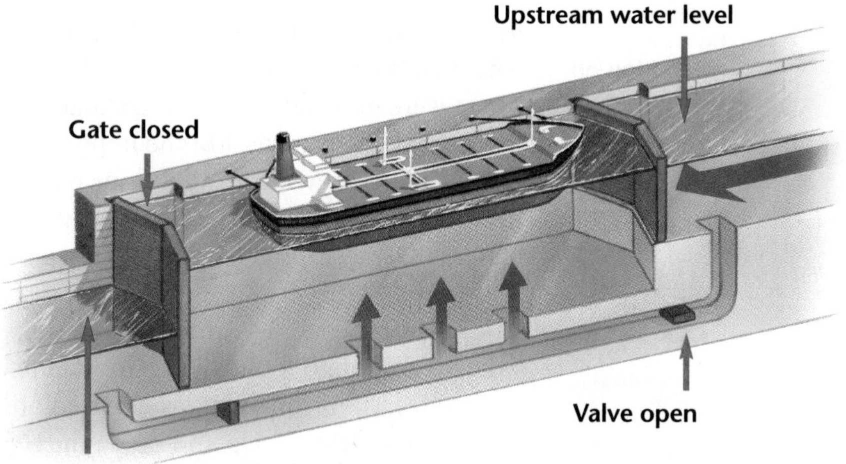
Upstream water level
Gate closed
Valve open
Downstream water level

Use the diagrams to trace how a boat "locks through" as it travels upstream. This technology allowed boats to travel to cities on the upper Mississippi. ▶

2 The gate closes, and water pours in. As water fills the lock—like a bathtub filling—it lifts the boat a meter or more. When the water in the lock is even with the water level upstream, the gates at the upstream end open. You untie your boat and move out into the river.

If you were going downstream, you would "lock through" in reverse. The water would empty out of the lock, lowering the water level to match the level downstream.

Science Activity

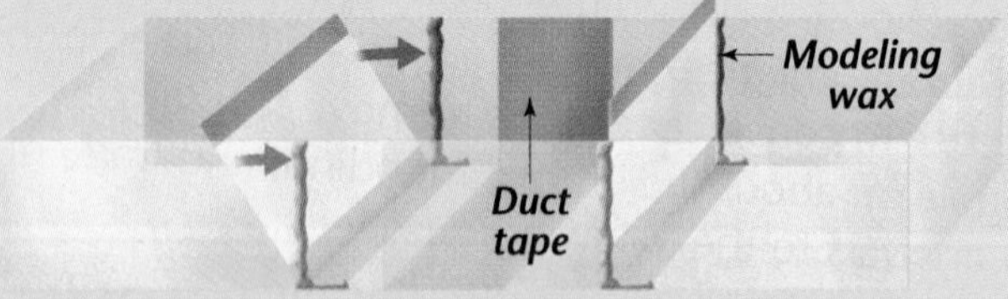
Modeling wax
Duct tape

Cut-out side view

Use a cardboard milk container to build a working model of a lock. Set up your lock following the illustration. Then demonstrate how your lock works, using a cork or pen cap as your ship and sailing it through the lock.

All Aboard

The whistle blows. The gleaming white steamboat pulls away from the dock just below Fort Snelling, Minnesota. You head downstream toward New Orleans. As you watch the paddlewheel splashing in the water, you think of the old-time steamboats that carried passengers up and down the Mississippi River in the 1800s.

Today you are cruising at a speed of 11.3 kilometers per hour. You want to stay awake until you enter Lock 3 at Red Wing, Minnesota. It's 4:30 P.M. on Monday now. You know that it's about 78.8 kilometers to Red Wing. It should take about 7 hours to reach the lock. So you'll be there at 11:30 P.M. and through the lock by midnight.

As your boat travels along the river, it will follow the schedule you see on this page. The highlight of your trip will be Mark Twain's hometown of Hannibal, Missouri. You will arrive there on Friday.

Look at the Upper Mississippi River schedule to answer the questions below. Distances are given from Fort Snelling.

- What is your average speed between Dubuque and Hannibal? Use the following equation:

$$speed = \frac{distance}{time}$$

Round to the nearest tenth.

- How long will you spend in Prairie du Chien?
- About how long does it take to travel from Prairie du Chien to Dubuque?

MISSISSIPPI RIVERBOAT

SCHEDULE

MAY to SEPTEMBER

UPPER MISSISSIPPI RIVERBOAT SCHEDULE

Port	Arrival Time	Departure Time	Distance From Fort Snelling
Fort Snelling, MN		4:30 P.M. Mon.	0 km
Lock 3, Red Wing, MN	11:30 P.M. Mon.	12: 00 midnight	78.8 km
Prairie du Chien, WI	11:00 P.M. Tues.	10:30 A.M. Wed.	337.8 km
Dubuque, IA	6:30 P.M. Wed.	7:00 P.M. Wed.	426.3 km
Hannibal, MO	1:00 A.M. Fri.	———	863.9 km

LOWER MISSISSIPPI RIVERBOAT SCHEDULE

Port	Arrival Time	Departure Time	Distance From Fort Snelling
Hannibal, MO		6 P.M. Fri.	863.9 km
Lock 26 at Alton, IL	a. ?	b. ?	1033 km
St. Louis, MO	c. ?	d. ?	1070.7 km
Cape Girardeau, MO	6:30 A.M. Sun.	———	e. ?

Math Activity

Now complete the riverboat schedule for the Lower Mississippi. Your boat will leave Hannibal at 6 P.M. Friday and will travel at a speed of 14.7 kilometers per hour for the rest of the journey.

- When will you arrive at Lock 26?
- You spend 34 minutes in the lock. When will you depart from Lock 26? Your boat travels on. When will it arrive in St. Louis?
- The boat will spend 4 hours in St. Louis and head to Cape Girardeau, arriving at 6:30 A.M. Sunday. How far is it from St. Louis to Cape Girardeau?

Language Arts

Mark Three! Mark Twain!

To steer a boat on the Mississippi, early riverboat pilots had to memorize landmarks at every bend and curve of the river, going both upstream and down. They had to know where the channel was deep enough for the boat, where the current was strong, where there were sandbars or sunken logs.

When Samuel Clemens was growing up in the small river town of Hannibal, Missouri, his ambition was to become a Mississippi River steamboat pilot. He was a pilot for a while. Later he became one of America's most famous writers, using the pen name Mark Twain. In the passage below from his book *Life on the Mississippi*, Twain describes a lesson he learned from an experienced pilot, Mr. Bixby.

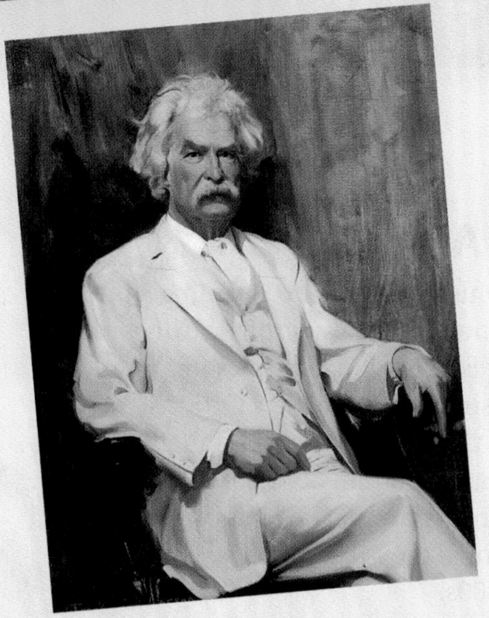

What's in a Name?

Mark Twain's name comes from a term that steamboat crews used to measure the depth of river water. *Twain* means "two." Dropping a weighted line, they would call out the depth: "Mark twain!"—2 fathoms deep; "Mark three!"—3 fathoms deep. (Note: One fathom equals 1.8 meters.)

"My boy," [Bixby said] "you've got to know the shape of the river perfectly. It is all there is left to steer by on a very dark night. Everything else is blotted out and gone. But mind you, it hasn't the same shape in the night that it has in the daytime."

"How on earth am I ever going to learn it, then?"

"How do you follow a hall at home in the dark? Because you know the shape of it. You can't see it."

"Do you mean to say that I've got to know all the million trifling variations of shape in the banks of this interminable [endless] river as well as I know the shape of the front hall at home?"

"On my honor, you've got to know them better than any man ever did know the shapes of the halls in his own house."

"I wish I was dead!"

"Now I don't want to discourage you, but —. . . . You see, this has got to be learned; there isn't any getting around it. . . The river is a very different shape on a pitch-dark night from what it is on a starlight night. All shores seem to be straight lines, then, and mighty dim ones, too; and you'd run them for straight lines, only you know better. . . . Then there's your gray mist. You take a night when there's one of these grisly, drizzly gray mists, and then there isn't any particular shape to a shore. A gray mist would tangle the head of the oldest man that ever lived. Well, then, different kinds of moonlight change the shape of the river in different ways. You see —"

"Oh, don't say any more, please! Have I got to learn the shape of the river according to all these five hundred thousand different ways? If I tried to carry all that cargo in my head, it would make me stoop-shouldered."

"No! You only learn the shape of the river; and you learn it with such absolute certainty that you can always steer by the shape that's in your head, and never mind the one that's before your eyes."

Language Arts Activity

Read the excerpt, focusing on what the dialogue tells you about the characters of Mark Twain and Mr. Bixby.

- What lesson does Mark Twain learn?
- How does Mr. Bixby feel about the Mississippi River? How can you tell?

Now, use dialogue to write an ending to this riverboat excerpt. Before you begin writing, think carefully about the characters, setting, and your conclusion.

Riverboat captains were licensed to navigate the river. ▶

Tie It Together

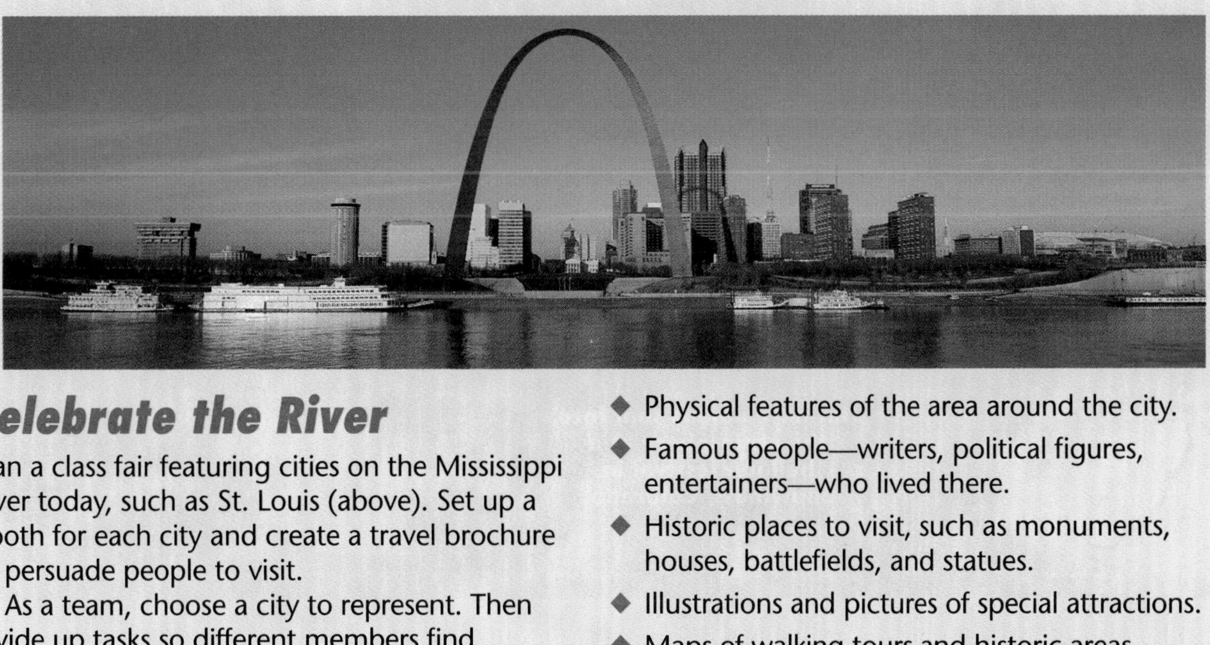

Celebrate the River

Plan a class fair featuring cities on the Mississippi River today, such as St. Louis (above). Set up a booth for each city and create a travel brochure to persuade people to visit.

As a team, choose a city to represent. Then divide up tasks so different members find information on the following topics:

- Interesting attractions and events that your city offers— zoos, museums, parks, sports events, music festivals, and so on.
- Influences of different groups on the city's food, customs, music, and architecture.
- Physical features of the area around the city.
- Famous people—writers, political figures, entertainers—who lived there.
- Historic places to visit, such as monuments, houses, battlefields, and statues.
- Illustrations and pictures of special attractions.
- Maps of walking tours and historic areas.
- Native plants and animals in the area.

Before starting your brochure, decide which attractions to highlight. Think of a slogan for your travel campaign. If you wish, make a poster. Celebrate life on the river today.

CHAPTER 14

The Atmosphere

Hot-air balloons soar into the atmosphere at a balloon festival in Snowmass, Colorado.

CALIFORNIA SCIENCE CONTENT STANDARDS

The following California Science Content Standards are addressed in this chapter:

2. Topography is reshaped by weathering of rock and soil and by the transportation and deposition of sediment.

- **d.** Earthquakes, volcanic eruptions, landslides, and floods change human and wildlife habitats.

4. Many phenomena on the Earth's surface are affected by the transfer of energy through radiation and convection currents.

- **b.** Solar energy reaches Earth through radiation, mostly in the form of visible light.
- **e.** Differences in pressure, heat, air movement, and humidity result in changes of weather.

5. Organisms in ecosystems exchange energy and nutrients among themselves and with the environment.

- **b.** Over time, matter is transferred from one organism to others in the food web, and between organisms and the physical environment.
- **e.** The number and types of organisms an ecosystem can support depends on the

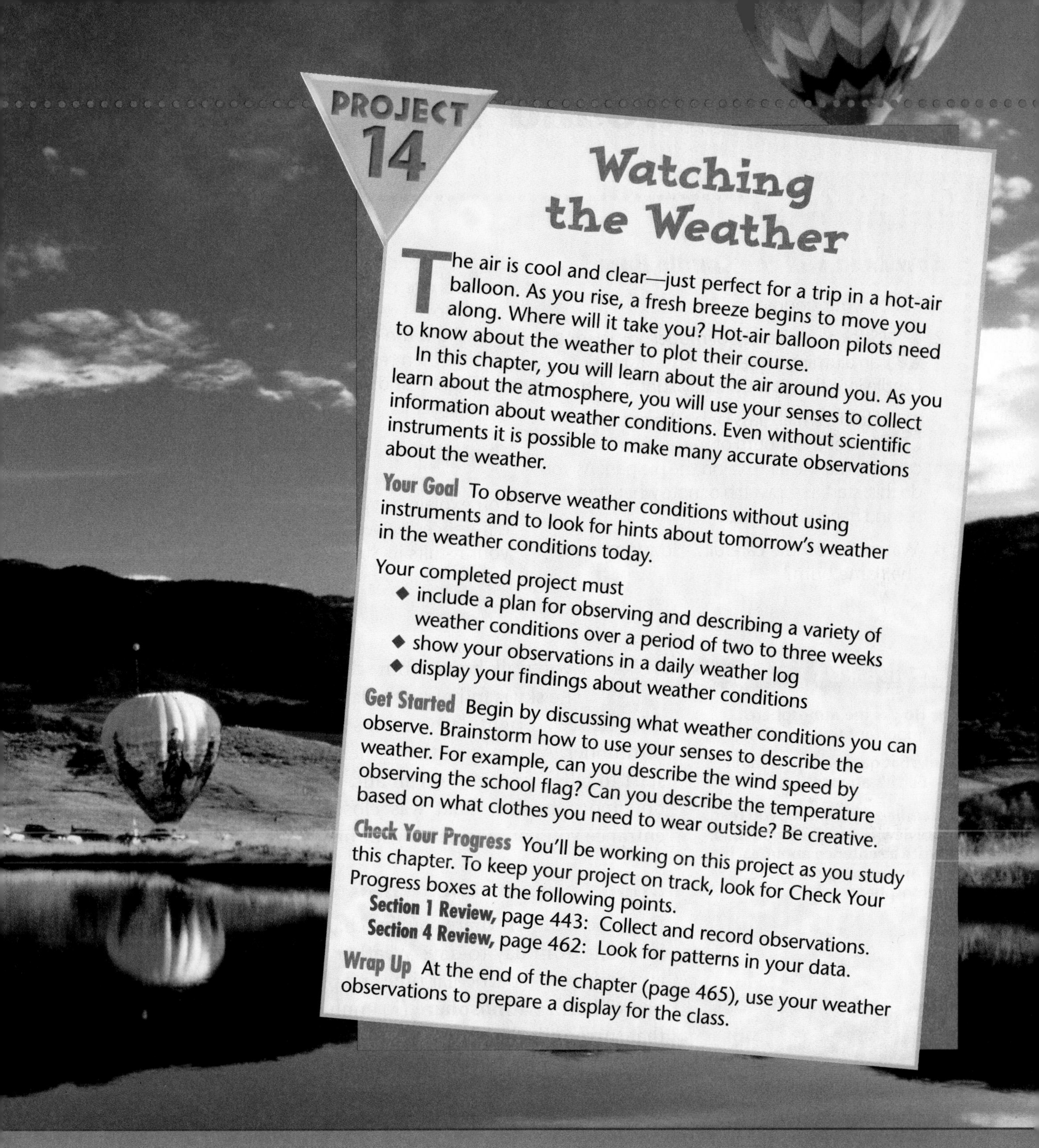

PROJECT 14

Watching the Weather

The air is cool and clear—just perfect for a trip in a hot-air balloon. As you rise, a fresh breeze begins to move you along. Where will it take you? Hot-air balloon pilots need to know about the weather to plot their course.

In this chapter, you will learn about the air around you. As you learn about the atmosphere, you will use your senses to collect information about weather conditions. Even without scientific instruments it is possible to make many accurate observations about the weather.

Your Goal To observe weather conditions without using instruments and to look for hints about tomorrow's weather in the weather conditions today.

Your completed project must

- include a plan for observing and describing a variety of weather conditions over a period of two to three weeks
- show your observations in a daily weather log
- display your findings about weather conditions

Get Started Begin by discussing what weather conditions you can observe. Brainstorm how to use your senses to describe the weather. For example, can you describe the wind speed by observing the school flag? Can you describe the temperature based on what clothes you need to wear outside? Be creative.

Check Your Progress You'll be working on this project as you study this chapter. To keep your project on track, look for Check Your Progress boxes at the following points.

Section 1 Review, page 443: Collect and record observations.
Section 4 Review, page 462: Look for patterns in your data.

Wrap Up At the end of the chapter (page 465), use your weather observations to prepare a display for the class.

resources available and abiotic factors, such as quantity of light and water, range of temperatures, and soil composition.

6. Sources of energy and materials differ in amounts, distribution, usefulness, and the time required for their formation.

a. The utility of energy sources is determined by factors that are involved in converting these sources to useful forms and the consequences of the conversion process.

b. Different natural energy and material resources, including air, soil, rocks, minerals, petroleum, fresh water, wildlife, and forests, and classify them as renewable or nonrenewable.

7. Scientific progress is made by asking meaningful questions and conducting careful investigations.

a. Develop a hypothesis.

h. Identify changes in natural phenomena over time without manipulating the phenomena (e.g., a tree limb, a grove of trees, a stream, a hillslope).

SECTION 1 The Air Around You

DISCOVER ACTIVITY

How Long Will the Candle Burn?

1. Put on your goggles.
2. Stick a small piece of modeling clay onto an aluminum pie pan. Push a short candle into the clay. Carefully light the candle.
3. Hold a small glass jar by the bottom. Lower the mouth of the jar over the candle until the jar rests on the pie pan. As you do this, start a stopwatch or note where the second hand is on a clock.
4. Watch the candle carefully. How long does the flame burn?
5. Wearing an oven mitt, remove the jar. Relight the candle and then repeat Steps 3 and 4 with a larger jar.

Think It Over

Inferring How would you explain any differences between your results in Steps 4 and 5?

GUIDE FOR READING

- **How is the atmosphere important to living things?**
- **What gases are present in Earth's atmosphere?**

Reading Tip **Before you read, preview Figure 2. As you read, write a sentence about each of the major gases in the atmosphere.**

As you walk home from school, the air is warm and still. The sky is full of thick, dark clouds. In the distance you see a bright flash. A few seconds later, you hear a crack of thunder. As you turn the corner onto your street, raindrops start to fall. You begin to run and reach your home just as the downpour begins. That was close! From the shelter of the entrance you pause to catch your breath and watch the storm.

Importance of the Atmosphere

Does the weather where you live change frequently, or is it fairly constant from day to day? **Weather** is the condition of Earth's atmosphere at a particular time and place. But what is the atmosphere? Earth's **atmosphere** (AT muh sfeer) is the layer of gases that surrounds the planet. To understand the relative size of the atmosphere, imagine that the planet Earth is the size of an apple.

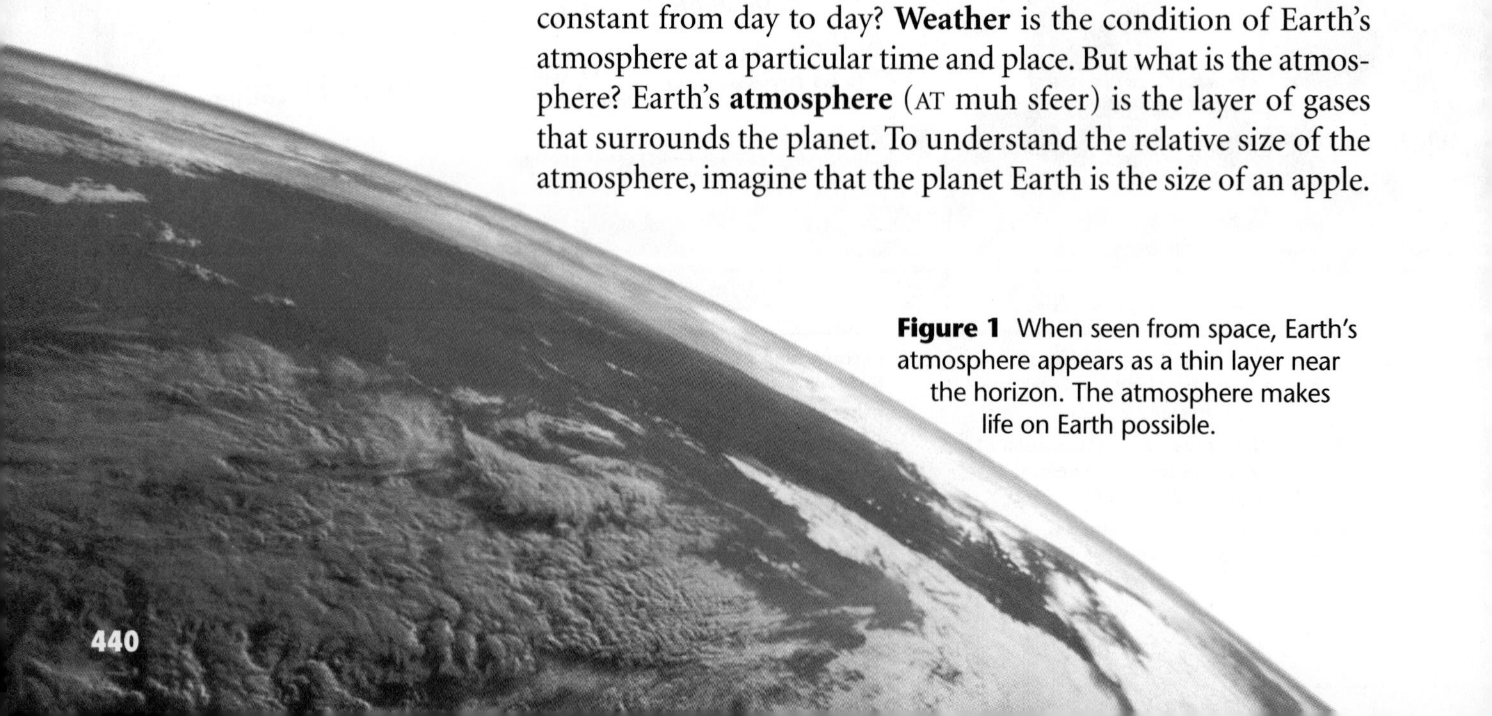

Figure 1 When seen from space, Earth's atmosphere appears as a thin layer near the horizon. The atmosphere makes life on Earth possible.

If you breathe on the apple, a thin film of water will form on its surface. Earth's atmosphere is like that water on the apple—a thin layer of gases on Earth's surface.

Earth's atmosphere makes conditions on Earth suitable for living things. The atmosphere contains oxygen and other gases that you and other living things need to live. In turn, living things affect the atmosphere. The atmosphere is constantly changing, with atoms and molecules of gases moving around the globe and in and out of living things, the land, and the water.

Living things also need warmth and liquid water. By trapping energy from the sun, the atmosphere keeps most of Earth's surface warm enough for water to exist as a liquid. In addition, Earth's atmosphere protects living things from dangerous radiation from the sun. It also prevents Earth's surface from being hit by most meteoroids, or chunks of rock from outer space.

☑ *Checkpoint* *What would conditions on Earth be like without the atmosphere?*

Language Arts CONNECTION

The word *atmosphere* comes from two Greek words: *atmos*, meaning "vapor," and *sphaira*, meaning "ball," or "globe." So the atmosphere is the vapors or gases surrounding a globe—in this case, Earth.

In Your Journal

As you read this chapter, write down all the words that end in *-sphere*. Look up the roots of each word in a dictionary. How does knowing the roots of each word help you understand its meaning?

Composition of the Atmosphere

The atmosphere is made up of a mixture of atoms and molecules of different kinds of gases. An atom is the smallest unit of a chemical element that can exist by itself. Molecules are made up of two or more atoms. **Earth's atmosphere is made up of nitrogen, oxygen, carbon dioxide, water vapor, and many other gases, as well as particles of liquids and solids.**

Nitrogen As you can see in Figure 2, nitrogen is the most abundant gas in the atmosphere. It makes up a little more than three fourths of the air we breathe. Each nitrogen molecule consists of two nitrogen atoms.

Gases in Dry Air

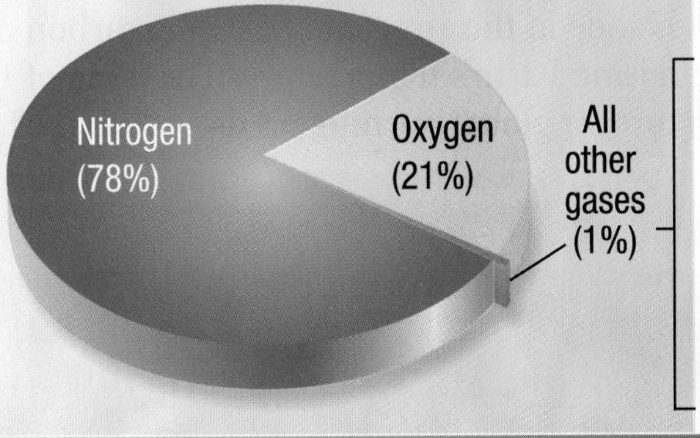
Nitrogen
(78%)
Oxygen
(21%)
All
other
gases
(1%)

Other Gases	Percentage by Volume
Argon	0.93
Carbon dioxide	0.036
Neon	0.0018
Helium	0.00052
Methane	0.00015
Krypton	0.00011
Hydrogen	0.00005

Figure 2 Dry air in the lower atmosphere always has the same composition of gases. *Interpreting Data What two gases make up most of the air?*

Try This

Breathe In, Breathe Out

Activity

How can you detect carbon dioxide in the air you exhale?

1. Put on your goggles.
2. Fill a glass or beaker halfway with limewater.

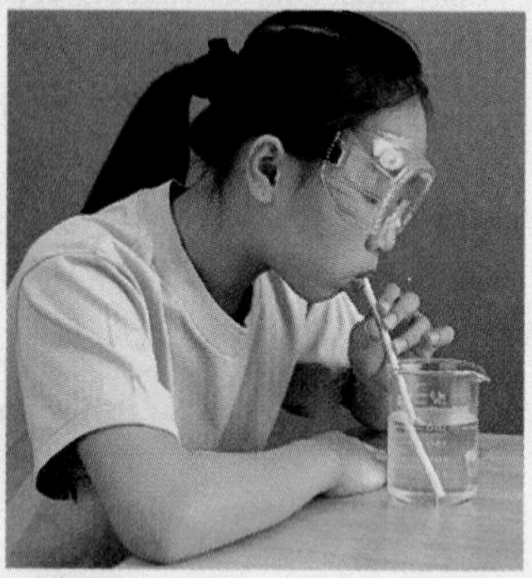

3. Using a straw, slowly blow air through the limewater for about a minute. **CAUTION:** *Do not suck on the straw or drink the limewater.*
4. What happens to the limewater?

Predicting What do you think would happen if you did the same experiment after jogging for 10 minutes? If you tried this, what might the results tell you about exercise and carbon dioxide?

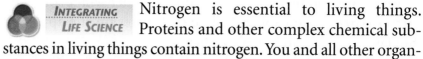

Integrating Life Science Nitrogen is essential to living things. Proteins and other complex chemical substances in living things contain nitrogen. You and all other organisms must have nitrogen in order to grow and to repair body cells.

Most living things cannot obtain nitrogen directly from the air. Instead, some bacteria convert nitrogen into substances called nitrates. Plants then absorb the nitrates from the soil and use them to make proteins. To obtain proteins, animals must eat plants or other animals.

Oxygen Most oxygen molecules have two oxygen atoms. Even though oxygen is the second-most abundant gas in the atmosphere, it makes up less than one fourth of the volume. Plants and animals take oxygen directly from the air and use it to release energy from food in a usable form.

Oxygen is also involved in other important processes. Any fuel you can think of, from the gasoline in a car to the candles on a birthday cake, uses oxygen as it burns. Without oxygen, a fire will go out. Burning uses oxygen rapidly. During other processes, oxygen is used slowly. For example, steel in cars and other objects reacts slowly with oxygen to form iron oxide, or rust.

Have you ever noticed a pungent smell in the air after a thunderstorm? This is the odor of ozone, which forms when lightning interacts with oxygen in the air. **Ozone** is a form of oxygen that has three oxygen atoms in each molecule instead of the usual two.

Carbon Dioxide Each molecule of carbon dioxide has one atom of carbon and two atoms of oxygen. Even though the atmosphere contains only a small amount of carbon dioxide, it is essential to life. Plants must have carbon dioxide to produce food. Animals, on the other hand, give off carbon dioxide as a waste product.

When fuels such as coal and gasoline are burned, they release carbon dioxide. Burning these fuels increases the amount of carbon dioxide in the atmosphere. Rising carbon dioxide levels may be raising Earth's temperature. The issue of Earth's rising temperature, or global warming, is discussed in Chapter 17.

Figure 3 To burn, these candles need oxygen, one of the gases in the atmosphere. *Predicting What would happen if the candles used up all of the oxygen around them?*

Other Gases Oxygen and nitrogen together make up 99 percent of dry air. Carbon dioxide and argon make up most of the other one percent. The remaining gases are called trace gases because only small amounts of them are present.

Water Vapor The composition of the air discussed so far has been for dry air. In reality, air is not dry because it contains water vapor. **Water vapor** is water in the form of a gas. Water vapor is invisible—it is not the same thing as steam, which is made up of tiny droplets of liquid water. Each water molecule contains two atoms of hydrogen and one atom of oxygen.

The amount of water vapor in the air varies greatly from place to place and from time to time. Air above a desert or polar ice sheet may contain almost no water vapor. In tropical rain forests, on the other hand, as much as five percent of the air may be water vapor.

Water vapor plays an important role in Earth's weather. Clouds form when water vapor condenses out of the air to form tiny droplets of liquid water or crystals of ice. If these droplets or crystals become large enough, they can fall as rain or snow.

Costa Rica

Figure 4 This lush vegetation grows in a rain forest in Costa Rica. The percentage of water vapor in the air in a rain forest may be as high as five percent.

Particles Pure air contains only gases. But pure air exists only in laboratories. In the real world, air also contains tiny solid and liquid particles of dust, smoke, salt, and other chemicals. Sometimes you can see particles in the air around you, but most of them are too small to see.

Section 1 Review

1. Describe two ways in which the atmosphere is important to life on Earth.
2. What are the four most common gases in dry air?
3. Why are the amounts of gases in the atmosphere usually shown as percentages of dry air?
4. **Thinking Critically Applying Concepts** How would the amount of carbon dioxide in the atmosphere change if there were no plants? If there were no animals?

CHAPTER PROJECT

Check Your Progress

Have you determined *how*, *where*, and *when*, you will make your observations? Organize a notebook to record them. Think of ways to compare weather conditions from day to day. Make your observations without weather instruments or TV weather reports. (*Hint:* You can estimate how much of the sky is covered by clouds.) For your own safety, do not try to make observations during storms.

Real-World Lab

You and Your Environment

How Clean Is the Air?

Sometimes you can actually see the atmosphere! How? Since air is normally transparent, it can only be visible because it contains particles. In this activity, you will use a vacuum cleaner to gather particles from the air.

Problem

How do weather factors affect the number of particles in the air?

Skills Focus

measuring, interpreting data

Materials

coffee filters
rubber band
thermometer
low-power microscope
vacuum cleaner with intake hose (1 per class)

Procedure

1. Predict what factors will affect the number of particles you collect. How might different weather factors affect your results?
2. In your notebook, make a data table like the one below.
3. Place the coffee filter over the nozzle of the vacuum cleaner hose. Fasten the coffee filter securely to the hose with a rubber band. Make sure the air passes through the coffee filter before entering the vacuum cleaner.
4. You will take air samples in the same place each day for five days. If possible, find a place outdoors. Otherwise, you can run the vacuum cleaner out a classroom window. **CAUTION:** *Do not use the vacuum cleaner outdoors on wet or rainy days.* If it is wet or rainy, collect the sample as soon as possible after it stops raining.
5. Hold the vacuum nozzle at least one meter above the ground each time you use the vacuum. Turn on the vacuum. Run the vacuum for 30 minutes. Shut off the vacuum.

DATA TABLE

Date and Time	Temperature	Amount of Precipitation	Wind Direction	Wind Speed	Number of Particles

6. While the vacuum is running, observe the weather conditions. Measure the temperature. Estimate the amount of precipitation, if any, since the previous observation. Note the direction from which the wind, if any, is blowing. Also note whether the wind is heavy, light, or calm. Record your observations.
7. Remove the coffee filter from the nozzle. Label the filter with the place, time, and date. Draw a circle on the filter to show the area that was over the vacuum nozzle.
8. Place the coffee filter on the stage of a microscope (40 power). Be sure that the part of the filter that was over the vacuum nozzle is directly under the microscope lens. Without moving the coffee filter, count all the particles you see. Record the number in your data table.
9. Repeat Steps 3–8 each clear day.

Analyze and Conclude

1. Was there a day of the week when you collected more particles?
2. What factors changed during the week that could have caused changes in the particle count?
3. Did the weather have any effect on your day-to-day results? If so, which weather factor do you think was most important?
4. Make a list of some possible sources of the particles you collected. Are these sources natural, or did the particles come from manufactured products?
5. How could you improve your method to get more particles out of the air?
6. **Apply** Identify areas in or around your school where there may be high levels of dust and other particles. What can people do to protect themselves in these areas?

Design an Experiment

Develop a hypothesis to explain how the number of particles in the air varies with the time of day. Design an experiment to test your hypothesis. Could you work with other classes to get data at different times of the day? Before carrying out your plan, get your teacher's approval.

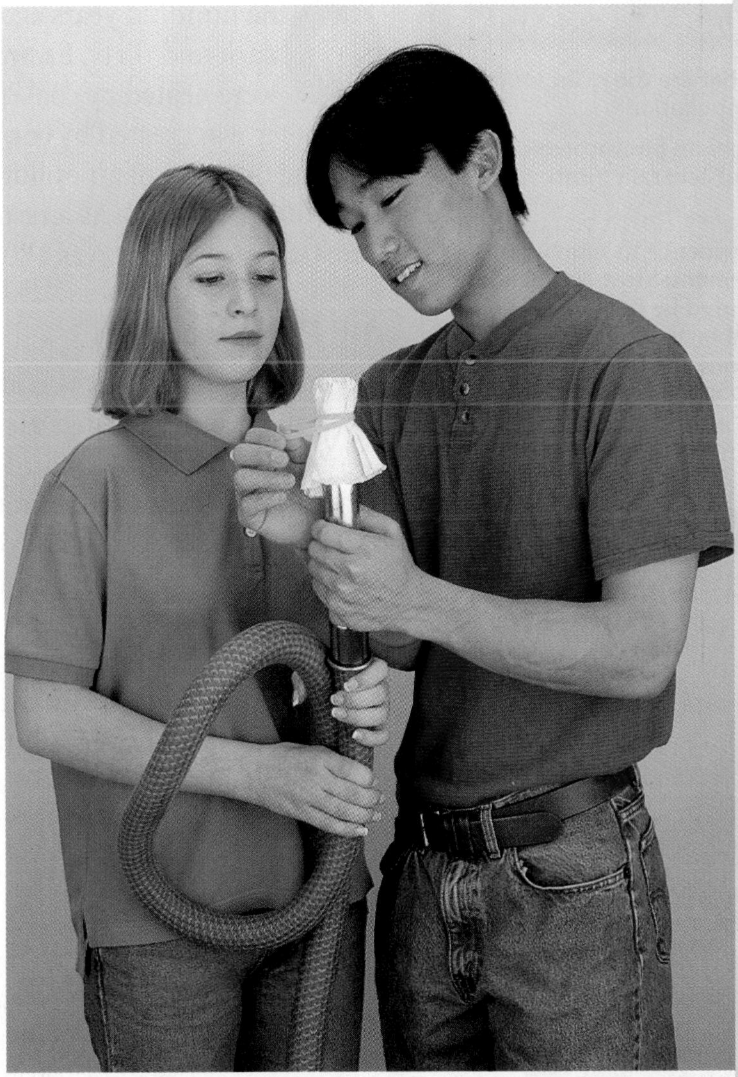

SECTION 2 Air Quality

DISCOVER ACTIVITY

What's On the Jar?

1. Put on your goggles.
2. Put a small piece of modeling clay on a piece of aluminum foil. Push a candle into the clay. Light the candle.
3. Wearing an oven mitt, hold a glass jar by the rim so that the bottom of the jar is just above the flame.

Think It Over

Observing What do you see on the jar? Where did it come from?

GUIDE FOR READING

- What are the main sources of air pollution?
- How do photochemical smog and acid rain form?

Reading Tip As you read, look for evidence to support this statement: Most air pollution is caused by human activities. What facts support this statement? What facts do not support it?

One hundred years ago, the city of London, England, was dark and dirty. Factories burned coal, and most houses were heated by coal. The air was full of soot. In 1905, the term *smog* was created by combining the words *sm*oke and f*og* to describe this type of air pollution. Today, people in London burn much less coal. As a result, the air in London now is much cleaner than it was 100 years ago.

Air Pollution

As you are reading this, you are breathing without even thinking about it. Breathing brings air into your lungs, where the oxygen you need is taken into your body. You may also breathe in tiny particles or even a small amount of harmful gases. In fact, these particles and gases are a concern to people everywhere.

If you live in a large city, you probably already know what air pollution is. You may have noticed a brown haze or an unpleasant smell in the air. Even if you live far from a city, the air around you may be polluted. Harmful substances in the air, water, or soil are known as **pollutants**. Figure 5 shows some of the effects of air pollution on human health.

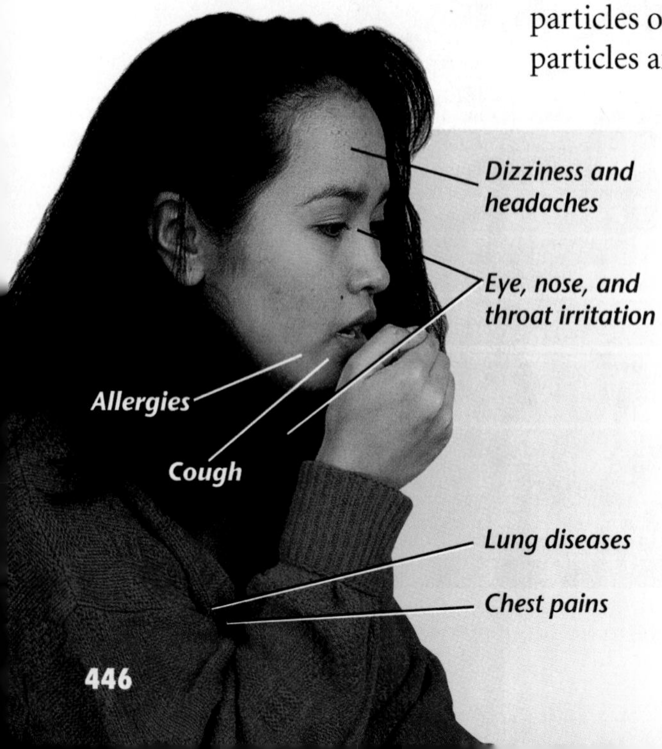
Dizziness and headaches
Eye, nose, and throat irritation
Allergies
Cough
Lung diseases
Chest pains

Figure 5 Air pollution can cause many different problems. Some air pollutants are natural, but most are caused by human activities. ***Interpreting Photographs*** *What parts of the body are most affected by air pollution?*

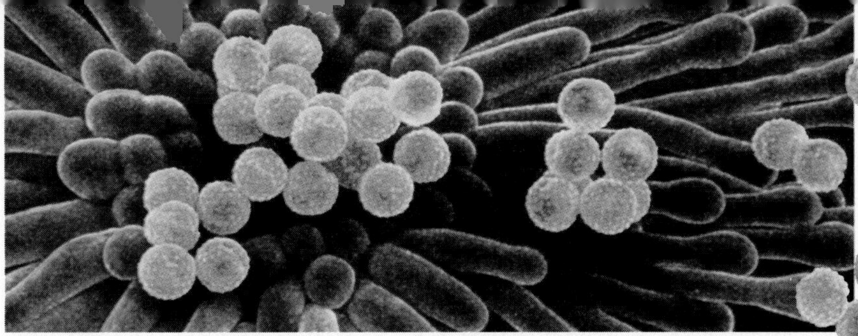

Figure 6 These pollen grains from a ragweed flower have been greatly magnified to show detail. Pollen can cause people who are allergic to it to sneeze.

Some air pollution occurs naturally, but much of it is caused by human activities. **Most air pollution is the result of burning fossil fuels such as coal, oil, gasoline, and diesel fuel.** Almost half of the air pollution from human activities comes from cars and other motor vehicles. A little more than one fourth comes from factories and power plants that burn coal and oil. Burning fossil fuels produces a number of air pollutants, including particles and gases that can form smog and acid rain.

☑ *Checkpoint* *What are two sources of air pollution that you see every day?*

Particles

As you know, air contains particles along with gases. When you draw these particles deep into your lungs, the particles can be harmful. Particles in the air come from both natural sources and human activities.

Natural Sources Many natural processes add particles to the atmosphere. When ocean waves splash salt water against rocks, some of the water sprays into the air and evaporates. Tiny salt particles stay in the air. The wind blows particles of molds and plant pollen. Forest fires, soil erosion, and dust storms add particles to the atmosphere. Erupting volcanoes spew out clouds of dust and ashes along with poisonous gases.

INTEGRATING HEALTH Even fairly clean air usually contains particles of dust and pollen. Figure 6 shows pollen, a fine, powdery material produced by many plants. The wind carries pollen not only to other plants, but also to people. One type of allergy, popularly called "hay fever," is caused by pollen from plants such as ragweed. Symptoms of hay fever include sneezing, a runny nose, red and itchy eyes, and headaches. Weather reports often include a "pollen count," which is the average number of pollen grains in a cubic meter of air.

Human Activities When people burn fuels such as wood and coal, particles made mostly of carbon enter the air. These particles of soot are what gives smoke its dark color. Farming and construction also release large amounts of soil particles into the air.

Figure 7 These people in Pontianak, Indonesia, are being given dust masks to protect them from smoke caused by widespread forest fires. *Inferring What effects do you think this smoke might have had on the people who live in this area?*

Sharpen your Skills

Predicting ACTIVITY

Are the amounts of pollutants in the air always at the same level, or do they change from time to time? At what time of the day do you think the major sources of air pollution— cars, trucks, power plants, and factories—might produce the most pollution? Overall, do you think there is more air pollution in the morning or in the evening? On Mondays or on Fridays? On what did you base your prediction?

Smog

London-type smog forms when particles in coal smoke combine with water droplets in humid air. Fortunately, London-type smog is no longer common in the United States. Today sunny cities like Los Angeles often have another type of smog. The brown haze that forms in cities is called **photochemical smog**. The *photo-* in photochemical means "light." Photochemical smog is caused by the action of sunlight on chemicals.

INTEGRATING CHEMISTRY Photochemical smog is formed by a complex process. All fossil fuels contain hydrocarbons, which are substances composed of carbon and hydrogen. When fossil fuels are burned, some hydrocarbons are not burned completely and escape into the air. At the same time, the high temperatures that accompany burning cause some of the nitrogen in the air to react with oxygen to form nitrogen oxides. **The nitrogen oxides, hydrocarbons, and other air pollutants then react with each other in the presence of sunlight to form a mix of ozone and other chemicals called photochemical smog.** The ozone in photochemical smog irritates breathing passages, harms plants, and damages rubber, paint, and some plastics.

☑ *Checkpoint* *How do natural conditions combine with human activities to create photochemical smog?*

Acid Rain

One result of air pollution is acid rain. The burning of coal that contains a lot of sulfur produces substances composed of oxygen and sulfur called sulfur oxides. **Acid rain forms when nitrogen oxides and sulfur oxides combine with water in the air to form nitric acid and sulfuric acid.**

Figure 8 This scientist is studying trees damaged by acid rain. Acid rain is one of the results of air pollution.

Rain, sleet, snow, fog, and even dry particles carry these two acids from the air to trees, lakes, and buildings. Rain is naturally slightly acidic, but rain that contains more acid than normal is known as **acid rain.** Acid rain is sometimes strong enough to damage the surfaces of buildings and statues.

As Figure 8 shows, needle-leafed trees such as pines and spruce are especially sensitive to acid rain. Acid rain may make tree needles turn brown or fall off. It also harms lakes and ponds. Acid rain can make water so acidic that plants, amphibians, fish, and insects can no longer survive in it.

Improving Air Quality

The United States government and state governments have passed a number of laws and regulations to reduce air pollution. For example, pollution-control devices are required equipment on cars. Factories and power plants must install filters in smokestacks to remove pollutants from smoke before it is released into the atmosphere. These filters are called scrubbers.

Air quality in this country has generally improved over the past 30 years. The amounts of most major air pollutants have decreased. Newer cars cause less pollution than older models. Recently-built power plants are less polluting than power plants that have been in operation for many years.

However, there are now more cars on the road and more power plants burning fossil fuels than in the past. Unfortunately, the air in many American cities is still polluted. Many people think that stricter regulations are needed to control air pollution. Others argue that reducing air pollution is very expensive and that the benefits of stricter regulations may not be worth the costs.

Section 2 Review

1. How is most air pollution produced?
2. Name two natural and two artificial sources of particles in the atmosphere.
3. How is photochemical smog formed? What kinds of harm does it cause?
4. What substances combine to form acid rain?
5. **Thinking Critically Inferring** Do you think that photochemical smog levels are higher during the winter or during the summer? Explain.

Science at Home

It's easy to see particles in the air. Gather your family members in a dark room. Open a window shade or blind slightly, or turn on a flashlight. Can they see tiny particles suspended in the beam of light? Discuss with your family where the particles came from. What might be some natural sources? What might be some human sources?

Cars and Clean Air

New technology and strict laws have brought cleaner air to many American cities. But in some places the air is still polluted. Cars and trucks still cause about half the air pollution in cities. And there are more cars on the road every year!

Worldwide, there are about 500 million cars. More cars will mean more pollution and more traffic jams. Unfortunately, cars stuck in traffic produce three times as much pollution as cars on the open road. What can people do to reduce air pollution by cars?

The Issues

Can Cars Be Made To Pollute Less?

In the past 20 years, cars have become more fuel-efficient and pollution levels have been lowered. Now engineers are running out of ways to make cars run more efficiently and produce less pollution. But technology does offer other answers.

Some vehicles use fuels other than gasoline. For instance, natural gas can power cars and trucks. Burning natural gas produces less pollution than burning gasoline.

Battery-powered electric cars produce no air pollution. However, the electricity to charge the batteries often comes from power plants that burn oil or coal. So electric cars still produce some pollution indirectly. Car makers have produced a few electric cars, but they are expensive and can make only fairly short trips.

Should People Drive Less? Many car trips are shorter than a mile—an easy distance for most people to walk. For longer trips, people might consider riding a bicycle. Many cars on the road carry just one person. Some people might consider riding with others in car pools or taking buses or subways.

Are Stricter Standards or Taxes the Answer? Some state governments have led efforts to reduce pollution. The state of California, for example, has strict anti-pollution laws. These laws set standards for gradually reducing pollutants released by cars. Stricter laws might make some old cars illegal.

Another approach is to make driving more expensive so that people use their cars less. That might mean higher gasoline taxes or fees for using the roads at busy times.

You Decide

1. Identify the Problem
In your own words, explain why automobiles make it hard to improve air quality. What kinds of pollution are caused by automobiles?

2. Analyze the Options
What are some ways to reduce the pollution caused by cars? Should these actions be voluntary, or should governments require them?

3. Find a Solution
How would you encourage people to try to reduce the pollution from cars? Create a visual essay from newspaper and magazine clippings. Write captions to explain your solution.

SECTION 3

Air Pressure

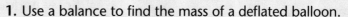

DISCOVER — ACTIVITY

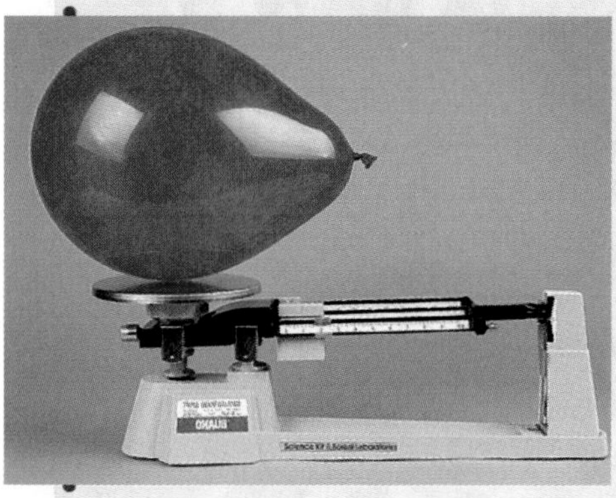
OHAUS

Does Air Have Mass?

1. Use a balance to find the mass of a deflated balloon.
2. Blow up the balloon and tie the neck closed. Do you think the mass of the inflated balloon will differ from the mass of the deflated balloon?
3. Find the mass of the inflated balloon. Compare this mass to the mass of the deflated balloon. Was your prediction correct?

Think It Over

Drawing Conclusions Did the mass of the balloon change after it was inflated? What can you conclude about whether air has mass?

GUIDE FOR READING

- **What are some of the properties of air?**
- **What instruments are used to measure air pressure?**
- **How does increasing altitude affect air pressure and density?**

Reading Tip **As you read this section, use the headings to make an outline about air pressure.**

One of the best parts of eating roasted peanuts is opening the jar. When a jar of peanuts is "vacuum packed," most of the air is pumped out, creating low pressure inside. When you break the seal, the "whoosh" you hear is air from the outside rushing into the jar. The "whoosh" is the result of a difference in pressure between the outside of the jar and the inside.

Properties of Air

It may seem to you that air has no mass. However, air consists of atoms and molecules, which have mass. So air must have mass. **Because air has mass, it also has other properties, including density and pressure.**

Density The amount of mass in a given volume of air is its **density**. You can calculate density by dividing mass by volume.

$$Density = \frac{Mass}{Volume}$$

If there are more molecules in a given volume of air, the density is greater. If there are fewer molecules, the density decreases.

Pressure The force pushing on an area or surface is known as **pressure**. A denser substance has more mass per unit volume than a less dense one. So denser air exerts more pressure than less dense air.

To understand pressure, think of carrying a heavy backpack. The weight presses the straps into your shoulders just as the pack does to the hiker in the photo.

When you take off a backpack, it feels as if all the pressure has been taken off your shoulders. But has it? The weight of the column of air above you remains, as shown in Figure 9.

Air pressure is the result of the weight of a column of air pushing down on an area. The weight of the column of air above your desk is about the same as the weight of a large school bus! So why doesn't air pressure crush your desk? The reason is that the molecules in air push in all directions—down, up, and sideways. So the air pushing down on the top of your desk is balanced by the air pushing up on the bottom of the desk.

Figure 9 There is a column of air above you all the time. The weight of the air in the atmosphere causes air pressure.

Measuring Air Pressure

Have you ever heard a weather report say that the air pressure is falling? Falling air pressure usually indicates that a storm is approaching. Rising air pressure usually means that the weather is clearing. A **barometer** (buh RAHM uh tur) is an instrument that is used to measure changes in air pressure. **There are two kinds of barometers: mercury barometers and aneroid barometers.**

Mercury Barometers The first barometers invented were mercury barometers. Figure 10 shows how a mercury barometer works. A **mercury barometer** consists of a glass tube open at the bottom end and partially filled with mercury. The space in the tube above the mercury is almost a vacuum—it contains no air. The open end of the tube rests in a dish of mercury. The air pressure pushing down on the surface of the mercury in the dish is equal to the

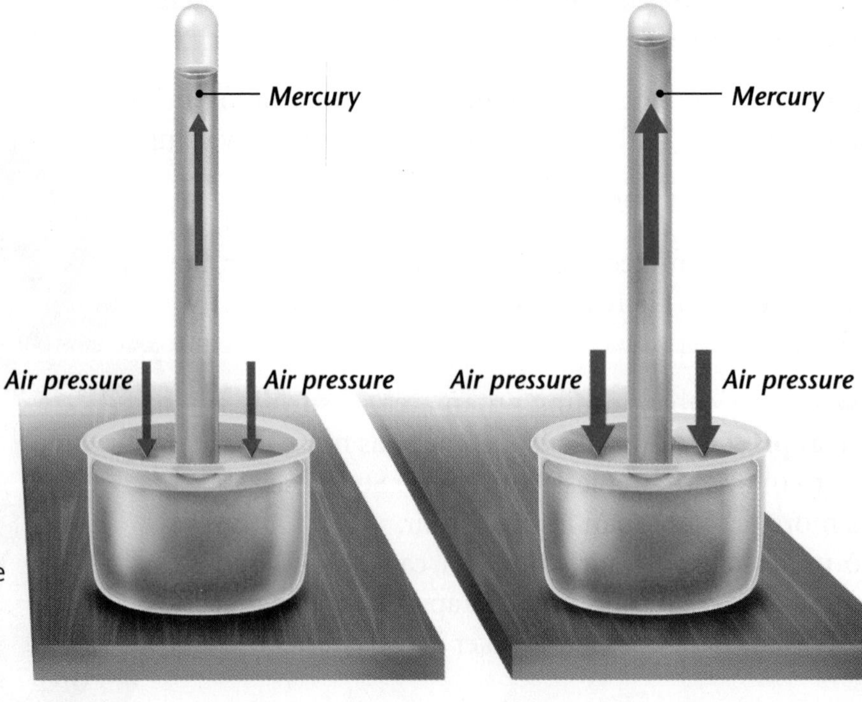
Mercury
Air pressure
Air pressure
Mercury
Air pressure
Air pressure

Figure 10 Air pressure pushes down on the surface of the mercury in the dish, causing the mercury in the tube to rise. *Predicting What happens when the air pressure increases?*

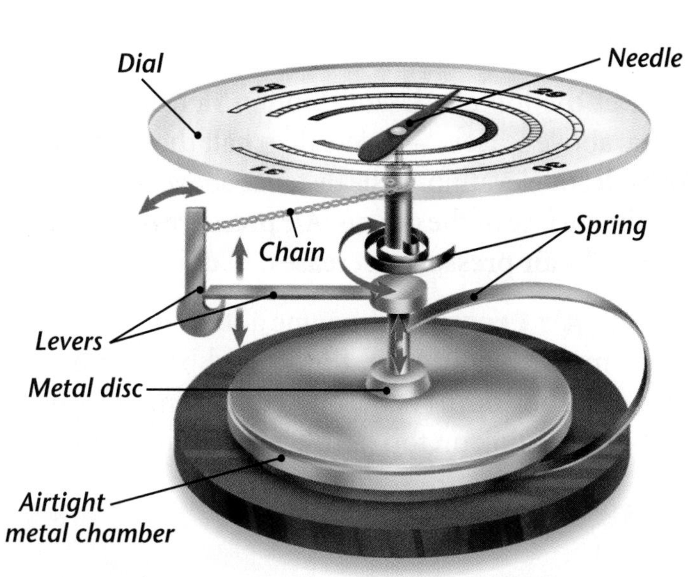
Dial
Needle
Chain
Spring
Levers
Metal disc
Airtight metal chamber

FALLING
RISING
FALLING PRESSURE
RISING PRESSURE

Figure 11 Changes in air pressure cause the walls of the airtight metal chamber to flex in and out. The needle on the dial indicates the air pressure.

weight of the column of mercury in the tube. At sea level the mercury column is about 76 centimeters high, on average.

When the air pressure increases, it presses down more on the surface of the mercury. Greater air pressure forces the column of mercury higher. What will happen to the column of mercury if the air pressure decreases? The column will fall.

Aneroid Barometers If you have a barometer on a desk or wall at home, it is probably an aneroid barometer. The word *aneroid* means "without liquid." An **aneroid barometer** (AN uh royd) has an airtight metal chamber, as shown in Figure 11. The metal chamber is sensitive to changes in air pressure. When air pressure increases, the thin walls of the chamber are pushed in. When the pressure drops, the walls bulge out. The chamber is connected to a dial by a series of springs and levers. As the shape of the chamber changes, the needle on the dial moves.

Aneroid barometers are smaller than mercury barometers and don't contain a liquid. Therefore, they are portable and often more practical for uses such as airplane instrument panels.

Units of Air Pressure Weather reports use several different units for air pressure. Most weather reports for the general public use inches of mercury. For example, if the column of mercury in a mercury barometer is 30 inches high, the air pressure is "30 inches of mercury" or just "30 inches."

National Weather Service maps indicate air pressure in millibars. One inch of mercury equals approximately 33.87 millibars, so 30 inches of mercury is approximately equal to 1,016 millibars.

☑ *Checkpoint* *Name two common units used to measure air pressure.*

TRY THIS

Soda-Bottle Barometer

ACTIVITY

Here's how to build a device that shows changes in air pressure.

1. Fill a 2-liter soda bottle one-half full with water.
2. Lower a long straw into the bottle so that the end of the straw is in the water. Seal the mouth of the bottle around the straw with modeling clay.
3. Squeeze the sides of the bottle. What happens to the level of the water in the straw?
4. Let go of the sides of the bottle. Watch the level of the water in the straw.

Inferring Explain your results in terms of air pressure.

Increasing Altitude

The air pressure at the top of Alaska's Mount McKinley—more than 6 kilometers above sea level—is less than half the air pressure at sea level. **Altitude,** or elevation, is the distance above sea level, the average level of the surface of the oceans. **Air pressure decreases as altitude increases. As air pressure decreases, so does density.**

Altitude Affects Air Pressure Imagine a stack of ten books. Which book has more weight on it, the second book from the top or the book at the bottom? The second book from the top has only the weight of one book on top of it. The book at the bottom

Skills Lab

Measuring

Working Under Pressure

Air pressure changes are related to changing weather conditions. In this lab, you will build and use your own barometer to measure air pressure.

Problem

How can a barometer detect changes in air pressure?

Materials

modeling clay
white glue
pencil
metric ruler
large rubber balloon
drinking straw, 12–15 cm long
cardboard strip, 10 cm x 25 cm
scissors
tape
wide-mouthed glass jar
rubber band

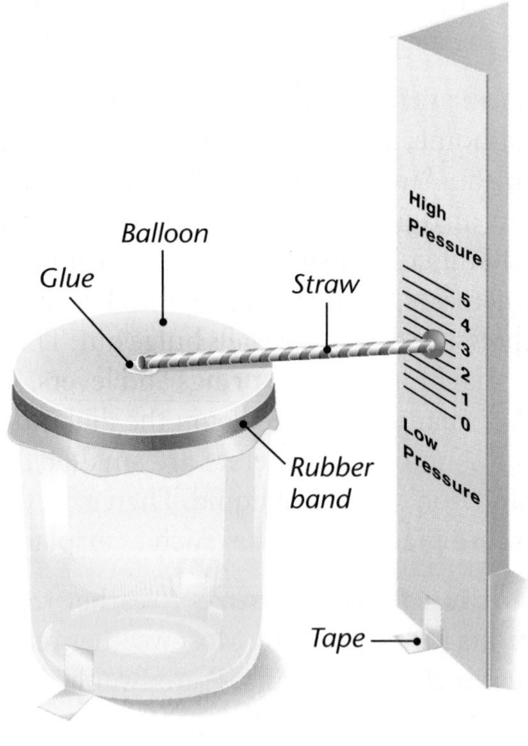

Balloon
Glue
Straw
High Pressure
5
4
3
2
1
0
Low Pressure
Rubber band
Tape

Procedure

1. Cut off the narrow opening of the balloon.
2. Fold the edges of the balloon outward. Carefully stretch the balloon over the open end of the glass jar. Use a rubber band to hold the balloon on the rim of the glass jar.
3. Place a small amount of glue on the center of the balloon top. Attach one end of the straw to the glue. Allow the other end to extend several centimeters beyond the edge of the glass jar. This is your pointer.

of the stack has the weight of all the other books pressing on it.

Air at sea level is like the bottom book. Recall that air pressure is the weight of the column of air pushing down on an area. Sea-level air has the weight of the whole atmosphere pressing on it. So air pressure is greatest at sea level. Air near the top of the atmosphere is like the second book from the top. There, the air has less weight pressing on it, and thus has lower air pressure.

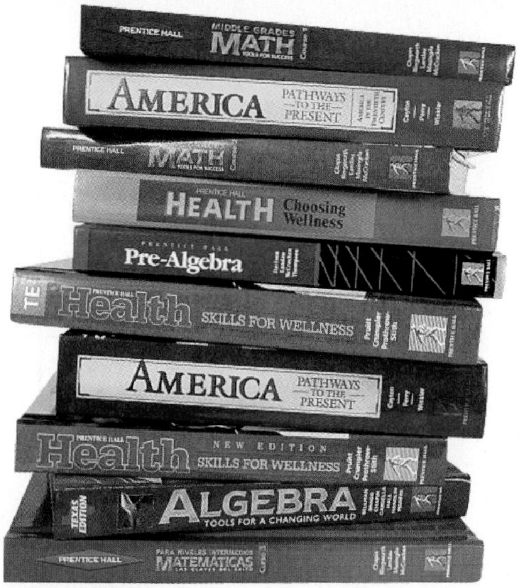

MATH
AMERICA
PATHWAYS TO THE PRESENT
HEALTH Choosing Wellness
Pre-Algebra
Health SKILLS FOR WELLNESS
AMERICA
PATHWAYS TO THE PRESENT
Health SKILLS FOR WELLNESS
ALGEBRA
TOOLS FOR A CHANGING WORLD
MATEMÁTICAS

DATA TABLE

Date and Time	Air Pressure	Weather Conditions

4. While the glue dries, fold the cardboard strip lengthwise and draw a scale along the edge with marks 0.5 cm apart. Write "High pressure" at the top of your scale and "Low pressure" at the bottom.
5. After the glue dries, add a pea-sized piece of modeling clay to the end of the pointer. Place your barometer and its scale in a location that is as free from temperature changes as possible. Arrange the scale and the barometer as shown in the diagram. Note that the pointer of the straw must just reach the cardboard strip.
6. Tape both the scale and the barometer to a surface so they do not move during your experiment.
7. In your notebook, make a data table like the one at the left. Record the date and time. Note the level of the straw on the cardboard strip.
8. Check the barometer twice a day. Record your observations in your data table.
9. Record the weather conditions for each day.

Analyze and Conclude

1. What change in atmospheric conditions must occur to cause the free end of the straw to rise? What change must occur for it to fall?
2. According to your observations, what kind of weather is usually associated with high air pressure? With low air pressure?
3. If the balloon had a tiny hole in it, what would happen to the accuracy of your barometer?
4. **Think About It** What effect, if any, would a great temperature change have on the accuracy of your barometer?

More to Explore

Compare changes in air pressure shown by your barometer with high and low air pressure readings shown on newspaper weather maps during the same time period. How do your readings compare with the readings in the newspapers?

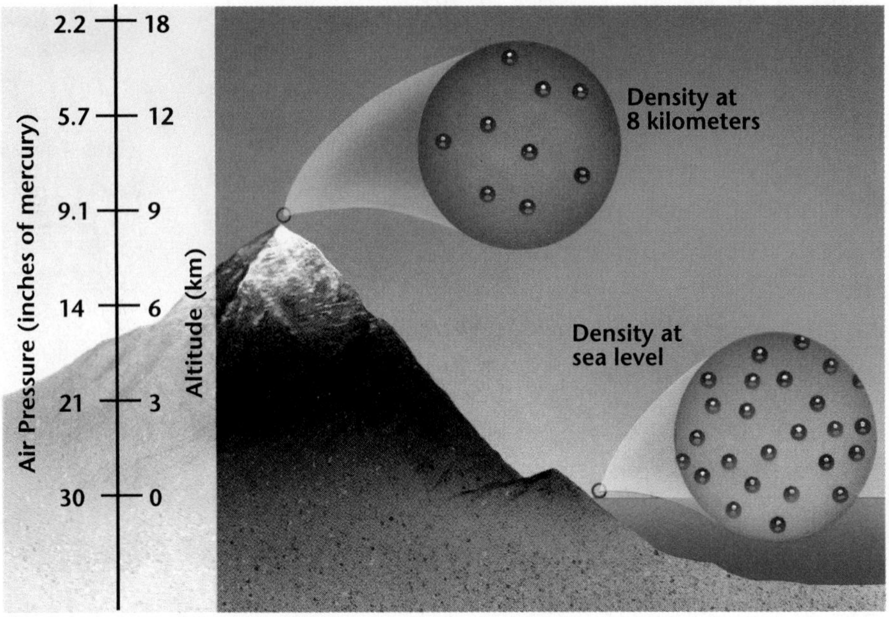

2.2
5.7
9.1
14
21
30
18
12
9
6
3
0
Air Pressure (inches of mercury)
Altitude (km)
Density at 8 kilometers
Density at sea level

Figure 12 The density of air decreases as altitude increases. Air at sea level has more gas molecules in each cubic meter than air at the top of a mountain.

Altitude Also Affects Density INTEGRATING LIFE SCIENCE If you were near the top of Mount McKinley and tried to run, you would get out of breath quickly. Why would you have difficulty breathing at high altitudes?

As you go up through the atmosphere, the air pressure decreases. As air pressure decreases, the density of the air decreases. So density decreases as altitude increases, as shown in Figure 12.

Whether air is at sea level or at 6 kilometers above sea level, the air still contains 21 percent oxygen. However, since the air is less dense at a high altitude, there are fewer oxygen molecules to breathe in each cubic meter of air than there are at sea level. You are taking in less oxygen with each breath. That is why you get out of breath quickly.

Section 3 Review

1. How does increasing the density of a gas affect its pressure?
2. Describe how a mercury barometer measures air pressure.
3. Why is the air at the top of a mountain hard to breathe?
4. **Thinking Critically Predicting** What changes in air pressure would you expect to see if you carried a barometer down a mine shaft? Explain.

Science at Home

Here's how you can show your family that air has pressure. Fill a glass with water. Place a piece of heavy cardboard over the top of the glass. Hold the cardboard in place with one hand as you turn the glass upside down. **CAUTION:** *Be sure the cardboard does not bend.* Now remove your hand from the cardboard. What happens? Explain to your family that the cardboard doesn't fall because the air pressure pushing up on it is greater than the weight of the water pushing down.

SECTION 4 Layers of the Atmosphere

DISCOVER ACTIVITY

Is Air There?

1. Use a heavy rubber band to tightly secure a plastic bag over the top of a wide-mouthed jar.
2. Gently try to push the bag into the jar. What happens? Is the air pressure higher inside or outside of the bag?
3. Remove the rubber band and line the inside of the jar with the plastic bag. Use the rubber band to tightly secure the edges of the bag over the rim of the jar.
4. Gently try to pull the bag out of the jar with your fingertips. What happens? Is the air pressure higher inside or outside of the bag?

Think It Over

Predicting Explain your observations in terms of air pressure. How do you think differences in air pressure would affect a weather balloon as it traveled up through the atmosphere?

GUIDE FOR READING

◆ **What are the characteristics of the main layers of the atmosphere?**

Reading Tip **Before you read, preview *Exploring Layers of the Atmosphere.* Make a list of unfamiliar words. Look for the meanings of these words as you read.**

Imagine taking a trip upward into the atmosphere in a hot-air balloon. You begin on a warm beach near the ocean, at an altitude of 0 kilometers.

You hear a roar as the balloon's pilot turns up the burner to heat the air in the balloon. The balloon begins to rise, and Earth's surface gets farther and farther away. As the balloon rises to an altitude of 3 kilometers, you realize that the air is getting colder. As you continue to rise, the air gets colder and colder. At 6 kilometers you begin to have trouble breathing. The air is becoming less dense. It's time to go back down.

What if you could have continued your balloon ride up through the atmosphere? As you rose farther up through the atmosphere, the air pressure and temperature would change dramatically. **The four main layers of the atmosphere are classified according to changes in temperature. These layers are the troposphere, the stratosphere, the mesosphere, and the thermosphere.**

The Troposphere

You live in the inner, or lowest, layer of Earth's atmosphere, the **troposphere** (TROH puh sfeer). *Tropo-* means "turning" or "changing"; conditions in the troposphere are more variable than in the other layers. The troposphere is where Earth's weather occurs.

Figure 13 This weather balloon will carry a package of instruments to measure weather conditions high in the atmosphere. *Applying Concepts Which is the first layer of the atmosphere the balloon passes through on its way up?*

Although hot-air balloons cannot travel very high into the troposphere, other types of balloons can. To measure weather conditions, scientists launch weather balloons that carry instruments up into the atmosphere. The balloons are not fully inflated before they are launched. Recall that air pressure decreases as you rise through the atmosphere. Leaving the balloon only partly inflated gives the gas inside the balloon room to expand as the air pressure outside the balloon decreases.

The depth of the troposphere varies from more than 16 kilometers above the equator to less than 9 kilometers above the North and South Poles. Even though it is the shallowest layer of the atmosphere, the troposphere contains almost all of the mass of the atmosphere.

As altitude increases in the troposphere, the temperature decreases. On average, for every 1-kilometer increase in altitude the air gets about 6.5 Celsius degrees cooler. At the top of the troposphere, the temperature stops decreasing and stays constant at about –60°C. Water here forms thin, feathery clouds of ice.

☑ ***Checkpoint*** ***Why are clouds at the top of the troposphere made of ice crystals instead of drops of water?***

The Stratosphere

The **stratosphere** extends from the top of the troposphere to about 50 kilometers above Earth's surface. *Strato-* is similar to *stratum*, which means "layer" or "spreading out."

The lower stratosphere is cold, about −60°C. You might be surprised to find out that the upper stratosphere is warmer than the lower stratosphere. Why is this? The upper stratosphere contains a layer of ozone, the three-atom form of oxygen. When the ozone in the stratosphere absorbs energy from the sun, the energy is converted into heat, warming the air.

As a weather balloon rises through the stratosphere, the air pressure outside the balloon continues to decrease. The volume of the balloon increases. Finally, the balloon bursts, and the instrument package falls back to Earth's surface.

The Mesosphere

Above the stratosphere, a drop in temperature marks the beginning of the next layer, the **mesosphere.** *Meso-* means "middle," so the mesosphere is the middle layer of the atmosphere. The mesosphere begins 50 kilometers above Earth's surface and ends at 80 kilometers. The outer mesosphere is the coldest part of the atmosphere, with temperatures near −90°C.

EXPLORING *Layers of the Atmosphere*

The atmosphere is divided into four layers: the troposphere, the stratosphere, the mesosphere, and the thermosphere. The thermosphere is further divided into the ionosphere and the exosphere.

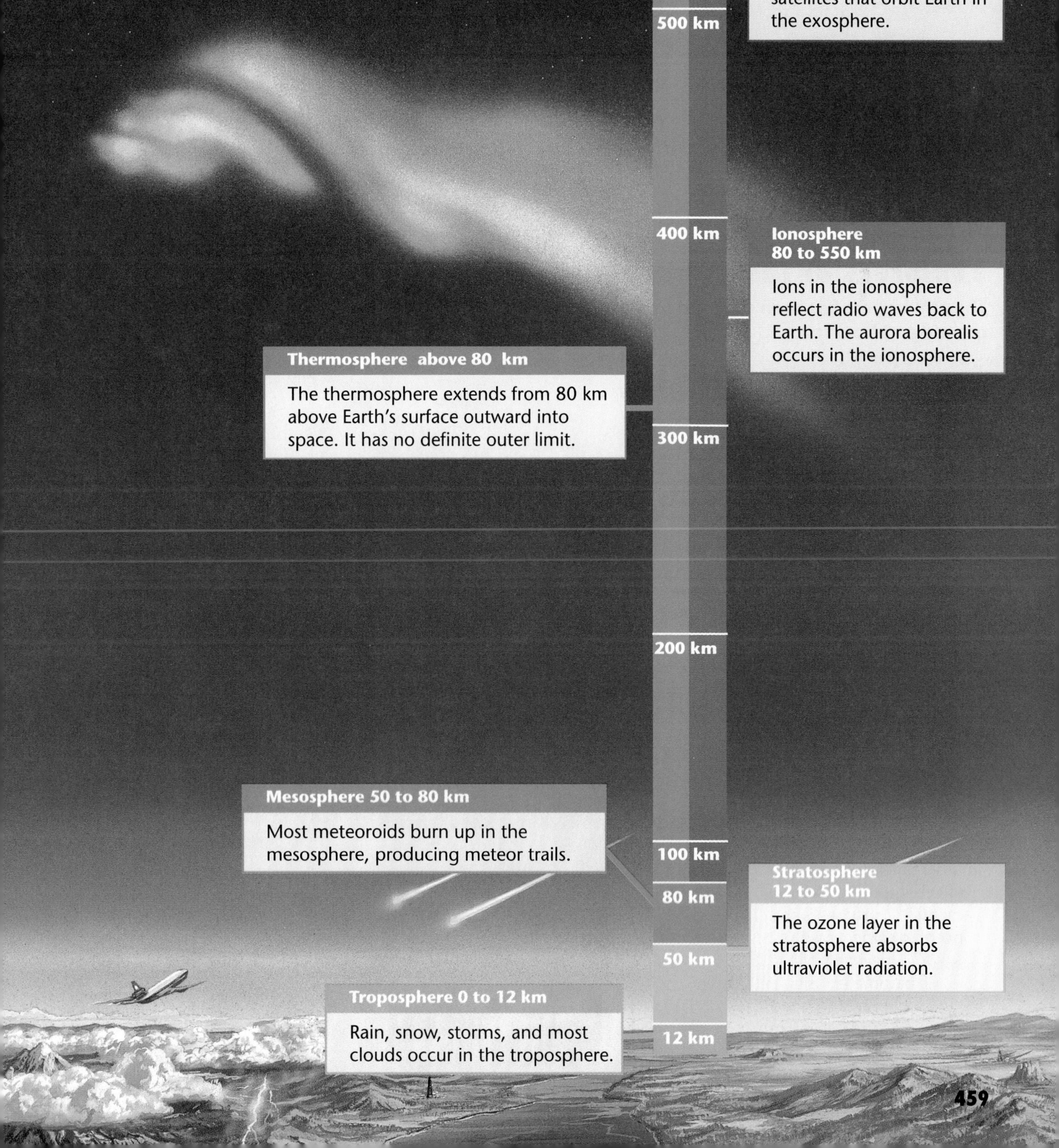

550 km
500 km
400 km
300 km
200 km
100 km
80 km
50 km
12 km
Exosphere above 550 km
Phone calls and television pictures often reach you by way of communications satellites that orbit Earth in the exosphere.
Ionosphere 80 to 550 km
Ions in the ionosphere reflect radio waves back to Earth. The aurora borealis occurs in the ionosphere.
Thermosphere above 80 km
The thermosphere extends from 80 km above Earth's surface outward into space. It has no definite outer limit.
Mesosphere 50 to 80 km
Most meteoroids burn up in the mesosphere, producing meteor trails.
Stratosphere 12 to 50 km
The ozone layer in the stratosphere absorbs ultraviolet radiation.
Troposphere 0 to 12 km
Rain, snow, storms, and most clouds occur in the troposphere.

INTEGRATING SPACE SCIENCE If you watch a shooting star streak across the night sky, you are seeing a meteoroid burn up as it enters the mesosphere. The mesosphere protects Earth's surface from being hit by most meteoroids, which are chunks of stone and metal from space. What you see as a shooting star, or meteor, is the trail of hot, glowing gases the burning meteoroid leaves behind.

☑ *Checkpoint* *What is the depth of the mesosphere?*

The Thermosphere

Near the top of the atmosphere, the air is very thin. The air 80 kilometers above Earth's surface is only about 0.001 percent as dense as the air at sea level. It's as though you took a cubic

SCIENCE & History

Explorers of the Atmosphere

The atmosphere has been explored from the ground and from space.

1746

Franklin's Experiment with Electricity

American statesman and inventor Benjamin Franklin and some friends in Philadelphia experimented with electricity in the atmosphere. To demonstrate that lightning is a form of electricity, Franklin flew a kite in a thunderstorm. However, Franklin did not hold the kite string in his hand, as this historical print shows.

1600 **1700** **1800**

1643

Torricelli Invents the Barometer

Italian physicist and mathematician Evangelista Torricelli improved existing scientific instruments and invented some new ones. In 1643 he invented the barometer, using a column of mercury 1.2 meters high.

1804

Gay-Lussac Studies the Upper Troposphere

French chemist Joseph-Louis Gay-Lussac ascended to a height of about 7 kilometers in a hydrogen balloon to study the upper troposphere. Gay-Lussac studied pressure, temperature, and humidity.

meter of air at sea level and expanded it into 100,000 cubic meters at the top of the mesosphere. The outermost layer of the atmosphere, the **thermosphere**, extends from 80 kilometers above Earth's surface outward into space. It has no definite outer limit. The atmosphere does not end suddenly at the outer edge of the thermosphere. Gas atoms and molecules there are so far apart that the air blends gradually with outer space.

The *thermo-* in thermosphere means "heat." Even though the air in the thermosphere is thin, it is very hot, up to 1,800°C. The temperature in the thermosphere is actually higher than the temperature in a furnace used to make steel! But why is the thermosphere so hot? Energy coming from the sun strikes the thermosphere first. Nitrogen and oxygen molecules convert energy from the sun into heat.

In Your Journal

Imagine you were one of the first people to go up into the atmosphere in a balloon. What would you need to take? Find out what the early explorers took with them in their balloons. Write at least two paragraphs about what you would take, and why.

1931

Piccard Explores the Stratosphere

Swiss-Belgian physicist Auguste Piccard made the first ascent into the stratosphere. He reached a height of about 16 kilometers in an airtight cabin attached to a huge hydrogen balloon. Piccard is shown here with the cabin.

1900 **2000**

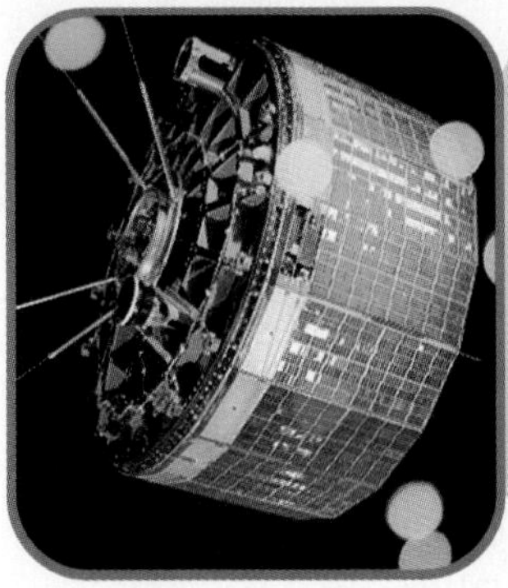

1960

First Weather Satellite Launched

TIROS-1, the first weather satellite equipped with a camera to send data back to Earth, was put into orbit by the United States. As later weather satellites circled Earth, they observed cloud cover and recorded temperatures and air pressures in the atmosphere.

1994

Space Shuttle Investigates the Atmosphere

The NASA space shuttle *Atlantis* traveled to a height of 300 kilometers in the thermosphere. *Atlantis* carried the ATLAS–3 research program, which observed the sun's influence on the atmosphere.

Figure 14 The aurora borealis, seen from Fairbanks, Alaska, creates a spectacular display in the night sky.

Despite the high temperature, however, you would not feel warm in the thermosphere. An ordinary thermometer would show a temperature well below 0°C. Why is that? Temperature is the average amount of energy of motion of each molecule of a substance. The gas molecules in the thermosphere move very rapidly, so the temperature is very high. However, the molecules are spaced far apart in the thin air. And there are not enough of them to collide with a thermometer and warm it very much. So an ordinary thermometer would not detect the molecules' energy.

The Ionosphere The thermosphere is divided into two layers. The lower layer of the thermosphere, called the **ionosphere** (eye AHN uh sfeer), begins 80 kilometers above the surface and ends at 550 kilometers. Energy from the sun causes gas molecules in the ionosphere to become electrically charged particles called ions. Radio waves bounce off ions in the ionosphere and then bounce back to Earth's surface.

The brilliant light displays of the **aurora borealis**—the Northern Lights—also occur in the ionosphere. The aurora borealis is caused by particles from the sun that enter the ionosphere near the North Pole. These particles strike oxygen and nitrogen atoms in the ionosphere, causing them to glow.

The Exosphere *Exo-* means "outer," so the **exosphere** is the outer layer of the thermosphere. The exosphere extends from 550 kilometers outward for thousands of kilometers. When you make a long-distance phone call or watch television, the signal may have traveled up to a satellite orbiting in the exosphere and then back down to your home. Satellites are also used for watching the world's weather and carrying telescopes that look deep into space.

Integrating Technology

Section 4 Review

1. Describe one characteristic of each of the four main layers of the atmosphere.
2. What is a shooting star? In which layer of the atmosphere would you see it?
3. What is the aurora borealis? In which layer of the atmosphere does it occur?
4. **Thinking Critically Drawing Conclusions** Why is the mesosphere the coldest part of the atmosphere?

Chapter Project

Check Your Progress

At this point, review your weather log. What do you notice about the weather on one day that might allow you to predict the next day's weather? What weather conditions changed the most from day to day? Continue to record your observations and start thinking about how you will present them.

Section 1 The Air Around You

Key Ideas

- Earth's atmosphere makes conditions on Earth suitable for living things.
- Earth's atmosphere is made up of molecules of nitrogen, oxygen, carbon dioxide, and water vapor, as well as some other gases and particles of liquids and solids.

Key Terms

weather, ozone, atmosphere, water vapor

Section 2 Air Quality

Integrating Environmental Science

Key Ideas

- Most air pollution results from the burning of fossil fuels such as coal, oil, gasoline, and diesel fuel.
- Nitrogen oxides, hydrocarbons, and other air pollutants react with each other in the presence of sunlight to form a mix of ozone and other chemicals called photochemical smog.
- Acid rain forms when nitrogen oxides and sulfur oxides combine with water in the air to form nitric acid and sulfuric acid.

Key Terms

pollutant, photochemical smog, acid rain

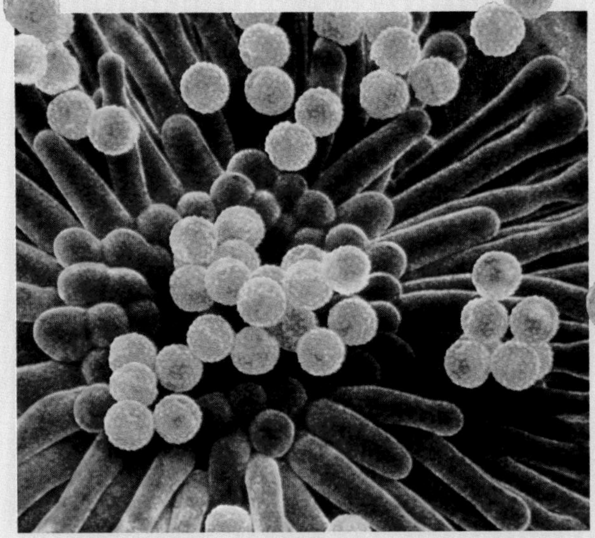

Section 3 Air Pressure

Key Ideas

- Properties of air include mass, density, and pressure.
- Air pressure is the result of the weight of a column of air pushing down on an area.
- Air pressure is measured with mercury barometers and aneroid barometers.
- Air pressure decreases as altitude increases. As air pressure decreases, so does density.

Key Terms

density, pressure, air pressure, barometer, mercury barometer, aneroid barometer, altitude

Section 4 Layers of the Atmosphere

Key Ideas

- The four main layers of the atmosphere are classified according to changes in temperature. These layers are the troposphere, the stratosphere, the mesosphere, and the thermosphere.
- Rain, snow, storms, and most clouds occur in the troposphere.
- Ozone in the stratosphere absorbs energy from the sun.
- Most meteoroids burn up in the mesosphere, producing meteor trails.
- The aurora borealis occurs in the ionosphere.
- Communications satellites orbit Earth in the exosphere.

Key Terms

troposphere, stratosphere, mesosphere, thermosphere, ionosphere, aurora borealis, exosphere

ACTIVITY — USING THE INTERNET

www.phschool.com/state_focus/california/

California Test Prep: Reviewing Content

Multiple Choice

Choose the letter of the answer that best completes each statement.

1. The most abundant gas in the atmosphere is
   a. ozone. **b.** carbon dioxide.
   c. oxygen. **d.** nitrogen.
2. Most air pollution is caused by
   a. dust and pollen.
   b. acid rain.
   c. erupting volcanoes.
   d. the burning of fossil fuels.
3. A barometer is used to measure
   a. temperature. **b.** smog.
   c. air pressure **d.** density.
4. The layers of the atmosphere are classified according to changes in
   a. altitude.
   b. temperature.
   c. pressure.
   d. density.
5. The inner layer, or "weather layer," of the atmosphere is called the
   a. mesosphere.
   b. troposphere.
   c. thermosphere.
   d. stratosphere.

True or False

If the statement is true, write true. If it is false, change the underlined word or words to make the statement true.

6. Plants need <u>carbon dioxide</u> from the atmosphere to make food.
7. Burning fuels add <u>nitrogen</u> to the atmosphere.
8. When sulfur and nitrogen oxides mix with water in the air, they form <u>smog</u>.
9. If the mass of a fixed volume of air increases, it becomes <u>less</u> dense.
10. Air pressure <u>increases</u> as you climb from land at sea level to the top of a mountain.

Checking Concepts

11. Name two ways in which carbon dioxide is added to the atmosphere.
12. Explain why it is difficult to include water vapor in a graph that shows the percentages of various gases in the atmosphere.
13. What is the difference between photochemical smog and London-type smog?
14. List the following layers of the atmosphere in order moving up from Earth's surface: thermosphere, stratosphere, troposphere, mesosphere.
15. Describe the temperature changes that occur as you move upward through the troposphere.
16. **Writing to Learn** You are a scientist who has a chance to join a research mission to explore the atmosphere. To win a place on this mission, you must write a persuasive letter telling which layer of the atmosphere you want to research and why you chose it.

Thinking Visually

17. **Concept Map** Copy the air pressure concept map onto a separate sheet of paper. Then complete it and add a title. (For more on concept maps, see the Skills Handbook.)

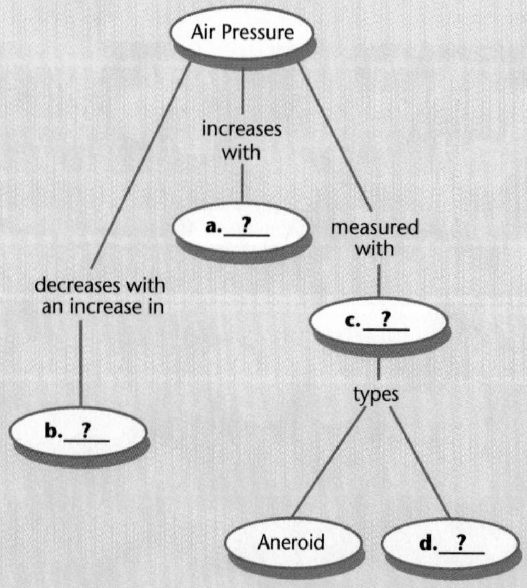
Air Pressure
increases with
a. ?
measured with
decreases with an increase in
c. ?
types
b. ?
Aneroid
d. ?

Test Prep: Skills

The table below shows temperature at various altitudes above Omaha, Nebraska, on a day in January. Use the table to answer the questions that follow.

Altitude (kilometers)	0	1.6	3.2	4.8	6.4	7.2
Temperature (°C)	0	–4	–9	–21	–32	–40

18. Graphing Make a line graph of the data in the table. Put temperature on the horizontal axis and altitude on the vertical axis. Label your graph.

19. Interpreting Graphs At about what height above the ground was the temperature –15°C?

20. Interpreting Graphs What was the approximate temperature 2.4 kilometers over Omaha?

21. Calculating Suppose an airplane was about 6.8 kilometers above Omaha on this day. What was the approximate temperature at 6.8 kilometers? How much colder was the temperature at 6.8 kilometers above the ground than at ground level?

Thinking Critically

22. Predicting Describe the changes in the atmosphere that you would experience while climbing a mountain four or more kilometers high. How might these changes affect you physically?

23. Applying Concepts Why can an aneroid barometer be used to measure elevation as well as air pressure?

24. Relating Cause and Effect How can burning high-sulfur coal in a power-generating plant harm a forest hundreds of kilometers away?

25. Classifying Which sources of air pollution occur naturally, and which are caused by humans?

Performance Assessment

CHAPTER PROJECT Wrap Up

Presenting Your Project For your class presentation, prepare a display of your weather observations. Include drawings, graphs, and tables that summarize the weather you observed. Practice presenting your project to your group. Do you need to make any improvements? If so, make them now.

Reflect and Record In your journal, write how you might improve your weather log. What weather conditions would you like to know more about? What factors could you have measured more accurately using instruments?

Getting Involved

In Your Community With some classmates, investigate air quality in and around your school or neighborhood. Listen to weather reports or check newspapers for the pollen count and for levels of other pollutants. With the approval of your teacher, design experiments using filters, dust masks, or other devices to examine air particles. Then write a report summarizing your findings and identifying sources where pollution could be reduced.

CHAPTER 15

Weather Factors

CALIFORNIA SCIENCE CONTENT STANDARDS

The following California Science Content Standards are addressed in this chapter:

3. Heat moves in a predictable flow from warmer objects to cooler objects until all objects are at the same temperature.

a. Energy can be carried from one place to another by heat flow, or by waves including water waves, light and sound, or by moving objects.

c. Heat flows in solids by conduction (which involves no flow of matter) and in fluids by conduction and also by convection (which involves flow of matter).

d. Heat energy is also transferred between objects by radiation; radiation can travel through space.

4. Many phenomena on the Earth's surface are affected by the transfer of energy through radiation and convection currents.

a. The sun is the major source of energy for phenomena on the Earth's surface, powering winds, ocean currents, and the water cycle.

b. Solar energy reaches Earth through radiation, mostly in the form of visible light.

d. Convection currents distribute heat in the atmosphere and oceans.

PROJECT 15

Your Own Weather Station

Spring rains are an important factor in helping these tulips grow.

A drenching spring rain is just what the flowers need! As the weather gets warmer, the garden will bloom. Warm days, soft winds, and plenty of rain—all of these are weather factors that affect growing things. In this chapter, you will learn about a variety of weather factors, including air pressure, temperature, wind speed and direction, relative humidity, precipitation, and the amount and types of clouds.

Your Goal To measure and record weather conditions using instruments. You will look for patterns in your data that can be used to predict the next day's weather.

In completing your project, you will

- develop a plan for measuring weather factors
- record your data in a daily log
- display your data in a set of graphs
- use your data and graphs to try to predict the weather
- follow the safety guidelines in Appendix A

Get Started Begin by previewing the chapter to see what weather factors you want to measure. Discuss with a group of your classmates what instruments you might use. Brainstorm what observations you should make each day.

Check Your Progress You'll be working on the project as you study this chapter. To keep your project on track, look for Check Your Progress boxes at the following points.

Section 2 Review, page 477: Prepare to make observations.
Section 3 Review, page 486: Collect and record data.
Section 5 Review, page 496: Graph your data and look for patterns.

Wrap Up At the end of the chapter (page 499), present your weather observations and explain how well you predicted the weather.

e. Differences in pressure, heat, air movement, and humidity result in changes of weather.

5. Organisms in ecosystems exchange energy and nutrients among themselves and with the environment.

e. The number and types of organisms an ecosystem can support depends on the resources available and abiotic factors, such as quantity of light and water, range of temperatures, and soil composition.

7. Scientific progress is made by asking meaningful questions and conducting careful investigations.

a. Develop a hypothesis.

b. Select and use appropriate tools and technology (including calculators, computers, balances, spring scales, microscopes, and binoculars) to perform tests, collect data, and display data.

c. Construct appropriate graphs from data and develop qualitative statements about the relationships between variables.

SECTION 1

Energy in the Atmosphere

DISCOVER ACTIVITY

Does a Plastic Bag Trap Heat?

1. Record the initial temperatures on two thermometers. (You should get the same readings.)
2. Place one of the thermometers in a plastic bag. Put a small piece of paper in the bag so that it shades the bulb of the thermometer. Seal the bag.
3. Place both thermometers on a sunny window ledge or near a light bulb. Cover the bulb of the second thermometer with a small piece of paper. Predict what you think will happen.
4. Wait five minutes. Then record the temperatures on the two thermometers.

Think It Over

Measuring Were the two temperatures the same? How could you explain any difference?

GUIDE FOR READING

- **In what form does energy from the sun travel to Earth?**
- **What happens to energy from the sun when it reaches Earth?**

Reading Tip **Before you read, skim the section for boldfaced words that are unfamiliar to you. As you read, find their meanings.**

Think of a sunny summer day. When you get up in the morning, the sun is low in the sky and the air is cool. As the sun rises, the temperature increases. By noon it is quite hot. As you will see in this chapter, heat is a major factor in the weather. The movement of heat in the atmosphere causes temperatures to change, winds to blow, and rain to fall.

Energy from the Sun

INTEGRATING PHYSICS Nearly all the energy in Earth's atmosphere comes from the sun. This energy travels to Earth as **electromagnetic waves,** a form of energy that can travel through space. Electromagnetic waves are classified according to wavelength, or distance between waves. The direct transfer of energy by electromagnetic waves is called **radiation.**

Most of the energy from the sun reaches Earth in the form of visible light and infrared radiation, and a small amount of ultraviolet radiation. Visible light is a mixture of all of the colors that you see in a rainbow: red, orange, yellow, green, blue, and violet. The different colors are the result of different wavelengths

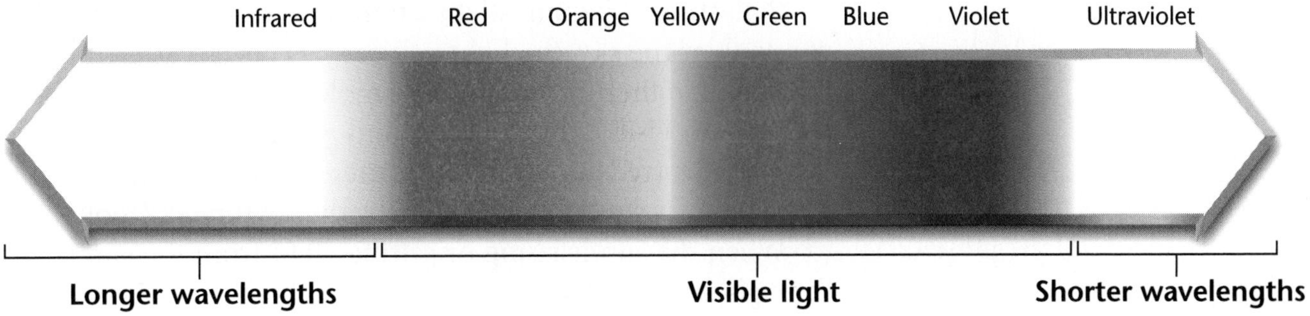
Infrared
Red
Orange
Yellow
Green
Blue
Violet
Ultraviolet
Longer wavelengths
Visible light
Shorter wavelengths

of visible light. Red and orange light have the longest wavelengths, while blue and violet light have the shortest wavelengths.

Infrared radiation is a form of energy with wavelengths that are longer than red light. Infrared radiation is not visible, but can be felt as heat. Heat lamps used to keep food warm in restaurants give off both visible red light and invisible infrared radiation. The sun also gives off **ultraviolet radiation,** which has wavelengths that are shorter than violet light. Sunburns are caused by ultraviolet radiation. This radiation can also cause skin cancer and eye damage.

Figure 1 Electromagnetic waves include infrared radiation, visible light, and ultraviolet radiation. *Interpreting Diagrams What type of radiation has wavelengths that are shorter than visible light? What type has wavelengths that are longer?*

☑ *Checkpoint* *Which color of visible light has the longest wavelengths?*

Energy in the Atmosphere

Before the sun's rays can reach Earth's surface, they must pass through the atmosphere. The path of the sun's rays is shown in *Exploring Energy in the Atmosphere* on the following page.

Some of the energy from the sun is absorbed within the atmosphere. Water vapor and carbon dioxide absorb some infrared radiation. The ozone layer in the stratosphere absorbs most of the ultraviolet radiation. Clouds, dust, and other gases also absorb energy from the sun.

Some of the sun's rays are reflected. Clouds in the atmosphere act like mirrors, reflecting some solar energy back into space. In addition, dust particles and molecules of gases in the atmosphere reflect light from the sun in all directions.

Reflection of light in all directions is called **scattering.** When you look at the sky, the light you see has been scattered by gas molecules in the atmosphere. Gas molecules scatter short wavelengths of visible light (blue and violet) more than long wavelengths (red and orange). Scattered light is therefore bluer than ordinary sunlight, which is why the daytime sky looks blue.

When the sun is rising or setting, light from the sun passes through a greater thickness of the atmosphere than when the sun is higher in the sky. More light from the blue end of the spectrum is removed by scattering before it reaches your eyes. The remaining light from the sun contains mostly red and orange light. The sun looks red, and clouds around it become very colorful.

☑ *Checkpoint* ***Why would particles from volcanic eruptions make sunsets and sunrises more red?***

EXPLORING *Energy in the Atmosphere*

Most of the energy that keeps Earth warm comes from the sun. Some of this energy is reflected or absorbed in the atmosphere. The rest of the energy reaches Earth's surface, where it is reflected or absorbed.

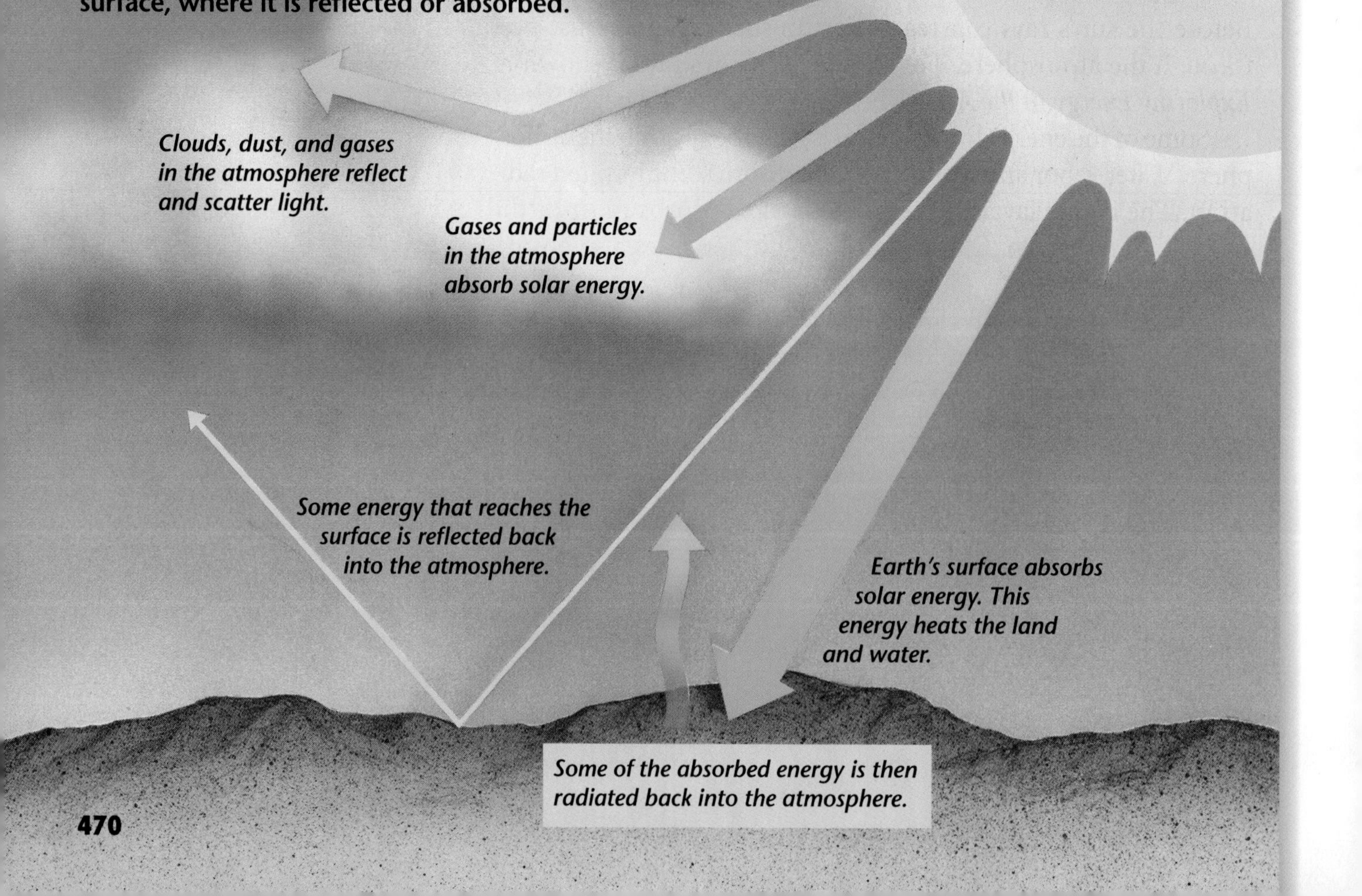

Solar energy is mostly visible light and infrared radiation, with a small amount of ultraviolet radiation.
Clouds, dust, and gases in the atmosphere reflect and scatter light.
Gases and particles in the atmosphere absorb solar energy.
Some energy that reaches the surface is reflected back into the atmosphere.
Earth's surface absorbs solar energy. This energy heats the land and water.
Some of the absorbed energy is then radiated back into the atmosphere.

Energy at Earth's Surface

Some of the sun's energy reaches Earth's surface and is reflected back into the atmosphere. Some of the energy, however, is absorbed by the land and water and changed into heat.

When Earth's surface is heated, it radiates some of the energy back into the atmosphere as infrared radiation. Most of this infrared radiation cannot travel all the way through the atmosphere back into space. Instead, much of it is absorbed by water vapor, carbon dioxide, methane, and other gases in the air. The energy from the absorbed radiation heats the gases in the air. These gases form a "blanket" around Earth that holds heat in the atmosphere. The process by which gases hold heat in the air is called the **greenhouse effect.**

Have you ever been inside a greenhouse during the winter? Even on a cold day, a greenhouse is warm. Greenhouses trap heat in two ways. First, infrared radiation given off in the interior cannot easily pass through glass and is trapped inside. Second, warm air inside the greenhouse cannot rise because the glass blocks the movement of air. What happens in Earth's atmosphere is similar to the first way that greenhouses trap heat.

The greenhouse effect is a natural process that keeps Earth's atmosphere at a temperature that is comfortable for most living things. Human activities over the last 200 years, however, have increased the amount of carbon dioxide in the atmosphere, which may be warming the atmosphere. You will learn more about the greenhouse effect in Chapter 4.

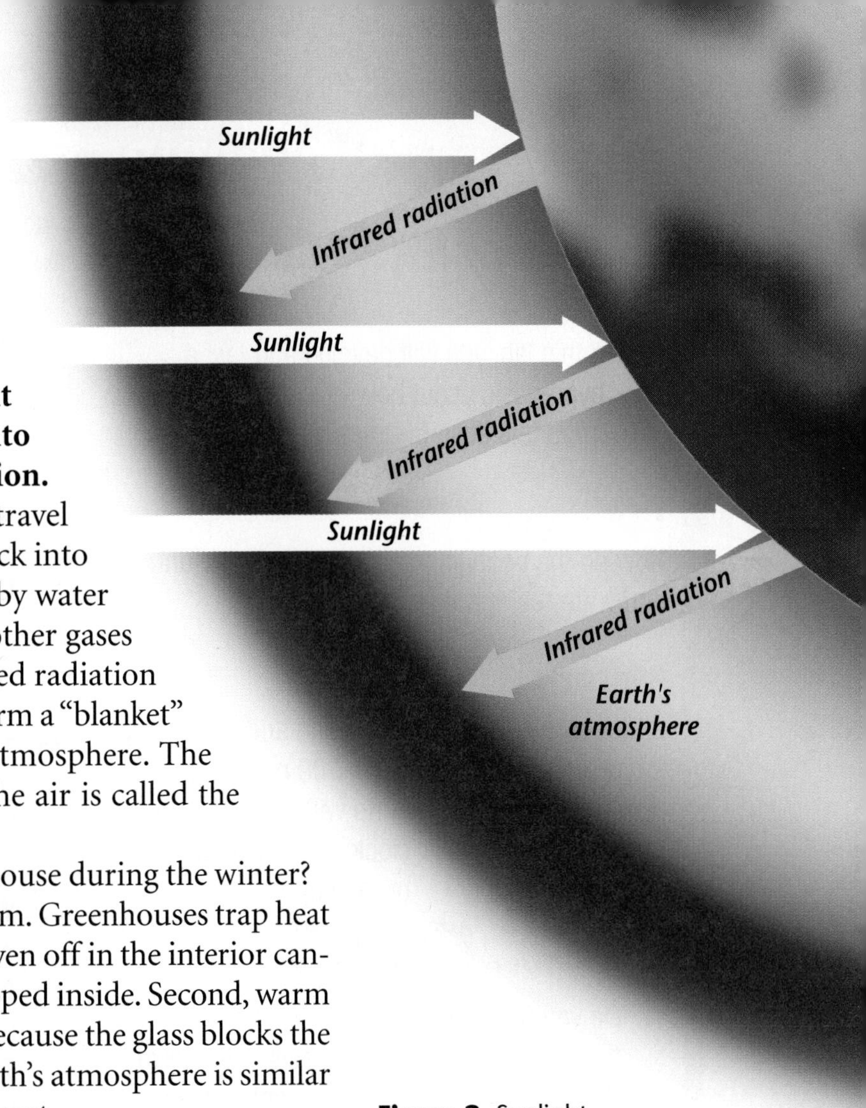
Sunlight
Infrared radiation
Sunlight
Infrared radiation
Sunlight
Infrared radiation
Earth's atmosphere

Figure 2 Sunlight travels through the atmosphere to Earth's surface. Earth's surface then gives off infrared radiation. Much of this energy is held by the atmosphere, warming it.

Section 1 Review

1. List three forms of radiation from the sun. How are these alike? How are they different?
2. What happens to the energy from the sun that is absorbed by Earth's surface?
3. Why is the sky blue? Why are sunsets often red?
4. **Thinking Critically Applying Concepts** What might conditions on Earth be like without the greenhouse effect?

Science at Home

With an adult family member, explore the role radiation plays in heating your home. Are some rooms warmer and sunnier in the morning? Are other rooms warmer and sunnier in the afternoon? How does opening and closing curtains or blinds affect the temperature of a room? Explain your observations to your family.

Skills Lab

Developing Hypotheses

Heating Earth's Surface

In this lab, you will develop and test a hypothesis about how quickly different materials absorb radiation.

Problem

How do the heating and cooling rates of sand and water compare?

Materials

2 thermometers
2 beakers, 400 mL
water, 300 mL
metric ruler
string
ring stand and ring clamp
sand, 300 mL
lamp with 100-W bulb
clock or stopwatch
graph paper

Procedure

1. Do you think sand or water will heat up faster? Record your hypothesis in the form of an "If . . . then. . . ." statement. Explain what information you used to form your hypothesis. Then follow these steps to test your hypothesis.
2. Copy the data table into your notebook. Add enough rows to record data for 15 minutes.
3. Fill one beaker with 300 mL of dry sand.
4. Fill the second beaker with 300 mL of water at room temperature.
5. Arrange the beakers beneath the ring stand.
6. Place one thermometer in each beaker.
7. Suspend the thermometers from the ring stand with string. This will hold the thermometers in place so they do not fall.
8. Adjust the height of the clamp so that the bulb of each thermometer is covered by about 0.5 cm of sand or water in a beaker.
9. Position the lamp so that it is about 20 cm above the sand and water. There should be no more than 8 cm between the beakers. **CAUTION:** *Be careful not to splash water onto the hot light bulb.*
10. Record the temperature of the sand and water in your data table.
11. Turn on the lamp. Read the temperature of the sand and water every minute for 15 minutes. Record the temperatures in the Light On column in the data table.
12. Which material do you think will cool off more quickly? Record your hypothesis. Again, give reasons why you think your hypothesis is correct.
13. Turn the light off. Read the temperature of the sand and water every minute for another 15 minutes. Record the temperatures in the Light Off column (16–30 minutes).

DATA TABLE

Temperature with Light On (°C)			Temperature with Light Off (°C)		
Time (min)	Sand	Water	Time (min)	Sand	Water
Start			16		
1			17		
2			18		
3			19		
4			20		
5			21		

Analyze and Conclude

1. Draw two line graphs to show the data for the temperature change in sand and water over time. Label the horizontal axis from 0 to 30 minutes and the vertical axis in degrees Celsius. Draw both graphs on the same piece of graph paper. Use a dashed line to show the temperature change in water and a solid line to show the temperature change in sand.
2. Calculate the total change in temperature for each material.
3. Based on your data, which material had the greater increase in temperature?
4. What can you conclude about which material absorbed heat faster? How do your results compare with your hypothesis?
5. Review your data again. In 15 minutes, which material cooled faster?
6. How do these results compare to your second hypothesis?
7. **Think About It** If your results did not support either of your hypotheses, why do you think the results differed from what you expected?
8. **Apply** Based on your results, which do you think will heat up more quickly on a sunny day: the water in a lake or the sand surrounding it? Which will cool off more quickly after dark?

More to Explore

Do you think all solid materials heat up as fast as sand? For example, consider gravel, crushed stone, or different types of soil. Write a hypothesis about their heating rates as an "If . . . then. . . ." statement. With the approval and supervision of your teacher, develop a procedure to test your hypothesis. Was your hypothesis correct?

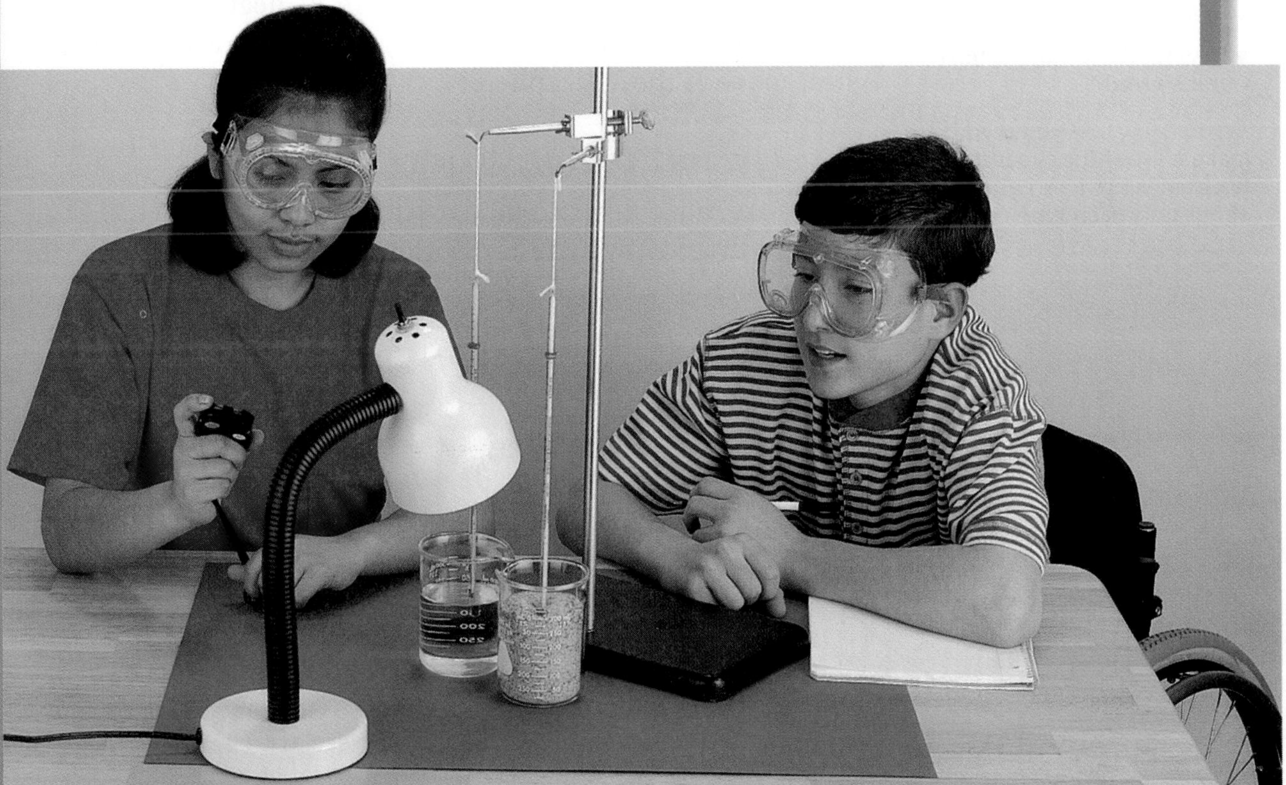

SECTION 2 Heat Transfer

DISCOVER ACTIVITY

What Happens When Air Is Heated?

1. Use heavy scissors to cut the flat part out of an aluminum pie plate. Use the tip of the scissors to poke a small hole in the middle of the flat part.
2. Cut the part into a spiral shape, as shown in the photo. Tie a 30-centimeter piece of thread to the middle of the spiral.
3. Hold the spiral over a source of heat, such as a candle, hot plate, or incandescent light bulb.

Think It Over
Inferring What happened to the spiral? Why do you think this happened?

GUIDE FOR READING

- **How is temperature measured?**
- **In what three ways is heat transferred?**

Reading Tip **As you read, make a list of the types of heat transfer. Write a sentence about how each type occurs.**

You know that energy from the sun is absorbed by Earth's surface. Some energy is then transferred from the surface to the atmosphere in the form of heat. The heat then moves from place to place within the atmosphere. But how does heat move in the atmosphere?

Energy and Temperature

Gases are made up of small particles, called molecules, that are constantly moving. The faster the molecules are moving, the more energy they have. Figure 3 shows how the motion of

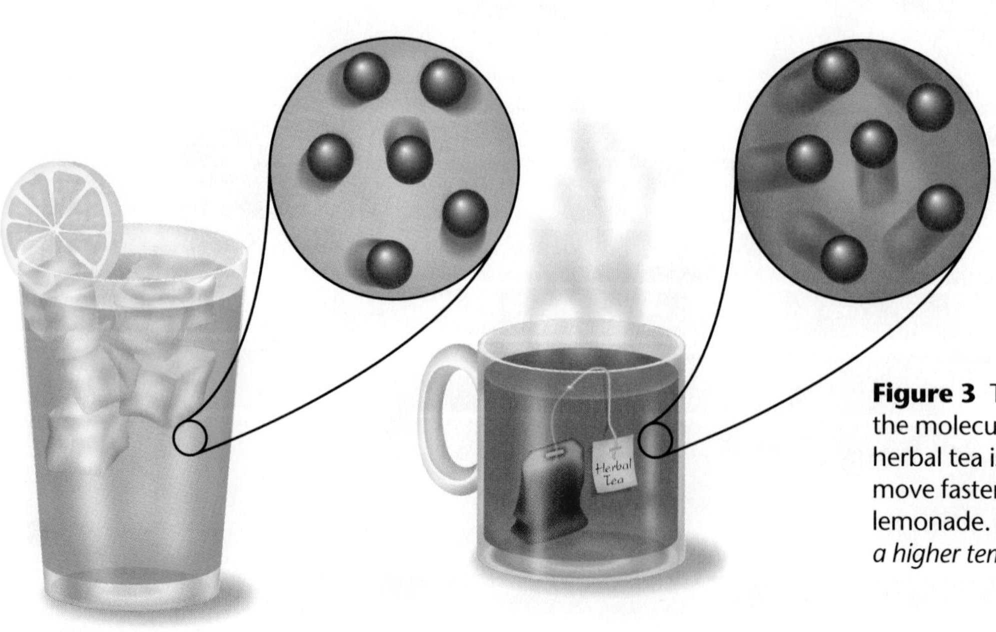
Herbal Tea

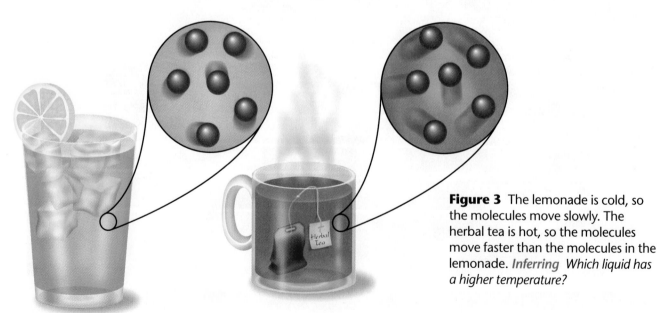

Figure 3 The lemonade is cold, so the molecules move slowly. The herbal tea is hot, so the molecules move faster than the molecules in the lemonade. ***Inferring*** *Which liquid has a higher temperature?*

molecules is related to the amount of energy they hold. The total energy of motion in the molecules of a substance is called **thermal energy.** On the other hand, **temperature** is the *average* amount of energy of motion of each molecule of a substance. That means that temperature is a measure of how hot or cold a substance is.

Measuring Temperature

Ask someone what the weather is like. The answer will probably include the temperature. Temperature is one of the most important elements of weather. **Air temperature is usually measured with a thermometer.** A **thermometer** is a thin glass tube with a bulb on one end that contains a liquid, usually mercury or colored alcohol.

Thermometers work because liquids expand when they are heated and contract when they are cooled. When the air temperature increases, the liquid in the bulb expands and rises up the column. What happens when the temperature decreases? The liquid in the bulb contracts and moves down the tube.

Temperature is measured in units called degrees. The two most common scales are shown in Figure 4. Scientists use the Celsius scale. On the Celsius scale, the freezing point of pure water is 0°C (read "zero degrees Celsius"). The boiling point of pure water is 100°C. Weather reports in the United States use the Fahrenheit scale. On the Fahrenheit scale, the freezing point of water is 32°F and the boiling point is 212°F.

☑ *Checkpoint* ***How many degrees Celsius are there between the freezing point of water and the boiling point of water?***

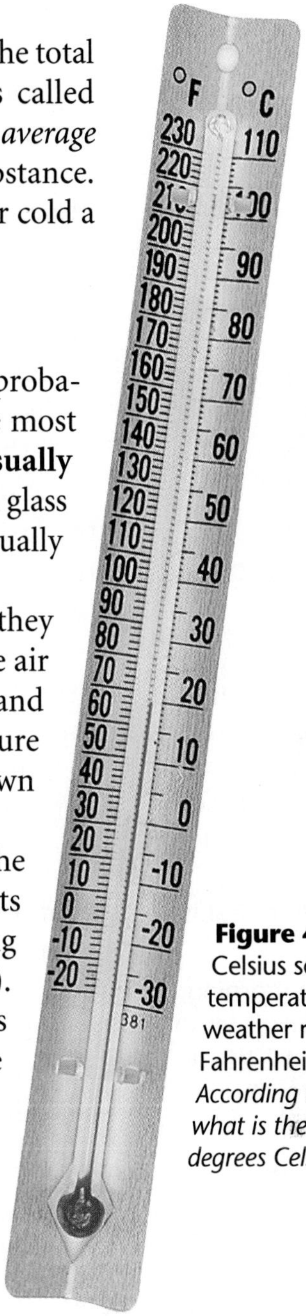
°F
°C
230
220
210
200
190
180
170
160
150
140
130
120
110
100
90
80
70
60
50
40
30
20
10
0
-10
-20
110
100
90
80
70
60
50
40
30
20
10
0
-10
-20
-30

Figure 4 Scientists use the Celsius scale to measure temperature. However, weather reports use the Fahrenheit scale. *Measuring According to this thermometer, what is the air temperature in degrees Celsius?*

How Heat Is Transferred

The energy transferred from a hotter object to a cooler one is referred to as **heat**. The types of heat transfer are shown in Figure 5 on the next page. **Heat is transferred in three ways: radiation, conduction, and convection.**

Radiation Have you ever felt the warmth of the sun's rays on your face? You were feeling energy coming directly from the sun as radiation. Recall that radiation is the direct transfer of energy by electromagnetic waves. The heat you feel from the sun or a campfire travels directly to you as infrared radiation. You cannot see infrared radiation, but you can feel it as heat.

Conduction Have you ever walked barefoot on hot sand? Your feet felt hot because heat moved directly from the sand into your feet. When a fast-moving molecule bumps into a nearby slower-moving molecule, it transfers some of its energy. The direct transfer of heat from one substance to another substance that it is touching is called **conduction.** The molecules that gain energy can in turn pass the energy along to other nearby molecules. When you walk on hot sand, the fast-moving molecules in the sand transfer heat into the slower-moving molecules in your feet.

The closer together the molecules in a substance are, the more effectively they can conduct heat. Conduction works well in some solids, such as metals, but not as well in liquids and gases. Air and water do not conduct heat very well.

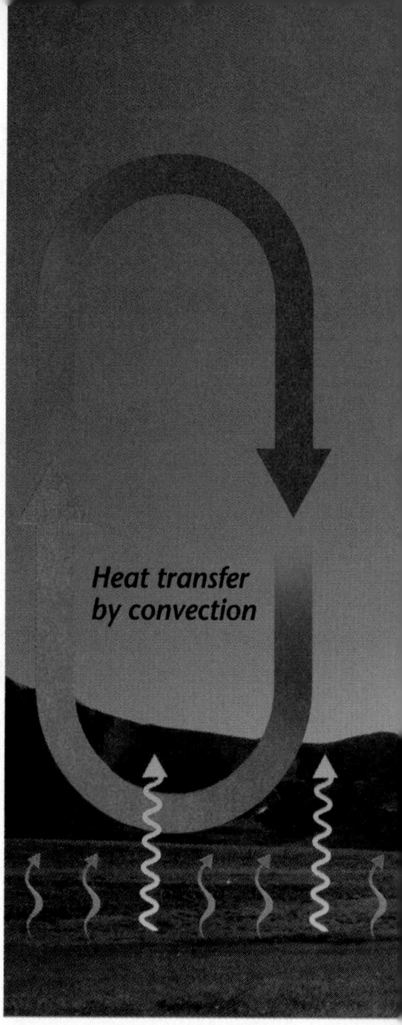
Heat transfer by convection

Convection How can you dry your boots over a hot-air vent, even though the furnace is in another room? Air from the furnace carries the heat to your boots. In fluids (liquids and gases), molecules can move from place to place. As the molecules move, they take their heat along with them. The transfer of heat by the movement of a fluid is called **convection.**

☑ *Checkpoint* ***Give at least one example each of radiation, conduction, and convection in your daily life.***

Heat Transfer in the Troposphere

Radiation, conduction, and convection work together to heat the troposphere. When Earth's surface absorbs solar energy during the day, the surface of the land becomes warmer than the air. Air near Earth's surface is warmed by radiation and conduction of heat from the surface to the air. However, heat is not easily conducted from one air molecule to another. Only the first few meters of the troposphere are heated by conduction. Thus, the air close to the ground is usually warmer than the air a few meters up.

Convection causes most of the heating of the troposphere. When the air near the ground is heated, the molecules have more energy. Because they have more energy, the molecules move

TRY THIS

Temperatures at Two Heights

ACTIVITY

How much difference do you think there is between air temperatures near the ground and air temperatures higher up? Give reasons for your prediction.

1. Take all of your measurements at a location that is sunny all day.
2. Early in the morning, measure the air temperature 1 cm and 1.25 m above the ground. Record the time of day and the temperature for both locations. Repeat your measurements late in the afternoon.
3. Record these measurements in the morning and afternoon for two more days.
4. Graph your data for each height with temperature on the vertical axis and time on the horizontal axis. Draw both lines on the same piece of graph paper using the same axes. Label both lines.

Interpreting Data At which height did the temperature vary the most? How can you explain the difference?

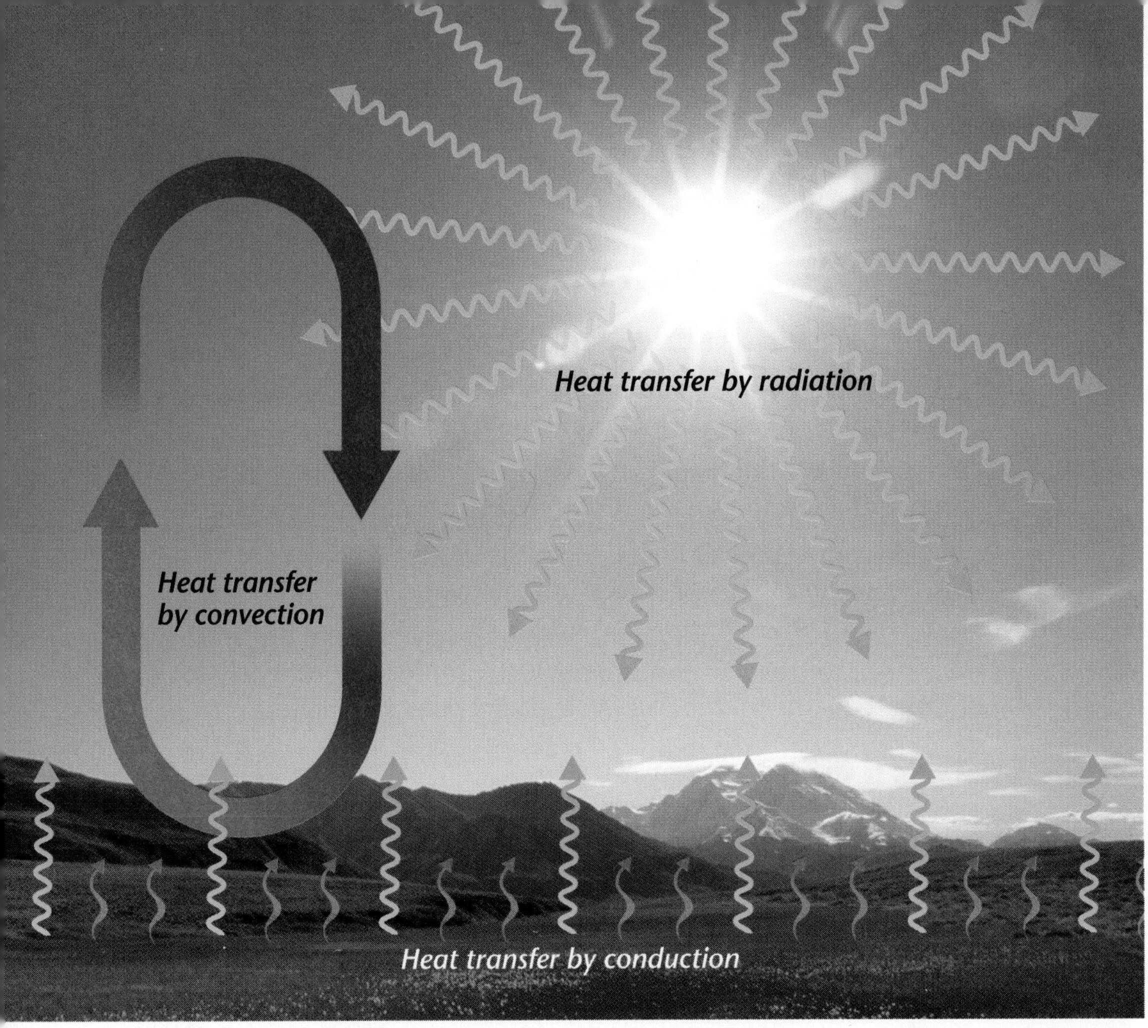
Heat transfer by radiation
Heat transfer by convection
Heat transfer by conduction

faster. As the molecules in the heated air move, they bump into each other and move farther apart. The air becomes less dense. Cooler, denser air sinks, forcing the warmer, less dense air to rise.

The upward movement of warm air and the downward movement of cool air form convection currents. Convection currents move heat throughout the troposphere.

Figure 5 All three types of heat transfer—radiation, convection, and conduction—occur near Earth's surface.

Section 2 Review

1. What is temperature?
2. Describe how a thermometer works.
3. Name three ways that heat can be transferred. Briefly explain how the three work together to heat the troposphere.
4. **Thinking Critically Applying Concepts** When you light a fire in a fireplace, warm air rises by convection and goes up the chimney. How, then, does a fireplace heat a room? Why do only the people directly in front of the fireplace feel the warmth of the fire?

CHAPTER PROJECT

Check Your Progress

Gather the instruments you will need to measure the weather factors. (*Hint:* Make sure you know how to take accurate measurements.) Plan when and where to measure weather factors. Be sure to take your measurements at the same location and at the same time of day.

SECTION 3 Winds

DISCOVER ACTIVITY

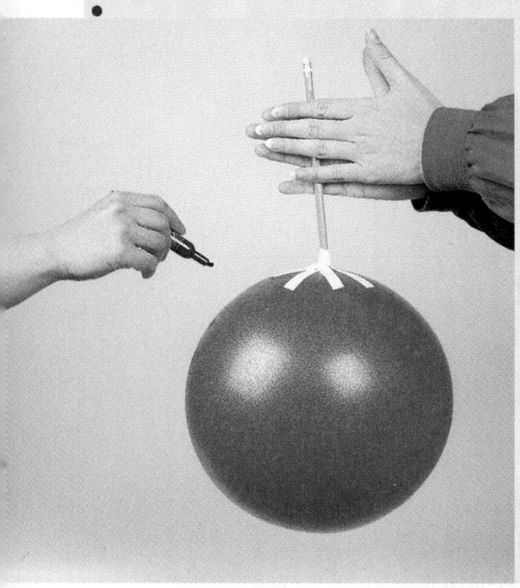

Which Way Does the Wind Turn?

Do this activity with a partner. Think of the ball as a model of Earth and the marker as representing wind.

1. Using heavy-duty tape, attach a pencil to a large smooth ball so that you can spin the ball from the top without touching it.
2. One partner should hold the pencil. Slowly turn the ball counterclockwise when seen from above.
3. While the ball is turning, the second partner should use a marker to try to draw a straight line from the "North Pole" to the "equator" of the ball. What shape does the line form?

Think It Over

Making Models If cold air were moving south from Canada into the United States, how would its movement be affected by Earth's rotation?

GUIDE FOR READING

- **What causes winds?**
- **What are local winds and global winds?**
- **Where are the major global wind belts located?**

Reading Tip **Before you read, preview the illustrations and read their captions. Write down any questions you have about winds. As you read, look for answers to your questions.**

The highest point in the northeastern United States, at 1,917 meters above sea level, is Mount Washington in New Hampshire. Sometimes winds near the top of this mountain are so strong that hikers cannot safely reach the summit! The greatest wind speed ever measured at Earth's surface—370 kilometers per hour—was measured on April 12, 1934, at the top of Mount Washington. What causes this incredible force?

What Causes Winds?

Because air is a fluid, it can move easily from place to place. The force that makes air move is caused by a difference of air pressure. Fluids tend to move from areas of high pressure to areas of low pressure. A **wind** is the horizontal movement of air from an area of high pressure to an area of lower pressure. **All winds are caused by differences in air pressure.**

Unequal heating of Earth's atmosphere causes these differences in air pressure. The sun is therefore the ultimate source of the energy that powers the wind. As you learned in the previous section, convection currents form when an area of Earth's surface is heated by the sun's rays. Air over the heated surface expands and becomes less dense. As the air becomes less dense, its air pressure decreases. If a nearby area is not heated as much, the air above the less-heated area will be cooler and denser. The cool, dense air has a higher air pressure so it flows underneath the warm, less dense air. This process forces the warm air to rise.

Measuring Wind

Winds are described by their direction and speed. Wind direction is determined with a wind vane. The wind swings the wind vane so that one end points into the wind. The name of a wind tells you where the wind is coming from. For example, a south wind blows from the south toward the north. A north wind blows to the south.

Wind speed is measured with an **anemometer** (an uh MAHM uh tur). An anemometer has three or four cups mounted at the ends of spokes that spin on an axle. The force of the wind against the cups turns the axle. A speedometer attached to the axle shows the wind speed.

A cool breeze can be very refreshing on a warm day. However, during the winter, a similar breeze can make you feel uncomfortably cold. The wind blowing over your skin removes body heat. The stronger the wind, the colder you feel. The increased cooling that a wind can cause is called the **wind-chill factor.** Thus a weather report may say, "The temperature is 20 degrees Fahrenheit. But with a wind speed of 30 miles per hour, the wind-chill factor makes it feel like 18 degrees below zero."

☑ *Checkpoint* ***Toward what direction does a west wind blow?***

TRY THIS

Build a Wind Vane

Here's how to build your own wind vane. ACTIVITY

1. Use scissors to cut out a pointer and a slightly larger tail fin from construction paper.
2. Make a slit 1 cm deep in each end of a soda straw.
3. Slide the pointer and tail fin into place on the straw, securing them with small pieces of tape.

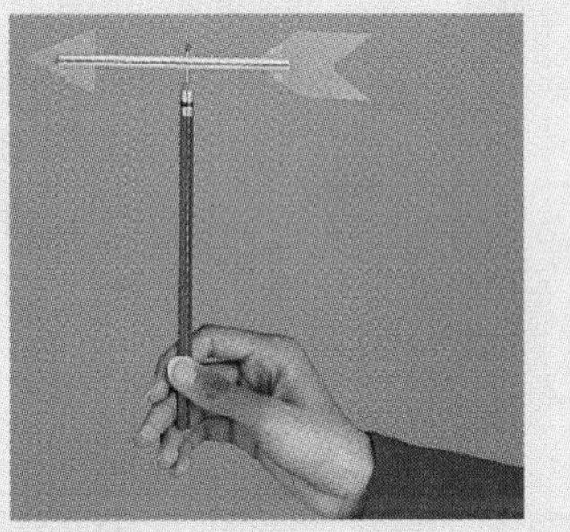

4. Hold the straw on your finger to find the point at which it balances.
5. Carefully push a pin through the balance point and into the eraser of a pencil. Move the wind vane back and forth to make sure it can spin freely.

Observing How can you use your wind vane to tell the direction of the wind?

Figure 6 The wind vane on the left points in the direction the wind is blowing from. The anemometer on the right measures wind speed. The cups catch the wind, turning faster when the wind blows faster.

Local Winds

Have you ever flown a kite at the beach on a hot summer day? Even if there is no wind inland, there may be a cool breeze blowing in from the water toward the beach. This breeze is an example of a local wind. **Local winds** are winds that blow over short distances. **Local winds are caused by unequal heating of Earth's surface within a small area.** Local winds form only when no winds are blowing from farther away.

Real-World Lab

You and Your Community

WHERE'S THE WIND?

Your city is planning to build a new community center. You and your classmates want to be sure that the doors will not be hard to open or close on windy days. You need to know which side of the building will be sheltered from the wind. You decide to measure wind speeds around a similar building.

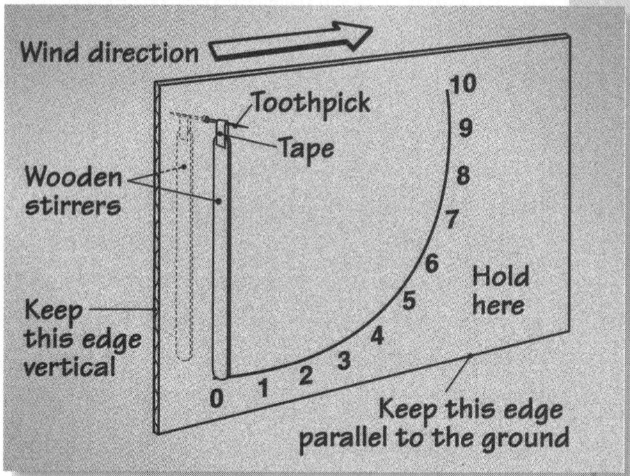

Wind direction
Toothpick
Tape
Wooden stirrers
Keep this edge vertical
Hold here
Keep this edge parallel to the ground
0
1
2
3
4
5
6
7
8
9
10

Problem

How can you determine wind patterns around a building?

Skills Focus

measuring, interpreting data, drawing conclusions

Materials

pen	round toothpick
wind vane	2 wooden coffee stirrers
meter stick	narrow masking tape

corrugated cardboard sheet, 15 cm x 20 cm

Procedure

1. You'll begin by making a simple anemometer that uses wooden coffee stirrers to indicate wind speed. On your piece of cardboard, draw a curved scale like the one shown in the diagram. Mark it in equal intervals from 0 to 10.
2. Carefully use the pen to make a small hole where the toothpick will go. Insert the toothpick through the hole.
3. Tape the wooden coffee stirrers to the toothpick as shown in the diagram, one on each side of the cardboard.
4. Copy the data table into your notebook.
5. Take your anemometer outside the school. Stand about 2–3 m away from the building and away from any corners or large plants.

Unequal heating often occurs on land that is next to a large body of water. It takes more energy to warm up a body of water than it does to warm up an equal area of land. This means that as the sun heats Earth's surface during the day, the land warms up faster than the water. The air over the land becomes warmer than the air over the water. The warm air expands and rises, creating a low-pressure area. Cool air blows inland from the water and moves underneath the warm air. A wind that blows

DATA TABLE

Location	Wind Direction	Wind Speed

6. Use the wind vane to find out what direction the wind is coming from. Hold your anemometer so that the card is straight, vertical, and parallel to the wind direction. Observe which number the wooden stirrer is closest to. Record your data.
7. Repeat your measurements on all the other sides of the building. Record your data.

Analyze and Conclude

1. Was the wind stronger on one side of the school building than the other sides? How can you explain your observation?
2. Do your classmates' results agree with yours? What might account for any differences?
3. **Apply** Based on your data, which side of the building provides the best location for a door?

More to Explore

What effect do plants have on the wind speed in an area? Could bushes and trees be planted so that they reduce the wind speed near the doors? What measurements could you make to find out?

1 2 3 4 5 6 7 8 9 10 11 12

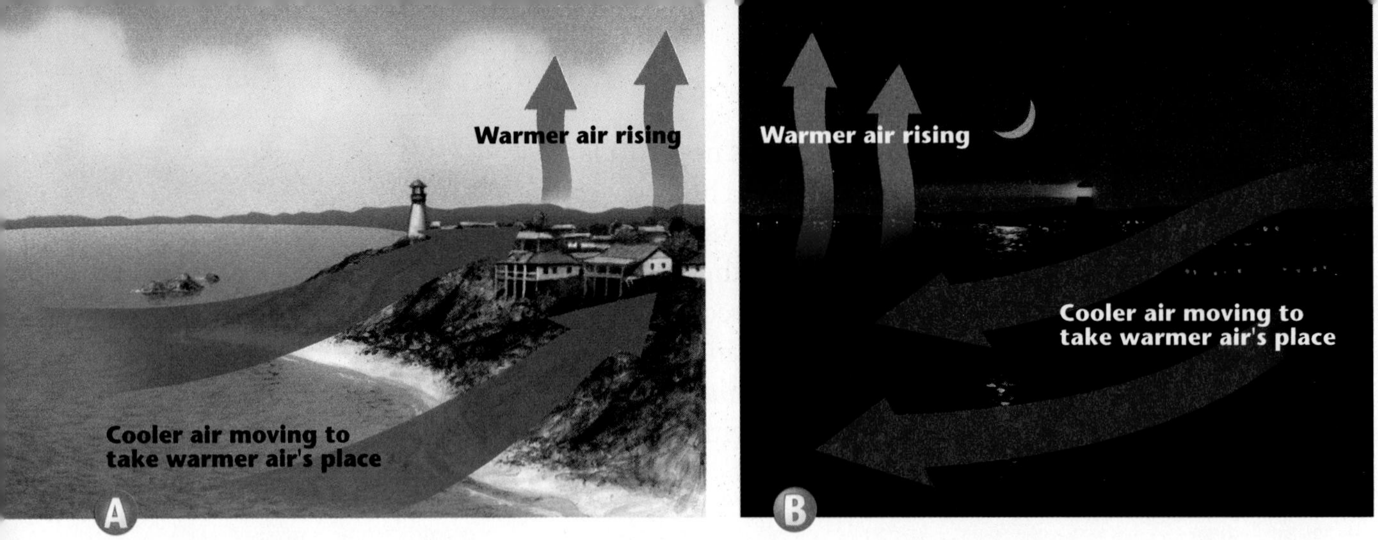
Warmer air rising
Cooler air moving to take warmer air's place
A
Warmer air rising
Cooler air moving to take warmer air's place
B

Figure 7 A. During the day, cool air moves from the sea to the land, creating a sea breeze. B. At night, cooler air moves from the land to the sea. *Forming Operational Definitions What type of breeze occurs at night?*

from an ocean or lake onto land is known as a **sea breeze** or a lake breeze. Figure 7A shows a sea breeze.

At night, the situation is reversed. Land cools more quickly than water, so the air over the land becomes cooler than the air over the water. As the warmer air over the water rises, cooler air moves from the land to take its place. The flow of air from land to a body of water is called a **land breeze.**

Monsoons

A process similar to land and sea breezes can occur over wider areas. In the summer in South and Southeast Asia, the land gradually gets warmer than the ocean. A large "sea breeze" blows steadily inland from the ocean all summer, even at night. In the winter, the land cools and becomes colder than the ocean. A "land breeze" blows steadily from the land to the ocean.

Sea and land breezes over a large region that change direction with the seasons are called **monsoons.** The summer monsoon in South Asia and Southeast Asia is very important for the crops grown there. The air blowing from the ocean during the rainy season is very warm and humid. As the humid air rises over the land, the air cools, producing heavy rains that supply the water needed by rice and other crops.

Figure 8 This heavy rain in Nepal is part of the summer monsoon, which blows from the ocean to the land. In the winter, the monsoon reverses and blows from the land to the ocean.

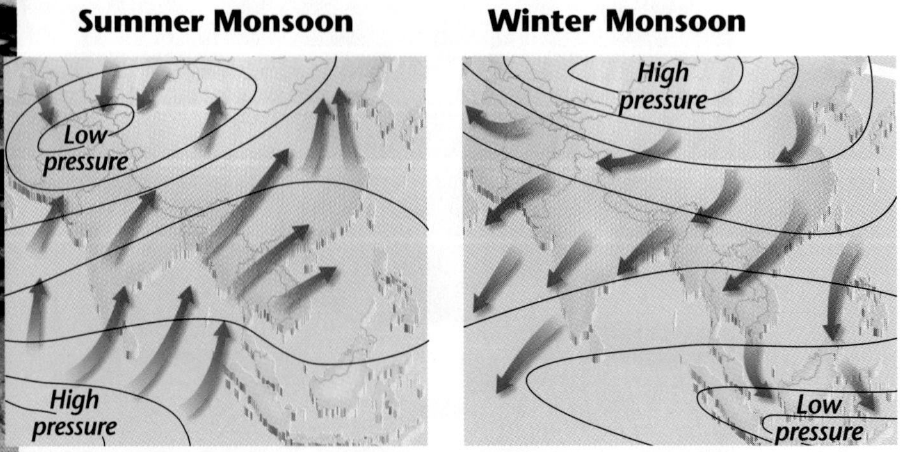
Summer Monsoon
Low pressure
High pressure
Winter Monsoon
High pressure
Low pressure

Global Winds

Winds that blow steadily from specific directions over long distances are called **global winds.** Like local winds, global winds are created by unequal heating of Earth's surface. Refer to Figure 9 to see how sunlight strikes Earth's surface. In the middle of the day near the equator, the sun is almost directly overhead. The direct rays from the sun heat Earth's surface intensely. Near the North Pole or South Pole, the sun's rays strike Earth's surface at a lower angle, even at noon. The sun's energy is spread out over a larger area, so it heats the surface less. As a result, temperatures near the poles are much lower than they are near the equator.

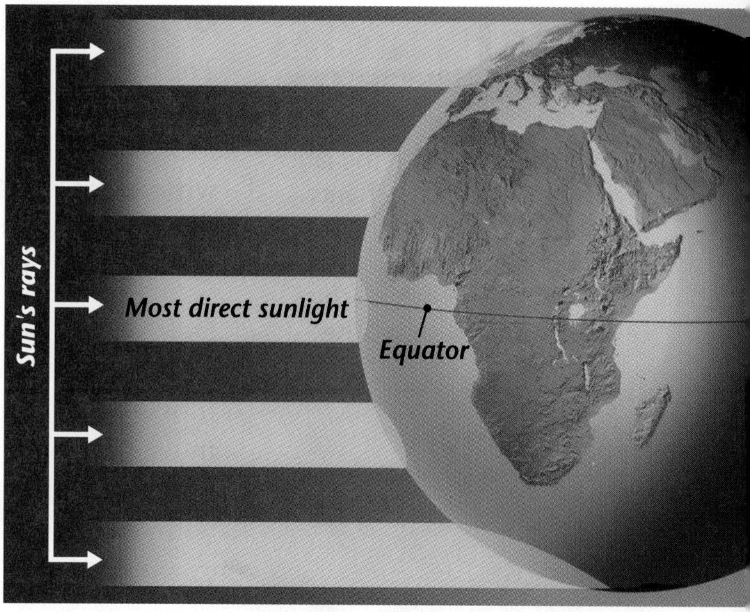
Sun's rays
Most direct sunlight
Equator

Figure 9 Near the equator, energy from the sun strikes Earth almost directly. Near the poles, the same amount of energy is spread out over a larger area.

Global Convection Currents Temperature differences between the equator and the poles produce giant convection currents in the atmosphere. Warm air rises at the equator, and cold air sinks at the poles. Therefore air pressure tends to be lower near the equator and greater near the poles, causing winds at Earth's surface to blow from the poles toward the equator. Higher in the atmosphere, air flows away from the equator toward the poles. **The movement of air between the equator and the poles produces global winds.**

The Coriolis Effect If Earth did not rotate, global winds would blow in a straight line from the poles toward the equator. Because Earth is rotating, global winds do not follow a straight path. As the winds move, Earth rotates from west to east underneath them, making it seem as if the winds have curved. The way Earth's rotation makes winds curve is called the **Coriolis effect** (kawr ee OH lis). It is named for the French mathematician who studied and explained it in 1835.

In the Northern Hemisphere, all global winds gradually turn toward the right. As you can see in Figure 10, a wind blowing toward the north gradually turns toward the northeast. In other words, a south wind gradually changes to a southwest wind. In the Southern Hemisphere, winds curve toward the left. A south wind becomes an southeast wind, and a north wind becomes a northwest wind.

Figure 10 As Earth rotates, the Coriolis effect turns winds in the Northern Hemisphere toward the right. ***Interpreting Diagrams*** *Which way do winds turn in the Southern Hemisphere?*

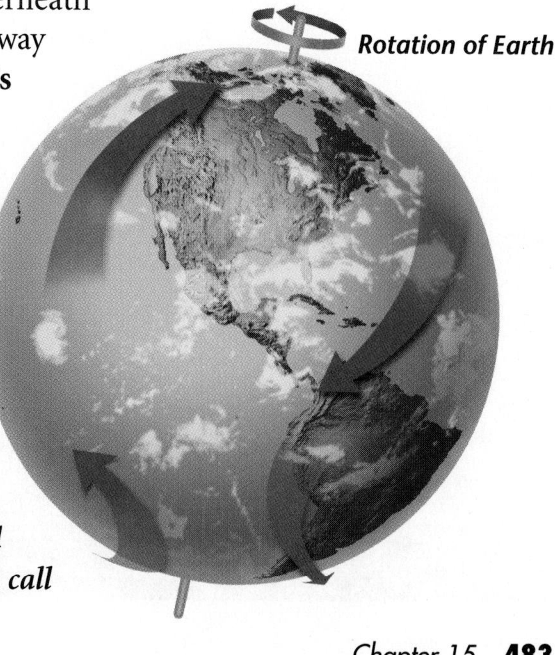
Rotation of Earth

☑ ***Checkpoint*** ***What happens to a wind blowing toward the south in the Northern Hemisphere? What would you call this wind?***

Social Studies CONNECTION

From colonial days to the late 1800s, American merchants traded new ships, lumber, cotton, tobacco, and furs for manufactured goods, such as textiles, from England. The eastbound voyage in the early 1800s took about three weeks. However, the westbound passage took almost twice as long—five to six weeks.

In Your Journal

Imagine that you are a sea captain making the voyage to England and back to America. Your family doesn't understand why your journey home takes almost twice as long as your journey to England. Write a letter to your family explaining why you have to travel farther south to take advantage of the prevailing winds on your return voyage.

Global Wind Belts

The Coriolis effect and other factors combine to produce a pattern of calm areas and wind belts around Earth. The calm areas include the doldrums and the horse latitudes. **The major global wind belts are the trade winds, the prevailing westerlies, and the polar easterlies.** As you read about each area, find it in *Exploring Global Winds.*

Doldrums Near the equator, the sun heats the surface strongly. Warm air rises steadily, creating an area of low pressure. Cool air moves into the area, but is warmed rapidly and rises before it moves very far. There is very little horizontal motion, so the winds near the equator are very weak. Regions near the equator with little or no wind are called the doldrums.

Horse Latitudes Warm air that rises at the equator divides and flows both north and south. **Latitude** is the distance from the equator, measured in degrees. At about 30° north and south latitudes, the air stops moving toward the poles and sinks. In each of these regions, another belt of calm air forms. Hundreds of years ago, sailors becalmed in these waters ran out of food and water for their horses and had to throw the horses overboard. Because of this, the latitudes 30° north and south of the equator are called the horse latitudes.

Trade Winds When the cold air over the horse latitudes sinks, it produces a region of high pressure. This high pressure causes surface winds to blow both toward the equator and away from it. The winds that blow toward the equator are turned west by the Coriolis effect. As a result, winds in the Northern Hemisphere between 30° north latitude and the equator blow generally from the northeast. In the Southern Hemisphere between 30° south latitude and the equator, the winds blow from the southeast. These steady easterly winds are called the trade winds. For hundreds of years, sailors relied on them to carry cargoes from Europe to the West Indies and South America.

Figure 11 The bark *Patriot,* built in 1809, carried goods to many parts of the world. ***Applying Concepts*** *How much effect do you think the prevailing winds have on shipping today?*

EXPLORING *Global Winds*

A series of wind belts circles Earth. Between the wind belts are calm areas where air is rising or falling.

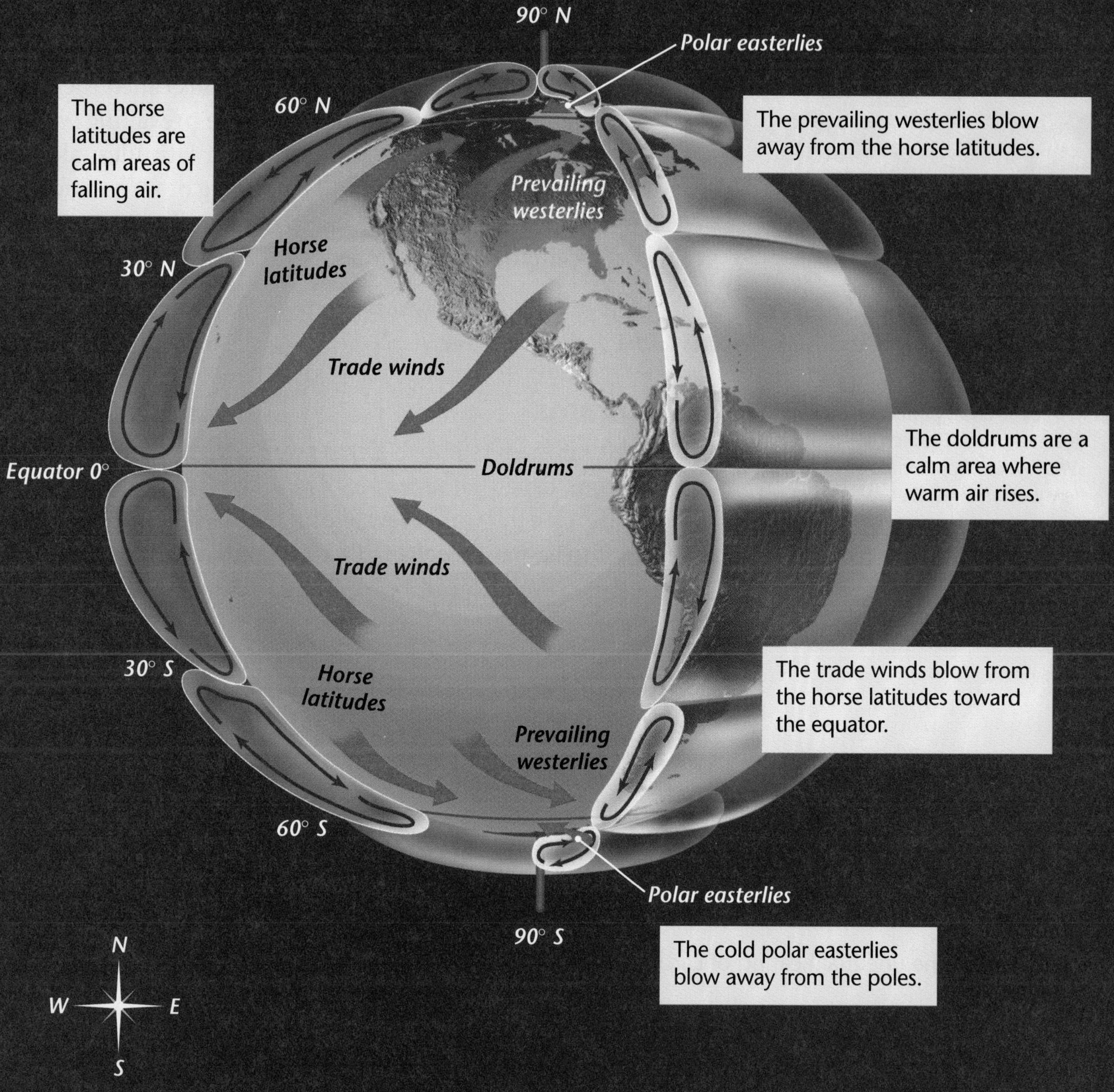

90° N
Polar easterlies
60° N
The horse latitudes are calm areas of falling air.
The prevailing westerlies blow away from the horse latitudes.
Prevailing westerlies
Horse latitudes
30° N
Trade winds
Equator 0°
Doldrums
The doldrums are a calm area where warm air rises.
Trade winds
30° S
Horse latitudes
The trade winds blow from the horse latitudes toward the equator.
Prevailing westerlies
60° S
Polar easterlies
90° S
The cold polar easterlies blow away from the poles.
N
W
E
S

Figure 12 By traveling east in a jet stream, pilots can save time and fuel. *Predicting* *What would happen if a plane flew west in a jet stream?*

Prevailing Westerlies In the mid-latitudes, winds that blow toward the poles are turned toward the east by the Coriolis effect. Because they blow from the west to the east, they are called prevailing westerlies. The prevailing westerlies blow generally from the southwest between 30° and 60° north latitudes and from the northwest between 30° and 60° south latitudes. The prevailing westerlies play an important part in the weather of the United States.

Polar Easterlies Cold air near the poles sinks and flows back toward lower latitudes. The Coriolis effect shifts these polar winds to the west, producing winds called the polar easterlies. The polar easterlies meet the prevailing westerlies at about 60° north and 60° south latitudes, along a region called the polar front. The mixing of warm and cold air along the polar front has a major effect on weather changes in the United States.

☑ *Checkpoint* ***In what region do the polar easterlies meet the prevailing westerlies?***

Jet Streams

About 10 kilometers above Earth's surface are bands of high-speed winds called **jet streams.** These winds are hundreds of kilometers wide but only a few kilometers deep. Jet streams blow from west to east at speeds of 200 to 400 kilometers per hour. As jet streams travel around Earth, they wander north and south along a wavy path.

Airplanes are aided by a jet stream when traveling east. Pilots can save fuel and time by flying east in a jet stream. However, airplanes flying at jet stream altitudes are slowed down when traveling west against the jet stream winds.

Section 3 Review

1. How does the unequal heating of Earth's surface cause winds?
2. How are local winds and global winds similar? How are they different?
3. Name and draw the three major wind belts.
4. **Thinking Critically Applying Concepts** Imagine you are flying from Seattle to San Francisco, which is almost exactly due south of Seattle. Should the pilot set a course due south? Explain your answer.

CHAPTER PROJECT

Check Your Progress

Check with your teacher to be sure you are using the weather instruments correctly. Are you recording units for each measurement? Collect and record measurements each day.

SECTION 4

Water in the Atmosphere

DISCOVER — ACTIVITY

How Does Fog Form?

1. Fill a narrow-necked plastic bottle with hot tap water. Pour out most of the water, leaving about 3 cm at the bottom. **CAUTION:** *Avoid spilling hot water. Do not use water that is so hot that you cannot safely hold the bottle.*
2. Place an ice cube on the mouth of the bottle. What happens?
3. Repeat Steps 1 and 2 using cold water instead of hot water. What happens?

Think It Over

Developing Hypotheses How can you explain your observations? Why is there a difference between what happens with the hot water and with the cold water?

GUIDE FOR READING

- **How is relative humidity measured?**
- **How do clouds form?**
- **What are the three main types of clouds?**

Reading Tip **Before you read, write a definition of "cloud." Revise your definition as you read about clouds.**

During a rainstorm, the air feels moist. On a clear, cloudless day, the air may feel dry. As the sun heats the land and oceans, the amount of water in the atmosphere changes. Water is always moving between the atmosphere and Earth's surface.

This movement of water between the atmosphere and Earth's surface, called the water cycle, is shown in Figure 13. Water vapor enters the air by evaporation from the oceans and other bodies of water. **Evaporation** is the process by which water molecules in liquid water escape into the air as water vapor. Water vapor is also added to the air by living things. Water enters the roots of plants, rises to the leaves, and is released as water vapor.

As part of the water cycle, some of the water vapor in the atmosphere condenses to form clouds. Rain and other forms of precipitation fall from the clouds toward the surface. The water then runs off the surface, or moves through the ground, back into the oceans, lakes, and streams.

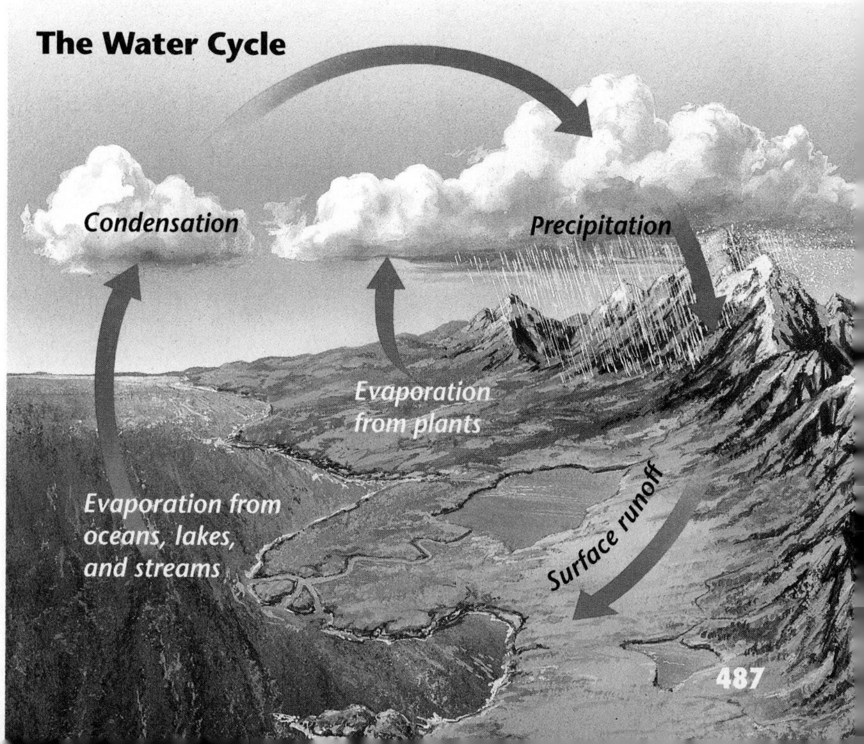
The Water Cycle
Condensation
Precipitation
Evaporation from plants
Evaporation from oceans, lakes, and streams
Surface runoff

Figure 13 In the water cycle, water moves from lakes and oceans into the atmosphere and falls back to Earth.

Humidity

Humidity is a measure of the amount of water vapor in the air. The percentage of water vapor in the air compared to the maximum amount the air could hold is called the **relative humidity.** For example, at 10°C, 1 cubic meter of air can hold a maximum of 8 grams of water vapor. If there actually were 8 grams of water vapor in the air, then the relative humidity of the air would be 100 percent. If the air held 4 grams of water vapor, the relative humidity would be half, or 50 percent. The amount of water vapor that the air can hold depends on its temperature. Warm air can hold more water vapor than cool air.

INTEGRATING LIFE SCIENCE "It's not the heat, it's the humidity." What does this common expression mean? Even on a hot day, you can still feel comfortable if the air is dry. Evaporation of moisture from your skin removes heat and helps to keep your body's temperature comfortable. You feel less comfortable on a hot day if the relative humidity is high. When the relative humidity is high, evaporation slows down. Evaporation therefore has less cooling effect on your body.

Measuring Relative Humidity

Relative humidity can be measured with a psychrometer. A **psychrometer** (sy KRAHM uh tur) has two thermometers, a wet-bulb thermometer and a dry-bulb thermometer. The bulb of the wet-bulb thermometer has a cloth covering that is moistened with water. Air is then blown over both thermometers. Because the wet-bulb thermometer is cooled by evaporation, its reading drops below that of the dry-bulb thermometer.

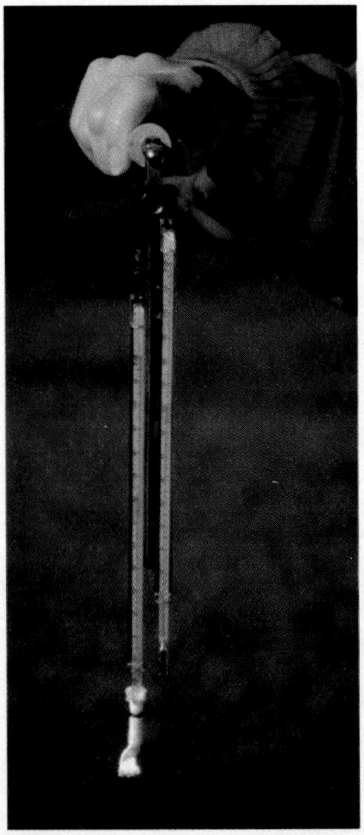

Relative Humidity

Dry-Bulb Reading (°C)	Difference Between Wet- and Dry-Bulb Readings (°C)				
	1	2	3	4	5
10	88	76	65	54	43
12	88	78	67	57	48
14	89	79	69	60	50
16	90	80	71	62	54
18	91	81	72	64	56
20	91	82	74	66	58
22	92	83	75	68	60
24	92	84	76	69	62
26	92	85	77	70	64
28	93	86	78	71	65
30	93	86	79	72	66

Figure 14 A sling psychrometer is used to measure relative humidity. First, find the wet-bulb and dry-bulb temperatures. Then find the dry-bulb temperature in the left column of the table. Find the difference between the wet- and dry-bulb temperatures across the top of the table. The number in the table where these two readings intersect indicates the relative humidity in percent.

If the relative humidity is high, the water on the wet bulb will evaporate slowly and the wet-bulb temperature will not change much. If the relative humidity is low, the water on the wet bulb will evaporate rapidly and the wet-bulb temperature will drop. The relative humidity can be found by comparing the temperatures of the wet-bulb and dry-bulb thermometers on a table like the one in Figure 14.

☑ *Checkpoint* ***What is the difference between humidity and relative humidity?***

How Clouds Form

What do clouds remind you of? They can look like people, animals, countries, and a thousand other fanciful forms. Of course, not all clouds are fluffy and white. Storm clouds can be dark and cover the whole sky.

Clouds of all kinds form when water vapor in the air becomes liquid water or ice crystals. The process by which molecules of water vapor in the air become liquid water is called **condensation.** How does water condense? As you know, cold air can hold less water vapor than warm air. As air cools, the amount of water vapor it can hold decreases. Some of the water vapor in the air condenses to form droplets of liquid water.

The temperature at which condensation begins is called the **dew point.** If the dew point is below the freezing point, the water vapor may change directly into ice crystals. When you look at a cloud, you are seeing millions of tiny ice crystals or water droplets.

For water vapor to condense, tiny particles must be present so the water has a surface on which to condense. Most of these particles are salt crystals, dust from soil, and smoke. Sometimes water vapor condenses onto solid surfaces, such as blades of grass, instead of particles. Water that condenses from the air onto a cold surface is called dew. Frost is ice that has been deposited directly from the air onto a cold surface.

Clouds form whenever air is cooled to its dew point and particles are present. But why does the air cool? If air is warmed near the ground, it

Sharpen your Skills

Interpreting Data

ACTIVITY

At lunchtime you use a psychrometer and get readings of 26°C on the dry-bulb thermometer and 21°C on the wet-bulb thermometer. Use Figure 14 to find the relative humidity.

Later in the day you use the psychrometer again and this time get readings of 20°C on the dry-bulb thermometer and 19°C on the wet-bulb thermometer. Find the new relative humidity. Is the relative humidity increasing or decreasing?

Figure 15 Dew forms when water vapor condenses out of the air onto a solid surface, such as this flower.

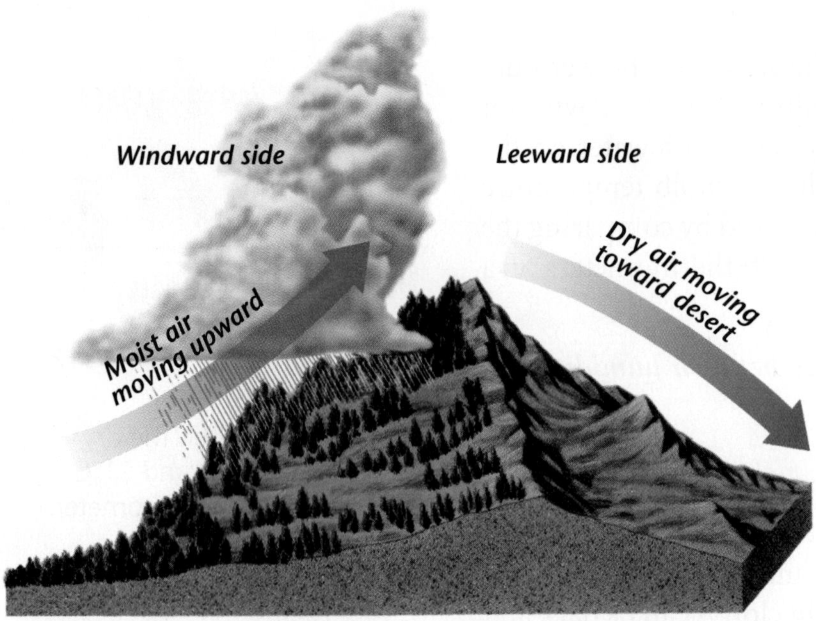
Windward side
Leeward side
Moist air moving upward
Dry air moving toward desert

Figure 16 Humid air cools as it is blown up the side of a mountain. *Predicting What happens when water vapor condenses out of the air?*

becomes less dense and rises in a convection current. When the rising air expands and becomes cooler, clouds may form.

When wind strikes the side of a hill or mountain, the air is forced upward. As the air rises along the slope, the air cools. Rain or snow falls on the windward side of the mountains, the side facing the oncoming wind.

By the time the air reaches the other side of the mountains, it has lost much of its water vapor. The air is cool and dry. The land on the leeward side of the mountains—downwind—is in a rain shadow. Just as very little light falls in a sun shadow, very little rain falls in a rain shadow. Not only has the air lost its water vapor while crossing the mountains, but the air has also grown warmer while flowing down the mountainside. This warm, dry air often creates a desert on the leeward side of the mountains.

☑ *Checkpoint* ***Why are the tops of some mountains almost always covered by clouds?***

Types of Clouds

As you know, clouds come in different shapes. **Meteorologists classify clouds into three main types: cumulus, stratus, and cirrus.** Clouds are also classified by their altitude. Each type of cloud is associated with a different type of weather.

Clouds that look like fluffy, rounded piles of cotton are called **cumulus** (KYOO myuh lus) clouds. The word *cumulus* means "heap" or "mass." Cumulus clouds form less than 2 kilometers above the ground, but may grow in size and height until they extend upward as much as 18 kilometers. Cumulus clouds usually indicate fair weather. Towering clouds with flat tops, called cumulonimbus clouds, often produce thunderstorms. The suffix *-nimbus* comes from a Latin word meaning "rain."

Clouds that form in flat layers are called **stratus** (STRAT us) clouds. *Strato* means "spread out." Stratus clouds usually cover all or most of the sky. As stratus clouds thicken, they may produce drizzle, rain, or snow. They are then called nimbostratus clouds.

Wispy, feathery clouds are called **cirrus** (SEER us) clouds. Cirrus clouds form only at high levels, above about 6 kilometers, where temperatures are very low. As a result, cirrus clouds are made mostly of ice crystals.

EXPLORING Clouds

The main types of clouds are cumulus, stratus, and cirrus. A cloud's name contains clues about its height and structure.

Cirrus clouds
Cirrus, cirrostratus, and cirrocumulus clouds are made up mostly of ice crystals.

Cumulonimbus clouds
Thunderstorms come from cumulonimbus clouds. For this reason cumulonimbus clouds are also called thunderheads.

Nimbostratus clouds
Nimbostratus clouds may produce rain or snow.

Cumulus clouds
Cumulus clouds are usually a sign of fair weather.

Cirrus
Cirrocumulus
Altocumulus
Altostratus
Cumulonimbus
Nimbostratus
Stratus
Cumulus
Fog

Figure 17 Fog often forms at night over cool lakes. ***Predicting*** *What will happen as the sun rises and warms the air above the lake?*

Cirrus clouds that have feathery "hooked" ends are sometimes called mare's tails. Cirrocumulus clouds, which look like rows of cotton balls, often indicate that a storm is on its way.

Part of a cloud's name may be based on its height. The names of clouds that form between about 2 and 6 kilometers above Earth's surface have the prefix *alto-*, which means "high." The two main types of these clouds are altocumulus and altostratus.

Clouds that form at or near the ground are called fog. Fog often forms when the ground cools at night after a warm, humid day. The ground cools the air just above the ground to the air's dew point. The next day the heat of the morning sun "burns" the fog off as its water droplets evaporate.

Section 4 Review

1. What instrument is used to measure relative humidity? How does it work?
2. What conditions are needed for clouds to form?
3. Describe each of the three main types of clouds.
4. **Thinking Critically Classifying** Classify each of the following cloud types as low-level, medium-level, or high-level: altocumulus, altostratus, cirrostratus, cirrus, cumulus, fog, nimbostratus, and stratus.

Science at Home

Fill a large glass half-full with cold water. Show your family members what happens as you add ice cubes to the water. Explain to your family that the water that appears on the outside of the glass comes from water vapor in the atmosphere. Also explain why the water on the outside of the glass only appears after you add ice to the water in the glass.

Section 5 Precipitation

Discover Activity

How Can You Make Hail?

1. Put on your goggles.
2. Put 15 g of salt into a beaker. Add 50 mL of water. Stir the solution until most of the salt is dissolved.
3. Put 15 mL of cold water in a clean test tube.
4. Place the test tube in the beaker.
5. Fill the beaker almost to the top with crushed ice. Stir the ice mixture every minute for six minutes.

6. Remove the test tube from the beaker and drop an ice chip into the test tube. What happens?

Think It Over

Inferring Based on your observation, what conditions are necessary for hail to form?

Guide for Reading

- **What are the main types of precipitation?**
- **How is precipitation measured?**

Reading Tip **As you read, make a list of the types of precipitation. Write a sentence describing how each type forms.**

In Arica, Chile, the average rainfall is less than 1 millimeter per year. Many years pass with no precipitation at all. On the other hand, the average rainfall on Mount Waialeale on the island of Kauai in Hawaii is about 12 meters per year. That's more than enough to cover a three-story house! As you can see, rainfall varies greatly around the world.

Water evaporates into the air from every water surface on Earth and from living things. This water eventually returns to the surface as precipitation. **Precipitation** (pree sip uh TAY shun) is any form of water that falls from clouds and reaches Earth's surface.

Precipitation always comes from clouds. But not all clouds produce precipitation. For precipitation to occur, cloud droplets or ice crystals must grow heavy enough to fall through the air. One way that cloud droplets grow is by colliding and combining with other cloud droplets. As the droplets grow larger, they fall faster and collect more and more small droplets. Finally, the droplets become heavy enough to fall out of the cloud as raindrops.

Types of Precipitation

In warm parts of the world, precipitation is almost always rain or drizzle. In colder regions, precipitation may fall as snow or ice. **Common types of precipitation include rain, sleet, freezing rain, hail, and snow.**

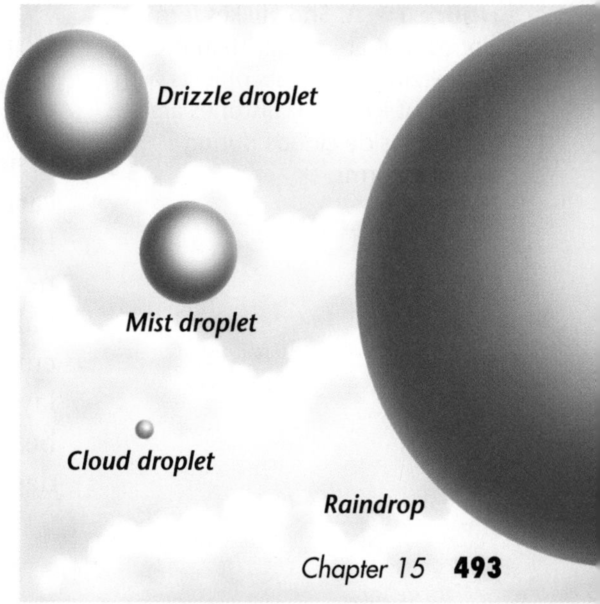
Drizzle droplet
Mist droplet
Cloud droplet
Raindrop

Figure 18 Droplets come in many sizes. Believe it or not, a raindrop has about one million times as much water in it as a cloud droplet.

A

STOP
TRUCKS OVER 5 TONS
B

C

Figure 19 A. Snowflakes form in clouds that are colder than 0°C. B. Freezing rain coats objects with a layer of ice. C. Hailstones are formed inside clouds during thunderstorms.

Rain The most common kind of precipitation is rain. Drops of water are called rain if they are at least 0.5 millimeter in diameter. Precipitation made up of smaller drops of water is called mist or drizzle. Mist and drizzle usually fall from nimbostratus clouds.

Sleet Sometimes raindrops fall through a layer of air below 0°C, the freezing point of water. As they fall, the raindrops freeze into solid particles of ice. Ice particles smaller than 5 millimeters in diameter are called sleet.

Freezing Rain At other times raindrops falling through cold air near the ground do not freeze in the air. Instead, the raindrops freeze when they touch a cold surface. This is called freezing rain. In an ice storm, a smooth, thick layer of ice builds up on every surface. The weight of the ice may break tree branches onto power lines, causing power failures. Freezing rain and sleet can make sidewalks and roads slippery and dangerous.

Hail Round pellets of ice larger than 5 millimeters in diameter are called hailstones. Hail forms only inside cumulonimbus clouds during thunderstorms. A hailstone starts as an ice pellet inside a cold region of a cloud. Strong updrafts in the cloud carry the hailstone up and down through the cold region many times. Each time the hailstone goes through the cold region, a new layer of ice forms around the hailstone. Eventually the hailstone becomes heavy enough to fall to the ground. If you cut a hailstone in half, you can often see shells of ice, like the layers of an onion. Because hailstones can grow quite large before finally falling to the ground, hail can cause tremendous damage to crops, buildings, and vehicles.

Snow Often water vapor in a cloud is converted directly into ice crystals called snowflakes. Snowflakes have an endless number of different shapes and patterns, all with six sides or branches. Snowflakes often join together into larger clumps of snow in which the six-sided crystals are hard to see.

☑ *Checkpoint* *How do hailstones form?*

Measuring Precipitation

Meteorologists measure rainfall with a rain gauge. A **rain gauge** is an open-ended can or tube that collects rainfall. The amount of rainfall is measured by dipping a ruler into the water or by reading a marked scale. To increase the accuracy of the measurement, the top of a rain gauge may have a funnel that collects ten times as much rain as the tube alone. The funnel collects a greater depth of water that is easier to measure. But to get the actual depth of rain, it is necessary to divide by ten.

Snowfall is measured using a ruler or by melting collected snow and measuring the depth of water it produces. On average, 10 centimeters of snow contains about the same amount of water as 1 centimeter of rain. Of course, light, fluffy snow contains far less water than heavy, wet snow.

Sharpen your Skills

Calculating

ACTIVITY

Make your own rain gauge by putting a funnel into a narrow, straight-sided glass jar. Here's how to calculate how much more rain your funnel collects than the jar alone.

1. First measure the diameter of the top of the funnel and square it.
   Example: $4 \times 4 = 16$
2. Then measure the diameter of the top of the jar and square it.
   Example: $2 \times 2 = 4$
3. Divide the first square by the second square.
   Example: $\frac{16}{4} = 4$
4. To find the actual depth of rain that fell, divide the depth of water in the jar by the ratio from Step 3.
   Example: $\frac{8 \text{ cm}}{4} = 2 \text{ cm}$

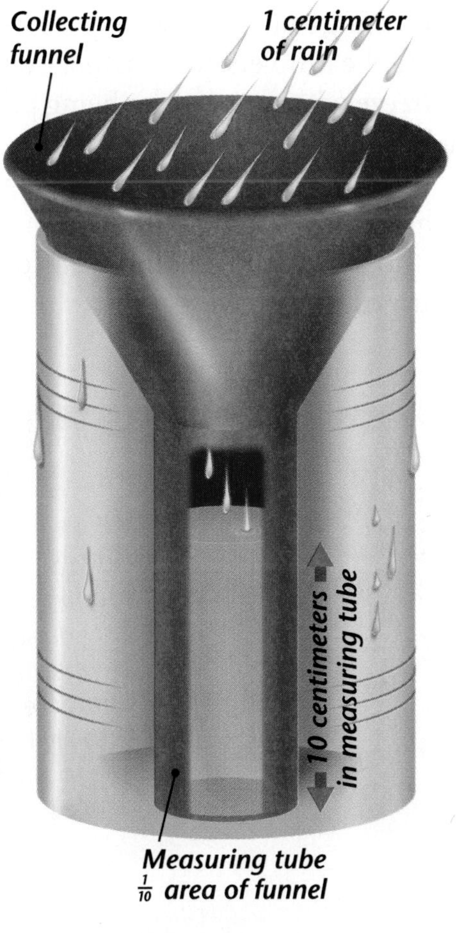
Collecting funnel
1 centimeter of rain
10 centimeters in measuring tube
Measuring tube
$\frac{1}{10}$ area of funnel

Figure 20 A rain gauge measures the depth of rain that falls. *Observing* *How much rain was collected in the measuring tube of this rain gauge?*

Figure 21 The corn in this photo was damaged by a long drought. *Applying Concepts How can cloud seeding be used to reduce the effect of droughts?*

Controlling Precipitation

In some regions, there may be periods that are much drier than usual. Long periods of unusually low precipitation are called **droughts.** Droughts can cause great hardship. In the farming regions of the Midwest, for example, droughts may cause entire crops to fail. The farmers suffer from lost income and consumers suffer from high food prices. In some less-developed countries, droughts can cause widespread hunger, or famine.

INTEGRATING TECHNOLOGY In recent years, scientists have been trying to produce rain during droughts. The most common method is called cloud seeding. In cloud seeding, tiny crystals of dry ice (solid carbon dioxide) and silver iodide are sprinkled into clouds from airplanes. Many clouds contain supercooled water droplets, which are actually below 0°C. The droplets don't freeze because there aren't enough particles around which ice crystals can form. Water vapor can condense on the particles of silver iodide, forming rain or snow. Dry ice works by cooling the droplets even further, so that they will freeze without particles being present.

Cloud seeding has also been used with some success to clear fog from airports. Dry ice is sprinkled into the fog, causing ice crystals to form. This removes some of the fog so pilots can see the runways. Unfortunately, cloud seeding clears only cold fogs, so its use for this purpose is limited.

Section 5 Review

1. Name the five common types of precipitation.
2. What device is used to measure precipitation?
3. What must happen before precipitation can fall from a cloud?
4. What kind of cloud produces hail?
5. **Thinking Critically Applying Concepts** If two open cans of different diameters were left out in the rain, how would the amount of water they collected compare? How would the depth of water in the cans compare?

CHAPTER PROJECT

Check Your Progress

Now you should be ready to begin graphing your weather data. Look for patterns in your graphs. Use your data to predict what the next day's weather will be. Compare your predictions with what actually happens the next day. Are you able to predict the weather with confidence?

SECTION 1 Energy in the Atmosphere

Key Ideas

- Energy from the sun travels to Earth as electromagnetic waves—mostly visible light, infrared radiation, and ultraviolet radiation.
- When Earth's surface is heated, it radiates some of the energy back into the atmosphere in the form of longer-wavelength radiation.

Key Terms

electromagnetic wave, radiation, infrared radiation, ultraviolet radiation, scattering, greenhouse effect

SECTION 2 Heat Transfer

INTEGRATING PHYSICS

Key Ideas

- The energy of motion in the molecules of a substance is called thermal energy.
- Three forms of heat transfer—radiation, conduction, and convection—work together to heat the troposphere.

Key Terms

thermal energy, temperature, thermometer, heat, conduction, convection

SECTION 3 Winds

Key Ideas

- All winds are caused by differences in air pressure, which are the result of unequal heating of Earth's surface.
- Local winds are caused by unequal heating of Earth's surface within a small area.
- The movement of air between the equator and the poles produces global winds.

Key Terms

wind, anemometer, wind-chill factor, local wind, sea breeze, land breeze, monsoon, global wind, Coriolis effect, latitude, jet stream

SECTION 4 Water in the Atmosphere

Key Ideas

- Relative humidity is the percentage of water vapor in the air compared to the amount of water vapor the air could hold. It can be measured with a psychrometer.
- Clouds of all kinds form when water vapor in the air becomes liquid water or solid ice.
- Meteorologists classify clouds into three main types: cumulus, stratus, and cirrus.

Key Terms

evaporation, humidity, relative humidity, psychrometer, condensation, dew point, cumulus, stratus, cirrus

SECTION 5 Precipitation

Key Ideas

- Common types of precipitation include rain, sleet, freezing rain, hail, and snow.
- Rain is measured with a rain gauge.
- Scientists have used cloud seeding to produce rain and to clear fog from airports.

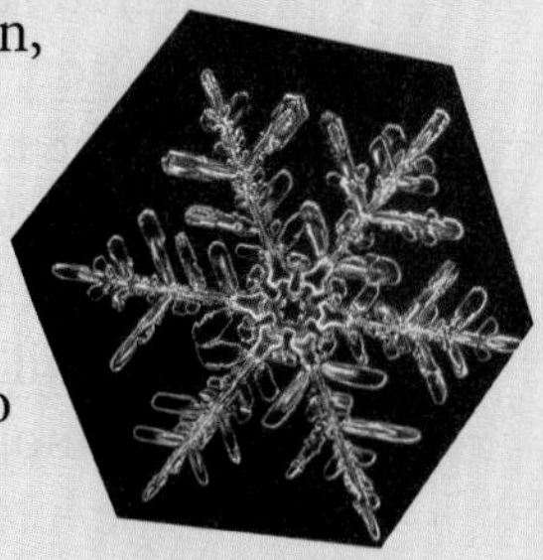

Key Terms

precipitation, rain gauge, drought

ACTIVITY — USING THE INTERNET

www.phschool.com/state_focus/california/

California Test Prep: Reviewing Content

Multiple Choice

Choose the letter of the best answer.

1. Energy from the sun travels to Earth's surface by
   a. radiation.
   b. convection.
   c. evaporation.
   d. conduction.
2. Rising warm air transports heat energy by
   a. conduction. b. convection.
   c. radiation. d. condensation.
3. A psychrometer is used to measure
   a. rainfall.
   b. relative humidity.
   c. temperature.
   d. humidity.
4. Clouds form because water vapor in the air
   a. warms. b. conducts.
   c. condenses. d. evaporates.
5. Rain, sleet, and hail are all forms of
   a. evaporation.
   b. condensation.
   c. precipitation.
   d. convection.

True or False

If the statement is true, write true. If it is false, change the underlined word or words to make the statement true.

6. Infrared radiation and ultraviolet radiation make up most of the energy Earth receives from the sun.
7. The process by which gases hold heat in the atmosphere is called the wind-chill factor.
8. Water molecules in liquid water escape into the atmosphere as water vapor in the process of evaporation.
9. The instrument used to measure wind speed is a thermometer.
10. Clouds that form near the ground are called fog.

Checking Concepts

11. What causes the greenhouse effect? How does it affect Earth's atmosphere?
12. What form of heat transfer is most important in heating the troposphere?
13. Describe how the movements of hot air at the equator and cold air at the poles produce global wind patterns.
14. Why do clouds usually form high in the air instead of near Earth's surface?
15. Describe sleet, hail, and snow in terms of how each one forms.
16. **Writing to Learn** Imagine you are a drop of water in the ocean. Write a diary describing your journey through the water cycle. How do you become a cloud? What type of conditions cause you to fall as precipitation? Use descriptive words to describe your journey.

Thinking Visually

17. **Concept Map** Copy the concept map about winds onto a separate sheet of paper. Then complete the map and add a title. (For more on concept maps, see the Skills Handbook.)

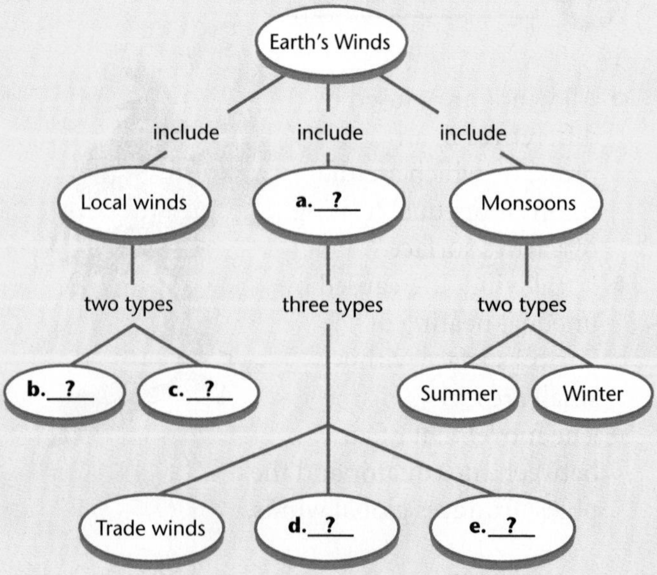
Earth's Winds
include
include
include
Local winds
a. ?
Monsoons
two types
three types
two types
b. ?
c. ?
Summer
Winter
Trade winds
d. ?
e. ?

Test Prep: Skills

Use the table below to answer Questions 18–21.

Average Monthly Rainfall

Month	Rainfall	Month	Rainfall
January	1 cm	July	49 cm
February	1 cm	August	57 cm
March	1 cm	September	40 cm
April	2 cm	October	20 cm
May	25 cm	November	4 cm
June	52 cm	December	1 cm

18. Graphing Use the information in the table to draw a bar graph that shows the rainfall each month at this location.

19. Calculating What is the total amount of rainfall each year at this location?

20. Classifying Which months of the year would you classify as "dry"? Which months would you classify as "wet"?

21. Drawing Conclusions The place represented by the rainfall data is in Southeast Asia. What do you think accounts for the extremely heavy rainfall that occurs during some months?

Thinking Critically

22. Relating Cause and Effect What circumstances could cause a nighttime land breeze in a city near the ocean?

23. Problem Solving If you use a psychrometer and get the same reading on both thermometers, what is the relative humidity?

24. Comparing and Contrasting How are hail and sleet alike? How are they different?

25. Classifying Classify the different types of clouds by the kind of weather associated with each type.

26. Relating Cause and Effect What is the source of the energy that powers Earth's winds?

Performance Assessment

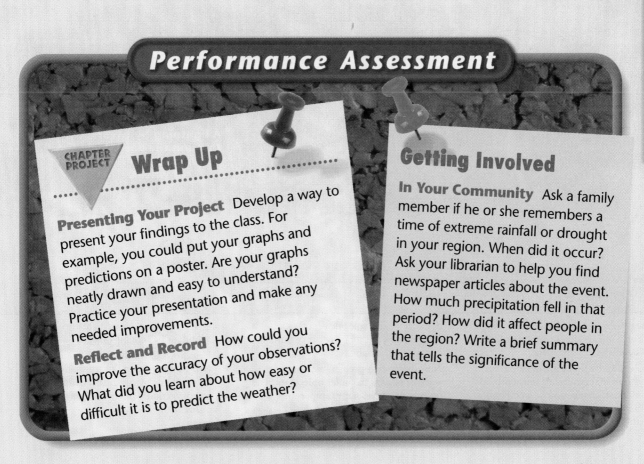

CHAPTER PROJECT Wrap Up

Presenting Your Project Develop a way to present your findings to the class. For example, you could put your graphs and predictions on a poster. Are your graphs neatly drawn and easy to understand? Practice your presentation and make any needed improvements.

Reflect and Record How could you improve the accuracy of your observations? What did you learn about how easy or difficult it is to predict the weather?

Getting Involved

In Your Community Ask a family member if he or she remembers a time of extreme rainfall or drought in your region. When did it occur? Ask your librarian to help you find newspaper articles about the event. How much precipitation fell in that period? How did it affect people in the region? Write a brief summary that tells the significance of the event.

CHAPTER

16 Weather Patterns

A lightning bolt tears through the dark sky, illuminating a field of wheat.

The following California Science Content Standards are addressed in this chapter:

2. Topography is reshaped by weathering of rock and soil and by the transportation and deposition of sediment.

b. Rivers and streams are dynamic systems that erode and transport sediment, change course, and flood their banks in natural and recurring patterns.

d. Earthquakes, volcanic eruptions, landslides, and floods change human and wildlife habitats.

3. Heat moves in a predictable flow from warmer objects to cooler objects until all objects are at the same temperature.

a. Energy can be carried from one place to another by heat flow, or by waves including water waves, light and sound, or by moving objects.

c. Heat flows in solids by conduction (which involves no flow of matter) and in fluids by conduction and also by convection (which involves flow of matter).

16 The Weather Tomorrow

When the sky turns dark and threatening, it's not hard to predict the weather. A storm is on its way. But wouldn' you rather know about an approaching storm before it actually arrives?

In this chapter you will learn about weather patterns, including the kinds of patterns that cause strong thunderstorms like this one. As you work through this chapter, you will get a chance to make your own weather forecasts and compare them to the forecasts of professionals. Good luck!

Your Goal To predict the weather for your own community and two other locations in the United States.

To complete the project you will
- compare weather maps for several days at a time
- look for repeating patterns in the weather
- draw maps to show your weather predictions

Get Started Begin by previewing Section 4 to learn about weather maps and symbols. Start a project folder to hold daily national weather maps from your local newspaper and a description of the symbols used on the maps. Choose two locations in the United States that are at least 1,000 kilometers away from your community and from each other.

Check Your Progress You'll be working on this project as you study this chapter. To keep your project on track, look for Check Your Progress boxes at the following points.

Section 1 Review, page 508: Collect weather maps and look for patterns.

Section 3 Review, page 524: Predict the next day's weather.

Section 4 Review, page 531: Compare your predictions to professional forecasts and to the actual weather.

Wrap Up At the end of the chapter (page 535), you will present your weather maps and discuss how well you predicted the weather.

4. Many phenomena on the Earth's surface are affected by the transfer of energy through radiation and convection currents.

d. Convection currents distribute heat in the atmosphere and oceans.

e. Differences in pressure, heat, air movement, and humidity result in changes of weather.

7. Scientific progress is made by asking meaningful questions and conducting careful investigations.

a. Develop a hypothesis.

c. Construct appropriate graphs from data and develop qualitative statements about the relationships between variables.

f. Read a topographic map and a geologic map for evidence provided on the maps, and construct and interpret a simple scale map.

h. Identify changes in natural phenome over time without manipulating the phenomena (e.g., a tree limb, a grov of trees, a stream, a hillslope).

SECTION 1

Air Masses and Fronts

DISCOVER — ACTIVITY

How Do Fluids of Different Densities Behave?

1. Put on your apron. Place a cardboard divider across the middle of a plastic shoe box.
2. Add a few drops of red food coloring to a liter of warm water. Pour the red liquid, which represents low-density warm air, into the shoe box on one side of the divider.
3. Add about 100 mL of table salt and a few drops of blue food coloring to a liter of cold water. Pour the blue liquid, which represents high-density cold air, into the shoe box on the other side of the divider.
4. What do you think will happen if you remove the divider?
5. Now quickly remove the divider. Watch carefully from the side. What happens?

Think It Over

Developing Hypotheses Based on this activity, write a hypothesis stating the effect of a mass of cold air running into a mass of warm air.

GUIDE FOR READING

- **What are the major types of air masses that affect the weather in North America?**
- **What are the main types of fronts?**
- **What are cyclones and anticyclones?**

Reading Tip **Before you read, use the headings to make an outline about air masses and fronts. Leave space to fill in details as you read.**

Listen to the evening news and you may hear a weather forecast like this: "A huge mass of Arctic air is moving our way, bringing freezing temperatures." Today's weather is influenced by air from thousands of kilometers away—perhaps from Canada or the Caribbean Sea. A huge body of air that has similar temperature, humidity, and air pressure throughout it is called an **air mass.** A single air mass may spread over an area of millions of square kilometers and be up to 10 kilometers high.

Types of Air Masses

Scientists classify air masses according to two characteristics: temperature and humidity. Whether an air mass is warm or cold depends on the temperature of the region over which the air mass forms. **Tropical,** or warm, air masses form in the tropics and have low air pressure. **Polar,** or cold, air masses form north of 50° north latitude and south of 50° south latitude. Polar air masses have high air pressure.

Whether an air mass is humid or dry depends on whether it forms over water or land. **Maritime** air masses form over oceans. Water evaporates from the oceans, so the air can become very humid. **Continental** air masses form over land, in the middle of continents, and are dry.

L
H
COLD
L
Today

Four major types of air masses influence the weather in North America: maritime tropical, continental tropical, maritime polar, and continental polar.** *Exploring North American Air Masses* on the next page shows where these air masses come from and what parts of North America they affect.

Maritime Tropical Warm, humid air masses form over oceans near the tropics. Maritime tropical air masses that form over the Gulf of Mexico and the Atlantic Ocean move first into the southeastern United States. These air masses then move north and northeast, where they influence weather in the central and eastern United States. In the west, maritime tropical air masses form over the Pacific Ocean. They affect mainly the weather on the West Coast. As they cross the coastal mountain ranges, the Pacific air masses lose moisture. They bring dry air to the eastern slopes.

In summer, maritime tropical air masses usually bring hot, humid weather. Most summer showers and thunderstorms in the United States develop in air masses that have formed over the Gulf of Mexico. In winter, a humid air mass can bring heavy rain or snow.

Maritime Polar Cool, humid air masses form over the icy cold North Pacific and North Atlantic oceans. Maritime polar air masses affect the West Coast more than the East Coast. Even in summer, these masses of cool, humid air often bring fog, rain, and cool temperatures to the West Coast.

Figure 1 This beach is on the southern Oregon coast. ***Applying Concepts*** *How does maritime polar air affect the weather at this location?*

EXPLORING North American Air Masses

Air masses can be warm or cold, and humid or dry. As an air mass moves into an area, it changes the weather there.

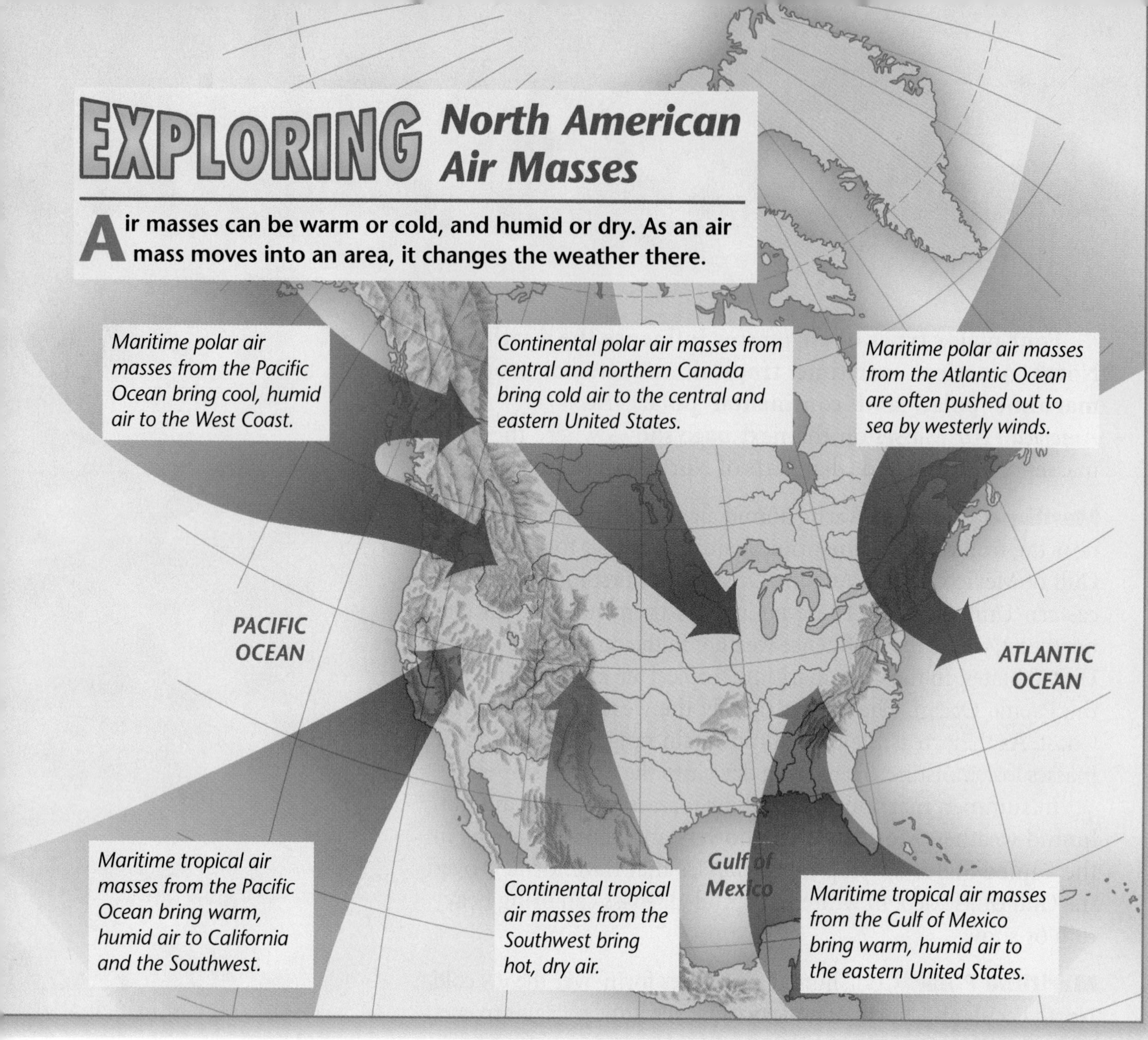

Maritime polar air masses from the Pacific Ocean bring cool, humid air to the West Coast.
Continental polar air masses from central and northern Canada bring cold air to the central and eastern United States.
Maritime polar air masses from the Atlantic Ocean are often pushed out to sea by westerly winds.
PACIFIC OCEAN
ATLANTIC OCEAN
Gulf of Mexico
Maritime tropical air masses from the Pacific Ocean bring warm, humid air to California and the Southwest.
Continental tropical air masses from the Southwest bring hot, dry air.
Maritime tropical air masses from the Gulf of Mexico bring warm, humid air to the eastern United States.

Continental Tropical Hot, dry air masses form only in summer over dry areas of the Southwest and northern Mexico. Continental tropical air masses cover a smaller area than other air masses. They occasionally move northeast, bringing hot, dry weather to the southern Great Plains.

Continental Polar Large continental polar air masses form over central and northern Canada and Alaska. As you would expect, continental polar air masses bring cool or cold air. In winter, continental polar air masses bring clear, cold, dry air to much of North America. Air masses that form near the Arctic Circle can bring bitterly cold weather with very low humidity. In summer, storms may occur when continental polar air masses move south and meet maritime tropical air masses moving north.

☑ *Checkpoint* *Where do continental polar air masses come from?*

How Air Masses Move

Recall that the prevailing westerlies are the major wind belts in the continental United States. The prevailing westerlies generally push air masses from west to east. For example, maritime polar air masses from the Pacific Ocean are blown onto the West Coast, bringing heavy rain or snow. Continental polar air masses from central Canada enter the United States between the Rocky Mountains and the Great Lakes. These cold, dry air masses are then blown east, where they affect the weather of the central and eastern United States.

Fronts

As huge masses of air move across the land and the oceans, they bump into each other. But the air masses do not easily mix. Why don't they? Think about a bottle of oil-and-vinegar salad dressing. The less dense oil floats on top of the more dense vinegar.

Something similar happens when two air masses with different temperatures and densities collide. The area where the air masses meet and do not mix becomes a **front.** The term *front,* which is borrowed from military language, means a battle area where opposing armies meet to fight. When air masses meet at a front, the collision often causes storms and changeable weather. A front may be 15 to 200 kilometers wide and extend as much as 10 kilometers up into the troposphere.

There are four types of fronts: cold fronts, warm fronts, stationary fronts, and occluded fronts. The kind of front that develops depends on the characteristics of the air masses and how they are moving. How does each type of front affect your local weather?

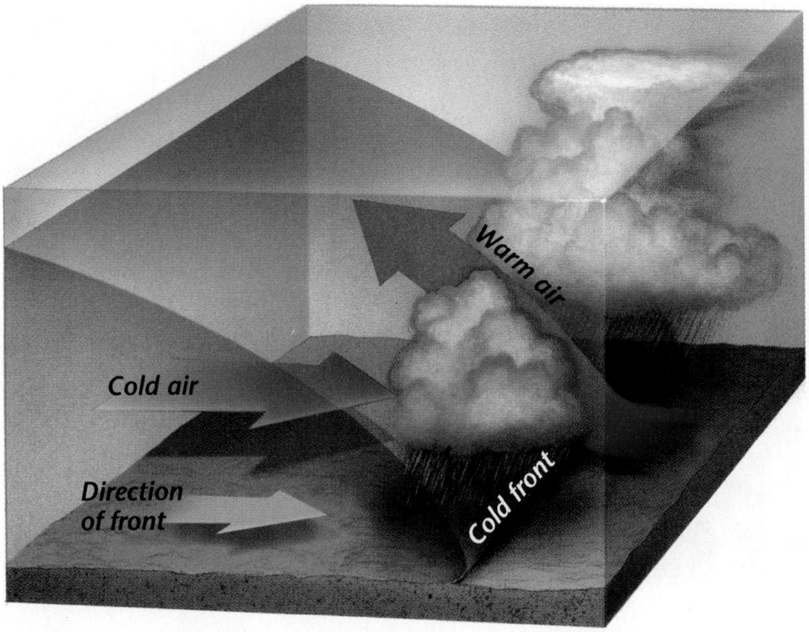
Warm air
Cold air
Direction of front
Cold front

Figure 2 A cold front forms when cold air moves underneath warm air, forcing the warm air to rise.

Cold Fronts As you know, cold air is dense and tends to sink. Warm air is less dense and tends to rise. When a rapidly moving cold air mass runs into a slowly moving warm air mass, the denser cold air slides under the lighter warm air. The warm air is pushed upward, as shown in Figure 2. The front that forms is called a cold front.

As the warm air rises, it cools. Remember that warm air can hold more water vapor than cool air. The rising air soon reaches the dew point, the temperature at which the water vapor in the air condenses into ice crystals or droplets of liquid water. Clouds form. If there is a lot of water vapor in the warm air, heavy rain or snow may fall. What will happen if the warm air mass contains only a little water vapor? In this case, the cold front may be accompanied by only cloudy skies.

Cold fronts move quickly, so they can cause abrupt weather changes, including violent thunderstorms. After a cold front passes through an area, cool, dry air moves in, often bringing clear skies and cooler temperatures.

Warm Fronts Clouds, storms, and rain also accompany warm fronts. At a warm front, a moving warm air mass collides with a slowly moving cold air mass. Because cold air is more dense than warm air, the warm air moves over the cold air, as shown in Figure 3. If the warm air is humid, showers and light rain fall along the front where the warm and cold air meet. If the warm air is dry, scattered clouds form. Because warm fronts move more slowly than cold fronts, the weather may be rainy or foggy for several days. After a warm front passes through an area, the weather is likely to be warm and humid. In winter, warm fronts bring snow.

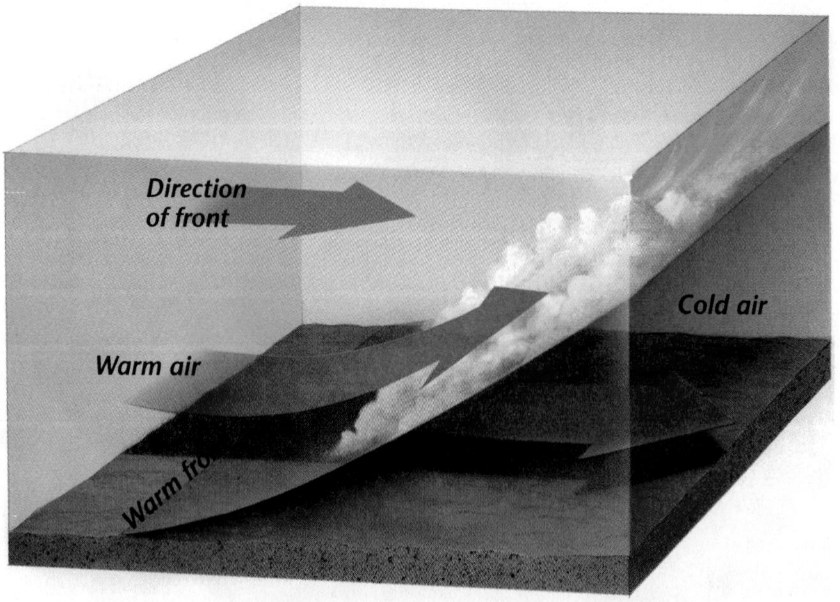
Direction of front
Cold air
Warm air

Figure 3 A warm front forms when warm air moves over cold air. *Interpreting Diagrams* *What kind of weather forms at a warm front?*

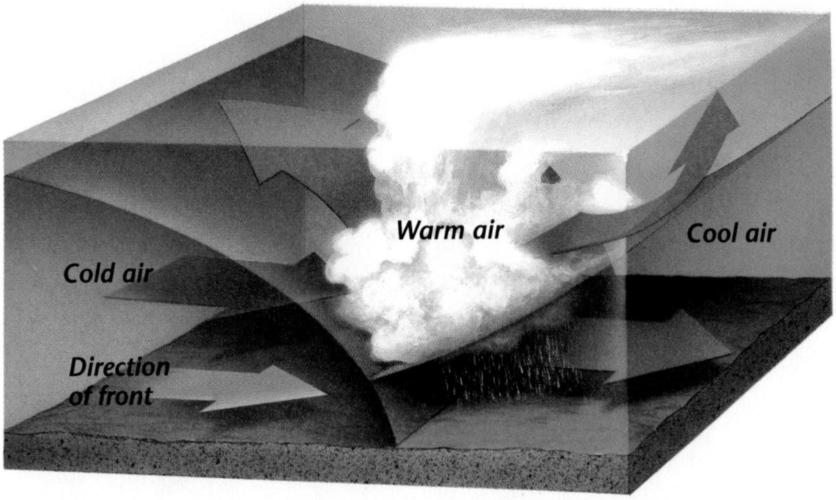
Warm air
Cool air
Cold air
Direction of front

Figure 4 When a cold air mass and a cool air mass come together, the warm air caught between them is forced upward. The result is an occluded front.

Stationary Fronts Sometimes cold and warm air masses meet, but neither one has enough force to move the other. The two air masses face each other in a "standoff." In this case, the front is called a stationary front. Where the warm and cool air meet, water vapor in the warm air condenses into rain, snow, fog, or clouds. If a stationary front remains stalled over an area, it may bring many days of clouds and precipitation.

Occluded Fronts The most complex weather situation occurs at an occluded front, shown in Figure 4. At an occluded front, a warm air mass is caught between two cooler air masses. The denser cool air masses move underneath the less dense warm air mass and push it upward. The two cooler air masses meet in the middle and may mix. The temperature near the ground becomes cooler. The warm air mass is cut off, or **occluded,** from the ground. As the warm air cools and its water vapor condenses, the weather may turn cloudy and rainy or snowy.

☑ *Checkpoint* ***What type of front forms when two air masses meet and neither one can move?***

Cyclones and Anticyclones

If you look at a weather map, you will see areas marked with an L. The L is short for "low," and indicates an area of relatively low air pressure. A swirling center of low air pressure is called a **cyclone,** from a Greek word meaning "wheel."

As warm air at the center of a cyclone rises, the air pressure decreases. Cooler air blows toward this low-pressure area from nearby areas where the air pressure is higher. Winds spiral inward toward the center of the system. Recall that in the Northern Hemisphere the Coriolis effect deflects winds to the right.

Sharpen your Skills

Classifying

ACTIVITY

At home, watch the weather forecast on television. Make a note of each time the weather reporter mentions a front. Classify the fronts mentioned or shown as cold, warm, stationary, or occluded. Also, note what type of weather is predicted to occur when the front arrives. Is each type of front always associated with the same type of weather?

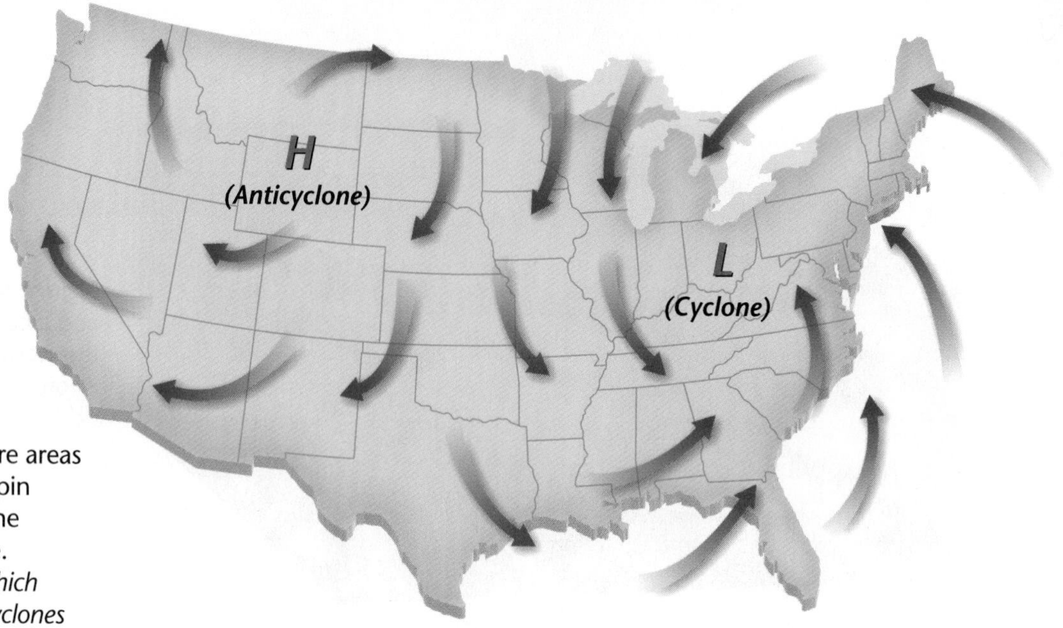
H
(Anticyclone)
L
(Cyclone)

Figure 5 Cyclones are areas of low pressure that spin counterclockwise in the Northern Hemisphere. *Interpreting Maps Which way do winds in anticyclones spin?*

Because of this, winds in a cyclone spin counterclockwise in the Northern Hemisphere, as shown in Figure 5.

Cyclones play a large part in the weather of the United States. As air rises in a cyclone, the air cools, forming clouds and precipitation. **Cyclones and decreasing air pressure are associated with storms and precipitation.**

As its name suggests, an anticyclone is the opposite of a cyclone in most ways. **Anticyclones** are high-pressure centers of dry air. Anticyclones are also called "highs"—H on a weather map. Winds spiral outward from the center of an anticyclone, moving toward areas of lower pressure. Because of the Coriolis effect, winds in an anticyclone spin clockwise in the Northern Hemisphere. Because air moves out from the center of the anticyclone, cool air moves downward from higher in the troposphere. As the cool air falls, it warms up, so its relative humidity drops. The descending air in an anticyclone causes dry, clear weather.

Section 1 Review

1. What two main characteristics are used to classify air masses?
2. What is a front? Name and describe four types of fronts.
3. What is a cyclone? What type of weather does it bring?
4. Why do maritime polar air masses have more effect on the West Coast than the East Coast?
5. **Thinking Critically Classifying** Classify the four major types of air masses according to whether they are dry or humid.

Check Your Progress

CHAPTER PROJECT

Collect newspaper weather maps for about a week, and arrange them in order. Look carefully at how symbols on the map have moved from one day to the next. What patterns do you see from day to day in different weather factors? How does the weather in your community differ from the weather in the two other locations you selected?

2 Storms

DISCOVER — ACTIVITY

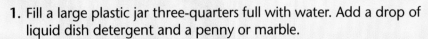

Can You Make a Tornado?

1. Fill a large plastic jar three-quarters full with water. Add a drop of liquid dish detergent and a penny or marble.
2. Put the lid on the jar tightly. Now move the jar in a circle until the water inside begins to spin.

Think It Over

Observing What happens to the water in the jar? Describe the pattern that forms. How is it like a tornado? Unlike a tornado?

GUIDE FOR READING

- **What are the main kinds of storms? How do they form?**
- **What measures can you take to ensure safety in a storm?**

Reading Tip **As you read, create a table comparing thunderstorms, tornadoes, hurricanes, and snowstorms. Include temperature, precipitation, and safety rules.**

Early in 1998, a series of powerful tornadoes roared through central Florida. With winds as high as 210 miles per hour, the tornadoes dropped cars into living rooms, crumpled trailers, and destroyed businesses and school buildings. They were the deadliest tornadoes ever to hit Florida. These tornadoes were not the only violent weather that year. In California the problem was rain. Record rainfalls brought devastating floods and mudslides.

What was causing these disasters? Meteorologists had an answer: El Niño. El Niño is a weather pattern related to the temperature of the water in the tropical Pacific Ocean. When temperatures there rise, they set off a series of events that can influence weather half a world away.

Have you ever experienced a tornado, hurricane, or other severe storm? When rain pours down, thunder crashes, or snowdrifts pile up, it may be hard to think about the actions of air pressure and air masses. Yet these are the causes of severe storms as well as the weather you experience every day.

A **storm** is a violent disturbance in the atmosphere. Storms involve sudden changes in air pressure, which in turn cause rapid air movements. Conditions that bring one kind of storm often cause other kinds of storms in the same area. For example, the conditions that cause thunderstorms can also cause tornadoes.

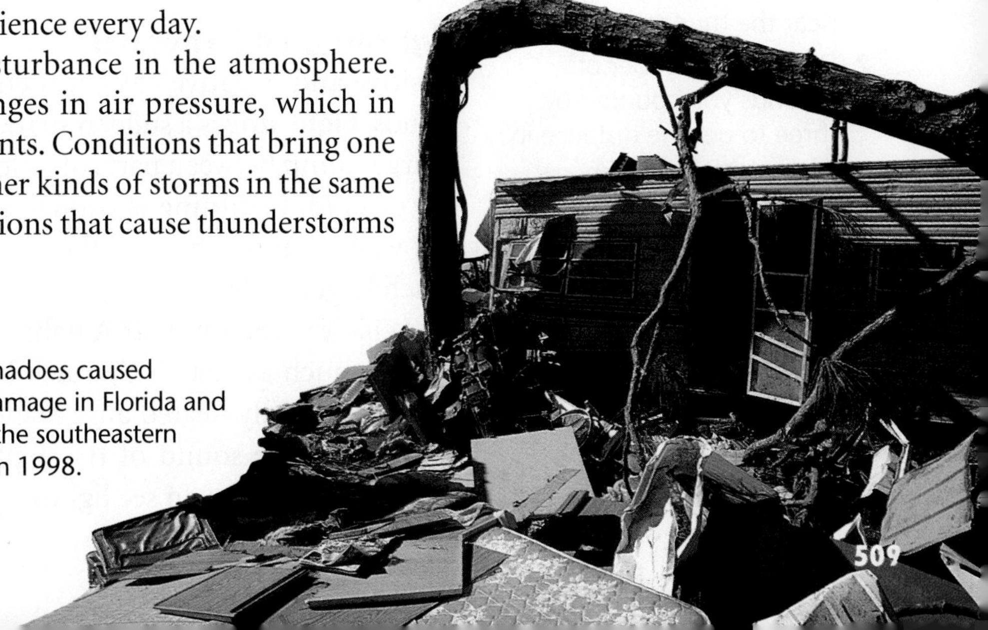

Figure 6 Tornadoes caused tremendous damage in Florida and other parts of the southeastern United States in 1998.

Figure 7 The anvil shape of this cloud is typical of cumulonimbus clouds that produce thunderstorms. *Applying Concepts Why do cumulonimbus clouds often form along cold fronts?*

Thunderstorms

Do you find thunderstorms frightening? Exciting? A little of both? As you watch the brilliant flashes of lightning and listen to long rolls of thunder, you have probably wondered what caused them.

How Thunderstorms Form Thunderstorms are heavy rainstorms accompanied by thunder and lightning. **Thunderstorms form within large cumulonimbus clouds, or thunderheads.** Most cumulonimbus clouds and thunderstorms form when warm air is forced upward at a cold front. Cumulonimbus clouds also form on hot, humid afternoons in the spring and summer. In both cases, the warm, humid air rises rapidly. As the air rises, it cools, forming dense thunderheads. Heavy rain falls, sometimes along with hail.

Thunderstorms produce strong upward and downward winds—updrafts and downdrafts—inside clouds. When a downdraft strikes the ground, the air spreads out in all directions, producing bursts of wind called wind shear. Wind shear has caused a number of airplane accidents during takeoff or landing.

Lightning and Thunder During a thunderstorm, areas of positive and negative electrical charges build up in the storm clouds. **Lightning** is a sudden spark, or energy discharge, as these charges jump between parts of a cloud or between the cloud and the ground. Lightning is similar to the shocks you sometimes feel when you touch a metal object on a very dry day, but on a much larger scale.

What causes thunder? A lightning bolt can heat the air near it to as much as 30,000°C, much hotter than the surface of the sun. The rapidly heated air expands suddenly and explosively. Thunder is the sound of the explosion. Because light travels faster than sound, you see lightning before you hear thunder.

TRY THIS

Lightning Distances

ACTIVITY

Because light travels faster than sound, you see a lightning flash before you hear the clap of thunder. Here's how to calculate your distance from a thunderstorm.

CAUTION: *Do this activity inside a building only.*

1. Count the number of seconds between the moment when you see the lightning and when you hear the thunder.
2. Divide the number of seconds you counted by three to get the distance in kilometers. Example:

$$\frac{15 \text{ s}}{3 \text{ s/km}} = 5 \text{ km}$$

Calculating Wait for another flash of lightning and calculate the distance again. How can you tell whether a thunderstorm is moving toward you or away from you?

Thunderstorm Safety *Integrating Health* When lightning strikes the ground, the hot, expanding air can shatter tree trunks or start forest fires. When lightning strikes people or animals, it acts like a powerful electric shock. Being struck by lightning can cause unconsciousness, serious burns, or even heart failure.

What should you do to remain safe if you are caught outside during a thunderstorm? **During thunderstorms, avoid touching metal objects because they can conduct electricity from lightning into your body.** Lightning usually strikes the tallest nearby object, such as a tree, house, or flagpole. To protect buildings from lightning, people install metal lightning rods at the highest point on a roof. Lightning rods intercept a lightning stroke and conduct the electricity through cables safely into the ground.

In open spaces, such as a golf course, people can be in danger because they are the tallest objects in the area. It is equally dangerous to seek shelter under a tree, because lightning may strike the tree and you at the same time. Instead, find a low area away from trees, fences, and poles. Crouch with your head down and your hands on your knees. If you are swimming or in a boat, get to shore and find shelter away from the water.

If you are inside a house during a thunderstorm, avoid touching telephones, electrical appliances, or plumbing fixtures, all of which can conduct electricity into the house. It is usually safe to stay in a car with a hard top during a thunderstorm because the electricity will move along the metal skin of the car and jump to the ground. However, do not touch any metal inside the car.

☑ *Checkpoint* *Why is lightning dangerous?*

Figure 8 Lightning occurs when electricity jumps within clouds or between a cloud and the ground.

Tornadoes

A tornado is one of the most frightening and destructive types of storms. A **tornado** is a rapidly whirling, funnel-shaped cloud that reaches down from a storm cloud to touch Earth's surface. If a tornado occurs over a lake or ocean, it is known as a waterspout. Tornadoes are usually brief, but can be deadly. They may touch the ground for 15 minutes or less and be only a few hundred meters across, but wind speeds may approach 480 kilometers per hour.

How Tornadoes Form **Tornadoes develop in low, heavy cumulonimbus clouds—the same clouds that bring thunderstorms.** Tornadoes are most likely to occur when thunderstorms are likely—in spring and early summer, often late in the afternoon when the ground is warm. The Great Plains often have the kind of weather pattern that is likely to create tornadoes: a warm, humid air mass moves north from the Gulf of Mexico into the lower Great Plains. A cold, dry air mass moves south from Canada. When the air masses meet, the cold air moves under the warm air, which rises. A squall line of thunderstorms is likely to form, with storms traveling from southwest to northeast. A single squall line can cause 10 or more tornadoes.

Tornadoes occur more often in the United States than in any other country. About 800 tornadoes occur in the United States

SCIENCE & History

Weather That Changed History

Unanticipated storms have caused incredible damage, killed numbers of people, and even changed the course of history.

1281 Japan

In an attempt to conquer Japan, Kublai Khan, the Mongol emperor of China, sent a fleet of ships carrying a huge army. A hurricane from the Pacific brought high winds and towering waves that sank the ships. The Japanese named the storm *kamikaze*, meaning "divine wind."

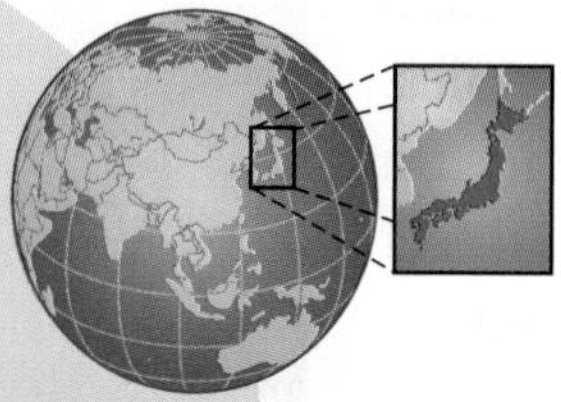

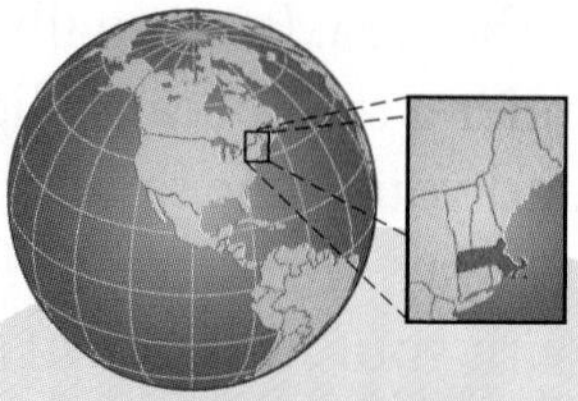

1620 Massachusetts

English Pilgrims set sail for the Americas in the *Mayflower.* They had planned to land near the mouth of the Hudson River, but turned back north because of rough seas and storms. When the Pilgrims landed farther north, they decided to stay and so established Plymouth Colony.

1300 1400 1500 1600

1588 England

King Philip II of Spain sent the Spanish Armada, a fleet of 130 ships, to invade England. Strong winds in the English Channel trapped the Armada near shore. Some Spanish ships escaped, but storms wrecked most of them.

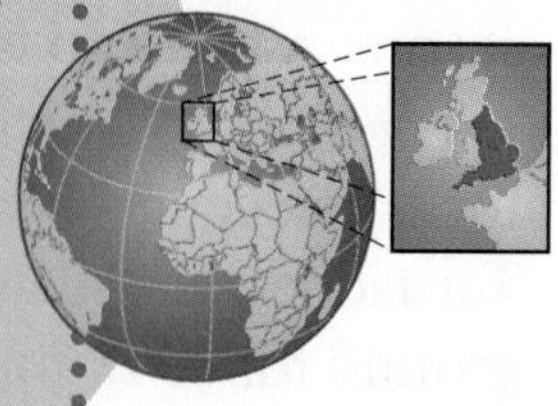

every year. Weather patterns on the Great Plains result in a "tornado alley," shown in Figure 9, that runs from north-central Texas across central Oklahoma, Kansas, and Nebraska. However, tornadoes can and do occur in nearly every part of the United States.

☑ *Checkpoint* *Where do tornadoes form?*

Tornado Safety A tornado can level houses on one street, but leave neighboring houses standing. Tornado damage comes from both strong winds and flying debris. The low pressure inside the tornado sucks up dust and other objects into the funnel. Tornadoes can move large objects—sheds, trailers, cars—and scatter debris many miles away. One tornado tore off a motel sign in Broken Bow, Oklahoma, and dropped it 30 miles away in Arkansas!

INTEGRATING HEALTH

In Your Journal

Some of these events happened before forecasters had the equipment to predict weather scientifically. Choose one of the events in the time line. Write a paragraph describing how history might have been different if the people involved had had accurate weather predictions.

1870 Great Lakes

Learning that more than 1,900 boats had sunk in storms on the Great Lakes in 1869, Congress decided to set up a national weather service, the Army Signal Corps. In 1891 the job of issuing weather warnings and forecasts went to a new agency, the U.S. Weather Bureau.

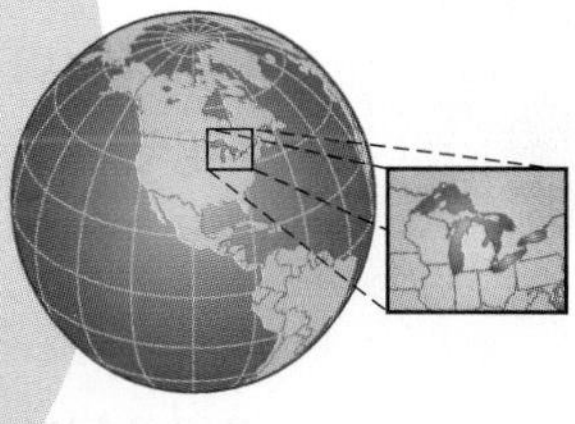

1700 1800 1900

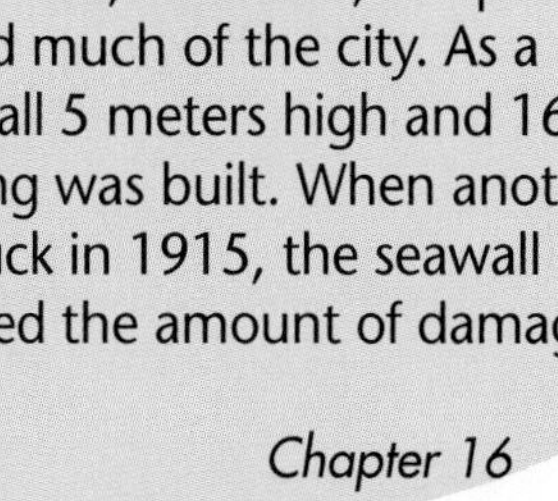

1837 North Carolina

The steamship *Home* sank during a hurricane off Ocracoke, North Carolina. In one of the worst storm-caused disasters at sea, 90 people died. In response, the U.S. Congress passed a law requiring seagoing ships to carry a life preserver for every passenger.

1915 Texas

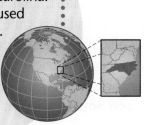

When a hurricane struck the port city of Galveston in 1900, it killed 6,000 people and destroyed much of the city. As a result, a seawall 5 meters high and 16 kilometers long was built. When another hurricane struck in 1915, the seawall greatly reduced the amount of damage.

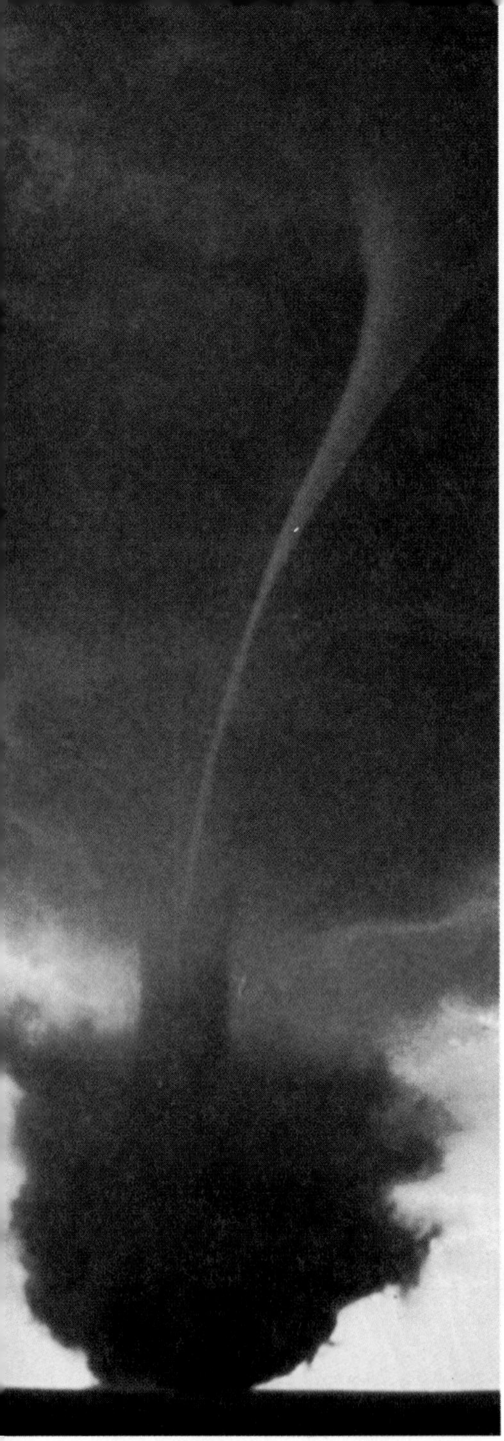

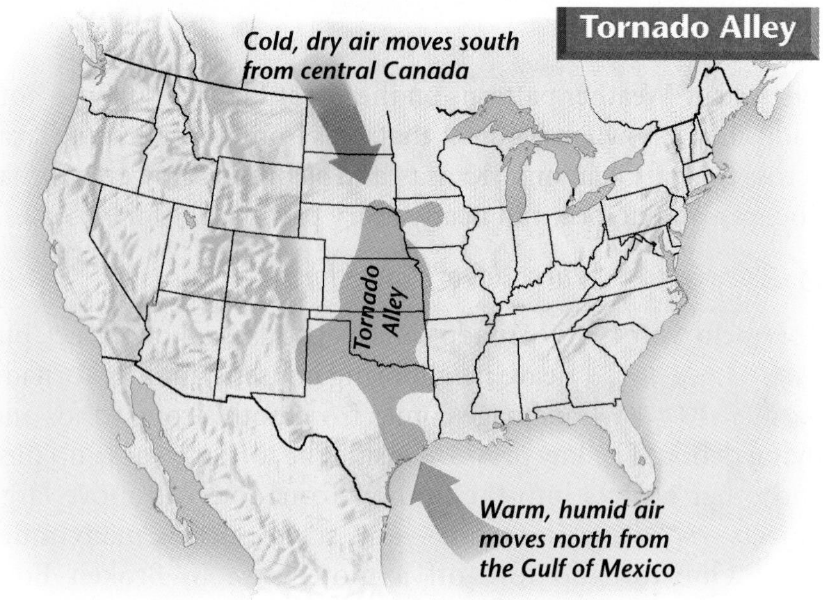
Tornado Alley
Cold, dry air moves south from central Canada
Tornado Alley
Warm, humid air moves north from the Gulf of Mexico

Figure 9 A tornado can cause a lot of damage in a short period of time. The map shows where tornadoes are most likely to occur in the United States.
Interpreting Maps Which states are partially located in "tornado alley"?

What should you do if a tornado is predicted in your area? A "tornado watch" is an announcement that tornadoes are possible in your area. Watch for approaching thunderstorms. A "tornado warning" is an announcement that a tornado has been seen in the sky or on weather radar. If you hear a tornado warning, move to a safe area as soon as you can. Do not wait until you actually see the tornado.

The safest place to be during a tornado is in the basement of a well-built building. If the building you are in does not have a basement, move to the middle of the ground floor. Stay away from windows and doors that could break and fly through the air. Lie on the floor under a sturdy piece of furniture, such as a large table. If you are outdoors or in a car or mobile home, move to a building or lie flat in a ditch.

☑ *Checkpoint* ***What is the difference between a tornado watch and a tornado warning?***

Hurricanes

Between June and November, people who live in the eastern United States hear weather reports much like this: "A hurricane warning has been issued for the Atlantic coast from Florida to North Carolina. Hurricane Michael has winds of over 160 kilometers per hour and is moving north at about 65 kilometers per hour." A **hurricane** is a tropical storm that has winds of 119 kilometers per hour or higher. A typical hurricane is about 600 kilometers across.

Hurricanes also form in the Pacific and Indian oceans. In the western Pacific Ocean, hurricanes are called typhoons. Although hurricanes may be destructive, they bring much-needed rainfall to South Asia and Southeast Asia.

How Hurricanes Form A typical hurricane that strikes the United States forms in the Atlantic Ocean north of the equator in August, September, or October. **A hurricane begins over warm water as a low-pressure area, or tropical disturbance.** If the tropical disturbance grows in size and strength, it becomes a tropical storm, which may then become a hurricane.

A hurricane gets its energy from the warm, humid air at the ocean's surface. As this air rises and forms clouds, more air is drawn into the system. As with other storm systems, winds spiral inward toward the areas of low pressure. Inside the storm are bands of very high winds and heavy rains. The lowest air pressure and warmest temperatures are at the center of the hurricane. The lower the air pressure at the center of a storm, the faster the winds blow toward the center. Hurricane winds may be as strong as 320 kilometers per hour.

The Eye of the Hurricane The center of a hurricane is a ring of clouds surrounding a quiet "eye," as shown in Figure 10. If you were in the path of a hurricane, you would notice that the wind gets stronger as the eye approaches. When the eye arrives, the weather changes suddenly. The winds grow calm and the sky may clear. After the eye passes, the storm resumes, but the wind blows from the opposite direction.

How Hurricanes Move Hurricanes last longer than other storms, usually a week or more. Hurricanes that form in the Atlantic Ocean are steered by easterly trade winds toward the Caribbean islands and the southeastern United States. After a hurricane passes over land, it no longer has warm, moist air to draw energy from. The hurricane gradually slows down and loses strength, although heavy rainfall may continue for a number of days.

Figure 10 In a hurricane, air moves rapidly around a low-pressure area called the eye. *Observing Where is the eye of the hurricane in the photograph?*

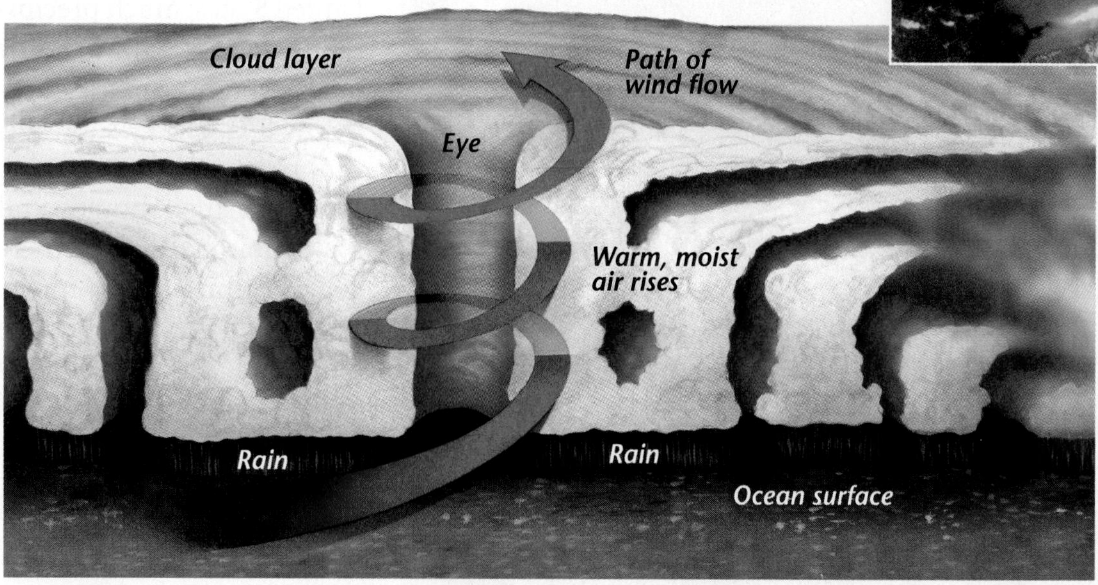
Cloud layer
Path of wind flow
Eye
Warm, moist air rises
Rain
Rain
Ocean surface

Visual Arts CONNECTION

Weather and storms are favorite subjects for artists. "Snow Storm" is an oil painting by English artist J.M.W. Turner (1775–1851). To convey a mood or feeling, artists choose certain colors and textures. How does Turner's choice of colors enhance the mood of the painting? What texture do you see in the sea and sky? How does the texture support the feeling of the painting?

In Your Journal

Write a paragraph or two about the mood of this painting. Describe how you would feel being out in the wind and waves. Before you begin writing, jot down words that describe what you would see, hear, touch, taste, and smell. Exchange your descriptive writing with a partner to get feedback.

Hurricane Damage When a hurricane comes ashore, it brings high waves and severe flooding as well as wind damage. Hurricanes uproot trees, smash buildings, and destroy power lines. Heavy rains flood roads.

One of the most dangerous features of a hurricane is the storm surge. The low pressure and high winds of the hurricane over the ocean raise the level of the water up to six meters above normal sea level. The result is a **storm surge,** a "dome" of water that sweeps across the coast where the hurricane lands. As the hurricane comes onshore, the water comes with it. Storm surges can cause great damage, washing away beaches and destroying buildings along the coast.

Hurricane Safety *INTEGRATING HEALTH* Until the 1950s, a fast-moving hurricane could strike with little warning. Since then, advances in communications and satellite tracking have made hurricanes less deadly. People now receive information well in advance of an approaching hurricane.

A "hurricane watch" is an announcement that hurricane conditions are *possible* in your area within the next 36 hours. People should be prepared to **evacuate** (ee VAK yoo ayt), or move away temporarily.

A "hurricane warning" means that hurricane conditions are *expected* within 24 hours. **If you hear a hurricane warning and are told to evacuate, leave the area immediately.** If you must stay in a house, move to the interior of the building, away from windows.

☑ *Checkpoint* *What is a storm surge?*

Winter Storms

In the winter in the northern United States, much precipitation falls as snow. **Snow falls when humid air cools below 0°C.** Heavy snowfalls can block roads, trapping people in their homes and making it hard for emergency vehicles to move. Extreme cold can damage crops and cause water pipes to freeze and burst.

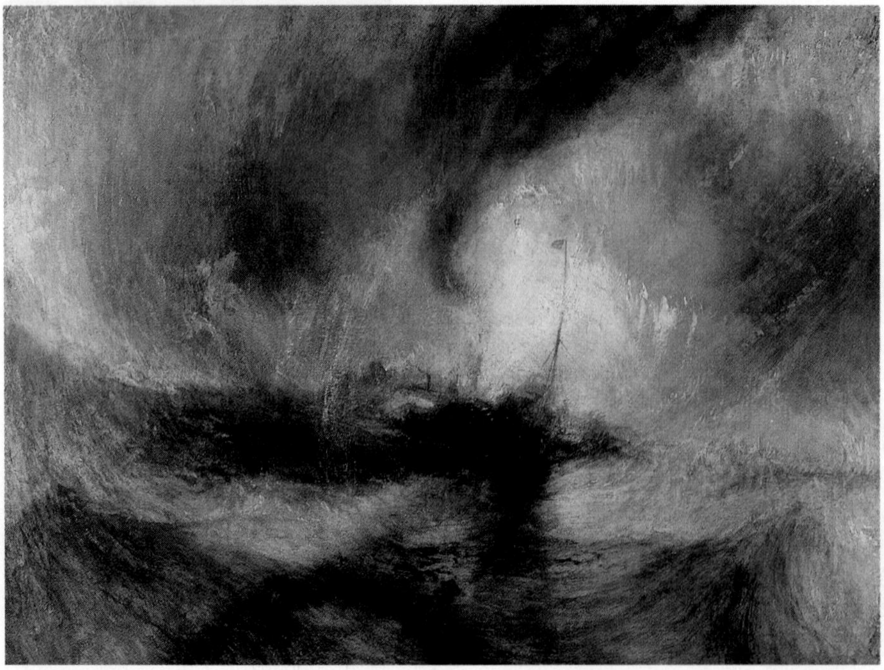

Figure 11 The British artist J.M.W. Turner painted "Snow Storm" in 1842.

Lake-effect Snow Two of the snowiest cities in the United States are Buffalo and Rochester in upstate New York. On average, nearly three meters of snow falls on each of these cities every winter. Why do Buffalo and Rochester get so much snow?

Study Figure 12. Notice that Buffalo is located to the east of Lake Erie, and Rochester is located to the south of Lake Ontario. In the fall and winter, the land near these lakes cools much more rapidly than the water in the lakes. Although the water in these lakes is cold, it is still much warmer than the surrounding land and air. When a cold, dry air mass moves from central Canada southeast across one of the Great Lakes, it picks up water vapor and heat from the lake. As soon as the air mass reaches the other side of the lake, the air rises and cools again. The water vapor condenses and falls as snow, usually within 40 kilometers of the lake.

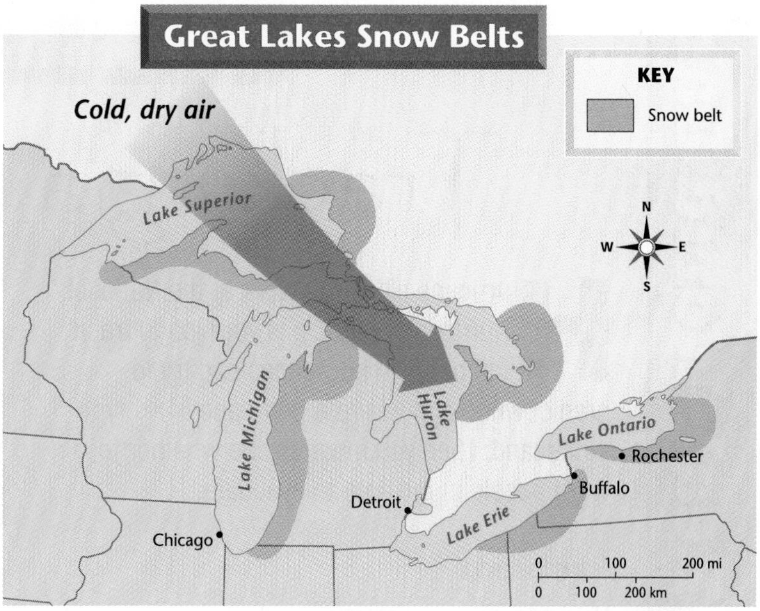

Great Lakes Snow Belts
KEY
Snow belt
Cold, dry air
Lake Superior
Lake Michigan
Lake Huron
Lake Ontario
Lake Erie
Rochester
Buffalo
Detroit
Chicago
N
S
E
W
0 100 200 mi
0 100 200 km

Figure 12 As cold dry air moves across the warmer water, it picks up water vapor. When the air reaches land and cools, lake-effect snow falls. *Interpreting Maps Which two cities receive large amounts of snow?*

Snowstorm Safety Imagine being out in a snowstorm when

INTEGRATING HEALTH

the wind suddenly picks up. High winds can blow falling snow sideways or pick up snow from the ground and suspend it in the air. This situation can be extremely dangerous because the blowing snow makes it easy to get lost. Also, strong winds cool a person's body rapidly. **If you are caught in a snowstorm, try to find shelter from the wind.** Cover exposed parts of your body and try to stay dry. If you are in a car, the driver should keep the engine running only if the exhaust pipe is clear of snow.

Section 2 Review

1. What weather conditions are most likely to cause thunderstorms and tornadoes?
2. What is the most common path for the hurricanes that strike the United States?
3. What safety precautions should you take if a tornado is predicted in your area? If a hurricane is predicted?
4. **Thinking Critically Applying Concepts** In the winter, cool, humid air from the Pacific Ocean blows across the cold land of southern Alaska. What kind of storm do you think this causes?

Science at Home

Interview a family member or other adult about a dramatic storm that he or she has experienced. Before the interview, make a list of questions you would like to ask. For example, how old was the person when the storm occurred? When and where did the storm occur? Write up your interview in a question-and-answer format, beginning with a short introduction.

Real-World Lab

Careers in Science

Tracking a Hurricane

Hurricane alert! You work at the National Hurricane Center. It is your job to track the paths of hurricanes and try to predict when and where a hurricane is likely to strike land. Then you must decide whether to warn people in the area to evacuate.

Problem

How can you predict when and where a hurricane will come ashore?

Skills Focus

interpreting data, predicting

Materials

ruler
red, blue, green, and brown pencils
tracing paper

Procedure

1. Look at the plotted path of the hurricane on the map. Each dot represents the location of the eye of the hurricane at six-hour intervals. The last dot shows where the hurricane was located at noon on August 30.
2. Predict the path you think the hurricane will take. Place tracing paper over the map below. Using a red pencil, place an X on your tracing paper where you think the hurricane will first reach land. Next to your X, write the date and time you think the hurricane will come ashore.

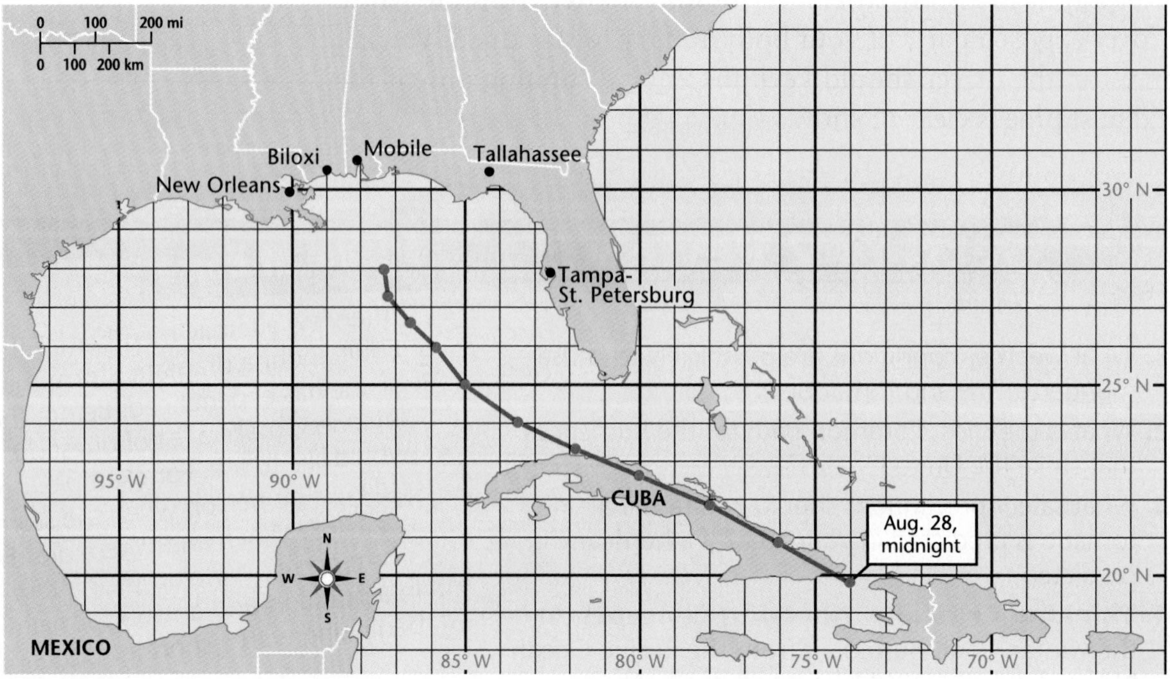

0 100 200 mi
0 100 200 km
Biloxi
Mobile
Tallahassee
New Orleans
Tampa-St. Petersburg
30° N
25° N
20° N
95° W
90° W
85° W
80° W
75° W
70° W
CUBA
Aug. 28, midnight
MEXICO
N
S
E
W

3. Hurricane warnings are issued for an area that is likely to experience a hurricane within 24 hours. On your tracing paper, shade in red the area for which you would issue a hurricane warning.
4. Using the following data table, plot the next five positions for the storm using a blue pencil. Use your ruler to connect the dots to show the hurricane's path.

Date and Time	Latitude	Longitude
August 30, 6:00 P.M.	28.3° N	86.8° W
August 31, midnight	28.4° N	86.0° W
August 31, 6:00 A.M.	28.6° N	85.3° W
August 31, noon	28.8° N	84.4° W
August 31, 6:00 P.M.	28.8° N	84.0° W

5. Based on the new data, decide if you need to change your prediction of where and when the hurricane will come ashore. Mark your new predictions in blue pencil on your tracing paper.
6. During September 1, you obtain four more positions. (Plot these points only after you have completed Step 5.) Based on these new data, mark in green pencil when and where you now think the hurricane will come ashore.

Date and Time	Latitude	Longitude
September 1, midnight	28.8° N	83.8° W
September 1, 6:00 A.M.	28.6° N	83.9° W
September 1, noon	28.6° N	84.2° W
September 1, 6:00 P.M.	28.9° N	84.8° W

7. The next day, September 2, you plot four more positions using a brown pencil. (Plot these points only after you have completed Step 6.)

Date and Time	Latitude	Longitude
September 2, midnight	29.4° N	85.9° W
September 2, 6:00 A.M.	29.7° N	87.3° W
September 2, noon	30.2° N	88.8° W
September 2, 6:00 P.M.	31.0° N	90.4° W

Analyze and Conclude

1. Describe in detail the complete path of the hurricane you tracked. Include where it came ashore and identify any cities that were in the vicinity.
2. How did your predictions in Steps 2, 5, and 6 compare to what actually happened?
3. What was unusual about your hurricane's path?
4. How do you think hurricanes with a path like this one affect the issuing of hurricane warnings?
5. Why do you have to be so careful when issuing warnings? What problems might be caused if you issued an unnecessary hurricane warning? What might happen if a hurricane warning were issued too late?
6. **Think About It** In this activity you only had data for the hurricane's position. If you were tracking a hurricane and issuing warnings, what other types of information would help you make decisions about the hurricane's path?

More to Explore

With your teacher's help, search the Internet for more hurricane tracking data. Map the data and try to predict where the hurricane will come ashore.

Hurricane Alert: To Stay or Not To Stay?

When a hurricane sweeps in from the ocean, the National Hurricane Center tracks the storm's course. Radio stations broadcast warnings. Sirens blow, and people in the storm path take steps to protect their homes and families.

State and local governments may try to keep people safe by closing state offices, setting up emergency shelters, and alerting the National Guard. As the danger increases, a state's governor can order the evacuation of people from dangerous areas. These actions are meant to protect public safety.

But not everyone wants to evacuate. Some people believe they have the right to stay. And officials cannot make people obey an evacuation order. How much can—or should—the government do to keep people safe?

The Issues

Why Play It Safe? Hurricanes can be extremely dangerous. High winds blow off roofs and shatter windows. Flash floods and storm surges can wash away houses. Even after the storm blows away, officials may need to keep people from returning home because of flooded sewers or broken power lines and gas mains.

In recent years, earlier and more accurate forecasts have saved lives. People now have time to prepare and to get out of the hurricane's path. Emergency officials urge people—especially the elderly, sick, or disabled—to leave early while the weather is still good. Most casualties happen when people are taken by surprise or ignore warnings. Those who decide to stay may later have to be rescued by boat or helicopter. These rescues add to the expense of the storm and may put the lives of rescuers in danger.

Why Ride Out the Storm? People have different reasons for not wanting to evacuate. Some want to protect their homes or businesses. Others don't want to leave pets or farm animals or go to public shelters. Store owners may stay open to sell disaster supplies. In addition, warnings may exaggerate the potential danger, urging people to leave when they might actually be safe. Since leaving can be expensive and disruptive, residents have to carefully evaluate the risks.

Is It a Matter of Rights? Should a government have the power to make people evacuate? Some citizens argue that the government should not tell them what to do as long as they are not harming others. They believe that individuals should have the right to decide for themselves. What do you think?

You Decide

1. Identify the Problem

In your own words, explain the controversy around hurricane evacuations.

2. Analyze the Options

Review and list the pros and cons of forcing people to evacuate. What people benefit? Who might be harmed? What more, if anything, should government officials do? What more could citizens do?

3. Find a Solution

Imagine that the radio has broadcast a hurricane warning. Write a dialogue in which you and members of your family discuss the options and decide whether or not to evacuate.

SECTION 3 Floods

DISCOVER ACTIVITY

What Causes Floods?

1. Fill a cup with water. Hold a funnel above a basin and pour the water very slowly into the funnel.
2. Refill the cup with the same amount of water you used in Step 1. Hold the funnel above the basin and this time pour the water rapidly into the funnel. What happens?

Think It Over

Inferring How is a funnel like a river valley? What do you think would happen if a large amount of water entered a river valley in a short period of time?

GUIDE FOR READING

- **What causes flooding?**
- **How can the dangers of floods be reduced?**

Reading Tip **As you read, draw a flowchart showing what can happen during a flood and how people should respond to it.**

Antelope Canyon in the northern Arizona desert is only a few meters wide in places. On August 12, 1997, a group of 12 hikers entered the dry, narrow canyon. That afternoon a severe thunderstorm dropped several inches of rain on the Kaibeto Plateau, 24 kilometers away. Dry stream channels that drain into Antelope Canyon quickly filled with rainwater. The water rushed into the canyon, creating a wall of water over 3 meters high. Tourists at the top of the canyon watched in horror as the water swept the hikers away. Only one hiker survived.

Are you surprised that floods can occur in a desert? Actually, floods like this are more common in the dry Southwest than in areas with more rain.

Figure 13 From the top, Antelope Canyon looks like a narrow slit in the ground.

1 Heavy rain falls on the plateau.
2 Instead of soaking into the hard soil, the water runs into the canyon.
3 The rainwater is funneled into the narrow canyon and floods it.

Figure 14 Flash floods occur when large amounts of rain are funneled into a narrow valley. This drawing shows what happened in the Antelope Canyon flood.

Flash Floods

Although movies feature the violent winds of tornadoes and hurricanes, floods are the most dangerous weather-related events in the United States. **Floods occur when so much water pours into a stream or river that it overflows its banks and covers the land on either side of the channel.** People who live along certain rivers know that melting snow and spring rains are likely to bring floods.

Unexpected floods are the most dangerous. Floods like the Antelope Canyon flood are called flash floods because the water rises very rapidly—"in a flash"—after it begins to rain heavily. A **flash flood** is a sudden, violent flood that occurs within a few hours, or even minutes, of a storm.

Most flash floods are due to large amounts of rain. For example, a line of thunderstorms may remain over an area, dropping heavy rain for several hours or days. Hurricanes or tropical storms bring downpours that quickly fill stream channels. A flash flood can also be caused by a dam breaking, releasing millions of liters of water all at once. Similarly, if ice that has jammed a river breaks free, the sudden rush of water can cause a flash flood.

☑ *Checkpoint* *Why are flash floods so dangerous?*

Flood Safety Measures

If you've never been in a flood, it's hard to imagine the awesome power of rushing water. What can people do to protect themselves and their homes?

Predicting Floods Advance warnings can help reduce flood damage and loss of life. Weather satellites supply information about snow cover so that scientists can estimate how much water will run into rivers when the snow melts. Radar can track and measure the size of an approaching rainstorm. Scientists check river gauges that measure water levels. With this information, forecasters can predict flood heights at different points along a river. Their goal is to issue warnings early enough to help people prepare and evacuate if necessary.

Sharpen your Skills

Communicating

ACTIVITY

Write a script for a 30-second public service radio announcement in which you tell about the dangers of floods. Include recommended safety steps to follow in case of a flood.

1

The car stalls in the water.

2

Moving water pushes against the car.

3

As the water rises, the car begins to float.

4

Sixty centimeters of water can wash a car away.

Figure 15 These drawings show what can happen to a car in a flood. *Applying Concepts Why is it dangerous to stay in a car in a flood?*

A "flood watch" is an announcement describing the area in which flooding is possible. Stay alert for more news. A "flood warning" is an announcement that floods have already been reported or are about to occur. It's time to take action!

Emergency Safety What should *you* do in case of a flood? When the danger becomes too great or the water rises too high, people are usually evacuated. **The first rule of flood safety: Move to higher ground and stay away from flood waters.** Don't try to cross streams and rivers that look as if they're flooded. Playing in flood waters may look like fun, but it's dangerous. A few centimeters of fast-moving water can sweep you off your feet. Even the storm drain on a city street can draw you in.

If your family is in a car, the driver shouldn't try to drive on a flooded road. Sometimes less than 60 centimeters of fast-moving water can sweep a car away, as shown in Figure 15. Everyone should leave the car and move to higher ground.

Figure 16 In the spring of 1997, the Red River of the North flooded regions of North Dakota and Minnesota. A large part of flooded downtown Grand Forks burned down because fire trucks could not get to the scene of the fire or connect to any fire hydrants.

Other Flood Hazards High water is not the only hazard in a flood. Floods can knock down electrical poles and wires, cutting off power supplies. Flood waters can also saturate soil, causing landslides or mudslides. If roads have been flooded or washed away, emergency vehicles such as fire trucks and ambulances may not be able to get through.

Flood waters can wash into wells and water treatment plants, polluting the water. Therefore, be careful with food and water that flood waters have touched. Boil water before drinking it to be sure it is safe.

Section 3 Review

1. How can precipitation cause flooding?
2. What should you do to stay safe during a flood?
3. What is the difference between a flood watch and a flood warning?
4. Name three tools that supply information used in forecasting floods and providing flood information.
5. **Thinking Critically Predicting** Describe two weather situations in which you would expect floods to occur.

CHAPTER PROJECT

Check Your Progress

Now you are ready to predict tomorrow's weather. Look at today's weather map. Then predict tomorrow's weather both where you live and in the two other locations you selected. (*Project Hint:* Refer to the weather patterns you have been observing.) Decide what symbols you will need to use. Then, on an outline map of the United States, draw symbols to show what you think tomorrow's weather will be. Continue to make predictions every day for at least a week.

SECTION 4 Predicting the Weather

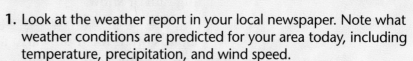

DISCOVER ACTIVITY

What's the Weather?

1. Look at the weather report in your local newspaper. Note what weather conditions are predicted for your area today, including temperature, precipitation, and wind speed.
2. Look out the window or think about what it was like the last time you were outside. Write down the actual weather conditions where you are.

Think It Over

Observing Does the weather report match what you observe? What is the same? What is different?

GUIDE FOR READING

- **How does technology help forecasters predict the weather?**
- **What types of information are shown on weather maps?**

Reading Tip **Before you read, preview Figure 19 and *Exploring Newspaper Weather Maps.* Write a list of any questions you have about weather maps.**

For centuries, people have tried to predict the weather. Every nation's folklore includes weather sayings. Many of these sayings are based on long-term observations. Sailors, pilots, farmers, and others who work outdoors are usually careful observers of clouds, winds, and other signs of coming changes in the weather. Here are two examples:

Evening red and morning gray
Will send the traveler on his way;
Evening gray and morning red
Will bring down rain upon his head.

Red sky in the morning,
sailors take warning;
Red sky at night, sailor's delight.

Why do these two weather sayings agree that a red morning sky means bad weather? Recall that in the United States storms usually move from west to east. Clouds in the west may indicate an advancing low-pressure area, bringing stormy weather. If there are high clouds in the west in the morning, the rising sun in the east turns these clouds red. The reverse is true at sunset. As the sun sets in the west, it turns clouds in the east red. Clouds in the east may indicate that a storm is moving away to the east.

Weather Forecasting

You can make many predictions from your own observations. For example, if a barometer shows that the air pressure is falling, you can expect a change in the weather. Falling air pressure usually indicates an approaching low-pressure area, possibly bringing rain or snow.

You can read weather signs in the clouds, too. Cumulus clouds often form on warm afternoons when warm air rises. If you see these clouds growing larger and taller, you can expect them to become cumulonimbus clouds, which may bring a thunderstorm. If you see thin cirrus clouds high in the sky, a low-pressure area may be approaching.

Even careful weather observers often turn to professional meteorologists for television weather information. You may hear the person who gives the television weather report referred to as a meteorologist. Despite their name, meteorologists don't study meteors. **Meteorologists** (mee tee uh RAWL uh jists) are scientists who study the causes of weather and try to predict it.

Figure 17 These meteorologists are releasing a weather balloon. The box attached to the balloon contains instruments that will record weather data—such as temperature, pressure, and humidity—high in the troposphere.

Meteorologists interpret information from a variety of sources, including local weather observers, instruments carried by balloons, satellites, and weather stations around the world. They use maps, charts, and computers to analyze the data and to prepare weather forecasts. Meteorologists use radar to track areas of rain or snow, so that forecasters can follow the path of a storm system.

Where do television and radio weather reporters get their information? A lot of weather information comes from the National Weather Service. However, weather forecasts for the general public may not have enough detail to be useful to farmers and pilots. There are also private weather-forecasting services, many of which use advanced, high-technology equipment. Private forecasting services are useful to people who need to answer questions like these: "Will the frost hurt the oranges in my orchard?" "Will the airport be fogged in?" "Will the trucks need to spread sand on the roads today?"

☑ *Checkpoint* *Where do meteorologists get weather information?*

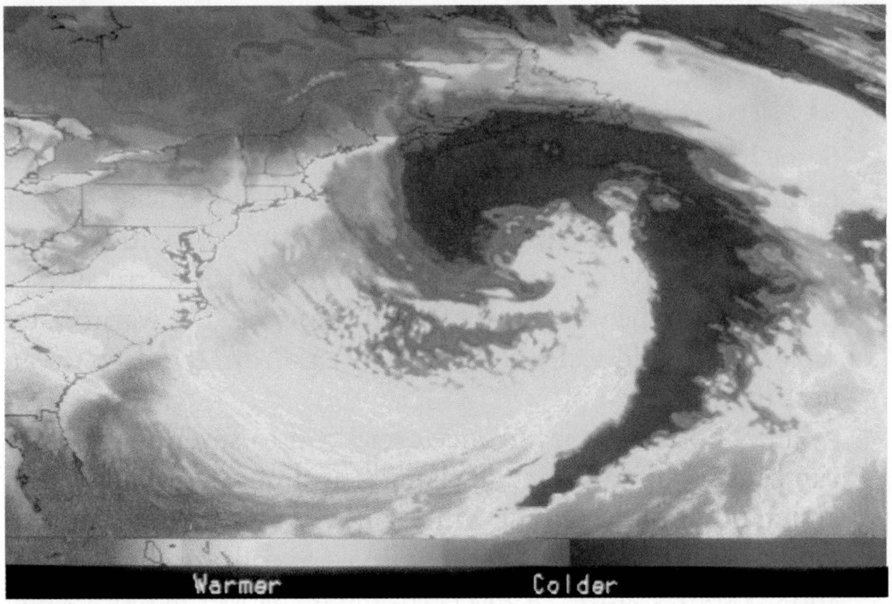
Warmer
Colder

Figure 18 This satellite photo shows an intense storm over the North Atlantic Ocean. *Observing What weather-related information can you see in the photo?*

Weather Technology

Techniques for predicting weather have changed rapidly in recent years. Short-range forecasts—forecasts for up to five days—are now fairly reliable. Meteorologists can also make long-range predictions that were once impossible. **Changes in technology have occurred in two areas: gathering weather data and using computers to make forecasts.**

Weather Balloons and Satellites As you learned in Chapter 14, weather balloons carry instruments high into the troposphere and stratosphere. The instruments measure temperature, air pressure, and humidity.

The first weather satellite was launched in 1960. Cameras on weather satellites in the exosphere can photograph Earth's surface, clouds, storms, and ice and snow cover. These images are then transmitted to meteorologists on Earth, who interpret the information.

Computer Forecasts Computers are widely used to help forecast weather. Instruments can now gather thousands of bits of data about temperature, air pressure, wind speed, and other factors. Computers process large amounts of information quickly to help forecasters make predictions. To make a forecast, the computer starts with weather conditions reported from weather stations over a large area. Conditions reported include wind speed and direction, humidity, sunlight, temperature, and air pressure. Then the computer works through thousands of calculations and makes forecasts for 12 hours, 24 hours, 36 hours, and so on. Each forecast builds on the previous forecast. When new weather data come in, the computer revises its forecasts.

INTEGRATING TECHNOLOGY

El Niño

Some long-term weather patterns may be caused by changes in ocean currents and global winds. Periodically, a warm-water event known as **El Niño** occurs in the tropical Pacific Ocean. During an El Niño event, winds shift and push warm surface water toward the west coast of South America. The warm water replaces the cold water that usually rises from the deep ocean near the coast.

El Niño events occur once every two to seven years. They can cause dramatic climate changes around the Pacific Ocean and in other places. In the winter of 1997 and 1998, a strong El Niño current caused droughts in Asia and Brazil, heavy rains and floods in California and Peru, and tornadoes in Florida and other parts of the southeastern United States.

Scientists have looked for clues and warnings to help predict the return of El Niño. One signal is rising surface temperatures in the tropical part of the Pacific Ocean. Using data gathered during past El Niño events, scientists were able to predict many of the results of the 1997–1998 El Niño.

☑ *Checkpoint* ***What evidence do scientists use to predict an El Niño?***

Sharpen your Skills

Interpreting Data

ACTIVITY

Use the key to Figure 19 to help you answer the questions about this weather station data.

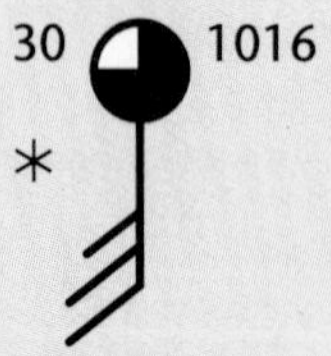

30
1016

1. What is the temperature at this station?
2. What is the wind speed?
3. Which way is the wind blowing?
4. What is the air pressure?
5. What percent of the sky is covered by clouds?
6. What type of precipitation, if any, is falling?

Reading Weather Maps

A weather map is a "snapshot" of conditions at a particular time over a large area. There are many different types of weather maps. Television forecasters often present maps generated by computers from radar information.

Weather Service Maps Data from more than 300 local weather stations all over the country are assembled into weather maps at the National Weather Service. The information collected by a typical reporting station is summarized in the key to Figure 19. The weather map, which has been simplified, includes most of the weather station data shown in the key.

On some weather maps, you see curved lines. These lines connect places where certain conditions—temperature or air pressure—are the same. **Isobars** are lines joining places on the map that have the same air pressure. (*Iso* means "equal" and *bar* means "pressure.") The numbers on the isobars are the pressure readings. Air pressure readings may be given in inches of mercury or in millibars or both. Figure 19 has isobars.

Isotherms are lines joining places that have the same temperature. The isotherm may be labeled with the temperature in degrees Fahrenheit, degrees Celsius, or both.

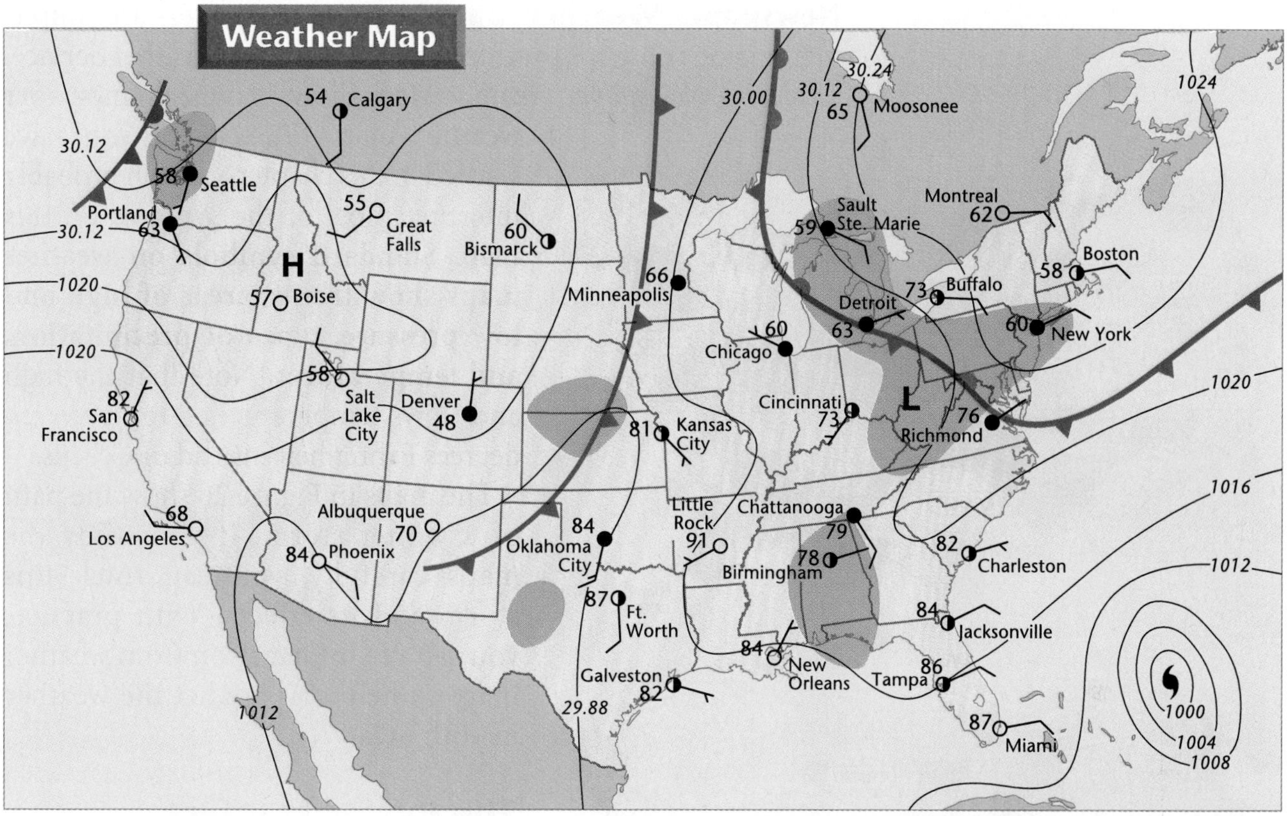

Weather Map
54 Calgary
30.12
58 Seattle
Portland
30.12
63
55 Great Falls
60 Bismarck
H
57 Boise
1020
1020
82 San Francisco
58 Salt Lake City
Denver 48
66 Minneapolis
60 Chicago
Cincinnati 73
81 Kansas City
68 Los Angeles
Albuquerque 70
84 Phoenix
84 Oklahoma City
87 Ft. Worth
Little Rock 91
Chattanooga 79
78 Birmingham
84 New Orleans
Galveston 82
29.88
1012
30.00
30.12
30.24
65 Moosonee
Montreal 62
59 Sault Ste. Marie
Boston 58
73 Buffalo
Detroit 63
60 New York
L
76 Richmond
82 Charleston
84 Jacksonville
86 Tampa
87 Miami
1024
1020
1016
1012
1000
1004
1008

EXPLANATION OF FRONTS

Cold Front
Boundary between a cold air mass and a warm air mass. Brings brief storms and cooler weather.

Warm Front
Boundary between a warm air mass and a cold air mass. Usually accompanied by precipitation.

Stationary Front
Boundary between a warm air mass and a cold air mass when no movement occurs. Brings long periods of precipitation.

Occluded Front
Boundary on which a warm front has been overtaken by a cold front. Brings precipitation.

Weather	Symbol
Drizzle	
Fog	≡
Hail	△
Haze	∞
Rain	•
Shower	▽
Sleet	
Smoke	
Snow	∗
Thunderstorm	
Hurricane	

Wind Speed (mph)	Symbol
1–2	
3–8	
9–14	
15–20	
21–25	
26–31	
32–37	
38–43	
44–49	
50–54	
55–60	
61–66	
67–71	
72–77	

Cloud Cover (%)	Symbol
0	○
10	
20–30	
40	
50	
60	
70–80	
90	
100	●

How Symbols Are Used on a Weather Map

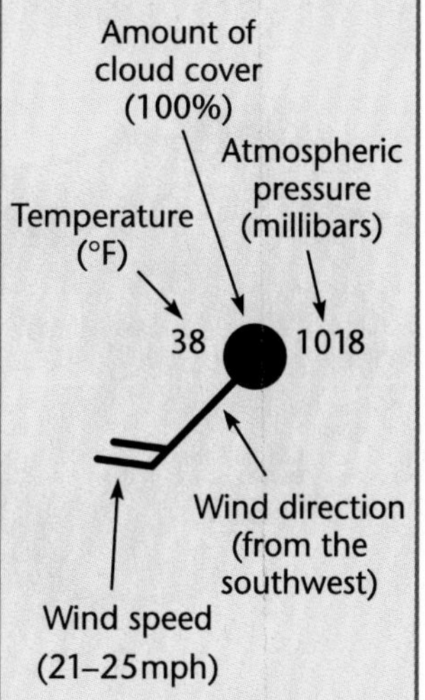

Amount of cloud cover (100%)
Atmospheric pressure (millibars)
Temperature (°F)
38
1018
Wind direction (from the southwest)
Wind speed (21–25mph)

Figure 19 This weather map shows data collected from weather stations all over the country. Below the map is an explanation of what the symbols at each city mean.

Newspaper Weather Maps Maps in newspapers are simplified versions of maps produced by the National Weather Service. *Exploring Newspaper Weather Maps* shows a typical newspaper weather map. From what you have learned in this chapter, you can probably interpret most of the symbols on this map. **Standard symbols on weather maps show fronts, areas of high and low pressure, types of precipitation, and temperatures.** Note that the high and low temperatures are given in degrees Fahrenheit instead of Celsius.

The maps in Figure 20 show the path of a winter storm. If you study the maps carefully, you can track this storm and its effects. With practice, you can use information from weather maps to help you predict the weather in your area.

The Butterfly Effect

Even with current technology, weather forecasting is tricky. The main reason is that weather patterns do not follow an orderly, step-by-step process.

A forecast for the weather six days from now is based on forecasts for all the days between now and then. A small change in the weather today can mean a larger change in the weather a week later! This is the so-called "butterfly effect." The name refers to a scientist's suggestion that even the flapping of a butterfly's wings causes a tiny disturbance in the atmosphere. This tiny event might cause a larger disturbance that could—eventually—grow into a hurricane.

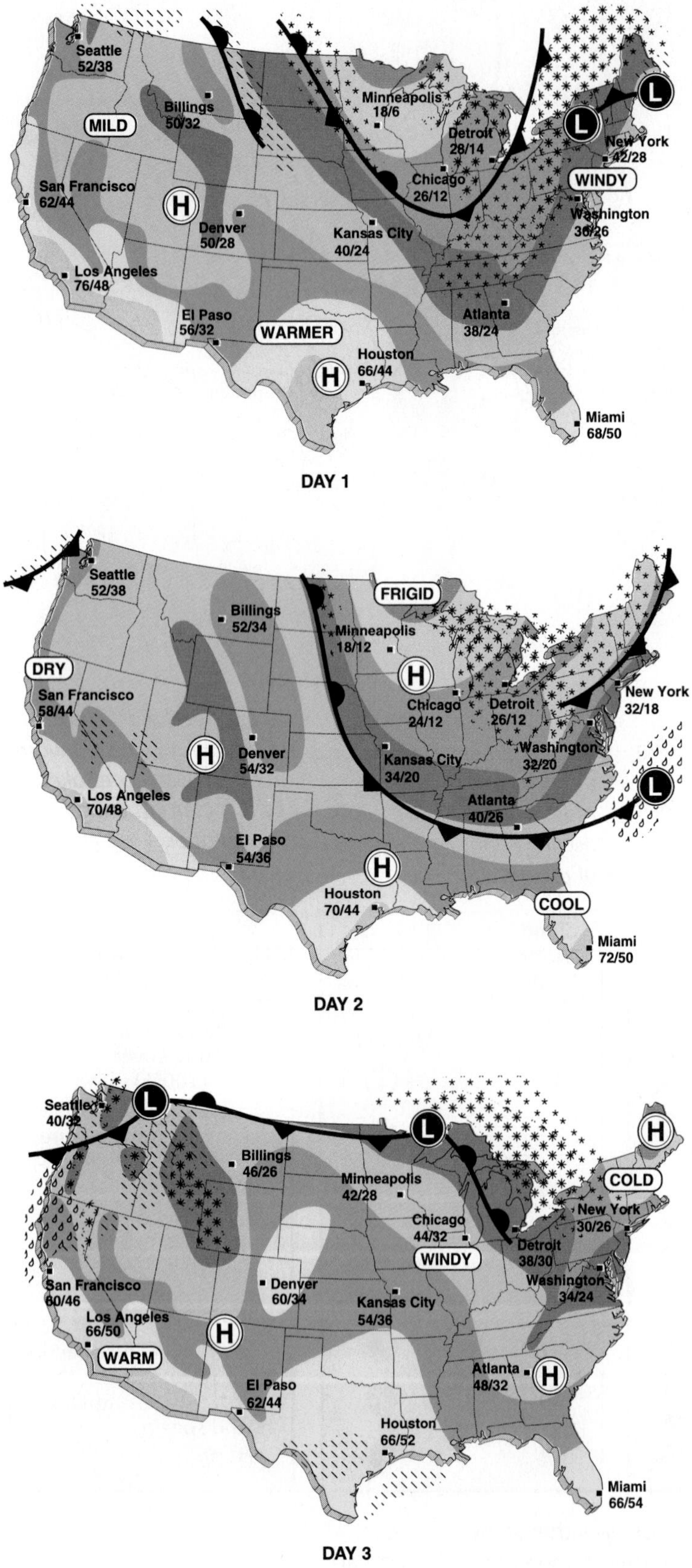
Seattle 52/38
Billings 50/32
MILD
Minneapolis 18/6
Detroit 28/14
L
L
New York 42/28
WINDY
San Francisco 62/44
H
Denver 50/28
Chicago 26/12
Kansas City 40/24
Washington 36/26
Los Angeles 76/48
El Paso 56/32
WARMER
Atlanta 38/24
Houston 66/44
H
Miami 68/50
DAY 1
Seattle 52/38
FRIGID
Billings 52/34
Minneapolis 18/12
DRY
H
San Francisco 58/44
Chicago 24/12
Detroit 26/12
New York 32/18
H
Denver 54/32
Washington 32/20
Kansas City 34/20
L
Los Angeles 70/48
Atlanta 40/26
El Paso 54/36
H
Houston 70/44
COOL
Miami 72/50
DAY 2
Seattle 40/32
L
L
H
Billings 46/26
Minneapolis 42/28
COLD
Chicago 44/32
New York 30/26
WINDY
Detroit 38/30
San Francisco 60/46
Denver 60/34
Washington 34/24
Kansas City 54/36
Los Angeles 66/50
H
WARM
Atlanta 48/32
H
El Paso 62/44
Houston 66/52
Miami 66/54
DAY 3

Figure 20 These weather maps show a storm moving from west to east over a three-day period.
Interpreting Diagrams What were the high and low temperatures in Chicago on Day 2? On Day 3?

EXPLORING Newspaper Weather Maps

Weather maps in newspapers use symbols to show fronts, high and low pressure areas, and precipitation. Color bands indicate different temperatures.

Major low-pressure areas are shown with an L. High-pressure areas are shown with an H.

Areas in the same temperature range are shown in the same color. For example, light green areas have high temperatures in the 40's.

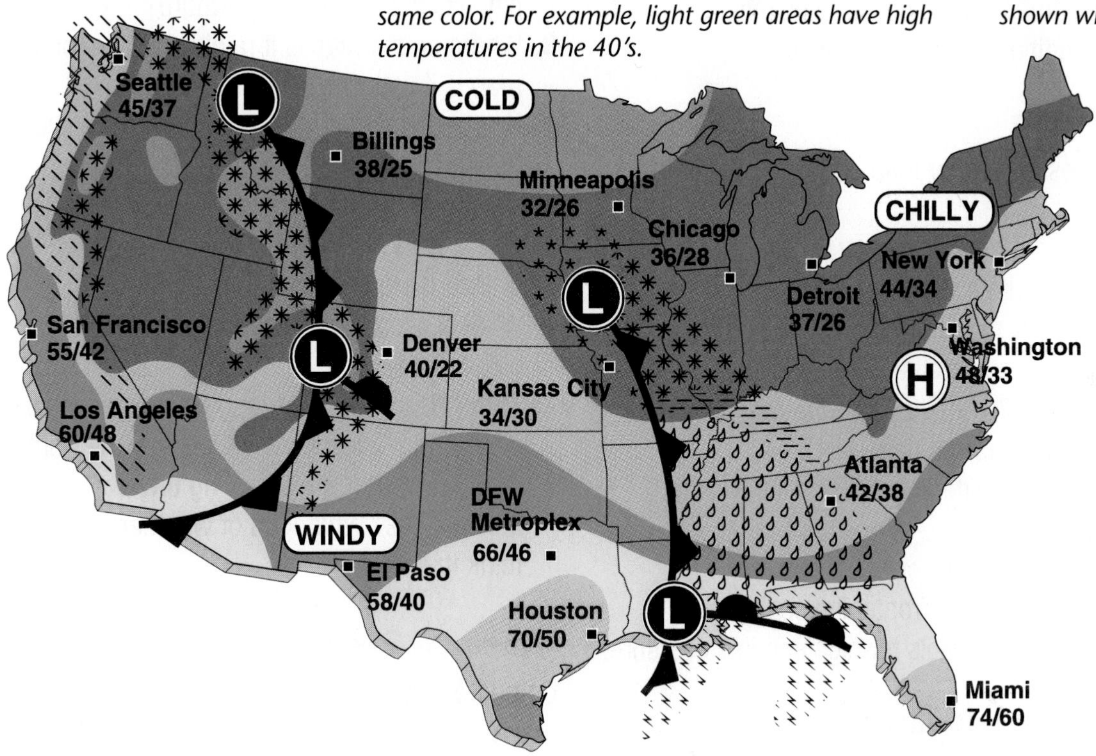

Seattle 45/37
COLD
Billings 38/25
Minneapolis 32/26
Chicago 36/28
CHILLY
New York 44/34
Detroit 37/26
San Francisco 55/42
Denver 40/22
Kansas City 34/30
Washington 48/33
H
L
Los Angeles 60/48
Atlanta 42/38
DFW Metroplex 66/46
WINDY
El Paso 58/40
Houston 70/50
Miami 74/60

Symbols that look like raindrops or snowflakes show precipitation.

The triangles showing a cold front point in the direction the cold air is moving. The half-circles indicating a warm front show the direction the warm air is moving.

Section 4 Review

1. What kinds of technology do meteorologists use to help predict the weather?
2. Name at least three types of information you could get from a weather map of your area.
3. What lines on a weather map connect points that have the same temperature?
4. **Thinking Critically Predicting** If you observe that air pressure is rising, what kind of weather do you think is coming?

CHAPTER PROJECT

Check Your Progress

After a week of predicting the weather, you are ready to compare your predictions to the actual weather that occurred. Then compare your predictions with those made by professional meteorologists. How accurate were your predictions? How accurate were the predictions made by professional meteorologists?

Interpreting Data

Reading a Weather Map

In this lab, you will interpret data from a weather map to describe weather conditions in various places.

Problem

How does a weather map communicate data?

Procedure

1. Examine the symbols on the weather map below. For more information about the symbols used on the map, refer to Figure 19 on page 529 and to *Exploring Newspaper Weather Maps* on page 531.
2. Observe the different colors on the weather map.
3. Find the symbols for snow and rain.
4. Locate the warm fronts and cold fronts.
5. Locate the symbols for high and low pressure.

Analyze and Conclude

1. What color represents the highest temperatures? What color represents the lowest temperatures?
2. What city has the highest temperature? What city has the lowest temperature?
3. Where on the map is it raining? Where on the map is it snowing?
4. How many different kinds of fronts are shown on the map?
5. How many areas of low pressure are shown on the map? How many areas of high pressure are shown on the map?
6. What season does this map represent? How do you know?
7. **Think About It** The triangles and semicircles on the front lines show which way the front is moving. What front is moving toward Minneapolis? What kind of weather do you think it will bring?

More to Explore

Compare this weather map with the weather map shown in a television news report. Which symbols on these maps are similar? Which symbols are different?

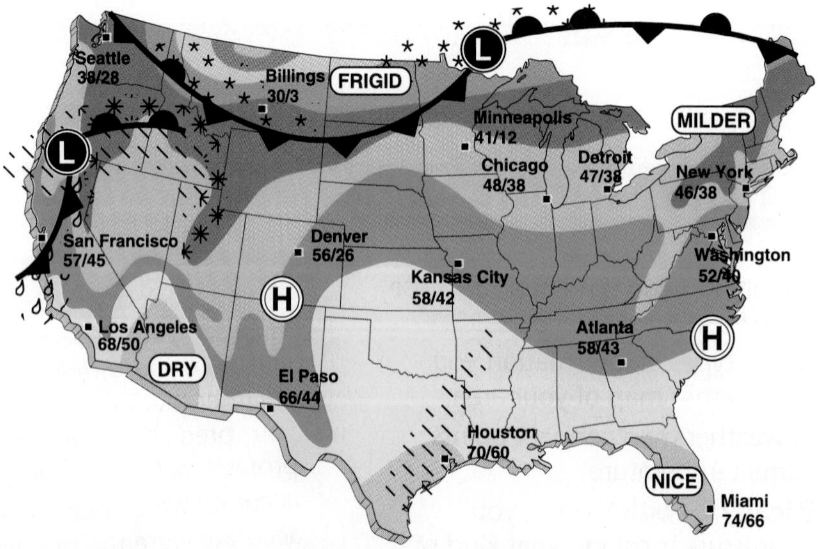

Seattle 38/28
Billings 30/3
FRIGID
L
Minneapolis 41/12
MILDER
Chicago 48/38
Detroit 47/38
New York 46/38
San Francisco 57/45
Denver 56/26
Washington 52/40
Kansas City 58/42
H
Los Angeles 68/50
Atlanta 58/43
DRY
El Paso 66/44
Houston 70/60
NICE
Miami 74/66

STUDY GUIDE

Section 1 Air Masses and Fronts

Key Ideas

- Four major types of air masses influence the weather in North America: maritime tropical, continental tropical, maritime polar, and continental polar.
- When air masses collide, they form four types of fronts: cold fronts, warm fronts, stationary fronts, and occluded fronts.
- Cyclones and decreasing air pressure are associated with storms and precipitation. Anticyclones bring high pressure and dry weather.

Key Terms

air mass	maritime	occluded
tropical	continental	cyclone
polar	front	anticyclone

Section 2 Storms

Key Ideas

- Thunderstorms and tornadoes form within large cumulonimbus clouds. During thunderstorms, avoid touching metal objects because they can conduct lightning into your body.
- The safest place to be during a tornado is in the basement of a well-built building.
- A hurricane begins over warm water as a low-pressure area. If you hear a hurricane warning and are told to evacuate, leave the area immediately.
- Snow falls when humid air cools below 0°C. If you are caught in a snowstorm, try to find shelter from the wind.

Key Terms

storm	tornado	storm surge
lightning	hurricane	evacuate

L
H
COLD
L
Today

Section 3 Floods

INTEGRATING HEALTH

Key Ideas

- Floods occur when so much water pours into a stream or river that it overflows its banks and covers the land on either side of the channel.
- The first rule of flood safety: Move to higher ground and stay away from flood waters.

Key Term

flash flood

Section 4 Predicting the Weather

Key Ideas

- Meteorologists interpret weather information from local weather observers, instruments carried by balloons, satellites, and weather stations around the world.
- Changes in weather technology have occurred in two areas: gathering weather data and using computers to make forecasts.
- Standard symbols on weather maps show fronts, areas of high and low pressure, types of precipitation, and temperatures.

Key Terms

meteorologist	isobar
El Niño	isotherm

ACTIVITY

USING THE INTERNET

www.phschool.com/state_focus/california/

California Test Prep: Reviewing Content

Multiple Choice

Choose the letter of the answer that best completes each statement.

1. An air mass that forms over an ocean is called
   a. tropical. b. continental.
   c. maritime. d. polar.
2. Cool, clear weather is usually brought by a
   a. warm front.
   b. cold front.
   c. stationary front.
   d. occluded front.
3. Winds spiraling inward toward a center of low pressure form a(n)
   a. anticyclone.
   b. front.
   c. isobar.
   d. cyclone.
4. Very large tropical storms with high winds are called
   a. hurricanes.
   b. tornadoes.
   c. thunderstorms.
   d. blizzards.
5. Most flash floods are caused by
   a. hailstorms.
   b. heavy rainfall.
   c. high winds.
   d. melting snow.

True or False

If the statement is true, write true. If it is false, change the underlined word or words to make it true.

6. Summers in the Southwest are hot and dry because of maritime tropical air masses.
7. A cold front over an area will bring many days of cloudy weather.
8. Foggy, rainy, or humid weather usually follows the passage of a warm front through an area.
9. Low cumulonimbus clouds may bring both thunderstorms and tornadoes.
10. On a weather map, isobars join places on the map with the same temperature.

Checking Concepts

11. What are the basic characteristics used to describe air masses?
12. Describe how wind patterns affect the movement of air masses in North America.
13. How does a cold front form?
14. Describe three hazards associated with floods.
15. What are some of the sources of information that meteorologists use to predict the weather?
16. **Writing to Learn** Imagine you are a meteorologist. Your assignment is to investigate a hurricane by flying into it with a large plane. Describe your experiences in a journal entry. Be sure to include descriptive words. How did it look? Sound? Feel?

Thinking Visually

17. **Compare/Contrast Table** Copy the compare/contrast table about hurricanes and tornadoes onto a separate sheet of paper. Then fill in the empty spaces and add a title. (For more on compare/contrast tables, see the Skills Handbook.)

Type of Storm	Hurricane	Tornado
Where storm forms	Over warm ocean water	a. ?
Size of storm	b. ?	Several hundred meters
How long storm lasts	A week or more	c. ?
Time of year	d. ?	Spring, early summer
Safety rules	Evacuate or move to the interior of a well-built building	e. ?

Test Prep: Skills

Use the map to answer Questions 18–21.

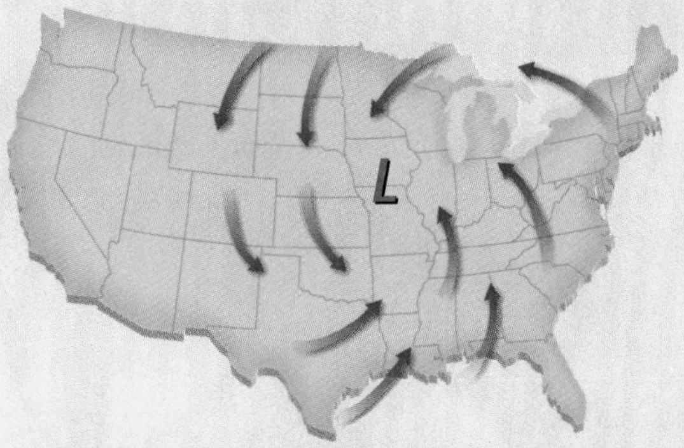
L

18. **Interpreting Maps** Does the map show a cyclone or an anticyclone? How can you tell?
19. **Interpreting Data** What do the arrows show about the movement of the winds in this pressure center? What else indicates wind direction?
20. **Making Models** Using this diagram as an example, draw a similar diagram to illustrate a high pressure area. Remember to indicate wind direction in your diagram.
21. **Posing Questions** If you saw a pressure center like this on a weather map, what prediction could you make about the weather? What questions would you need to ask in order to make a better prediction?

Thinking Critically

22. **Classifying** Classify the major types of air masses that influence weather in the United States in two ways: by temperature and by where they form.
23. **Applying Concepts** Would you expect hurricanes to form over the oceans off the northeast and northwest coasts of the United States? Explain.
24. **Relating Cause and Effect** How do differences in air density influence the movement of cold and warm fronts?
25. **Making Judgments** What do you think is the most important thing people should do to reduce the dangers of storms?

CHAPTER 16 ASSESSMENT

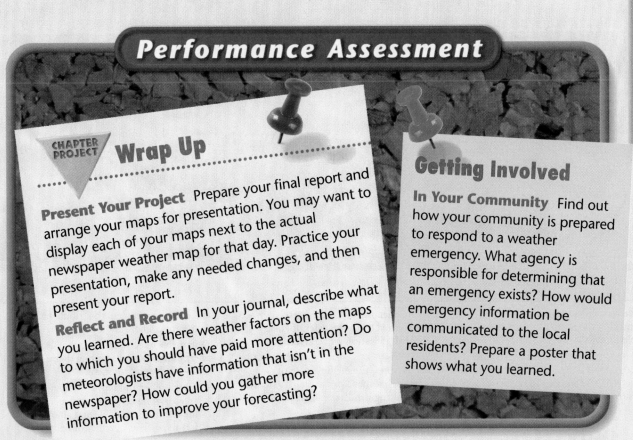

Performance Assessment

CHAPTER PROJECT Wrap Up

Present Your Project Prepare your final report and arrange your maps for presentation. You may want to display each of your maps next to the actual newspaper weather map for that day. Practice your presentation, make any needed changes, and then present your report.

Reflect and Record In your journal, describe what you learned. Are there weather factors on the maps to which you should have paid more attention? Do meteorologists have information that isn't in the newspaper? How could you gather more information to improve your forecasting?

Getting Involved

In Your Community Find out how your community is prepared to respond to a weather emergency. What agency is responsible for determining that an emergency exists? How would emergency information be communicated to the local residents? Prepare a poster that shows what you learned.

CHAPTER 17

Climate and Climate Change

The following California Science Content Standards are addressed in this chapter:

1. Plate tectonics explains important features of the Earth's surface and major geologic events.
   - **c.** Lithospheric plates that are the size of continents and oceans move at rates of centimeters per year in response to movements in the mantle.

4. Many phenomena on the Earth's surface are affected by the transfer of energy through radiation and convection currents.
   - **a.** The sun is the major source of energy for phenomena on the Earth's surface, powering winds, ocean currents, and the water cycle.
   - **d.** Convection currents distribute heat in the atmosphere and oceans.

5. Organisms in ecosystems exchange energy and nutrients among themselves and with the environment.
   - **e.** The number and types of organisms an ecosystem can support depends on the resources available and abiotic factors, such as quantity of light and

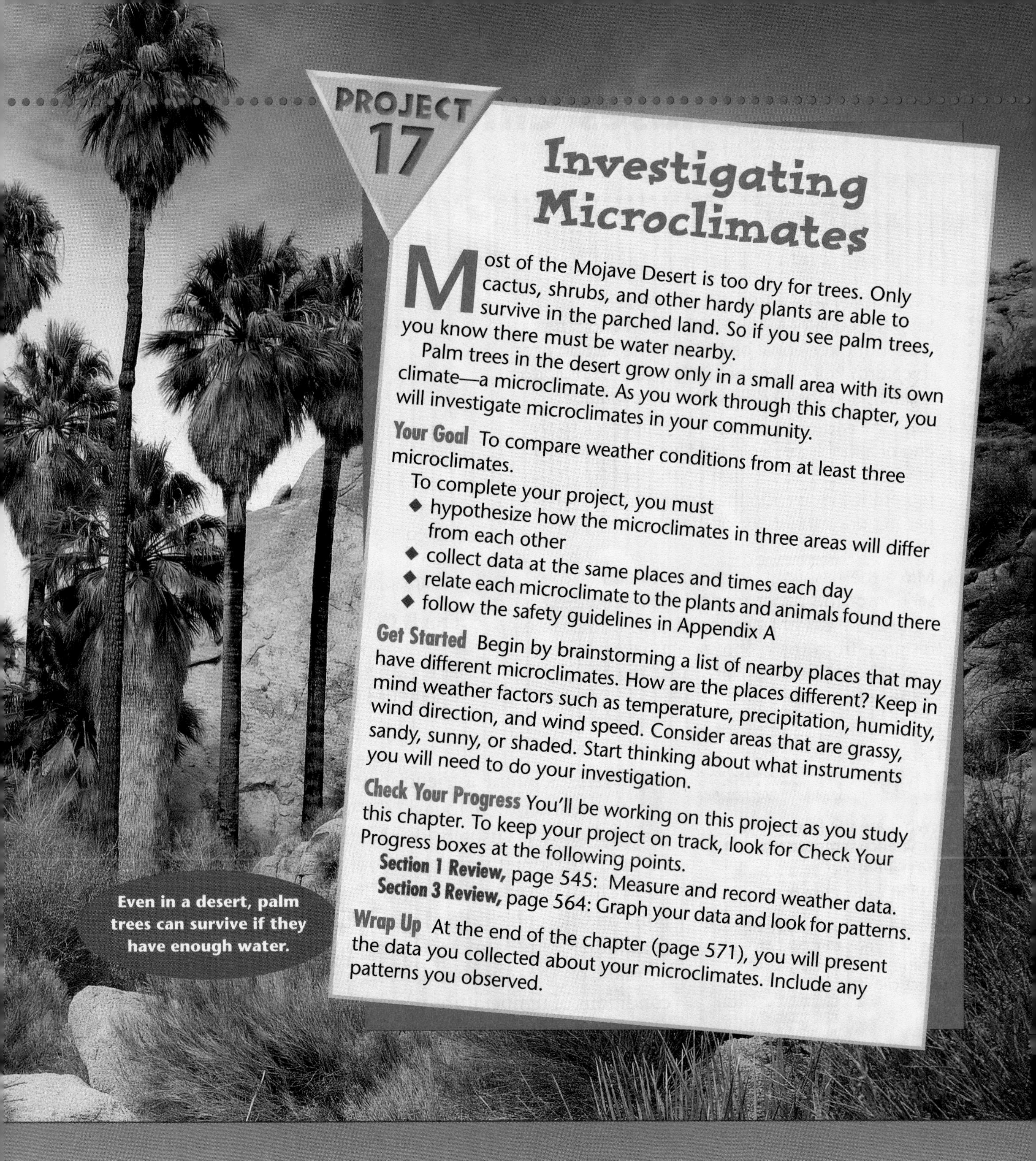

Even in a desert, palm trees can survive if they have enough water.

PROJECT 17

Investigating Microclimates

Most of the Mojave Desert is too dry for trees. Only cactus, shrubs, and other hardy plants are able to survive in the parched land. So if you see palm trees, you know there must be water nearby.

Palm trees in the desert grow only in a small area with its own climate—a microclimate. As you work through this chapter, you will investigate microclimates in your community.

Your Goal To compare weather conditions from at least three microclimates.

To complete your project, you must

- hypothesize how the microclimates in three areas will differ from each other
- collect data at the same places and times each day
- relate each microclimate to the plants and animals found there
- follow the safety guidelines in Appendix A

Get Started Begin by brainstorming a list of nearby places that may have different microclimates. How are the places different? Keep in mind weather factors such as temperature, precipitation, humidity, wind direction, and wind speed. Consider areas that are grassy, sandy, sunny, or shaded. Start thinking about what instruments you will need to do your investigation.

Check Your Progress You'll be working on this project as you study this chapter. To keep your project on track, look for Check Your Progress boxes at the following points.

Section 1 Review, page 545: Measure and record weather data.

Section 3 Review, page 564: Graph your data and look for patterns.

Wrap Up At the end of the chapter (page 571), you will present the data you collected about your microclimates. Include any patterns you observed.

water, range of temperatures, and soil composition.

6. Sources of energy and materials differ in amounts, distribution, usefulness, and the time required for their formation.
   a. The utility of energy sources is determined by factors that are involved in converting these sources to useful forms and the consequences of the conversion process.
   b. Different natural energy and material resources, including air, soil, rocks, minerals, petroleum, fresh water, wildlife, and forests, and classify them as renewable or nonrenewable.
7. Scientific progress is made by asking meaningful questions and conducting careful investigations.
   a. Develop a hypothesis.
   c. Construct appropriate graphs from data and develop qualitative statements about the relationships between variables.
   f. Read a topographic map and a geologic map for evidence provided on the maps, and construct and interpret a simple scale map.

SECTION 1 What Causes Climate?

DISCOVER ACTIVITY

How Does Earth's Shape Affect Climate Zones?

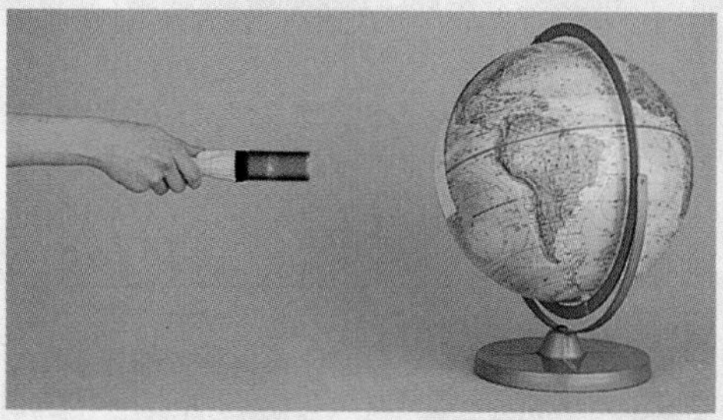

1. On a globe, tape a strip of cash register paper from the equator to the North Pole. Divide the tape into three equal parts. Label the section near the North Pole *poles,* the section near the equator *equator,* and the middle section *mid-latitudes.*
2. Tape the end of an empty toilet paper roll to the end of a flashlight. Hold the flashlight about 30 cm from the equator. Turn on the flashlight to represent the sun. On the paper strip, have a partner draw the shape of the area the light shines on.
3. Move the flashlight up slightly to aim at the section of the paper marked "mid-latitudes." Keep the flashlight horizontal and at the same distance from the globe. Again have a partner draw the shape of the area that the light shines on.
4. Move the flashlight up again to shine on the section of the paper marked "poles." Keep the flashlight horizontal and at the same distance from the globe. Draw the shape of the area that the light shines on.

Think It Over

Observing How does the shape of the area that is illuminated change? Do you think the sun's rays heat Earth's surface evenly?

GUIDE FOR READING

- **What are the factors that influence temperature and precipitation?**
- **What causes the seasons?**

Reading Tip **As you read, use the headings to make an outline of the factors that affect climate.**

If you telephone a friend in another state and ask, "What's the weather there today?" she might answer: "It's gray, cool, and rainy. It's usually like that this time of year." Your friend has told you something about both weather and climate.

Weather is day-to-day events. The weather may be cloudy and rainy one day and clear and sunny the next. Weather refers to the condition of the atmosphere at a particular place and time. **Climate,** on the other hand, refers to the average, year-after-year conditions of temperature, precipitation, winds, and clouds in an area. How would you describe the climate where you live?

Two main factors—temperature and precipitation—determine the climate of a region. A climate region is a large area with similar climate conditions throughout. For example, the climate in the southeastern United States is humid, with moderate temperatures.

◀ **These polar bears—two males and their mother—are taking it easy in the polar zone.**

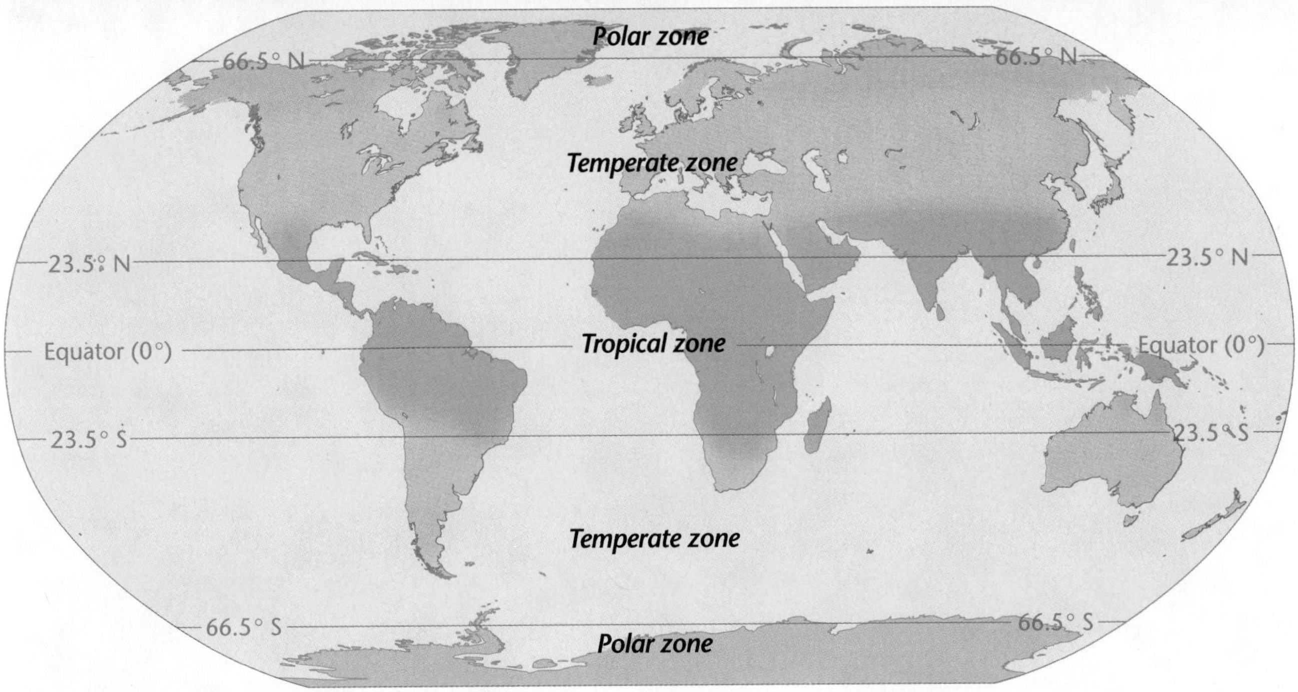
Polar zone
66.5° N
66.5° N
Temperate zone
23.5° N
23.5° N
Equator (0°)
Tropical zone
Equator (0°)
23.5° S
23.5° S
Temperate zone
66.5° S
66.5° S
Polar zone

Figure 1 Earth has three main temperature zones.
Interpreting Maps In which temperature zone is most of the United States located?

Factors Affecting Temperature

Tropical countries, such as Panama, are usually hot. Northern countries, such as Finland, are usually cold. Why are some places warm and others cold? **The main factors that influence temperature are latitude, altitude, distance from large bodies of water, and ocean currents.**

Latitude In general, climates of locations farther from the equator are cooler than climates of areas closer to the equator. Why is this? As you found out if you tried the Discover activity, the sun's rays hit Earth's surface most directly at the equator. At the poles, the same amount of solar radiation is spread out over a larger area, and therefore brings less warmth.

Recall that latitude is the distance from the equator, measured in degrees. Based on latitude, Earth's surface can be divided into the three temperature zones shown in Figure 1. The **tropical zone** is the area near the equator, between about 23.5° north latitude and 23.5° south latitude. The tropical zone receives direct or nearly direct sunlight all year round, making climates there warm.

In contrast, the sun's rays always strike at a lower angle near the North and South poles. As a result, the areas near both poles have cold climates. These **polar zones** extend from about 66.5° to 90° north and 66.5° to 90° south latitudes.

The **temperate zones** are between the tropical and the polar zones—from about 23.5° to 66.5° north and 23.5° to 66.5° south latitudes. In summer, the sun's rays strike the temperate zones more directly. In winter, the sun's rays strike at a lower angle. As a result, the weather in the temperate zones ranges from warm or hot in summer to cool or cold in winter.

Figure 2 Mount Kilimanjaro in Tanzania, Africa, is near the equator. *Applying Concepts Why is there snow on top of the mountain?*

Altitude The peak of Mount Kilimanjaro towers high above the African plains. At nearly 6 kilometers above sea level, Kilimanjaro is covered in snow all year round. Yet it is located near the equator, at 3° south latitude. Why is Mount Kilimanjaro so cold?

In the case of high mountains, altitude is a more important climate factor than latitude. Recall from Chapter 1 that the temperature of the troposphere decreases about 6.5 Celsius degrees for every 1-kilometer increase in altitude. As a result, highland areas everywhere have cool climates, no matter what their latitude. At nearly 6 kilometers, the air at the top of Mount Kilimanjaro is about 39 Celsius degrees colder than the air at sea level at the same latitude.

Distance From Large Bodies of Water Oceans or large lakes can also affect temperatures. Oceans greatly moderate, or make less extreme, the temperatures of nearby land. Water heats up more slowly than land; it also cools down more slowly. Therefore, winds from the ocean keep coastal regions from reaching extremes of hot and cold. Much of the west coasts of North America, South America, and Europe have mild **marine climates,** with relatively warm winters and cool summers.

The centers of North America and Asia are too far inland to be warmed or cooled by the oceans. Most of Canada and Russia, as well as the central United States, have **continental climates.** Continental climates have more extreme temperatures than marine climates. Winters are cold, while summers are warm or hot.

Ocean Currents Many marine climates are influenced by ocean currents, streams of water within the oceans that move in regular patterns. In general, warm ocean currents carry warm water from the tropics toward the poles. Cold currents bring cold water from the polar zones toward the equator. The surface of the water warms or cools the air above it. The warmed or cooled air then moves over the nearby land. So a warm current brings warm air to the land it touches. A cold current brings cool air.

As you read about the following currents, trace their paths on the map in Figure 3. The best-known warm-water current is the Gulf Stream. The Gulf Stream begins in the Gulf of Mexico, then flows north along the east coast of the United States. When it crosses the North Atlantic, it becomes the North Atlantic Drift. This warm current gives Ireland and southern England a mild, wet climate despite their relatively high latitude.

In contrast, the cool California Current flows from Alaska southward down the West Coast. The California Current makes climates of places along the West Coast cooler than you would expect at their latitudes.

☑ *Checkpoint* ***What effect do oceans have on the temperatures of nearby land areas?***

Sharpen your Skills

Inferring

ACTIVITY

Look at the currents in the South Pacific, South Atlantic, and Indian oceans. What pattern can you observe? Now compare currents in the South Atlantic to those in the North Atlantic. What might be responsible for differences in the current patterns?

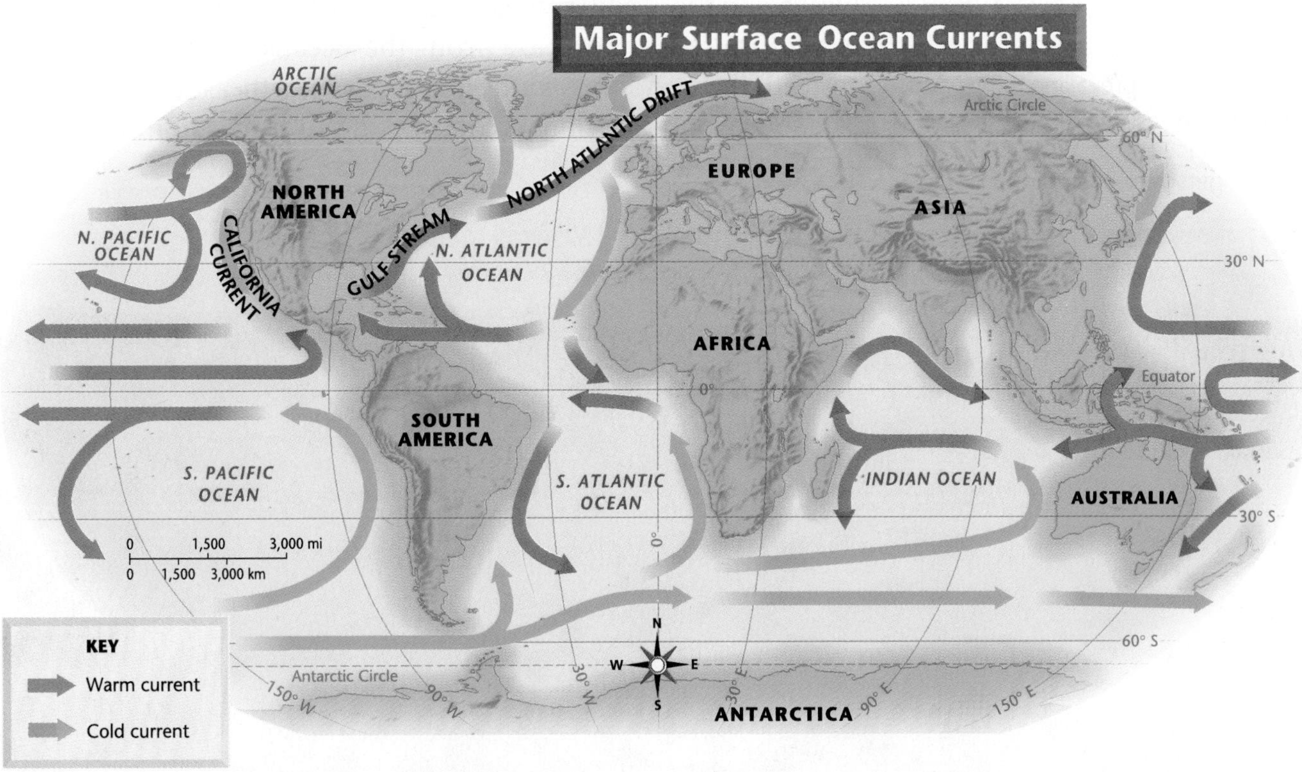
Major Surface Ocean Currents
ARCTIC OCEAN
NORTH ATLANTIC DRIFT
Arctic Circle
60° N
EUROPE
ASIA
NORTH AMERICA
N. PACIFIC OCEAN
CALIFORNIA CURRENT
GULF STREAM
N. ATLANTIC OCEAN
30° N
AFRICA
Equator
0°
SOUTH AMERICA
S. PACIFIC OCEAN
S. ATLANTIC OCEAN
INDIAN OCEAN
AUSTRALIA
30° S
0 1,500 3,000 mi
0 1,500 3,000 km
60° S
KEY
Warm current
Cold current
Antarctic Circle
150° W
90° W
30° W
30° E
90° E
150° E
N
S
E
W
ANTARCTICA

Figure 3 On this map, warm currents are shown in red and cold currents in blue.

Factors Affecting Precipitation

The amount of rain and snow that falls in an area each year determines how wet or dry its climate is. But what determines how much precipitation an area gets? **The main factors that affect precipitation are prevailing winds and the presence of mountains.**

Prevailing Winds As you know, weather patterns depend on the movement of huge air masses. Air masses are moved from place to place by prevailing winds, the directional winds that usually blow in a region. Air masses can be warm or cool, dry or humid. The amount of water vapor in the air mass influences how much rain or snow will fall.

Warm air can carry more water vapor than cold air can. When warm air rises and cools, water comes out of the air as precipitation. For example, surface air near the equator is generally hot and humid. As the air rises and cools, heavy rains fall, nourishing thick tropical forests. In contrast, sinking cold air is usually dry. Because the air becomes warmer as it sinks, it can hold more water vapor. The water vapor stays in the air and little or no rain falls. The result may be a desert.

The amount of water vapor in prevailing winds also depends on where the winds come from. Winds that blow inland from oceans carry more water vapor than winds that blow from over land. For example, the Sahara in Africa is near both the Atlantic Ocean and the Mediterranean Sea. Yet the Sahara is very dry. This is because few winds blow from the oceans toward this area. Instead, the prevailing winds are the dry northeast trade winds. The source of these winds is cool, sinking air from southwest Asia.

Figure 4 The prevailing winds that blow across the Sahara begin far inland. Since the air is dry, the Sahara gets very little rain.

SAHARA
AFRICA
ATLANTIC
OCEAN

Mountain Ranges A mountain range in the path of prevailing winds can also influence where precipitation falls. As you have learned, when humid winds blow from the ocean toward coastal mountains, they are forced to rise up to pass over the mountains. The rising warm air cools and its water vapor condenses, forming clouds. Rain or snow falls on the **windward** side of the mountains, the side the oncoming wind hits.

By the time the air reaches the other side of the mountains, it has lost much of its water vapor, so it is cool and dry. The land on the **leeward** side of the mountains—downwind—is in a rain shadow.

The Owens Valley in California, shown in Figure 5, is in the rain shadow of the Sierra Nevada, about 80 kilometers west of Death Valley. Humid winds blow eastward from the Pacific Ocean. In the photo, you can see that this humid air has left snow on top of the mountains. Then the air flowed down the leeward side of the mountains. As it moved downward, the air became warmer. The desert in the Owens Valley, on the eastern side of the Sierra Nevada, was formed by this hot, dry air.

☑ *Checkpoint* ***Why does precipitation fall mainly on the windward sides of mountains?***

Sierra Nevada
Owens Valley
Moist air
Coastal Ranges
Pacific Ocean

Figure 5 The Sierra Nevada runs through eastern California, parallel to the Pacific coast. To the east of the Sierras is the Owens Valley, shown above. *Inferring Is the Owens Valley on the windward or leeward side of the mountains?*

Microclimates

Have you ever noticed that it is cooler and more humid in a grove of trees than in an open field? The same factors that affect large climate regions also affect smaller areas. A small area with specific climate conditions may have its own **microclimate.** Inland mountains, lakes, forests, and other natural features can influence climate nearby, resulting in a microclimate.

You might find a microclimate in a downtown area with clusters of tall buildings, or on a windy peninsula jutting out into the ocean. Even a small park, if it is usually sunnier or windier than nearby areas, may have its own microclimate. The grass on a lawn can be covered in dew and produce conditions like a rain forest, while the pavement in the parking lot is dry, like a desert.

Math TOOLBOX

Angles

Light from the sun strikes Earth's surface at different angles. An angle is made up of two lines that meet at a point. Angles are measured in degrees. A full circle has 360 degrees.

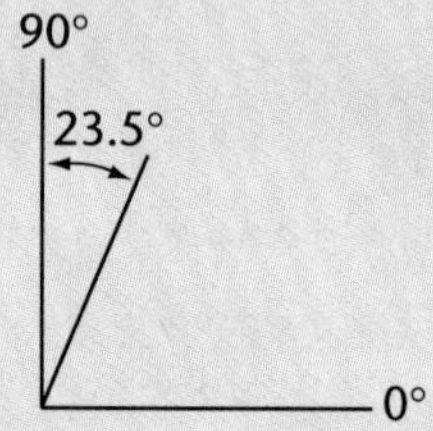

90°
23.5°
0°

When the sun is directly overhead near the equator, it is at an angle of 90° to Earth's surface. A 90° angle is called a right angle. It is one fourth of a circle.

When the sun is near the horizon, it is at an angle of close to 0° to Earth's surface.

Earth's axis is tilted at an angle of 23.5°. About what fraction of a right angle is this?

The Seasons

INTEGRATING SPACE SCIENCE Although you can describe the average weather conditions of a climate region, these conditions are not constant all year long. Instead, most places on Earth outside the tropics have four seasons: winter, spring, summer, and autumn.

You might think that Earth is closer to the sun during the summer and farther away during winter. If this were true, every place on Earth would have summer at the same time. Actually, when it is summer in the Northern Hemisphere it is winter in the Southern Hemisphere. So the seasons are *not* a result of changes in the distance between Earth and the sun.

Tilted Axis *Exploring the Seasons* on page 545 shows how Earth's axis is tilted in relation to the sun. **The seasons are caused by the tilt of Earth's axis as Earth travels around the sun.** The axis is an imaginary line through Earth's center that passes through both poles. Earth turns, or rotates, around this axis once each day. Earth's axis is not straight up and down, but is tilted at an angle of 23.5°. The axis always points in the same direction—toward the North Star. As Earth travels around the sun, the north end of the axis is pointed away from the sun for part of the year and toward the sun for part of the year.

Winter or Summer Look at *Exploring the Seasons* on the next page. Which way is the north end of Earth's axis tilted in June? Notice that the Northern Hemisphere receives more direct rays from the sun. Also, in June the days in the Northern Hemisphere are longer than the nights. The combination of more direct rays and longer days makes Earth's surface warmer in the Northern Hemisphere than at any other time of the year. It is summer.

In June, when the north end of Earth's axis is tilted toward the sun, the south end of the axis is tilted away from the sun. The Southern Hemisphere receives fewer direct rays from the sun. The days are shorter than the nights. As a result, the Southern Hemisphere is experiencing winter.

Now look at the situation in December, six months later. Which way is the north end of Earth's axis tilted now? The Northern Hemisphere receives fewer direct rays from the sun and has shorter days. It is winter in the Northern Hemisphere and summer in the Southern Hemisphere.

Twice during the year, in March and September, neither end of Earth's axis is tilted toward the sun. At both of these times, one hemisphere has spring while the other has autumn.

EXPLORING the Seasons

The seasons are a result of Earth's tilted axis. The seasons change as the amount of energy each hemisphere receives from the sun changes.

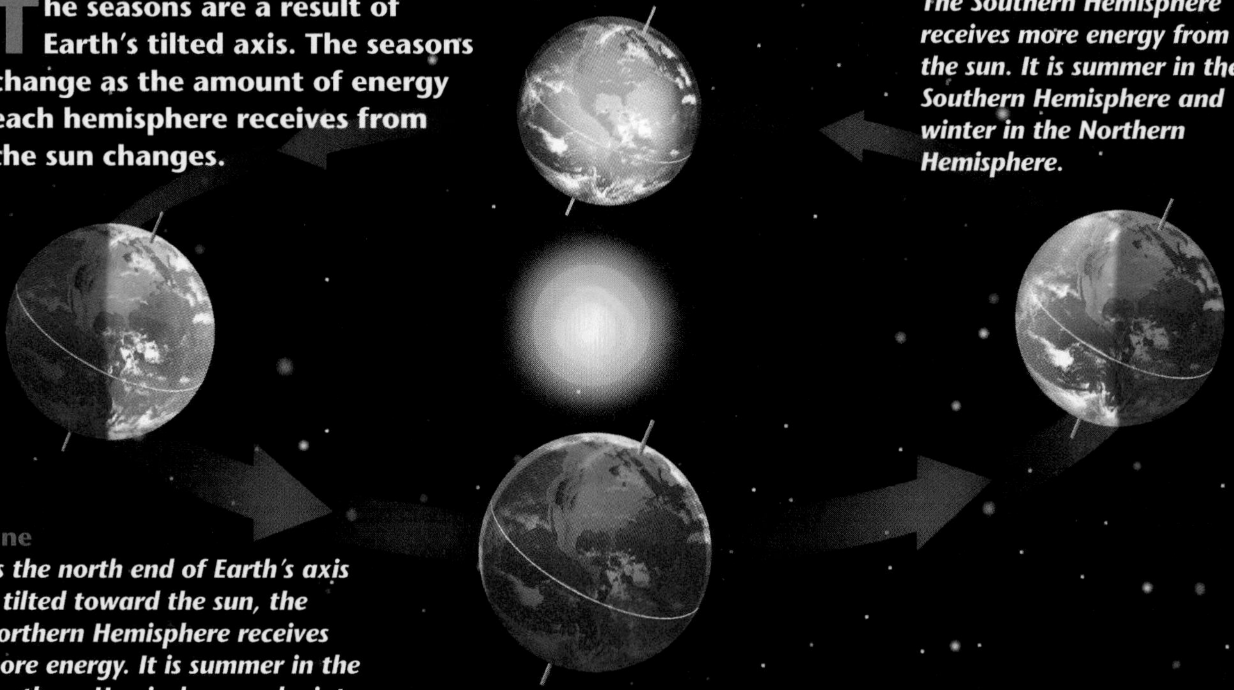

December

The south end of Earth's axis is tilted toward the sun. The Southern Hemisphere receives more energy from the sun. It is summer in the Southern Hemisphere and winter in the Northern Hemisphere.

June

As the north end of Earth's axis is tilted toward the sun, the Northern Hemisphere receives more energy. It is summer in the Northern Hemisphere and winter in the Southern Hemisphere.

March and September

Neither end of Earth's axis is tilted toward the sun. Both hemispheres receive the same amounts of energy.

Section 1 Review

1. Name the four main factors that influence the temperature of an area.
2. How do prevailing winds affect the amount of precipitation an area receives?
3. On which side of mountains—leeward or windward—does precipitation fall?
4. How does the tilt of Earth's axis cause the seasons?
5. **Thinking Critically Developing Hypotheses** How might Earth's climates be different if Earth were not tilted on its axis?

CHAPTER PROJECT

Check Your Progress

Have you chosen your microclimate study sites? If your sites are on private property, get permission. Set up a logbook so that you can record your data. How do you think the conditions in these sites will differ? Write down your hypotheses. Now you are ready to measure daily weather conditions for your microclimates. (*Hint:* Be sure to take your measurements at the same time each day.)

Skills Lab

Controlling Variables

Sunny Rays and Angles

In this lab, you will investigate how the angle of the sun's rays affects the amount of energy absorbed by different parts of Earth's surface.

Problem

How does the angle of a light source affect the rate of temperature change of a surface?

Materials

books	graph paper	pencil
scissors	ruler	clear tape
watch or clock	3 thermometers	protractor

100-W incandescent lamp
black construction paper

Procedure

1. Cut a strip of black construction paper 5 cm by 10 cm. Fold the paper in half and tape two sides to form a pocket.
2. Repeat Step 1 to make two more pockets.
3. Place the bulb of a thermometer inside each pocket.
4. Place the pockets with thermometers close together, as shown in the photo. Place one thermometer in a vertical position (90° angle), one at a 45° angle, and the third one in a horizontal position (0° angle). Use a protractor to measure the angles. Support the thermometers with books.
5. Position the lamp so that it is 30 cm from each of the thermometer bulbs. Make sure the lamp will not move during the activity.
6. Copy a data table like the one below into your notebook.
7. In your data table, record the temperature on all three thermometers. (All three temperatures should be the same.)
8. Switch on the lamp. In your data table, record the temperature on each thermometer every minute for 15 minutes. **CAUTION:** *Be careful not to touch the hot lampshade.*
9. After 15 minutes, switch off the lamp.

Analyze and Conclude

1. In this experiment, what was the manipulated variable? What was the responding variable? How do you know which is which?
2. Graph your data. Label the horizontal axis and vertical axis of your graph as shown on the sample graph. Use solid, dashed, and dotted lines to show the results from each thermometer, as shown in the key.
3. Based on your data, at which angle did the temperature increase the most?
4. At which angle did the temperature increase the least?

DATA TABLE

	Temperature (°C)		
Time (min.)	0° Angle	45° Angle	90° Angle
Start			
1			
2			
3			
4			
5			

5. What part of Earth's surface does each thermometer represent?
6. Why is air at the North Pole still very cold in the summer even though the Northern Hemisphere is tilted toward the sun?
7. **Think About It** In this experiment, what variables were held constant?

Design an Experiment

Design an experiment to find out how the results of this investigation would change if the lamp were placed farther from the thermometers. Then design another experiment to find out what would happen if the lamp were placed closer to the thermometers.

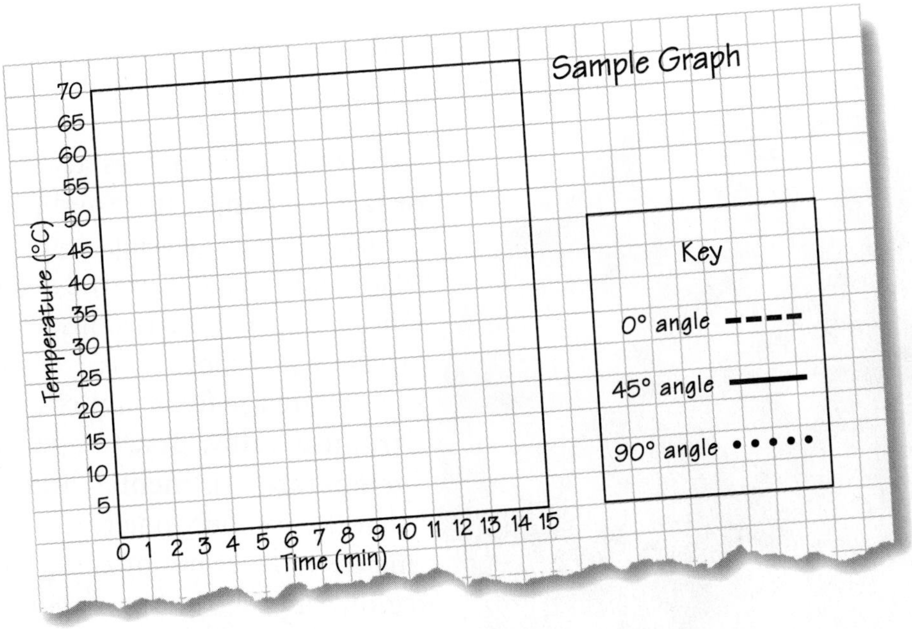

Sample Graph
Temperature (°C)
70
65
60
55
50
45
40
35
30
25
20
15
10
5
0 1 2 3 4 5 6 7 8 9 10 11 12 13 14 15
Time (min)
Key
0° angle
45° angle
90° angle

SECTION 2 Climate Regions

DISCOVER ACTIVITY

What Are Different Climate Types?

1. Collect pictures from magazines and newspapers of a variety of land areas around the world.
2. Sort the pictures into categories according to common weather characteristics.

Think It Over

Forming Operational Definitions Choose several words that describe the typical weather for each of your categories. What words would you use to describe the typical weather where you live?

GUIDE FOR READING

- **What factors are used to define climates?**
- **What are the five main climate regions?**

Reading Tip **Before you read, preview *Exploring Climate Regions.* Write a list of any questions you have about climate regions.**

When the Spanish settlers came to California in the 1700s, they brought with them plants from home. The padres, or priests, who established missions planted vineyards and orchards. They found that grapes, figs, and olives grew as well in California as they had in Spain. What do Spain and California have in common? They have similar climates.

Classifying Climates

The Spanish padres traveled a long distance but found a familiar climate. Suppose you traveled from your home to a place where the weather, the sunlight, and even the plants and trees were very different from what you are used to. Would you know what caused those differences?

Scientists classify climates according to two major factors: temperature and precipitation. They use a system developed around 1900 by Wladimir Köppen (KEP un). This system identifies broad climate regions, each of which has smaller subdivisions.

There are five main climate regions: tropical rainy, dry, temperate marine, temperate continental, and polar. Note that there is only one category of dry climates, whether hot or cold. These climate regions are shown in *Exploring Climate Regions* on pages 124–125.

◀ **Olive trees**

Exploring Climate Regions also shows a sixth type of climate: highlands. Recall that temperatures are cooler at the tops of mountains than in the surrounding areas. So a highland climate can occur within any of the other zones.

Maps show boundaries between the climate regions. In the real world, of course, no clear boundaries mark where one climate region ends and another begins. Each region blends gradually into the next.

☑ *Checkpoint* *What are the five main climate regions?*

Tropical Rainy Climates

The tropics have two types of rainy climates: tropical wet and tropical wet-and-dry. Trace the equator on *Exploring Climate Regions* with your finger. Tropical wet climates are found in low-lying lands near the equator. If you look north and south of tropical wet climates on the map, you can see two bands of tropical wet-and-dry climates.

Tropical Wet In areas that have a tropical wet climate, many days are rainy, often with afternoon thunderstorms. With year-round heat and heavy rainfall, vegetation grows lush and green. Dense rain forests grow in these rainy climates. **Rain forests** are forests in which plenty of rain falls all year-round. Tall trees such as teak and mahogany form the top layer, or canopy, while smaller bushes and vines grow near the ground. There are also many animals in the rain forest, including colorful parrots and toucans, bats, insects, frogs, and snakes.

In the United States, only the windward sides of the Hawaiian islands have a tropical wet climate. Rainfall is very heavy—over 10 meters per year on the windward side of the Hawaiian island of Kauai. The rain forests in Hawaii have a large variety of plants, including ferns, orchids, and many types of vines and trees.

Figure 6 Lush tropical rain forests grow in the tropical wet climate. ***Relating Cause and Effect*** *What climate factors encourage this growth?*

EXPLORING Climate Regions

Climate regions are classified according to a combination of temperature and precipitation. Climates in highland regions change rapidly as altitude changes.

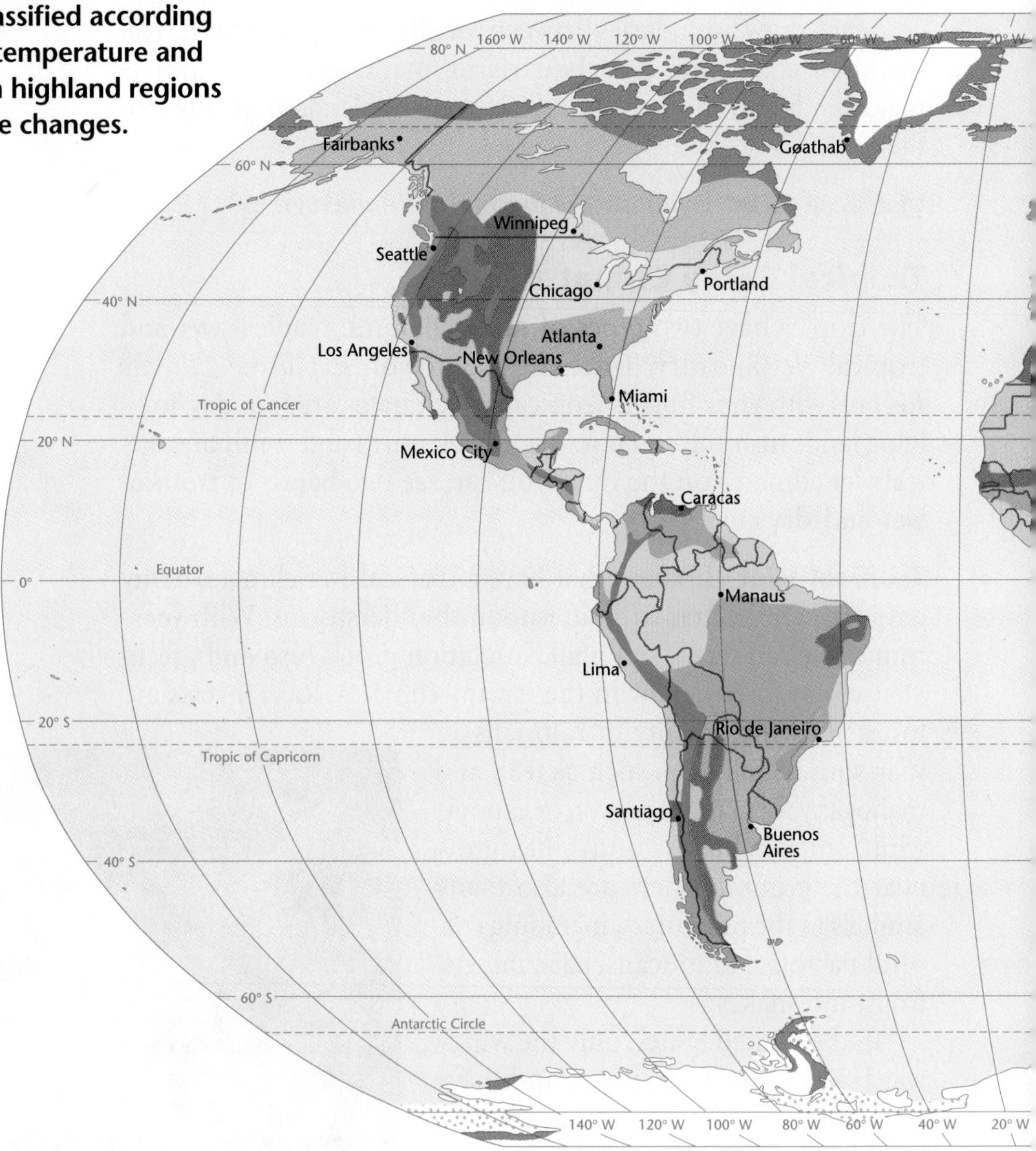

80° N
160° W
140° W
120° W
100° W
80° W
60° W
40° W
20° W
60° N
40° N
20° N
0°
20° S
40° S
60° S
Tropic of Cancer
Equator
Tropic of Capricorn
Antarctic Circle
Fairbanks
Gøathab
Winnipeg
Seattle
Chicago
Portland
Atlanta
Los Angeles
New Orleans
Miami
Mexico City
Caracas
Manaus
Lima
Rio de Janeiro
Santiago
Buenos Aires

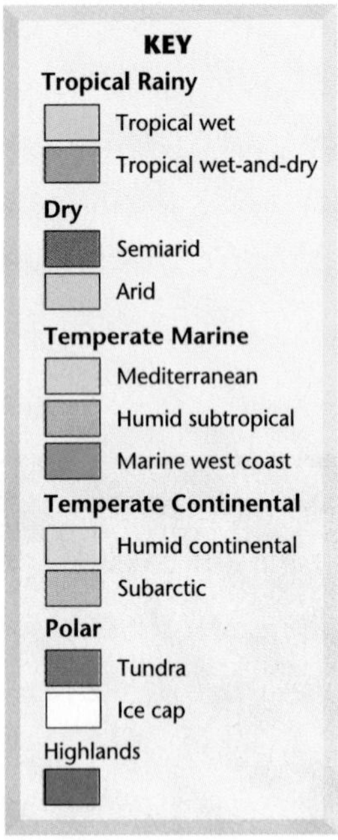

KEY
Tropical Rainy
Tropical wet
Tropical wet-and-dry
Dry
Semiarid
Arid
Temperate Marine
Mediterranean
Humid subtropical
Marine west coast
Temperate Continental
Humid continental
Subarctic
Polar
Tundra
Ice cap
Highlands

Tropical Rainy

Temperature always 18°C or above.

Tropical wet *Always hot and humid, with heavy rainfall (at least 6 centimeters a month) all year round.*
Tropical wet-and-dry *Always hot, with alternating wet and dry seasons; heavy rainfall in the wet season.*

Dry

Occurs wherever potential evaporation is greater than precipitation. May be hot or cold.

Arid *Desert, with little precipitation, usually less than 25 centimeters a year.*
Semiarid *Dry but receives about 25 to 50 centimeters of precipitation a year.*

Temperate Marine

Average temperature 10°C or above in the warmest month, between –3° and 18°C in the coldest month.

Mediterranean *Warm, dry summers and rainy winters.*
Humid subtropical *Hot summers and cool winters.*
Marine west coast *Mild winters and cool summers, with moderate precipitation year round.*

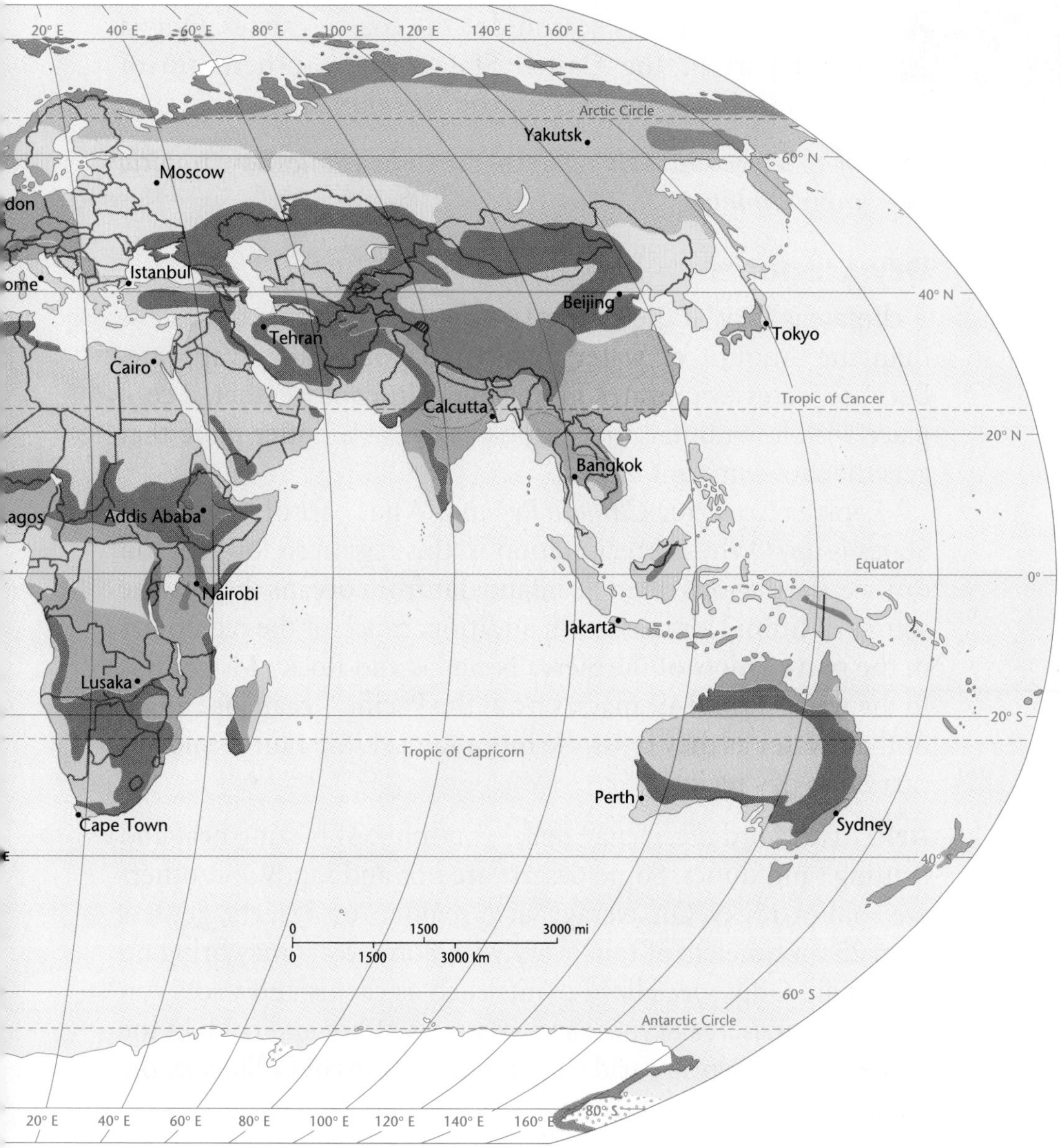
20° E
40° E
60° E
80° E
100° E
120° E
140° E
160° E
Arctic Circle
Yakutsk
60° N
Moscow
don
Istanbul
ome
40° N
Beijing
Tokyo
Tehran
Cairo
Tropic of Cancer
Calcutta
20° N
Bangkok
Lagos
Addis Ababa
Equator
0°
Nairobi
Jakarta
Lusaka
20° S
Tropic of Capricorn
Perth
Sydney
Cape Town
40° S
0
1500
3000 mi
0
1500
3000 km
60° S
Antarctic Circle
80° S

Temperate Continental
Average temperature 10°C or above in the warmest month, –3°C or below in the coldest month.

Humid continental *Hot, humid summers and cold winters, with moderate precipitation year round.*
Subarctic *Short, cool summers and long, cold winters. Light precipitation, mainly in summer.*

Polar
Average temperature below 10°C in the warmest month.

Tundra *Always cold with a short, cool summer—warmest temperature about 10°C.*
Ice cap *Always cold, average temperature at or below 0°C.*

Highlands
Generally cooler and wetter than nearby lowlands, temperature decreasing with altitude.

Figure 7 A reticulated giraffe gazes across the grasses and shrubby trees of the African savanna. Savannas are found in tropical wet-and-dry climates.

Tropical Wet-and-Dry Tropical wet-and-dry climates get slightly less rain than tropical climates and have distinct dry and rainy seasons. Instead of rain forests, there are tropical grasslands called **savannas**. Scattered clumps of trees that can survive the dry season dot the coarse grasses. Only a small part of the United States—the southern tip of Florida—has a tropical wet-and-dry climate.

☑ *Checkpoint* ***What parts of the United States have tropical rainy climates?***

Dry Climates

A climate is "dry" if the amount of precipitation that falls is less than the amount of water that could potentially evaporate. Because water evaporates more slowly in cool weather, a cool place with low rainfall may not be as dry as a hotter place that gets the same amount of rain.

Look at *Exploring Climate Regions.* What part of the United States is dry? Why is precipitation in this region so low? As you can see, dry regions often lie inland, far from oceans that are the source of humid air masses. In addition, much of the region lies in the rain shadow of the Sierra Nevadas and Rocky Mountains to the west. Humid air masses from the Pacific Ocean lose much of their water as they cross the mountains. Little rain or snow is carried to dry regions.

Arid The word *desert* may make you think of blazing heat and drifting sand dunes. Some deserts are hot and sandy, but others are cold or rocky. On average, arid regions, or **deserts,** get less than 25 centimeters of rain every year. Some years may bring no rain at all. Only specialized plants such as cactus and yucca can survive the desert's dryness and extremes of hot and cold. In the United States there are arid climates in portions of California, the Great Basin, and the southwest.

Figure 8 Dry-land wheat farming is common in the steppe region of the Great Plains. *Comparing and Contrasting How are steppes similar to savannas, shown in Figure 7? How are they different?*

Semiarid Locate the semiarid regions on *Exploring Climate Regions.* As you can see, large semiarid areas are usually located on the edges of deserts. A steppe is dry but gets enough rainfall for short grasses and low bushes to grow. For this reason, a **steppe** may also be called a prairie or grassland.

The Great Plains are the steppe region of the United States. Many kinds of short grasses and wildflowers grow here, along with scattered forests. Livestock grazing is an important part of the economy of the Great Plains. Beef cattle, sheep, and goats graze on the short grasses of the region. Farm crops include grains, such as wheat and oats, and sunflowers.

Temperate Marine Climates

Look at *Exploring Climate Regions,* along the coasts of continents in the temperate zones. You will find the third main climate region, temperate marine. There are three kinds of temperate marine climates. Because of the moderating influence of oceans, all three are humid and have mild winters.

Marine West Coast The coolest temperate marine climates are found on the west coasts of continents north of 40° north latitude and south of 40° south latitude. Humid ocean air brings cool, rainy summers and mild, rainy winters.

In North America, the marine west coast climate extends from northern California to southern Alaska. In the Pacific Northwest of the United States, humid air from the Pacific Ocean rises as it hits the western slopes of the Coastal Ranges. As the air cools, large amounts of rain or snow fall on the western slopes.

Because of the heavy precipitation, thick forests of tall trees grow in this region, including coniferous, or cone-bearing, trees such as Sitka spruce, Douglas fir, redwoods, and Western red cedar. One of the main industries of this region is harvesting and processing wood for lumber, paper, and furniture.

TRY THIS

Modeling a Humid Climate

ACTIVITY

Here's how you can create humidity.

1. Put the same amount of water in each of two small plastic bowls.
2. Place a sheet of transparent plastic wrap over each bowl. Secure each sheet with a rubber band.
3. Place one bowl on a warm, sunny windowsill or near a radiator. Put the other bowl in a cool location.
4. Wait a day and then look at the two bowls. What do you see on the plastic wrap over each bowl?

Inferring Would you expect to find more water vapor in the air in a warm climate or in a cool one? Why? Explain your results in terms of solar energy.

Figure 9 Seattle, Washington, is in the marine west coast climate region. Here the summers are cool and rainy, and winters are wet and mild.

Figure 10 A. Much of Italy has a Mediterranean climate, with warm, dry summers and cool, rainy winters. B. Rice is a major food crop in places with a humid subtropical climate, as in parts of China. *Comparing and Contrasting How are Mediterranean and humid subtropical climates similar? How do they differ?*

Mediterranean A coastal climate that is drier and warmer than west coast marine is known as Mediterranean. Find the Mediterranean climates in *Exploring Climate Regions.* In the United States, the southern coast of California has a Mediterranean climate. This climate is mild, with two seasons. In winter, marine air masses bring cool, rainy weather. Summers are somewhat warmer, with little rain.

Mediterranean climates have two main vegetation types. One is made up of dense shrubs and small trees, called chaparral (chap uh RAL). The other vegetation type includes grasses with a few oak trees.

Agriculture is an important part of the economy of California's Mediterranean climate region. Some crops, including olives and grapes, were originally introduced by Spanish settlers. With the help of irrigation, farmers grow many different crops, including rice, oranges, and many vegetables, fruits, and nuts.

Humid Subtropical The warmest temperate marine climates are on the edges of the tropics. **Humid subtropical** climates are wet and warm, but not as constantly hot as the tropics. Locate the humid subtropical climates in *Exploring Climate Regions.*

The southeastern United States has a humid subtropical climate. Summers are hot, with much more rainfall than in winter. Maritime tropical air masses move inland, bringing tropical weather conditions, including thunderstorms and occasional hurricanes, to southern cities such as Houston, New Orleans, and Atlanta. Winters are cool to mild, with more rain than snow. However, polar air masses moving in from the north can bring freezing temperatures and severe frosts.

Mixed forests of oak, ash, hickory, and pines grow in the humid subtropical region of the United States. Cotton was once the most important crop grown in this region. Other crops, including oranges, grapefruits, peaches, peanuts, sugar cane, and rice, are now more important to the economy.

☑ *Checkpoint* ***What is the main difference between a humid subtropical climate and a tropical climate?***

Temperate Continental Climates

Temperate continental climates are found on continents in the Northern Hemisphere. Because they are not influenced very much by oceans, temperate continental climates have extremes of temperature. Why do continental climates occur only in the Northern Hemisphere? The parts of continents in the Southern Hemisphere south of 40° south latitude are not far enough from oceans for dry continental air masses to form.

Humid Continental Shifting tropical and polar air masses bring constantly changing weather to humid continental climates. In winter, continental polar air masses move south, bringing bitterly cold weather. In summer, tropical air masses move north, bringing heat and high humidity. Humid continental climates receive moderate amounts of rain in the summer. Smaller amounts of rain or snow fall in winter.

What parts of the United States have a humid continental climate? The eastern part of the region—the Northeast—has a range of forest types, from mixed forests in the south to coniferous forests in the north. Much of the western part of this region—the Midwest—was once tall grasslands, but is now farmland. Farmers in the Midwest grow wheat, corn, other grains, and soybeans. These crops are used as food for people and for hogs, poultry, and beef cattle.

Subarctic The **subarctic** climates lie north of the humid continental climates. The world's largest subarctic regions are in Russia, Canada, and Alaska. Summers in the subarctic are short and cool. Winters are long and bitterly cold.

In North America, coniferous trees such as spruce and fir make up a huge northern forest that stretches from Alaska to Canada's east coast. Many large mammals, including bears, wolves, and moose, live in the forest. Small mammals such as beavers, porcupines, and red squirrels, and birds such as grouse and owls also live in the forest. Wood products from the northern forest are an important part of the economy.

Sharpen your Skills

Classifying

ACTIVITY

The table shows some climate data for three cities.

	City A	City B	City C
Average January Temperature (°C)	12.8	18.9	–5.6
Average July Temperature (°C)	21.1	27.2	20
Annual Precipitation (cm)	33	152	109

Describe the climate you would expect each city to have. Identify which city is Miami, which is Los Angeles, and which is Portland, Maine. Use *Exploring Climate Regions* on pages 550–551 to help identify each city's climate.

Figure 11 Subarctic climates have cool summers and cold winters. Parts of this region are called "spruce-moose belts."

Polar Climates

The polar climate is the coldest climate region. Ice cap and tundra climates are found only in the far north and south, near the North and South poles.

Figure 12 Emperor penguins live on the ice cap of Antarctica.

Ice Cap As you can see in *Exploring Climate Regions*, ice cap climates are found mainly on Greenland and in Antarctica. With average temperatures always at or below freezing, the land in ice cap climate regions is covered with ice and snow. Intense cold makes the air dry. Lichens and a few low plants may grow on the rocks.

Tundra The **tundra** climate region stretches across northern Alaska, Canada, and Russia. Short, cool summers follow bitterly cold winters. Because of the cold, some layers of the tundra soil are always frozen. This permanently frozen tundra soil is called **permafrost.** Because of the permafrost, water cannot drain away, so the soil is wet and boggy in summer.

It is too cold on the tundra for trees to grow. Despite the harsh climate, during the short summers the tundra is filled with life. Mosquitoes and other insects hatch in the ponds and marshes above the frozen permafrost. Mosses, grasses, lichens, wildflowers, and shrubs grow quickly during the short summers. Herds of caribou and musk oxen eat the vegetation and are in turn preyed upon by wolves. Some birds, such as the white-tailed ptarmigan, live on the tundra year-round. Others, such as the arctic tern and many waterfowl, spend only the summer there.

☑ *Checkpoint* ***What type of vegetation is found on the tundra?***

Figure 13 The tundra is often very cold, but still many plants and animals live there. *Observing How are these musk oxen adapted to the cold climate?*

Highlands

Why are highlands a distinct climate region? Remember that temperature falls as altitude increases, so highland regions are colder than the regions that surround them. Increasing altitude produces climate changes similar to the climate changes you would expect with increasing latitude. In the tropics, highlands are like cold islands overlooking the warm lowlands.

The climate on the lower slopes of a mountain range is like that of the surrounding countryside. The foothills of the Rocky Mountains, for instance, share the semiarid climate of the Great Plains. But as you go higher up into the mountains, temperatures become lower. Climbing 1,000 meters up in elevation is like traveling 1,200 kilometers north. The climate higher in the mountains is like that of the subarctic: cool with coniferous trees. Animals typical of the subarctic zone—such as moose and porcupines—live in the mountain forest.

Above a certain elevation—the tree line—no trees can grow. The climate above the tree line is like that of the tundra. Only low plants, mosses, and lichens can grow there.

Figure 14 The top of this mountain is too cold and windy for trees to grow. **Classifying** *What climate zone does this mountaintop resemble?*

Section 2 Review

1. What two factors are used to classify climates?
2. Briefly describe each of the five main climate types.
3. Give three examples of how the climate of a region affects what plants and animals can live there.
4. **Thinking Critically Applying Concepts** Which of these two places has more severe winters—central Russia or the west coast of France? Why?
5. **Thinking Critically Classifying** Classify the main climate regions according to whether or not trees usually grow in each one.

Science at Home

Describe to your family the characteristics of each of the climate regions found in the United States. Which climate region does your family live in? What plants and animals live in your climate region? What characteristics do these plants and animals have that make them well-adapted to living in your climate region?

Real-World Lab

Careers in Science

Cool Climate Graphs

You are a land-use planner who has been hired by a company that builds recreational facilities. Your company is considering buying land near at least one of four cities, all at about the same latitude. Your job is to decide which of the cities would be the best place to build a water park and which is the best place to build a ski-touring center.

Problem

Based on climate data, which city is the best place for each type of recreational facility?

Skills Focus

graphing, interpreting data, drawing conclusions

Materials

calculator
ruler
3 pieces of graph paper
black, blue, red, and green pencils
climate map on pages 550–551
U.S. map with city names and latitude lines

Procedure

1. Work in groups of three. Each person should graph the data for a different city: A, B, or C.
2. On graph paper, use a black pencil to label the axes as on the climate graph below. Title your climate graph City A, City B, or City C.
3. Use your green pencil to make a bar graph of the monthly average amount of precipitation. Place a star below the name of each month that has more than a trace of snow.
4. Use a red pencil to plot the average monthly maximum temperature. Make a dot for the temperature in the middle of each space for the month. When you have plotted data for all 12 months, connect the points into a smooth curved line.
5. Use a blue pencil to plot the average monthly minimum temperature for your city. Use the same procedure as in Step 4.
6. Calculate the total average annual precipitation for this city and include it in your observations. Do this by adding the average precipitation for each month.

Washington, D.C., Climate Averages

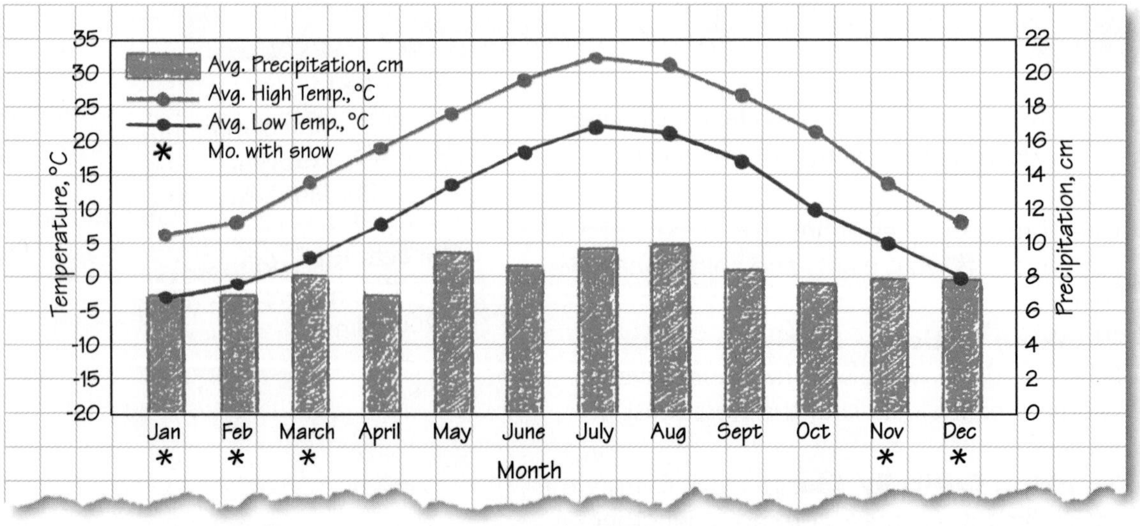
Avg. Precipitation, cm
Avg. High Temp., °C
Avg. Low Temp., °C
* Mo. with snow
Temperature, °C
35
30
25
20
15
10
5
0
-5
-10
-15
-20
Precipitation, cm
22
20
18
16
14
12
10
8
6
4
2
0
Jan
Feb
March
April
May
June
July
Aug
Sept
Oct
Nov
Dec
Month

Climate Data												
Washington, D.C.	Jan	Feb	Mar	April	May	June	July	Aug	Sept	Oct	Nov	Dec
Average High Temp. (°C)	6	8	14	19	24	29	32	31	27	21	14	8
Average Low Temp. (°C)	-3	-2	3	8	14	19	22	21	17	10	5	0
Average Precipitation (cm)	6.9	6.9	8.1	6.9	9.4	8.6	9.7	9.9	8.4	7.6	7.9	7.9
Months With Snow	*	*	*	trace	—	—	—	—	—	trace	*	*
City A	Jan	Feb	Mar	Apr	May	Jun	July	Aug	Sept	Oct	Nov	Dec
Average High Temp. (°C)	13	16	16	17	17	18	18	19	21	21	17	13
Average Low Temp. (°C)	8	9	9	10	11	12	12	13	13	13	11	8
Average Precipitation (cm)	10.4	7.6	7.9	3.3	0.8	0.5	0.3	0.3	0.8	3.3	8.1	7.9
Months With Snow	trace	trace	trace	—	—	—	—	—	—	—	—	trace
City B	Jan	Feb	Mar	Apr	May	Jun	July	Aug	Sept	Oct	Nov	Dec
Average High Temp. (°C)	5	7	10	16	21	26	29	27	23	18	11	6
Average Low Temp. (°C)	–9	–7	–4	1	6	11	14	13	8	2	–4	–8
Average Precipitation (cm)	0.8	1.0	2.3	3.0	5.6	5.8	7.4	7.6	3.3	2.0	1.3	1.3
Months With Snow	*	*	*	*	*	—	—	—	trace	*	*	*
City C	Jan	Feb	Mar	Apr	May	Jun	July	Aug	Sept	Oct	Nov	Dec
Average High Temp. (°C)	7	11	13	18	23	28	33	32	27	21	12	8
Average Low Temp. (°C)	–6	–4	–2	1	4	8	11	10	5	1	–3	–7
Average Precipitation (cm)	2.5	2.3	1.8	1.3	1.8	1	0.8	0.5	0.8	1	2	2.5
Months With Snow	*	*	*	*	*	trace	—	—	trace	trace	*	*

Analyze and Conclude

Compare your climate graphs and observations. Use all three climate graphs, plus the graph for Washington, D.C., to answer these questions.

1. Which of the four cities has the least change in average temperatures during the year?
2. In which climate region is each city located?
3. Which of the cities listed below matches each climate graph?

Colorado Springs, Colorado	latitude 39° N
San Francisco, California	latitude 38° N
Reno, Nevada	latitude 40° N
Washington, D.C.	latitude 39° N

4. Even though these cities are at approximately the same latitude, why are their climate graphs so different?
5. **Apply** Which city would be the best location for a water slide park? For a cross-country ski touring center? What other factors should you consider when deciding where to build each type of recreational facility? Explain.

More to Explore

What type of climate does the area where you live have? Find out what outdoor recreational facilities your community has. How is each one particularly suited to the climate of *your* area?

3 Long-Term Changes in Climate

DISCOVER — ACTIVITY

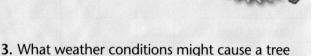

What Story Can Tree Rings Tell?

1. Look at the photo of tree rings on page 561. Tree rings are the layers of new wood that form as a tree grows each year.
2. Look closely at the tree rings. Note whether they are all the same thickness.
3. What weather conditions might cause a tree to form thicker or thinner tree rings?

Think It Over

Inferring How could you use tree rings to tell you about weather in the past?

GUIDE FOR READING

- **What principle do scientists follow in studying ancient climates?**
- **What changes occur on Earth's surface during an ice age?**
- **What theories have been proposed to explain natural climate change?**

Reading Tip **Before you read, preview the art and photos and read the captions. Write a prediction about how Earth's climate has changed through time.**

One of the greatest Native American cultures in the American Southwest was the Ancestral Pueblos. These farming people built great pueblos, or "apartment houses," of stone and sun-baked clay, with hundreds of rooms. By about the year 1000, the Ancestral Pueblos were flourishing. They grew crops of corn, beans, and squash and traded extensively with other groups of people. But in the late 1200s, the climate became drier, reducing the size of their crops. After a long period of drought, the Ancestral Pueblos migrated to other areas.

Although weather can vary from day to day, climates usually change more slowly. But climates do change, both in small areas and throughout the world. Although climate change is usually slow, its consequences are great. Climate changes have affected many civilizations, including the Ancestral Pueblos.

Figure 15 The Ancestral Pueblos lived in these buildings, now in Mesa Verde National Park in southwestern Colorado, about 1,000 years ago.

Studying Climate Change

In studying ancient climates, scientists follow an important principle: If plants or animals today need certain conditions to live, then similar plants and animals in the past also required those conditions. For example, today magnolia and palm trees grow only in warm, moist climates. Scientists assume that the ancestors of these trees required similar conditions. Thus, 80-million-year-old fossils of these trees in Greenland are good evidence that the climate of Greenland was warm and moist 80 million years ago.

Tree rings can also be used to learn about ancient climates. Every summer, a tree grows a new layer of wood under its bark. These layers form rings when seen in a cross section, as shown in Figure 16. In cool climates, the amount the tree grows—the thickness of a ring—depends on the length of the warm growing season. In dry climates, the thickness of each ring depends on the amount of rainfall. By looking at cross sections of trees, scientists can count backward from the outer ring to see whether previous years were warm or cool, wet or dry. A thin ring indicates that the year was cool or dry. A thick ring indicates that the year was warm or wet.

A third source of information about ancient climates is pollen records. Each type of plant has a particular type of pollen. The bottoms of some lakes are covered with thick layers of mud and plant material, including pollen, that fell to the bottom of the lake over thousands of years. Scientists can drill down into these layers and bring up cores to examine. By looking at the pollen present in each layer, scientists can tell what types of plants lived in the area. The scientists can then infer that the climate that existed when the pollen was deposited was similar to the climate where the same plants grow today.

Figure 16 Scientists have learned about past climates by studying tree rings. They can learn much from giant sequoias, some of which may be 3,000–4,000 years old.

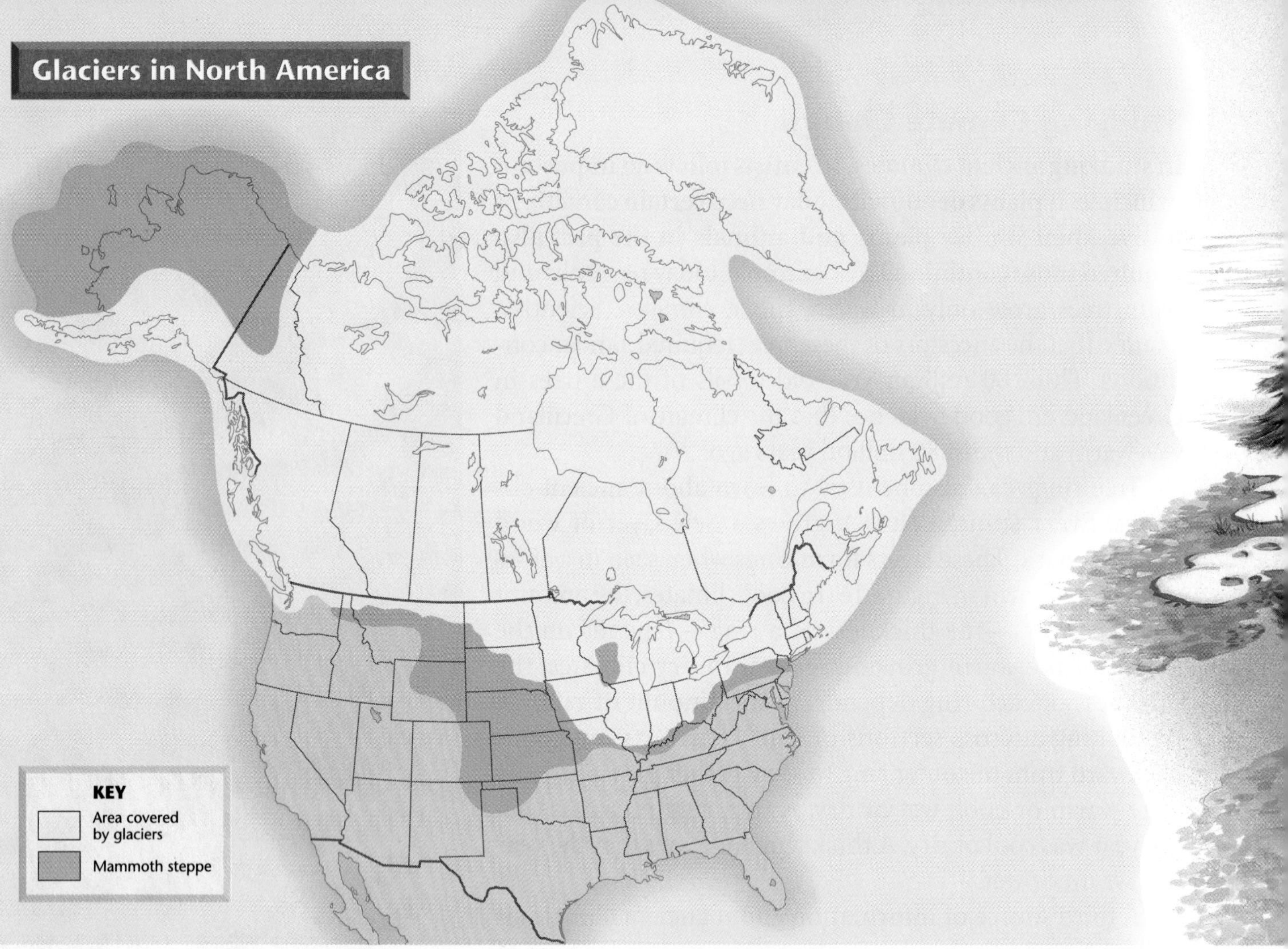
Glaciers in North America
KEY
Area covered by glaciers
Mammoth steppe

Figure 17 The map shows the parts of North America that were covered by glaciers 18,000 years ago. On the steppe near the glaciers lived many mammals that are now extinct, including woolly mammoths and scimitar-toothed cats.

Ice Ages

Throughout Earth's history, climates have gradually changed. Over millions of years, warm periods have alternated with cold periods known as **ice ages,** or glacial episodes. **During each ice age, huge sheets of ice called glaciers covered large parts of Earth's surface.**

From fossils and other evidence, scientists have concluded that in the past two million years there have been at least four major ice ages. Each one lasted 100,000 years or longer. Long, warmer periods known as interglacials occurred between the ice ages. Some scientists think that we are now in a warm period between ice ages.

The most recent major ice age ended only about 10,500 years ago. Ice sheets covered much of northern Europe and North America, reaching as far south as present-day Iowa and Nebraska. In some places, the ice was more than 3 kilometers thick. So much water was frozen in the ice sheets that the average sea level was much lower than it is today. When the ice sheets melted, the rising oceans flooded coastal areas. Inland, large lakes formed.

☑ *Checkpoint* *Why were the oceans lower during the ice ages than they are now?*

Causes of Climate Change

Why do climates change? Scientists have formed several hypotheses. **Possible explanations for major climate changes include variations in the position of Earth relative to the sun, changes in the sun's energy output, and the movement of continents.**

Earth's Position Changes in Earth's position relative to the sun may have affected climates. According to one hypothesis, as Earth revolves around the sun, the time of year when Earth is closest to the sun shifts from January to July and back again over a period of about 26,000 years.

The angle at which Earth's axis tilts and the shape of Earth's orbit around the sun also change slightly over long periods of time. The combined effects of these changes in Earth's movements may be the main cause of ice ages.

INTEGRATING SPACE SCIENCE

Solar Energy Short-term changes in climate have been linked to changes in the number of **sunspots**—dark, cooler regions on the surface of the sun. Sunspots increase and decrease in regular 11-year cycles. Sunspot cycles could in turn be caused by changes in the sun's energy output.

Social Studies CONNECTION

Prehistoric people who lived during the last ice age faced a harsh environment. To endure the cold, they learned to make clothing from animal skins. They also used fires for warmth and cooking.

In Your Journal

Make a list of five ways your life would change if the climate suddenly became colder.

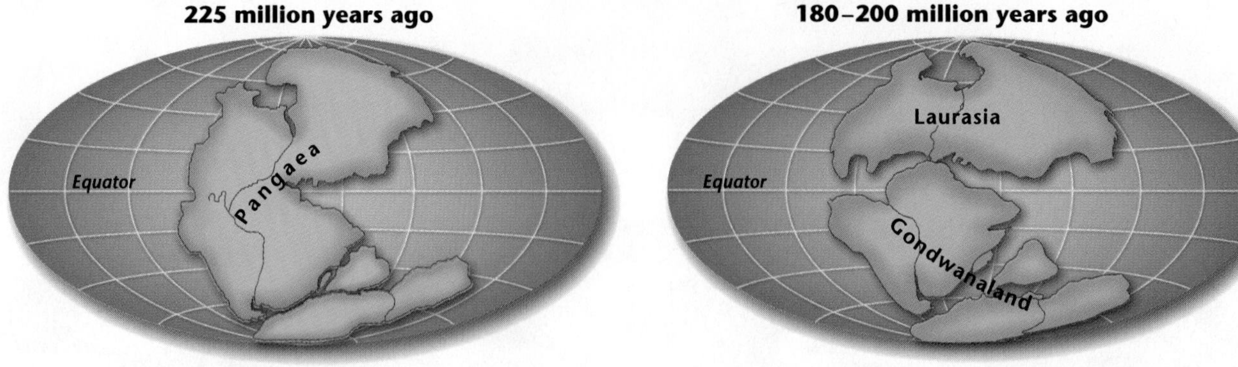
225 million years ago
Equator
Pangaea
180–200 million years ago
Laurasia
Equator
Gondwanaland

Figure 18 The continents have moved over millions of years. *Interpreting Maps* *Which present-day continents broke away from Gondwanaland? Which broke away from Laurasia?*

Recently, satellite measurements have shown that the amount of energy the sun produces increases and decreases slightly from year to year. These changes may cause Earth's temperature to increase and decrease. More observations are needed to test this hypothesis.

Movement of Continents Earth's continents have not always been located where they are now. About 225 million years ago, most of the land on Earth was part of a single continent called Pangaea (pan JEE uh).

As Figure 18 shows, most continents were far from their present positions. Continents that are now in the polar zones were once near the equator. This movement explains how tropical plants such as magnolias and palm trees could once have grown in Greenland.

Over millions of years, the continents broke away and gradually moved to their present positions. The movements of continents over time changed the locations of land and sea. These changes affected the global patterns of winds and ocean currents, which in turn slowly changed climates. And as the continents continue to move, climates will continue to change.

Section 3 Review

1. What types of evidence do scientists use to study changes in climate?
2. How was the climate during an ice age different from the climate today?
3. List three factors that could be responsible for changing Earth's climates.
4. **Thinking Critically** **Predicting** What kinds of climate changes might be caused by a volcanic eruption? Would these changes be permanent? Explain.

CHAPTER PROJECT

Check Your Progress

What types of weather conditions have you measured at each site? Have you been recording all the data in your logbook? You should now be ready to graph and analyze your data. Are the weather conditions at all of your test areas similar, or do you see differences? What do you think causes the different conditions? What organisms did you observe at your sites?

INTEGRATING ENVIRONMENTAL SCIENCE

SECTION 4

Global Changes in the Atmosphere

DISCOVER ACTIVITY

What Is the Greenhouse Effect?

1. Cut two pieces of black construction paper to fit the bottoms of two shoe boxes.
2. Place a thermometer in one end of each box. Read the temperatures on the thermometers. (They should be the same.) Cover one box with plastic wrap.
3. Place the boxes together where sunlight or a light bulb can shine on them equally. Make sure the thermometers are shaded by the sides of the boxes.
4. What do think will happen to the temperatures on the thermometers? Wait 15 minutes and read the thermometers again. Record the temperatures.

Think It Over

Inferring How can you explain the temperature difference between the box with the plastic wrap and the open box? Why does the inside of a car left in direct sunlight get so warm?

GUIDE FOR READING

- **How might human activities be affecting the temperature of Earth's atmosphere?**
- **How have human activities affected the ozone layer?**

Reading Tip **As you read, draw a concept map showing how human activities can cause changes in the atmosphere and climate.**

Have you ever seen a headline like the one below? If you hate cold winters and love summer sports, you may wonder what would be wrong with a slightly warmer world. Some experts agree with you, but many scientists are worried about such climate change.

ANYWHERE U.S.A. DAILY NEWS

Earth's Average Temperature Expected to Increase by 3 Celsius Degrees

Most changes in world climates are caused by natural factors. In the last hundred years, however, human activities have also had an effect on Earth's climate and atmosphere. Two of the most important worldwide issues are global warming and thinning of the ozone layer.

Global Warming

Over the last 120 years, the average temperature of the troposphere has risen by about 0.5 Celsius degree. Was this increase part of natural variations, or was it caused by human activities? What effects could higher temperatures have? Scientists have done a great deal of research to try to answer these questions.

Sunlight
Infrared radiation cannot pass through greenhouse roof

Figure 19 Sunlight enters the greenhouse and is absorbed. The interior of the greenhouse radiates back energy in the form of infrared radiation, or heat. The heat is trapped and held inside the greenhouse, warming it. *Applying Concepts What gases in Earth's atmosphere can trap heat like a greenhouse?*

The Greenhouse Effect Recall that gases in Earth's atmosphere hold in heat from the sun, keeping the atmosphere at a comfortable temperature for living things. The process by which gases in Earth's atmosphere trap solar energy is called the greenhouse effect.

Gases in the atmosphere that trap solar energy are called **greenhouse gases.** Water vapor, carbon dioxide, and methane are some of the greenhouse gases. **Human activities that add greenhouse gases to the atmosphere may be warming Earth's atmosphere.** For example, the burning of wood, coal, oil, and natural gas adds carbon dioxide to the air. If the increased carbon dioxide traps more heat, the result could be **global warming,** a gradual increase in the temperature of Earth's atmosphere.

The amount of carbon dioxide in the atmosphere has been steadily increasing. Some scientists predict that if the level of carbon dioxide doubles by the year 2100, the average global temperature could go up by 1.5 to 3.5 Celsius degrees.

Another Hypothesis Not everyone agrees about the causes of global warming. Some scientists think that the 0.5 Celsius degree rise in global temperatures over the past 120 years may be part of natural variations in climate rather than a result of increases in carbon dioxide.

As you learned in Section 3, satellite measurements have shown that the amount of energy the sun produces increases and decreases from year to year. These changes in solar energy could be causing periods of warmer and cooler climates. Or climate change could be a result of changes in both carbon dioxide levels and amounts of solar energy.

Possible Effects Global warming has some potential advantages. Farmers in cool areas could plant two crops a year. Places that are too cold for farming today could become farmland. However, many effects of global warming are likely to be less positive. Higher temperatures would cause water to evaporate from exposed soil, such as plowed farmland. Dry soil blows away easily. Thus some fertile fields might become "dust bowls."

A rise in temperatures of even a few degrees could warm up water in the oceans. As ocean surface temperatures increased, the number of hurricanes might increase.

As the water warmed, it would expand, raising sea levels around the world. Glaciers and polar ice caps might partially melt, which would also increase sea levels. Sea levels have already risen by 10 to 20 centimeters over the last 100 years, and could rise another 25 to 80 centimeters by the year 2100. Even such a small rise in sea levels would flood low-lying coastal areas.

☑ *Checkpoint* *What are three possible effects of global warming?*

Ozone Depletion

Another global change in the atmosphere involves the ozone layer, which you learned about in Chapter 14. Ozone in the stratosphere filters out much of the harmful ultraviolet radiation from the sun.

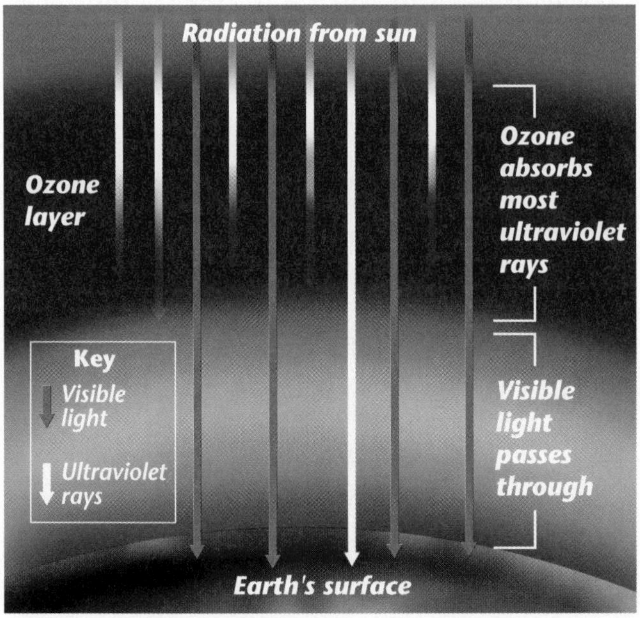

Radiation from sun
Ozone layer
Ozone absorbs most ultraviolet rays
Key
Visible light
Ultraviolet rays
Visible light passes through
Earth's surface

Figure 20 The ozone layer blocks much of the ultraviolet radiation coming from the sun. Visible light can pass through the ozone layer.

TRY THIS

It's Your Skin!

ACTIVITY

How well do sunscreens block out ultraviolet rays? Here's how to compare sunscreens.

1. Close the blinds or curtains in the room. Place one square of sun-sensitive paper inside each of three plastic sandwich bags.
2. Place three drops of one sunscreen on the outside of one bag. Spread the sunscreen as evenly as possible. Label this bag with the SPF number of the sunscreen.
3. On another bag, repeat Step 2 using a sunscreen with a different SPF. Wash your hands after spreading the sunscreen. Leave the third bag untreated as a control.
4. Place the bags outside in direct sunlight. Bring them back inside after 3 minutes or after one of the squares of paper has turned completely white.

Drawing Conclusions Did both of the sunscreens block ultraviolet radiation? Did one of the sunscreens block more ultraviolet radiation than the other one? Explain your results.

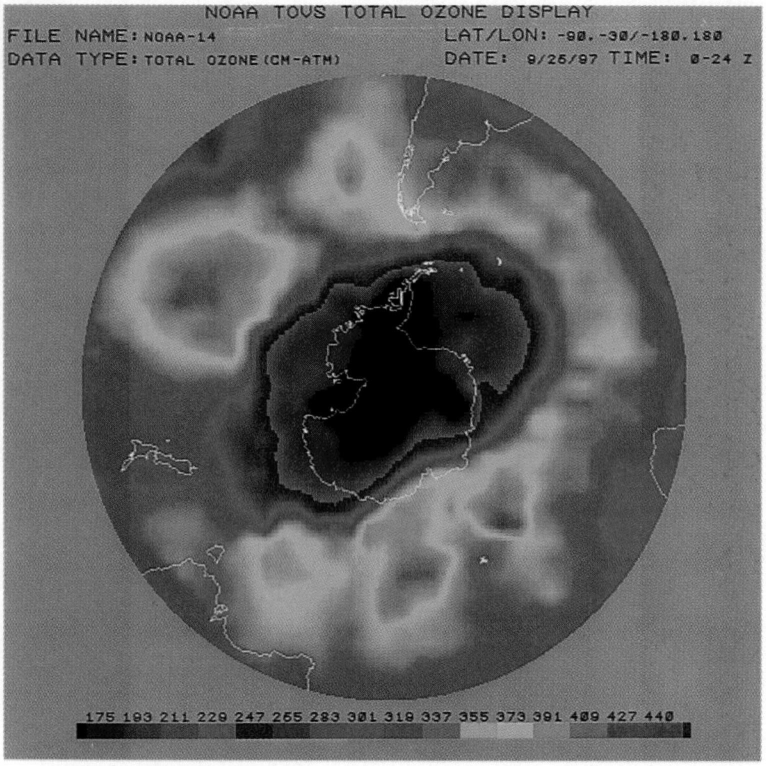
NOAA TOVS TOTAL OZONE DISPLAY
FILE NAME: NOAA-14
LAT/LON: -90.-30/-180.180
DATA TYPE: TOTAL OZONE (CM-ATM)
DATE: 9/25/97 TIME: 0-24 Z
175 193 211 229 247 265 283 301 319 337 355 373 391 409 427 440

Figure 21 This satellite image shows the concentration of ozone in the air over the South Pole. The dark area shows where the ozone layer is the thinnest.

In the 1970s, scientists noticed that the ozone layer over Antarctica was growing thinner each spring. By 1992, the area of thinner ozone was more than twice as large as the continental United States. What created the ozone hole? **Chemicals produced by humans have been damaging the ozone layer.**

The main cause of ozone depletion is a group of chlorine compounds called **chlorofluorocarbons,** or CFCs. CFCs were used in air conditioners and refrigerators, as cleaners for electronic parts, and in spray cans. Most chemical compounds released into the air eventually break down. CFCs, however, can last for decades and rise all the way to the stratosphere. In the stratosphere, ultraviolet radiation breaks down the CFC molecules into atoms, including chlorine. The chlorine atoms then break ozone down into oxygen atoms.

Because ozone blocks ultraviolet radiation, a decrease in ozone means an increase in the amount of ultraviolet radiation that reaches Earth's surface. If you have ever been sunburned, you can understand one effect of stronger ultraviolet radiation! Ultraviolet radiation can also cause eye damage and several kinds of skin cancer.

In the late 1970s, the United States and many other countries banned the use of CFCs in spray cans. In 1992, more than 90 nations agreed to phase out production of CFCs. Because ozone depletion affects the whole world, such agreements must be international to be effective.

Section 4 Review

1. What human actions increase the amount of carbon dioxide in Earth's atmosphere?
2. How could increases in carbon dioxide in the air affect world temperatures?
3. What chemicals are the major cause of ozone depletion in the stratosphere?
4. **Thinking Critically Predicting** How might global warming change conditions where you live? How would this affect your life?

Science at Home

Visit a drugstore with your family. Compare the SPF (sun protection factor) of the various sunscreens for sale. Explain why it is important to protect your skin from ultraviolet radiation. Ask your family members to determine the best value for their money in terms of SPF rating and price.

SECTION 1 What Causes Climate?

Key Ideas

- The climate of a region is determined by its temperature and precipitation.
- The main factors that influence temperature are latitude, altitude, distance from large bodies of water, and ocean currents.
- The main factors that affect precipitation are prevailing winds and the presence of mountains.
- The different seasons are a result of the tilt of Earth's axis as Earth travels around the sun.

Key Terms

climate
tropical zone
polar zone
temperate zone
marine climate
continental climate
windward
leeward
microclimate

SECTION 2 Climate Regions

Key Ideas

- Climates are classified according to temperature and precipitation.
- There are five main climate regions: tropical rainy, dry, temperate marine, temperate continental, and polar. Highlands are often considered to be a sixth climate region.

Key Terms

rain forest
savanna
desert
steppe
humid subtropical
subarctic
tundra
permafrost

SECTION 3 Long-Term Changes in Climate

Key Ideas

- Scientists assume that plants and animals in the past required the same conditions as similar plants and animals today.
- During each ice age, huge sheets of ice covered large parts of Earth's surface.
- Possible explanations for major climate changes include movement of continents, variations in the position of Earth relative to the sun, and changes in the sun's energy output.

Key Terms

ice age
sunspot

SECTION 4 Global Changes in the Atmosphere

INTEGRATING ENVIRONMENTAL SCIENCE

Key Ideas

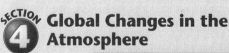

- Human activities that add greenhouse gases to the atmosphere may be warming Earth's atmosphere.
- Chemicals produced by humans have been damaging the ozone layer.

Key Terms

greenhouse gas
global warming
chlorofluorocarbons

ACTIVITY

USING THE INTERNET

www.phschool.com/state_focus/california/

California Test Prep: Reviewing Content

Multiple Choice

Choose the letter of the best answer.

1. Temperatures are highest in the tropical zone because
   a. the land is flat.
   b. the sun's rays strike most directly.
   c. Earth's axis is tilted toward the sun.
   d. ocean currents warm the region.
2. Continental climates are found
   a. on every continent.
   b. only near the equator.
   c. only in the Northern Hemisphere.
   d. only in the Southern Hemisphere.
3. In a wet-and-dry tropical climate, the most common vegetation is
   a. coniferous forests.
   b. savanna grasslands.
   c. tropical rain forest.
   d. steppe grasslands.
4. Extremely cold periods in Earth's history have resulted in huge
   a. tree rings. b. sunspots.
   c. pollen deposits. d. glaciers.
5. Chlorofluorocarbons, or CFCs, are the main cause of
   a. ozone depletion.
   b. global warming.
   c. the greenhouse effect.
   d. ice ages.

True or False

If the statement is true, write true. If it is false, change the underlined word or words to make it true.

6. The prevailing winds affect how much sunlight falls on an area.
7. When the north end of Earth's axis is tilted toward the sun, it is summer in the Southern Hemisphere.
8. Climate regions are classified according to temperature and precipitation.
9. A thin tree ring indicates that a year was cool or dry.
10. An increase in nitrogen in the atmosphere may be making world temperatures increase.

Checking Concepts

11. Identify the parts of the United States that are located in each of the three temperature zones.
12. How are "dry" climates defined? How do the two types of dry climate differ?
13. How does the movement of continents explain major changes in climate over time?
14. In order to be effective, why must agreements aimed at preventing or reducing ozone depletion be international?
15. **Writing to Learn** In what climate region do you live? Write a description of your local climate and identify some of the things—such as latitude, bodies of water, or wind patterns—that affect the climate.

Thinking Visually

16. **Concept Map** Copy the concept map about climate onto a separate sheet of paper. Then complete it and add a title. (For more on concept maps, see the Skills Handbook.)

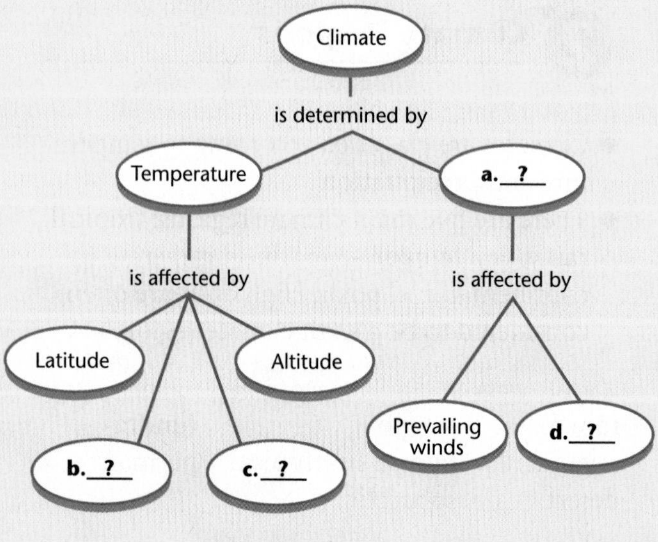
Climate
is determined by
Temperature
a. ?
is affected by
is affected by
Latitude
Altitude
Prevailing winds
d. ?
b. ?
c. ?

Test Prep: Skills

Use the map of world temperature zones to answer Questions 17–19.

17. Interpreting Maps Name each of the five zones shown on the map.

18. Measuring What is the name of the temperature zone that includes the equator? How many degrees of latitude does this zone cover?

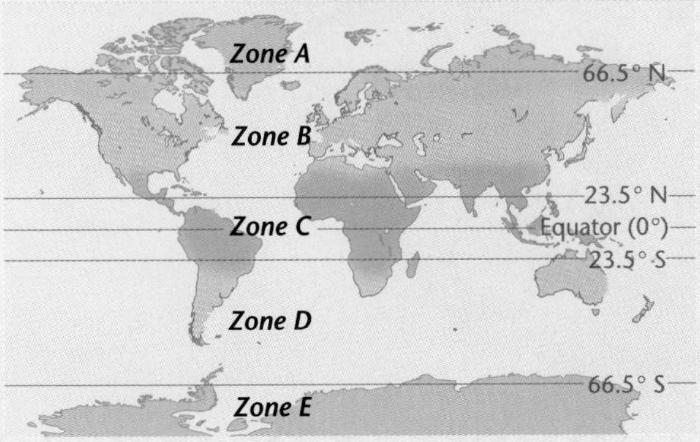

Zone A
66.5° N
Zone B
23.5° N
Zone C
Equator (0°)
23.5° S
Zone D
66.5° S
Zone E

19. Interpreting Data Which of the five zones shown on the map has the greatest amount of land area suitable for people to live?

Thinking Critically

20. Relating Cause and Effect Describe three ways in which water influences climate.

21. Comparing and Contrasting How is global warming different from earlier changes in Earth's climate?

22. Making Judgments What is the most important thing that needs to be done about global warming?

23. Relating Cause and Effect Why do parts of the United States have a semiarid climate while neighboring areas have a humid continental climate?

CHAPTER 17 ASSESSMENT

Performance Assessment

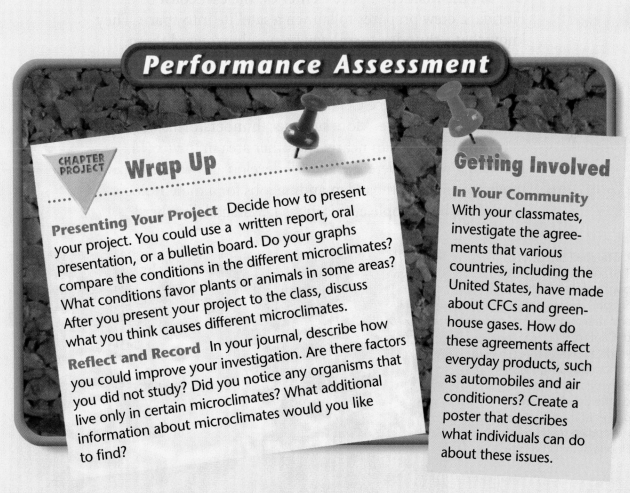

CHAPTER PROJECT

Wrap Up

Presenting Your Project Decide how to present your project. You could use a written report, oral presentation, or a bulletin board. Do your graphs compare the conditions in the different microclimates? What conditions favor plants or animals in some areas? After you present your project to the class, discuss what you think causes different microclimates.

Reflect and Record In your journal, describe how you could improve your investigation. Are there factors you did not study? Did you notice any organisms that live only in certain microclimates? What additional information about microclimates would you like to find?

Getting Involved

In Your Community With your classmates, investigate the agreements that various countries, including the United States, have made about CFCs and greenhouse gases. How do these agreements affect everyday products, such as automobiles and air conditioners? Create a poster that describes what individuals can do about these issues.

Eyes On EARTH

At the Kennedy Space Center on the east coast of Florida, a crew prepares to launch a satellite into space. They know that a thunderstorm may be moving toward them. Should they launch the mission or delay? Before deciding, the crew contacts meteorologists for the latest weather forecast.

The Kennedy Space Center is about 100 kilometers east of the center of the state. More summer thunderstorms occur in central Florida than nearly any other area in the world. Predicting when severe storms will develop and where they will move is one of the most demanding jobs for a meteorologist. One of the best people at this job is J. Marshall Shepherd.

J. Marshall Shepherd
The son of two school principals, J. Marshall Shepherd was born in 1969 and raised in the small town of Canton, Georgia. Today he works for NASA as a research meteorologist for Mission to Planet Earth. He's an expert on the development of powerful thunderstorms. He studied meteorology at Florida State University.

Unit d States
TRMM
Tropical Rainfall Measuring Mission

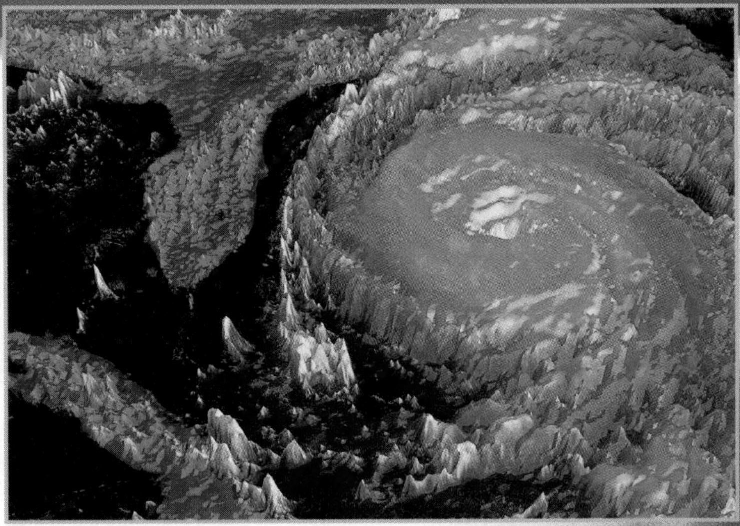

Hurricane Fran roars over the Caribbean Sea near Florida and the island of Cuba. White clouds swirl around the "eye" at the center of the hurricane (upper right).

Getting Started at a Science Fair

Marshall Shepherd is an "old hand" at predicting the weather. He's been at it since sixth grade, when his teacher suggested that he enter a science fair. Marshall titled his science project "Can a Sixth-Grader Predict the Weather?" First he toured the local TV station in Atlanta to see what instruments meteorologists use to measure basic weather variables.

> **"The shape of Florida is part of the reason that so many storms form here."**

"Then I did a little background reading and decided I could build some of those instruments out of basic materials around the house," he recalls.

Using household materials and a few inexpensive items at supply stores, Marshall Shepherd built everything he needed for his project. He constructed a weather station with an anemometer to measure wind speed, a wind vane to measure wind direction, a barometer to measure air pressure, a hair hygrometer to measure humidity, and a rain gauge.

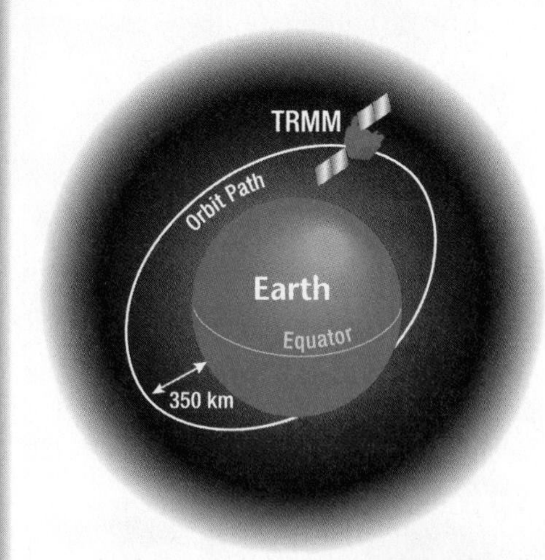
TRMM
Orbit Path
Earth
Equator
350 km

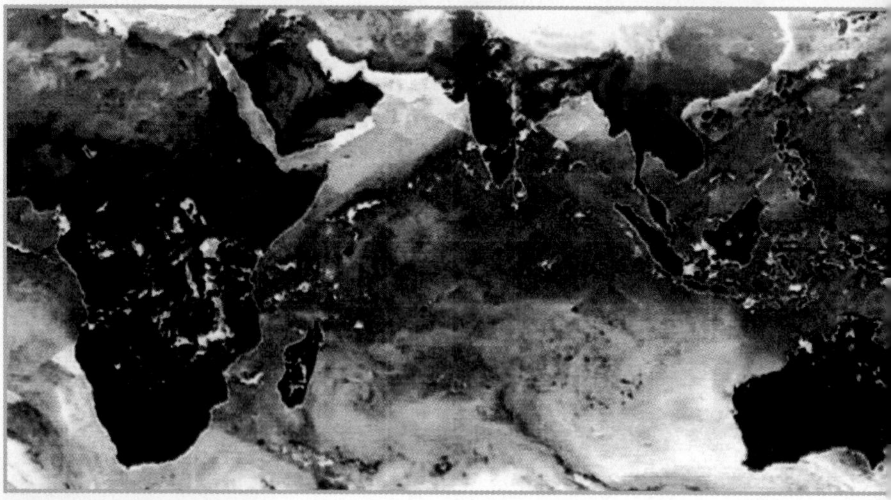

▲TRMM, a device that records weather conditions from space, orbits Earth at an altitude of 350 kilometers. It flies over each position on Earth at a different time each day.

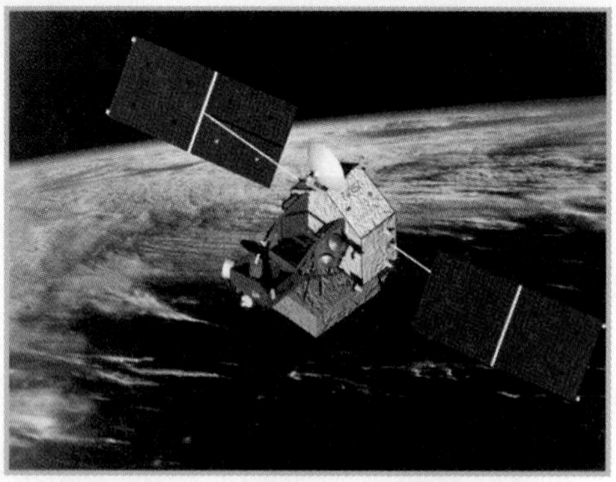

TRMM observatory is about the size of a small room and weighs as much as a medium-sized truck. It contains two solar panels and instruments to record weather data.

"From these basic instruments, I took weather observations around my neighborhood," he explains. "I developed a model of day-to-day weather over a six-month period and found some very interesting and accurate results." Marshall's instruments and scientific work on this project won prizes for him at local, district, and state science fairs.

"From that point on, I was involved with science projects," he recalls. By the time he graduated from high school, he had a definite goal. "One day, I planned to be a research scientist at NASA (National Aeronautics and Space Administration)," he stated.

Predicting Severe Storms

Hurricane Andrew—the most powerful hurricane ever to strike Florida—swept through Southern Florida and Louisiana in 1992. Marshall was in college at the time. "My college research paper was on hurricane tracking using radar. I actually did some work with Hurricane Andrew," he says. "That's how I got interested in tropical weather."

In graduate school, Marshall Shepherd investigated the way powerful thunderstorms form and move, especially those in central Florida. The long, narrow shape of Florida is part of the reason that so many storms form there. "When you have land heating faster than water, you get something called sea-breeze circulation," he explains. "On a typical summer day, a sea-breeze forms on both the west coast and the east coast of Florida. They tend to move toward the center. When they collide, you get intense thunderstorm development."

Designing New Instruments

Now Marshall Shepherd works at NASA, where his projects contribute to NASA's Mission to Planet Earth.

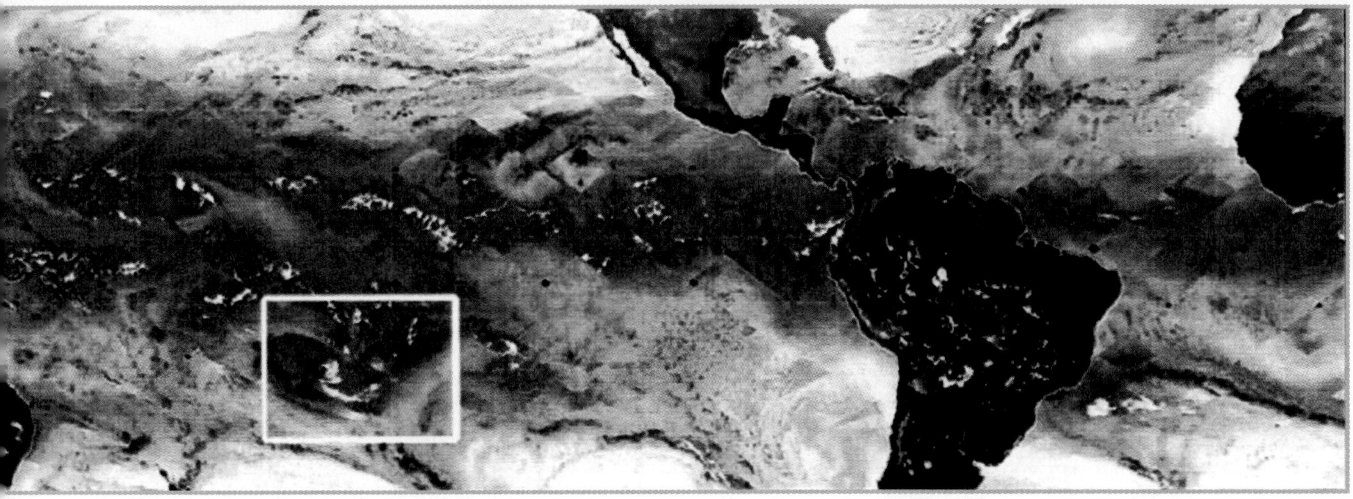

This map was generated by TRMM. The white rectangle identifies a cyclone.

This long-term program uses information from satellites, aircraft, and ground studies to explore environmental changes around the world.

Marshall Shepherd's knowledge of thunderstorms is especially valuable in interpreting data from TRMM (Tropical Rainfall Measuring Mission), a device that measures tropical and subtropical rainfall. Rainfall cycles in tropical regions affect weather throughout the world.

Marshall Shepherd's work involves both observation and calculation. As he did in sixth grade, he designs and builds instruments. But now his devices are some of the most advanced in the world. He no longer takes his instruments into a neighborhood to measure weather conditions directly. Instead, his specialty is "remote sensing"—making observations of weather conditions (rainfall, water vapor, and so on) from a distance.

After collecting data, Marshall uses a computer to analyze it. He and others have designed a computer program that uses the data to predict the development of severe storms. So when a crew at the Kennedy Space Center must decide whether or not to launch a rocket, they rely on predictions from programs similar to ones that Marshall Shepherd has worked on.

Looking Ahead

Marshall Shepherd's personal goals go beyond Mission to Planet Earth. "With the upcoming international space station, scientists are going to have the opportunity to do research from space. My goal is to conduct Earth-directed meteorological research from the space station as well as from the ground. I'll use some of the new instruments we are currently developing." He describes another important goal back home on Earth—"to reach out, inspire, and expose students to science."

In Your Journal

Marshall Shepherd credits his success to having detailed goals. "I always write down goals, and check them off as they happen," he says. Think of an important task that you would like to accomplish over the next year. Identify the steps and note target dates you will need to meet in order to reach your goal. How do those steps help bring you closer to achieving your goal?

CHAPTER

18 Populations and Communities

CALIFORNIA
SCIENCE CONTENT STANDARDS

The following California Science Content Standards are addressed in this chapter:

5. Organisms in ecosystems exchange energy and nutrients among themselves and with the environment.

a. Energy entering ecosystems as sunlight is transferred by producers into chemical energy through photosynthesis, and then from organism to organism in food webs.

b. Over time, matter is transferred from one organism to others in the food web, and between organisms and the physical environment.

c. Populations of organisms can be categorized by the functions they serve in an ecosystem.

d. Different kinds of organisms may play similar ecological roles in similar biomes.

e. The number and types of organisms an ecosystem can support depends on the resources available and abiotic factors, such as quantity of light and water, range of temperatures, and soil composition.

7. Scientific progress is made by asking meaningful questions and conducting careful investigations.

PROJECT 18

What's a Crowd?

How many sunflowers are there in this photograph? Certainly too many to count! But there is a limit to how many more sunflowers can grow in this fertile field. The limit is determined by what the sunflowers need to survive.

In this chapter, you will explore how living things obtain the things they need from their surroundings. You will also learn how organisms interact with the living and nonliving things around them. As you study this chapter, you will observe plants as sample organisms.

Your Goal To design and conduct an experiment to determine the effect of crowding on plant growth.

To complete your project successfully, you must

- develop a plan for planting different numbers of seeds in identical containers
- observe and collect data on the growing plants
- present your results in a written report and a graph
- follow the safety guidelines in Appendix A

Get Started With your group, brainstorm ideas for your plan. What conditions do plants need to grow? How will you arrange your seeds in their containers? What types of measurements will you make when the plants begin to grow? Submit your draft plan to your teacher for review.

Check Your Progress You'll be working on this project as you study this chapter. To keep your project on track, look for Check Your Progress boxes at the following points.

Section 1 Review, page 583: Plant the seeds. Measure the plants' growth and record your observations.

Section 3 Review, page 600: Analyze your data and prepare your report.

Wrap Up At the end of the chapter (page 603), your group will present your results and conclusions to the class.

c. Construct appropriate graphs from data and develop qualitative statements about the relationships between variables.

e. Recognize whether evidence is consistent with a proposed explanation.

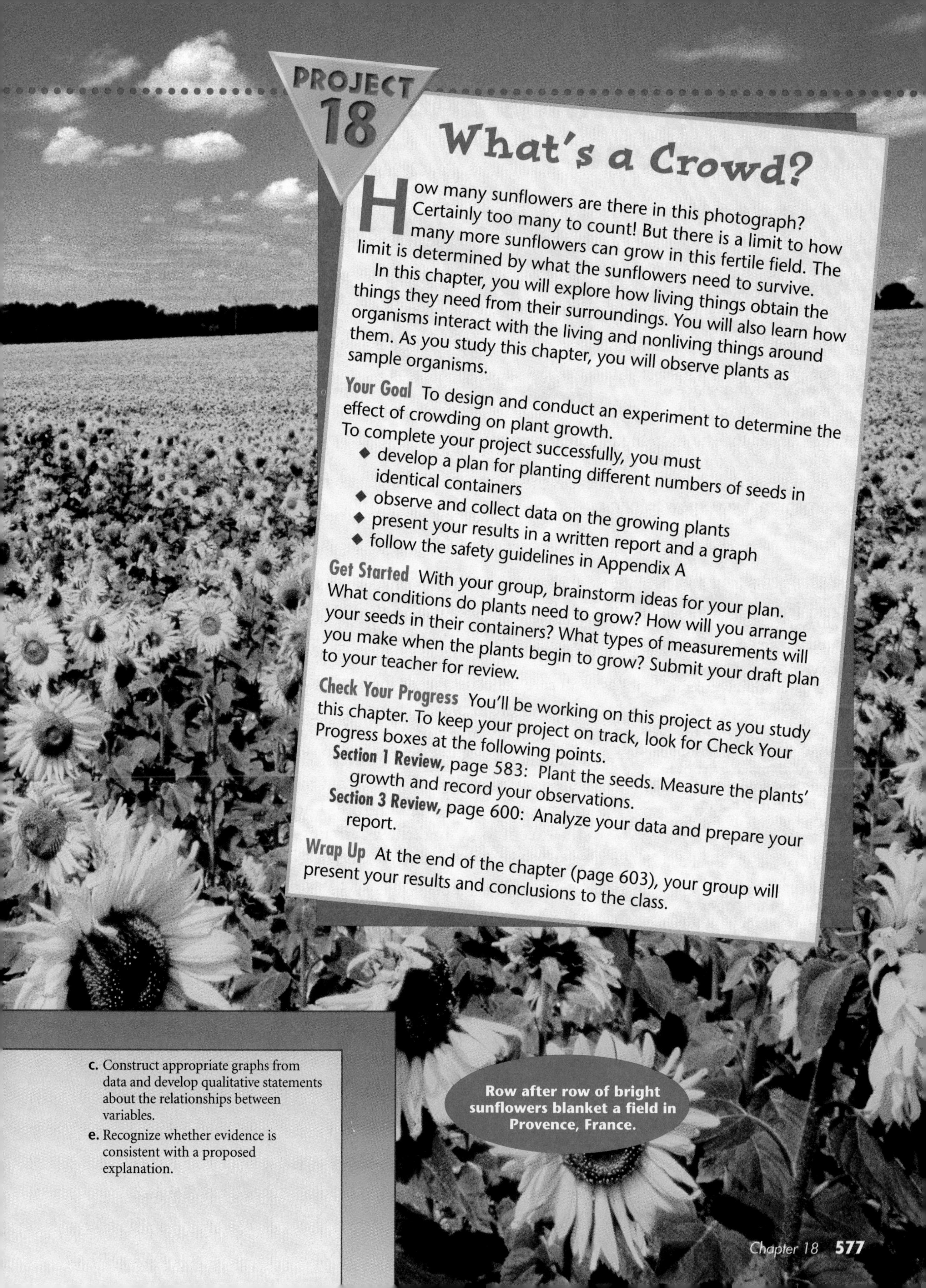

Row after row of bright sunflowers blanket a field in Provence, France.

SECTION 1 Living Things and the Environment

DISCOVER ACTIVITY

What's in the Scene?

1. Choose a magazine picture of a nature scene. Paste the picture onto a sheet of paper, leaving space all around the picture.
2. Identify all the things in the picture that are alive. Use a colored pencil to draw a line from each living thing, or organism. Label the organism if you know its name.
3. Use a different colored pencil to draw a line from each nonliving thing and label it.

Think It Over

Inferring How do the organisms in the picture depend on the nonliving things? Using a third color, draw lines connecting organisms to the nonliving things they need.

GUIDE FOR READING

- **What needs are met by an organism's surroundings?**
- **What are the levels of organization within an ecosystem?**

Reading Tip **Write the section headings in your notebook. As you read, make a list of main ideas and supporting details under each heading.**

As the sun rises on a warm summer morning, the Nebraska town is already bustling with activity. Some residents are hard at work building homes for their families. They are building underground, where it is dark and cool. Other inhabitants are collecting seeds for breakfast. Some of the town's younger residents are at play, chasing each other through the grass.

Suddenly, an adult spots a threatening shadow approaching—an enemy has appeared in the sky! The adult cries out several times, warning the others. Within moments, the town's residents disappear into their underground homes. The town is silent and still, except for a single hawk circling overhead.

Have you guessed what kind of town this is? It is a prairie dog town on the Nebraska plains. As these prairie dogs dug their burrows, searched for food, and hid from the hawk, they interacted with their environment, or surroundings. The prairie dogs interacted with living things, such as the grass and the hawk, and with nonliving things, such as the soil. All the living and nonliving things that interact in a particular area make up an **ecosystem.**

Black-tailed prairie dogs ▼

A prairie is just one of the many different ecosystems found on Earth. Other ecosystems in which living things make their homes include mountain streams, deep oceans, and dense forests.

Habitats

A prairie dog is one type of organism, or living thing. Organisms live in a specific place within an ecosystem. **An organism obtains food, water, shelter, and other things it needs to live, grow, and reproduce from its surroundings.** The place where an organism lives and that provides the things the organism needs is called its **habitat.**

A single ecosystem may contain many habitats. For example, in a forest ecosystem, mushrooms grow in the damp soil, bears live on the forest floor, termites live in fallen tree trunks, and flickers build nests in the trunks.

Organisms live in different habitats because they have different requirements for survival. A prairie dog obtains the food and shelter it needs from its habitat. It could not survive in a tropical rain forest or on the rocky ocean shore. Likewise, the prairie would not meet the needs of a gorilla, a penguin, or a hermit crab.

Figure 1 A stream tumbles over mossy rocks in a lush Tennessee forest. This ecosystem contains many different habitats. *Comparing and Contrasting How is the mushrooms' habitat in the forest different from the flicker's habitat?*

Biotic Factors

An organism interacts with both the living and nonliving things in its environment. The living parts of an ecosystem are called **biotic factors** (by AHT ik factors). Biotic factors in the prairie dogs' ecosystem include the grass and plants that provide seeds and berries. The hawks, ferrets, badgers, and eagles that hunt the prairie dogs are also biotic factors. In addition, worms, fungi, and bacteria are biotic factors that live in the soil underneath the prairie grass. These organisms keep the soil rich in nutrients as they break down the remains of other living things.

☑ *Checkpoint* *Name a biotic factor in your environment.*

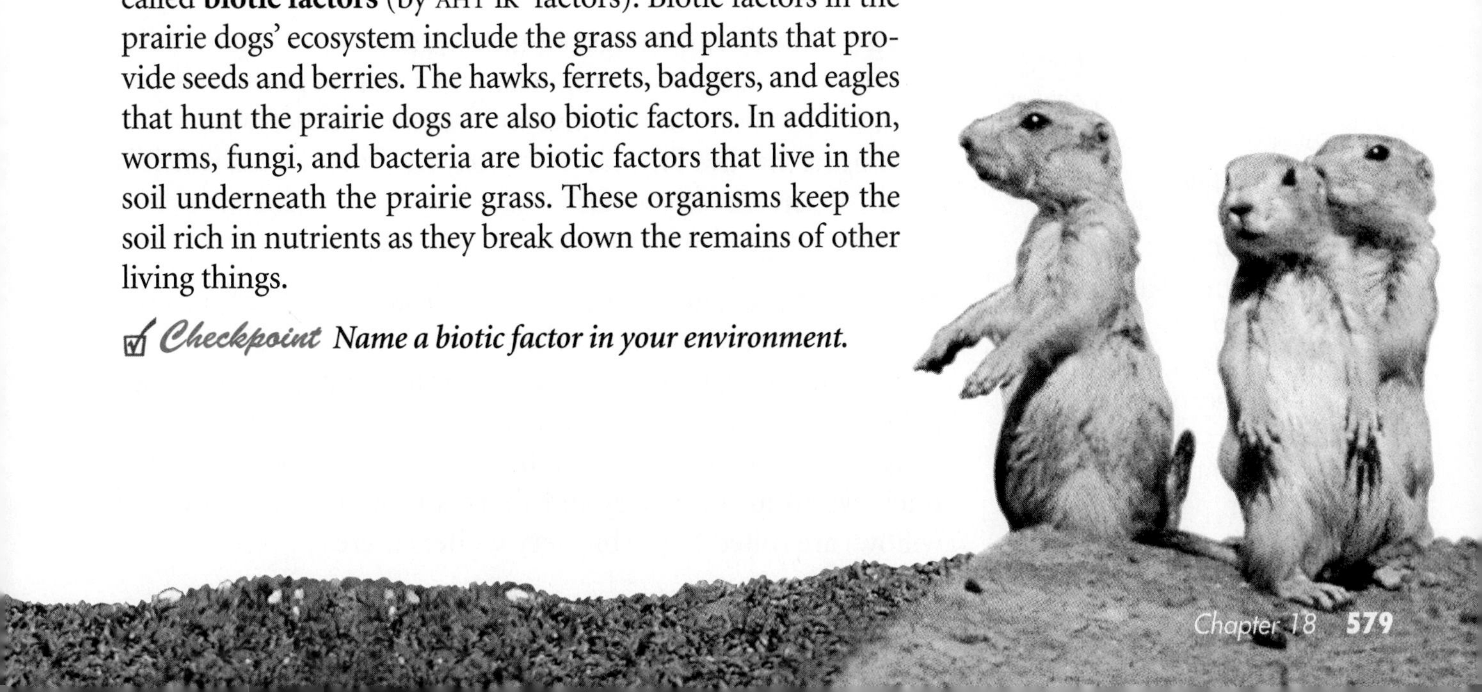

Figure 2 This eastern banjo frog is burrowing in the sand to stay cool in the hot Australian desert. ***Interpreting Photographs*** *With which abiotic factors is the frog interacting in this scene?*

Try This

With or Without Salt?

ACTIVITY

In this activity you will explore salt as an abiotic factor.

1. Label four 600-mL beakers A, B, C, and D. Fill each with 500 mL of room-temperature spring water.
2. Set beaker A aside. It will contain fresh water. To beaker B, add 2.5 grams of noniodized salt. Add 7.5 grams of salt to beaker C and 15 grams of salt to beaker D. Stir beakers B, C, and D.
3. Add 1/8 teaspoon of brine shrimp eggs to each beaker.
4. Cover each beaker with a square of paper. Keep them away from direct light or heat. Wash your hands.
5. Observe the beakers daily for three days.

Drawing Conclusions In which beakers did the eggs hatch? What can you conclude about the amount of salt in the shrimps' natural habitat?

Abiotic Factors

The nonliving parts of an ecosystem are called **abiotic factors** (ay by AHT ik factors). Abiotic factors that affect living things in the prairie are similar to those found in most ecosystems. They include water, sunlight, oxygen, temperature, and soil.

Water All living things require water to carry out their life processes. Water also makes up a large part of the bodies of most organisms. Your body, for example, is about 65 percent water. A watermelon consists of more than 95 percent water! Water is particularly important to plants and algae. These organisms use water, along with sunlight and carbon dioxide, to make food in a process called **photosynthesis** (foh toh SIN thuh sis). Other living things eat the plants and algae to obtain energy.

Sunlight Because sunlight is necessary for photosynthesis, it is an important abiotic factor for plants, algae, and other living things. In places that do not receive sunlight, such as dark caves, plants cannot grow. Without plants or algae to provide a source of food, few other organisms can live.

Oxygen Most living things require oxygen to carry out their life processes. Oxygen is so important to the functioning of the human body that you can live only a few minutes without it. Organisms that live on land obtain oxygen from the air, which is about 20 percent oxygen. Fish and other water organisms obtain dissolved oxygen from the water around them.

Temperature The temperatures that are typical of an area determine the types of organisms that can live there. For example, if you took a trip to a warm tropical island, you would see palm trees, bright hibiscus flowers, and tiny lizards. These organisms could not survive on the frozen plains of Siberia. But the thick, warm fur of wolves and short, strong branches of dwarf willows are suited to the blustery winters there.

Some animals alter their environments to overcome very hot or very cold temperatures. For example, prairie dogs dig underground dens to find shelter from the blazing summer sun. They line the dens with grass. The grass keeps the prairie dogs warm during the cold and windy winters.

Soil Soil is a mixture of rock fragments, nutrients, air, water, and the decaying remains of living things. Soil in different areas consists of varying amounts of these materials. The type of soil in an area influences the kinds of plants that can grow there. Many animals, such as the prairie dogs, use the soil itself as a home. Billions of microscopic organisms such as bacteria also live in the soil. These tiny organisms play an important role in the ecosystem by breaking down the remains of other living things.

☑ *Checkpoint* *How do biotic factors differ from abiotic factors?*

Populations

In 1900, travelers saw a prairie dog town in Texas covering an area twice the size of the city of Dallas. The sprawling town contained more than 400 million prairie dogs! These prairie dogs were all members of one species, or single kind, of organism. A **species** (SPEE sheez) is a group of organisms that are physically similar and can reproduce with each other to produce fertile offspring.

All the members of one species in a particular area are referred to as a **population.** The 400 million prairie dogs in the Texas town are one example of a population. All the pigeons in New York City make up a population, as do all the daisies in a field. In contrast, all the trees in a forest do not make up a population, because they do not all belong to the same species. There may be pines, maples, birches, and many other tree species in the forest.

The area in which a population lives can be as small as a single blade of grass or as large as the whole planet. Scientists studying a type of organism usually limit their study to a population in a defined area. For example, they might study the population of bluegill fish in a pond, or the population of alligators in the Florida Everglades.

Some populations, however, do not stay in a contained area. For example, to study the population of finback whales, a scientist might need to use the entire ocean.

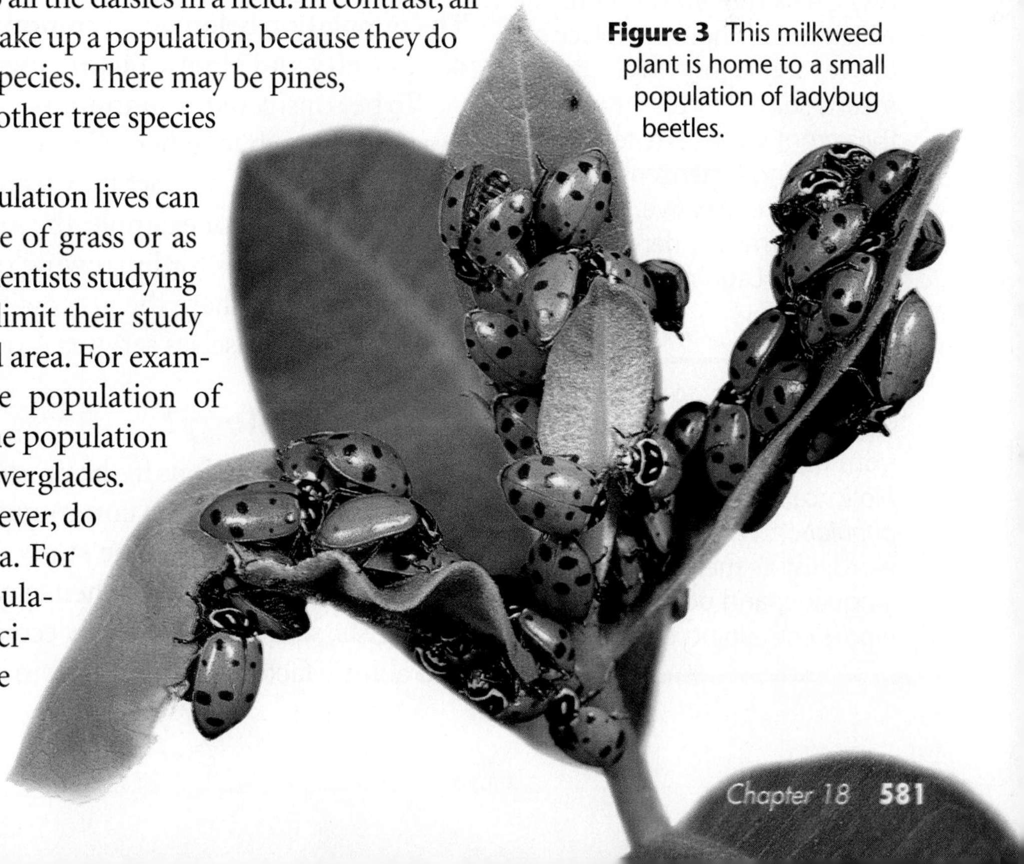

Figure 3 This milkweed plant is home to a small population of ladybug beetles.

Organism
Population

Communities

Of course, most ecosystems contain more than one type of organism. The prairie, for instance, includes prairie dogs, hawks, grasses, badgers, and snakes, along with many other organisms. All the different populations that live together in an area make up a **community.**

Figure 4 shows the levels of organization in the prairie ecosystem. **The smallest unit of organization is a single organism, which belongs to a population of other members of its species. The population belongs to a community of different species. The community and abiotic factors together form an ecosystem.**

To be considered a community, the different populations must live close enough together to interact. One way the populations in a community may interact is by using the same resources, such as food and shelter. For example, the tunnels dug by the prairie dogs also serve as homes for burrowing owls and black-footed ferrets. The prairie dogs share the grass with other animals. Meanwhile, prairie dogs themselves serve as food for many species.

What Is Ecology?

Because the populations in the prairie ecosystem interact with one another, any changes in a community affect all the different populations that live there. The study of how living things interact with each other and with their environment is called **ecology.** Ecologists, scientists who study ecology, look at how all the biotic and abiotic factors in an ecosystem are related.

Language Arts CONNECTION

The word *ecology* comes from two Greek root words: *oikos,* which means house or place to live, and *logos,* which means *study.* Put together, these root words create a term for studying organisms in the place where they live. Many science terms are derived from Greek and Latin root words.

In Your Journal

Use a dictionary to find root words for the following terms from this section: *habitat, biotic, community,* and *population.* For each root word, list its meaning, original language, and other English words containing the root.

Community

Ecosystem

Figure 4 The smallest level of ecological organization is an individual organism. The largest is the entire ecosystem.

As part of their work, ecologists study how organisms react to changes in their environment. Living things constantly interact with their surroundings, responding to changes in the conditions around them. Some responses are very quick. When a prairie dog sees a hawk overhead, it gives a warning bark. The other prairie dogs hear the bark and respond by returning to their burrows to hide. Other responses to change in the environment occur more slowly. For example, after a fire on the prairie, it takes some time for the grass to reach its former height and for all the animals to return to the area.

Section 1 Review

1. What basic needs are provided by an organism's habitat?
2. List these terms in order from the smallest unit to the largest: population, organism, ecosystem, community.
3. Explain how water and sunlight are two abiotic factors that are important to all organisms.
4. Why do ecologists study both biotic and abiotic factors in an ecosystem?
5. **Thinking Critically Applying Concepts** Would all the insects in a forest be considered a population? Why or why not?

CHAPTER PROJECT

Check Your Progress

After your teacher has reviewed your plan, prepare the containers and plant the seeds. Design a data table to record the information you will use to compare the growth in the different containers. When the plants begin to grow, examine them daily and record your observations. Be sure to continue caring for your plants according to your plan. (*Hint:* Use a metric ruler to measure your growing plants. Besides size, look for differences in leaf color and the number of buds among the plants.)

Skills Lab

Making Models

A World in a Jar

In this lab, you will study the interactions that take place between biotic and abiotic factors in a model ecosystem.

Problem

How can organisms live in a closed ecosystem?

Materials

aquarium gravel
plastic stirring rod
2-day-old tap water
2 guppies
metric ruler
dip net
4 aquatic plants
4 small pond snails
large jar with cover (about 2 liters)
UL-listed lamp with a 60-watt bulb

Procedure

1. In this lab, you will put guppies, snails, and plants together in a sealed jar of water. Record your prediction about whether this habitat will meet the needs of these organisms.
2. Find a safe location for the jar away from windows and other areas where light and temperature are likely to change often. There should be an electrical outlet nearby for the lamp.
3. Add aquarium gravel to the jar to a depth of 3 cm. Add water to about 6 cm from the top.
4. Place the plants in the jar one at a time. Use a stirring rod to gently brush aside a little gravel. Position the roots of each plant against the bottom of the jar. Move gravel back over the roots to hold the plant in place.
5. Using a dip net, carefully place the guppies in the water. Gently place the snails in the jar. Put the lid on the jar, and close it tightly.
6. Position the lamp so that the light shines into the jar. The light bulb should be 15 to 20 cm from the jar. **CAUTION:** *Lighted bulbs get very hot. Do not allow the bulb to touch any objects.*
7. Observe the jar every day. Record your observations in your notebook.
8. Within 5 days, the water in the jar should turn slightly green. The green color indicates the presence of algae. If the water is bright green, move the light away from the jar. If the water is not green after 5 days, move the light closer to the jar. Record in your notebook any changes to the setup.
9. Observe the jar for at least one more week.

Analyze and Conclude

1. What biotic and abiotic factors are part of the ecosystem in the jar?
2. Are any biotic or abiotic factors able to enter the sealed jar? If so, which one(s)?
3. Where did the green algae come from?
4. Draw a diagram of the interactions between the biotic and abiotic factors in the jar.
5. Would the guppies, snails, and plants be able to live alone in separate jars? Why or why not?
6. **Think About It** Explain how your jar and its contents model an ecosystem. How is your model different from an ecosystem on Earth?

More to Explore

Make a plan to model a saltwater or land ecosystem. How would this model be different from the freshwater ecosystem? Obtain your teacher's approval before carrying out your plan.

SECTION 2 Studying Populations

DISCOVER ACTIVITY

What's the Population of Beans in a Jar?

1. Fill a plastic jar with dried beans. This is your model population.
2. Your goal is to determine the number of beans in the jar, but you will not have time to count every bean. You may use any of the following to help you determine the size of the bean population: a ruler, a small beaker, another large jar. Set a timer for two minutes when you are ready to begin.

3. After two minutes, record your answer. Then count the actual number of beans. How close was your answer?

Think It Over

Forming Operational Definitions In this activity, you came up with an estimate of the size of the bean population. Write a definition of the term *estimate* based on what you did.

How would you like to change jobs for the day? Instead of being a student, today you are an ecologist. You are working on a project to study the bald eagle population in your area. One question you might ask is how the population has changed over time. Is the number of bald eagles more, less, or the same as it was 50 years ago? To answer these questions, you must first determine the present size of the bald eagle population.

GUIDE FOR READING

- How do ecologists determine the size of a population?
- What causes populations to change in size?
- What factors limit population growth?

Reading Tip **Before you read, predict some factors that might cause a population to increase or decrease.**

Population Density

One way to state the size of a population is in terms of **population density**— the number of individuals in a specific area. Population density can be written as an equation:

$$\text{Population density} = \frac{\text{Number of individuals}}{\text{Unit area}}$$

For instance, suppose you counted 50 monarch butterflies in a garden measuring 10 square meters. The population density would be 50 butterflies per 10 square meters, or 5 butterflies per square meter.

Bald eagles in Alaska ▶

Figure 5 These cone-shaped structures are nests built by cliff swallows in Dinosaur National Monument, Utah. Counting the nests is one way to estimate the cliff swallow population.

Determining Population Size

In your work as an ecologist, how can you determine the size of the population you are studying? **Some methods of determining the size of a population are direct and indirect observations, sampling, and mark-and-recapture studies.**

Direct Observation The most obvious way to determine the size of a population is to count, one by one, all of its members. You could count all the bald eagles that live along a river, all the red maple trees in a forest, or all the elephants in a valley in Kenya.

Indirect Observation The members of a population may be small or hard to find. It may then be easier to observe their tracks or other signs rather than the organisms themselves. Look at the mud nests built by cliff swallows in Figure 5. Each nest has one entrance hole. By counting the entrance holes, you can determine the number of swallow families nesting in this area. Suppose that the average number of swallows per nest is four: two parents and two offspring. If there are 120 nests in an area, you can find the number of swallows by multiplying 120 by 4, or 480 swallows.

Sampling In most cases, it is not possible to count every member of a population. The population may be very large, or it may be spread over a wide area. It may be hard to find every individual or to remember which ones have already been counted. Instead, ecologists usually make an estimate. An **estimate** is an approximation of a number, based on reasonable assumptions.

One type of estimating involves counting the number of organisms in a small area (a sample), and then multiplying to find the number in a larger area. To get an accurate estimate, the sample should have the same population density as the larger area. For example, suppose you count 8 red maples in a 10 meter-by-10 meter area of the forest. If the entire forest were 100 times that size, you would multiply your count by 100 to estimate the total population, or 800 red maples.

Mark-and-Recapture Studies Another estimating method is a technique called "mark and recapture." This technique gets its name because some animals are first captured, marked, and released into the environment. Then another group of animals is captured. The

Sharpen your Skills

Calculating

ACTIVITY

A bed of oysters measures 100 meters long and 50 meters wide. In a one-square-meter area you count 20 oysters. Estimate the population of oysters in the bed. (*Hint:* Drawing a diagram may help you set up your calculation.)

number of marked animals in this second group indicates the population size. For example, if half the animals in the second group are marked, it means that the first sample represented about half the total population.

Here's an example showing how mark and recapture works. First, deer mice in a field are caught in a trap that does not harm the mice. Ecologists count the mice and mark each mouse with a dot of hair dye before releasing it again. Two weeks later, the researchers return and capture mice again. They count how many mice have marks, showing that they were captured the first time, and how many are unmarked. Using a mathematical formula, the scientists can estimate the total population of mice in the field. You can try this technique for yourself in the Real-World Lab at the end of this section.

Figure 6 This young hawk is part of a mark-and-recapture study in a Virginia marsh. *Inferring What is the purpose of the silver band on the hawk's leg?*

Checkpoint *When is sampling used to estimate a population?*

Changes in Population Size

By returning to a location often and using one of the methods described above, ecologists can monitor the size of a population over time. **Populations can change in size when new members enter the population or when members leave the population.**

Births and Deaths The major way in which new individuals are added to a population is through the birth of offspring. The **birth rate** of a population is the number of births in a population in a certain amount of time. For example, suppose a population of 1,000 snow geese produces 1,400 goslings in a year. The birth rate in this population would be 1,400 goslings per year.

Similarly, the major way that individuals leave a population is by dying. The **death rate** is the number of deaths in a population in a certain amount of time. Suppose that in the same population, 500 geese die in a year. The death rate would be 500 geese per year.

Figure 7 The birth of new individuals can increase the size of a population. This cheetah mother added five offspring to the population in her area.

The Population Equation When the birth rate in a population is greater than the death rate, the population will generally increase in size. This statement can be written as a mathematical statement using the "is greater than" sign:

If birth rate > death rate, population size increases.

For example, in the snow goose population, the birth rate of 1,400 goslings per year was greater than the death rate of 500 geese per year, and the population would increase in size.

However, if the death rate in a population is greater than the birth rate, the population size will generally decrease. This can also be written as a mathematical statement:

If death rate > birth rate, population size decreases.

Immigration and Emigration The size of a population also can change when individuals move into or out of the population, just as the population of your town changes when families move into town or move away. **Immigration** (im ih GRAY shun) means moving into a population. **Emigration** (em ih GRAY shun) means leaving a population. Emigration can occur when part of a population gets cut off from the rest of the population. For instance, if food is scarce, some members of an antelope herd may wander off in search of better grassland. If they become permanently separated from the original herd, they will no longer be part of that population.

Graphing Changes in Population You can see an example of changes in a population of rabbits in Figure 8. The vertical axis shows the numbers of rabbits in the population, while the horizontal axis shows time. The graph shows the size of the population over a 10-year period.

☑ *Checkpoint* *Name two ways individuals can join a population.*

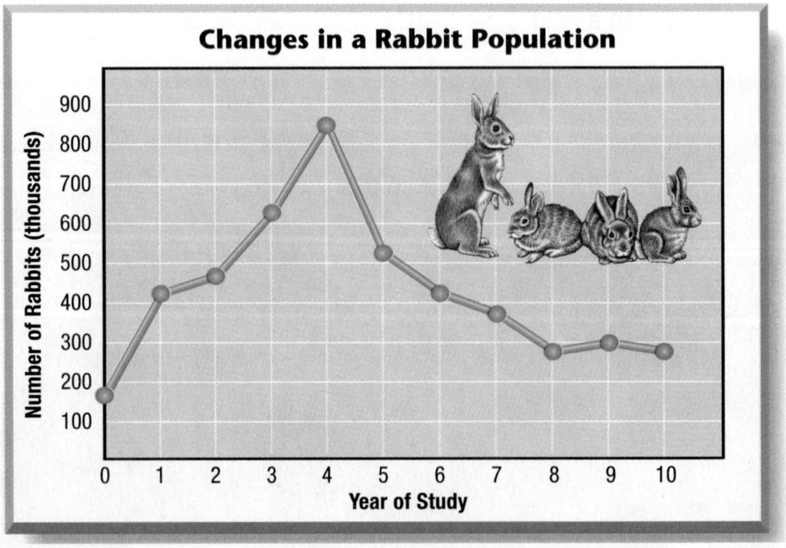

Changes in a Rabbit Population
Number of Rabbits (thousands)
900
800
700
600
500
400
300
200
100
0
1
2
3
4
5
6
7
8
9
10
Year of Study

Figure 8 From Year 0 to Year 4, more rabbits joined the population than left it, so the population increased. From Year 4 to Year 8, more rabbits left the population than joined it, so the population decreased. From Year 8 to Year 10, the rates of rabbits leaving and joining the population were about equal, so the population remained steady. ***Interpreting Graphs*** *In what year did the rabbit population reach its highest point? What was the size of the population in that year?*

Figure 9 These gannets seem to have heard the saying "Birds of a feather flock together." When there are more birds than the space can support, the population will have exceeded the carrying capacity of the shore.

Limiting Factors

When conditions are good, a population will generally increase. But a population does not keep growing forever. Eventually, some factor in its environment causes the population to stop growing. A **limiting factor** is an environmental factor that prevents a population from increasing. **Some limiting factors for populations are food, space, and weather conditions.**

Food Organisms require food to survive. In an area where food is scarce, this becomes a limiting factor. Suppose a giraffe needs to eat 10 kilograms of leaves each day to survive. The trees in an area can provide 100 kilograms of leaves a day while remaining healthy. Five giraffes could live easily in this area, since they would only require a total of 50 kilograms of food. But 15 giraffes could not all survive—there would not be enough food for all of them. No matter how much shelter, water, and other resources there might be, the population will not grow much higher than 10 giraffes. The largest population that an environment can support is called its **carrying capacity.** The carrying capacity of this environment is 10 giraffes.

Space The birds in Figure 9 are rarely seen on land. These birds, called gannets, spend most of their lives flying over the ocean. They only land on this rocky shore to nest. But as you can see, the shore is very crowded. If a pair of gannets does not have room to build a nest, that pair will not be able to produce any offspring.

TRY THIS

Elbow Room

ACTIVITY

Using masking tape, mark off several one-meter squares on the floor of your classroom. Your teacher will form groups of 2, 4, and 6 students. Each group's task is to put together a small jigsaw puzzle in one of the squares. All the group members must keep their feet within the square. Time how long it takes your group to finish the puzzle.

Making Models How long did it take each group to complete the task? How does this activity show that space can be a limiting factor? What is the carrying capacity of puzzle-solvers in a square meter?

Figure 10 A snowstorm can limit the size of the orange crop.

Those gannets will not contribute to an increase in the gannet population. This means that space for nesting is a limiting factor for these gannets. If the shore were bigger, more gannets would be able to nest there, and the population would increase.

Space is often a limiting factor for plants. The amount of space in which a plant grows can determine how much sunlight, water, and other necessities the plant can obtain. For example, many pine seedlings sprout each year in a forest. But as the trees get bigger, those that are too close together do not have room to spread their roots underground. Other tree branches block out the sunlight they need to live. Some of the seedlings die, limiting the size of the pine population.

Weather Weather conditions such as temperature and amount of rainfall can also limit population growth. Many insect species breed in the warm spring weather. As winter begins, the first frost kills many of the insects. This sudden rise in the death rate causes the insect population to decrease.

A single severe weather event can dramatically change the size of a population by killing many organisms. For instance, a flood or hurricane can wash away nests and burrows just as it damages the homes of humans. If you live in a northern state, you may have seen an early frost limit the population of tomato plants in a vegetable garden.

Section 2 Review

1. List four ways of determining population size.
2. How is birth rate related to population size?
3. List three limiting factors for populations. Choose one and explain how this factor can limit population growth.
4. Explain why it is often necessary for ecologists to estimate the size of a population.
5. **Thinking Critically Problem Solving** A field measures 50 meters by 90 meters. In one square meter, you count 3 grasshoppers. Estimate the total population of grasshoppers in the field. What method did you use to make your estimate?

Science at Home

Choose a page of a dictionary or other book that has a lot of type on it. Challenge your family members to estimate the number of words on the page. After everyone has come up with an estimate, have each person explain the method he or she used. Now count the actual number of words on the page. Whose estimate was closest?

Careers in Science

Counting Turtles

Real-World Lab

For three years, ecologists have been using the mark-and-recapture method to monitor the population of turtles in a pond. In this lab, you will model recapturing the turtles to complete the study. Then you will analyze the results.

Problem

How can the mark-and-recapture method help ecologists monitor the size of a population?

Skills Focus

calculating, graphing, predicting

Materials

model paper turtle population
calculator
graph paper

Procedure

1. The data table shows the results from the first three years of the study. Copy it into your notebook, leaving spaces for your data as shown.
2. Your teacher will give you a box representing the pond. Fifteen of the turtles have been marked, as shown in the data table for Year 4.
3. Capture a member of the population by randomly selecting one turtle. Set it aside.
4. Repeat Step 3 nine times. Record the total number of turtles you captured.
5. Examine each turtle to see whether it has a mark. Count the number of recaptured (marked) turtles. Record this number in your data table.

Analyze and Conclude

1. Use the equation below to estimate the turtle population for each year. The first year is done for you as a sample. If your answer is a decimal, round it to the nearest whole number so that your estimate is in "whole turtles." Record the population for each year in the last column of the data table.

$$\text{Total population} = \frac{\text{Number marked} \times \text{Total number captured}}{\text{Number recaptured (with marks)}}$$

Sample (Year 1):

$$\frac{32 \times 28}{15} = 59.7 \text{ or } 60 \text{ turtles}$$

2. Graph the estimated total populations for the four years. Mark years on the horizontal axis. Mark population size on the vertical axis.
3. Describe how the turtle population has changed over the four years of the study. Suggest three possible causes for the changes.
4. **Apply** Use your graph to predict the turtle population in Year 5. Explain your prediction.

DATA TABLE

Year	Number Marked	Total Number Captured	Number Recaptured (with Marks)	Estimated Total Population
1	32	28	15	
2	25	21	11	
3	23	19	11	
4	15			

Getting Involved

Find out whether any wildlife populations in your area are being monitored by national, state, or local agencies. Make a poster or write an article for the school paper about the population and the method being used to study it.

SCIENCE AND SOCIETY

Animal Overpopulation: How Can People Help?

Populations of white-tailed deer are growing rapidly in many parts of the United States. As populations soar, food becomes a limiting factor. Many deer die of starvation. Others grow up small and unhealthy. In search of food, hungry deer move closer to where humans live. There they eat farm crops, garden vegetables, shrubs, and even trees. This affects birds and small animals that depend on the plants for shelter or food. In addition, increased numbers of deer near roads can cause more automobile accidents.

People admire the grace, beauty, and swiftness of deer. Most people don't want these animals to suffer from starvation or illness. Should people take action to limit growing deer populations?

The Issues

Should People Take Direct Action?

Many people argue that hunting is the simplest way to reduce animal populations. Wildlife managers look at the supply of resources in an area and determine its carrying capacity. Then hunters are issued licenses to help reduce the number of deer to the level that can be supported.

Other people favor nonhunting approaches to control deer populations. One plan is to trap the deer and relocate them. But this method is expensive and requires finding another location that can accept the deer without unbalancing its own system. Few such locations are available.

Scientists are also working to develop chemicals to reduce the birth rate in deer populations. This plan will help control overpopulation, but it is effective for only one year at a time.

Should People Take Indirect Action?

Some suggest bringing in natural enemies of deer, such as wolves, mountain lions, and bears, to areas with too many deer. But these animals could also attack cattle, dogs, cats, and even humans. Other communities have built tall fences around areas they don't want deer to invade. Although this solution can work for people with small yards, it is impractical for farmers or ranchers.

Should People Do Nothing? Some people oppose any kind of action. They support leaving the deer alone and allowing nature to take its course. Animal populations in an area naturally cycle up and down over time. Doing nothing means that some deer will die of starvation or disease. But eventually, the population will be reduced to a size within the carrying capacity of the environment.

You Decide

1. Identify the Problem

In your own words, explain the problem created by the overpopulation of white-tailed deer.

2. Analyze the Options

List the ways that people can deal with overpopulation of white-tailed deer. State the negative and positive points of each method.

3. Find a Solution

Suppose you are an ecologist in an area that has twice as many deer as it can support. Propose a way for the community to deal with the problem.

Section 3 Interactions Among Living Things

Discover — Activity

How Well Can You Hide a Butterfly?

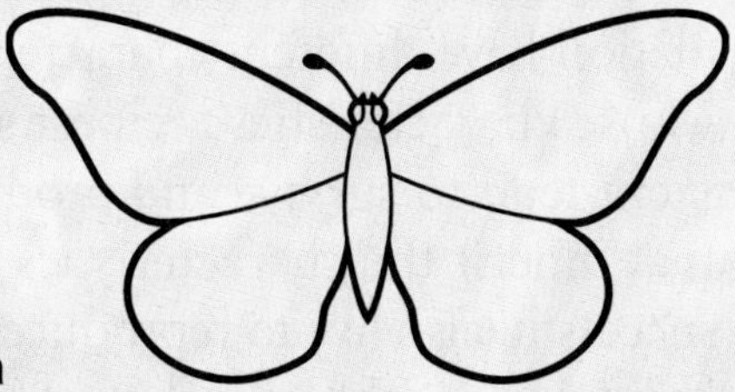

1. Using the outline at the right, trace a butterfly on a piece of paper.
2. Look around the classroom and pick a spot where you will place your butterfly. The butterfly must be placed completely in the open. Color your butterfly so it will blend in with the spot you choose.
3. Tape your butterfly to its spot. Someone will now enter the room to look for the butterflies. This person will have one minute to find all the butterflies he or she can. Will your butterfly be found?

Think It Over

Predicting Over time, how do you think the population size would change for butterflies that blend in with their surroundings?

Guide for Reading

- How do an organism's adaptations help it to survive?
- What are the major types of interactions among organisms?
- What are the three forms of symbiotic relationships?

Reading Tip As you read, use the section headings to make an outline. Fill in details under each heading.

Imagine giving a big hug to the plant in the photo. Ouch! The sharp spines on its trunk would make you think twice before hugging—or even touching—the saguaro (suh GWAHR oh) cactus. But if you could spend a day hidden inside a saguaro, you would see that many species do interact with this spiky plant.

As the day breaks, you hear a twittering noise coming from a nest tucked in one of the saguaro's arms. Two young red-tailed hawks are preparing to fly for the first time. Farther down the trunk, a tiny elf owl peeks out of its nest in a small hole. The elf owl is so small it could fit in your palm! A rattlesnake slithers around the base of the saguaro, looking for lunch. Spying a nearby shrew, the snake moves in for the kill. With a sudden movement, it strikes the shrew with its sharp fangs.

The activity around the saguaro doesn't stop after the sun goes down. At night, long-nosed bats feed on the nectar from the saguaro's blossoms. They stick their faces into the flowers to feed, covering their long snouts with a dusting of white pollen in the process. As the bats move from plant to plant, they carry the pollen along. This enables the cactuses to reproduce.

◀ Saguaro cactus in the Arizona desert

Red-tailed hawk
Flycatcher
Hawk nest
Woodpecker
Elf owl
Purple martin
Wasps
Saguaro cactus
Roadrunner

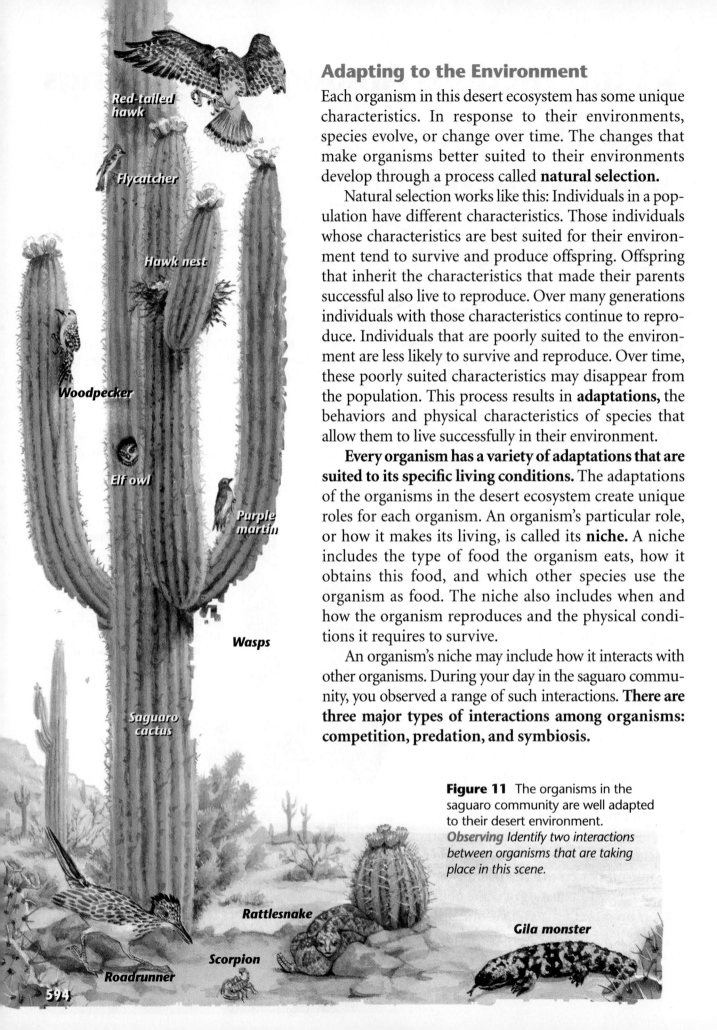

Adapting to the Environment

Each organism in this desert ecosystem has some unique characteristics. In response to their environments, species evolve, or change over time. The changes that make organisms better suited to their environments develop through a process called **natural selection.**

Natural selection works like this: Individuals in a population have different characteristics. Those individuals whose characteristics are best suited for their environment tend to survive and produce offspring. Offspring that inherit the characteristics that made their parents successful also live to reproduce. Over many generations individuals with those characteristics continue to reproduce. Individuals that are poorly suited to the environment are less likely to survive and reproduce. Over time, these poorly suited characteristics may disappear from the population. This process results in **adaptations,** the behaviors and physical characteristics of species that allow them to live successfully in their environment.

Every organism has a variety of adaptations that are suited to its specific living conditions. The adaptations of the organisms in the desert ecosystem create unique roles for each organism. An organism's particular role, or how it makes its living, is called its **niche.** A niche includes the type of food the organism eats, how it obtains this food, and which other species use the organism as food. The niche also includes when and how the organism reproduces and the physical conditions it requires to survive.

An organism's niche may include how it interacts with other organisms. During your day in the saguaro community, you observed a range of such interactions. **There are three major types of interactions among organisms: competition, predation, and symbiosis.**

Figure 11 The organisms in the saguaro community are well adapted to their desert environment.
Observing *Identify two interactions between organisms that are taking place in this scene.*

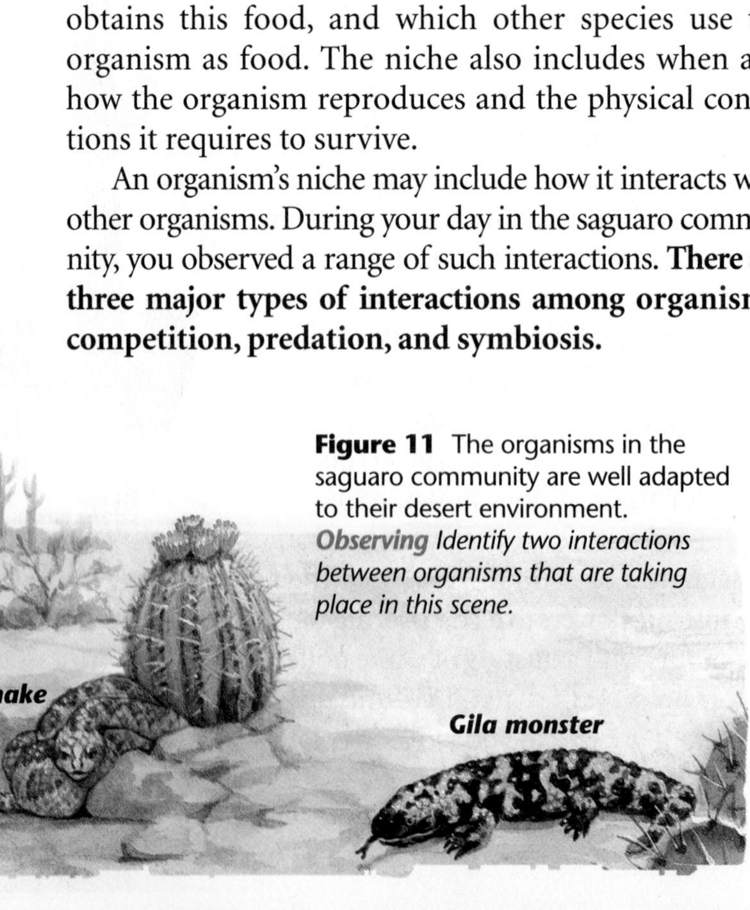
Rattlesnake
Scorpion
Gila monster

The Cape May warbler *feeds at the tips of branches near the top of the tree.*
The bay-breasted warbler *feeds in the middle part of the tree.*
The yellow-rumped warbler *feeds in the lower part of the tree and at the bases of the middle branches.*

Figure 12 Each of these warblers occupies a different niche in its spruce tree habitat. By feeding in different areas of the tree, the birds avoid competing with each other for food.

Competition

Different species can share the same habitat, such as the many animals that live in and around the saguaro. Different species can also share similar food requirements. For example, the red-tailed hawk and the elf owl both live on the saguaro and eat similar food. However, these two species do not occupy exactly the same niche. The hawk is active during the day, while the owl is active mostly at night. If two species occupy the same niche, one of the species will eventually die off. The reason for this is **competition,** the struggle between organisms to survive in a habitat with limited resources.

An ecosystem cannot satisfy the needs of all the living things in a particular habitat. There is a limited amount of food, water, and shelter. Organisms that survive have adaptations that enable them to reduce competition. For example, the three species of warblers in Figure 12 live in the same spruce forest habitat. They all eat insects that live in the spruce trees. How do these birds avoid competing for the limited insect supply? Each warbler "specializes" in feeding in a certain part of a spruce tree. By finding their own places to feed, the three species can coexist.

INTEGRATING CHEMISTRY Many plants use chemicals to ward off their competition. Plants often compete with one another for growing space and water. Some shrubs release toxic, or poisonous, chemicals into the ground around them. These chemicals keep grass and weeds from growing around the shrubs, sometimes forming a ring of bare ground a meter or two wide.

☑ *Checkpoint* *Why can't two species occupy the same niche?*

Predation

A tiger shark lurks beneath the surface of the clear blue water, looking for shadows of young albatrosses floating above it. The shark sees a chick and silently swims closer. Suddenly, the shark bursts through the water and seizes the albatross with one snap of its powerful jaw. This interaction between two organisms has an unfortunate ending for the albatross.

An interaction in which one organism kills and eats another is called **predation.** The organism that does the killing, in this case the tiger shark, is the **predator.** The organism that is killed, the albatross, is the **prey.**

Predator Adaptations Predators have adaptations that help them catch and kill their prey. For example, a cheetah can run very fast for a short time, enabling it to catch its prey. A jellyfish's tentacles contain a poisonous substance that paralyzes tiny water

EXPLORING *Defense Strategies*

Organisms display a wide array of adaptations that help them avoid becoming prey.

Camouflage ▲
These delicate spiny bugs are a perfect match for their branch habitat. The more an organism resembles its surroundings, the less likely it is that a predator will notice it. Some animals, such as flounder, can even change their colors to match a variety of settings.

Protective Coverings
This sea urchin sends a clear message to predators: "Don't touch!" Porcupines, hedgehogs, and cactuses all use the same spiny strategy. After a few painful encounters, a predator will look for less prickly prey. ▼

animals. You can probably think of many predators that have claws, sharp teeth, or stingers. Some plants, too, have adaptations for catching prey. The sundew is covered with sticky bulbs on stalks—when a fly lands on the plant, it remains snared in the sticky goo while the plant digests it.

Some predators have adaptations that enable them to hunt at night. For example, the big eyes of an owl let in as much light as possible to help it see in the dark. Bats can hunt without seeing at all. Instead, they locate their prey by producing pulses of sound and listening for the echoes. This precise method enables a bat to catch a flying moth in complete darkness.

Prey Adaptations How do prey organisms manage to avoid being killed by such effective predators? In *Exploring Defense Strategies,* below, you can see some examples of how an organism's physical characteristics can help protect it.

Warning Coloring ▲
A frog this bright certainly can't hide. How could such a color be an advantage? The bright red and blue of this poison arrow frog warn predators not to eat it—glands on the frog's back that release toxic chemicals make it a bad choice for a meal.

Mimicry
If you've ever been stung by a bee, you'd probably keep your distance from this insect. But actually this "bee" is a harmless fly. The fly's resemblance to a stinging bee protects it from birds and other predators, who are fooled into staying away. ▼

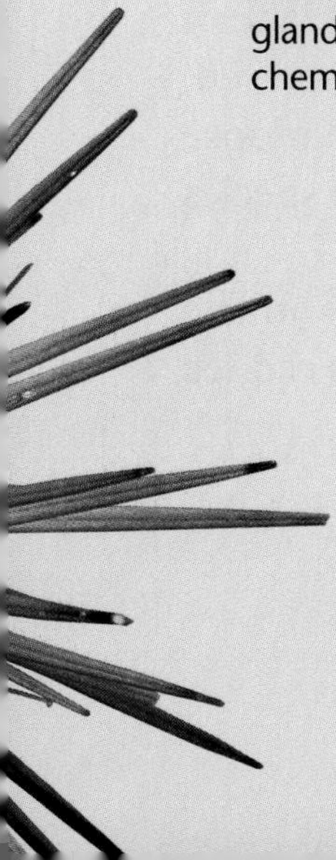

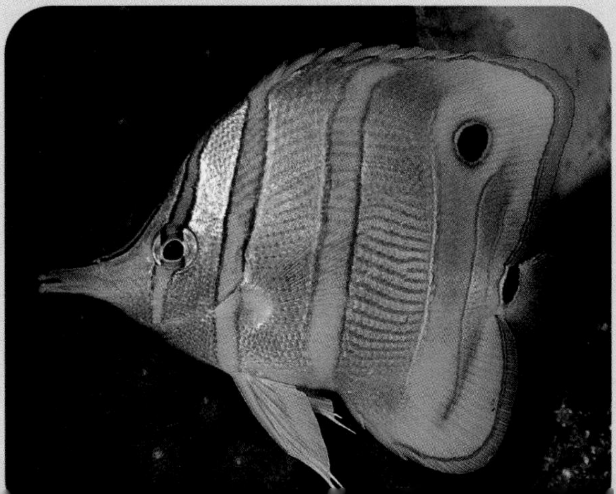

◄ **False Coloring**
Which way is this butterfly fish swimming? The black dot on its tail is a false eye. A predator may bite this end of the fish, allowing it to escape with only part of its tail missing.

Figure 13 The populations of wolves and moose on Isle Royale are related. The predator wolf population depends on the size of the prey moose population, and vice versa.
Predicting How might a disease in the wolf population one year affect the moose population the next year?

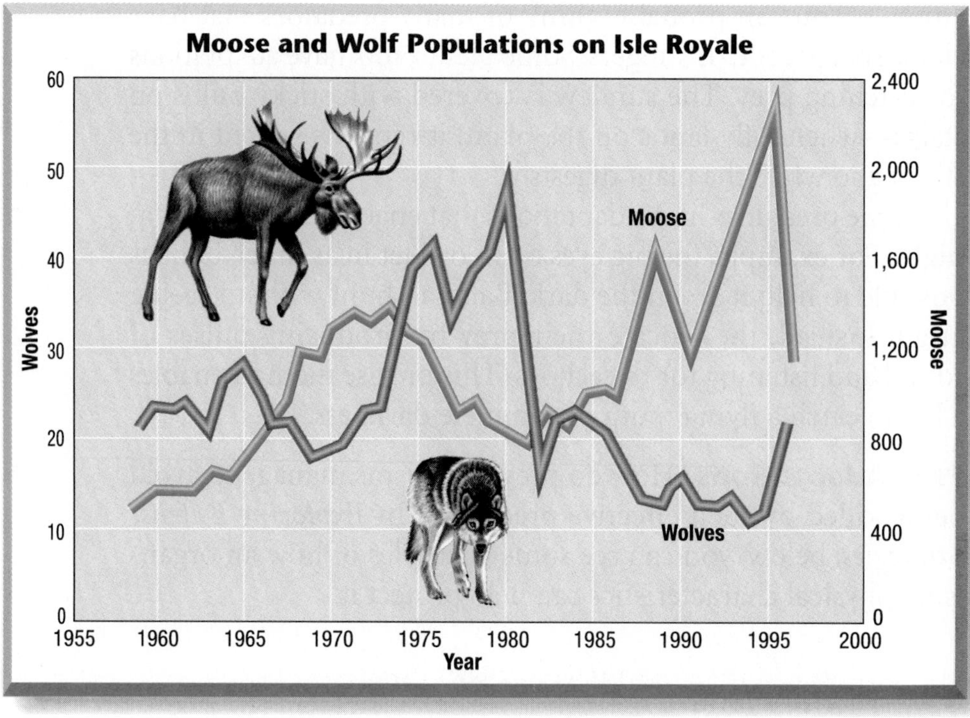

Moose and Wolf Populations on Isle Royale
Wolves
60
50
40
30
20
10
0
Moose
2,400
2,000
1,600
1,200
800
400
0
Moose
Wolves
1955
1960
1965
1970
1975
1980
1985
1990
1995
2000
Year

The Effect of Predation on Population Size Predation can have a major effect on the size of a population. As you learned in Section 2, when the death rate exceeds the birth rate in a population, the size of the population usually decreases. If predators are very effective at hunting their prey, the result is often a decrease in the size of the prey population. But a decrease in the prey population in turn affects the predator population.

To see how predator and prey populations can affect each other, look at the graph above. The graph shows the number of moose and wolves living on Isle Royale, an island in Lake Superior. From 1965 to 1975, the number of prey moose increased. The wolves now had enough to eat, so more of them survived. Within a few years, the wolf population began to increase. The growing number of wolves killed more and more moose. The moose population decreased. By 1980, the lack of moose had greatly affected the wolves. Some wolves starved, and others could not raise as many young. Soon the moose population began to climb again. This cycle for the two species has continued.

Of course, other factors also affect the populations on Isle Royale. For instance, cold winters and disease can also reduce the size of one or both of the populations.

☑ *Checkpoint* ***If predation removes more members of a population than are born, how will the population change?***

Symbiosis

Many of the interactions in the saguaro community you read about earlier are examples of symbiosis. **Symbiosis** (sim bee OH sis) is a close relationship between two species that benefits at least one of the species. **The three types of symbiotic relationships are mutualism, commensalism, and parasitism.**

Mutualism A relationship in which both species benefit is called **mutualism** (MYOO choo uh liz um). The relationship between the saguaro and the long-eared bats is an example of mutualism. The bat benefits because the cactus flowers provide it with food. The saguaro benefits as its pollen is carried to another plant on the bat's nose.

INTEGRATING HEALTH At this very moment, you are participating in a mutualistic relationship with a population of bacteria in your large intestine. These bacteria, called *Escherichia coli,* live in the intestines of most mammals. These bacteria break down some foods that the mammal cannot digest. The bacteria benefit by receiving food and a place to live. You also benefit from the relationship because the bacteria provide you with vitamin K, a nutrient that is needed to make your blood clot.

Commensalism A relationship in which one species benefits and the other species is neither helped nor harmed is called **commensalism** (kuh MEN suh liz um). The red-tailed hawks' interaction with the saguaro is an example of commensalism. The hawks are helped by having a place to build their nest, while the cactus is not affected by the birds.

Commensalism is not very common in nature because two species are usually either helped or harmed a little by any interaction. For example, by creating a small hole for its nest in the cactus trunk, the elf owl slightly damages the cactus.

Sharpen your Skills

Classifying ACTIVITY

Classify each interaction as an example of mutualism, commensalism, or parasitism. Explain your answers.

- a remora fish attaches itself to the underside of a shark without harming the shark, and eats leftover bits of food from the shark's meals
- a vampire bat drinks the blood of horses
- bacteria living in cows' stomachs help them break down the cellulose in grass

Figure 14 Three yellow-billed oxpeckers get a cruise and a snack aboard an obliging hippopotamus. The oxpeckers eat ticks living on the hippo's skin. Since both the birds and the hippo benefit from this interaction, it is an example of mutualism.

Figure 15 The white objects on this sphinx moth larva are wasp cocoons. When the wasps emerge, they will feed on the larva. *Applying Concepts Which organism in this interaction is the parasite? Which organism is the host?*

Parasitism The third type of symbiosis is called parasitism. **Parasitism** (PA ruh sit iz um) involves one organism living on or inside another organism and harming it. The organism that benefits is called a **parasite,** and the organism it lives on or in is called a **host.** The parasite is usually smaller than the host. In a parasitic relationship, the parasite benefits from the interaction while the host is harmed.

Some common parasites you may be familiar with are fleas, ticks, and leeches. These parasites have adaptations that enable them to attach to their host and feed on its blood. Other parasites live inside the host's body, such as tapeworms that live inside the digestive systems of many mammals, such as dogs and wolves.

Unlike a predator, a parasite does not usually kill the organism it feeds on. If the host dies, the parasite loses its source of food. An interesting example of this rule is shown by a species of mite that lives in the ears of moths. The mites almost always live in just one of the moth's ears. If they live in both ears, the moth's hearing is so badly affected that it is likely to be quickly caught and eaten by its predator, a bat.

Section 3 Review

1. How do an organism's adaptations help it to survive?
2. Name and define the three major types of interactions among organisms.
3. List the three types of symbiosis. For each one, explain how the two organisms are affected.
4. A walking stick is an insect that resembles a small twig. How do you think this insect avoids predators?
5. **Thinking Critically Comparing and Contrasting** How are parasitism and predation similar? How are they different?

CHAPTER PROJECT

Check Your Progress

By now you should be making your final observations of your plants and planning your report. How can you present your data in a graph? Think about what you should put on each axis of your graph. (*Hint:* Draft the written portion of your report early enough to look it over and make any necessary changes.)

SECTION 1 Living Things and the Environment

Key Ideas

- An organism's habitat provides food, water, shelter, and other things the organism needs to live, grow, and reproduce.
- An ecosystem includes both biotic and abiotic factors. Abiotic factors found in many environments include water, sunlight, oxygen, temperature, and soil.
- A population consists of a single species. The different populations living together in one area make up a community. The community plus abiotic factors form an ecosystem.
- Ecologists study how the biotic and abiotic factors interact within an ecosystem.

Key Terms

ecosystem
habitat
biotic factor
abiotic factor
photosynthesis
species
population
community
ecology

SECTION 2 Studying Populations

INTEGRATING MATHEMATICS

Key Ideas

- Ecologists can estimate population size by direct and indirect observations, sampling, and mark-and-recapture studies.
- A population changes in size as a result of changes in the birth rate or death rate, or when organisms move into or out of the population.
- Population size is controlled by limiting factors such as food, space, and weather conditions.

Key Terms

population density
estimate
birth rate
death rate
immigration
emigration
limiting factor
carrying capacity

SECTION 3 Interactions Among Living Things

Key Ideas

- Over time, species of organisms develop specialized adaptations and behaviors that help them succeed in their environments.
- The major types of interactions among organisms are competition, predation, and symbiosis.
- Predators have many adaptations that enable them to catch their prey, while prey organisms have adaptations to protect themselves from predators.
- Symbiosis is a close relationship between two species. The three types of symbiotic relationships are mutualism, commensalism, and parasitism.

Key Terms

natural selection
adaptation
niche
competition
predation
predator
prey
symbiosis
mutualism
commensalism
parasitism
parasite
host

ACTIVITY
USING THE INTERNET
www.phschool.com/state_focus/california/

CHAPTER 18 ASSESSMENT

California Test Prep: Reviewing Content

Multiple Choice

Choose the letter of the best answer.

1. A prairie dog, a hawk, and a badger all are members of the same
a. habitat. **b.** community.
c. species. **d.** population.

2. Which of the following is *not* an example of a population?
a. the pets in your neighborhood
b. the people in a city
c. the rainbow trout in a stream
d. the ants in an anthill

3. All of the following are examples of limiting factors for populations *except*
a. space **b.** food
c. time **d.** weather

4. Which of these relationships is an example of parasitism?
a. a bird building a nest on a tree branch
b. a bat pollinating a saguaro cactus
c. a flea living on a cat's blood
d. *Escherichia coli* bacteria making vitamin K in your intestine

5. In which type of interaction do both species benefit?
a. predation **b.** mutualism
c. commensalism **d.** parasitism

True or False

If the statement is true, write true. If it is false, change the underlined word or words to make the statement true.

6. Grass is an example of a(n) <u>abiotic</u> factor in a habitat.

7. A rise in birth rate while the death rate remains steady will cause a population to <u>increase</u> in size.

8. The struggle between organisms for limited resources is called <u>mutualism</u>.

9. A parasite lives on or inside its <u>predator</u>.

10. An organism's specific role in its habitat is called its <u>niche</u>.

Checking Concepts

11. Name two biotic and two abiotic factors you might find in a forest ecosystem.

12. Explain how sunlight is used by plants and algae. How is this process important to other living things in an ecosystem?

13. Describe how ecologists use the technique of sampling to estimate population size.

14. Give an example showing how space can be a limiting factor for a population.

15. What are two adaptations that prey organisms have developed to protect themselves? Describe how each adaptation protects the organism.

16. Writing to Learn Write a description of your niche in the environment. Include details about your habitat, including both biotic and abiotic factors around you. Be sure to describe your feeding habits as well as any interactions you have with members of other species.

Thinking Visually

17. Concept Map Copy the concept map about interactions among organisms onto a separate sheet of paper. Complete the concept map and add a title. (For more on concept maps, see the Skills Handbook.)

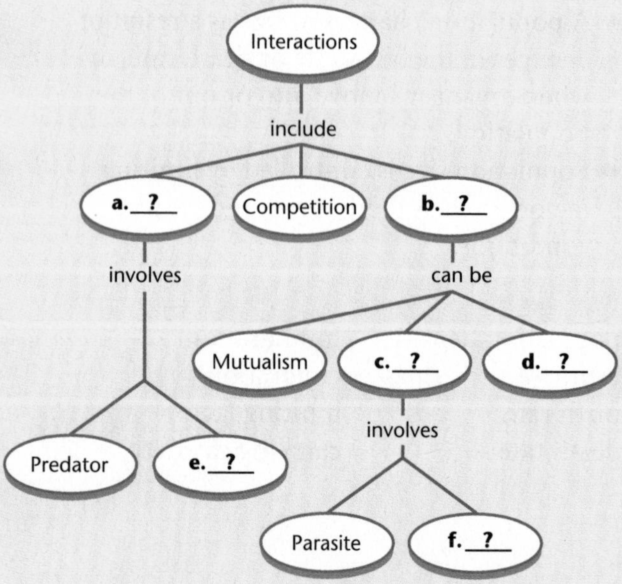
Interactions
include
a. ?
Competition
b. ?
involves
can be
Mutualism
c. ?
d. ?
involves
Predator
e. ?
Parasite
f. ?

Test Prep: Skills

Ecologists monitoring a deer population collected data during a 30-year study. Use the data to answer Questions 18–21.

18. **Graphing** Make a line graph using the data in the table. Plot years on the horizontal axis and population on the vertical axis.

Year	0	5	10	15	20	25	30
Population (thousands)	15	30	65	100	40	25	10

19. **Interpreting Data** In which year did the deer population reach its highest point? Its lowest point?
20. **Communicating** Write a few sentences describing how the deer population changed during the study.
21. **Developing Hypotheses** In Year 16 of the study, this region experienced a very severe winter. How might this have affected the deer population?

Thinking Critically

22. **Making Generalizations** Explain why ecologists usually study a specific population of organisms rather than studying the entire species.
23. **Problem Solving** As a summer job working for an ecologist, you have been assigned to estimate the population of grasshoppers in a field. Propose a method to get an estimate and explain how you would carry it out.
24. **Comparing and Contrasting** Explain how parasitism and mutualism are similar and how they are different.
25. **Relating Cause and Effect** Competition for resources in an area is usually more intense within a single species than between two different species. Can you suggest an explanation for this observation? (*Hint:* Consider how niches help organisms avoid competition.)

Performance Assessment

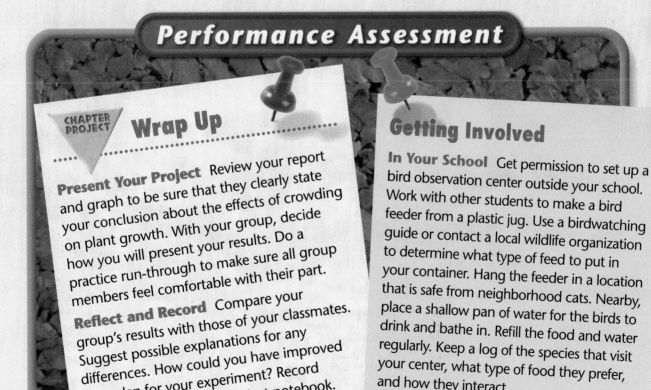

CHAPTER PROJECT Wrap Up

Present Your Project Review your report and graph to be sure that they clearly state your conclusion about the effects of crowding on plant growth. With your group, decide how you will present your results. Do a practice run-through to make sure all group members feel comfortable with their part.

Reflect and Record Compare your group's results with those of your classmates. Suggest possible explanations for any differences. How could you have improved your plan for your experiment? Record these thoughts in your project notebook.

Getting Involved

In Your School Get permission to set up a bird observation center outside your school. Work with other students to make a bird feeder from a plastic jug. Use a birdwatching guide or contact a local wildlife organization to determine what type of feed to put in your container. Hang the feeder in a location that is safe from neighborhood cats. Nearby, place a shallow pan of water for the birds to drink and bathe in. Refill the food and water regularly. Keep a log of the species that visit your center, what type of food they prefer, and how they interact.

CHAPTER

19 Ecosystems and Biomes

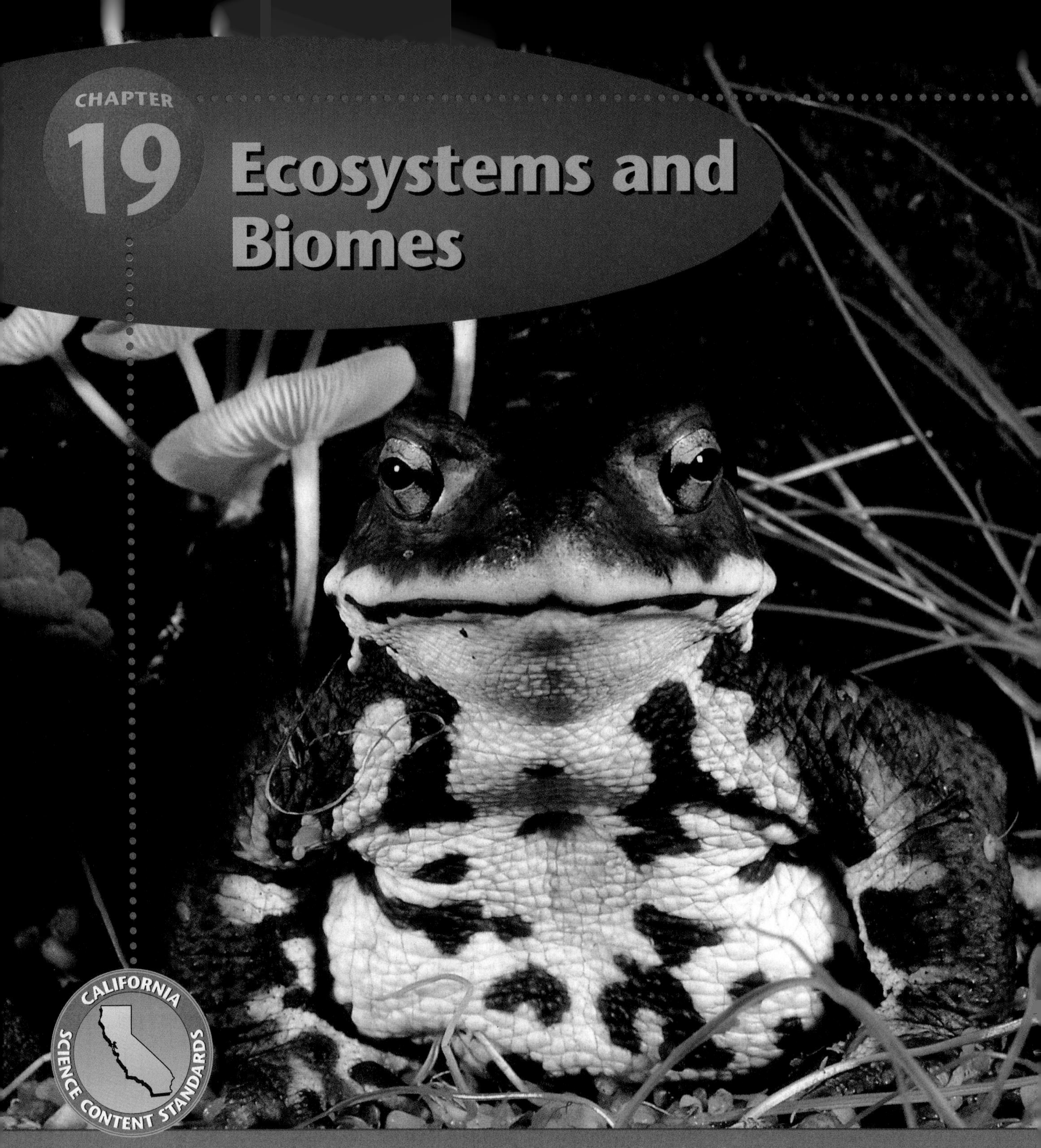
CALIFORNIA
SCIENCE CONTENT STANDARDS

The following California Science Content Standards are addressed in this chapter:

1. Plate tectonics explains important features of the Earth's surface and major geologic events.
   - c. Lithospheric plates that are the size of continents and oceans move at rates of centimeters per year in response to movements in the mantle.
2. Topography is reshaped by weathering of rock and soil and by the transportation and deposition of sediment.
   - d. Earthquakes, volcanic eruptions, landslides, and floods change human and wildlife habitats.
5. Organisms in ecosystems exchange energy and nutrients among themselves and with the environment.
   - a. Energy entering ecosystems as sunlight is transferred by producers into chemical energy through photosynthesis, and then from organism to organism in food webs.
   - b. Over time, matter is transferred from one organism to others in the food web, and between organisms and the physical environment.

PROJECT 19

Breaking It Down

This toad is right at home in its habitat. It is surrounded by living leaves, grass, and mushrooms, as well as nonliving rocks, soil, and air.

Nothing in this toad's ecosystem is wasted. Even when the living things die, they will be recycled by other organism like the mushrooms. This natural breakdown process is called decomposition. In this chapter, you will study decomposition and other processes in ecosystems.

When fallen leaves and other waste products decompose, a fluffy, brown mixture called compost is formed. You can observe decomposition firsthand by building a compost chamber.

Your Goal To design an experiment to learn more about the process of decomposition.

To complete your project successfully, you must

- build two compost chambers
- investigate the effect of one of the following variables on decomposition: moisture, oxygen, temperature, or activity of soil organisms
- analyze your data and present your results
- follow the safety guidelines in Appendix A

Get Started Your teacher will provide you with a sample of compost material. Observe the wastes in the mixture with a hand lens. Write a hypothesis about which kinds of waste will decay and which will not. Begin thinking about which variable you will test.

Check Your Progress You'll be working on this project as you study this chapter. To keep your project on track, look for Check Your Progress boxes at the following points.

Section 1 Review, page 612: Build your compost chambers and design your experimental plan.

Section 2 Review, page 617: Observe your compost chambers and collect data.

Section 4 Review, page 635: Analyze your data.

Wrap Up At the end of the chapter (page 643), you will compare the compost produced in each of your compost chambers. Will your results support your hypothesis?

c. Populations of organisms can be categorized by the functions they serve in an ecosystem.

d. Different kinds of organisms may play similar ecological roles in similar biomes.

e. The number and types of organisms an ecosystem can support depends on the resources available and abiotic factors, such as quantity of light and water, range of temperatures, and soil composition.

7. Scientific progress is made by asking meaningful questions and conducting careful investigations.

a. Develop a hypothesis.

b. Select and use appropriate tools and technology to perform tests, collect data, and display data.

e. Recognize whether evidence is consistent with a proposed explanation

SECTION 1

Energy Flow in Ecosystems

DISCOVER ACTIVITY

Where Did Your Dinner Come From?

1. Across the top of a page, list the different types of foods you ate for dinner last night.
2. Under each item, write the name of the plant, animal, or other organism that is the source of that food. Some foods have more than one source. For example, bread is made from flour (which is made from a plant such as wheat) and yeast (which is a fungus).

Think It Over

Classifying Count the different organisms that contributed to your dinner. How many of your food sources were plants? How many were animals?

GUIDE FOR READING

- **What energy roles do organisms play in an ecosystem?**
- **How much energy is available at each level of an energy pyramid?**

Reading Tip **As you read, create a flowchart showing one possible path of energy through an ecosystem.**

Pushing off from its perch on an oak tree limb, the kestrel glides over a field dotted with yellow flowers. In the middle of the field, the bird pauses. It hovers above the ground like a giant hummingbird. Despite strong gusts of wind, the bird's head remains steady as it looks for prey. It takes a lot of energy for the kestrel to hover in this way, but from this position it can search the field below for food.

Soon the kestrel spots a mouse munching the ripening seedhead of a blade of grass. Seconds later the kestrel swoops down and grasps the mouse in its talons. The bird carries the mouse back to the tree to feed.

Meanwhile, a lynx spider hides among the petals of a nearby flower. An unsuspecting bee lands on the flower for a sip of nectar. The spider grabs the bee and injects its venom into the bee's body. The venom kills the bee before it can respond with its own deadly sting.

This sunny field is an ecosystem, made up of living and nonliving things that interact with one another. You can see that many interactions in this ecosystem involve eating. The spider eats a bee that eats nectar, while the kestrel eats a mouse that eats grass. Ecologists study such feeding patterns to learn how energy flows within an ecosystem.

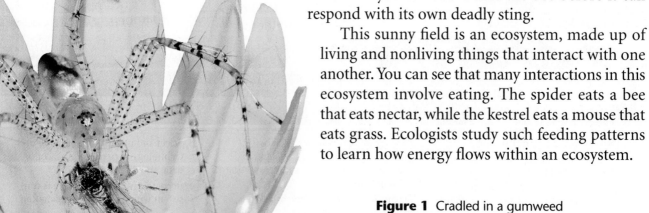

Figure 1 Cradled in a gumweed flower, a green lynx spider attacks an unsuspecting bee. These organisms are involved in feeding interactions.

Energy Roles

Do you play an instrument in your school band? If so, you know that each instrument has a role in a piece of music. For instance, the flute may provide the melody, while the drum provides the beat. Although the two instruments are quite different, they both play important roles in creating the band's music. In the same way, each organism has a role in the movement of energy through its ecosystem. This role is part of the organism's niche in the ecosystem. The kestrel's role is different from that of the giant oak tree where it was perched. But all parts of the ecosystem, like all parts of the band, are necessary for the ecosystem to work.

An organism's energy role is determined by how it obtains energy and how it interacts with the other living things in its ecosystem. **An organism's energy role in an ecosystem may be that of a producer, consumer, or decomposer.**

Producers Energy first enters most ecosystems as sunlight. Some organisms, such as plants, algae, and certain microorganisms, are able to capture the energy of sunlight and store it as food energy. As Figure 2 shows, these organisms use the sun's energy to turn water and carbon dioxide into molecules such as sugars and starches. As you recall from Chapter 18, this process is called photosynthesis.

An organism that can make its own food is a **producer.** Producers are the source of all the food in an ecosystem. For example, the grass and oak tree are the producers for the field ecosystem you read about at the beginning of the section.

In a few ecosystems the producers obtain energy from a source other than sunlight. One such ecosystem is found in rocks deep beneath the ground. Since the rocks are never exposed to sunlight, how is energy brought into this ecosystem? Certain bacteria in this ecosystem produce their own food using the energy in a gas, hydrogen sulfide, that is found in their environment.

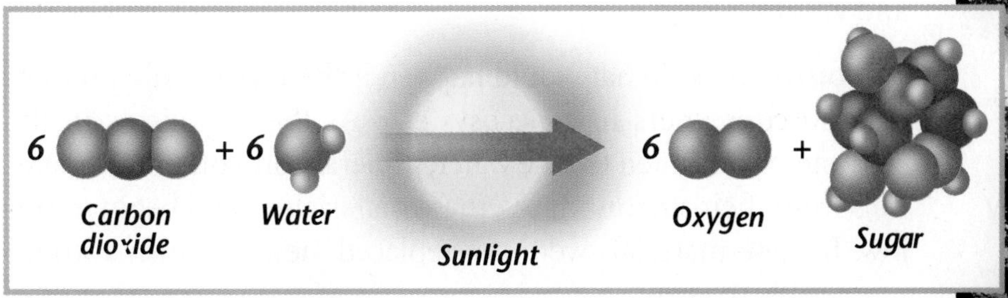
6
+ 6
6
+
Carbon dioxide
Water
Sunlight
Oxygen
Sugar

Figure 2 The sunlight streaming through this redwood forest is the source of energy for the ecosystem. Plants convert the sun's energy to stored food energy through the process of photosynthesis.
Interpreting Diagrams What substances are needed for photosynthesis? What substances are produced?

A
B
C

Figure 3 Consumers are classified by what they eat. **A.** An agile gerenuk stands on its hind legs to reach these leaves. Consumers that eat plants are called herbivores. **B.** Carnivores like this collared lizard eat only animals. **C.** A black vulture is a scavenger, a carnivore that feeds on the remains of dead organisms.

Consumers Other members of the ecosystem cannot make their own food. These organisms depend on the producers for food and energy. An organism that obtains energy by feeding on other organisms is a **consumer.**

Consumers are classified by what they eat. Consumers that eat only plants are called **herbivores.** This term comes from the Latin words *herba,* which means grass or herb, and *vorare,* which means to eat. Some familiar herbivores are caterpillars, cattle, and deer. Consumers that eat only animals are called **carnivores.** This term comes from the same root word *vorare,* plus the Latin word for flesh, *carnis.* Lions, spiders, and snakes are some examples of carnivores. A consumer that eats both plants and animals is called an **omnivore.** The Latin word *omni* means all. Crows, goats, and most humans are examples of omnivores.

Some carnivores are scavengers. A **scavenger** is a carnivore that feeds on the bodies of dead organisms. Scavengers include catfish and vultures.

Sharpen your Skills

Observing ACTIVITY

Sprinkle a few drops of water on a slice of bread. Enclose the bread in a sealable plastic bag. Seal the bag tightly with tape and put it in a warm, dark place. Observe the bread daily for about two weeks. **CAUTION:** *Do not open the bag.* Write a few sentences describing the changes you observe. What is responsible for the change?

Decomposers What would happen if there were only producers and consumers in an ecosystem? As the organisms in the ecosystem continued to take water, minerals, and other raw materials from their surroundings, these materials would begin to run low. If these materials were not replaced, new organisms would not be able to grow.

All the organisms in an ecosystem produce waste and eventually die. If these wastes and dead organisms were not somehow removed from the ecosystem, they would pile up until they overwhelmed the living things. Organisms that break down wastes and dead organisms and return the raw materials to the environment are called **decomposers.** Two major groups of decomposers are bacteria and fungi, such as molds and mushrooms. While obtaining energy for their own needs, decomposers return simple molecules to the environment. These molecules can be used again by other organisms.

Figure 4 A cluster of honey mushrooms grows among dead leaves. Mushrooms are familiar decomposers.

☑ *Checkpoint* ***What do herbivores and carnivores have in common?***

Food Chains and Food Webs

As you have read, energy enters most ecosystems as sunlight, and is converted into sugar and starch molecules by producers. This energy is transferred to each organism that eats a producer, and then to other organisms that feed on these consumers. The movement of energy through an ecosystem can be shown in diagrams called food chains and food webs.

A **food chain** is a series of events in which one organism eats another and obtains energy. You can follow one food chain from the field ecosystem below. The first organism in a food chain is always a producer, such as the grass in the field. The second organism is a consumer that eats the producer, and is called a first-level consumer. The mouse is a first-level consumer. Next, a second-level consumer eats the first-level consumer. The second-level consumer in this example is the kestrel.

A food chain shows one possible path along which energy can move through an ecosystem. But just as you do not eat the same thing every day, neither do most other organisms. Most producers and consumers are part of many food chains. A more realistic way to show the flow of energy through an ecosystem is a food web. A **food web** consists of the many overlapping food chains in an ecosystem.

Kestrel
(Second-level consumer)
Grass
(Producer)
Mouse
(First-level consumer)

Figure 5 These organisms make up one food chain in a field ecosystem. *Classifying Which organism shown is acting as an herbivore? Which is a carnivore?*

EXPLORING a Food Web

A food web consists of many interconnected food chains. Trace the path of energy through the producers, consumers, and decomposers.

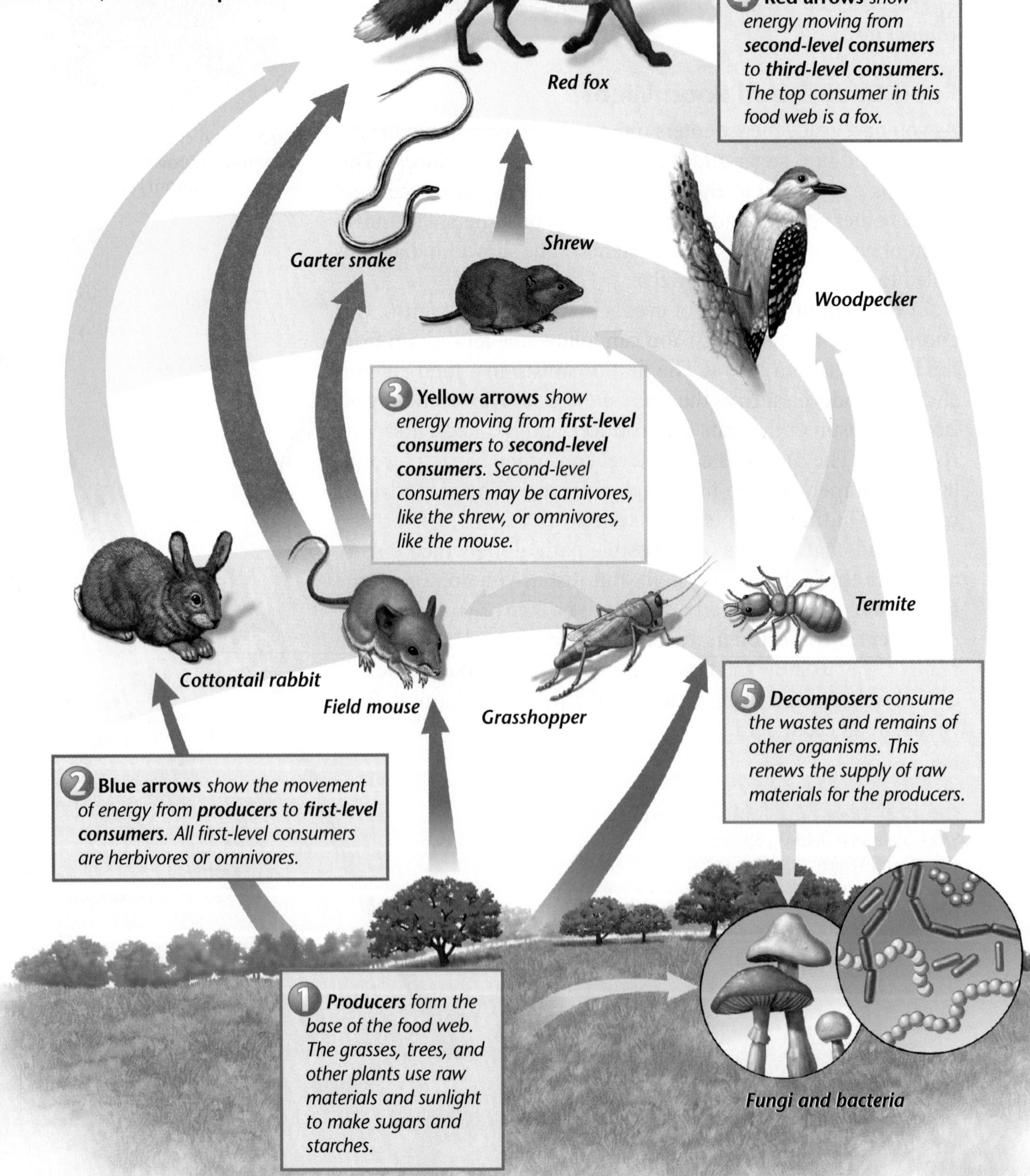

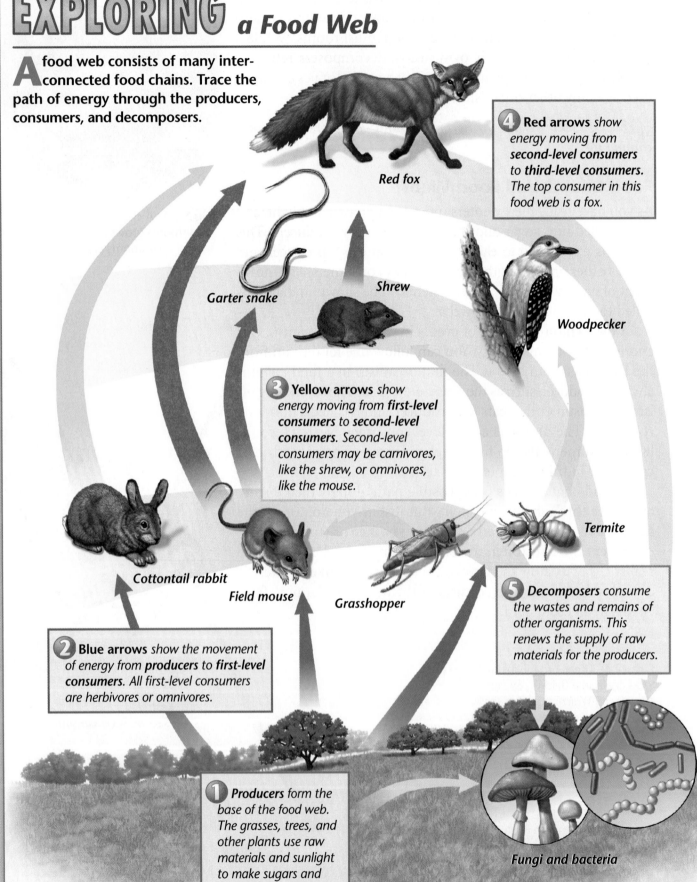

Red fox
4 Red arrows show energy moving from second-level consumers to third-level consumers. The top consumer in this food web is a fox.
Garter snake
Shrew
Woodpecker
3 Yellow arrows show energy moving from first-level consumers to second-level consumers. Second-level consumers may be carnivores, like the shrew, or omnivores, like the mouse.
Cottontail rabbit
Field mouse
Grasshopper
Termite
5 Decomposers consume the wastes and remains of other organisms. This renews the supply of raw materials for the producers.
2 Blue arrows show the movement of energy from producers to first-level consumers. All first-level consumers are herbivores or omnivores.
1 Producers form the base of the food web. The grasses, trees, and other plants use raw materials and sunlight to make sugars and starches.
Fungi and bacteria

In *Exploring a Food Web* on the facing page, you can trace the many food chains in a woodland ecosystem. Note that an organism may play more than one role in an ecosystem. For example, an omnivore such as the mouse is a first-level consumer when it eats grass. But when the mouse eats a grasshopper, it is a second-level consumer.

☑ *Checkpoint* ***What are the organisms in one food chain shown in the food web on the facing page?***

Energy Pyramids

When an organism in an ecosystem eats, it obtains energy. The organism uses some of this energy to move, grow, reproduce, and carry out other life activities. This means that only some of the energy will be available to the next organism in the food web.

A diagram called an **energy pyramid** shows the amount of energy that moves from one feeding level to another in a food web. The organisms at each level use some of the energy to carry out their life processes. **The most energy is available at the producer level. At each level in the pyramid, there is less available energy than at the level below.** An energy pyramid gets its name from the shape of the diagram—wider at the base and narrower at the top, resembling a pyramid.

In general, only about 10 percent of the energy at one level of a food web is transferred to the next, higher, level. The other

Figure 6 Organisms use energy to carry out their life activities. A lioness uses energy to chase her zebra prey. The zebras use energy to flee.

TRY THIS

Weaving a Food Web

ACTIVITY

This activity shows how the organisms in a food web are interconnected.

1. Your teacher will assign you a role in the food web.
2. Hold one end of each of several pieces of yarn in your hand. Give the other ends of your yarn to the other organisms to which your organism is linked.
3. Your teacher will now eliminate one of the organisms. Everyone who is connected to that organism should drop the yarn connecting them to it.

Making Models How many organisms were affected by the removal of one organism? What does this activity show about the importance of each organism in a food web?

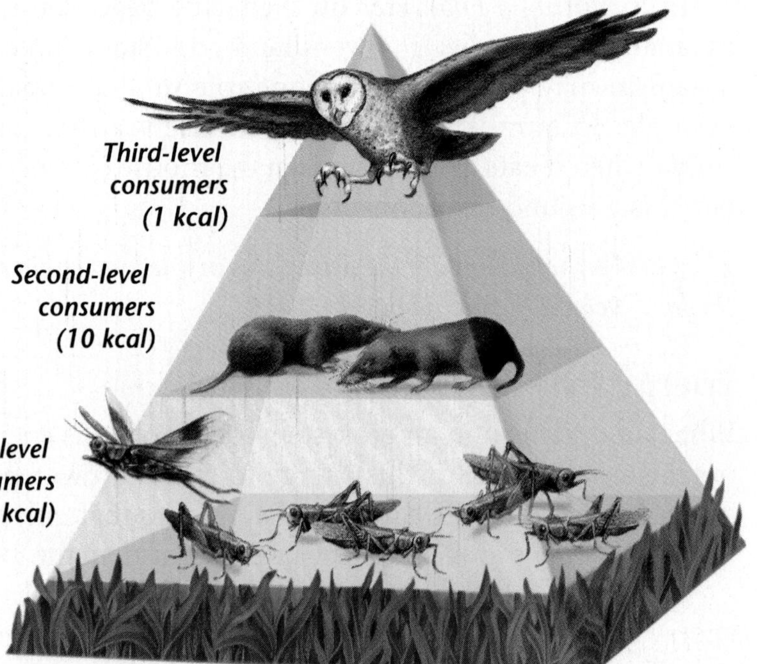
Third-level consumers (1 kcal)
Second-level consumers (10 kcal)
First-level consumers (100 kcal)
Producers (1,000 kcal)

Figure 7 This energy pyramid diagram shows the energy available at each level of a food web. Energy is measured in kilocalories, or kcal. ***Calculating*** *How many times more energy is available at the producer level than at the second-level consumer level?*

90 percent of the energy is used for the organism's life processes or is lost as heat to the environment. Because of this, most food webs only have three or four feeding levels. Since 90 percent of the energy is lost at each step, there is not enough energy to support many feeding levels.

But the organisms at higher feeding levels of an energy pyramid do not necessarily require less energy to live than organisms at lower levels. Since so much energy is lost at each level, the amount of energy in the producer level limits the number of consumers the ecosystem can support. As a result, there usually are few organisms at the highest level in a food web.

Section 1 Review

1. Name the three energy roles of organisms in an ecosystem. How does each type of organism obtain energy?
2. How does the amount of available energy change from one level of an energy pyramid to the next level up?
3. Name and define the four types of consumers.
4. What is the source of energy for most ecosystems?
5. **Thinking Critically Making Generalizations** Why are food webs a more realistic way of portraying ecosystems than food chains?

CHAPTER PROJECT

Check Your Progress

By now you should have constructed your compost chambers and chosen a variable to investigate. Design your plan for observing the effect of this variable on the decomposition process. Submit your plan to your teacher for approval. (*Hint:* As part of your plan, include how you will collect data to measure decomposition in your compost chambers.)

SECTION 2
Cycles of Matter

DISCOVER

ACTIVITY

Are You Part of a Cycle?

1. Hold a small mirror a few centimeters from your mouth.
2. Exhale onto the mirror.
3. Observe the surface of the mirror.

Think It Over

Inferring What is the substance that forms on the mirror? Where did this substance come from?

GUIDE FOR READING

- **What three major processes make up the water cycle?**
- **How is carbon dioxide used by producers?**

Reading Tip **As you read, use the section headings to make an outline of the section.**

A pile of crumpled cars is ready for loading into a giant compactor. Junkyard workers have already removed many of the cars' parts. The aluminum and copper pieces were removed so that they could be recycled, or used again. Now a recycling plant will reclaim the steel in the bodies of the cars. Earth has a limited supply of aluminum, copper, and the iron needed to make steel. Recycling old cars is one way to provide a new supply of these materials.

Recycling Matter

The way matter is recycled in ecosystems is similar to the way the metal in old cars is recycled. Like the supply of metal for building cars, the supply of matter in an ecosystem is limited. If matter could not be recycled, ecosystems would quickly run out of the raw materials necessary for life.

Energy, on the other hand, is not recycled. You must constantly supply a car with energy in the form of gasoline. Ecosystems must also be constantly supplied with energy, usually in the form of sunlight. Gasoline and the sun's energy cannot be recycled—they must be constantly supplied.

As you read in Section 1, energy enters an ecosystem and moves from the producers to the consumers to the decomposers. In contrast, matter cycles through an ecosystem over and over. Matter in an ecosystem includes water, oxygen, carbon, nitrogen, and many other substances. To understand how these substances cycle through an ecosystem, you need to know a few basic terms that describe the structure of matter. Matter is made

Cars awaiting recycling at a Utah plant ▼

Figure 8 In the water cycle, water moves continuously from Earth's surface to the atmosphere and back. *Interpreting Diagrams* *In which step of the water cycle does water return to Earth's surface?*

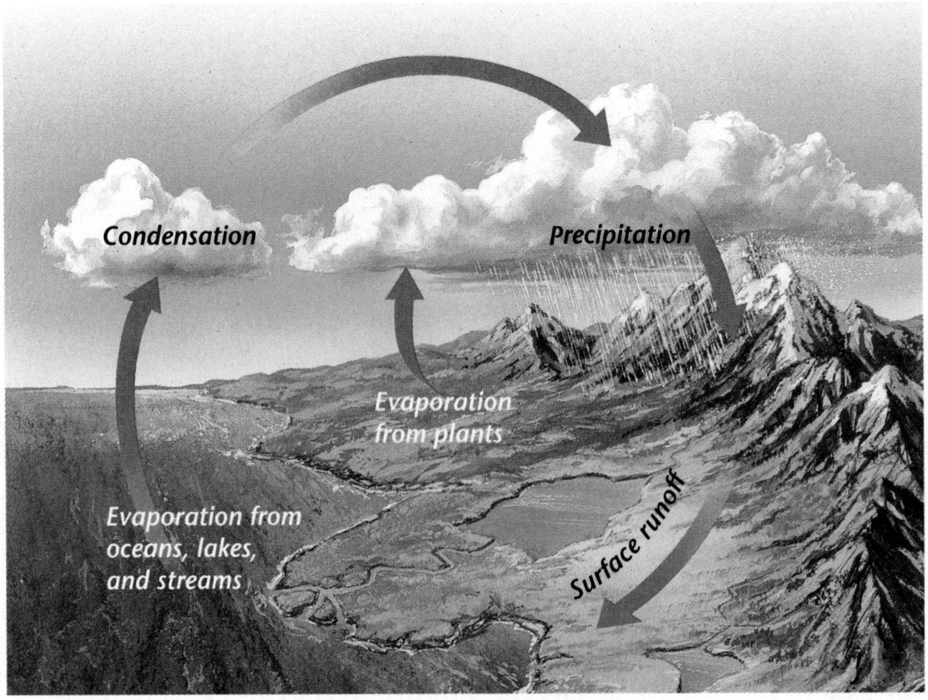
Condensation
Precipitation
Evaporation from plants
Evaporation from oceans, lakes, and streams
Surface runoff

up of tiny particles called atoms. Combinations of two or more atoms chemically bonded together are called molecules. For example, a molecule of water consists of two hydrogen atoms bonded to one oxygen atom. In this section, you will learn about some of the most important cycles of matter: the water cycle, the carbon and oxygen cycles, and the nitrogen cycle.

Sharpen your Skills

Developing Hypotheses

ACTIVITY

You're having cocoa at a friend's house on a cold, rainy day. As your friend boils some water, you notice that a window next to the stove is covered with water droplets. Your friend thinks the window is leaking. Using what you know about the water cycle, can you propose another explanation for the water droplets on the window?

The Water Cycle

How could you determine whether life has ever existed on another planet in the solar system? One piece of evidence scientists look for is the presence of water. This is because water is the most common compound in all living cells on Earth. Water is necessary for life as we know it.

Water is recycled through the water cycle. The **water cycle** is the continuous process by which water moves from Earth's surface to the atmosphere and back. **The processes of evaporation, condensation, and precipitation make up the water cycle**. As you read about these processes, follow the cycle in Figure 8.

Evaporation The process by which molecules of liquid water absorb energy and change to the gas state is called **evaporation.** In the water cycle liquid water evaporates from Earth's surface and forms water vapor, a gas, in the atmosphere. Most water evaporates from the surfaces of oceans and lakes. The energy for evaporation comes from the sun.

Some water is also given off by living things. For example, plants take in water through their roots and release water vapor from their leaves. You take in water when you drink and eat. You release liquid water in your wastes and water vapor when you exhale.

Condensation What happens next to the water vapor in the atmosphere? As the water vapor rises higher in the atmosphere, it cools down. When it cools to a certain temperature the vapor turns back into tiny drops of liquid water. The process by which a gas changes to a liquid is called **condensation.** The water droplets collect around particles of dust in the air, eventually forming clouds like those in Figure 8.

Precipitation As more water vapor condenses, the drops of water in the cloud grow larger and heavier. Eventually the heavy drops fall back to Earth as a form of **precipitation**—rain, snow, sleet, or hail. Most precipitation falls back into oceans or lakes. The precipitation that falls on land may soak into the soil and become groundwater. Or the precipitation may run off the land, ultimately flowing into a river or ocean once again.

☑ ***Checkpoint*** ***What change of state occurs when water from the surface of the ocean enters the atmosphere as water vapor?***

The Carbon and Oxygen Cycles

Two other chemicals necessary for life are carbon and oxygen. The processes by which they are recycled are linked together, as shown in Figure 9. Carbon is the building block for the matter that makes up the bodies of living things. It is present in the atmosphere in the gas carbon dioxide. Producers take in carbon dioxide from

Figure 9 This scene shows how the carbon and oxygen cycles are linked together. Producers use carbon dioxide to carry out photosynthesis. In this process, carbon is used to create sugar molecules such as those found in apples. The producers release oxygen, which is then used by other organisms. These organisms take in carbon in food and release it in the form of carbon dioxide again.

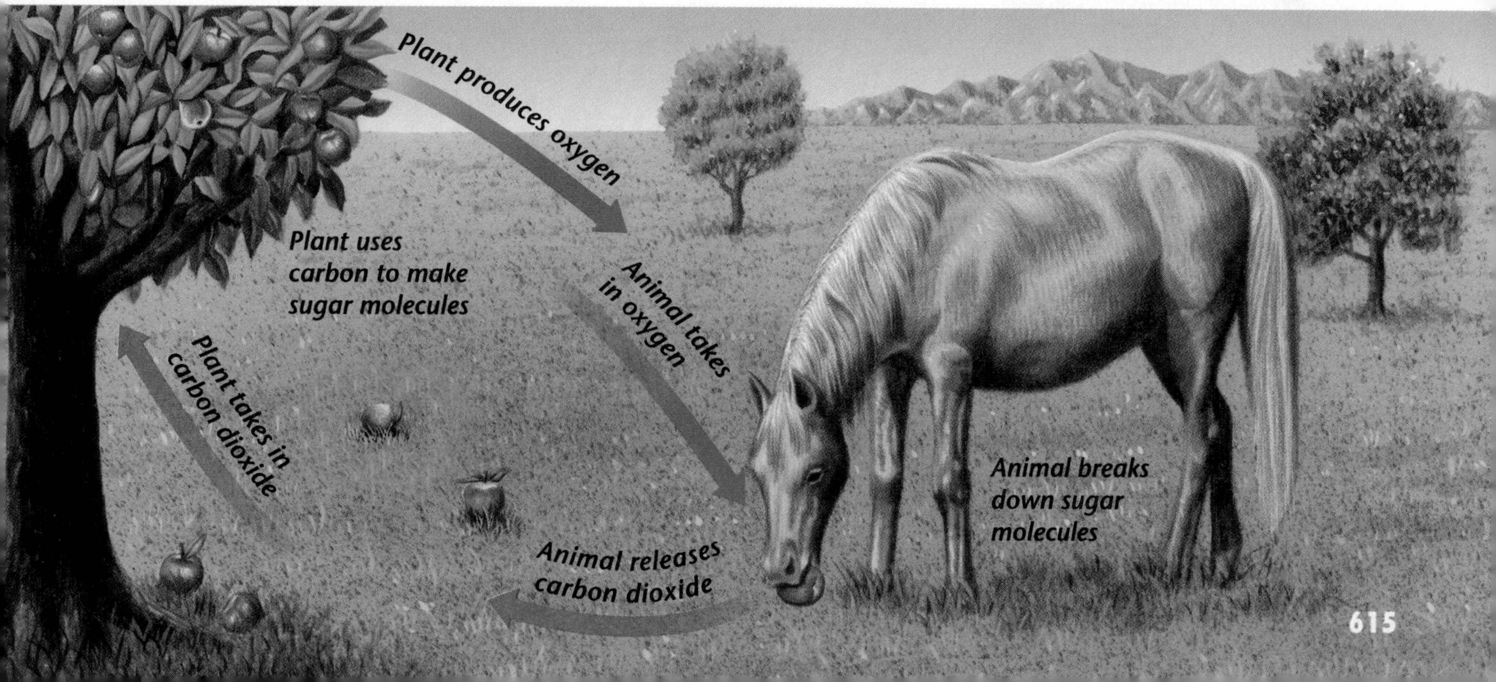
Plant produces oxygen
Plant uses carbon to make sugar molecules
Animal takes in oxygen
Plant takes in carbon dioxide
Animal breaks down sugar molecules
Animal releases carbon dioxide

the atmosphere during photosynthesis. **In this process, the producers use carbon from the carbon dioxide to produce other carbon-containing molecules.** These molecules include sugars and starches. To obtain energy from these molecules, consumers break them down into simpler molecules. Consumers release water and carbon dioxide as waste products.

At the same time, oxygen is also cycling through the ecosystem. Producers release oxygen as a result of photosynthesis. Other organisms take in oxygen from the atmosphere and use it in their life processes.

Checkpoint *How is oxygen returned to the environment?*

The Nitrogen Cycle

Like carbon, nitrogen is a necessary building block in the matter that makes up living things. Since the air around you is about 78 percent nitrogen gas, you might think that it would be easy for living things to obtain nitrogen. However, most organisms cannot use the nitrogen gas in the air. Nitrogen gas is called "free" nitrogen, meaning it is not combined with other kinds of atoms. Most organisms can use nitrogen only once it has been "fixed," or combined with other elements to form nitrogen-containing compounds. You can follow this process in Figure 10 below.

Figure 10 In the nitrogen cycle, nitrogen moves from the air to the soil, into living things, and back into the air.
Interpreting Diagrams *How do consumers obtain nitrogen?*

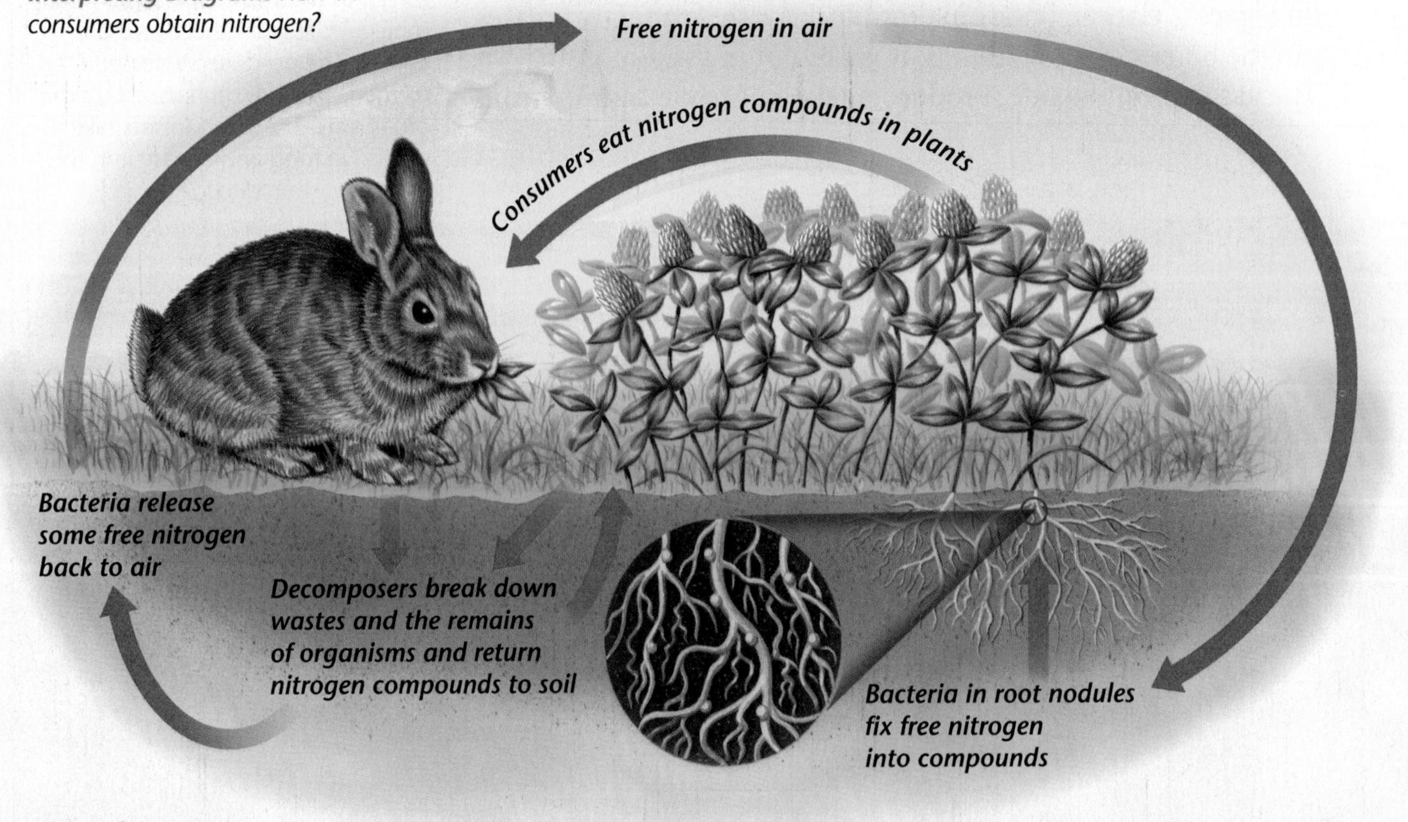

Free nitrogen in air
Consumers eat nitrogen compounds in plants
Bacteria release some free nitrogen back to air
Decomposers break down wastes and the remains of organisms and return nitrogen compounds to soil
Bacteria in root nodules fix free nitrogen into compounds

Nitrogen Fixation The process of changing free nitrogen gas into a usable form of nitrogen is called **nitrogen fixation.** Most nitrogen fixation is performed by certain kinds of bacteria. Some of these bacteria live in bumps called **nodules** (NAHJ oolz) on the roots of certain plants. These plants, known as legumes, include clover, beans, peas, alfalfa, and peanuts.

The relationship between the bacteria and the legumes is an example of mutualism. As you recall from Chapter 18, a symbiotic relationship in which both species benefit is called mutualism. Both the bacteria and the plant benefit from this relationship: The bacteria feed on the plant's sugars, and the plant is supplied with nitrogen in a usable form.

INTEGRATING TECHNOLOGY Many farmers make use of the nitrogen-fixing bacteria in legumes to enrich their fields. Every few years, a farmer may plant a legume such as alfalfa in a field. The bacteria in the alfalfa roots build up a new supply of nitrogen compounds in the soil. The following year, the new crops planted in the field benefit from the improved soil.

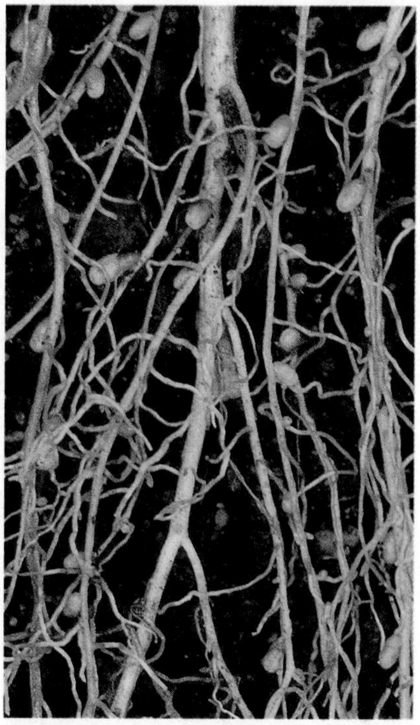

Figure 11 Lumpy nodules are clearly visible on the roots of this clover plant. Bacteria inside the nodules carry out nitrogen fixation.

Return of Nitrogen to the Environment Once the nitrogen has been fixed into chemical compounds, it can be used by organisms to build proteins and other complex substances. Decomposers break down these complex compounds in animal wastes and in the bodies of dead organisms. This returns simple nitrogen compounds to the soil. Nitrogen can cycle from the soil to producers and consumers many times. At some point, however, bacteria break down the nitrogen compounds completely. These bacteria release free nitrogen back into the air. Then the cycle starts again.

Section 2 Review

1. Name and define the three major processes that occur during the water cycle.
2. Explain the role of plants in the carbon cycle.
3. How is nitrogen fixation a necessary part of the nitrogen cycle?
4. Where do nitrogen-fixing bacteria live?
5. **Thinking Critically Comparing and Contrasting** Explain how the movement of matter through an ecosystem is different than the movement of energy through an ecosystem.

CHAPTER PROJECT

Check Your Progress

Once your teacher has approved your plan, place the waste into your compost chambers. Record your hypothesis about the effect of the variable you are investigating. Observe the two containers daily. (*Hint:* If there are no signs of decomposition after several days, you may wish to stir the contents of each chamber. Stirring allows more oxygen to enter the mixture.)

SECTION 3 Biogeography

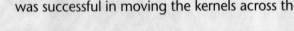

DISCOVER ACTIVITY

How Can You Move a Seed?

1. Place a few corn kernels at one end of a shallow pan.
2. Make a list of ways you could move the kernels to the other side of the pan. You may use any of the simple materials your teacher has provided.
3. Now try each method. Record whether or not each was successful in moving the kernels across the pan.

Think It Over

Predicting How might seeds be moved from place to place on Earth?

GUIDE FOR READING

- **How does dispersal of organisms occur?**
- **What factors can limit the distribution of a species?**

Reading Tip **As you read, look for reasons why organisms live in certain places in the world. Make a list of these reasons.**

◀ Australian wallaby

Imagine how European explorers must have felt when they saw the continent of Australia for the first time. Instead of familiar grazing animals such as horses and deer, they saw what looked like giant rabbits with long tails. Peering into the branches of eucalyptus trees, these explorers saw bearlike koalas. And who could have dreamed up an egg-laying animal with a beaver's tail, a duck's bill, and a thick coat of fur? You can see why people who heard the first descriptions of the platypus accused the explorers of lying!

Ecologists had many questions about the plants and animals of Australia. Why had no one ever seen a kangaroo, a eucalyptus tree, or a koala in Europe? Why were there no reindeer, camels, or gorillas in Australia?

Different species live in different parts of the world. The study of where organisms live is called **biogeography.** The word *biogeography* is made up of three Greek word roots: *bio,* meaning "life"; *geo,* meaning "Earth"; and *graph,* meaning "description." Together, these root words tell what biogeographers do—they describe where living things are found on Earth.

Continental Drift

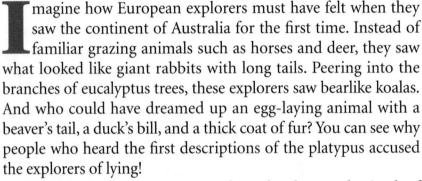

INTEGRATING EARTH SCIENCE In addition to studying where species live today, biogeographers also study how these species spread into different parts of the world. One factor that has affected how species are distributed is the motion of Earth's continents.The continents are huge blocks of solid rock floating on a layer of hot, dense liquid. The very slow motion of the continents is called **continental drift.**

Pangaea
Equator

1 *225 million years ago*

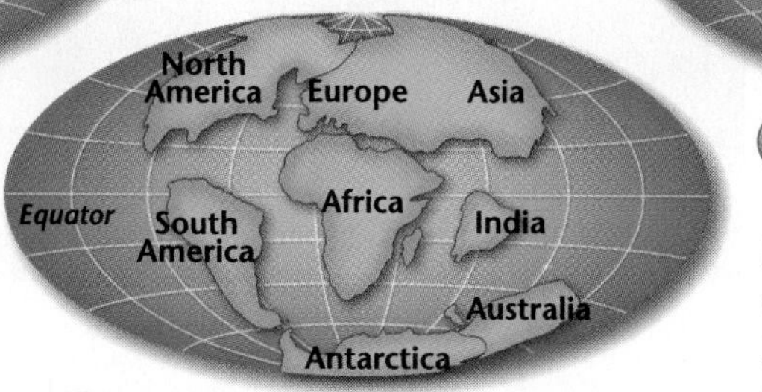
North America
Europe
Asia
Equator
South America
Africa
India
Australia
Antarctica

2 *65 million years ago*

North America
Europe
Asia
India
Africa
Equator
South America
Australia
Antarctica

3 *Present day*

Figure 12 The continents have drifted far from their positions 225 million years ago. Their movement is one factor affecting the distribution of organisms.

Figure 12 shows how much the continents have moved. About 225 million years ago, all the continents were touching each other. But after millions of years of slow drifting, they have moved apart. Looking at the globe today, it is hard to believe that at one time India was next to Antarctica, or that Europe and North America once were connected.

The movement of the continents has had a great impact on the distribution of species. Consider Australia, for example. Millions of years ago Australia drifted apart from the other land masses. Organisms from other parts of the world could not reach the isolated island. Kangaroos, koalas, and other unique species developed in this isolation.

Means of Dispersal

The movement of organisms from one place to another is called **dispersal.** Organisms may be dispersed in several different ways. **Dispersal can be caused by wind, water, or living things, including humans.**

Wind and Water Many animals move into new areas by simply walking, swimming, or flying. But plants and small organisms need assistance to move from place to place. Wind provides a means of dispersal for seeds, the spores of fungi, tiny spiders, and many other small, light organisms. Similarly, water transports objects that float, such as coconuts and leaves. Insects and small animals may get a free ride to a new home on top of these floating rafts.

Other Living Things Organisms may also be dispersed by other living things. For example, a goldfinch may eat seeds in one area and deposit them elsewhere in its wastes. A duck may carry algae or fish eggs on its feet from pond to pond. And if your dog or cat has ever come home covered with sticky plant burs, you know another way seeds can get around.

Figure 13 The stiff brown pods of the milkweed plant contain seeds fringed with silky threads. *Inferring By what means of dispersal are milkweed seeds spread?*

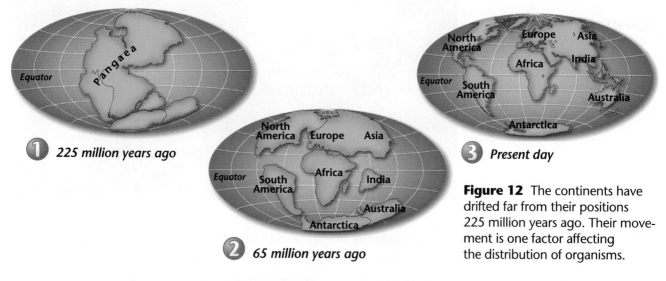

Figure 14 Clumps of purple loosestrife line the banks of a Massachusetts river. Loosestrife is an exotic species that has thrived in its new home, often crowding out native species.

Humans are important to the dispersal of other species. As people move around the globe, they take plants, animals, and other organisms with them. Sometimes this is intentional, such as when people bring horses to a new settlement. Sometimes it is unintentional, such as when someone carries a parasite into a country.

Species that have naturally evolved in an area are referred to as **native species.** When an organism is carried into a new location by people, it is referred to as an **exotic species.** Some exotic species are so common in their new environment that people think of them as native. For example, you probably know the dandelion, one of the most common flowering plants in North America. But the dandelion is not a native species. It was brought by colonists who valued its leaves for eating and for tea for the sick.

☑ *Checkpoint* *How can humans disperse a species?*

Limits to Dispersal

With all these means of dispersal, you might expect to find the same organisms everywhere in the world. Of course, that's not so. Why not? What determines the limits of a species' distribution? **Three factors that limit dispersal of a species are physical barriers, competition, and climate.**

Physical Barriers Barriers such as water, mountains, and deserts are hard to cross. These features can limit the movement of organisms. For example, once Australia became separated from the other continents, the ocean acted as a barrier to dispersal. Organisms could not easily move to or from Australia.

Competition When an organism enters a new area, it must compete for resources with the species already there. To survive, the organism must find a unique niche. If the existing species are thriving, they may outcompete the new species. In this case competition is a barrier to dispersal. Sometimes, however, the new species is more successful than the existing species. The native species may be displaced.

Social Studies CONNECTION

Many important crops are actually exotic species. When settlers in new lands brought crops with them from their old homes, they caused the dispersal of these species. Some examples of crops dispersed by people are peanuts, potatoes, cotton, corn, and rice.

In Your Journal

Choose a crop to investigate. Research your crop to learn where it is a native species and how it spread to different parts of the world. In what conditions does it grow well? (*Hint:* Almanacs and encyclopedias are good sources of this information.)

Climate The typical weather pattern in an

INTEGRATING EARTH SCIENCE

area over a long period of time is the area's **climate.** Climate is different from weather, which is the day-to-day conditions in an area. Climate is largely determined by temperature and precipitation.

Differences in climate can be a barrier to dispersal. For example, conditions at the top of the mountain shown in Figure 15 are very different from those at the base. The base is warm and dry. Low shrubs and cactuses grow there. Just up the mountain, mostly grasses grow. Higher up the mountain, the climate becomes cooler and wetter. Larger trees such as pines, oaks, and firs can grow. The squirrel in the closeup lives in this region. Climate differences act as a barrier that keeps the squirrel species from dispersing down or up the mountain. Near the top of the mountain, it is very cold and windy. Small alpine wildflowers and mosses grow best in this region.

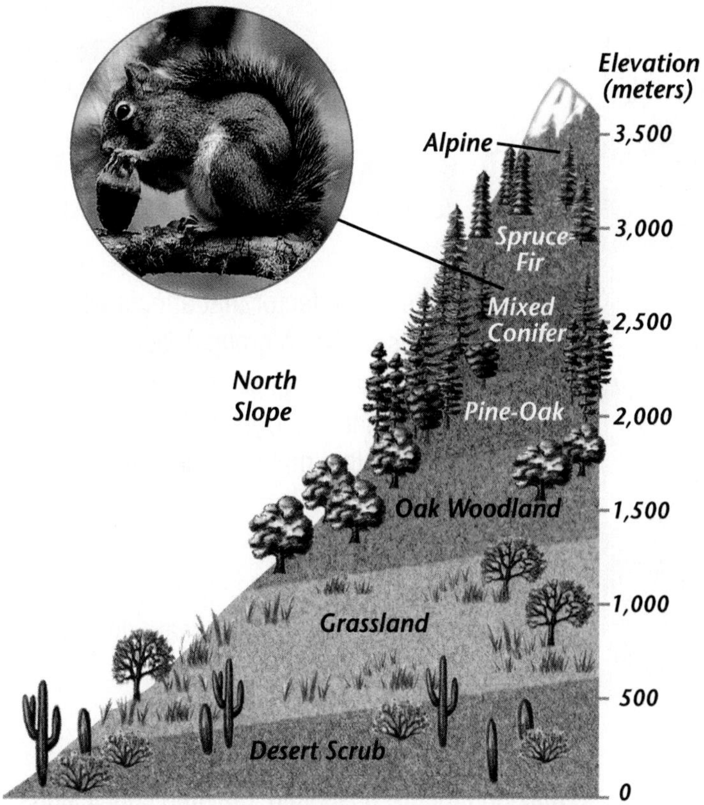

Elevation (meters)
Alpine
3,500
3,000
Spruce-Fir
Mixed Conifer
2,500
North Slope
Pine-Oak
2,000
Oak Woodland
1,500
1,000
Grassland
500
Desert Scrub
0

Figure 15 Climate conditions change at different elevations on this mountainside. These conditions determine the distribution of species on the mountain. Each zone begins at a lower elevation on the north slope of the mountain, which is cooler than the south slope.

Places with similar climates tend to have similar niches for species to occupy. For example, most continents have a large area of flat, grassy plains. The organisms that occupy the niche of "large, grazing mammal" on each continent have some similarities. In North America, the large, grazing mammals of the grasslands are bison; in Africa, they are wildebeests and antelopes; in Australia, they are kangaroos.

Section 3 Review

1. List three ways that species can disperse.
2. Explain how mountain ranges and climate can each limit a species' distribution.
3. What is biogeography?
4. Give an example of a physical barrier. How might it affect where species are found?
5. **Thinking Critically Predicting** If an exotic insect species were introduced to your area, do you think it would be easy or difficult to eliminate the species? Give reasons to support your answer.

Science at Home

Take an adult family member on a seed hunt. When you spot a new seed, place a plastic bag over your hand. Pick up the seed with the bag and then turn the bag inside out to hold the seed. When you get home, observe the seeds and compare them to one another. Based on your observations, classify the seeds by their methods of dispersal. Staple the bags to a sheet of heavy paper in the groups in which you have classified them.

Real-World Lab

How It Works

BIOMES IN MINIATURE

Climate is one factor that affects where organisms live. A group of ecosystems with similar climates and organisms is called a biome. In this lab, you will investigate some key factors that make biomes different from each other.

Problem

What biotic and abiotic factors create different biomes around the world?

Skills Focus

making models, observing, drawing conclusions

Materials

scissors
index card
10 impatiens seeds
5 lima bean seeds
about 30 rye grass seeds
empty, clean cardboard milk carton
sandy soil or potting soil
clear plastic wrap
lamp
tape
stapler

Procedure

1. Your teacher will assign your group a biome. You will also observe the other groups' biomes. Based on the chart below, predict how well you think each of the three kinds of seeds will grow in each set of conditions. Record these predictions in your notebook. Then copy the data table on the facing page four times, once for each biome.
2. Staple the spout of the milk carton closed. Completely cut away one of the four sides of the carton. Poke a few holes in the opposite side for drainage, then place that side down.
3. Fill the carton to 3 centimeters from the top with the type of soil given in the table. Divide the surface of the soil into three sections by making two lines in it with a pencil.
4. In the section near the spout, plant the impatiens seeds. In the middle section, plant the lima bean seeds. In the third section, scatter the rye grass seeds on the surface.

GROWING CONDITIONS

Biome	Soil Type	Hours of Light Per Day	Watering Instructions
Forest	Potting soil	1–2 hours direct light	Let the surface dry, then add water.
Desert	Sandy soil	5–6 hours direct light	Let the soil dry to a depth of 2.5 cm below the surface.
Grassland	Potting soil	5–6 hours direct light	Let the surface dry, then add water.
Rain forest	Potting soil	No direct light; indirect light for 5–6 hours	Keep the surface of the soil moist.

DATA TABLE

Name of biome: ________

Day	Impatiens	Lima Beans	Rye Grass
1			
2			
3			

5. Water all the seeds well. Then cover the open part of the carton with plastic wrap.
6. On an index card, write the name of your biome, the names of the three types of seeds in the order you planted them, and the names of your group members. Tape the card to the carton. Put it in a warm place where it will not be disturbed.
7. Once the seeds sprout, provide your biome with light and water as specified in the chart. Keep the carton covered with plastic wrap except when you add water.
8. Observe all the biomes daily for at least one week. Record your observations.

Analyze and Conclude

1. In which biome did each type of seed grow best? In which biome did each type of seed grow least well?
2. How was each type of seed affected by the soil type, amount of light, and availability of water? How do your results relate to biomes in nature?
3. Ecologists studying land biomes often begin a description of the biome by describing key abiotic factors and the typical plants. Why do you think they do this?
4. **Apply** Describe the rainfall pattern and other abiotic factors that make up the climate where you live. How do those factors affect the kinds of plants and animals that live there?

Design an Experiment

After reading Section 4, write a plan for setting up a model rain forest or desert terrarium. Include typical plants found in that biome. Obtain your teacher's approval before trying this activity.

Grassland
rye grass
lima beans
impatiens

SECTION 4 Earth's Biomes

DISCOVER — ACTIVITY

How Much Rain Is That?

The table shows the average amount of precipitation that falls each year in four different regions. With your classmates, you will create a full-size bar graph on a wall to help you visualize these amounts of rain.

Biome	Rainfall (cm)
Mojave Desert	15
Illinois prairie	70
Smoky Mountains	180
Costa Rican rain forest	350

1. Using a meter stick, measure a strip of adding-machine paper 15 centimeters long. Label this piece of paper "Mojave Desert."
2. Repeat Step 1 for the other three locations. If necessary, tape strips of paper together to make the correct length. Label each strip.
3. Now find a place where you can display the four strips vertically. If the wall of your classroom is not tall enough, you may need to use another wall in your school building. Follow your teacher's instructions to hang your precipitation strips.

Think It Over

Developing Hypotheses Which ecosystem receives the most precipitation? Which receives the least? What effect do you think the amount of rainfall might have on the types of species that live in these ecosystems?

GUIDE FOR READING

- **What determines the type of biome found in an area?**
- **Where can photosynthesis occur in water biomes?**

Reading Tip **As you read, make a list of the biomes described in this section. Under each biome name, take notes on the characteristics of that biome.**

Congratulations! You and your classmates have been selected as the student members of an around-the-world scientific expedition. Your mission is to study the major types of ecosystems on Earth. You will be collecting data on the climate conditions and typical organisms found in each of these ecosystems. The result of this expedition will be a database of information on the biomes you visit. A **biome** is a group of ecosystems with similar climates and organisms.

Classifying ecosystems into biomes helps ecologists describe the world. As you might expect, not all ecologists agree on the exact number and kinds of biomes. The scientists guiding your expedition have chosen to focus on six major land biomes and two major water biomes.

Be sure to pack a variety of clothing for your journey. During your trip, you will visit places ranging from frozen, windy Arctic plains to steamy tropical jungles. **In fact, it is mostly the climate conditions—temperature and rainfall—in an area that determine its biome.** This is because climate limits the distribution of plants in the area. In turn, the types of plants determine the kinds of animals that live there.

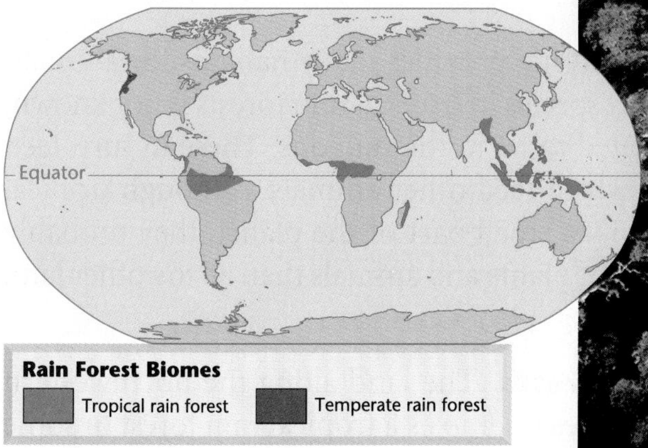
Equator
Rain Forest Biomes
Tropical rain forest
Temperate rain forest

Rain Forest Biomes

The first stop on your expedition is a tropical rain forest close to the equator. The rain forest is warm and humid—in fact, it's pouring rain! Fortunately, you remembered to pack a poncho. After just a short shower, the sun reappears. But even though the sun is shining, very little light penetrates the thick vegetation.

Plants are everywhere in the rain forest. Some, such as the ferns, orchids, and vines you observe hanging from tree limbs, even grow on other plants. Among the plants are many species of birds as bright as the numerous flowers all around you.

Tropical Rain Forests Tropical rain forests are found in warm regions close to the equator. Tropical rain forests typically receive a lot of rain. The warm temperatures do not vary much throughout the year, and the sunlight is fairly constant all year.

Tropical rain forests contain an astounding variety of species. For example, scientists studying a 100-square-meter area of one rain forest identified 300 different kinds of trees! These trees form several distinct layers. The tall trees form a leafy roof called the **canopy.** A few giant trees poke out above the canopy. Below the canopy, a second layer of shorter trees and vines form an **understory.** Understory plants grow well in the shade formed by the canopy. Finally, some plants thrive in the near-darkness of the forest floor.

Figure 16 Tropical rain forests contain an amazing variety of plants and other organisms. In the large photo, a river winds through the lush Indonesian rain forest. The top closeup shows a young orangutan swinging from tree limbs. In the bottom closeup, a tarantula climbs over a brightly colored bracket fungus on the forest floor.

The abundant plant life provides many habitats for animals. The number of insect species in tropical rain forests is not known, but has been estimated to be in the millions. These in turn feed many bird species, which feed other animals. Although tropical rain forests cover only a small part of the planet, they probably contain more species of plants and animals than all the other land biomes combined.

Temperate Rain Forests The land along the northwestern coast of the United States resembles a tropical rain forest in some ways. This region receives more than 300 centimeters of rain a year. Huge trees grow there, including cedars, redwoods, and Douglas firs. However, it is difficult to classify this region. It is too far north and too cool to be a tropical rain forest. Instead many ecologists refer to this ecosystem as a temperate rain forest. The term *temperate* means having moderate temperatures.

Desert Biomes

The next stop on your expedition is a desert. It couldn't be more different from the tropical rain forest you just left. You step off the bus into the searing summer heat. At midday, you cannot even walk into the desert—the sand feels as hot as the hot water that comes from your bathroom faucet at home.

A **desert** is an area that receives less than 25 centimeters of rain per year. The amount of evaporation in a desert is greater than the amount of precipitation. Some of the driest deserts may not receive any rain at all in a year! Deserts often also undergo large shifts in temperature during the course of a day. A scorching hot desert like the

Figure 17 Desert organisms have adaptations that enable them to live in the harsh conditions of their biome. For example, this shovel-snouted lizard "dances" to avoid burning its feet on the hot sand dunes of the Namib Desert in Africa. ***Making Generalizations*** *Describe the climate conditions of a typical desert.*

Equator
Desert and Grassland Biomes
Desert
Grassland

Namib Desert cools rapidly each night when the sun goes down. Other deserts, such as the Gobi in central Asia, are cooler, even experiencing freezing temperatures in the winter.

The organisms that live in the desert are adapted to the lack of rain and to the extreme temperatures. For example, the trunk of a saguaro cactus has folds that work like the pleats in an accordion. The trunk of the cactus expands to hold more water when it is raining. Many desert animals are most active at night when the temperatures are cooler. A gila monster, for instance, spends much of its time in a cool underground burrow. It may go for weeks without coming up to the surface of the desert.

☑ *Checkpoint* ***What are some adaptations that help an organism to live in the desert?***

Grassland Biomes

The next stop on the expedition is a grassland called a prairie. The temperature here is much more comfortable than that in the desert. The breeze carries the scent of soil warmed by the sun. This rich soil supports grass as tall as you and your classmates. Sparrows flit among the grass stems, looking for their next meal. Startled by your approach, a rabbit quickly bounds away.

Like other grasslands located in the middle latitudes, this prairie receives more rain than deserts, but not enough for many trees to grow. A **grassland** receives between 25 and 75 centimeters of rain each year, and is typically populated by grasses and other non-woody plants. Grasslands that are located closer to the equator than prairies, called **savannas,** receive as much as 120 centimeters of

TRY THIS

Desert Survival

ACTIVITY

Use a hand lens to carefully observe a small potted cactus. Be careful of the spines! With a pair of scissors, carefully snip a small piece from the tip of the cactus. Observe the inside of the plant. Note any characteristics that seem different from those of other plants.

Observing How is the inside of the cactus different from the outside? Suggest how the features you observe might be related to its desert habitat.

Figure 18 Migrating wildebeest make their way across a vast Kenyan savanna.

Equator
Forest Biomes
Deciduous forest
Boreal forest

Figure 19 This Michigan forest in autumn is a beautiful example of a deciduous forest. The closeup shows a red fox, a common resident of North American deciduous forests. *Comparing and Contrasting How do deciduous forests differ from rain forests?*

rain each year. Scattered shrubs and small trees grow on savannas along with the grass.

Grasslands are home to many of the largest animals on Earth—herbivores such as bison, antelopes, zebras, rhinoceros, giraffes, and kangaroos. Grazing by these large herbivores helps to maintain the grasslands. They keep young trees and bushes from sprouting and competing with the grass for water and sunlight.

Deciduous Forest Biomes

Your trip to the next biome takes you to another forest. It is now late summer. Cool mornings here give way to warm days. Several members of the expedition are busy recording the numerous plant species. Others are looking through their binoculars, trying to identify the songbirds in the trees. You step carefully to avoid a small salamander on the forest floor. Chipmunks chatter at all the disturbance.

You are now visiting the deciduous forest biome. The trees found in this forest, called **deciduous trees** (dee SIJ oo us), shed their leaves and grow new ones each year. Oaks and maples are examples of deciduous trees. Deciduous forests receive enough rain to support the growth of trees and other plants, at least 50 centimeters per year. Temperatures vary during the year. The growing season usually lasts five to six months. As in the rain forest, different plants grow to different heights, ranging from a canopy of tall trees to small ferns and mosses on the forest floor.

The variety of plants in the forest creates many different habitats. You and your classmates note that different species of birds live at each level, eating the insects and fruits that live and grow there. You observe opossums, mice, and a skunk looking for food in the thick layer of damp leaves on the ground. Other common North American deciduous forest species include wood thrushes, white-tailed deer, and black bears.

If you were to return to this biome in the winter, you would not see much of the wildlife you are now observing. One reason is that many of the bird species migrate to warmer areas. Some of the mammals enter a low-energy state similar to sleep called **hibernation.** During hibernation an animal relies on fat it has stored in its body.

☑ *Checkpoint* *What are deciduous trees?*

Sharpen your Skills

Inferring ACTIVITY

Observe the map on the facing page showing the locations of deciduous and boreal forests. How do they compare? Can you suggest a reason why no boreal forests are shown in the Southern Hemisphere?

Boreal Forest Biomes

Now the expedition heads north into a colder climate. The expedition leaders claim they can identify the next biome, a boreal forest, by its smell. When you arrive, you catch a whiff of the spruce and fir trees that blanket the hillsides. Feeling the chilly early fall air, you pull a jacket and hat out of your bag.

This forest contains **coniferous trees** (koh NIF ur us), that produce their seeds in cones and have leaves shaped like needles. The boreal forest is sometimes referred to by its Russian name, the *taiga* (TY guh). Winters in these forests are very cold. The yearly

Figure 20 Common organisms of the boreal forest include moose like this one in Alaska's Denali National Park, and porcupines.

snowfall can reach heights well over your head—or even two or three times your height! Even so, the summers are rainy and warm enough to melt all the snow.

A limited number of trees have adapted to the cold climate of boreal forests. Fir, spruce, and hemlock are the most common species because their thick, waxy needles keep water from evaporating. Since water is frozen for much of the year in these areas, prevention of water loss is a necessary adaptation for trees in the boreal forest.

Many of the animals of the boreal forest eat the seeds produced by the conifers. These animals include red squirrels, insects, and birds such as finches and chickadees. Some of the larger herbivores, such as porcupines, deer, elk, moose, and beavers, eat tree bark and new shoots. This variety of herbivores in the boreal forest supports a variety of large predators, including wolves, bears, wolverines, and lynxes.

Tundra Biomes

The driving wind brings tears to the eyes of the members of the expedition as you arrive at your next stop. It is now fall. The slicing wind gives everyone an immediate feel for this biome, the tundra. The **tundra** is an extremely cold, dry, land biome. Expecting deep snow, many are surprised that the tundra may receive no more precipitation than a desert. Most of the soil in the tundra is frozen all year. This frozen soil is called **permafrost**.

Figure 21 Far from being a barren terrain, the tundra explodes with color in summer. Mosses, wildflowers, and shrubs flourish despite the short growing season. *Relating Cause and Effect* *Why are there no tall trees on the tundra?*

Equator
Tundra Biomes, Mountains, and Ice
Tundra
Mountains
Ice

During the short summer the top layer of soil on the tundra thaws, but the underlying soil remains frozen.

Plants on the tundra include mosses, grasses, shrubs, and dwarf forms of a few trees, such as willows. Looking across the tundra, you observe that the landscape is already brown and gold. The short growing season is over. Most of the plant growth takes place during the long summer days when many hours of sunshine combine with the warmest temperatures of the year. North of the Arctic Circle the sun does not set during midsummer.

Figure 22 Many waterfowl spend summers on the tundra. This black brant is tending her nest.

If you had visited the tundra during the summer, the animals you might remember most are insects. Swarms of black flies and mosquitos provide food for many birds. The birds take advantage of the plentiful food and long days by eating as much as they can. Then, when winter approaches again, many birds migrate south to warmer climates.

Mammals of the tundra include caribou, foxes, wolves, and hares. The animals that remain in the tundra during the winter grow thick fur coats. What can these animals find to eat on the tundra in winter? The caribou scrape snow away to find lichens, which are fungi and algae that grow together on rocks. Wolves follow the caribou and look for weak members of the herd to prey upon.

☑ *Checkpoint* *What is the climate of the tundra?*

Mountains and Ice

Some areas of land on Earth do not fall into one of the major land biomes. These areas include mountain ranges and land that is covered with thick sheets of ice.

You read in Section 3 that the climate conditions of a mountain change from its base to its summit. As a result, different species of plants and other organisms inhabit different parts of the mountain. If you hiked to the top of a tall mountain, you would pass through a series of biomes. At the base of the mountain, you might find a grassland. As you climbed, you might pass through a deciduous forest, and then a boreal forest. Finally, as you neared the top, the trees would disappear. Your surroundings would resemble the rugged tundra.

Some land on Earth is covered year-round with thick ice sheets. Most of the island of Greenland and the continent of Antarctica fall into this category. Some organisms are adapted to life on the ice, including penguins, polar bears, and seals.

Sharpen your Skills

Interpreting Data

ACTIVITY

An ecologist has collected climate data from two locations. The total yearly precipitation is 250 cm in Location A and 14 cm in Location B. The graph below shows the average monthly temperature in the two locations. Based on this information, of which biome is each location a part? Explain.

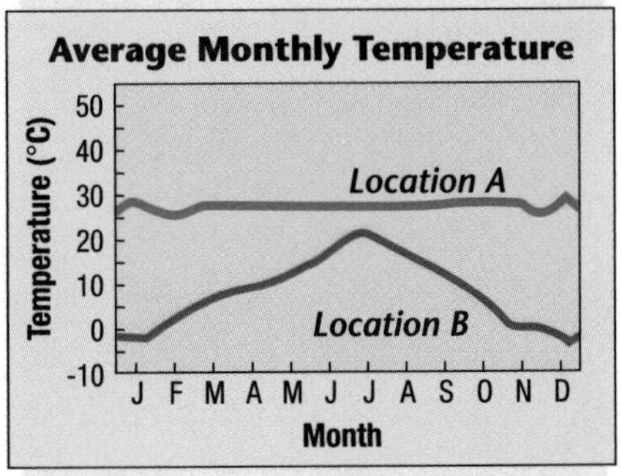
Average Monthly Temperature
Temperature (°C)
50
40
30
20
10
0
-10
Location A
Location B
J F M A M J J A S O N D
Month

Figure 23 Ponds and rivers are two types of freshwater habitats. **A.** At the edge of a pond, two western pond turtles sun themselves on a log. **B.** A brown bear fishes for salmon in the rushing waters of a river. *Comparing and Contrasting How are these habitats similar? How are they different?*

Freshwater Biomes

The next stops for the expedition are located in water biomes. Since almost three quarters of Earth's surface is covered with water, it is not surprising that many living things make their homes in the water. Water biomes include both freshwater and saltwater (also called marine) biomes. All of these are affected by the same abiotic factors: temperature, sunlight, oxygen, and salt content.

An especially important factor in water biomes is sunlight. Sunlight is necessary for photosynthesis in the water just as it is on land. **However, because water absorbs sunlight, there is only enough light for photosynthesis near the surface or in shallow water.** The most common producers in most water biomes are algae rather than plants.

Ponds and Lakes First stop among the freshwater biomes is a calm pond. Ponds and lakes are bodies of standing, or still, fresh water. Lakes are generally larger and deeper than ponds. Ponds are often shallow enough that sunlight can reach the bottom even in the center of the pond, allowing plants to grow there. Plants that grow along the shore have their roots in the soil, while their leaves stretch to the sunlit water at the surface. In the center of a lake, algae floating at the surface are the major producers.

Many animals are adapted for life in the still water. Along the shore of the pond you observe insects, snails, frogs, and salamanders. Sunfish live in the open water, feeding on insects and algae from the surface. Scavengers such as catfish live near the pond bottom. Bacteria and other decomposers also feed on the remains of other organisms.

Streams and Rivers When you arrive at a mountain stream, you immediately notice how different it is from the still waters of a lake. Where the stream begins, called the headwaters, the cold, clear water flows rapidly. Animals that live in this part must be adapted to the strong current. Trout, for instance, have streamlined bodies that allow them to swim despite the pull of the rushing water. Insects and other small animals may have hooks or suckers to help them cling to rocks. Few plants or algae can grow in this fast-moving water. Instead, first-level consumers rely on leaves and seeds that fall into the stream.

As the river flows along, it is joined by other streams. The current slows. The water becomes cloudy with soil. With fewer rapids, the slower-moving, warmer water contains less oxygen. Different organisms are adapted to live in this lower part of the river. More plants take root among the pebbles on the river bottom, providing homes for insects and frogs. As is true in every biome, organisms are adapted to live in this specific habitat.

☑ *Checkpoint* ***What are two abiotic factors that affect organisms in a river?***

Marine Biomes

Next the members of the expedition head down the coast to explore some marine biomes. The oceans contain many different habitats. These habitats differ in sunlight amount, water temperature, wave action, and water pressure. Different organisms are adapted to life in each type of habitat. The first habitat, called an **estuary** (ES choo ehr ee), is found where the fresh water of a river meets the salt water of the ocean.

Estuaries The shallow, sunlit water, plus a large supply of nutrients carried in by the river, makes an estuary a very rich habitat for living things. The major producers in estuaries are plants, such as marsh grasses, as well as algae.

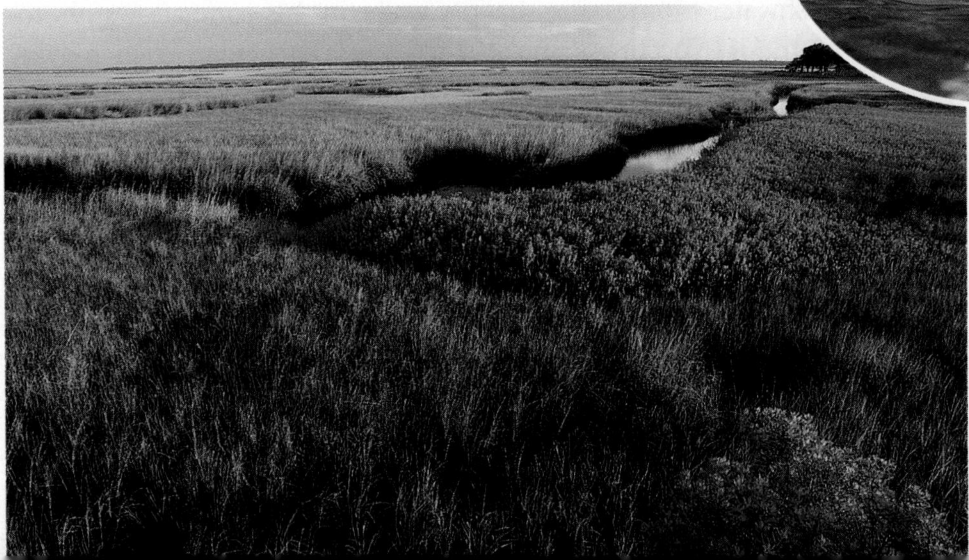

Figure 24 Fresh river water and salty ocean water meet in an estuary. Estuaries such as this Georgia salt marsh provide a rich habitat for many organisms, including a wading tricolored heron.

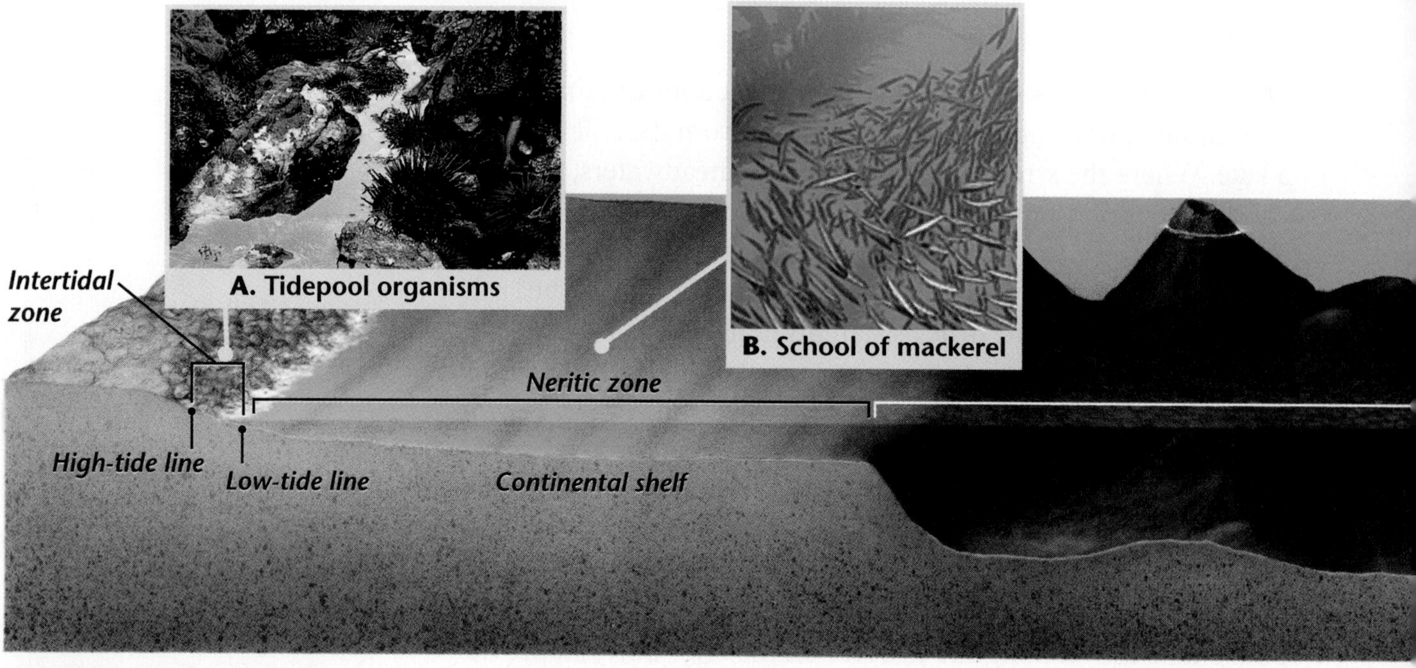
A. Tidepool organisms
B. School of mackerel
Intertidal zone
Neritic zone
High-tide line
Low-tide line
Continental shelf

Figure 25 The marine biome is divided into several zones. **A.** Tidepools are common in the intertidal zone. This zone lies between the highest high-tide line and lowest low-tide line. **B.** Many fish, such as these silvery mackerel, inhabit the shallow waters over the continental shelf, called the neritic zone. **C.** A humpback whale feeds on algae at the surface of the open-ocean zone. **D.** This eerie deep-sea gulper is a predator in the deepest part of the ocean.

These organisms provide food and shelter for a variety of animals, including crabs, worms, clams, oysters, and fish. Many of these organisms use the calm waters of estuaries for breeding grounds.

Intertidal Zone Next, you take a walk along the rocky shoreline. The part of the shore between the highest high-tide line and the lowest low-tide line is called the **intertidal zone.** Organisms here must be able to withstand the pounding action of waves, sudden changes in temperature, and being both covered with water and then exposed to the air. It is a difficult place to live! You observe many animals, such as barnacles and sea stars, clinging to the rocks. Others, such as clams and crabs, burrow in the sand.

Neritic Zone Now it's time to set out to sea to explore the waters near shore. From your research vessel, your group will explore the next type of marine habitat. The edge of a continent extends into the ocean for a short distance, like a shelf. Below the low-tide line is a region of shallow water, called the **neritic zone** (nuh RIT ik), that extends over the continental shelf. Just as in freshwater biomes, the shallow water in this zone allows photosynthesis to occur. As a result, this zone is particularly rich in living things. Many large schools of fish such as sardines and anchovies feed on the algae in the neritic zone. In the warm ocean waters of the tropics, coral reefs may form in the neritic zone. Though a coral reef may look like stone, it is actually a living home to a wide variety of other organisms.

Surface Zone Out in the open ocean, light penetrates through the water only to a depth of a few hundred meters. Algae floating in these surface waters carry out photosynthesis. These algae

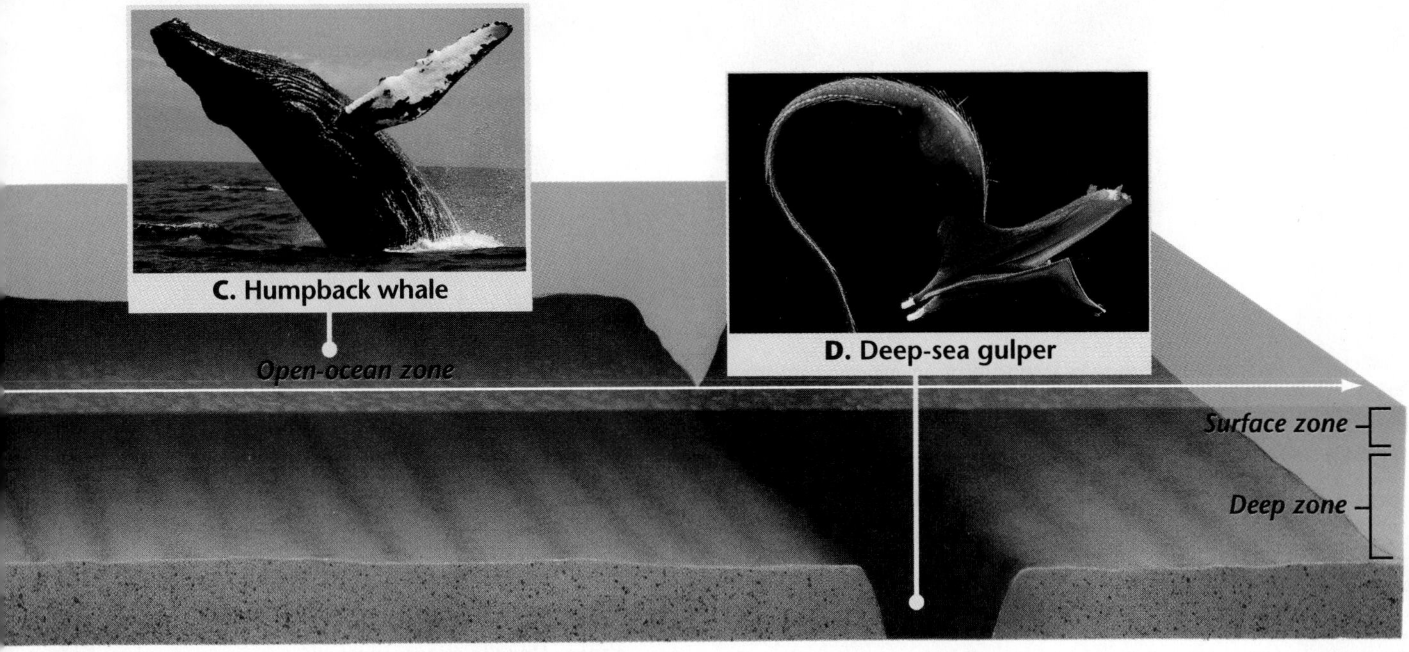
C. Humpback whale
Open-ocean zone
D. Deep-sea gulper
Surface zone
Deep zone

are the producers that form the base of almost all open-ocean food webs. Other marine animals, such as tuna, swordfish, and whales, depend directly or indirectly on the algae for food.

Deep Zone The deep zone is located in the open ocean below the surface zone. Throughout most of the deep ocean, the water is completely dark. Your expedition will need to use a submarine with bright headlights to explore this region. How can anything live in a place with no sunlight? Most animals in this zone feed on remains of organisms that sink down from the surface zone. The deepest parts of the deep zone are home to bizarre-looking animals, such as giant squid that glow in the dark and fish with rows and rows of sharp teeth.

After you have recorded your deep-zone observations, your long expedition is over at last. You can finally return home.

Section 4 Review

1. How does climate determine a biome's characteristics?
2. Where in water biomes can photosynthesis occur?
3. Which land biome receives the most precipitation? Which two receive the least?
4. In which biome would you find large herbivores such as antelope and elephants? Explain your answer.
5. **Thinking Critically Comparing and Contrasting** How are the three forest biomes (rain forests, deciduous forests, and boreal forests) alike? How are they different?

CHAPTER PROJECT

Check Your Progress

By now you should be ready to start analyzing the data you have collected about your compost chambers. Do your observations of the two chambers support your hypothesis? Begin to prepare your report.

Observing

CHANGE IN A TINY COMMUNITY

The types of organisms in an ecosystem may change gradually over time. You will learn more about this process, called succession, in the next section. In this lab you will observe succession in a pond community.

Problem

How does a pond community change over time?

Materials

hay solution
small baby-food jar
plastic dropper
coverslip
pond water
wax pencil
microscope slide
microscope

Procedure

1. Use a wax pencil to label a small jar with your name.
2. Fill the jar about three-fourths full with hay solution. Add pond water until the jar is nearly full. Examine the mixture, and record your observations in your notebook.
3. Place the jar in a safe location out of direct sunlight where it will remain undisturbed. Always wash your hands thoroughly with soap after handling the jar or its contents.
4. After two days, examine the contents of the jar, and record your observations.
5. Use a plastic dropper to collect a few drops from the surface of the solution in the jar. Make a slide following the procedures in the box at the right. **CAUTION:** *Slides and coverslips are fragile, and their edges are sharp. Handle them carefully.*
6. Examine the slide under a microscope using both low and high power following the procedures in the box at the right. Draw each type of organism you observe. Estimate the number of each type in your sample. The illustration below shows some of the organisms you might see.
7. Repeat Steps 5 and 6 with a drop of solution taken from the side of the jar beneath the surface.
8. Repeat Steps 5 and 6 with a drop of solution taken from the bottom of the jar. When you are finished, follow your teacher's directions about cleaning up.
9. After 3 days, repeat Steps 5 through 8.
10. After 3 more days, repeat Steps 5 through 8 again. Then follow your teacher's directions for returning the solution.

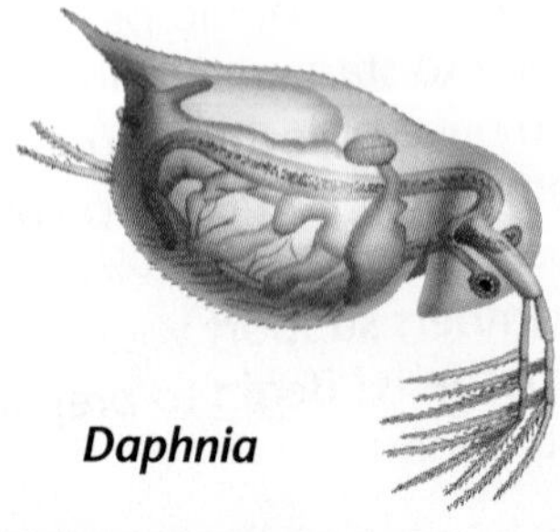

Daphnia

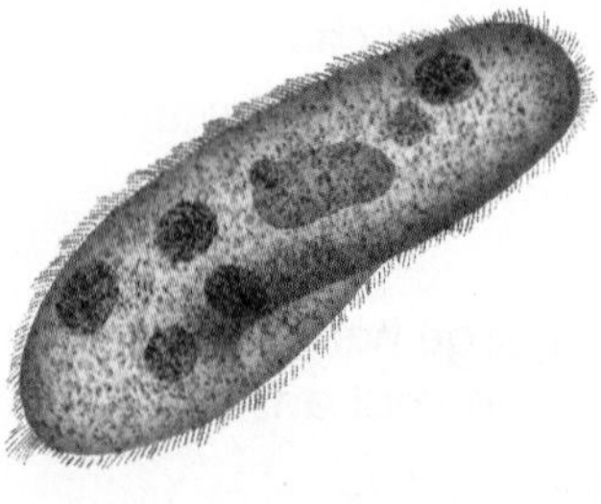

Paramecium

Spirogyra

Making and Viewing a Slide

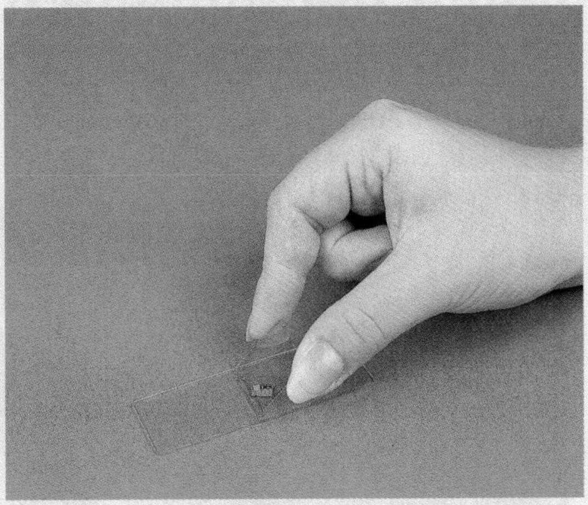

A. Place one drop of the solution to be examined in the middle of a microscope slide. Place one edge of a coverslip at the edge of the drop, as shown above. Gently lower the coverslip over the drop. Try not to trap any air bubbles.

B. Place the slide on the stage of a microscope so the drop is over the opening in the stage. Adjust the stage clips to hold the slide.

C. Look from the side of the microscope, and use the coarse adjustment knob to move the low-power objective close to, but not touching, the coverslip.

D. Look through the eyepiece, and use the coarse adjustment knob to raise the body tube and bring the slide into view. Use the fine adjustment knob to bring the slide into focus.

E. To view the slide under high power, look from the side of the microscope, and revolve the nosepiece until the high-power objective clicks into place just over, but not touching, the slide.

F. While you are looking through the eyepiece, use the fine adjustment knob to bring the slide into focus.

Analyze and Conclude

1. Identify as many of the organisms you observed as possible. Use the diagrams on the facing page and any other resources your teacher provides.
2. How did the community change over the time that you made your observations?
3. What factors may have influenced the changes in this community?
4. Where did the organisms you observed in the jar come from?
5. **Think About It** Do you think your observations gave you a complete picture of the changes in this community? Explain your answer.

Design an Experiment

Write a hypothesis about the effect on a community of changing one biotic or abiotic factor. Design a plan to test your hypothesis. Obtain your teacher's permission before carrying out your experiment.

SECTION 5
Succession

DISCOVER ACTIVITY

What Happened Here?

1. The two photographs at the right show the same area in Yellowstone National Park in Wyoming. Photograph A was taken soon after a major fire. Photograph B was taken a few years later. Observe the photographs carefully.
2. Make a list of all the differences you notice between the two scenes.

A

B

Think It Over

Posing Questions How would you describe what happened during the time between the two photographs? What questions do you have about this process?

GUIDE FOR READING

◆ **How are primary and secondary succession different?**

Reading Tip **Before you read, write a definition of what you think the term *succession* might mean. As you read, revise your definition.**

In 1988, a huge fire raged through Yellowstone National Park. The fire was so hot that it jumped from tree to tree without burning along the ground between them. In an instant, huge trees burst into flame from the intense heat. It took weeks for the fires to burn themselves out. All that remained of that part of the forest were thousands of blackened tree trunks sticking out of the ground like charred toothpicks.

You might think it unlikely that Yellowstone could recover from such a disastrous fire. But within just a few months, signs of life had returned. First tiny green shoots of new grass appeared in the black ground. Then small tree seedlings began to grow again. The forest was coming back!

Natural disasters such as fires, floods, volcanoes, hurricanes, earthquakes, and landslides can change communities and wildlife habitats in a very short period of time. But even without a disaster, communities change. The series of predictable changes that occur in a community over time is called **succession.** This section describes two types of succession: primary succession and secondary succession.

Primary Succession

Primary succession is the series of changes that occur in an area where no ecosystem previously existed. Such an area might be a new island formed by the eruption of an undersea volcano, or an area of rock uncovered by a melting sheet of ice.

You can follow the series of changes an area might undergo in Figure 26 below. These scenes show an area after a violent volcanic eruption. At first there is no soil, just ash and rock. The first species to populate the area are called **pioneer species.** Pioneer species are often lichens and mosses carried to the area by wind or water. These species can grow on bare rocks with little or no soil. As these organisms grow, they help break up the rocks. When they die, they provide nutrients that enrich the thin layer of soil that is forming on the rocks.

Over time, plant seeds land in the new soil and begin to grow. The specific plants that grow depend on the biome of the area. For example, in a cool, northern area, early seedlings might include alder and cottonwood trees. As the soil grows older and richer, these trees might be replaced by spruce and hemlock. Eventually, succession may lead to a community of organisms that does not change unless the ecosystem is disturbed. Reaching this stable community can take centuries.

☑ *Checkpoint* *What are some pioneer species?*

Figure 26 Primary succession occurs in an area where no ecosystem previously existed. **A.** After a volcanic eruption, the ground surface consists of ash and rock. **B.** The first organisms to appear are lichens and moss. **C.** Weeds and grasses take root in the thin layer of soil. **D.** Eventually, tree seedlings and shrubs sprout. *Applying Concepts What determines the particular species that appear during succession?*

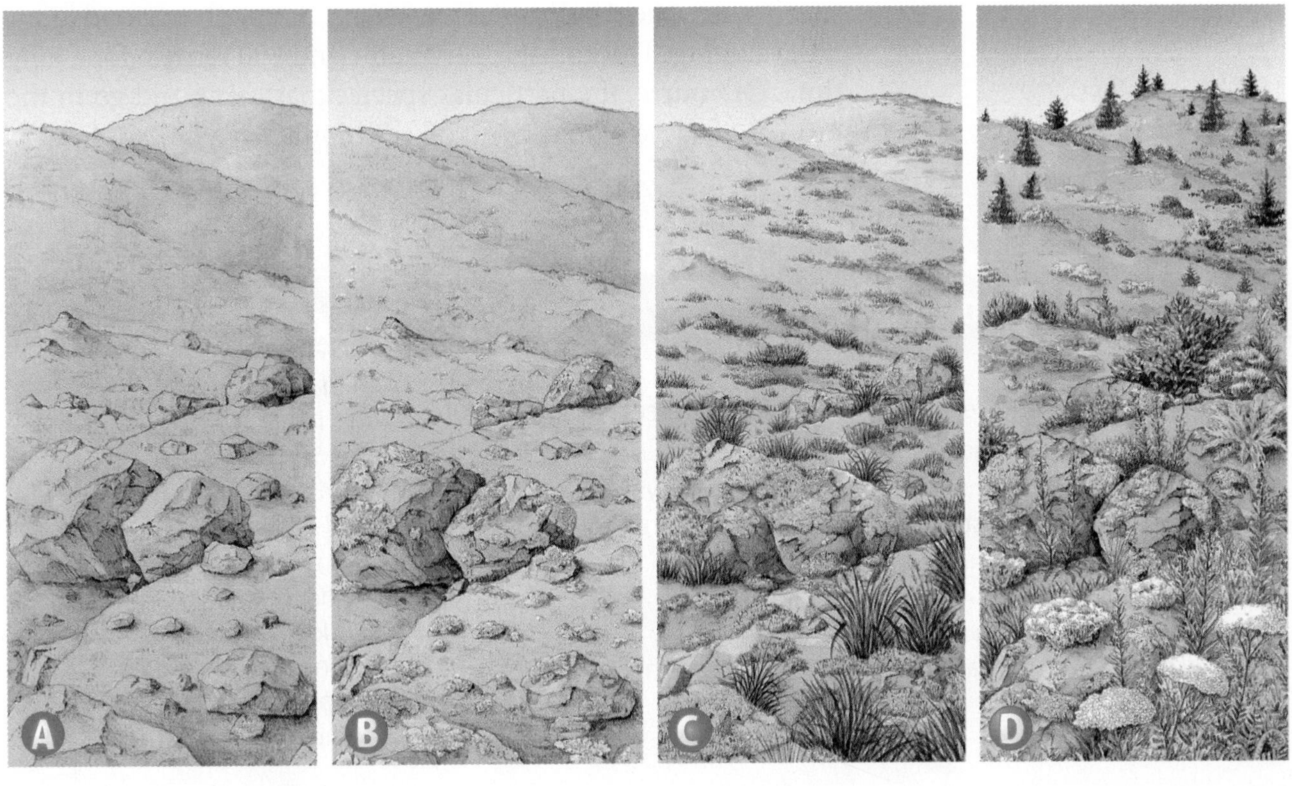
A
B
C
D

A
B
C
D

Figure 27 Secondary succession occurs following a disturbance to an ecosystem, such as clearing a forest for farmland. When the farm is abandoned, the forest gradually returns. **A.** After two years, weeds and wildflowers fill the field. **B.** After five years, pine seedlings and other plants populate the field. **C.** After 30 years, a pine forest has grown up. **D.** After 100 years, a mixed forest of pine, oak, and hickory is developing in the field.

Secondary Succession

The changes following the Yellowstone fire were an example of secondary succession. **Secondary succession** is the series of changes that occur after a disturbance in an existing ecosystem. Natural disturbances that have this effect include fires, hurricanes, and tornadoes. Human activities, such as farming, logging, or mining, may also disturb an ecosystem. **Unlike primary succession, secondary succession occurs in a place where an ecosystem has previously existed.**

Secondary succession occurs somewhat more rapidly than primary succession. Consider, for example, an abandoned field in the southeastern United States. Follow the process of succession in such a field in Figure 27. After a century, a hardwood forest is developing. This forest is very stable and will remain for a long time. Of course, the particular species that come and go in the process of succession depend on the biome.

Section 5 Review

1. How are primary and secondary succession different?
2. What is a pioneer species?
3. Give two examples of natural disturbances and two examples of human disturbances that can result in secondary succession.
4. **Thinking Critically Classifying** Grass poking through the cracks in a sidewalk is an example of succession. Is this primary or secondary succession? Explain.

Science at Home

Interview an older family member or neighbor who has lived in your neighborhood for a long time. Ask the person to describe how the neighborhood has changed over time. Have areas that were formerly grassy been paved or developed? Have any farms, parks, or lots returned to a wild state? Write a summary of your interview. Can you classify any of the changes as examples of succession?

SECTION 1 Energy Flow in Ecosystems

Key Ideas

- The energy role of an organism is that of a producer, consumer, or decomposer.
- Producers are the source of all the food in an ecosystem. Most producers use sunlight to make food molecules through photosynthesis.
- Consumers include herbivores, carnivores, omnivores, and scavengers.
- Decomposers return nutrients to the environment where they can be used again.
- A food web shows the feeding relationships that exist in an ecosystem.
- At each level in an energy pyramid, there is less available energy than at the level below.

Key Terms

producer	omnivore	food chain
consumer	scavenger	food web
herbivore	decomposer	energy pyramid
carnivore		

SECTION 2 Cycles of Matter

INTEGRATING CHEMISTRY

Key Ideas

- Matter, such as water, carbon dioxide, oxygen, and nitrogen, cycles through an ecosystem. Energy must be supplied constantly.
- The processes of evaporation, condensation, and precipitation form the water cycle.
- Producers use carbon dioxide to produce other carbon-containing molecules.
- Free nitrogen in the atmosphere cannot be used by most living things. Nitrogen must be fixed by certain types of bacteria.

Key Terms

water cycle	condensation	nitrogen fixation
evaporation	precipitation	nodules

SECTION 3 Biogeography

Key Ideas

- Means of dispersal of organisms include continental drift, wind, water, and living things.
- Three factors that limit dispersal are physical barriers, competition, and climate.

Key Terms

biogeography	native species
continental drift	exotic species
dispersal	climate

SECTION 4 Earth's Biomes

Key Ideas

- Temperature and precipitation mostly determine the type of ecosystem found in an area.
- Land biomes include rain forests, deserts, grasslands, deciduous forests, boreal forests, and tundras.
- There is only enough sunlight for photosynthesis to occur near the surface or in shallow areas of water biomes.

Key Terms

biome	savanna	permafrost
canopy	deciduous trees	estuary
understory	hibernation	intertidal zone
desert	coniferous trees	neritic zone
grassland	tundra	

SECTION 5 Succession

Key Idea

- Primary succession occurs where no previous ecosystem exists. Secondary succession occurs after a disturbance.

Key Terms

succession	pioneer species
primary succession	secondary succession

ACTIVITY

USING THE INTERNET

www.phschool.com/state_focus/california/

California Test Prep: Reviewing Content

Multiple Choice

Choose the letter of the best answer.

1. A diagram that shows how much energy is available at each feeding level in an ecosystem is a(n)
   a. food chain. b. food web.
   c. succession. d. energy pyramid.
2. Which of the following organisms are typical decomposers?
   a. grasses and ferns
   b. bacteria and mushrooms
   c. mice and deer
   d. lions and snakes
3. Which of the following is *not* recycled in an ecosystem?
   a. carbon b. nitrogen
   c. water d. energy
4. Organisms may be dispersed in all the following ways *except* by
   a. wind. b. water.
   c. temperature. d. other organisms.
5. Much of Canada is covered in pine and spruce forests. The winter is cold and long. What is this biome?
   a. tundra b. boreal forest
   c. deciduous forest d. grassland

True or False

If the statement is true, write true. If it is false, change the underlined word or words to make the statement true.

6. An organism that eats the remains of dead organisms is called a(n) herbivore.
7. The step of the water cycle is which liquid water changes to water vapor is evaporation.
8. The study of the past and present distribution of species on Earth is called succession.
9. Precipitation and temperature are the two major abiotic factors that determine what types of plants can grow in an area.
10. The land biome that gets the highest average amount of precipitation is the tropical grassland biome.

Checking Concepts

11. Name and briefly define each of the three energy roles organisms can play in an ecosystem.
12. How are food chains and food webs different?
13. What is the source of energy for most ecosystems?
14. Describe the role of nitrogen-fixing bacteria in the nitrogen cycle.
15. Explain the difference between a native species and an exotic species.
16. How has continental drift affected the distribution of species on Earth?
17. What organisms are the producers in most marine ecosystems?
18. **Writing to Learn** Choose any of the biomes described in this chapter. Imagine that you are a typical animal found in that biome. Write a paragraph describing the conditions and other organisms in your animal's biome.

Thinking Visually

19. **Flowchart** Copy the flowchart below on a separate sheet of paper. Complete the flowchart to show how carbon cycles through an ecosystem. (For more on flowcharts, see the Skills Handbook.)

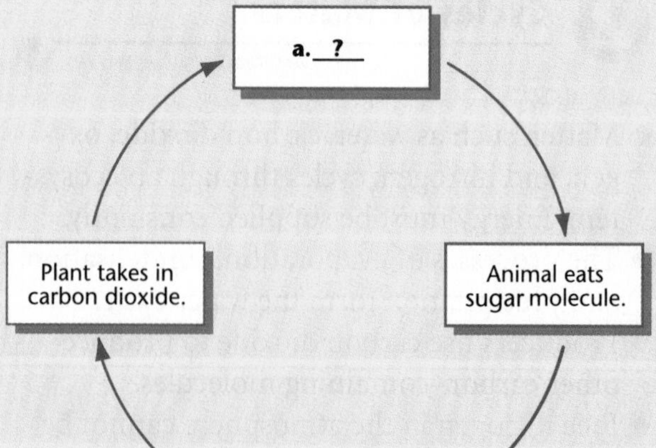
a. ?
Animal eats sugar molecule.
b. ?
Plant takes in carbon dioxide.

Test Prep: Skills

Use the diagram of a food web below to answer Questions 20–22.

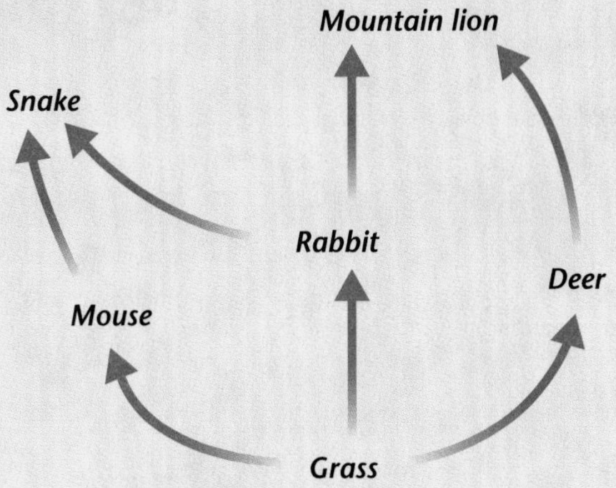
Mountain lion
Snake
Rabbit
Deer
Mouse
Grass

20. Classifying Identify the energy role of each organism in this food web. For consumers, specify whether they are first-level, second-level, or third-level.

21. Inferring Which level of the food web contains the greatest amount of available energy?

22. Predicting If a disease were to kill most of the rabbits in this area, predict how the snakes, deer, and mountain lions would be affected.

Thinking Critically

23. Relating Cause and Effect Every few years, a farmer plants clover in a wheatfield. Explain this practice.

24. Comparing and Contrasting How are the desert biome and the tundra biome similar? How are they different?

25. Inferring Polar bears are very well adapted to life around the Arctic Ocean. Their white fur camouflages them in the snow. They can swim and hunt in very cold water. Is the distribution of polar bears limited by physical barriers, competition, or climate? Explain your answer.

26. Predicting A volcano has just erupted in the ocean near Hawaii, forming a new island. How might succession change this island over time?

Performance Assessment

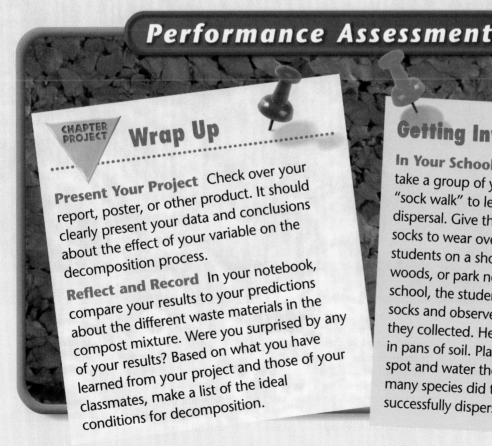

CHAPTER PROJECT Wrap Up

Present Your Project Check over your report, poster, or other product. It should clearly present your data and conclusions about the effect of your variable on the decomposition process.

Reflect and Record In your notebook, compare your results to your predictions about the different waste materials in the compost mixture. Were you surprised by any of your results? Based on what you have learned from your project and those of your classmates, make a list of the ideal conditions for decomposition.

Getting Involved

In Your School With your classmates, take a group of younger students on a "sock walk" to learn about seed dispersal. Give the students thick white socks to wear over their shoes. Lead the students on a short walk through a field, woods, or park near your school. Back at school, the students can remove the socks and observe how many seeds they collected. Help them plant the socks in pans of soil. Place the pans in a sunny spot and water them regularly. How many species did the students successfully disperse?

CHAPTER

20 Living Resources

CALIFORNIA
SCIENCE CONTENT STANDARDS

The following California Science Content Standards are addressed in this chapter:

5. Organisms in ecosystems exchange energy and nutrients among themselves and with the environment.

- **e.** The number and types of organisms an ecosystem can support depends on the resources available and abiotic factors, such as quantity of light and water, range of temperatures, and soil composition.

6. Sources of energy and materials differ in amounts, distribution, usefulness, and the time required for their formation.

- **a.** The utility of energy sources is determined by factors that are involved in converting these sources to useful forms and the consequences of the conversion process.
- **b.** Different natural energy and material resources, including air, soil, rocks, minerals, petroleum, fresh water, wildlife, and forests, and classify them as renewable or nonrenewable.
- **c.** Natural origin of the materials used to make common objects.

7. Scientific progress is made by asking meaningful questions and conducting careful investigations.

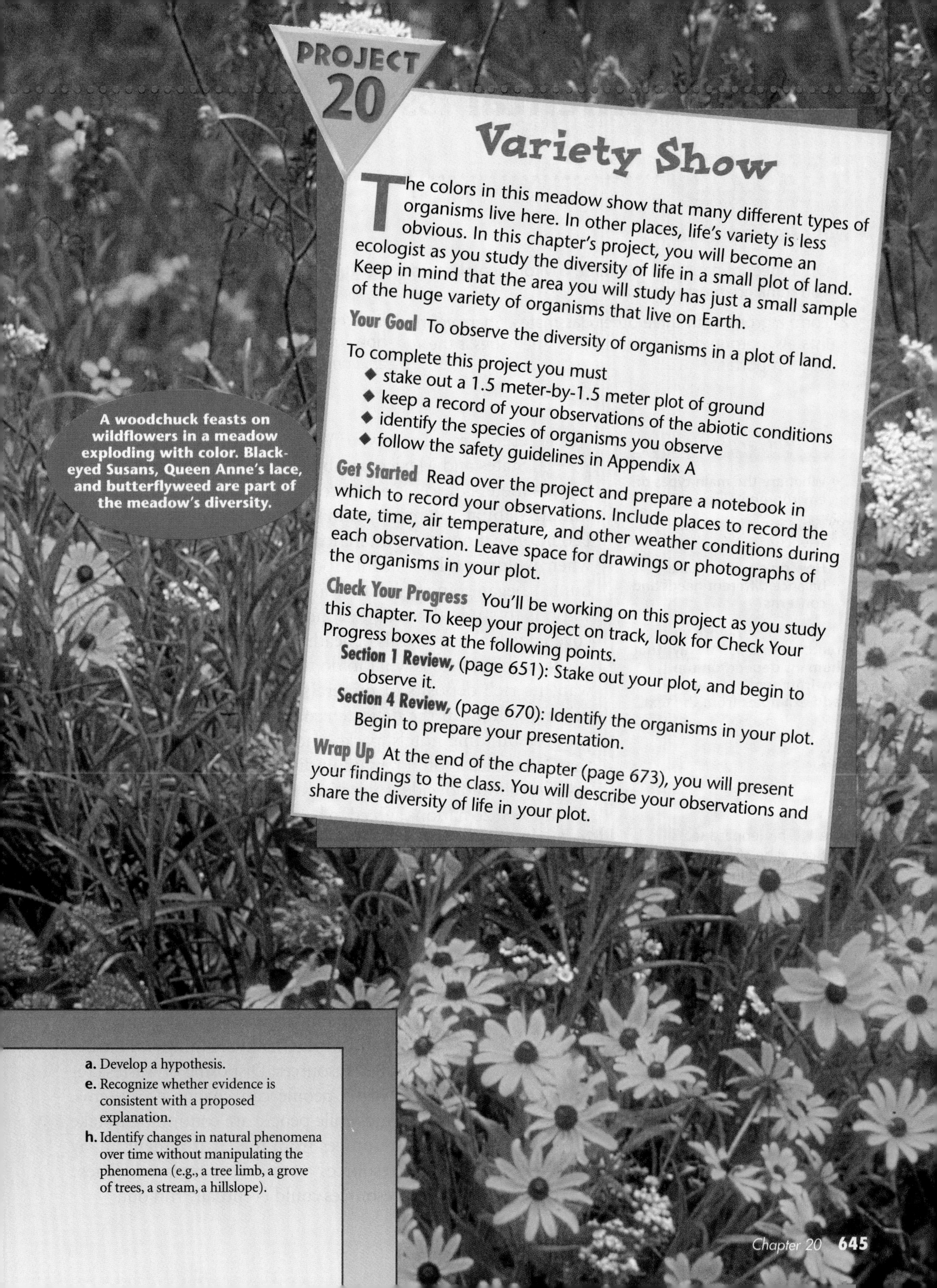

A woodchuck feasts on wildflowers in a meadow exploding with color. Black-eyed Susans, Queen Anne's lace, and butterflyweed are part of the meadow's diversity.

PROJECT 20

Variety Show

The colors in this meadow show that many different types of organisms live here. In other places, life's variety is less obvious. In this chapter's project, you will become an ecologist as you study the diversity of life in a small plot of land. Keep in mind that the area you will study has just a small sample of the huge variety of organisms that live on Earth.

Your Goal To observe the diversity of organisms in a plot of land.

To complete this project you must

- stake out a 1.5 meter-by-1.5 meter plot of ground
- keep a record of your observations of the abiotic conditions
- identify the species of organisms you observe
- follow the safety guidelines in Appendix A

Get Started Read over the project and prepare a notebook in which to record your observations. Include places to record the date, time, air temperature, and other weather conditions during each observation. Leave space for drawings or photographs of the organisms in your plot.

Check Your Progress You'll be working on this project as you study this chapter. To keep your project on track, look for Check Your Progress boxes at the following points.

Section 1 Review, (page 651): Stake out your plot, and begin to observe it.

Section 4 Review, (page 670): Identify the organisms in your plot. Begin to prepare your presentation.

Wrap Up At the end of the chapter (page 673), you will present your findings to the class. You will describe your observations and share the diversity of life in your plot.

a. Develop a hypothesis.

e. Recognize whether evidence is consistent with a proposed explanation.

h. Identify changes in natural phenomena over time without manipulating the phenomena (e.g., a tree limb, a grove of trees, a stream, a hillslope).

SECTION 1 Environmental Issues

DISCOVER ACTIVITY

How Do You Decide?

1. On a sheet of paper, list the three environmental issues you think are most important.
2. Form a group with three other classmates. Share your lists. As a group decide which one of the issues is the most important.

Think It Over

Forming Operational Definitions Based on your group's discussion, how would you define the term *environmental issue?*

GUIDE FOR READING

- **What are the main types of environmental issues?**
- **What is environmental science?**
- **How do decision makers balance different needs and concerns?**

Reading Tip **Before you read, make a list of ways that humans depend on the environment. As you read, add examples from the text.**

Here's a puzzle for you: What is bigger than the United States and Mexico combined; is covered with two kilometers of ice; is a source of oil, coal, and iron; and is a unique habitat for many animals? The answer is Antarctica. People once thought of Antarctica as a useless, icy wasteland. But when explorers told of its huge populations of seals and whales, hunters began going to Antarctica. Then scientists set up research stations to study the unique conditions there. They soon discovered valuable minerals beneath the thick ice.

Now the puzzle is what to do with Antarctica. Many people want its rich deposits of minerals and oil. Others worry that mining will harm the delicate ecosystems there. Some people propose building hotels, parks, and ski resorts. But others feel that Antarctica should remain undisturbed. It is not even obvious who should decide Antarctica's fate.

In 1998, 26 nations agreed to ban mining and oil exploration in Antarctica for at least 50 years. As resources become more scarce elsewhere in the world, the debate will surely continue. What is the best use of Antarctica?

Figure 1 This leopard seal's habitat could be affected if oil drilling is allowed in Antarctica. This tradeoff is an example of an environmental issue.

Types of Environmental Issues

People have always used Earth's resources. But as the human population has grown, so has its effect on the environment. People compete with each other and with other living things for Earth's limited resources. Disposing of wastes created by people can change ecosystems. And while people are continuing to take resources from the environment, many resources cannot be replaced. These resources could eventually run out.

Figure 2 Cherries are a renewable resource. After they are harvested, new cherries will grow in their place. In contrast, the aluminum and iron used to make these kitchen tools are nonrenewable resources.

The three main types of environmental issues are resource use, population growth, and pollution. These issues are all connected, making them very difficult to solve.

Resource Use Anything in the environment that is used by people is a natural resource. Some natural resources, called **renewable resources,** are naturally replaced in a relatively short time. Renewable resources include sunlight, wind, and trees. But it is possible to use up some renewable resources. For example, if people cut down trees faster than they can grow back, the supply of this resource will decrease.

Natural resources that are not replaced as they are used are called **nonrenewable resources.** Most nonrenewable resources, such as coal and oil, exist in a limited supply. As nonrenewable resources are used, the supply may eventually be depleted.

Population Growth Figure 3 shows how the human population has changed in the last 3,000 years. You can see that the population grew very slowly until about A.D. 1650. Around that time, improvements in medicine, agriculture, and sanitation enabled people to live longer. The death rate decreased. But as the population has continued to grow, the demand for resources has also grown.

Pollution Any change to the environment that has a negative effect on living things is called **pollution.** Pollution is an issue because it is often the result of an activity that benefits humans. For example, generating electricity by burning coal can result in air pollution. Some pesticides used to kill insects that eat crops are harmful to other animals.

☑ *Checkpoint* ***What is a natural resource?***

Figure 3 If two's company, six billion is certainly a crowd! The human population has grown rapidly in the last few centuries. *Calculating How much has the population grown since 1650?*

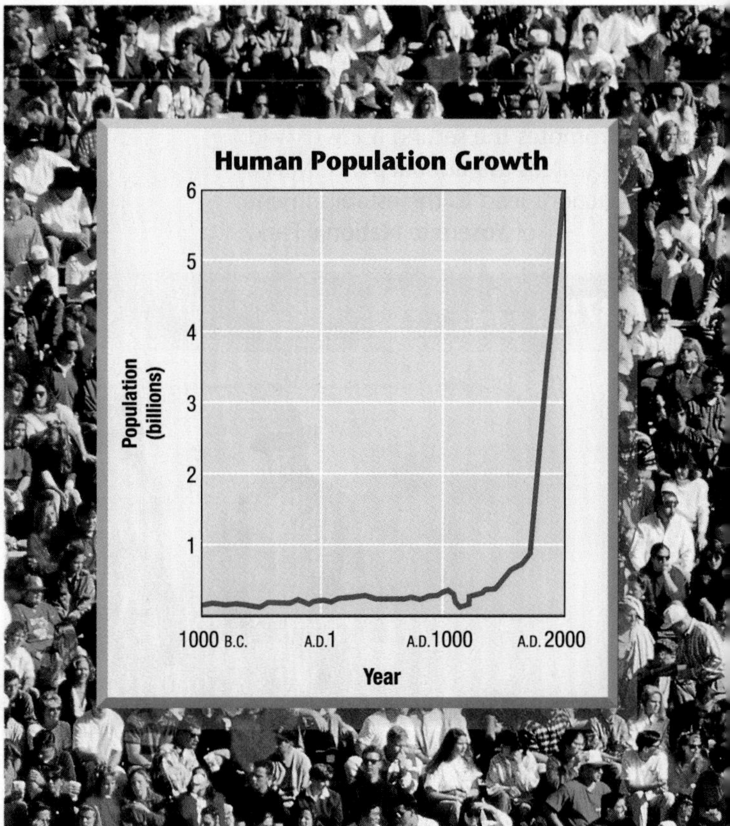
Human Population Growth
Population (billions)
6
5
4
3
2
1
1000 B.C.
A.D.1
A.D.1000
A.D.2000
Year

Approaches to Environmental Issues

Dealing with environmental issues means making choices. These choices can be made at personal, local, national, or global levels. Whether to ride in a car, take a bus, or ride your bicycle to the mall is an example of a personal choice. Whether to build a landfill or an incinerator for disposing of a town's wastes is a local choice. Whether the United States should allow oil drilling in a wildlife refuge is a national choice. How to protect Earth's atmosphere is a global choice.

Choices that seem personal are often part of much larger issues. Choices of what you eat, what you wear, and how you travel all affect the environment in a small way. When the choices made by millions of people are added together, each person's actions can make a difference.

SCIENCE & *History*

Making a Difference

Can one individual change the way people think? The leaders featured in this time line have influenced the way that many people think about environmental issues.

1892

California writer John Muir founds the Sierra Club. The group promotes the setting aside of wild areas as national parks. Muir's actions lead to the establishment of Yosemite National Park.

1905

Forestry scientist Gifford Pinchot is appointed the first director of the United States Forest Service. His goal is to manage forests scientifically to meet current and future lumber needs.

1875 — **1900** — **1925**

1903

President Theodore Roosevelt establishes the first National Wildlife Refuge on Pelican Island, Florida, to protect the brown pelican.

Theodore Roosevelt (left) and John Muir (right)

The first step in making environmental decisions is to understand how humans interact with the environment. **Environmental science is the study of the natural processes that occur in the environment and how humans can affect them.**

When people make decisions about environmental issues, the information provided by environmental scientists is a starting point. The next step is to decide what to do with the information. But environmental decisions also involve discussions of values, not just facts and figures. Environmental decisions usually require considering many different points of view. Most of these viewpoints fall into one of these three categories: development, preservation, or conservation.

☑ **Checkpoint** *What is an example of a local choice about an environmental issue?*

In Your Journal

Find out more about one of the people featured in this time line. Write a short biography of the person's life explaining how he or she became involved in environmental issues. What obstacles did the person overcome to accomplish his or her goal?

1949

Naturalist Aldo Leopold publishes *A Sand County Almanac.* This classic book links wildlife management to the science of ecology.

1969

At the age of 79, journalist Marjory Stoneman Douglas founds Friends of the Everglades. This grassroots organization is dedicated to preserving the unique Florida ecosystem. She continues to work for the Everglades until her death in 1998.

1950 **1975** **2000**

1962

Biologist Rachel Carson writes *Silent Spring,* which describes the harmful effects of pesticides on the environment. The book raises awareness of how human activities can affect the environment.

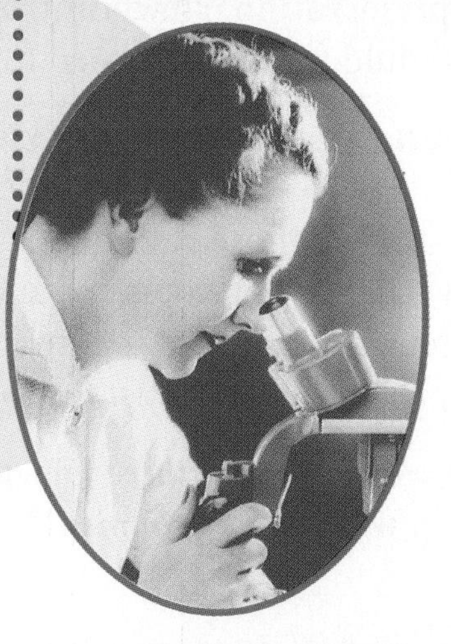

1977

Biologist Wangari Maathai founds the Green Belt Movement. This organization encourages restoring forests in Kenya and other African nations.

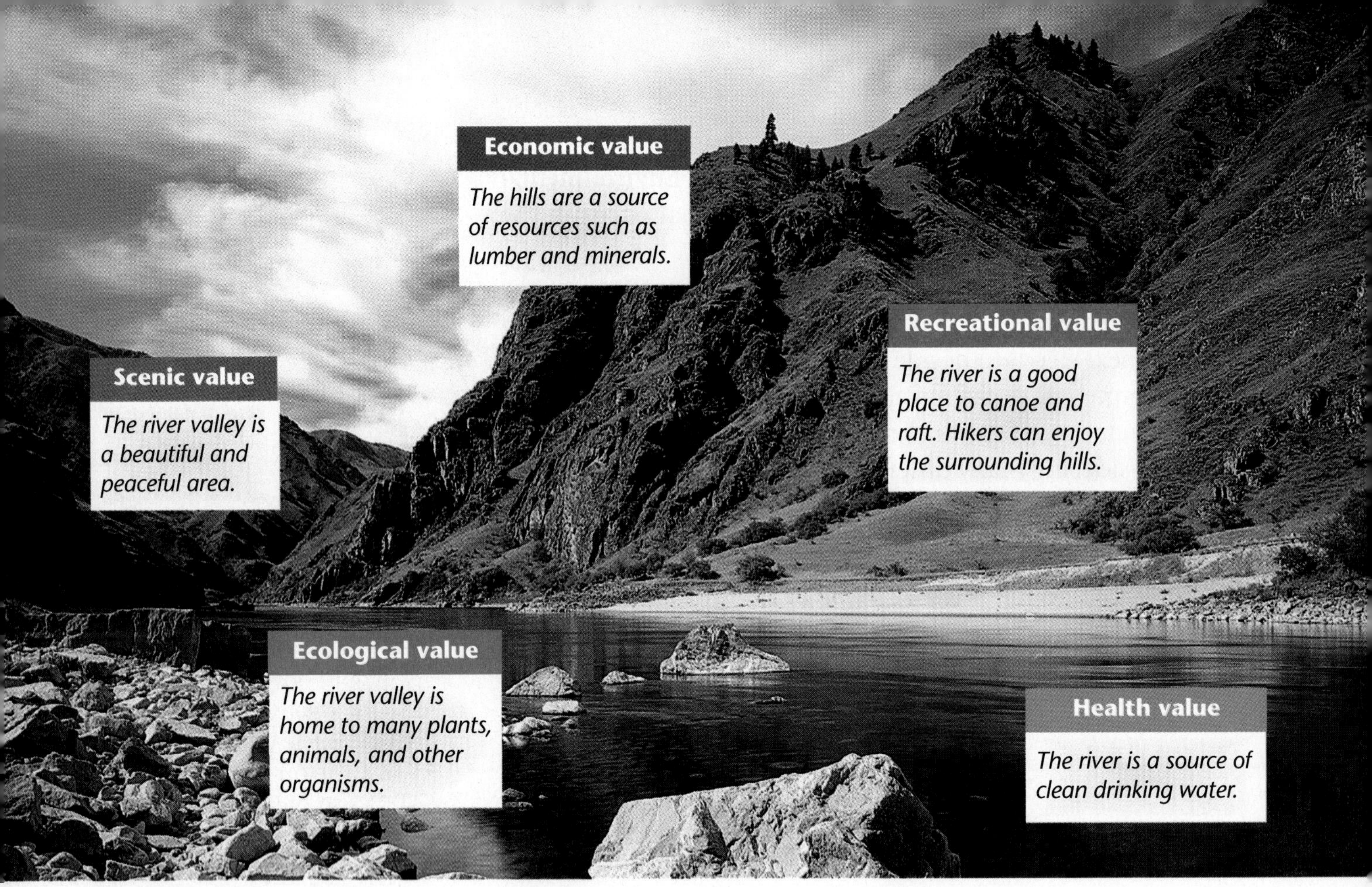
Economic value
The hills are a source of resources such as lumber and minerals.
Recreational value
The river is a good place to canoe and raft. Hikers can enjoy the surrounding hills.
Scenic value
The river valley is a beautiful and peaceful area.
Ecological value
The river valley is home to many plants, animals, and other organisms.
Health value
The river is a source of clean drinking water.

Figure 4 The environment is valued for many different reasons. *Applying Concepts In what other ways might this area be valuable?*

Development The belief that humans should be able to freely use and benefit from all of Earth's resources is referred to as the **development viewpoint.** This viewpoint considers the environment in terms of economics. Economics involves business, money, and jobs. According to the development viewpoint, the most valuable parts of the environment are those resources that are most useful to human beings.

Preservation The belief that all parts of the environment are equally important, no matter how useful they are to humans, is the **preservation viewpoint.** This viewpoint considers humans to be the caretakers of nature. Preservationists feel that Earth and its resources should be a source of beauty, comfort, and recreation. The preservation viewpoint is that living things and ecosystems should not be disturbed for the benefit of people.

Conservation The **conservation viewpoint** is the belief that people should use resources from the environment as long as they do not destroy those resources. Conservationists feel that people must balance development and preservation. The conservation viewpoint is that people should manage Earth's resources for the future, not just for today.

Checkpoint ***What are three viewpoints about how humans should interact with the environment?***

Weighing Costs and Benefits

Lawmakers work with many different government agencies to make environmental decisions. Together they must consider the needs and concerns of people with many different viewpoints. **To help balance these different opinions, decision makers weigh the costs and benefits of a proposal.**

Costs and benefits are often economic. Will a proposal provide jobs? Will it cost too much money? But costs and benefits are not only measured in terms of money. For example, building an incinerator might reduce the beauty of a natural landscape (a scenic cost). But the incinerator might be safer than an existing open dump site (a health benefit). It is also important to consider short-term and long-term effects. A proposal's short-term costs might be outweighed by its long-term benefits.

Consider the costs and benefits of drilling for oil in Antarctica. Drilling for oil would have many costs. It would be very expensive to set up a drilling operation in such a cold and distant place. Transporting the oil would be difficult and costly. An oil spill in the seas around Antarctica could harm the fish, penguins, and seals there.

On the other hand, there would be many benefits to drilling in Antarctica. A new supply of oil would provide fuel for heat, electricity, and transportation. The plan would create many new jobs. There would be a greater opportunity to study Antarctica's ecosystems. Do the benefits of drilling outweigh the costs? This is the kind of question lawmakers ask when they make environmental decisions.

Sharpen your Skills

Communicating

ACTIVITY

Form a group with two other students. Each person will be assigned a different viewpoint toward the environment. Hold a panel discussion in which each person proposes how the continent of Antarctica should be used. What similarities and differences are there among your responses?

Section 1 Review

1. List the three main types of environmental issues.
2. Define environmental science.
3. What is one way to balance different viewpoints on an environmental issue?
4. How has the growth of the human population affected the environment?
5. List three costs and three benefits of drilling for oil on Antarctica.
6. **Thinking Critically Comparing and Contrasting** Compare renewable and nonrenewable resources. Give an example of each type of resource.

Check Your Progress

CHAPTER PROJECT

Stake out a square plot measuring 1.5 meters on each side. Record the date, time, temperature, and weather. Observe the organisms in your plot, and record them with notes and drawings. Include enough detail so that you can identify any unfamiliar organisms later. (*Hint:* Also note evidence such as feathers or footprints that shows that other organisms may have visited the plot.)

Real-World Lab

You and Your Community

Is Paper a Renewable Resource?

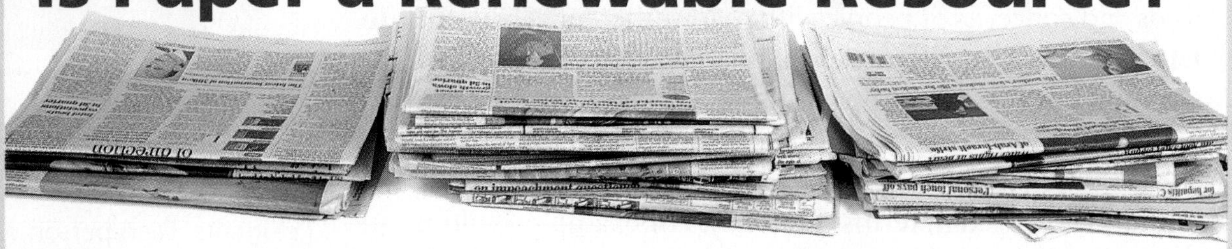

Recycling is a common local environmental issue. In this lab, you will explore how well paper can be recycled.

Problem

What happens when paper is recycled?

Skills Focus

observing, designing experiments

Materials

newspaper	microscope	water
eggbeater	square pan	screen
plastic wrap	mixing bowl	heavy book
microscope slide		

Procedure

1. Tear off a small piece of newspaper. Place the paper on a microscope slide and examine it under a microscope. Record your observations.
2. Tear a sheet of newspaper into pieces about the size of postage stamps. Place the pieces in the mixing bowl. Add enough water to cover the newspaper. Cover the bowl and let the mixture stand overnight.
3. The next day, add more water to cover the paper if necessary. Use the eggbeater to mix the wet paper until it is smooth. This thick liquid is called paper pulp.
4. Place the screen in the bottom of the pan. Pour the pulp onto the screen, spreading it out evenly. Then lift the screen above the pan, allowing most of the water to drip into the pan.
5. Place the screen and pulp on several layers of newspaper to absorb the rest of the water. Lay a sheet of plastic wrap over the pulp. Place a heavy book on top of the plastic wrap to press more water out of the pulp.
6. After 30 minutes, remove the book. Carefully turn over the screen, plastic wrap, and pulp. Remove the screen and plastic wrap. Let the pulp sit on the newspaper for one or two more days to dry. Replace the newspaper layers if necessary.
7. When the pulp is dry, observe it closely. Record your observations.

Analyze and Conclude

1. What kind of structures did you observe when you examined torn newspaper under a microscope? What are these structures made of? Where do they come from?
2. What do you think happens to the structures you observed when paper is recycled?
3. Based on your results, predict how many times a sheet of newspaper can be recycled.
4. **Apply** Should paper be classified as a renewable or nonrenewable resource? Explain.

Design an Experiment

Using procedures like those in this lab, design an experiment to recycle three different types of paper, such as shiny magazine paper, paper towels, and cardboard. Find out how the resulting papers differ. Obtain your teacher's approval for your plans before you try your experiment.

Section 2 Forests and Fisheries

Discover Activity

What Happened to the Tuna?

1. Use the data in the table to make a line graph. Label the axes of the graph and add a title. (To review graphing, see the Skills Handbook.)
2. Mark the high and low points on the graph.

Year	Western Atlantic Bluefin Tuna Population
1970	240,000
1975	190,000
1980	90,000
1985	60,000
1990	45,000
1994	60,000

Think It Over

Inferring How did the tuna population change during this period? Can you suggest a possible reason for this change?

Guide for Reading

- **How can forests and fisheries be managed?**

Reading Tip **As you read, make a list of ways to conserve forests and fisheries.**

At first glance, a bluefin tuna and a pine tree may not seem to have much in common. One is an animal and the other is a plant. One lives in the ocean and the other lives on land. However, tuna and pine trees are both living resources. Tuna are a source of food for people. People don't eat pine trees, but they do use them to make lumber, paper, and turpentine. People also use pine needles as mulch in gardens.

Every day you use many different products that are made from living organisms. In this section, you will read about two major types of living resources: forests and fisheries. As you read, think about how they are similar and how they are different.

Forest Resources

Forests are a resource because they contain valuable materials. Many products are made from the flowers, fruits, seeds, and other parts of forest plants. Some of these products, such as maple syrup, rubber, and nuts, come from living trees. Other products, such as lumber and pulp for paper, require cutting trees down. Conifers, including pine and spruce, are used for construction and for making paper. Hardwoods, such as oak, cherry, and maple, are used for furniture because of their strength and beauty.

Trees and other plants produce oxygen that other organisms need to survive. They also absorb carbon dioxide and many pollutants from the air. Trees also help prevent flooding and control soil erosion. Their roots absorb rainwater and hold the soil together.

Figure 5 One important use of forest resources is for building housing.

Figure 6 Clear-cutting has left large portions of these hillsides bare. *Interpreting Photographs What problems might clear-cutting cause?*

Managing Forests

There are about 300 million hectares of forests in the United States. That's nearly a third of the nation's area! Many forests are located on publicly owned land. Others are owned by private timber and paper companies or by individuals. Forest industries provide jobs for 1.5 million people.

Because new trees can be planted to replace trees that are cut down, forests can be renewable resources. The United States Forest Service and environmental organizations work with forestry companies to conserve forest resources. They try to develop logging methods that maintain forests as renewable resources.

Logging Methods There are two major methods of logging: clear-cutting and selective cutting. **Clear-cutting** is the process of cutting down all the trees in an area at once. Cutting down only some trees in a forest and leaving a mix of tree sizes and species behind is called **selective cutting.**

Each logging method has advantages and disadvantages. Clear-cutting is usually quicker and cheaper than selective cutting. It may also be safer for the loggers. In selective cutting, the loggers must move the heavy equipment and logs around the remaining trees in the forest. But selective cutting is usually less damaging to the forest environment than clear-cutting. When an area of forest is clear-cut, the habitat changes. Clear-cutting exposes the soil to wind and rain. Without the protection of the tree roots, the soil is more easily blown or washed away. Soil washed into streams may harm the fish and other organisms that live there.

Sustainable Forestry Forests can be managed to provide a sustained yield. A **sustainable yield** is a regular amount of a renewable resource such as trees that can be harvested without

Social Studies CONNECTION

Many of the world's living resources are owned by no one—they are shared by everyone. A word that is sometimes used to describe such a shared resource is a "commons." This word comes from a time when villages were built around common areas of open land. All the town's residents grazed their cattle on the commons. This worked well as long as there weren't too many people. But as more and more people brought their cattle to the commons, the area would become overgrazed. There would not be enough pasture to feed even one cow—the "tragedy of the commons."

In Your Journal

Suppose you live in a farming community with a central commons. Propose a solution that will allow residents to use the commons while protecting it from overuse.

reducing the future supply. This works sort of like a book swap: as long as you donate a book each time you borrow one, the total supply of books will not be affected. Planting a tree to replace one being cut down is like donating a book to replace a borrowed one.

Part of forest management is planning how frequently the trees must be replanted to keep a constant supply. Different species grow at different rates. Trees with softer woods, such as pines, usually mature faster than trees with harder woods, such as hickory, oak, and cherry. Forests containing faster-growing trees can be harvested and replanted more often. For example, pine forests may be harvested every 20 to 30 years. On the other hand, some hardwood forests may be harvested only every 40 to 100 years. One sustainable approach is to log small patches of forest. This way, different sections of forest can be harvested every year.

Certified Wood Forests that are managed in a sustainable way can be certified by the Forest Stewardship Council. Once a forest is certified, all wood logged from that forest may carry a "well-managed" label. This label allows businesses and individuals to select wood from forests that are managed for sustainable yields.

☑ *Checkpoint* *What is a sustainable yield?*

A
Original forest
Clear cutting
Replanted growth
B
Original forest
Selective cutting
Diverse regrowth

Figure 7 Two logging methods are clear-cutting and selective cutting. **A.** After clear-cutting, the new trees are usually all the same age and species. **B.** Selective cutting results in a more diverse forest.

Sharpen your Skills

Calculating

ACTIVITY

In a recent year, the total catch of fish in the world was 112.9 million metric tons. Based on the data below, calculate the percent of this total each country caught.

Country	Catch (millions of metric tons)
China	24.4
Japan	6.8
United States	5.6
Peru	8.9

Fisheries

Until recently, the oceans seemed like an unlimited resource. The waters held such huge schools of fish, it seemed impossible that they could ever disappear. And fish reproduce in incredible numbers. A single codfish can lay as many as nine million eggs in a single year! But people have discovered that this resource has limits. After many years of big catches, the number of sardines off the California coast suddenly declined. The same thing happened to the huge schools of cod off the New England coast. What caused these changes?

An area with a large population of valuable ocean organisms is called a **fishery.** Some major fisheries include the Grand Banks off Newfoundland, Georges Bank off New England, and Monterey Canyon off California. Fisheries like these are valuable renewable resources. But if fish are caught at a faster rate than they can breed, the population decreases. This situation is known as overfishing.

Scientists estimate that 70 percent of the world's major fisheries have been overfished. But if those fish populations are allowed to recover, a sustainable yield of fish can once again be harvested. **Managing fisheries for a sustainable yield includes setting fishing limits, changing fishing methods, developing aquaculture techniques, and finding new resources.**

Fishing Limits Laws can help protect individual fish species. Laws may also limit the amount that can be caught or require that fish be at least a certain size. This ensures that young fish

Figure 8 A fishing boat returns to harbor at the end of a long day. Overfishing has forced the crews of many boats to find other work until the fisheries recover.

survive long enough to reproduce. Also, setting an upper limit on the size of fish caught ensures that breeding fish remain in the population. But if a fishery has been severely overfished, the government may need to completely ban fishing until the populations can recover.

Fishing Methods Today fishing practices are regulated by laws. Some fishing crews now use nets with a larger mesh size to allow small, young fish to escape. Some methods have been outlawed. These methods include poisoning fish with cyanide and stunning them by exploding dynamite underwater. These techniques kill all the fish in an area rather than selecting certain fish.

Aquaculture The practice of raising fish and other water-dwelling organisms for food is called **aquaculture.** The fish may be raised in artificial ponds or bays. Salmon, catfish, and shrimp are farmed in this way in the United States.

However, aquaculture is not a perfect solution. The artificial ponds and bays often replace natural habitats such as salt marshes. Maintaining the farms can cause pollution and spread diseases into wild fish populations.

New Resources Today about 9,000 different fish species are harvested for food. More than half the animal protein eaten by people throughout the world comes from fish. One way to help feed a growing human population is to fish for new species. Scientists and chefs are working together to introduce people to deep-water species such as monkfish and tile fish, as well as easy-to-farm freshwater fish such as tilapia.

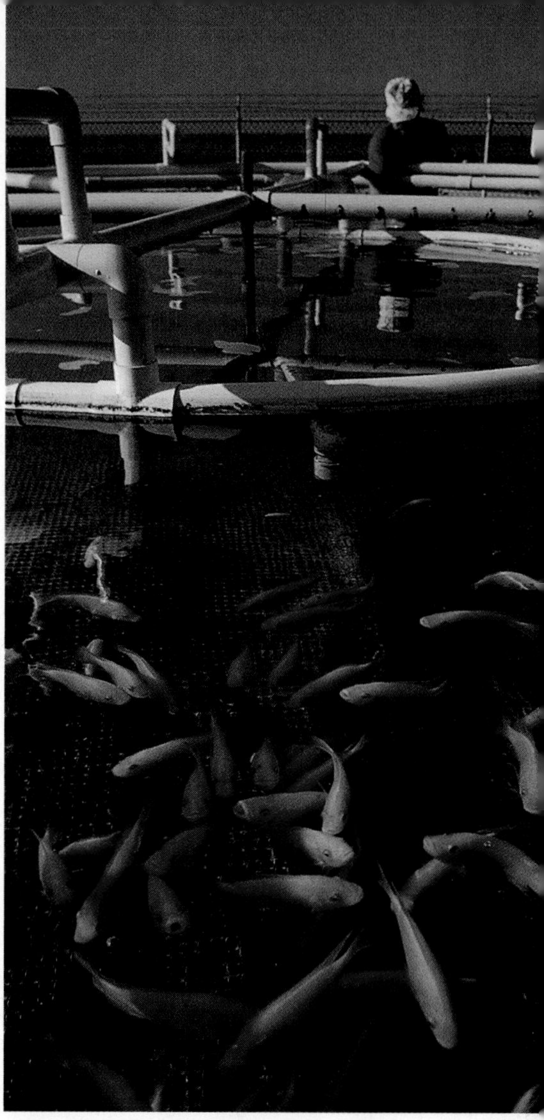

Figure 9 As fishing limits become stricter, aquaculture is playing a larger role in meeting the worldwide demand for fish. This fish farm in Hawaii raises tilapia.

Section 2 Review

1. Describe one example of a sustainable forestry practice.
2. What are three ways fisheries can be managed so that they will continue to provide fish for the future?
3. Why are forests considered renewable resources?
4. **Thinking Critically** **Comparing and Contrasting** Describe the advantages and disadvantages of clear-cutting and selective cutting.

Science at Home

With a family member, conduct a "Forest and Fishery" survey of your home. Make a list of all the things that are made from either forest or fishery products. Then ask other family members to predict how many items are on the list. Are they surprised by the answer?

Skills Lab

Interpreting Data

Tree Cookie Tales

Tree cookies aren't snacks! They're slices of a tree trunk that contain clues about the tree's age, past weather conditions, and fires that occurred during its life. In this lab, you'll interpret the data hidden in a tree cookie.

Problem

What can tree cookies reveal about the past?

Materials

tree cookie
metric ruler
hand lens
colored pencils
calculator (optional)

Procedure

1. Use a hand lens to examine your tree cookie. Draw a simple diagram of your tree cookie. Label the bark, tree rings, and center, or pith.
2. Notice the light-colored and dark-colored rings. The light ring results from fast springtime growth. The dark ring, where the cells are smaller, results from slower summertime growth. Each pair of light and dark rings represents one year's growth, so the pair is called an annual ring. Observe and count the annual rings.
3. Compare the spring and summer portions of the annual rings. Identify the thinnest and thickest rings.
4. Measure the distance from the center to the outermost edge of the last summer growth ring. This is the radius of your tree cookie. Record your measurement.
5. Measure the distance from the center to the outermost edge of the 10th summer growth ring. Record your measurement.
6. Examine your tree cookie for any other evidence of its history, such as damaged bark or burn marks. Record your observations.

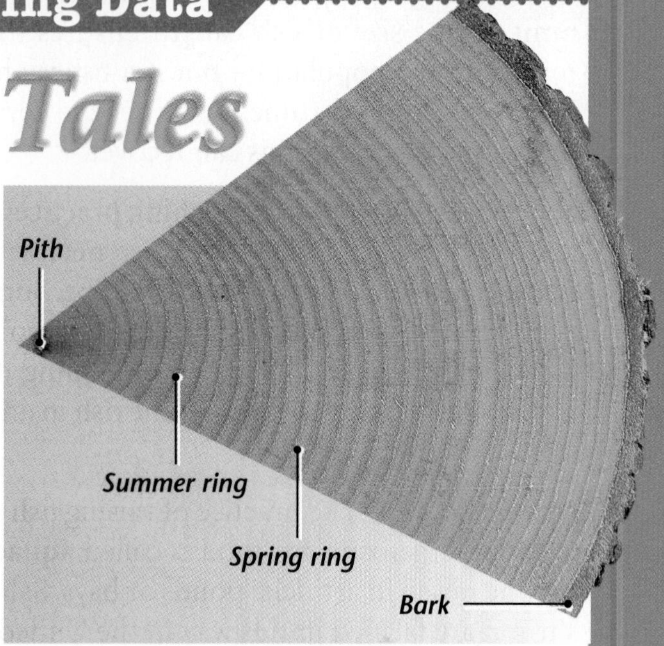
Pith
Summer ring
Spring ring
Bark

Analyze and Conclude

1. How old was your tree? How do you know?
2. What percent of the tree's growth took place during the first 10 years of its life? (*Hint:* Divide the distance from the center to the 10th growth ring by the radius. Then multiply by 100. This gives you the percent of growth that occurred during the tree's first 10 years.)
3. How did the spring rings compare to the summer rings for the same year? Suggest a reason.
4. Why might the annual rings be narrower for some years than for others?
5. Using evidence from your tree cookie, summarize the history of the tree.
6. **Think About It** Suppose you had cookies from two other trees of the same species that grew near your tree. How could you verify the interpretations you made in this lab?

More to Explore

Examine and compare several tree cookies. Record any similarities and differences you observe. Do you think any of the tree cookies came from trees growing in the same area? Support your answer with specific evidence.

SECTION 3 Biodiversity

DISCOVER ACTIVITY

How Much Variety Is There?

1. You will be given two cups of seeds and a paper plate. The seeds in Cup A represent the trees in a section of tropical rain forest. The seeds in Cup B represent the trees in a section of deciduous forest.
2. Pour the seeds from Cup A onto the plate. Sort the seeds by type. Count the different types of seeds. This number represents the number of different kinds of trees in that type of forest.
3. Pour the seeds back into Cup A.
4. Repeat Steps 2 and 3 with the seeds in Cup B.
5. Share your results with your class. Use the class results to calculate the average number of different kinds of seeds in each type of forest.

Think It Over

Inferring How does the variety of trees in the tropical rain forest compare with the variety of trees in a deciduous forest? Can you suggest any advantages of having a wide variety of species?

GUIDE FOR READING

- **What factors affect an area's biodiversity?**
- **Which human activities threaten biodiversity?**
- **How can biodiversity be protected?**

Reading Tip **Before you read, use the headings to make an outline on biodiversity.**

No one knows exactly how many species live on Earth. So far, more than 1.7 million species have been identified. The number of different species in an area is called its **biodiversity.** It is difficult to estimate the total biodiversity on Earth because many areas of the planet have not been thoroughly studied. Some experts think that the deep oceans alone could contain 10 million new species! Protecting this diversity is a major environmental issue today.

Factors Affecting Biodiversity

Biodiversity varies from place to place on Earth. **Factors that affect biodiversity in an ecosystem include area, climate, and diversity of niches.**

Area Within an ecosystem, a large area will contain more species than a small area. For example, suppose you were counting tree species in a forest. You would find far more tree species in a 10-square-meter area than in a 1-square-meter area.

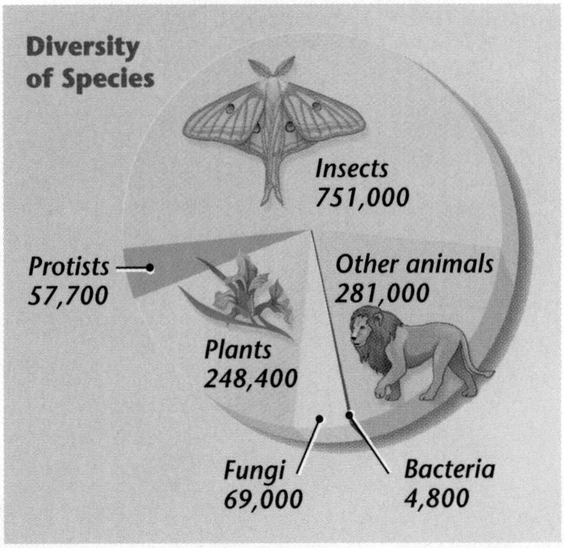

Diversity of Species
Insects 751,000
Protists 57,700
Other animals 281,000
Plants 248,400
Fungi 69,000
Bacteria 4,800

Figure 10 Organisms of many kinds are part of Earth's biodiversity. *Interpreting Graphs* *Which group of organisms has the greatest number of species?*

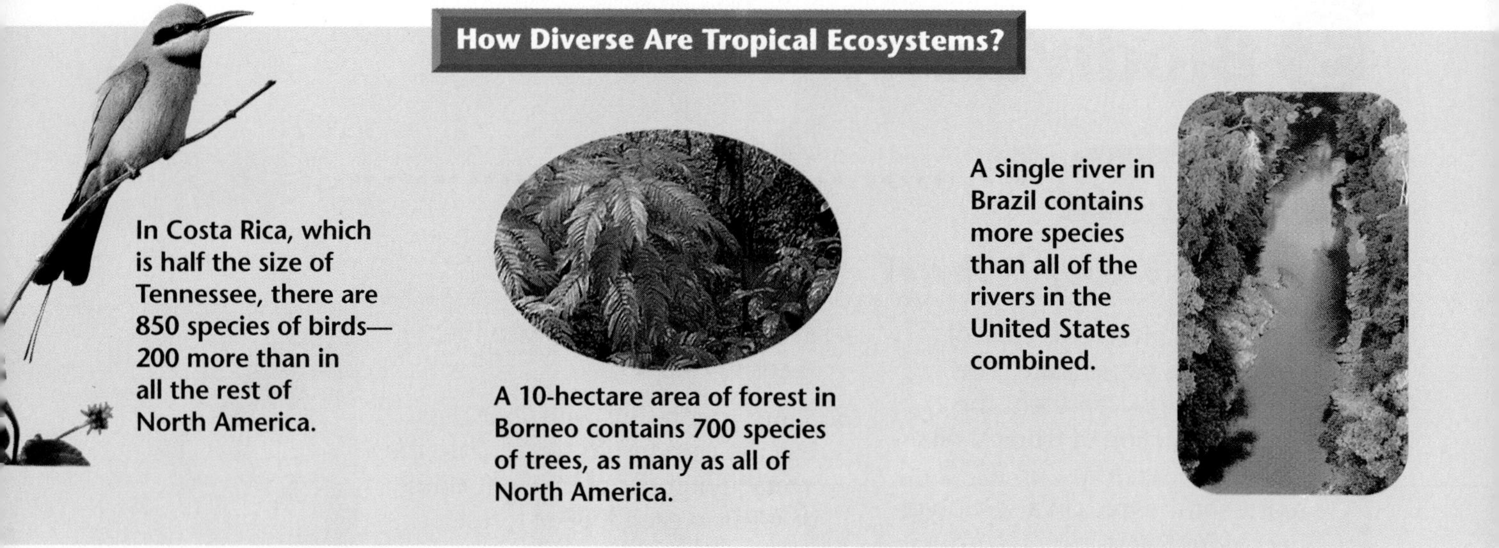
How Diverse Are Tropical Ecosystems?
In Costa Rica, which is half the size of Tennessee, there are 850 species of birds—200 more than in all the rest of North America.
A 10-hectare area of forest in Borneo contains 700 species of trees, as many as all of North America.
A single river in Brazil contains more species than all of the rivers in the United States combined.

Figure 11 Tropical ecosystems tend to be more diverse than those further from the equator.

Climate In general, the number of species increases from the poles toward the equator. The tropical rain forests of Latin America, southeast Asia, and central Africa are the most diverse ecosystems in the world. These forests cover about 7 percent of Earth's land surface and contain over half of the world's species.

The reason for the great biodiversity in the tropics is not fully understood. Many scientists hypothesize that it has to do with climate. For example, tropical rain forests have fairly constant temperatures and large amounts of rainfall throughout the year. Many plants in these regions have year-round growing seasons. This means that food is available for other organisms year-round.

Figure 12 Coral reefs are the second most diverse ecosystems. *Applying Concepts What is one reason why coral reefs are so diverse?*

Niche Diversity Coral reefs make up less than 1 percent of the oceans' area. But reefs are home to 20 percent of the world's saltwater fish species. Coral reefs are the second most diverse ecosystems in the world. Found only in shallow, warm waters, coral reefs are often called the rain forests of the sea. A reef provides many different niches for organisms that live under, on, and among the coral. This enables more species to live in the reef than in a more uniform habitat such as a flat sandbar.

☑ *Checkpoint* ***What is one possible reason that tropical regions have the greatest biodiversity?***

The Value of Biodiversity

Perhaps you are wondering how biodiversity is important. Does it matter whether there are 50 or 5,000 species of ferns in some faraway rain forest? Is it necessary to protect every one of these species?

There are many reasons why preserving biodiversity is important. The simplest reason is that wild organisms and ecosystems are a source of beauty and recreation.

Figure 13 Ecosystem tours such as safaris can provide income for local people. These tourists are observing giraffes in Botswana.

Economic Value Many plants, animals, and other organisms are essential for human survival. In addition to providing food and oxygen, these organisms supply raw materials for clothing, medicine, and other products. No one knows how many other useful species have not yet been identified.

Ecosystems are economically valuable, too. For example, many companies now run wildlife tours in rain forests, savannas, mountain ranges, and other locations. This ecosystem tourism, or "ecotourism," is an important source of jobs and money for nations such as Brazil, Costa Rica, and Kenya.

Value to the Ecosystem All the species in an ecosystem are connected to one another. Species may depend on each other for food and shelter. A change that affects one species will surely affect all the others.

Some species play a particularly important role. A species that influences the survival of many other species in an ecosystem is called a **keystone species.** If a keystone species disappears, the entire ecosystem may change. For example, the sea stars in Figure 14 are a keystone species in their ecosystem. The sea stars prey mostly on the mussels that live in tide pools. When researchers removed the sea stars from an area, the mussels began to outcompete many of the other species in the tide pool. The sea star predators had kept the population of mussels in check, allowing other species to live. When the keystone species disappeared, the balance in the ecosystem was destroyed.

Figure 14 These sea stars on the Washington coast are an example of a keystone species. By preying on mussels, the sea stars keep the mussels from taking over the ecosystem.

Figure 15 Just as diversity of species is important to an ecosystem, diversity of genes is important within a species. Diverse genes give these potatoes their rainbow of colors.

Gene Pool Diversity

The organisms in a healthy population have a diversity of traits. These traits are determined by genes. **Genes** are the structures in an organism's cells that carry its hereditary information. Every organism receives a combination of genes from its parents. Genes determine the organism's characteristics, from its size and appearance to its ability to fight disease. The organisms in one species share many genes. But each organism also has some genes that differ from those of other individuals. These individual differences make up the total gene "pool" of that species.

Species that lack a diverse gene pool are less able to adapt to disease, parasites, or drought. For example, most agricultural crops, such as wheat and corn, have very little diversity. These species are bred to be very uniform. If a disease or parasite attacks, the whole population could be affected. A fungus once wiped out much of the corn crop in the United States in this way. Fortunately, there are many wild varieties of corn that have slightly different genes. At least some of these plants contain genes that make them more resistant to the fungus. Scientists were able to breed corn that was not affected by the fungus. Keeping a diverse gene pool helps ensure that crop species can survive such problems.

☑ *Checkpoint* *What do an organism's genes determine?*

Extinction of Species

The disappearance of all members of a species from Earth is called **extinction.** Extinction is a natural process. Many species that once lived on Earth, from dinosaurs to dodos, are now extinct. But in the last few centuries, the number of species becoming extinct has increased dramatically.

Once a population drops below a certain level, the species may not be able to recover. For example, millions of passenger pigeons once darkened the skies in the United States. People hunted the birds for sport and food, killing many hundreds of thousands. This was only part of the total population of passenger pigeons. But at some point, there were not enough birds to reproduce and increase the population. Only after the birds disappeared did people realize that the species could not survive without its enormous numbers.

Species in danger of becoming extinct in the near future are considered **endangered species.** Species that could become endangered in the near future are considered **threatened species.**

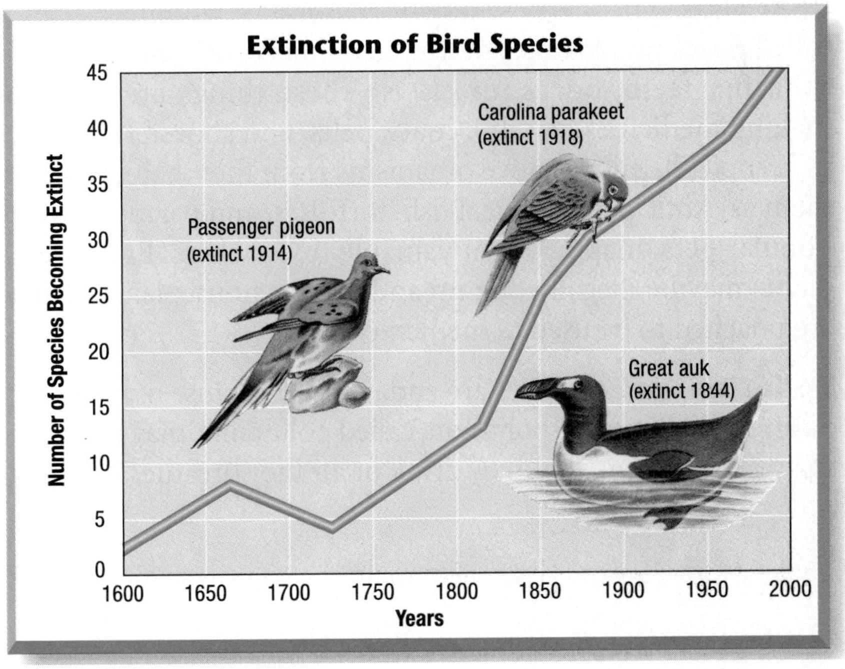
Extinction of Bird Species
Number of Species Becoming Extinct
45
40
35
30
25
20
15
10
5
0
1600
1650
1700
1750
1800
1850
1900
1950
2000
Years
Carolina parakeet
(extinct 1918)
Passenger pigeon
(extinct 1914)
Great auk
(extinct 1844)

Figure 16 This graph shows the rate of extinction of bird species in the last 400 years.
Interpreting Graphs How many bird species became extinct in 1750? In 1850? In 1950?

Threatened and endangered species are found on every continent and in every ocean. Some are well-known animals such as Africa's black rhinoceros. Others are little known, such as hutias, rodents that live on only a few Caribbean islands. Ensuring that these species survive is one way to protect Earth's biodiversity.

Causes of Extinction

A natural event, such as an earthquake, volcano, landslide, or flood, can damage an ecosystem or wildlife habitat, wiping out populations or even some species. **Human activities can also threaten biodiversity. These activities include habitat destruction, poaching, pollution, and introduction of exotic species.**

Habitat Destruction The major cause of extinction is **habitat destruction,** the loss of a natural habitat. This can occur when forests are cleared to build towns or create grazing land. Plowing grasslands or filling in wetlands greatly changes those ecosystems. Some species may not be able to survive such changes to their habitats.

Breaking larger habitats into smaller, isolated pieces, or fragments, is called **habitat fragmentation.** For example, building a road through a forest disrupts habitats. This makes trees more vulnerable to wind damage. Plants may be less likely to successfully disperse their seeds. Habitat fragmentation is also very harmful to large mammals. These animals usually need large areas of land to find enough food to survive. They may not be able to obtain enough resources in a small area. They may also be injured trying to cross to another area.

Figure 17 Building this subdivision caused the habitats in the area to change. Open land was replaced by houses, streets, and yards.
Inferring How would these changes affect species in this area?

Poaching The illegal killing or removal of wildlife species is called **poaching.** Many endangered animals are hunted for their skin, fur, teeth, horns, or claws. These things are used for making medicines, jewelry, coats, belts, and shoes.

People illegally remove organisms from their habitats to sell them as exotic pets. Tropical fish, tortoises, and parrots are very popular pets, making them valuable to poachers. Endangered plants may be illegally dug up and sold as houseplants. Others are poached to be used as medicines.

Pollution Some species are endangered because of pollution. Substances that cause pollution, called pollutants, may reach animals through the water they drink or air they breathe. Pollutants

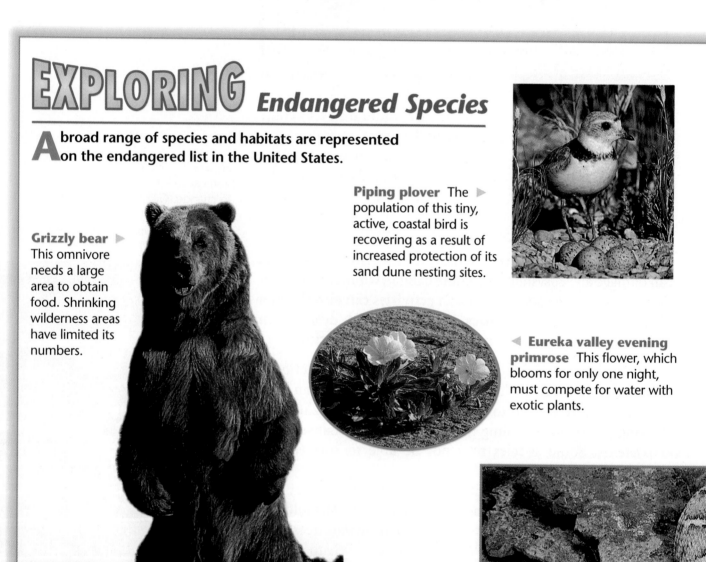

EXPLORING *Endangered Species*

A broad range of species and habitats are represented on the endangered list in the United States.

Piping plover The population of this tiny, active, coastal bird is recovering as a result of increased protection of its sand dune nesting sites.

Grizzly bear This omnivore needs a large area to obtain food. Shrinking wilderness areas have limited its numbers.

Eureka valley evening primrose This flower, which blooms for only one night, must compete for water with exotic plants.

may also settle in the soil. From there they are absorbed by plants, and build up in other organisms through the food chain. Pollutants may kill or weaken organisms or cause birth defects.

Exotic Species Introducing exotic species into an ecosystem can threaten biodiversity. When European sailors began visiting Hawaii hundreds of years ago, rats from their ships escaped onto the islands. Without any predators in Hawaii, the rats multiplied quickly. They ate the eggs of the nene goose. To protect the geese, people brought the rat-eating mongoose from India to help control the rat population. Unfortunately, the mongooses preferred eating eggs to rats. With both the rats and the mongoose eating its eggs, the nene goose is now endangered.

◄ **Steller's sea lion** This mammal competes with fishermen for its prey along the Pacific coast.

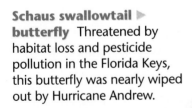

▲ **Whooping crane** Threatened by habitat destruction and disease, half of the remaining population of this wading bird is in captivity. The species seems to be recovering well since its lowest point in the 1940s.

Schaus swallowtail butterfly ► Threatened by habitat loss and pesticide pollution in the Florida Keys, this butterfly was nearly wiped out by Hurricane Andrew.

◄ **New Mexico ridgenose rattlesnake** Illegal collectors have reduced the population of this rare snake, the largest known group of which lives in a single canyon.

Protecting Biodiversity

Many people are working to preserve the world's biodiversity. Some focus on protecting individual endangered species, such as the giant panda or the Florida panther. Others try to protect entire ecosystems, such as the Great Barrier Reef in Australia. **Many programs to protect biodiversity combine scientific and legal approaches.**

Captive Breeding One scientific approach to protecting severely endangered species is captive breeding. **Captive breeding** is the mating of animals in zoos or wildlife preserves. Scientists care for the young to increase their chance of survival. These offspring are then released back into the wild.

A captive breeding program was the only hope for the California condor. California condors are the largest birds in North America. They became endangered as a result of habitat destruction, poaching, and pollution. By the mid-1980s there were fewer than ten California condors in the wild. Fewer than 30 were in zoos. Scientists captured all the wild condors and brought them to the zoos. Soon afterward, the first California condor chick was successfully bred in captivity. Today, there are more than 100 California condors in zoos. Some condors have even been returned to the wild. Though successful, this program has cost more than $20 million. It is not possible to save many species in this costly way.

Laws and Treaties Laws can help protect individual species. Some nations have made it illegal to sell endangered species or products made from them. In the United States, the Endangered Species Act of 1973 prohibits importing or trading products made from threatened or endangered species. This law also requires the development of plans to save endangered species.

Figure 18 Captive breeding programs use a scientific approach to protect endangered species.
A. California condor chicks raised in captivity need to learn what adult condors look like. Here, a scientist uses a puppet to feed and groom a chick.
B. These young green turtles were hatched in the laboratory. Now a researcher is releasing the turtles into their natural ocean habitat.

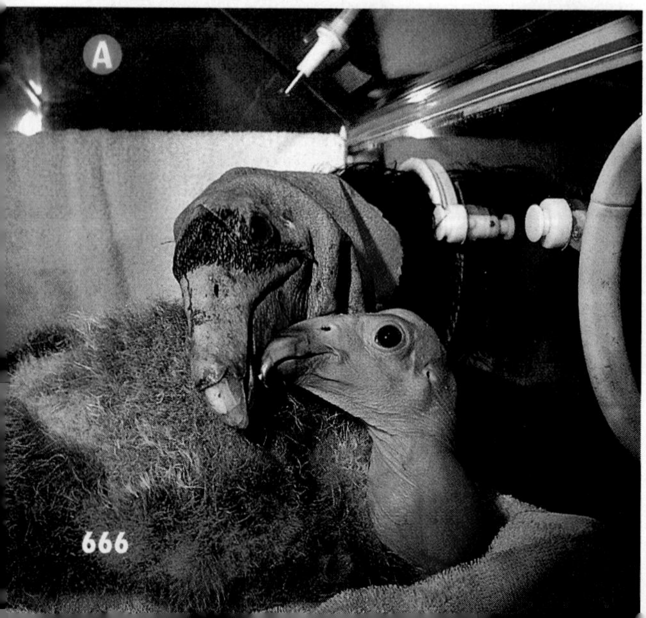
A

B

American alligators, Pacific gray whales, and green sea turtles are just a few of the species that have begun to recover as a result of legal protection.

The most important international treaty protecting wildlife is the Convention on International Trade in Endangered Species. Eighty nations signed this treaty in 1973. This treaty lists nearly 700 threatened and endangered species that cannot be traded for profit. Laws like these are difficult to enforce. Even so, they have helped to reduce the poaching of many endangered species, including African elephants, snow leopards, sperm whales, and mountain gorillas.

STATE OF CALIFORNIA
THE RESOURCES AGENCY
DEPARTMENT OF FISH AND GAME
BOLSA CHICA
ECOLOGICAL RESERVE
PROPERTY ACQUIRED by
STATE LANDS COMMISSION

Figure 19 Preserving whole habitats is probably the most effective way to protect biodiversity.

Habitat Preservation The most effective way to preserve biodiversity is to protect whole ecosystems. Preserving whole habitats saves not only endangered species, but also other species that depend on them.

Beginning in 1872 with Yellowstone National Park, the world's first national park, many countries have set aside wildlife habitats as parks and refuges. In addition, private organizations have purchased millions of hectares of endangered habitats throughout the world. Today, there are about 7,000 nature parks, preserves, and refuges in the world.

To be most effective, reserves must have the characteristics of diverse ecosystems. For example, they must be large enough to support the populations that live there. The reserves must contain a variety of niches. And of course, it is still necessary to keep the air, land, and water clean, remove exotic species, and control poaching.

Section 3 Review

1. What are three factors that affect biodiversity?
2. List four possible causes of extinction.
3. Give an example of a legal approach and a scientific approach to preventing extinction.
4. Which are the most diverse ecosystems on Earth?
5. Identify three ways in which biodiversity is important.
6. **Thinking Critically Making Generalizations** Explain how the statement "In the web of life, all things are connected" relates to keystone species.

Science at Home

Obtain a map of your community or state. With a family member, identify any city, state, or national parks, reserves, or refuges in your area. Create a travel brochure highlighting one of these areas. Describe the habitats there. Find out whether any endangered or threatened species live in the park. Include their pictures in your brochure.

SECTION 4 The Search for New Medicines

DISCOVER ACTIVITY

How Are Plant Chemicals Separated?

1. Using a black marking pen, draw a dot about 2 centimeters from the end of a strip of filter paper.
2. Pour a few centimeters of water into a clear plastic cup.
3. Tape the top edge of the filter paper strip to a pencil. Place the pencil across the top of the cup so that the ink dot hangs just below the water surface. If necessary, turn the pencil to adjust the length of the paper.

4. Observe what happens to the black dot.

Think It Over

Observing How many different colors of ink did you separate from the black ink? This process models one method of separating individual chemicals contained in plants.

GUIDE FOR READING

- **Why are many rain forest plants sources of medicines?**

Reading Tip **As you read, identify statements that show how biodiversity is related to human health.**

You lace up your hiking boots, and sling your collecting bag over your shoulder. It's time to head out for another day of searching in the cool, damp forest. Stepping carefully to avoid mud, you walk beneath the giant evergreens. Their needle-covered branches form a thick roof above your head. Rotting logs covered with ferns, seedlings, and brightly colored fungi line your path. You scan the ground for telltale signs of the object of your search. What are you looking for in this forest? A plant that can save lives!

Pacific yew tree

This ancient forest is the temperate rain forest of the Pacific Northwest. Many of its giant trees are more than 200 years old. Like tropical rain forests, temperate rain forests are diverse ecosystems. They contain many species that are found nowhere else. Some of these species are threatened or endangered, including the bull trout, Olympic salamander, and the life-saving plant you are looking for—the Pacific yew tree.

Plants and Medicines

People have always valued plants for their ability to heal wounds and fight diseases. For example, aspirin was originally made from the bark of the willow tree. The active chemical in aspirin can now be made in a laboratory.

TAXOL
112
Taxol

Figure 20 Scientists studied Pacific yew tree seedlings to learn more about the cancer-fighting substance taxol. In the closeup, a researcher examines taxol crystals.

The ability to fight disease is a result of the plants' adaptations to their environment. Plants in many ecosystems produce chemicals that protect them from predators, parasites, and diseases. This is particularly true in rain forests, where so many organisms make their living by eating plants. **Some chemicals that rain forest plants produce to protect their leaves and bark can also be used to fight human diseases.**

The Story of Taxol

The Pacific yew tree is very resistant to diseases and insects. Scientists began studying the bark of the Pacific yew to find out why it was so hardy. They separated chemicals from the bark. During this analysis, the scientists discovered unusual crystals in the bark. These crystals are made from a chemical called **taxol,** the substance that protects the Pacific yew tree.

Scientists next experimented with taxol in the laboratory. They discovered that taxol crystals affect cancer cells in an unusual way. Typically, cancer cells grow and divide very rapidly. This quick growth forms a mass of cells called a tumor. When cancer cells are exposed to taxol, the taxol forms structures that look like tiny cages around each cancer cell. These structures prevent the cancer cells from dividing. As a result, the cancer cannot grow and spread.

After more research, doctors were ready to test taxol on cancer patients. The taxol treatments often were able to shrink certain types of tumors. Sometimes they even stopped the cancer from spreading in the body. Taxol is now used to treat more than 12,000 cancer patients each year.

☑ *Checkpoint* *How is taxol helpful to Pacific yew trees?*

Figure 21 This researcher is pressing leaves as part of a species survey in a forest reserve.

A Threatened Supply of Taxol

The demand for taxol as a cancer treatment has grown rapidly. Now many scientists have become concerned about the supply of Pacific yew trees. It takes the bark of three Pacific yew trees to produce enough pure taxol for one cancer patient's treatment. If the bark is removed from a yew tree, the tree cannot survive. And by the time researchers discovered taxol's value as a cancer-fighting drug, a large portion of the yew trees' temperate rain forests were gone.

Taxol has a very complex chemical structure. Chemists have been working for many years to reproduce this structure. In 1996, chemists successfully created taxol in the laboratory for the first time. This discovery could help protect the remaining Pacific yew trees for future generations.

Biodiversity and Medicine

Almost half of all medicines sold today contain chemicals originally found in wild organisms. What other medicines are growing undiscovered in the forests of the world? So far, only about 2 percent of the world's known plant species have been studied for possible medical use. In 1995 the American Medical Association called for the protection of Earth's biodiversity. Their goal was to preserve the undiscovered medicines that may exist in nature. Governments, scientists, and private companies are working together to find new species all over the world. Perhaps they will find new sources of cancer-fighting drugs.

Section 4 Review

1. What adaptations of rain forest plants make them a likely source of medicines?
2. Describe the ecosystem in which Pacific yew trees are found.
3. How does taxol affect cancer cells?
4. **Thinking Critically** **Inferring** Suppose a group of scientists is planning an expedition to identify new species in the South American rain forest. Why might a company that manufactures medicines be interested in supporting their expedition?

CHAPTER PROJECT

Check Your Progress

Visit your plot regularly to make observations. Use field guides to identify the plants, animals, and other organisms you observe. Record their locations within your plot along with their common and scientific names. By now you should also be planning how to present your findings. Consider using a series of drawings, a flip chart, a computer presentation, or a video of your plot with closeups of the species you have identified. (*Hint:* Be sure to include the data you collected on abiotic factors.)

STUDY GUIDE

CHAPTER 20 REVIEW

Section 1 Environmental Issues

Key Ideas

- Three types of environmental issues are resource use, population growth, and pollution.
- Environmental science is the study of the natural processes that occur in the environment and how humans can affect them.
- Making environmental decisions requires balancing different viewpoints and weighing the costs and benefits of proposals.

Key Terms

renewable resources
nonrenewable resources
pollution
development viewpoint
preservation viewpoint
conservation viewpoint

Section 2 Forests and Fisheries

Key Ideas

- Because new trees can be planted to replace those that are cut down, forests can be renewable resources.
- Managing fisheries involves setting fishing limits, changing fishing methods, developing aquaculture techniques, and finding new resources.

Key Terms

clear-cutting	fishery
selective cutting	aquaculture
sustainable yield	

Section 3 Biodiversity

Key Ideas

- Factors that affect biodiversity include area, climate, and diversity of niches.
- Tropical rain forests are the most diverse ecosystems in the world. Coral reefs are the second most diverse ecosystems in the world.
- Diversity of organisms is a source of beauty, inspiration, and recreation. Many species and ecosystems also have economic value. Some species play critical roles in their ecosystems.
- Human activities that threaten biodiversity include habitat destruction, poaching, pollution, and introduction of exotic species.
- Three techniques for protecting biodiversity are regulating capture and trade, captive breeding, and habitat preservation.

Key Terms

biodiversity	threatened species
keystone species	habitat destruction
genes	habitat fragmentation
extinction	poaching
endangered species	captive breeding

Section 4 The Search for New Medicines

INTEGRATING HEALTH

Key Ideas

- Many plants make chemicals that protect them from predators, parasites, and disease. These chemicals may fight human diseases.
- The cancer-fighting drug taxol comes from Pacific yew trees, which have been affected by logging of the forests where they grow.
- The possible discovery of other medicines is one reason to protect biodiversity.

Key Term

taxol

ACTIVITY

USING THE INTERNET

www.phschool.com/state_focus/california/

C H A P T E R 20 A S S E S S M E N T

California Test Prep: Reviewing Content

Multiple Choice

Choose the letter of the best answer.

1. The viewpoint that humans should be able to benefit from all of Earth's resources is the
   a. conservation viewpoint.
   b. development viewpoint.
   c. scientific viewpoint.
   d. preservation viewpoint.
2. The most diverse ecosystems in the world are
   a. coral reefs. **b.** deserts.
   c. grasslands. **d.** tropical rain forests.
3. If all members of a species disappear from Earth, that species is
   a. extinct. **b.** endangered.
   c. nonrenewable. **d.** threatened.
4. The illegal removal from the wild or killing of an endangered species is called
   a. habitat destruction.
   b. poaching.
   c. pollution.
   d. captive breeding.
5. Taxol, which comes from Pacific yew trees, is a medicine that is used to fight
   a. heart disease. **b.** cancer.
   c. lung disease. **d.** diabetes.

True or False

If the statement is true, write true. If it is false, change the underlined word or words to make the statement true.

6. The three main types of environmental issues today are resource use, pollution, and population growth.
7. Forests and fisheries are examples of nonrenewable resources.
8. A sustainable yield is a number of trees that can be regularly harvested without affecting the health of the forest.
9. A species that influences the survival of many other species in an ecosystem is called a(n) endangered species.
10. The most effective way to protect biodiversity is through habitat fragmentation.

Checking Concepts

11. Give an example of a personal or local environmental issue and an example of a national or global environmental issue.
12. How are environmental decisions made?
13. Compare the effects of clear-cutting and selective cutting on forest ecosystems.
14. Describe one way to prevent overfishing.
15. Explain how habitat destruction affects species.
16. **Writing to Learn** You are a member of the county land use commission. Hundreds of people are moving to your county every day. You must make a decision regarding how to manage a 5,000-hectare woodland area in your county. Choose one point of view: development, preservation, or conservation. Write an editorial for a newspaper explaining your position.

Thinking Visually

17. **Concept Map** Copy the biodiversity concept map below onto a sheet of paper. Complete it and add a title. (For more on concept maps, see the Skills Handbook.)

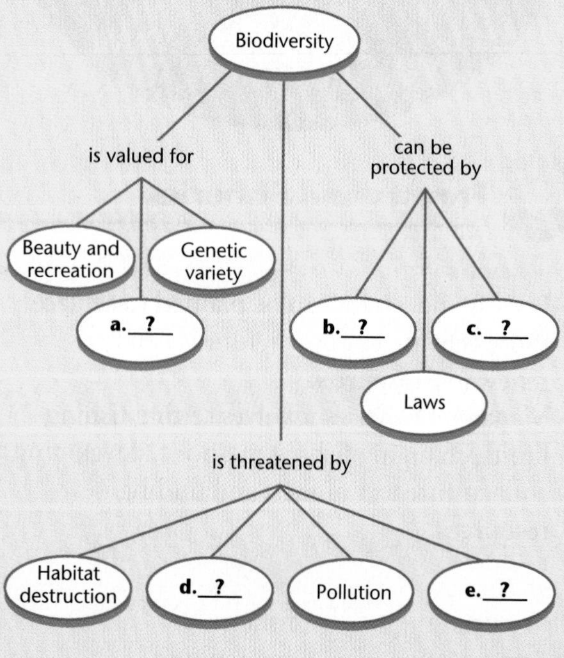

Biodiversity
is valued for
can be protected by
Beauty and recreation
Genetic variety
a. ?
b. ?
c. ?
Laws
is threatened by
Habitat destruction
d. ?
Pollution
e. ?

Test Prep: Skills

One study identifies the reasons that mammal and bird species are endangered or threatened. Use the table to answer Questions 18–20.

Reason	Mammals	Birds
Poaching	31%	20%
Habitat loss	32%	60%
Exotic species	17%	12%
Other causes	20%	8%

18. **Graphing** Make a bar graph comparing the reasons that mammals and birds are endangered and threatened. Show percents for each animal group on the vertical axis and reasons on the horizontal axis.
19. **Interpreting Data** What is the major reason that mammals become endangered or threatened? What mainly endangers or threatens birds?
20. **Developing Hypotheses** Suggest explanations for the differences between the data for mammals and birds.

Thinking Critically

21. **Relating Cause and Effect** Explain how human population growth affects other species on Earth.
22. **Making Generalizations** Describe how an exotic species can threaten other species in an ecosystem.
23. **Predicting** How could the extinction of a species today affect your life 20 years from now?
24. **Relating Cause and Effect** Explain why many human medicines are made from chemicals that come from plants.
25. **Making Judgments** Suppose you were given $1 million toward saving an endangered turtle species. You could use the money to start a captive breeding program for the turtles. Or you could use the money to purchase and protect part of the turtle's habitat. How would you spend the money? Explain your answer.

CHAPTER 20 ASSESSMENT

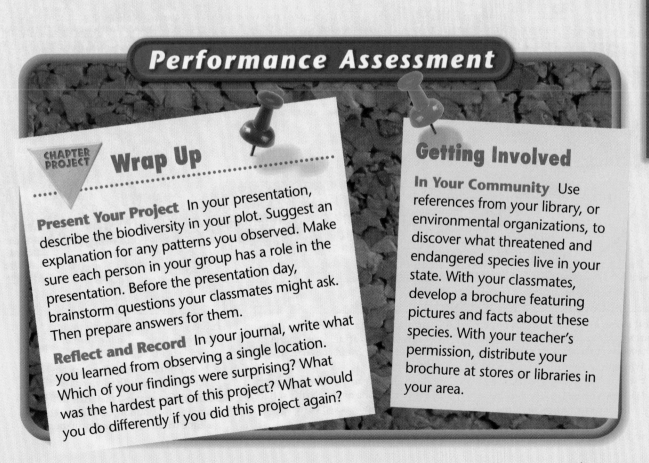

Performance Assessment

CHAPTER PROJECT

Wrap Up

Present Your Project In your presentation, describe the biodiversity in your plot. Suggest an explanation for any patterns you observed. Make sure each person in your group has a role in the presentation. Before the presentation day, brainstorm questions your classmates might ask. Then prepare answers for them.

Reflect and Record In your journal, write what you learned from observing a single location. Which of your findings were surprising? What was the hardest part of this project? What would you do differently if you did this project again?

Getting Involved

In Your Community Use references from your library, or environmental organizations, to discover what threatened and endangered species live in your state. With your classmates, develop a brochure featuring pictures and facts about these species. With your teacher's permission, distribute your brochure at stores or libraries in your area.

CHAPTER 21

Energy Resources

Electricity makes downtown Los Angeles sparkle at dusk.

CALIFORNIA SCIENCE CONTENT STANDARDS

The following California Science Content Standards are addressed in this chapter:

3. Heat moves in a predictable flow from warmer objects to cooler objects until all objects are at the same temperature.

- **b.** When fuel is consumed, most of the energy released becomes heat energy.
- **c.** Heat flows in solids by conduction (which involves no flow of matter) and in fluids by conduction and also by convection (which involves flow of matter).

4. Many phenomena on the Earth's surface are affected by the transfer of energy through radiation and convection currents.

- **a.** The sun is the major source of energy for phenomena on the Earth's surface, powering winds, ocean currents, and the water cycle.
- **b.** Solar energy reaches Earth through radiation, mostly in the form of visible light.
- **c.** Heat from Earth's interior reaches the surface primarily through convection.

6. Sources of energy and materials differ in amounts, distribution, usefulness, and the time required for their formation.

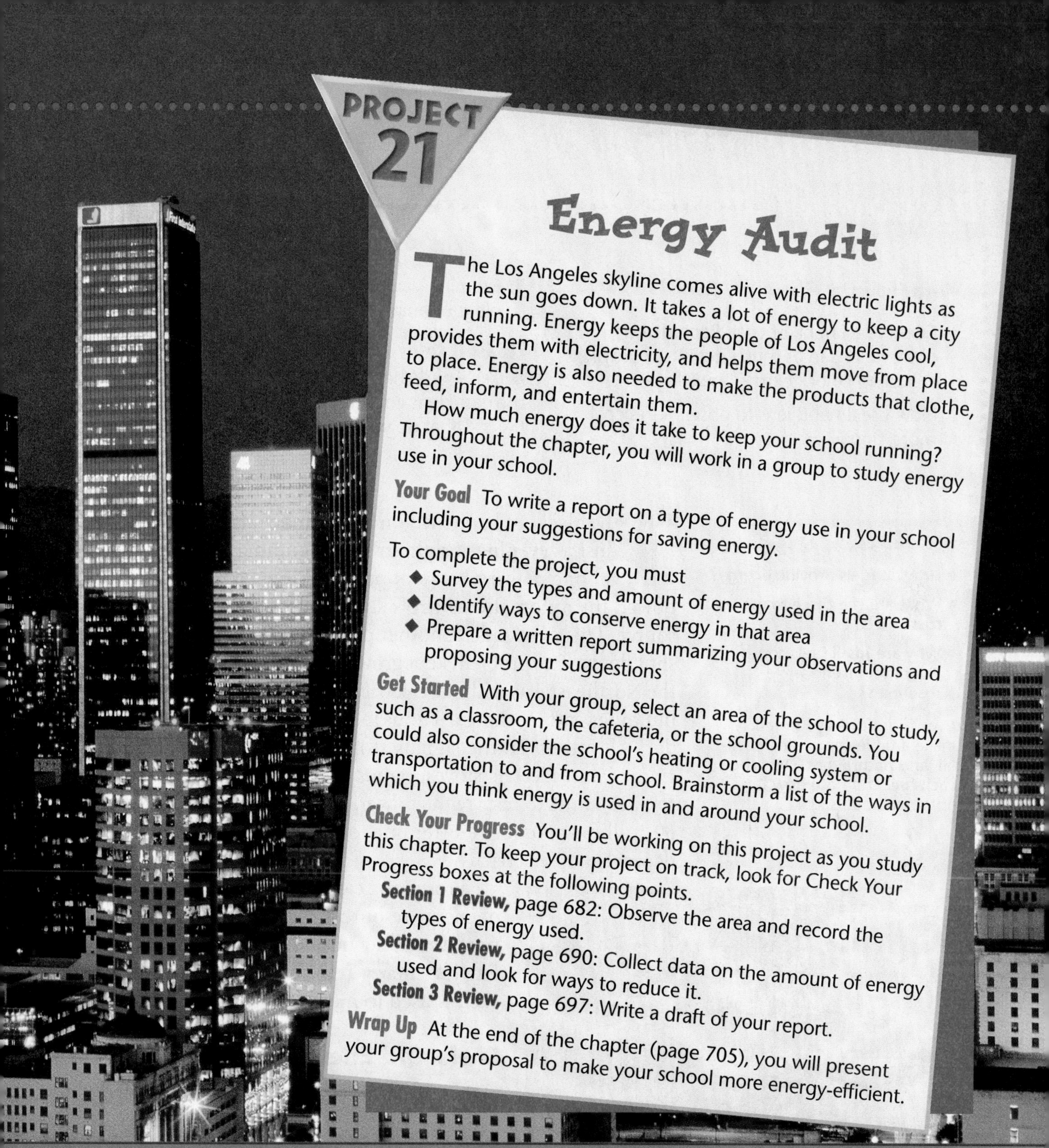

PROJECT 21

Energy Audit

The Los Angeles skyline comes alive with electric lights as the sun goes down. It takes a lot of energy to keep a city running. Energy keeps the people of Los Angeles cool, provides them with electricity, and helps them move from place to place. Energy is also needed to make the products that clothe, feed, inform, and entertain them.

How much energy does it take to keep your school running? Throughout the chapter, you will work in a group to study energy use in your school.

Your Goal To write a report on a type of energy use in your school including your suggestions for saving energy.

To complete the project, you must

- Survey the types and amount of energy used in the area
- Identify ways to conserve energy in that area
- Prepare a written report summarizing your observations and proposing your suggestions

Get Started With your group, select an area of the school to study, such as a classroom, the cafeteria, or the school grounds. You could also consider the school's heating or cooling system or transportation to and from school. Brainstorm a list of the ways in which you think energy is used in and around your school.

Check Your Progress You'll be working on this project as you study this chapter. To keep your project on track, look for Check Your Progress boxes at the following points.

Section 1 Review, page 682: Observe the area and record the types of energy used.

Section 2 Review, page 690: Collect data on the amount of energy used and look for ways to reduce it.

Section 3 Review, page 697: Write a draft of your report.

Wrap Up At the end of the chapter (page 705), you will present your group's proposal to make your school more energy-efficient.

a. The utility of energy sources is determined by factors that are involved in converting these sources to useful forms and the consequences of the conversion process.

b. Different natural energy and material resources, including air, soil, rocks, minerals, petroleum, fresh water, wildlife, and forests, and classify them as renewable or nonrenewable.

7. Scientific progress is made by asking meaningful questions and conducting careful investigations.

a. Develop a hypothesis.

d. Communicate the steps and results from an investigation in written reports and verbal presentations.

e. Recognize whether evidence is consistent with a proposed explanation.

SECTION 1
Fossil Fuels

DISCOVER — ACTIVITY

What's in a Piece of Coal?

1. Observe a chunk of coal. Record your observations in as much detail as possible, including color, texture, and shape.
2. Now use a hand lens to observe the coal more closely.
3. Examine your coal for fossils, imprints of plant or animal remains.

Think It Over

Observing What did you notice when you used the hand lens compared to your first observations? What do you think coal is made of?

GUIDE FOR READING

- **How do fuels provide energy?**
- **What are the three major fossil fuels?**
- **Why are fossil fuels considered nonrenewable resources?**

Reading Tip **As you read, make a table comparing coal, oil, and natural gas. Describe each fuel and note how it is obtained and used.**

The blackout happened on a November afternoon in 1965, just as evening rush hour was beginning. One small part in one power plant stopped working. To replace the lost power, the automatic controls shifted electricity from another source. This overloaded another part of the system, causing it to shut down. The problem kept growing. Within minutes, much of the Northeast was without electricity! Lights went out, plunging buildings into darkness. Thousands of people were trapped in dark elevators. Traffic signals stopped working, causing huge traffic jams. Electric stoves, radios, clocks—nothing worked. It took 13 hours to restore the power. During that time, more than 30 million people were reminded just how much their lives depended on electricity.

Producing electricity is an important use of energy resources. Other uses include transportation and heating. As you read about Earth's energy resources, think about how each is used to meet people's energy needs.

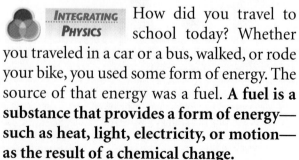

◀ Electric power lines stretch against the evening sky.

Fuels and Energy

INTEGRATING PHYSICS How did you travel to school today? Whether you traveled in a car or a bus, walked, or rode your bike, you used some form of energy. The source of that energy was a fuel. **A fuel is a substance that provides a form of energy—such as heat, light, electricity, or motion—as the result of a chemical change.**

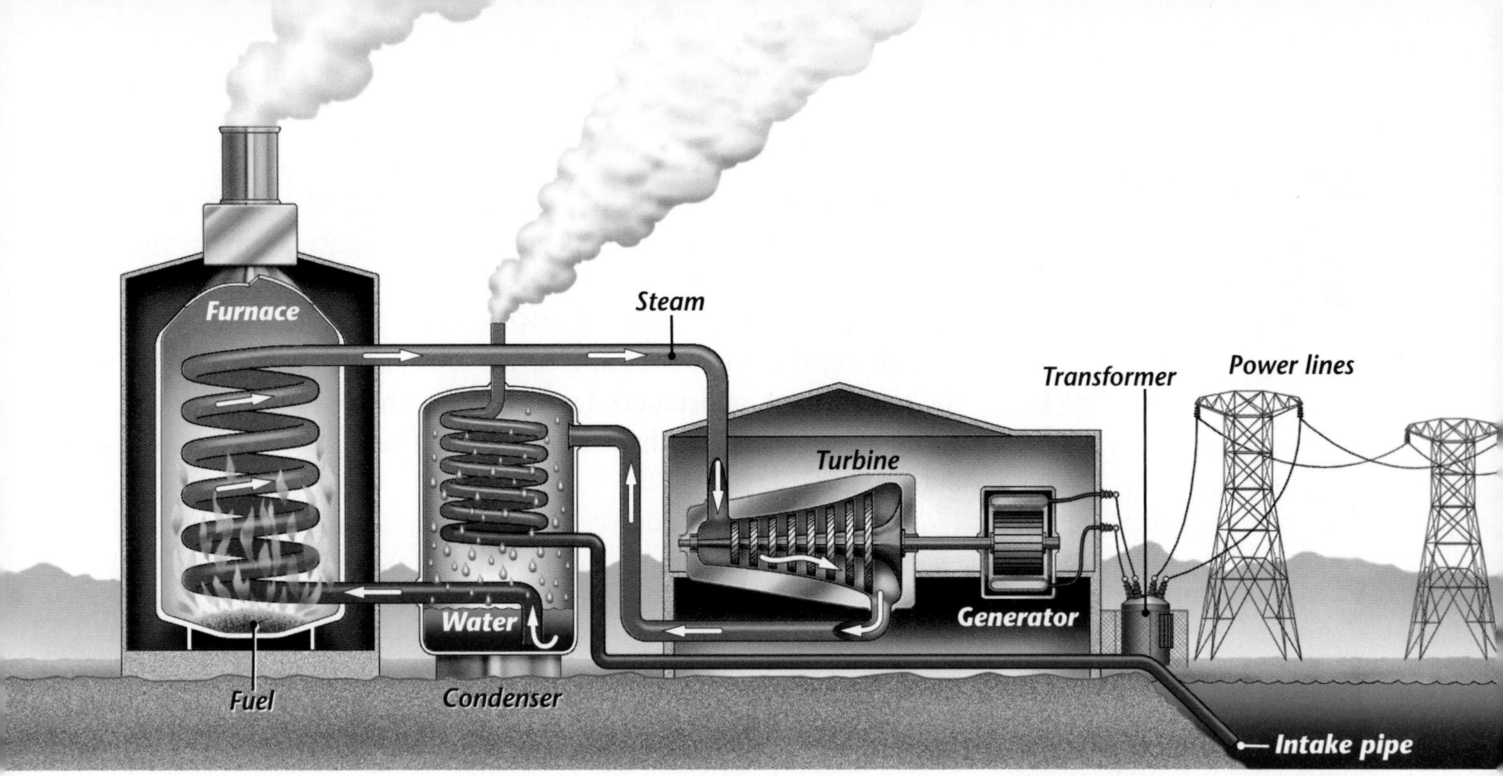
Furnace
Steam
Transformer
Power lines
Turbine
Water
Generator
Fuel
Condenser
Intake pipe

Figure 1 Electric power plants generate electricity by converting energy from one form to another. In the furnace, fuel is burned, releasing thermal energy. This energy is used to boil water and make steam. The mechanical energy of the moving steam turns the blades of a turbine. The turbine turns the shaft of the generator, producing an electric current.

Energy can be converted from one form to another. To see how, rub your hands together quickly for several seconds. Did you feel them become warmer? When you moved your hands, they had mechanical energy, the energy of motion. The friction of your hands rubbing together converted some of this mechanical energy to thermal energy, which you felt as heat.

Combustion Fuels contain stored chemical energy, which can be released by burning. The process of burning a fuel is called **combustion.** For example, the fuel used by most cars is gasoline. When gasoline is burned in a car engine, it undergoes a chemical change. The gasoline combines with oxygen, producing carbon dioxide and water. The combustion of gasoline also converts some of the stored chemical energy into thermal energy. This thermal energy is converted to mechanical energy that moves the car.

Production of Electricity The energy stored in fuels can be used to generate electricty. In most power plants, the thermal energy produced by burning fuel is used to boil water, making steam, as shown in Figure 1. The mechanical energy of the steam turns the blades of a turbine. The shaft of the turbine is connected to a generator. The generator consists of powerful magnets surrounded by coils of copper wire. As the shaft rotates, the magnets turn inside the wire coil, producing an electric current. The electric current flows through power lines to homes and industries.

☑ *Checkpoint* *What are three energy conversions that might occur in a power plant?*

Sharpen your Skills

Graphing ACTIVITY

Use the data in the table below to make a circle graph showing the uses of energy in the United States. (To review circle graphs, see the Skills Handbook.)

End Use of Energy	Percent of Total Energy
Transportation	26.5
Industry	38.1
Homes and businesses	35.4

What Are Fossil Fuels?

Most of the energy used today comes from organisms that lived hundreds of millions of years ago. As these plants, animals, and other organisms died, their remains piled up. Layers of sand, rock, and mud buried the dead organisms. Over time, heat and pressure changed the material into other substances. **Fossil fuels** are the energy-rich substances formed from the remains of once-living organisms. **The three major fossil fuels are coal, oil, and natural gas.**

Fossil fuels are made of hydrocarbons. **Hydrocarbons** are energy-rich chemical compounds that contain carbon and hydrogen atoms. During combustion, the carbon and hydrogen combine with oxygen in the air to form carbon dioxide and water. This process releases energy in the forms of heat and light.

Fossil fuels have more hydrocarbons per kilogram than most other fuels. For this reason, they are an excellent source of energy. Combustion of one kilogram of coal, for example, provides twice as much heat as burning one kilogram of wood. Oil and natural gas provide three times the energy of wood.

☑ *Checkpoint* *Why do fossil fuels yield more energy than other fuels?*

Coal

Coal is a solid fossil fuel formed from plant remains. People have burned coal to produce heat for thousands of years. But coal was only a minor source of energy compared to wood until the 1800s. As Europe and the United States entered the Industrial Revolution, the need for fuel increased rapidly.

Figure 2 Coal is formed from the remains of trees and other plants that grew in swamps hundreds of millions of years ago.

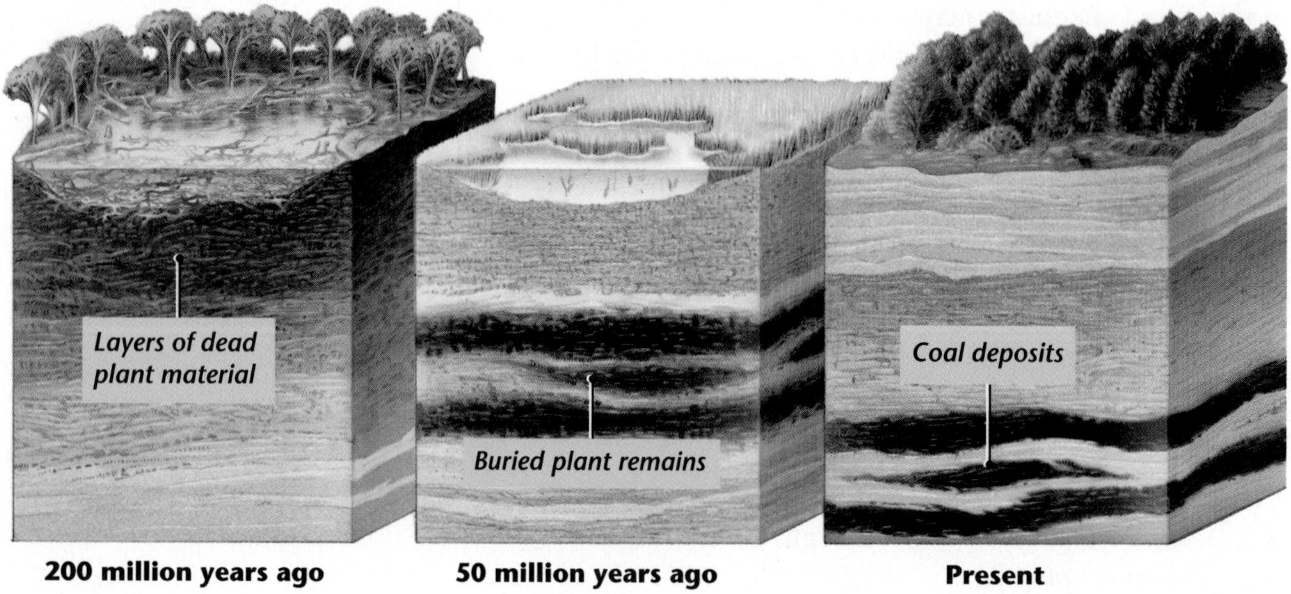
Layers of dead plant material
Buried plant remains
Coal deposits
200 million years ago
50 million years ago
Present

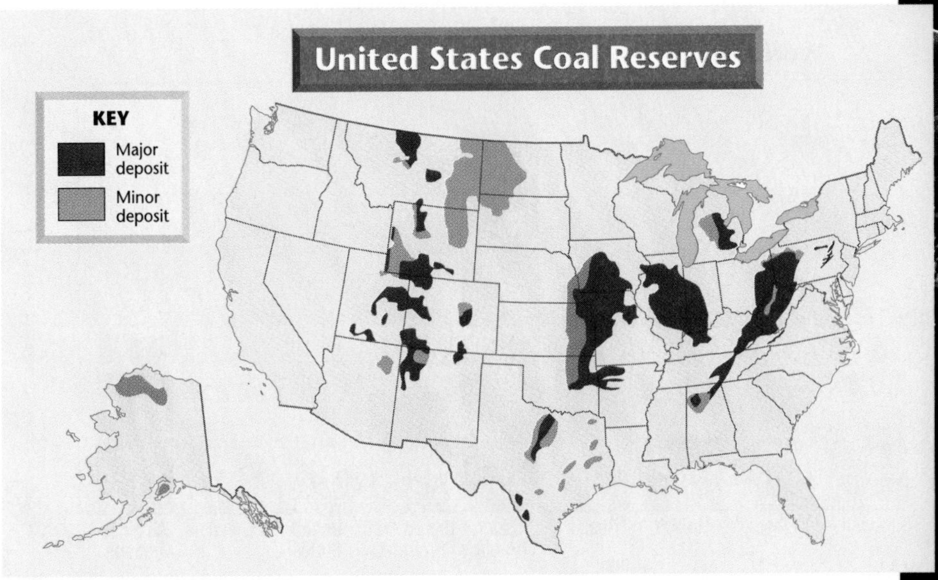
United States Coal Reserves
KEY
Major deposit
Minor deposit

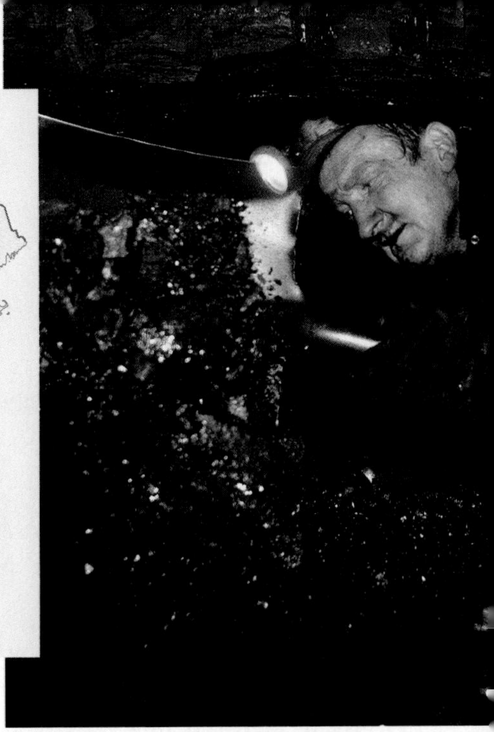

As forests were cut down, firewood became more expensive. It became worthwhile to find, mine, and transport coal. Coal fueled the huge steam engines that powered trains, ships, and factories during the Industrial Revolution.

Today, coal provides 23 percent of the energy used in the United States. The major use of coal is to fuel electric power plants.

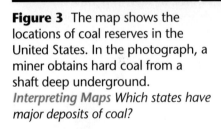

Figure 3 The map shows the locations of coal reserves in the United States. In the photograph, a miner obtains hard coal from a shaft deep underground. *Interpreting Maps Which states have major deposits of coal?*

Coal Mining Before it can be used to produce energy, coal has to be removed from the ground, or mined.

INTEGRATING TECHNOLOGY

Some coal is located very deep underground or is mixed with other materials, making it too difficult to obtain. Known deposits of coal (and other fossil fuels) that can be obtained using current technology are called **reserves.**

A century ago, miners had to break the coal apart with hand tools. Today they use machines to chop the coal into chunks and lift it to the surface. The coal is then cleaned to remove rocks, sand, and other materials that do not burn. Removing them also makes the coal lighter, reducing the cost of transporting it.

Coal as an Energy Source Coal is the most plentiful fossil fuel in the United States. It is fairly easy to transport, and provides a lot of energy when burned. But coal also has some disadvantages. Coal mining can increase erosion. Runoff from mines can cause water pollution. Finally, burning most types of coal results in more air pollution than other fossil fuels.

In addition, coal mining can be a dangerous job. Thousands of miners have been killed or injured in accidents in the mines. Many more suffer from "black lung," a disease caused by years of breathing coal dust. Fortunately, the mining industry has been working hard to improve conditions. New safety procedures and better equipment, including robots and drills that produce less coal dust, have made coal mining safer.

Figure 4 A farmer in Ireland turns over blocks of soft peat. Peat is formed in the early stages of the process of coal formation.

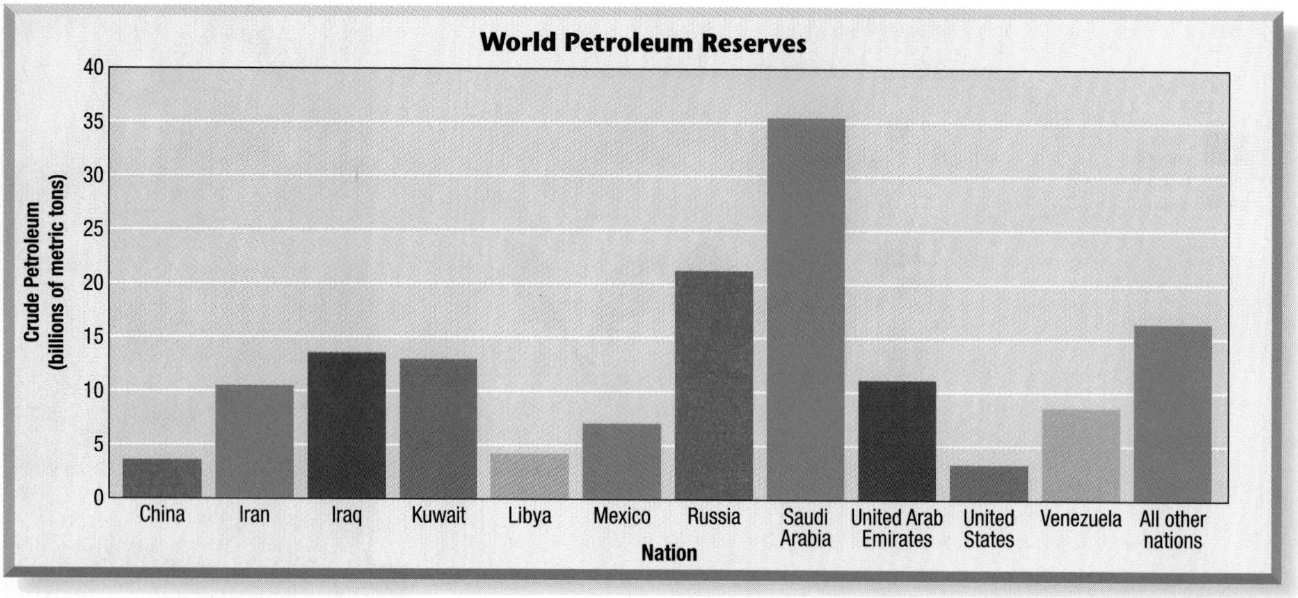
World Petroleum Reserves
Crude Petroleum (billions of metric tons)
40
35
30
25
20
15
10
5
0
China
Iran
Iraq
Kuwait
Libya
Mexico
Russia
Saudi Arabia
United Arab Emirates
United States
Venezuela
All other nations
Nation

Figure 5 Known petroleum deposits, called reserves, are located in many parts of the world. *Interpreting Graphs Which two nations have the largest reserves?*

Oil

Oil is a thick, black, liquid fossil fuel. It formed from the remains of small animals, algae, and protists that lived in oceans and shallow inland seas hundreds of millions of years ago. **Petroleum** is another name for oil, from the Latin words *petra* (rock) and *oleum* (oil). Most oil deposits are located underground in tiny holes in sandstone or limestone. The oil fills the holes somewhat like water trapped in the holes of a sponge.

Petroleum accounts for more than one third of the energy produced in the world. Fuel for most cars, airplanes, trains, and ships comes from petroleum. Many homes are heated by oil.

The United States consumes about one third of all the oil produced in the world. But only three percent of the world's supply is located in this country. The difference must be purchased from countries with large oil supplies.

Locating Oil Deposits Because it is usually located deep below the surface, finding oil is difficult. Scientists can use sound waves to test an area for oil without drilling. This technique relies on the fact that sound waves bounce off objects and return as echoes. Scientists send pulses of sound down into the rocks below ground. Then they measure how long it takes the echoes to return. The amount of time depends on whether the sound waves must travel through solid rock or liquid oils. This information can indicate the most likely places to find oil. However, only about one out of every six wells drilled produces a usable amount of oil.

Integrating Technology

Figure 6 An oil rig bobs up and down as it pumps oil from a Texas oil field.

Refining Oil When oil is first pumped out of the ground, it is called crude oil. Crude oil can be a runny or a thick liquid. In order to be made into useful products, crude oil must undergo a process called refining. A factory where crude oil is separated into fuels and other products by heating is called a **refinery.**

In addition to gasoline and heating oil, many products you use every day are made from crude oil. **Petrochemicals** are compounds that are made from oil. Petrochemicals are used in plastics, paints, medicines, and cosmetics.

☑ *Checkpoint* *How is petroleum used?*

Natural Gas

The third major fossil fuel is natural gas, a mixture of methane and other gases. Natural gas forms from the same organisms as petroleum. Because it is less dense than oil, natural gas often rises above an oil deposit, forming a pocket of gas in the rock.

Pipelines transport the gas from its source to the places where it is used. If all the gas pipelines in the United States were connected, they would reach to the moon and back—twice! Natural gas can also be compressed into a liquid and stored in tanks as fuel for trucks and buses.

Natural gas has several advantages. It produces large amounts of energy, but lower levels of many air pollutants than coal or oil. It is also easy to transport once the network of pipelines is built. One disadvantage of natural gas is that it is highly flammable. A gas leak can cause a violent explosion and fire.

Gas companies help to prevent dangerous explosions from leaks. If you use natural gas in your home, you probably are familiar with the "gas" smell that alerts you whenever there is unburned gas in the air. You may be surprised to learn that natural gas actually has no odor at all. What causes the strong smell? The gas companies add a chemical with a distinct smell to the gas before it is piped to homes and businesses so that any leaks will be noticed.

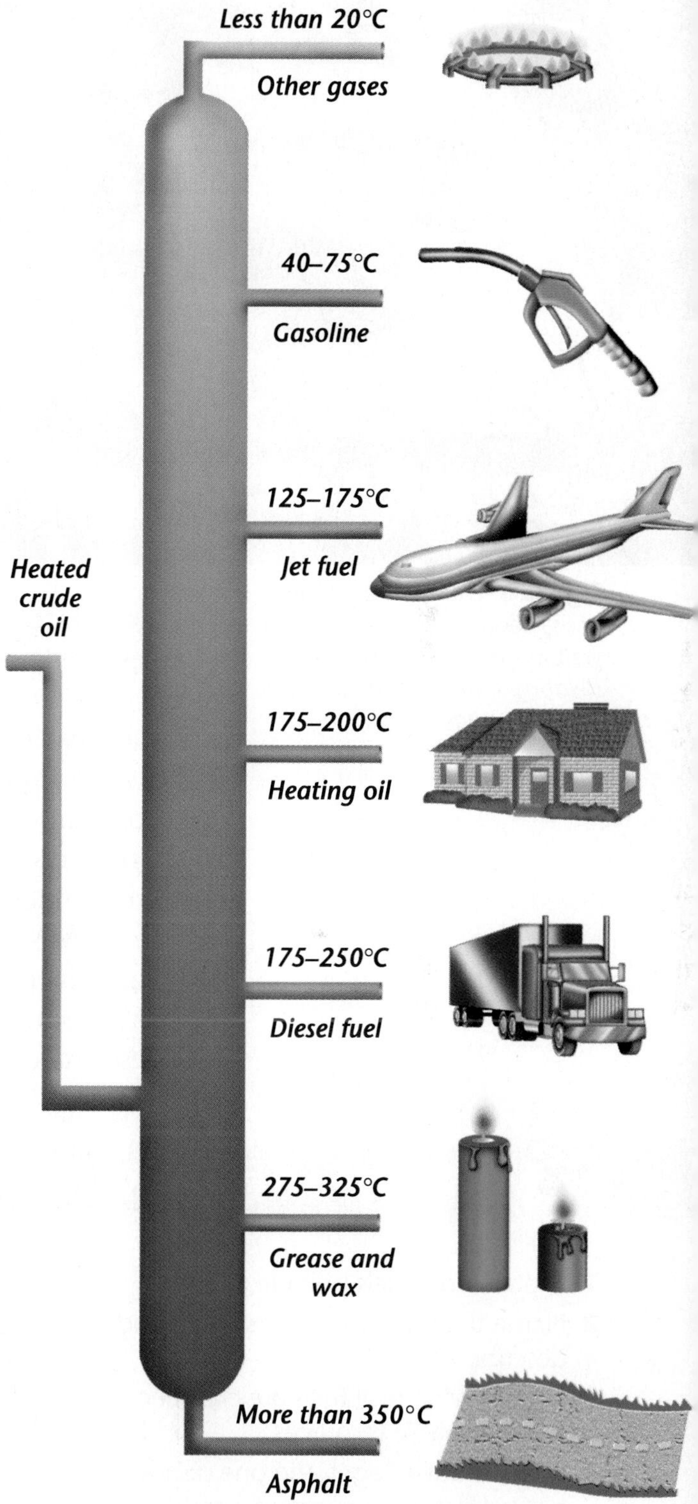
Less than 20°C
Other gases
40–75°C
Gasoline
125–175°C
Jet fuel
Heated crude oil
175–200°C
Heating oil
175–250°C
Diesel fuel
275–325°C
Grease and wax
More than 350°C
Asphalt

Figure 7 Crude oil is refined to make many different products. In the refining process, heat causes the different molecules in crude oil to separate. Different substances vaporize at specific temperatures.

STANDARD
Chevron

Figure 8 During the gasoline crisis, people frequently had to wait in long lines to buy gas. *Relating Cause and Effect What caused the gasoline shortage?*

Fuel Supply and Demand

The many advantages of using fossil fuels as an energy source have made them essential to modern life. **But remember that fossil fuels take hundreds of millions of years to form. For this reason, fossil fuels are considered a nonrenewable resource.** For example, Earth's known oil reserves took 500 million years to form. One fourth of this oil has already been used. If fossil fuels continue to be used more rapidly than they are formed, the reserves will eventually be used up.

Many of the nations that consume large amounts of fuel have very limited reserves of their own. They have to buy oil, natural gas, and coal from the regions that have large supplies. The uneven distribution of fossil fuel reserves has often been a cause of political problems in the world. For example, in the 1970s, a group of oil-exporting nations decided to reduce their oil exports to the United States. As the supply of gasoline fell, prices rose very rapidly. People sometimes waited in line for hours to buy gasoline. This shortage reminded Americans of their dependence on oil imported from other nations.

New sources of energy are needed to replace the decreasing fossil fuel reserves. The rest of this chapter will describe some other sources of energy, as well as ways to make current fuel resources last longer.

Section 1 Review

1. Explain how fuels provide energy.
2. Name the three major fossil fuels and briefly describe each.
3. Explain why fossil fuels are classified as nonrenewable resources.
4. List two advantages and one disadvantage of natural gas as an energy source.
5. **Thinking Critically** **Applying Concepts** Why is it impossible to know exactly how large the world's oil reserves are?

CHAPTER PROJECT

Check Your Progress

With your team, observe your selected area of the school. Determine which types of energy use take place in this area: heating, cooling, lighting, mechanical devices, electronic equipment, or moving vehicles. Record the specific types and amounts of energy use in a data table. To find the amounts, you will need to collect data from electric meters or fuel gauges. (*Hint:* Observe your area at several different times of the day, since the pattern of energy use may vary.)

SECTION 2 Renewable Sources of Energy

DISCOVER ACTIVITY

Can You Capture Solar Energy?

1. Pour 250 milliliters of water into each of two sealable, clear plastic bags.
2. Measure and record the water temperature in each bag. Seal the bags.
3. Put one bag in a dark or shady place. Put the other bag in a place where it will receive direct sunlight.
4. Predict what the temperature of the water in each bag will be after 30 minutes.
5. Measure and record the ending temperatures.

Think It Over

Developing Hypotheses How did the water temperature in each bag change? What could account for these results?

As the sun rises over the rim of the canyon where your family is camping, you feel its warmth on your face. The night's chill disappears quickly. A breeze stirs, carrying with it the smell of the campfire. Maybe you'll take a morning dip in the warm water of a nearby hot spring.

This relaxing scene is far from the city, with its bustling cars and trucks, factories and power plants. But there are energy resources all around you here, too. The sun warms the air, the wind blows, and heat from inside Earth warms the waters of the spring. These sources of energy are all renewable—that is, they are constantly being supplied. You can see why people are trying to find ways to use these renewable resources instead of fossil fuels. As you read about each source of renewable energy, think about how it could help meet people's energy needs.

GUIDE FOR READING

- **How does the sun provide energy?**
- **What are some renewable sources of energy?**

Reading Tip **Before you read, preview the headings in this section. Predict some sources of energy that are renewable.**

Energy From the Sun

The warmth you feel on a sunny day is **solar energy,** energy from the sun. **The sun constantly gives off energy in the form of light and heat.** Solar energy is the source, directly or indirectly, of most other renewable energy resources. In one day, Earth receives enough solar energy to meet the energy needs of the entire world for 40 years. Solar energy does not cause pollution, and it will not run out for billions of years.

So why hasn't solar energy replaced fossil fuels? One reason is that solar energy is only available when the sun is shining. A backup energy source must be available on cloudy days and at night. Another problem is that

Figure 9 Aimed at the sun, these mirrors provide power to an electric plant in New South Wales, Australia. *Inferring How does the shape of these mirrors make them more effective?*

although Earth receives a lot of energy from the sun every day, this energy is very spread out. To obtain enough power, it is necessary to collect this energy from a huge area.

Solar Technologies

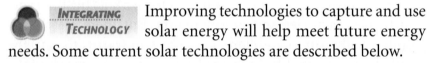

INTEGRATING TECHNOLOGY Improving technologies to capture and use solar energy will help meet future energy needs. Some current solar technologies are described below.

Solar Plants One way to capture the sun's energy involves using giant mirrors. In a solar plant, rows of mirrors focus the sun's rays to heat a tank of water. The water boils, making steam that can be used to generate electricity.

Solar Cells Solar energy can be converted directly into electricity in a solar cell. A solar cell consists of a "sandwich" of very thin layers of the element silicon and other materials. The upper and lower parts of the sandwich have a negative and a positive terminal, like a battery. When light hits the cell, electrons move across the layers, producing an electric current.

The amount of electricity produced by solar cells depends on the area of the cell and the amount of light available. Solar cells are used to power calculators, lights, telephones, and other small devices. However, it would take more than 5,000 solar cells the size of your palm to produce enough electricity for a typical American home. Building solar cells on a large scale is very expensive. As a result, solar cells are used mostly in areas where fossil fuels are difficult to transport.

☑ *Checkpoint* ***What are solar cells made of and how do they work?***

Solar Heating Systems Solar energy can be used to heat buildings. As shown in *Exploring a Solar House,* there are two types of solar heating systems: passive and active.

A **passive solar system** converts sunlight into thermal energy without using pumps or fans. If you have ever stepped into a car on a sunny day, you have experienced passive solar heating. Solar energy passes through the car's windows as light. The sun's rays heat the seats and other parts of the car, which then transfer heat to the air. The heated air is trapped inside, so the car gets warmer. The same principle can be used to heat a home.

An **active solar system** captures the sun's energy, then uses fans and pumps to distribute the heat. Light strikes the black metal surface of a solar collector. There, it is converted to thermal energy. Water is pumped through pipes in the solar collector to absorb the thermal energy. The heated water flows to a storage tank. Pumps and fans distribute the heat throughout the building.

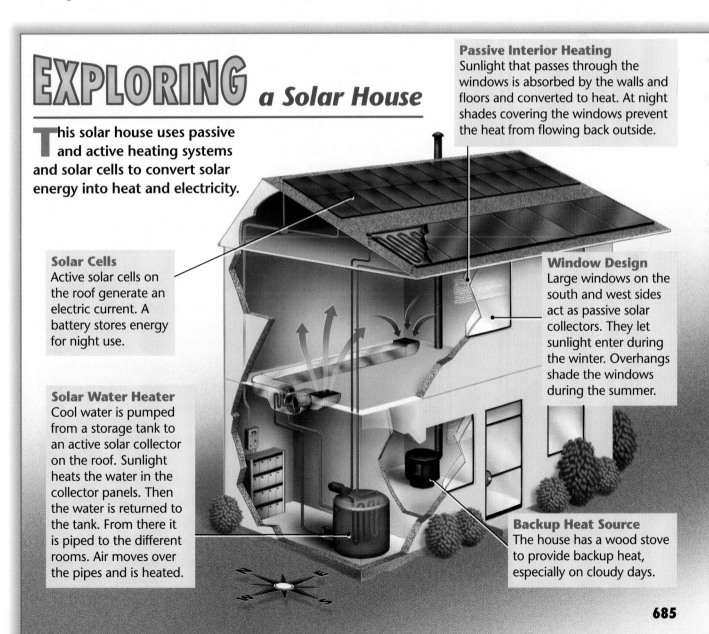

EXPLORING *a Solar House*

This solar house uses passive and active heating systems and solar cells to convert solar energy into heat and electricity.

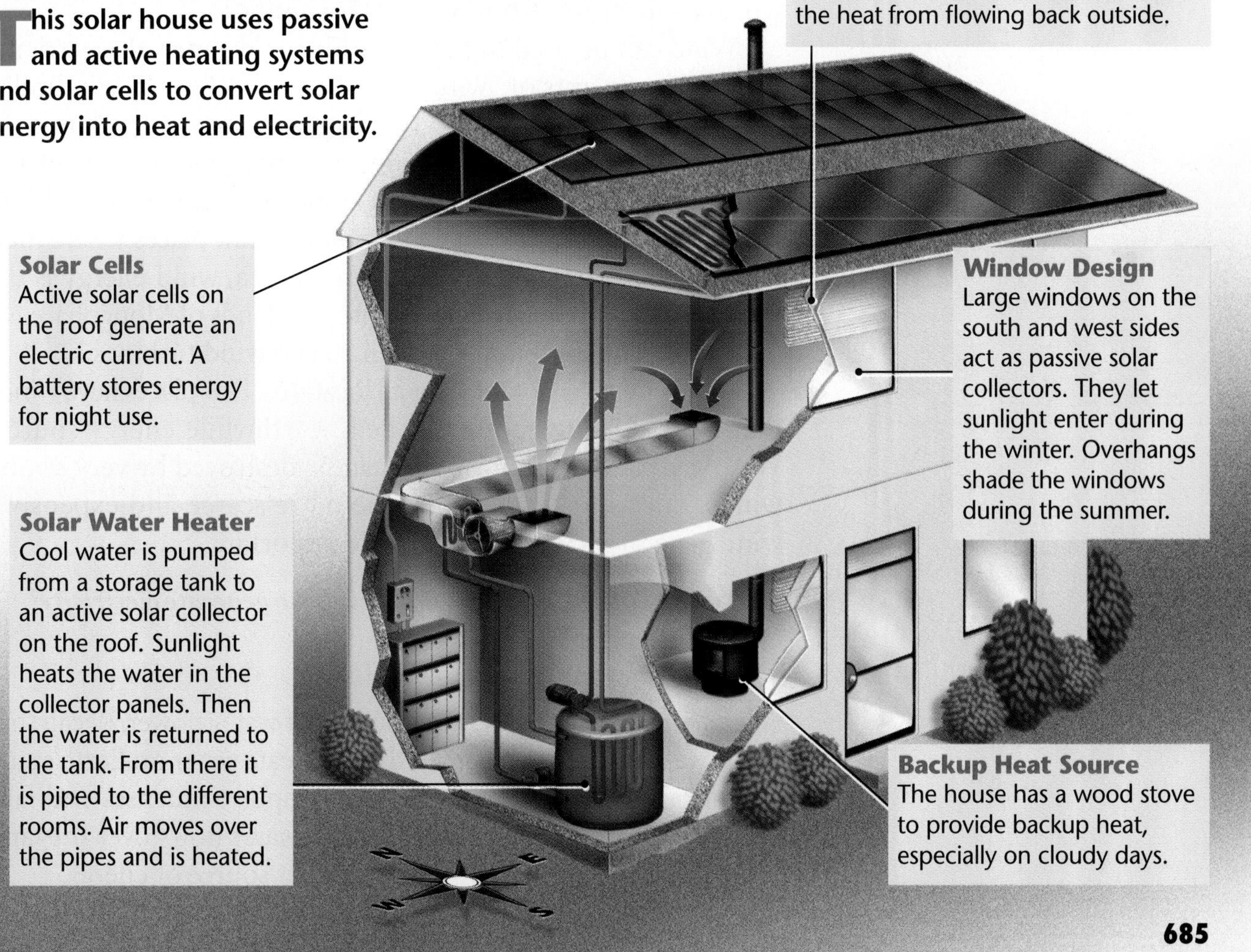

Passive Interior Heating
Sunlight that passes through the windows is absorbed by the walls and floors and converted to heat. At night shades covering the windows prevent the heat from flowing back outside.
Solar Cells
Active solar cells on the roof generate an electric current. A battery stores energy for night use.
Window Design
Large windows on the south and west sides act as passive solar collectors. They let sunlight enter during the winter. Overhangs shade the windows during the summer.
Solar Water Heater
Cool water is pumped from a storage tank to an active solar collector on the roof. Sunlight heats the water in the collector panels. Then the water is returned to the tank. From there it is piped to the different rooms. Air moves over the pipes and is heated.
Backup Heat Source
The house has a wood stove to provide backup heat, especially on cloudy days.
N
E
S
W

Figure 10 This wind farm in the Mojave Desert is one of many in the state of California. *Making Generalizations What are some advantages of wind power?*

Capturing the Wind

The sun is one source of renewable energy. **Other renewable sources of energy include wind, water, tides, biomass material, Earth's interior, and hydrogen.**

Wind energy is actually an indirect form of solar energy. The sun heats Earth's surface unevenly. As a result of this uneven heating, different areas of the atmosphere have different temperatures and air pressure. The differences in pressure cause winds as air moves from one area to another.

Wind can be used to turn a turbine and generate electricity. Wind power plants or "wind farms" consist of many windmills. Together, the windmills generate large amounts of power.

Although wind now provides less than one percent of the world's electricity, it is the fastest-growing energy source. Wind energy is free and does not cause pollution. In places where fuels are difficult to transport, such as Antarctica, wind energy is the major source of power. In the remote grasslands of Mongolia, electricity is obtained from more than 70,000 wind turbines.

Wind energy is not ideal for all locations. Few places have winds that blow steadily enough to be a worthwhile energy source. Wind generators are noisy and can be destroyed by very strong winds. But as fossil fuels become more scarce and expensive, wind generators will become more important.

☑ *Checkpoint* *How can wind be used to generate electricity?*

The Power of Flowing Water

Solar energy is also the indirect source of water power. Recall that in the water cycle, energy from the sun heats water on Earth's surface, forming water vapor. The water vapor condenses and falls back to Earth as rain and snow. As the water flows over the land into lakes and oceans, it provides another source of energy.

Flowing water can turn a turbine and generate electricity in the same way as steam or wind. A dam across a river blocks the flow of water, creating an artificial lake called a reservoir. Water flows through tunnels at the bottom of the dam. As the water moves through the tunnels, it turns turbines connected to a generator.

Figure 11 Flowing water provides the power to turn the water wheel of this historic mill in Tennessee.

Hydroelectric power is electricity produced by flowing water. This type of power is the most widely used source of renewable energy in the world today. Once a dam and power plant are built, producing the electricity is inexpensive. Another benefit is that hydroelectric power does not create air pollution. Unlike wind or solar energy, flowing water provides a steady supply of energy.

But hydroelectric power does have limitations. In the United States, for example, most of the suitable rivers have already been dammed. And dams can have negative effects on the environment. You can read more about the pros and cons of hydroelectric dams in *Science and Society* on page 692.

Tidal Energy

Another source of moving water is the tides. The gravity of the moon and sun causes the water on Earth's surface to regularly rise and fall on its shores. Along some coastlines, enormous amounts of water move into bays at the high tide. The water flows out to sea again when the tide goes out.

A few tidal power plants have been built to take advantage of this regular motion. A low dam across the entrance to a shallow bay holds water in the bay at high tide. As the tide goes out, water flowing past turbines in the dam generate electricity, as in a hydroelectric power plant.

Only a few coastal areas in the world are suitable for building tidal power plants. A dam across a bay also blocks boats and fish from traveling up the river. For these reasons, tidal power will probably never become a major source of energy.

☑ *Checkpoint* ***How are tidal power plants similar to hydroelectric power plants? How are they different?***

Social Studies CONNECTION

Early settlers in the eastern United States often built mills along streams. The mills captured the power of flowing water at dams or waterfalls, where the water turned water wheels connected to machines. Saw mills sawed logs into boards, and grist mills ground wheat into flour. A mill site often formed the center of a new town.

In Your Journal

Suppose you are writing a news story about an old mill. Describe the mill's early importance to the settlers, how a town grew up around it, and how it is used today.

Biomass Fuels

The oldest fuel used for heat and light is wood. As trees carry out photosynthesis, they use the sun's energy to convert carbon dioxide and water into more complicated molecules. Burning wood breaks down these molecules again and releases energy.

Wood is one of a group of fuels, called **biomass fuels,** made from living things. Other biomass fuels include leaves, food wastes, and even manure. As fossil fuel supplies shrink, people are taking a closer look at biomass fuels. For instance, when oil prices rose in the early 1970s, Hawaiian sugar-cane farmers thought of a way to use sugar-cane wastes. They began burning the wastes to generate electricity instead of discarding the wastes in landfills. Now almost one fourth of the electricity used on the island of Kauai comes from biomass material.

Biomass materials can be also converted into other fuels. For example, corn, sugar cane, and other crops can be used to make alcohol. Adding the alcohol to gasoline forms a mixture called **gasohol.** Gasohol can be used as fuel for cars. When bacteria decompose wastes, they convert the wastes into methane gas. The methane produced in some landfills is used to heat buildings.

Alcohol and methane are renewable resources. But producing them in large quantities is more expensive than using fossil fuels. And though wood is renewable, it takes time for new trees to grow and replace those that have been cut down. As a result, biomass fuels are not widely used today in the United States. But as fossil fuels become scarcer, biomass fuels may play a larger role in meeting energy needs.

Figure 12 This corn field is a rich source of biomass fuel. After the corn is harvested, the stalks and leaves can be burned to provide energy. ***Comparing and Contrasting*** *How are biomass fuels similar to energy sources such as wind and water? How are these fuels different?*

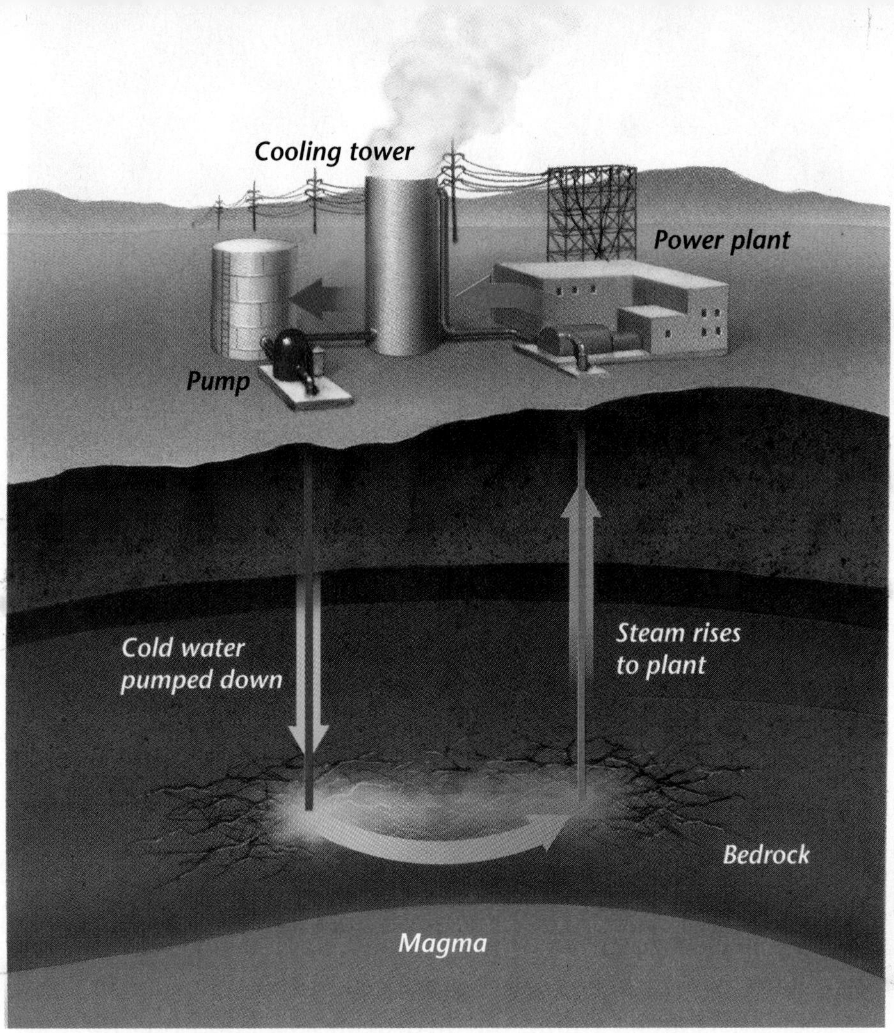
Cooling tower
Power plant
Pump
Cold water
pumped down
Steam rises
to plant
Bedrock
Magma

Figure 13 A geothermal power plant uses heat from Earth's interior as an energy source. Cold water is piped deep into the ground, where it is heated by magma. The resulting steam can be used for heat or to generate electricity.

Tapping Earth's Energy

Below Earth's surface are pockets of very hot, liquid rock called magma. In some places, magma is found very close to the surface. It may even erupt out of the ground as volcanic lava. The intense heat from Earth's interior that warms the magma is called **geothermal energy.**

In certain regions, such as Iceland and New Zealand, the magma heats underground water to the boiling point. The hot water and steam are valuable sources of energy. In Reykjavik, Iceland, 90 percent of homes are heated by water warmed underground in this way. Geothermal energy can also be used to generate electricity, as shown in Figure 13.

Geothermal energy is an unlimited source of cheap energy. But it has disadvantages, just like every other energy source. There are only a few places where magma comes close to Earth's surface. Elsewhere, a very deep well is required to tap this energy. Drilling deep wells is very expensive. Even so, geothermal energy is likely to play a part in meeting energy needs in the future.

☑ *Checkpoint* *How can geothermal energy be used to generate electricity?*

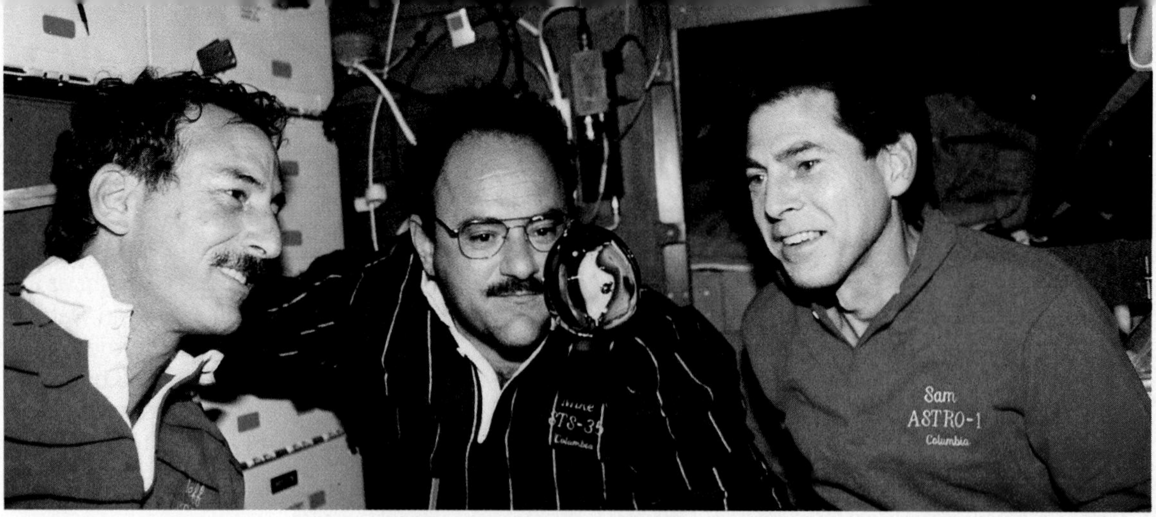
Sam
ASTRO-1
Columbia

Figure 14 The object fascinating these three astronauts is a bubble of water—the harmless by-product of the hydrogen fuel cells used on the space shuttle.

Hydrogen Power

Now that you have read about so many energy sources, consider a fuel with this description: It burns cleanly, forming only water as a by-product. It creates no smoke, smog, or acid rain. It can be handled and transported through pipelines, much like natural gas. This fuel exists on Earth in large supply.

This ideal-sounding fuel is real—it's hydrogen. However, there is an obstacle. Almost all the hydrogen on Earth is combined with oxygen in the form of water. Pure hydrogen can be obtained by passing an electric current through water. But it takes more energy to obtain the hydrogen than is produced by burning it again.

Scientists aren't ruling out hydrogen as a good fuel for the future. At present, hydroelectric plants decrease their activity when the demand for electricity is low. Instead, they could run at full power all the time, using the excess electricity to produce hydrogen. Similarly, solar power plants often generate more electricity than is needed during the day. This extra electricity could be used to produce hydrogen. If a way can be found to produce hydrogen cheaply, it could someday be an important source of energy.

Section 2 Review

1. What is solar energy?
2. How are the energy of wind and flowing water each related to solar energy?
3. How are active and passive solar heating systems different?
4. List three examples of biomass fuels.
5. What limits the use of geothermal energy?
6. **Thinking Critically Predicting** Which of the renewable sources of energy do you think is most likely to be used in your community in 100 years? Give reasons to support your answer.

CHAPTER PROJECT

Check Your Progress

Continue to collect data on how much energy is used in your group's area of the school. Begin to brainstorm ideas for reducing energy usage in this area. For example, is there a way to use some electrical devices for shorter periods of time? (*Hint:* Interviewing some adults who are responsible for the operation of the school building may give you some good ideas. Be sure to check with your teacher before interviewing anyone.)

Cooking With Sunshine

In the future, will you cook your meals with sunshine instead of electricity? That's certainly a possibility. In this lab, you'll investigate how solar energy can be used to cook food.

Problem

What is the best shape for a solar cooker?

Skills Focus

predicting, designing experiments, forming operational definitions

Suggested Materials

scissors	glue	3 thermometers
3 dowels	tape	marshmallows
3 sheets of aluminum foil		clock or watch
3 sheets of oaktag paper		

Procedure

Part 1 Capturing Solar Energy

1. Read over the entire lab. Then predict which shape will produce the largest temperature increase when placed in the sun.
2. Glue a sheet of aluminum foil, shiny side up, to each sheet of oaktag paper. Before the glue dries, gently smooth out any wrinkles in the foil.
3. Bend one sheet into a V shape. Bend another sheet into a U shape. Leave the last sheet flat.
4. Place the aluminum sheets in direct sunlight, using wood blocks or books to hold the U- and V-shapes in position.
5. Tape a dowel to each thermometer. Record the starting temperature on each thermometer.
6. Use the dowels to hold the thermometer bulbs in the center of the aluminum shapes. After 15 minutes, record the final temperature on each thermometer.

Part 2 Designing a Solar Cooker

7. Use the results from Step 6 to design a solar cooker that can toast a marshmallow. Prepare a written description of your plan for your teacher's approval. Include an operational definition of a "well-toasted" marshmallow.
8. After your teacher has approved your plan, test your design by placing a marshmallow on a wooden dowel. Record the time it takes to toast the marshmallow.

Analyze and Conclude

1. What was the role of the aluminum foil in this investigation? What other materials could you have used instead? Explain.
2. Which of the three shapes—V, U, or flat—produced the largest increase in temperature? Propose an explanation for this result.
3. What other variables might have affected your results? Explain.
4. **Apply** What are some possible advantages of a solar cooker based on this design? What are some possible disadvantages?

More to Explore

Try adapting your design to heat water. Show your new design to your teacher before trying it.

SCIENCE AND SOCIETY

Hydroelectric Dams: Are They All Here to Stay?

There are hundreds of hydroelectric dams on United States rivers. These dams provide electricity for millions of people. Hydroelectric dams provide clean, inexpensive, and renewable energy. They are a good source of power.

Recently, however, people have learned that dams can have negative effects on river ecosystems. Some people have even suggested removing certain dams. But is this wise? When do the benefits of dams outweigh the problems?

The Issues

How Do Dams Affect the Environment? Because dams change water depth and flow, they can alter the temperature of a river. The water may become too cold or too warm for fish that normally live there. A change in temperature can also reduce the number of algae in a river. This affects other organisms in the river food web.

Some species of fish, such as salmon, herring, and menhaden, hatch in rivers but then travel to the ocean. To breed, they must return to the river. Dams can block the movement of these fish populations. For example, the Columbia River Basin, which has more than 50 dams, once contained more than 10 million salmon. Today it is home to only 2 million salmon.

What Are the Effects of Removing Dams? Some people say that the only way to restore ecosystems is to remove dams. However, these dams supply a small but important part of the nation's electricity. Removing them could force the United States to use more nonrenewable fossil fuels. Fossil fuels also produce more pollution than hydroelectric plants.

The reservoirs behind hydroelectric dams supply water for irrigation and drinking. These supplies would be difficult to replace. In addition, a series of dams on a river can reduce flooding downstream during heavy rains.

What Can People Do? Removing dams might restore some river ecosystems. For example, Edwards Dam on the Kennebec River in Maine was removed in 1999 to allow several threatened fish species to spawn. Edwards Dam provided only a small percent of Maine's electric power. This small amount was easier to replace than the power provided by a much larger dam.

There are other ways to protect migrating fish. Fish ladders, for example, are step-like waterways that help fish pass over dams. Fish can even be carried around dams in trucks. Still, these methods are costly and not always successful.

The government issues licenses for hydroelectric dams. In considering license renewals, officials examine environmental impact as well as energy production.

You Decide

1. Identify the Problem
In your own words, explain some of the major issues surrounding hydroelectric dams.

2. Analyze the Options
Examine the pros and cons of removing dams. What are the benefits? What are the costs? Who will be affected by the change?

3. Find a Solution
The license of a nearby dam is up for review. The dam provides electricity, but also blocks the migration of fish. What do you recommend? Explain.

SECTION 3 Nuclear Energy

DISCOVER ACTIVITY

Why Do They Fall?

1. Line up 15 dominoes to form a triangle, as shown.
2. Knock over the first domino so that it falls against the second row of dominoes. Observe the results.
3. Set up the dominoes again, but then remove the dominoes in the third row from the lineup.
4. Knock over the first domino again. Observe what happens.

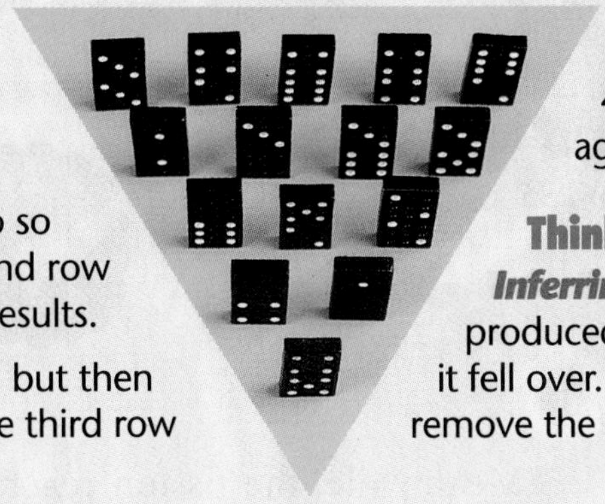

Think It Over

Inferring Suppose each domino produced a large amount of energy when it fell over. Why might it be helpful to remove the dominoes as you did in Step 3?

GUIDE FOR READING

- **What happens during fission and fusion reactions?**
- **How does a nuclear power plant produce electricity?**

Reading Tip **As you read, create a Venn diagram to compare and contrast nuclear fission and nuclear fusion.**

Wouldn't it be great if people could use the same method as the sun to produce energy? In a way, they can! The kind of reactions that power the sun involve the central cores of atoms. The central core of an atom that contains the protons and neutrons is called the **nucleus** (plural nuclei). The reactions that involve nuclei, called nuclear reactions, involve tremendous amounts of energy. Two types of nuclear reactions are fission and fusion.

Fission Reactions and Energy

Nuclear reactions convert matter into energy. In 1905, Albert Einstein developed a formula that described the relationship between energy and matter. You have probably seen this famous equation, $E = mc^2$. In the equation, the E represents energy and the m represents mass. The c, which represents the speed of light, is a very large number. This equation states that when matter is changed into energy, an enormous amount of energy is released.

Nuclear fission is the splitting of an atom's nucleus into two smaller nuclei. The fuel for the reaction is a large atom that has an unstable nucleus, such as uranium-235 (U-235). A neutron is shot at the U-235 atom at high speed. **When the neutron hits the U-235 nucleus, the nucleus splits apart into two smaller nuclei and two or more neutrons.** The total mass of all these particles is a bit less than the mass of the original nucleus. The small amount of mass that makes up the difference has been converted into energy—a lot of energy, as described by Einstein's equation.

Figure 15 Albert Einstein, shown here in 1930, described the relationship between energy and matter.

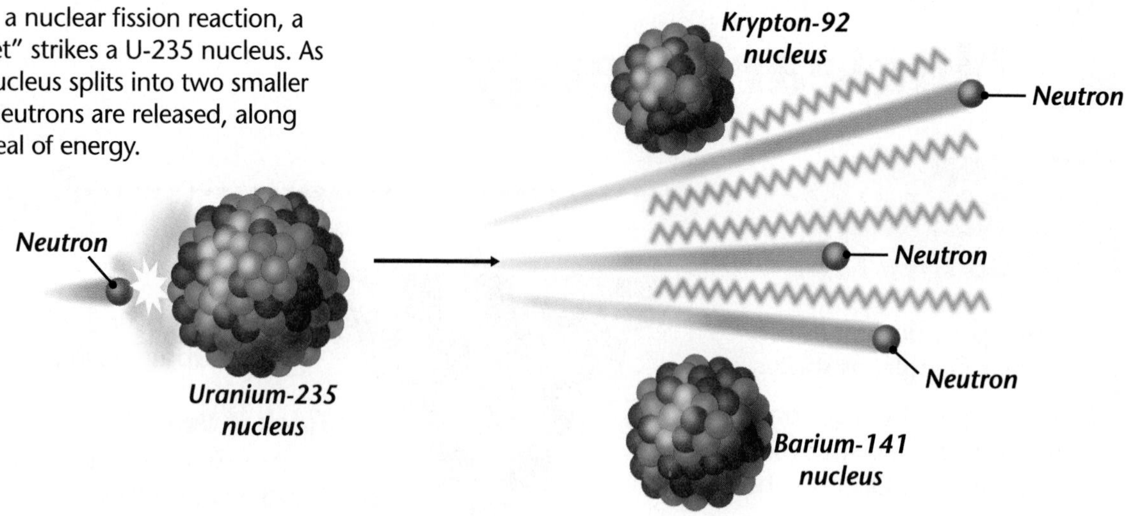
Krypton-92
nucleus
Neutron
Neutron
Neutron
Uranium-235
nucleus
Neutron
Barium-141
nucleus

Figure 16 In a nuclear fission reaction, a neutron "bullet" strikes a U-235 nucleus. As a result, the nucleus splits into two smaller nuclei. More neutrons are released, along with a great deal of energy.

Meanwhile, the fission reaction has produced three more neutrons. If any of these neutrons strikes another nucleus, the fission reaction is repeated. More neutrons and more energy are released. If there are enough nuclei nearby, the process continues over and over in a chain reaction, just like a row of dominoes falling. In a nuclear chain reaction, the amount of energy released increases rapidly with each step in the chain.

What happens to all the energy released by these fission reactions? If a nuclear chain reaction is not controlled, the released energy causes a huge explosion. The explosion of an atomic bomb is an uncontrolled nuclear reaction. A few kilograms of matter explode with more force than several thousand tons of a nonnuclear explosive such as dynamite. However, if the chain reaction is controlled, the energy is released as heat, which can be used to generate electricity.

TRY THIS

Shoot the Nucleus

ACTIVITY

In an open area of your classroom, make a model of a nuclear fission reaction. Place a handful of marbles on the floor in a tight cluster, so that they touch one another. Step back about a half-meter from the marbles. Shoot another marble at the cluster.

Making Models What does the marble you shot at the cluster represent? What effect did the marble have on the cluster? How is this similar to a nuclear fission reaction?

Nuclear Power Plants

Controlled nuclear fission reactions take place inside nuclear power plants. **In a nuclear power plant, the heat released from the reactions is used to change water into steam. As in other types of power plants, the steam then turns the blades of a turbine to generate electricity.** Look at the diagram of a nuclear power plant in Figure 17. In addition to the generator, it has two main parts: the reactor vessel and the heat exchanger.

Reactor Vessel The **reactor vessel** is the section of a nuclear reactor where nuclear fission occurs. The reactor contains rods of U-235, called **fuel rods.** When several fuel rods are placed close together, a series of fission reactions occurs. The reactions are controlled by placing **control rods** made of the metal cadmium between the fuel rods. The cadmium absorbs the neutrons released during the fission reactions. As the cadmium control rods are removed, the fission reactions speed up. If the reactor vessel starts to get too hot, the control rods are moved back in place to slow the chain reaction.

Heat Exchanger Heat is removed from the reactor vessel by water or another fluid that is pumped through the reactor. This fluid passes through a heat exchanger. There, the fluid boils water to produce steam, which runs the electrical generator. The steam is condensed again and pumped back to the heat exchanger.

☑ *Checkpoint* *How are fission reactions controlled?*

The Risks of Nuclear Fission

When it was first demonstrated, people thought that nuclear fission would provide an almost unlimited source of clean, safe energy. Today nuclear power plants generate much of the world's electricity—about 20 percent in the United States and more than 70 percent in France. But these plants have some problems.

In 1986, in Chernobyl, Ukraine, the reactor vessel in a nuclear power plant overheated. The fuel rods generated so much heat that they started to melt, a condition called a **meltdown.** The excess heat increased the steam pressure in the generator. A series of explosions blew parts of the roof off and injured or killed dozens of plant workers and firefighters. Radioactive materials escaped into the environment. Today, the soil in an area the size of Florida remains contaminated with radioactive waste.

Sharpen your Skills

Calculating ACTIVITY

A single pellet of U-235 the size of a breath mint can produce as much energy as 615 liters of fuel oil. An average home uses 5,000 liters of oil a year. How many U-235 pellets would be needed to supply the same amount of energy?

Figure 17 In a nuclear plant, uranium fuel undergoes fission, producing heat. The heat boils water, and the resulting steam drives the turbines that generate electricity. *Interpreting Diagrams From which part of the power plant is heat released to the environment?*

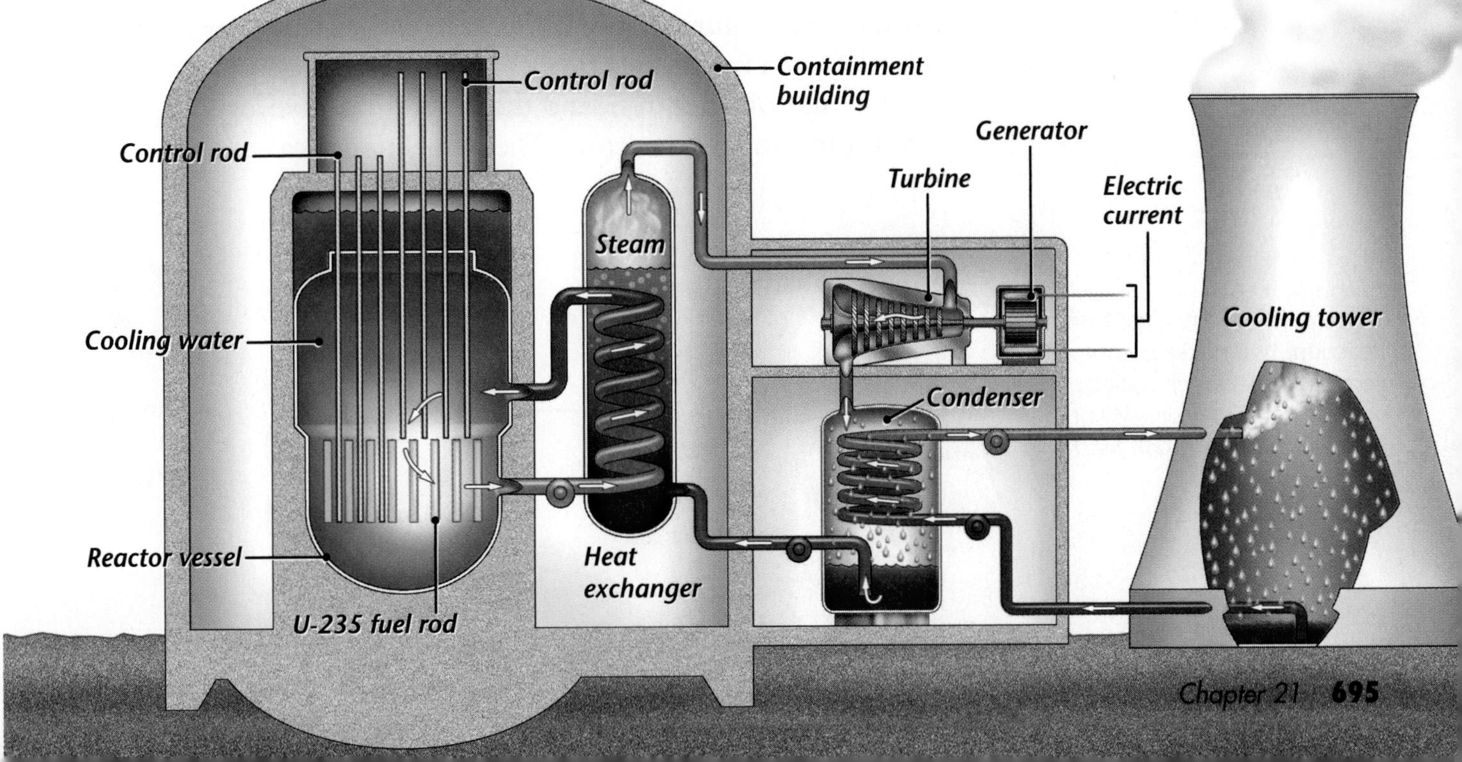

Control rod
Containment building
Control rod
Generator
Turbine
Electric current
Steam
Cooling tower
Cooling water
Condenser
Reactor vessel
Heat exchanger
U-235 fuel rod

Figure 18 One problem with nuclear power is disposal of the used radioactive fuel rods. In this plant in France, the fuel rods are stored in a deep pool of water.

Chernobyl and less-serious accidents at other nuclear power plants have led to public concerns about nuclear plant safety.

The danger of a meltdown is a serious concern. However, a meltdown can be avoided by careful planning. A more difficult problem is the disposal of radioactive wastes produced by power plants. Radioactive wastes remain dangerous for many thousands of years. Scientists must find a way to safely store these wastes for a long period of time. Finally, nuclear power has turned out to be a much more costly source of power than was originally expected. The safety features required for nuclear plants make the plants very expensive.

☑ *Checkpoint* *What are three problems with using nuclear fission as an energy source?*

The Quest to Control Fusion

A second type of nuclear reaction is fusion. **Nuclear fusion** is the combining of two atomic nuclei to produce a single larger nucleus. **As shown in Figure 19, two kinds of hydrogen nuclei are forced together in a fusion reaction.** One kind (hydrogen-2) has one proton and one neutron, and the other kind (hydrogen-3) has one proton and two neutrons. The tremendous heat and pressure

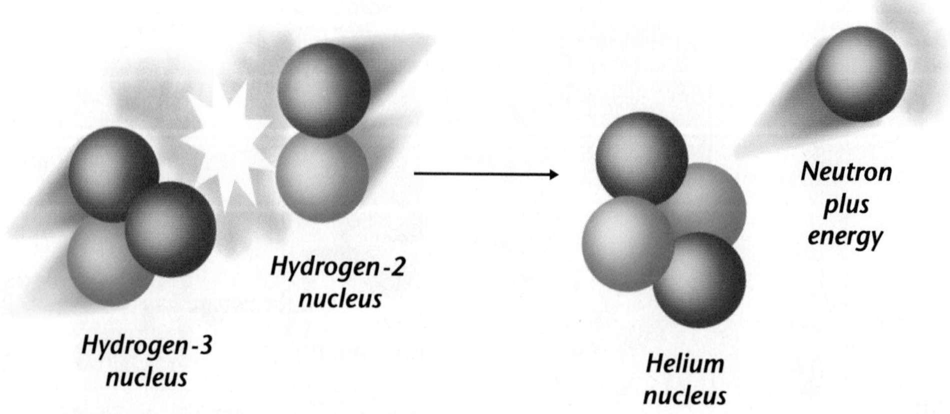
Hydrogen-2
nucleus
Hydrogen-3
nucleus
Helium
nucleus
Neutron
plus
energy

Figure 19 In a nuclear fusion reaction, two nuclei combine to form a single larger nucleus. *Interpreting Diagrams What is released during a fusion reaction?*

cause them to combine and create a helium nucleus with two protons and two neutrons. This helium nucleus has slightly less mass than the total mass of the two hydrogen nuclei. The difference is converted to energy.

Nuclear fusion would have many advantages as an energy source. Fusion can produce much more energy per atom than nuclear fission. The fuel for a nuclear fusion reactor is also readily available. Water, which is plentiful in Earth's oceans, contains one of the kinds of hydrogen needed for fusion. Fusion should be safer and less polluting than nuclear fission. You can see why scientists are eager to find a way to build a nuclear fusion reactor!

Although some fusion bombs have been exploded, scientists have not yet been able to control a large-scale fusion reaction. The biggest problem is temperature. In the sun, nuclear fusion occurs at 15 million degrees Celsius. Such conditions are almost impossible to create on Earth. Very great pressure would also work to contain a fusion reaction. But no material has been found that could serve as a reactor vessel under such high pressure. Extremely powerful magnetic fields can contain a fusion reaction. However, it takes more energy to generate these fields than the fusion reaction produces.

Although many more years of research are expected, some scientists believe that they will eventually be able to control fusion reactions. If they succeed, the quest for a clean, cheap energy source may be over at last.

Figure 20 Researchers at Los Alamos National Laboratory in New Mexico are studying fusion as an energy source. This machine creates strong magnetic fields that allow fusion to occur for short periods of time.

Section 3 Review

1. Draw and label a simple diagram of a nuclear fission reaction. Include the following labels: U-235 nucleus, neutrons, smaller nuclei, and energy.
2. How can the energy released in a fission reaction be used to produce electricity?
3. Explain the purpose of control rods.
4. Give two reasons that people have not been able to use nuclear fusion as an energy source.
5. **Thinking Critically Classifying** Is nuclear fission a renewable or nonrenewable energy source? Is nuclear fusion renewable or nonrenewable? Explain.

CHAPTER PROJECT

Check Your Progress

By now you should begin preparing the written report of your findings about energy use in your group's area of the school. Your report should include the major ways energy is used in your chosen area. You should also include recommendations on how energy use might be reduced.

Skills Lab

Designing Experiments

Keeping Comfortable

Two ways to use less energy are to keep heat out of your home when the weather is hot, and to keep heat in when the weather is cold. In this lab, you will design an experiment to compare how well different materials do this.

Problem

How well do different materials stop heat transfer?

Suggested Materials

thermometers, ice water, hot water, watch or clock, beakers

containers and lids made of paper, plastic foam, plastic, glass, and metal

Design a Plan

Part 1 Measuring Temperature Changes

1. Use a pencil to poke a hole in the lid of a paper cup. Fill the cup about halfway with cold water.
2. Put the lid on the cup. Insert a thermometer into the water through the hole. When the temperature stops dropping, place the cup in a beaker. Add hot water to the beaker until the water level is about 1 cm below the lid.
3. Record the water temperature once every minute until it has increased by 5°C. Use the time it takes for the temperature to increase 1°C as a measure of the effectiveness of the paper cup in preventing heat transfer.

Part 2 Comparing Materials

4. Use the ideas from Part 1 to design a controlled experiment to rank the effectiveness of different materials in preventing heat transfer.
5. Use these questions to help you plan your experiment:
   - What hypothesis will you test?
   - Which materials do you predict will be the best and worst at preventing heat transfer? How will you define these terms?
   - What will your manipulated variable be? What will your responding variable be?
   - What variables do you need to control? How will you control them?
   - What step-by-step procedures will you use?
   - What kind of data table will you use?
6. After your teacher has reviewed your plans, make any necessary changes in your design. Then perform your experiment.

Analyze and Conclude

1. In Part 1, what was the starting temperature of the hot water? What was the starting temperature of the cold water? In which direction did the heat flow? How do you know?
2. If the materials in Part 1 are used to represent your home in very hot weather, which material would represent the rooms in your home? Which would represent the outdoor weather? Which would represent the walls of the building?
3. Which material was most effective at preventing the transfer of heat? Which was the least effective? Explain.
4. **Think About It** Would experiments similar to this one provide you with enough information to choose materials to build a home? Explain.

More to Explore

Create a plan to compare how well the materials would work if the hot water were inside the cup and the cold water were outside. With your teacher's permission, carry out your plan.

SECTION 4 Energy Conservation

DISCOVER **ACTIVITY**

Which Bulb Is More Efficient?

1. Record the light output (listed in lumens) from the packages of a 60-watt incandescent light bulb and a 15-watt compact fluorescent bulb.
2. Place the fluorescent bulb in a lamp socket. **CAUTION:** *Make sure the lamp is unplugged.*
3. Plug in the lamp and turn it on. Hold the end of a thermometer about 8 centimeters from the bulb.
4. Record the temperature after 5 minutes.
5. Turn off and unplug the lamp. When the bulb is cool, remove it. Repeat Steps 2, 3, and 4 with the incandescent light bulb.

Think It Over

Inferring Based on the number of lumens, what is the difference between the amount of light given off by the two types of bulbs? The incandescent bulb uses 4 times as much electricity. Why do you think this might be?

GUIDE FOR READING

- **What are two ways to make sure there will be enough energy for the future?**
- **How does insulation help conserve energy?**

Reading Tip **Before you read, list ways to conserve energy. As you read, add to the list.**

Imagine what would happen if the world ran out of fossil fuels today. Eighty percent of the electric power would disappear. Most buildings would lose their heating and cooling. Forests would disappear as people began to burn wood for heat and cooking. Almost all transportation would stop. Cars, buses, trains, airplanes, and ships would be stranded wherever they ran out of fuel. Since radios, televisions, computers, and telephones depend on electricity, communication would be greatly reduced.

Although fossil fuels won't run out immediately, they also won't last forever. Most people think that it makes sense to start planning now to avoid a fuel shortage in the future. **One approach to the problem is to find new sources of energy. The second way is to make the fuels that are available now last as long as possible while other solutions are being developed.**

Electricity Production by Energy Source

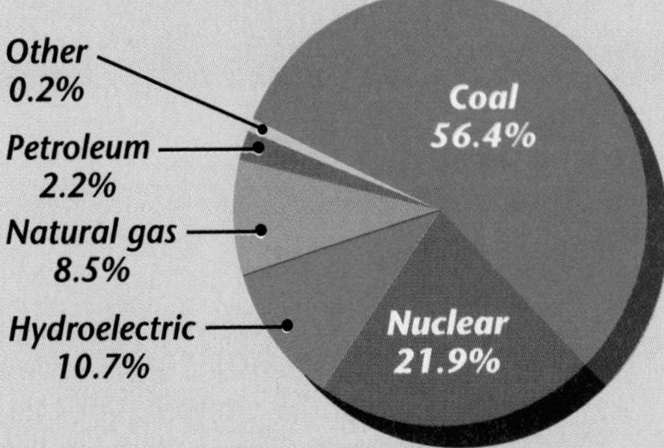
Other 0.2%
Petroleum 2.2%
Natural gas 8.5%
Hydroelectric 10.7%
Coal 56.4%
Nuclear 21.9%

Figure 21 Nonrenewable fossil fuels generate over two thirds of the nation's electricity.

Conservation and Efficiency

Reducing energy use is called **energy conservation.** For example, if you walk to the store instead of getting a ride, you are conserving the gasoline needed to drive to the store. Reducing energy use is a solution to energy problems that will help no matter what form of energy is used in the future.

A way to get as much work as possible out of fuels is to use them efficiently. **Efficiency** is the percentage of energy that is actually used to perform work. The rest of the energy is "lost" to the surroundings, usually as heat. People have developed many ways to increase energy efficiency.

Lighting Lights can use as much as 10 percent of the electricity in your home, but much of that electricity is wasted. An incandescent light bulb converts less than 10 percent of the electricity it uses into light. The rest is given off as heat. You can prove this to yourself by holding your hand close to an incandescent light bulb. But don't touch it! Compact fluorescent bulbs, on the other hand, use only about one fourth as much energy to provide the same amount of light.

☑ *Checkpoint* *Which type of light bulb is more energy-efficient?*

SCIENCE & History

Energy-Efficient Devices

Scientists and engineers have developed many technologies that improve energy efficiency and reduce energy use.

1932
Fiberglass Insulation

Long strands of glass fibers trap air and keep buildings from losing heat. Less fuel is used for heating.

1958
Solar Cells

More than 150 years ago, scientists discovered that silicon can convert light into electricity. The first useful application of solar cells was to power the radio on a satellite. Now solar cells are even used on experimental cars like the one below.

1930 **1940** **1950**

1936
Fluorescent Lighting

Fluorescent bulbs were introduced to the public at the 100th anniversary celebration of the United States Patent Office. Because these bulbs use less energy than incandescent bulbs, most offices and schools use fluorescent lights.

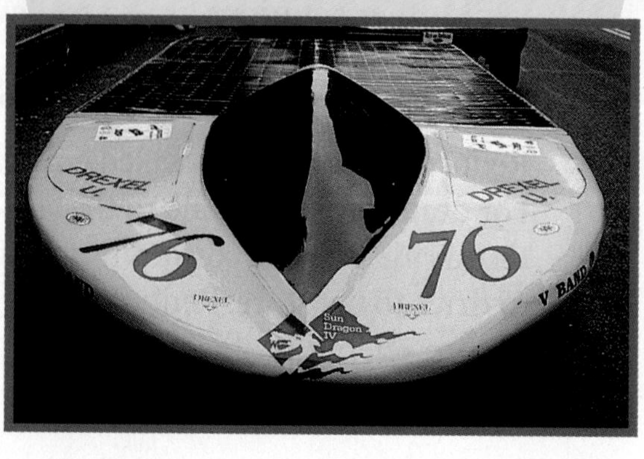
DREXEL U.
76
DREXEL U.
76
Sun Dragon IV

Heating and Cooling One method of increasing the efficiency of heating and cooling systems is insulation. **Insulation** is a layer of material that helps block the transfer of heat between the air inside and outside a building. You have probably seen insulation made of fiberglass, which looks like fluffy pink cotton candy. The mat of thin glass fibers trap air. **This layer of trapped air helps keep the building from losing or gaining heat from the outside.** A layer of fiberglass 15 centimeters thick insulates a room as well as a brick wall 2 meters thick or a stone wall almost 6 meters thick!

Buildings lose a lot of heat around the windows. Look at the windows in your school or home. Was the building built after 1980? Have the windows been replaced recently? If so, you will most likely see two panes of glass with space between them. The air between the panes of glass acts as insulation.

In Your Journal

Design an advertisement for one of the energy-saving inventions described in this time line. The advertisement may be a print, radio, or television ad. Be sure that your advertisement clearly explains the benefits of the invention.

1967

Microwave Ovens

The first countertop microwave oven for the home was introduced. Microwaves cook food by heating the water the food contains. The microwave oven heats only the food, not the air, racks, and oven walls as in a conventional oven. Preheating is also not required, saving even more energy.

1997

Smart Roads

The Department of Transportation demonstrated that cars can be controlled by computers. Sensors built into the road control all the cars, making traffic flow more smoothly. This uses less energy.

1970 1980 1990 2000

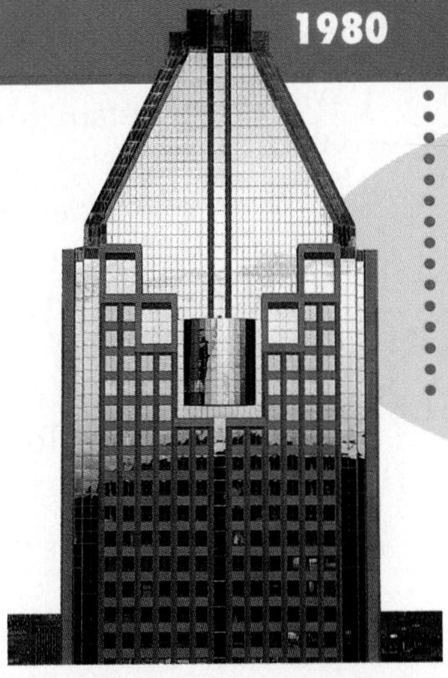

1981

High-Efficiency Window Coatings

Materials that reflect sunlight were first used to coat windows in the early 1980s. This coating reduces the air conditioning needed to keep the inside of the building cool.

Figure 22 A single city bus can transport dozens of people, reducing the number of cars on the roads and saving energy. *Applying Concepts How does riding a bus conserve energy?*

Transportation Engineers have improved the energy efficiency of cars by designing better engines and tires. Another way to save energy is to reduce the number of cars on the road. In many communities, public transit systems provide an alternative to driving. Other cities encourage carpooling. If four people travel together in one car, they use much less energy than they would by driving separately. Many cities now set aside lanes for cars containing two or more people.

In the future, cars that run on electricity may provide the most energy savings of all. Electric power plants can convert fuel into electricity more efficiently than a car engine converts gasoline into motion. Therefore, a car that runs on electricity is more energy-efficient than one that runs directly on fuel.

What You Can Do

You can reduce your personal energy use by changing your behavior in some simple ways.

- Keep your home cooler in winter and warmer in summer. Instead of turning up the heat, put on a sweater. Use fans instead of air conditioners.
- Use natural lighting instead of electric lights when possible.
- Turn off the lights or television when you leave a room.
- Walk or ride a bike for short trips. Ride buses and trains.
- Recycle, especially metal products. Recycling an aluminum can uses only 5 percent of the energy making a new can uses!

The items in this list are small things, but multiplied by millions of people they add up to a lot of energy saved for the future.

Section 4 Review

1. What are two ways to make energy resources last longer?
2. Explain how putting insulation in a building conserves energy.
3. How does carpooling conserve energy?
4. **Thinking Critically Predicting** An office building contains only incandescent lights. The building next door contains fluorescent lights. Predict which building has higher energy bills. Explain your answer.

Science at Home

With an adult family member, conduct an energy audit of your home. Look for places where energy is being lost, such as cracks around windows and doors. Also look for ways to reduce energy use, such as running the dishwasher only when it is full. Together, create a list of energy-saving suggestions for your family. Post the list where everyone can see it.

STUDY GUIDE

Section 1 Fossil Fuels

Key Ideas

- A fuel is a substance that provides a form of energy as a result of a chemical change.
- Energy can be converted from one form to another.
- The three major fossil fuels are coal, oil, and natural gas. These fuels release more energy when they are burned than most other substances do.
- Because fossil fuels take hundreds of millions of years to form, they are considered nonrenewable resources.

Key Terms

combustion
fossil fuels
hydrocarbons
reserves
petroleum
refinery
petrochemicals
nonrenewable resources

Section 2 Renewable Sources of Energy

Key Ideas

- Solar energy is plentiful and renewable, and does not cause pollution. However, a backup energy source is needed.
- Because the sun causes winds and drives the water cycle, wind power and water power are considered indirect forms of solar energy.
- Biomass fuels, geothermal energy, and hydrogen power are other renewable energy sources that are currently in limited use.

Key Terms

solar energy
passive solar system
active solar system
hydroelectric power
biomass fuels
gasohol
geothermal energy

Section 3 Nuclear Energy

INTEGRATING CHEMISTRY

Key Ideas

- Nuclear reactions include fission reactions and fusion reactions.
- In a fission reaction, the impact of a neutron splits an atom's nucleus into two smaller nuclei and two or more neutrons. A large amount of energy is released in the process.
- In a nuclear power plant, the thermal energy released from controlled fission reactions is used to generate electricity.
- Disadvantages of nuclear power include the risk of a meltdown and radioactive waste.
- Scientists have not yet been able to control a major nuclear fusion reaction.

Key Terms

nucleus
nuclear fission
reactor vessel
fuel rods
control rods
meltdown
nuclear fusion

Section 4 Energy Conservation

Key Ideas

- To avoid an energy shortage in the future, people must find new sources of energy and conserve the fuels that are available now.
- Insulation keeps a building from losing heat to, or gaining heat from, the outside.
- Ways to conserve energy use in transportation include making more efficient vehicles, carpooling, and using public transit.

Key Terms

energy conservation
efficiency
insulation

ACTIVITY

USING THE INTERNET

www.phschool.com/state_focus/california/

CHAPTER 21 ASSESSMENT

California Test Prep: Reviewing Content

Multiple Choice

Choose the letter of the best answer.

1. Which of the following is *not* a fossil fuel?
   a. coal
   b. wood
   c. oil
   d. natural gas
2. Wind and water energy are both indirect forms of
   a. nuclear energy.
   b. electrical energy.
   c. solar energy.
   d. geothermal energy.
3. Which of the following is *not* a biomass fuel?
   a. methane
   b. gasohol
   c. hydrogen
   d. sugar-cane wastes
4. The particle used to start a nuclear fission reaction is a(n)
   a. neutron.
   b. nucleus.
   c. proton.
   d. atom.
5. A part of a nuclear power plant that undergoes a fission reaction is called a
   a. turbine.
   b. control rod.
   c. heat exchanger.
   d. fuel rod.

True or False

If the statement is true, write true. If it is false, change the underlined word or words to make the statement true.

6. Products made from petroleum are called <u>hydrocarbons</u>.
7. The process of burning a fuel for energy is <u>combustion</u>.
8. Geothermal energy is an example of a <u>nonrenewable</u> energy source.
9. Solar energy is harnessed to run calculators using <u>solar satellites</u>.
10. Most of the energy used in the United States today comes from <u>fossil fuels</u>.

Checking Concepts

11. Explain why coal mining is a difficult task.
12. Describe how coal forms.
13. Describe three features of a solar home. (Your answer may include passive or active solar systems.)
14. Explain how wind can be used to generate electricity.
15. What factors limit the use of tides as an energy source?
16. How is a nuclear fission reaction controlled in a nuclear power plant?
17. Define *energy efficiency.* Give three examples of inventions that increase energy efficiency.
18. **Writing to Learn** Suppose you had no electricity. Write a journal entry describing a typical weekday, including your meals, classes, and after-school activities. Explain how you might get things done without electricity.

Thinking Visually

19. **Compare/Contrast Table** Copy the table about types of energy onto a separate sheet of paper. Then complete the table and add a title. The first line is filled in as an example. (For more on compare/contrast tables see the Skills Handbook.)

Energy Type	Advantages	Disadvantages
Coal	Produces large amount of energy; easy to transport	Causes air pollution when burned; difficult to mine
Petroleum		
Solar		
Wind		
Water		
Geothermal		
Nuclear		

Test Prep: Skills

The table below shows how the world's energy production changed between 1973 and 1995. Use the information in the table to answer Questions 20–23.

Source of Energy	Energy Units Produced 1973	Energy Units Produced 1995
Coal	1,498	2,179
Gas	964	1,775
Hydroelectric	107	242
Nuclear	54	646
Oil	2,730	3,228
TOTAL Energy Units	5,353	8,070

20. **Interpreting Data** How did the total energy production change between 1973 and 1995?
21. **Calculating** What percentage of the total world energy production did nuclear power provide in 1973? In 1995?
22. **Classifying** Classify the different types of energy according to whether they are renewable or nonrenewable. How important was renewable energy to the world's energy production in 1995?
23. **Drawing Conclusions** Which energy source was the most important in the world in 1995?

Critical Thinking

24. **Comparing and Contrasting** Discuss how the three major fossil fuels are alike and how they are different.
25. **Classifying** State whether each of the following energy sources is renewable or nonrenewable: coal, solar power, methane, hydrogen. Give a reason for each answer.
26. **Making Judgments** Write a short paragraph explaining why you agree or disagree with the following statement: "The United States should build more nuclear power plants to prepare for the future shortage of fossil fuels."

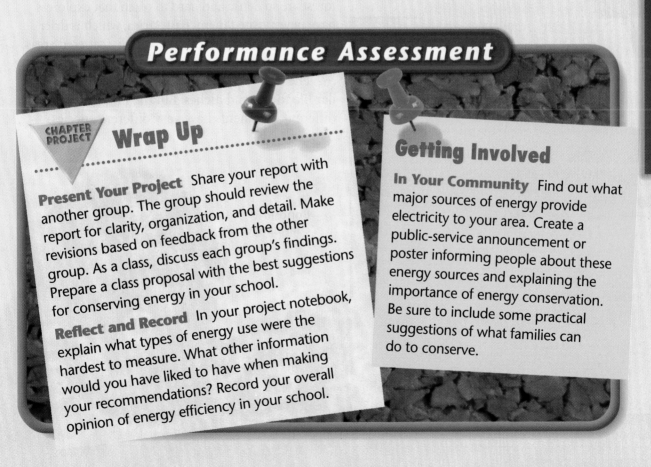

Performance Assessment

CHAPTER PROJECT Wrap Up

Present Your Project Share your report with another group. The group should review the report for clarity, organization, and detail. Make revisions based on feedback from the other group. As a class, discuss each group's findings. Prepare a class proposal with the best suggestions for conserving energy in your school.

Reflect and Record In your project notebook, explain what types of energy use were the hardest to measure. What other information would you have liked to have when making your recommendations? Record your overall opinion of energy efficiency in your school.

Getting Involved

In Your Community Find out what major sources of energy provide electricity to your area. Create a public-service announcement or poster informing people about these energy sources and explaining the importance of energy conservation. Be sure to include some practical suggestions of what families can do to conserve.

African Rain Forests

Preserving Diversity

What forest—

is home to a beetle with wings larger than a sparrow's?

contains a frog that's 30 cm long?

is home to gorillas, chimpanzees, and pygmy hippos?

▲ Ball python

▲ Comet moth

It's an African rain forest. Thousands of plants and animals live here, from colorful orchids to fruit bats, tree frogs, and elephants.

The rain forests of Africa grow in a band near the equator. About 80 percent of the rain-forested area is in central Africa, in the vast basin of the great Congo River. Some parts of the central African rain forest are so dense and hard to reach that explorers have never visited them. East Africa, which is drier and more heavily populated, has only scattered areas of rain forest.

The rain forest regions of the world have similar life forms and niches. But the rain forests of different continents have very different species.

African Rain Forests

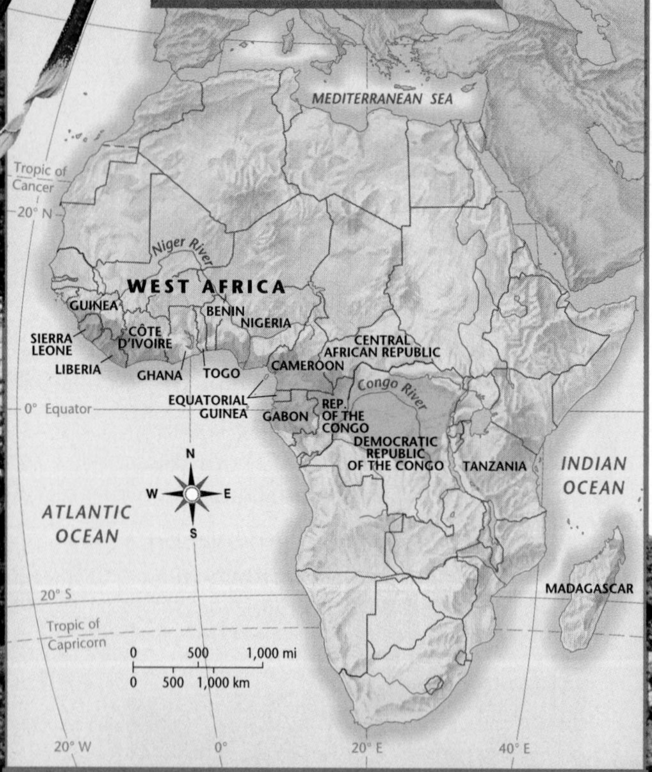
MEDITERRANEAN SEA
Tropic of Cancer
20° N
Niger River
WEST AFRICA
GUINEA
SIERRA LEONE
LIBERIA
CÔTE D'IVOIRE
GHANA
TOGO
BENIN
NIGERIA
CAMEROON
CENTRAL AFRICAN REPUBLIC
Congo River
EQUATORIAL GUINEA
GABON
REP. OF THE CONGO
DEMOCRATIC REPUBLIC OF THE CONGO
TANZANIA
0° Equator
INDIAN OCEAN
ATLANTIC OCEAN
N
W
E
S
MADAGASCAR
20° S
Tropic of Capricorn
0
500
1,000 mi
0
500
1,000 km
20° W
0°
20° E
40° E

Major areas of tropical rain forest, shown in green on the map, cover only 7 percent of Africa.

Bonobo chimpanzee ▶

Layers of the Rain Forest

From above, the rain forest may look like a mass of broccoli. But it's really many forests in one—like different levels in an apartment building.

Each layer from the forest floor to the emergent, or top, layer varies in climate and is home to different plants and animals. The emergent layer captures the most rain, sunlight, heat, and wind. Colobus monkeys swing from vines and branches. Vast numbers of birds live in the trees.

Over time, African rain forest plants and animals have developed unusual adaptations to life at different layers of the forest. Some monkeys living in the canopy have long, muscular legs. They can run and leap through the branches. Guenons and baboons have strong teeth and jaws that allow them to crunch fruits, nuts, and seeds. Other monkeys have shorter tails but longer front legs. They live mainly on the forest floor.

In the understory, small animals such as frogs and squirrels "fly." They have tough membranes that stretch between their front and hind legs and allow them to glide from branch to branch.

The forest floor is dark, humid, and still. Termites feed on dead leaves and brush. Many plants have large leaves that allow them to catch the dim light. Some animals, such as frogs and insects, grow to gigantic sizes. Others are little, like the pygmy hippo that runs through the forest.

Science Activity

Design a rain forest animal that is adapted to life at a certain level of the rain forest. Consider how your animal lives, how it travels, and what food it eats. Outline its characteristics and explain how each adaptation helps the animal survive. Draw a sketch.

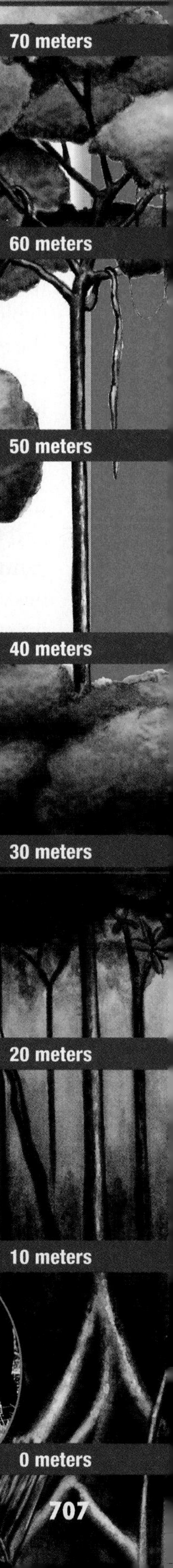

70 meters
60 meters
50 meters
40 meters
30 meters
20 meters
10 meters
0 meters

The emergent layer is formed by a few taller trees that poke through the canopy. Some of these trees are as much as 70 meters high—about as tall as a 17-story building. ***Colobus monkeys*** *(above) live at this level.*

The canopy, from 10 to 40 meters high, is the dense "roof" of the rain forest. The crowns of trees capture sunlight to use in photosynthesis. Rainwater and sunlight filter through thick vegetation. ***Epiphytic orchids*** *grow to the top of the canopy (below).*

The understory has trees and plants that need little light. Pythons lurk in the vegetation. On the forest floor live other animals like the ***pygmy hippo*** *and the gorilla.*

Mathematics

Reaching for Sunlight

Most rain forest trees are evergreens with broad leathery leaves. Some, like the African yellowwood, are conifers. Because the forest is so dense, trees must grow tall and straight to reach sunlight at the top of the canopy.

Along rivers, the floor and understory of the rain forest are a tangle of plants. Early explorers traveling the rivers assumed that the entire rain forest had similar thick vegetation, or jungle. In fact, the rain forest floor is surprisingly bare.

The canopy trees block the sunlight from plants below. Shaded by the dense canopy, the understory and forest floor are humid and dark. Water drips from the leaves of the canopy high overhead. Young trees have the best chance to grow when trees fall, opening up sunny clearings.

West Africa's tropical forests contain many valuable trees. African mahogany and teak are used to make furniture, tools, and boats. Oil from the oil palm is used in soaps, candles, and some foods. Trees such as ebony that can tolerate shade, grow slowly and develop dark, hard, long-lasting wood.

Trees of the Rain Forest

Tree	Maximum Height
African oil palm	18 m
African yellowwood	20 m
Cape fig	7 m
Ebony	30 m
Kapok	70 m
Raffia palm	12 m
Teak	46 m

African oil palms ▲ grow in Nigeria.

◀ This African sculpture is made of wood from the African rain forest.

Math Activity

The table on this page gives the height of some of the trees in the rain forest. Use the information in the table to make a bar graph. On the horizontal axis, label the trees. Use the vertical axis to show the height of the trees.

- Which tree has the greatest maximum height? The least maximum height?
- What is the height difference between the tallest and the shortest trees?
- What is the average height of all the trees shown in the graph?

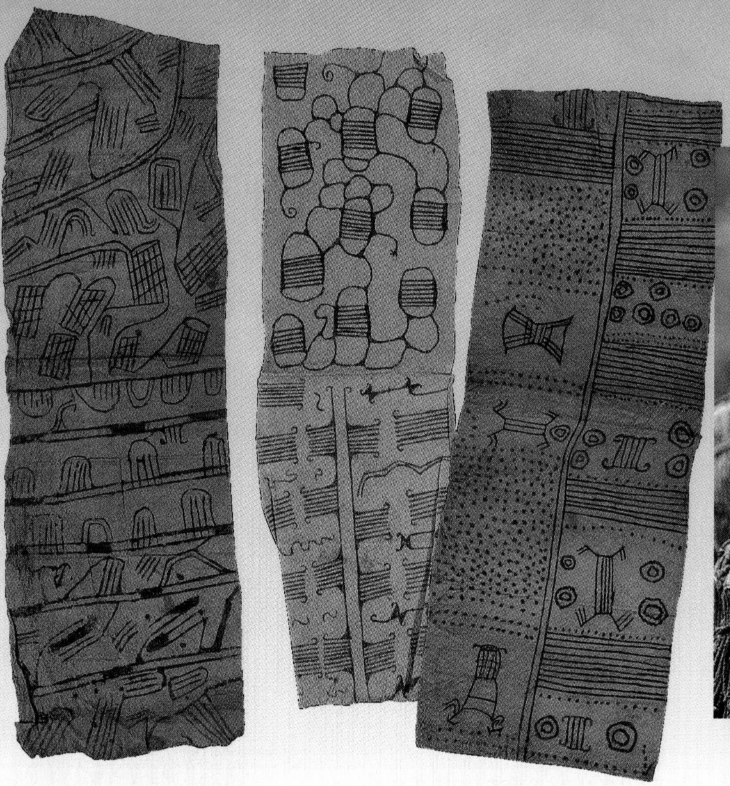

The Mbuti (above) hunt and fish along the Congo River. Their clothing is made of bark cloth (left).

Ituri Forest People

The native peoples of the African rain forest live as they have for thousands of years—by hunting and gathering. The forest supplies them with everything they need—food, water, firewood, building materials, and medicines.

One group of rain forest dwellers is the Mbuti people. The Mbuti live in the Ituri forest of the Democratic Republic of the Congo. Many of the Mbuti are quite small. The men hunt game, such as gazelle and antelope. The women gather wild fruits, nuts, and greens. Their traditional Mbuti clothing is made of tree bark and is wrapped around the waist. The bark is beaten to make it soft. Then it's decorated with geometric designs.

Most Mbuti live as nomads, with no single settled home. Every few months they set up new hunting grounds. They build temporary dome-shaped huts of branches and leaves. Hunting groups of about 10 to 25 families live together. They divide the hunting area among the family groups. On occasion, larger groups gather for ceremonies with dances and ritual music.

Modern Africa has brought changes to the forest people, especially for those who live near the edges of the rain forest. For a few months of the year, some Mbuti work as laborers for farmers who live in villages at the edge of the forest. When their work is finished, the Mbuti return to the Ituri forest. Most forest people prefer not to cultivate their own land. Since the farmers don't hunt, they trade their goods for meat. In exchange for meat, the Mbuti receive goods such as iron tools, cooking pots, clothes, bananas, and other farm produce.

Social Studies Activity

List the goods that forest people and farmers might have to trade. Assume that no modern conveniences, such as tractors and stoves, are available. Write a paragraph or two explaining how goods might be exchanged. Assign a value to the farmers' goods and the Mbuti goods, depending upon each group's needs. For example, decide how much meat a farmer should pay for medicines from the rain forest. How would the trading process change if money were exchanged?

Climbing the Canopy

Much of the rain forest is still a mystery because it's so difficult for scientists to study the canopy. Native forest people sometimes climb these tall trees using strong, thick vines called lianas as support. But rain forest scientists have had to find different methods. Naturalist Gerald Durrell, working in the African rain forest, was lucky enough to find another way to observe the canopy. He describes it here:

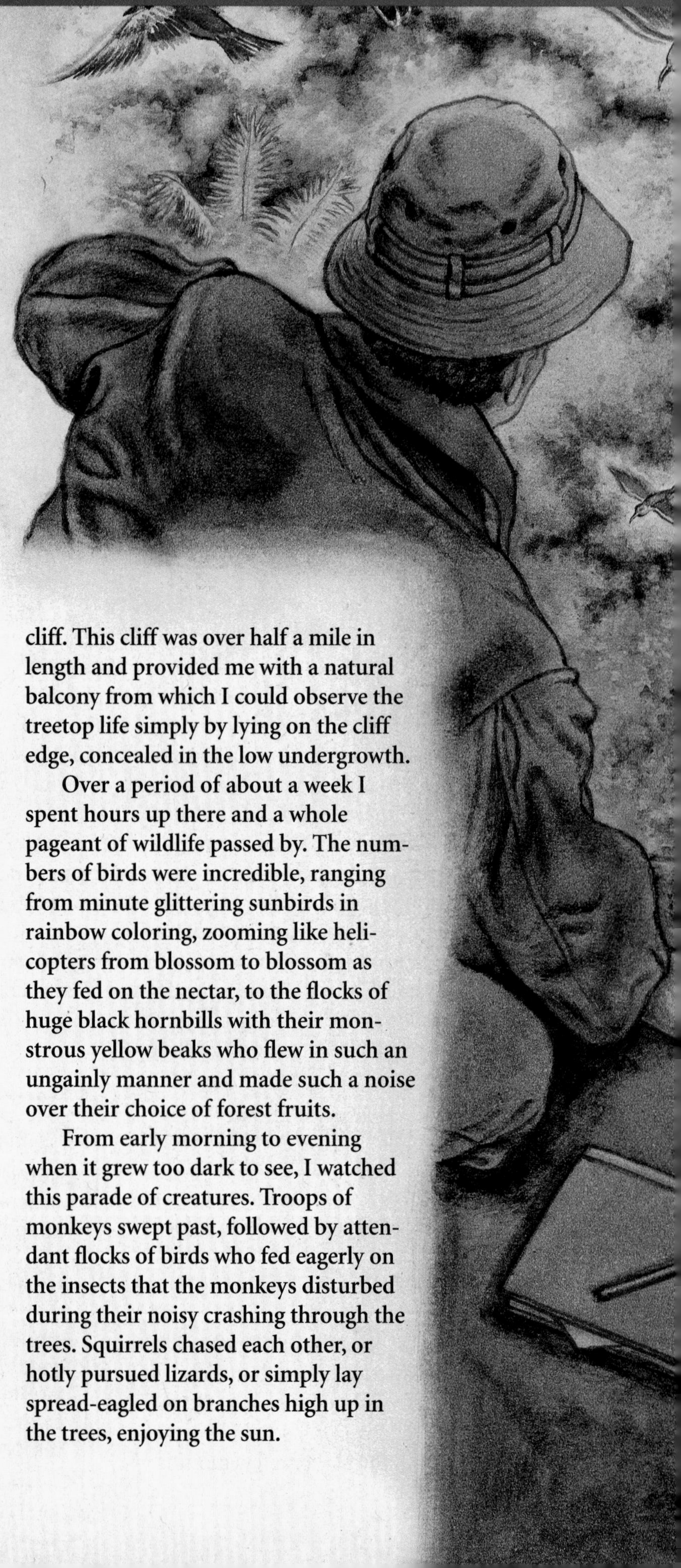

While the canopy is one of the most richly inhabited regions of the forest it is also the one that causes the naturalist the greatest frustration. There he is, down in the gloom among the giant tree trunks, hearing the noises of animal life high above him and having half-eaten fruit, flowers, or seeds rained on him by legions of animals high in their sunlit domain—all of which he cannot see. Under these circumstances the naturalist develops a very bad temper and a permanent crick in the neck.

However, there was one occasion when I managed to transport myself into the forest canopy, and it was a magical experience. It happened in West Africa when I was camped on the thickly forested lower slopes of a mountain called N'da Ali. Walking through the forest one day I found I was walking along the edge of a great step cut out of the mountain. The cliff face, covered with creepers, dropped away for about 50 yards, so that although I was walking through forest, just next to me and slightly below was the canopy of the forest growing up from the base of the cliff. This cliff was over half a mile in length and provided me with a natural balcony from which I could observe the treetop life simply by lying on the cliff edge, concealed in the low undergrowth.

Over a period of about a week I spent hours up there and a whole pageant of wildlife passed by. The numbers of birds were incredible, ranging from minute glittering sunbirds in rainbow coloring, zooming like helicopters from blossom to blossom as they fed on the nectar, to the flocks of huge black hornbills with their monstrous yellow beaks who flew in such an ungainly manner and made such a noise over their choice of forest fruits.

From early morning to evening when it grew too dark to see, I watched this parade of creatures. Troops of monkeys swept past, followed by attendant flocks of birds who fed eagerly on the insects that the monkeys disturbed during their noisy crashing through the trees. Squirrels chased each other, or hotly pursued lizards, or simply lay spread-eagled on branches high up in the trees, enjoying the sun.

Language Arts Activity

- Besides being an experienced naturalist and writer, Gerald Durrell is also a careful observer. In this selection, he describes in detail the "magical experience" of being in the canopy. Reread Durrell's description. Now work with a partner to write and design a pamphlet that will persuade visitors to come to an African rain forest. For your pamphlet, write strong, lively descriptions of what you might see, hear, and experience. Be persuasive.

British conservationist Gerald Durrell wrote about his adventures with wildlife around the world. He established a zoo on the British island of Jersey and worked to preserve threatened species. In the photo, Durrell holds an anteater.

Tie It Together

Celebrate Diversity

Rain forests have the greatest biodiversity—variety of plant and animal life—of any ecosystem on Earth. Many species have yet to be discovered! Plan a display for your school to celebrate biodiversity in the rain forests. Include drawings, photos, and detailed captions.

- On a large map, locate and label Earth's tropical rain forests. Divide into groups to choose one rain forest region to research, such as Africa, Brazil, Costa Rica, Hawaii, Indonesia, or Borneo.
- Have your group study several animal and plant species in its chosen rain forest. You might choose monkeys, butterflies, birds, orchids, or medicinal plants.
- For each species, describe its appearance, where it occurs in the rain forest, its role in the ecosystem, and how it is useful to humans.

Think Like a Scientist

Although you may not know it, you think like a scientist every day. Whenever you ask a question and explore possible answers, you use many of the same skills that scientists do. Some of these skills are described on this page.

Observing

When you use one or more of your five senses to gather information about the world, you are **observing.** Hearing a dog bark, counting twelve green seeds, and smelling smoke are all observations. To increase the power of their senses, scientists sometimes use microscopes, telescopes, or other instruments that help them make more detailed observations.

An observation must be an accurate report of what your senses detect. It is important to keep careful records of your observations in science class by writing or drawing in a notebook. The information collected through observations is called evidence, or data.

Inferring

When you interpret an observation, you are **inferring,** or making an inference. For example, if you hear your dog barking, you may infer that someone is at your front door. To make this inference, you combine the evidence—the barking dog—and your experience or knowledge—you know that your dog barks when strangers approach—to reach a logical conclusion.

Notice that an inference is not a fact; it is only one of many possible explanations for an observation. For example, your dog may be barking because it wants to go for a walk. An inference may turn out to be incorrect even if it is based on accurate observations and logical reasoning. The only way to find out if an inference is correct is to investigate further.

Predicting

When you listen to the weather forecast, you hear many predictions about the next day's weather—what the temperature will be, whether it will rain, and how windy it will be. Weather forecasters use observations and knowledge of weather patterns to predict the weather. The skill of **predicting** involves making an inference about a future event based on current evidence or past experience.

Because a prediction is an inference, it may prove to be false. In science class, you can test some of your predictions by doing experiments. For example, suppose you predict that larger paper airplanes can fly farther than smaller airplanes. How could you test your prediction?

ACTIVITY Use the photograph to answer the questions below.

Observing Look closely at the photograph. List at least three observations.

Inferring Use your observations to make an inference about what has happened. What experience or knowledge did you use to make the inference?

Predicting Predict what will happen next. On what evidence or experience do you base your prediction?

Classifying

Could you imagine searching for a book in the library if the books were shelved in no particular order? Your trip to the library would be an all-day event! Luckily, librarians group together books on similar topics or by the same author. Grouping together items that are alike in some way is called **classifying.** You can classify items in many ways: by size, by shape, by use, and by other important characteristics.

Like librarians, scientists use the skill of classifying to organize information and objects. When things are sorted into groups, the relationships among them become easier to understand.

ACTIVITY

Classify the objects in the photograph into two groups based on any characteristic you choose. Then use another characteristic to classify the objects into three groups.

Making Models

Have you ever drawn a picture to help someone understand what you were saying? Such a drawing is one type of model. A model is a picture, diagram, computer image, or other representation of a complex object or process. **Making models** helps people understand things that they cannot observe directly.

Scientists often use models to represent things that are either very large or very small, such as the planets in the solar system, or the parts of a cell. Such models are physical models—drawings or three-dimensional structures that look like the real thing. Other models are mental models—mathematical equations or words that describe how something works.

ACTIVITY

This student is using a model to demonstrate what causes day and night on Earth. What do the flashlight and the tennis ball in the model represent?

Communicating

Whenever you talk on the phone, write a letter, or listen to your teacher at school, you are communicating. **Communicating** is the process of sharing ideas and information with other people. Communicating effectively requires many skills, including writing, reading, speaking, listening, and making models.

Scientists communicate to share results, information, and opinions. Scientists often communicate about their work in journals, over the telephone, in letters, and on the Internet. They also attend scientific meetings where they share their ideas with one another in person.

ACTIVITY

On a sheet of paper, write out clear, detailed directions for tying your shoe. Then exchange directions with a partner. Follow your partner's directions exactly. How successful were you at tying your shoe? How could your partner have communicated more clearly?

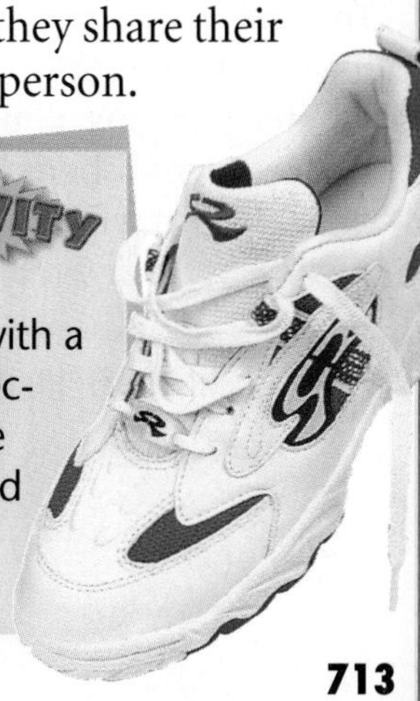

Making Measurements

When scientists make observations, it is not sufficient to say that something is "big" or "heavy." Instead, scientists use instruments to measure just how big or heavy an object is. By measuring, scientists can express their observations more precisely and communicate more information about what they observe.

Measuring in SI

The standard system of measurement used by scientists around the world is known as the International System of Units, which is abbreviated as SI (in French, *Système International d'Unités*). SI units are easy to use because they are based on multiples of 10. Each unit is ten times larger than the next smallest unit and one tenth the size of the next largest unit. The table lists the prefixes used to name the most common SI units.

Common SI Prefixes

Prefix	Symbol	Meaning
kilo-	k	1,000
hecto-	h	100
deka-	da	10
deci-	d	0.1 (one tenth)
centi-	c	0.01 (one hundredth)
milli-	m	0.001 (one thousandth)

Length To measure length, or the distance between two points, the unit of measure is the **meter (m).** One meter is the approximate distance from the floor to a doorknob. Long distances, such as the distance between two cities, are measured in kilometers (km). Small lengths are measured in centimeters (cm) or millimeters (mm). Scientists use metric rulers and meter sticks to measure length.

Common Conversions

1 km = 1,000 m
1 m = 100 cm
1 m = 1,000 mm
1 cm = 10 mm

ACTIVITY

The larger lines on the metric ruler in the picture show centimeter divisions, while the smaller, unnumbered lines show millimeter divisions. How many centimeters long is the shell? How many millimeters long is it?

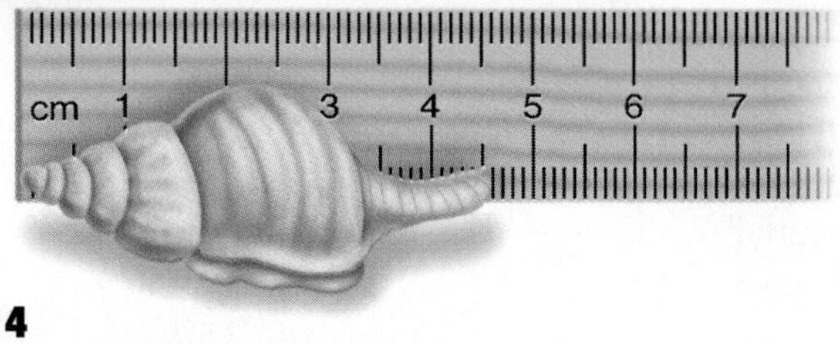
cm
1
3
4
5
6
7

Liquid Volume To measure the volume of a liquid, or the amount of space it takes up, you will use a unit of measure known as the **liter (L).** One liter is the approximate volume of a medium-sized carton of milk. Smaller volumes are measured in milliliters (mL). Scientists use graduated cylinders to measure liquid volume.

Common Conversion

1 L = 1,000 mL

ACTIVITY

The graduated cylinder in the picture is marked in milliliter divisions. Notice that the water in the cylinder has a curved surface. This curved surface is called the *meniscus*. To measure the volume, you must read the level at the lowest point of the meniscus. What is the volume of water in this graduated cylinder?

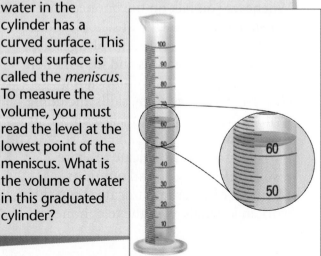

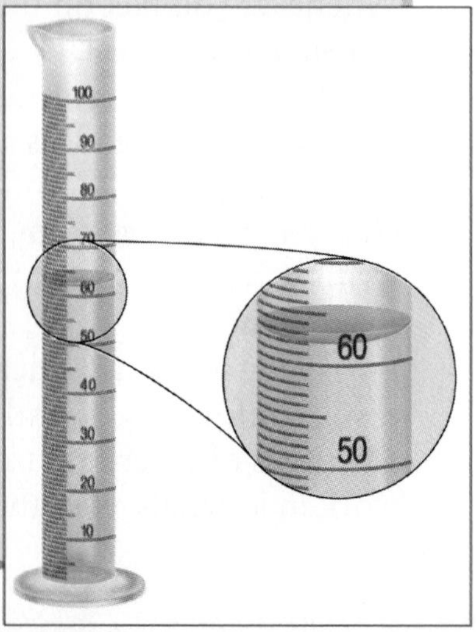
100
90
80
70
60
50
40
30
20
10
60
50

Mass To measure mass, or the amount of matter in an object, you will use a unit of measure known as the **gram (g)**. One gram is approximately the mass of a paper clip. Larger masses are measured in kilograms (kg). Scientists use a balance to find the mass of an object.

Common Conversion

1 kg = 1,000 g

0.1 KG

ACTIVITY

The electronic balance displays the mass of an apple in kilograms. What is the mass of the apple? Suppose a recipe for applesauce called for one kilogram of apples. About how many apples would you need?

Temperature
To measure the temperature of a substance, you will use the **Celsius scale.** Temperature is measured in degrees Celsius (°C) using a Celsius thermometer. Water freezes at 0°C and boils at 100°C.

°C
110
100
90
80
70
60
50
40
30
20
10
0
-10
-20

ACTIVITY

What is the temperature of the liquid in degrees Celsius?

Converting SI Units

To use the SI system, you must know how to convert between units. Converting from one unit to another involves the skill of **calculating**, or using mathematical operations. Converting between SI units is similar to converting between dollars and dimes because both systems are based on multiples of ten.

Suppose you want to convert a length of 80 centimeters to meters. Follow these steps to convert between units.

1. Begin by writing down the measurement you want to convert—in this example, 80 centimeters.
2. Write a conversion factor that represents the relationship between the two units you are converting. In this example, the relationship is *1 meter = 100 centimeters.* Write this conversion factor as a fraction, making sure to place the units you are converting from (centimeters, in this example) in the denominator.
3. Multiply the measurement you want to convert by the fraction. When you do this, the units in the first measurement will cancel out with the units in the denominator. Your answer will be in the units you are converting to (meters, in this example).

Example

80 centimeters = __?__ meters

$$80 \text{ cen}\cancel{\text{timeters}} \times \frac{1 \text{ meter}}{100 \text{ cen}\cancel{\text{timeters}}} = \frac{80 \text{ meters}}{100}$$

$$= 0.8 \text{ meters}$$

ACTIVITY

Convert between the following units.

1. 600 millimeters = __?__ meters
2. 0.35 liters = __?__ milliliters
3. 1,050 grams = __?__ kilograms

Conducting a Scientific Investigation

In some ways, scientists are like detectives, piecing together clues to learn about a process or event. One way that scientists gather clues is by carrying out experiments. An experiment tests an idea in a careful, orderly manner. Although all experiments do not follow the same steps in the same order, many follow a pattern similar to the one described here.

Posing Questions

Experiments begin by asking a scientific question. A scientific question is one that can be answered by gathering evidence. For example, the question "Which freezes faster—fresh water or salt water?" is a scientific question because you can carry out an investigation and gather information to answer the question.

Developing a Hypothesis

The next step is to form a hypothesis. A **hypothesis** is a possible explanation for a set of observations or answer to a specific question. In science, a hypothesis must be testable. Hypotheses are based on your observations and previous knowledge. An example of a hypothesis is "Salt water takes longer to freeze than fresh water."

You then use the words "*If... then...*" to make a prediction based on the hypothesis. An example is, "*If I add salt to fresh water, then the water will take longer to freeze.*" Such a prediction outlines a possible experiment.

CONTAINER 1
CONTAINER 2
CONTAINER 3

Designing an Experiment

Next you need to plan a way to test your hypothesis. Your plan should be written out as a step-by-step procedure and should describe the observations or measurements you will make.

Two important steps involved in designing an experiment are controlling variables and forming operational definitions.

Controlling Variables In a well-designed experiment, you need to keep all variables the same except for one. A **variable** is any factor that can change in an experiment. The factor that you change is called the **manipulated variable.** In this experiment, the manipulated variable is the amount of salt added to the water. Other factors, such as the amount of water or the starting temperature, are kept constant.

The factor that changes as a result of the manipulated variable is called the responding variable. The **responding variable** is what you measure or observe to obtain your results. In this experiment, the responding variable is how long the water takes to freeze.

An experiment in which all factors except one are kept constant is a **controlled experiment.** Most controlled experiments include a test called the control. In this experiment, Container 3 is the control. Because no salt is added to Container 3, you can compare the results from the other containers to it. Any difference in results must be due to the addition of salt alone.

Forming Operational Definitions
Another important aspect of a well-designed experiment is having clear operational definitions. An **operational definition** is a statement that describes how a particular variable is to be measured or how a term is to be defined. For example, in this experiment, how will you determine if the water has frozen? You might decide to insert a stick in each container at the start of the experiment. Your operational definition of "frozen" would be the time at which the stick can no longer move.

EXPERIMENTAL PROCEDURE

1. *Fill 3 containers with 300 milliliters of cold tap water.*
2. *Add 10 grams of salt to Container 1; stir. Add 20 grams of salt to Container 2; stir. Add no salt to Container 3.*
3. *Place the 3 containers in a freezer.*
4. *Check the containers every 15 minutes. Record your observations.*

Interpreting Data

The observations and measurements you make in an experiment are called data. At the end of an experiment, you need to analyze the data to look for any patterns or trends. Patterns often become clear if you organize your data in a data table or graph. Then think through what the data reveal. Do they support your hypothesis? Do they point out a flaw in your experiment? Do you need to collect more data?

Drawing Conclusions

A conclusion is a statement that sums up what you have learned from an experiment. When you draw a conclusion, you need to decide whether the data you collected support your hypothesis or not. You may need to repeat an experiment several times before you can draw any conclusions from it. Conclusions often lead you to pose new questions and plan new experiments to answer them.

ACTIVITY

Is a ball's bounce affected by the height from which it is dropped? Using the steps just described, plan a controlled experiment to investigate this problem.

Thinking Critically

Has a friend ever asked for your advice about a problem? If so, you may have helped your friend think through the problem in a logical way. Without knowing it, you used critical-thinking skills to help your friend. Critical thinking involves the use of reasoning and logic to solve problems or make decisions. Some critical-thinking skills are described below.

Comparing and Contrasting

When you examine two objects for similarities and differences, you are using the skill of **comparing and contrasting.** Comparing involves identifying similarities, or common characteristics. Contrasting involves identifying differences. Analyzing objects in this way can help you discover details that you might otherwise overlook.

ACTIVITY

Compare and contrast the two animals in the photo. First list all the similarities that you see. Then list all the differences.

Applying Concepts

When you use your knowledge about one situation to make sense of a similar situation, you are using the skill of **applying concepts.** Being able to transfer your knowledge from one situation to another shows that you truly understand a concept. You may use this skill in answering test questions that present different problems from the ones you've reviewed in class.

ACTIVITY

You have just learned that water takes longer to freeze when other substances are mixed into it. Use this knowledge to explain why people need a substance called antifreeze in their car's radiator in the winter.

Interpreting Illustrations

Diagrams, photographs, and maps are included in textbooks to help clarify what you read. These illustrations show processes, places, and ideas in a visual manner. The skill called **interpreting illustrations** can help you learn from these visual elements. To understand an illustration, take the time to study the illustration along with all the written information that accompanies it. Captions identify the key concepts shown in the illustration. Labels point out the important parts of a diagram or map, while keys identify the symbols used in a map.

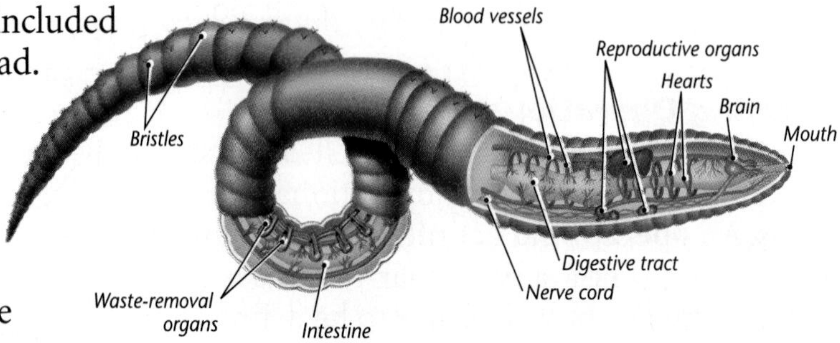
Blood vessels
Reproductive organs
Hearts
Brain
Mouth
Bristles
Digestive tract
Nerve cord
Waste-removal organs
Intestine

▲ **Internal anatomy of an earthworm**

ACTIVITY

Study the diagram above. Then write a short paragraph explaining what you have learned.

Relating Cause and Effect

If one event causes another event to occur, the two events are said to have a cause-and-effect relationship. When you determine that such a relationship exists between two events, you use a skill called **relating cause and effect.** For example, if you notice an itchy, red bump on your skin, you might infer that a mosquito bit you. The mosquito bite is the cause, and the bump is the effect.

It is important to note that two events do not necessarily have a cause-and-effect relationship just because they occur together. Scientists carry out experiments or use past experience to determine whether a cause-and-effect relationship exists.

ACTIVITY You are on a camping trip and your flashlight has stopped working. List some possible causes for the flashlight malfunction. How could you determine which cause-and-effect relationship has left you in the dark?

Making Generalizations

When you draw a conclusion about an entire group based on information about only some of the group's members, you are using a skill called **making generalizations.** For a generalization to be valid, the sample you choose must be large enough and representative of the entire group. You might, for example, put this skill to work at a farm stand if you see a sign that says, "Sample some grapes before you buy." If you sample a few sweet grapes, you may conclude that all the grapes are sweet—and purchase a large bunch.

ACTIVITY A team of scientists needs to determine whether the water in a large reservoir is safe to drink. How could they use the skill of making generalizations to help them? What should they do?

Making Judgments

When you evaluate something to decide whether it is good or bad, or right or wrong, you are using a skill called **making judgments.** For example, you make judgments when you decide to eat healthful foods or to pick up litter in a park. Before you make a judgment, you need to think through the pros and cons of a situation, and identify the values or standards that you hold.

ACTIVITY Should children and teens be required to wear helmets when bicycling? Explain why you feel the way you do.

Problem Solving

When you use critical-thinking skills to resolve an issue or decide on a course of action, you are using a skill called **problem solving.** Some problems, such as how to convert a fraction into a decimal, are straightforward. Other problems, such as figuring out why your computer has stopped working, are complex. Some complex problems can be solved using the trial and error method—try out one solution first, and if that doesn't work, try another. Other useful problem-solving strategies include making models and brainstorming possible solutions with a partner.

Organizing Information

As you read this textbook, how can you make sense of all the information it contains? Some useful tools to help you organize information are shown on this page. These tools are called *graphic organizers* because they give you a visual picture of a topic, showing at a glance how key concepts are related.

Concept Maps

Concept maps are useful tools for organizing information on broad topics. A concept map begins with a general concept and shows how it can be broken down into more specific concepts. In that way, relationships between concepts become easier to understand.

A concept map is constructed by placing concept words (usually nouns) in ovals and connecting them with linking words. Often, the most general concept word is placed at the top, and the words become more specific as you move downward. Often the linking words, which are written on a line extending between two ovals, describe the relationship between the two concepts they connect. If you follow any string of concepts and linking words down the map, it should read like a sentence.

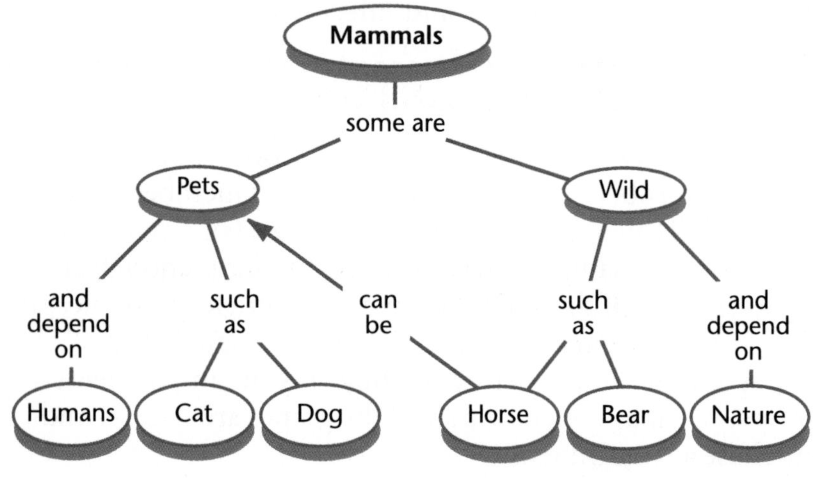
Mammals
some are
Pets
Wild
and depend on
such as
can be
such as
and depend on
Humans
Cat
Dog
Horse
Bear
Nature

Some concept maps include linking words that connect a concept on one branch of the map to a concept on another branch. These linking words, called cross-linkages, show more complex interrelationships among concepts.

Compare/Contrast Tables

Compare/contrast tables are useful tools for sorting out the similarities and differences between two or more items. A table provides an organized framework in which to compare items based on specific characteristics that you identify.

To create a compare/contrast table, list the items to be compared across the top of a table. Then list the characteristics that will form the basis of your comparison in the left-hand column. Complete the table by filling in information about each characteristic, first for one item and then for the other.

Characteristic	Baseball	Basketball
Number of Players	9	5
Playing Field	Baseball diamond	Basketball court
Equipment	Bat, baseball, mitts	Basket, basketball

Venn Diagrams

Another way to show similarities and differences between items is with a Venn diagram. A Venn diagram consists of two or more circles that partially overlap. Each circle represents a particular concept or idea. Common characteristics, or similarities, are written within the area of overlap between the two circles. Unique characteristics, or differences, are written in the parts of the circles outside the area of overlap.

To create a Venn diagram, draw two overlapping circles. Label the circles with the names of the items being compared. Write the unique characteristics in each circle outside the area of overlap. Then write the shared characteristics within the area of overlap.

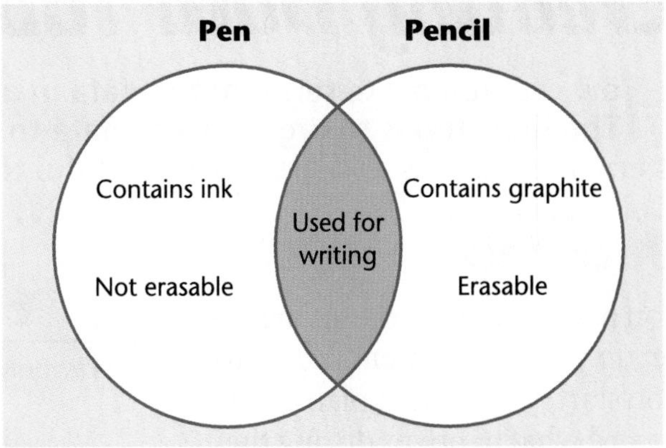

Pen
Pencil
Contains ink
Not erasable
Used for writing
Contains graphite
Erasable

Flowcharts

A flowchart can help you understand the order in which certain events have occurred or should occur. Flowcharts are useful for outlining the stages in a process or the steps in a procedure.

To make a flowchart, write a brief description of each event in a box. Place the first event at the top of the page, followed by the second event, the third event, and so on. Then draw an arrow to connect each event to the one that occurs next.

Preparing Pasta

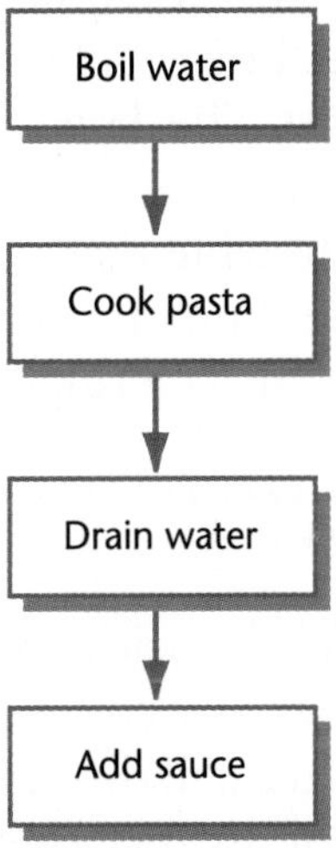

Boil water
Cook pasta
Drain water
Add sauce

Cycle Diagrams

A cycle diagram can be used to show a sequence of events that is continuous, or cyclical. A continuous sequence does not have an end because, when the final event is over, the first event begins again. Like a flowchart, a cycle diagram can help you understand the order of events.

To create a cycle diagram, write a brief description of each event in a box. Place one event at the top of the page in the center. Then, moving in a clockwise direction around an imaginary circle, write each event in its proper sequence. Draw arrows that connect each event to the one that occurs next, forming a continuous circle.

Steps in a Science Experiment

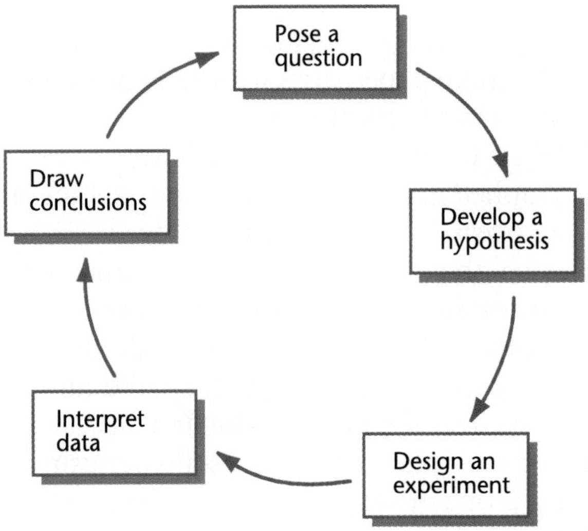

Pose a question
Develop a hypothesis
Design an experiment
Interpret data
Draw conclusions

SKILLS HANDBOOK

Creating Data Tables and Graphs

How can you make sense of the data in a science experiment? The first step is to organize the data to help you understand them. Data tables and graphs are helpful tools for organizing data.

Data Tables

You have gathered your materials and set up your experiment. But before you start, you need to plan a way to record what happens during the experiment. By creating a data table, you can record your observations and measurements in an orderly way.

Suppose, for example, that a scientist conducted an experiment to find out how many Calories people of different body masses burn while doing various activities. The data table shows the results.

CALORIES BURNED IN 30 MINUTES OF ACTIVITY

Body Mass	Experiment 1 Bicycling	Experiment 2 Playing Basketball	Experiment 3 Watching Television
30 kg	60 Calories	120 Calories	21 Calories
40 kg	77 Calories	164 Calories	27 Calories
50 kg	95 Calories	206 Calories	33 Calories
60 kg	114 Calories	248 Calories	38 Calories

Notice in this data table that the manipulated variable (body mass) is the heading of one column. The responding variable (for Experiment 1, the number of Calories burned while bicycling) is the heading of the next column. Additional columns were added for related experiments.

Bar Graphs

To compare how many Calories a person burns doing various activities, you could create a bar graph. A bar graph is used to display data in a number of separate, or distinct, categories. In this example, bicycling, playing basketball, and watching television are three separate categories.

Calories Burned by a 30-kilogram Person in Various Activities

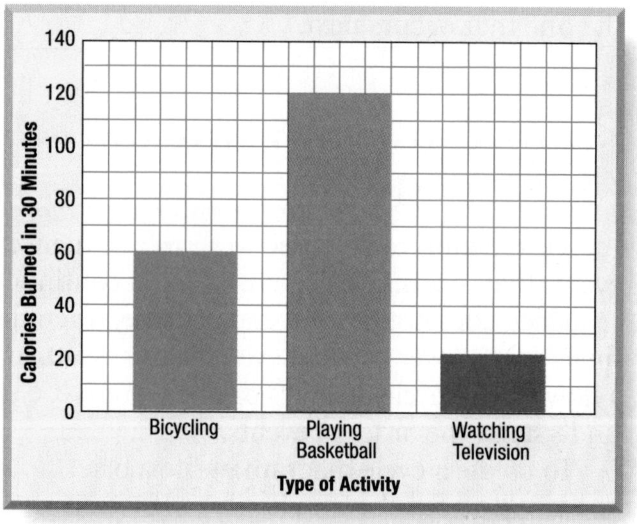
140
120
100
80
60
40
20
0
Calories Burned in 30 Minutes
Bicycling
Playing Basketball
Watching Television
Type of Activity

To create a bar graph, follow these steps.

1. On graph paper, draw a horizontal, or *x*-, axis and a vertical, or *y*-, axis.
2. Write the names of the categories to be graphed along the horizontal axis. Include an overall label for the axis as well.
3. Label the vertical axis with the name of the responding variable. Include units of measurement. Then create a scale along the axis by marking off equally spaced numbers that cover the range of the data collected.
4. For each category, draw a solid bar using the scale on the vertical axis to determine the appropriate height. For example, for bicycling, draw the bar as high as the 60 mark on the vertical axis. Make all the bars the same width and leave equal spaces between them.
5. Add a title that describes the graph.

Line Graphs

Effect of Body Mass on Calories Burned While Bicycling

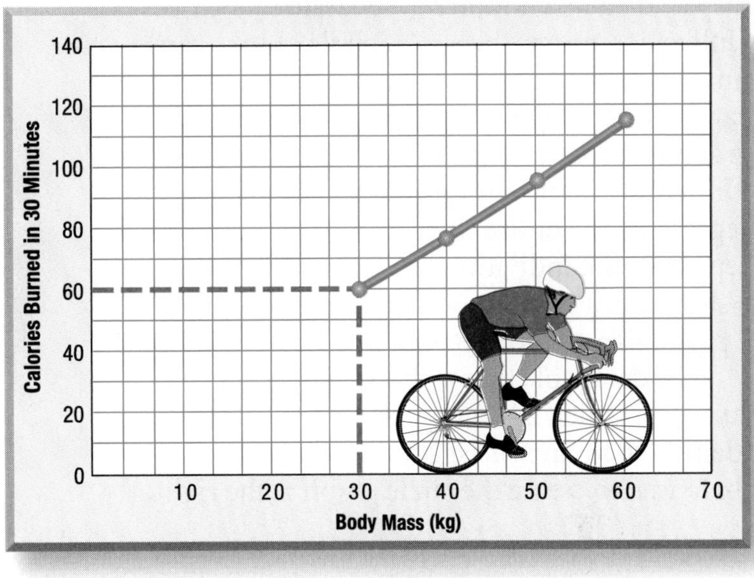
Calories Burned in 30 Minutes
140
120
100
80
60
40
20
0
10
20
30
40
50
60
70
Body Mass (kg)

To see whether a relationship exists between body mass and the number of Calories burned while bicycling, you could create a line graph. A line graph is used to display data that show how one variable (the responding variable) changes in response to another variable (the manipulated variable). You can use a line graph when your manipulated variable is *continuous,* that is, when there are other points between the ones that you tested. In this example, body mass is a continuous variable because there are other body masses between 30 and 40 kilograms (for example, 31 kilograms). Time is another example of a continuous variable.

Line graphs are powerful tools because they allow you to estimate values for conditions that you did not test in the experiment. For example, you can use the line graph to estimate that a 35-kilogram person would burn 68 Calories while bicycling.

To create a line graph, follow these steps.

1. On graph paper, draw a horizontal, or *x*-, axis and a vertical, or *y*-, axis.
2. Label the horizontal axis with the name of the manipulated variable. Label the vertical axis with the name of the responding variable. Include units of measurement.
3. Create a scale on each axis by marking off equally spaced numbers that cover the range of the data collected.
4. Plot a point on the graph for each piece of data. In the line graph above, the dotted lines show how to plot the first data point (30 kilograms and 60 Calories). Draw an imaginary vertical line extending up from the horizontal axis at the 30-kilogram mark. Then draw an imaginary horizontal line extending across from the vertical axis at the 60-Calorie mark. Plot the point where the two lines intersect.
5. Connect the plotted points with a solid line. (In some cases, it may be more appropriate to draw a line that shows the general trend of the plotted points. In those cases, some of the points may fall above or below the line.)
6. Add a title that identifies the variables or relationship in the graph.

ACTIVITY

Create line graphs to display the data from Experiment 2 and Experiment 3 in the data table.

ACTIVITY

You read in the newspaper that a total of 4 centimeters of rain fell in your area in June, 2.5 centimeters fell in July, and 1.5 centimeters fell in August. What type of graph would you use to display these data? Use graph paper to create the graph.

Circle Graphs

Like bar graphs, circle graphs can be used to display data in a number of separate categories. Unlike bar graphs, however, circle graphs can only be used when you have data for *all* the categories that make up a given topic. A circle graph is sometimes called a pie chart because it resembles a pie cut into slices. The pie represents the entire topic, while the slices represent the individual categories. The size of a slice indicates what percentage of the whole a particular category makes up.

The data table below shows the results of a survey in which 24 teenagers were asked to identify their favorite sport. The data were then used to create the circle graph at the right.

Sports That Teens Prefer

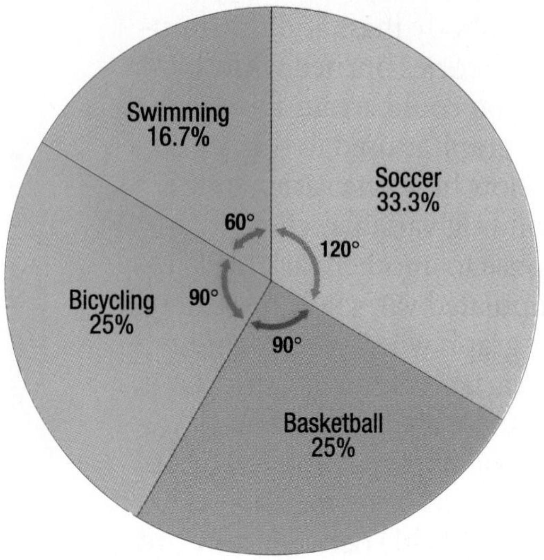
Swimming
16.7%
Soccer
33.3%
60°
120°
Bicycling
25%
90°
90°
Basketball
25%

FAVORITE SPORTS

Sport	Number of Students
Soccer	8
Basketball	6
Bicycling	6
Swimming	4

To create a circle graph, follow these steps.

1. Use a compass to draw a circle. Mark the center of the circle with a point. Then draw a line from the center point to the top of the circle.
2. Determine the size of each "slice" by setting up a proportion where x equals the number of degrees in a slice. (NOTE: A circle contains 360 degrees.) For example, to find the number of degrees in the "soccer" slice, set up the following proportion:

$$\frac{\text{students who prefer soccer}}{\text{total number of students}} = \frac{x}{\text{total number of degrees in a circle}}$$

$$\frac{8}{24} = \frac{x}{360}$$

Cross-multiply and solve for x.

$$24x = 8 \times 360$$

$$x = 120$$

The "soccer" slice should contain 120 degrees.

3. Use a protractor to measure the angle of the first slice, using the line you drew to the top of the circle as the 0° line. Draw a line from the center of the circle to the edge for the angle you measured.
4. Continue around the circle by measuring the size of each slice with the protractor. Start measuring from the edge of the previous slice so the wedges do not overlap. When you are done, the entire circle should be filled in.
5. Determine the percentage of the whole circle that each slice represents. To do this, divide the number of degrees in a slice by the total number of degrees in a circle (360), and multiply by 100%. For the "soccer" slice, you can find the percentage as follows:

$$\frac{120}{360} \times 100\% = 33.3\%$$

6. Use a different color to shade in each slice. Label each slice with the name of the category and with the percentage of the whole it represents.
7. Add a title to the circle graph.

ACTIVITY

In a class of 28 students, 12 students take the bus to school, 10 students walk, and 6 students ride their bicycles. Create a circle graph to display these data.

Laboratory Safety

Safety Symbols

These symbols alert you to possible dangers in the laboratory and remind you to work carefully.

Safety Goggles Always wear safety goggles to protect your eyes in any activity involving chemicals, flames or heating, or the possibility of broken glassware.

Lab Apron Wear a laboratory apron to protect your skin and clothing from damage.

Breakage You are working with materials that may be breakable, such as glass containers, glass tubing, thermometers, or funnels. Handle breakable materials with care. Do not touch broken glassware.

Heat-resistant Gloves Use an oven mitt or other hand protection when handling hot materials. Hot plates, hot glassware, or hot water can cause burns. Do not touch hot objects with your bare hands.

Heating Use a clamp or tongs to pick up hot glassware. Do not touch hot objects with your bare hands.

Sharp Object Pointed-tip scissors, scalpels, knives, needles, pins, or tacks are sharp. They can cut or puncture your skin. Always direct a sharp edge or point away from yourself and others. Use sharp instruments only as instructed.

Electric Shock Avoid the possibility of electric shock. Never use electrical equipment around water, or when the equipment is wet or your hands are wet. Be sure cords are untangled and cannot trip anyone. Disconnect the equipment when it is not in use.

Corrosive Chemical You are working with an acid or another corrosive chemical. Avoid getting it on your skin or clothing, or in your eyes. Do not inhale the vapors. Wash your hands when you are finished with the activity.

Poison Do not let any poisonous chemical come in contact with your skin, and do not inhale its vapors. Wash your hands when you are finished with the activity.

Physical Safety When an experiment involves physical activity, take precautions to avoid injuring yourself or others. Follow instructions from your teacher. Alert your teacher if there is any reason you should not participate in the activity.

Animal Safety Treat live animals with care to avoid harming the animals or yourself. Working with animal parts or preserved animals also may require caution. Wash your hands when you are finished with the activity.

Plant Safety Handle plants in the laboratory or during field work only as directed by your teacher. If you are allergic to certain plants, tell your teacher before doing an activity in which those plants are used. Avoid touching harmful plants such as poison ivy, poison oak, or poison sumac, or plants with thorns. Wash your hands when you are finished with the activity.

Flames You may be working with flames from a lab burner, candle, or matches. Tie back loose hair and clothing. Follow instructions from your teacher about lighting and extinguishing flames.

No Flames Flammable materials may be present. Make sure there are no flames, sparks, or other exposed heat sources present.

Fumes When poisonous or unpleasant vapors may be involved, work in a ventilated area. Avoid inhaling vapors directly. Only test an odor when directed to do so by your teacher, and use a wafting motion to direct the vapor toward your nose.

Disposal Chemicals and other laboratory materials used in the activity must be disposed of safely. Follow the instructions from your teacher.

Hand Washing Wash your hands thoroughly when finished with the activity. Use antibacterial soap and warm water. Lather both sides of your hands and between your fingers. Rinse well.

General Safety Awareness You may see this symbol when none of the symbols described earlier appears. In this case, follow the specific instructions provided. You may also see this symbol when you are asked to develop your own procedure in a lab. Have your teacher approve your plan before you go further.

Science Safety Rules

To prepare yourself to work safely in the laboratory, read over the following safety rules. Then read them a second time. Make sure you understand and follow each rule. Ask your teacher to explain any rules you do not understand.

Dress Code

1. To protect yourself from injuring your eyes, wear safety goggles whenever you work with chemicals, burners, glassware, or any substance that might get into your eyes. If you wear contact lenses, notify your teacher.
2. Wear a lab apron or coat whenever you work with corrosive chemicals or substances that can stain.
3. Tie back long hair to keep it away from any chemicals, flames, or equipment.
4. Remove or tie back any article of clothing or jewelry that can hang down and touch chemicals, flames, or equipment. Roll up or secure long sleeves.
5. Never wear open shoes or sandals.

General Precautions

6. Read all directions for an experiment several times before beginning the activity. Carefully follow all written and oral instructions. If you are in doubt about any part of the experiment, ask your teacher for assistance.
7. Never perform activities that are not assigned or authorized by your teacher. Obtain permission before "experimenting" on your own. Never handle any equipment unless you have specific permission.
8. Never perform lab activities without direct supervision.
9. Never eat or drink in the laboratory.
10. Keep work areas clean and tidy at all times. Bring only notebooks and lab manuals or written lab procedures to the work area. All other items, such as purses and backpacks, should be left in a designated area.
11. Do not engage in horseplay.

First Aid

12. Always report all accidents or injuries to your teacher, no matter how minor. Notify your teacher immediately about any fires.
13. Learn what to do in case of specific accidents, such as getting acid in your eyes or on your skin. (Rinse acids from your body with lots of water.)
14. Be aware of the location of the first-aid kit, but do not use it unless instructed by your teacher. In case of injury, your teacher should administer first aid. Your teacher may also send you to the school nurse or call a physician.
15. Know the location of emergency equipment, such as the fire extinguisher and fire blanket, and know how to use it.
16. Know the location of the nearest telephone and whom to contact in an emergency.

Heating and Fire Safety

17. Never use a heat source, such as a candle, burner, or hot plate, without wearing safety goggles.
18. Never heat anything unless instructed to do so. A chemical that is harmless when cool may be dangerous when heated.
19. Keep all combustible materials away from flames. Never use a flame or spark near a combustible chemical.
20. Never reach across a flame.
21. Before using a laboratory burner, make sure you know proper procedures for lighting and adjusting the burner, as demonstrated by your teacher. Do not touch the burner. It may be hot. And never leave a lighted burner unattended!
22. Chemicals can splash or boil out of a heated test tube. When heating a substance in a test tube, make sure that the mouth of the tube is not pointed at you or anyone else.
23. Never heat a liquid in a closed container. The expanding gases produced may blow the container apart.
24. Before picking up a container that has been heated, hold the back of your hand near it. If you can feel heat on the back of your hand, the container is too hot to handle. Use an oven mitt to pick up a container that has been heated.

Using Chemicals Safely

25. Never mix chemicals "for the fun of it." You might produce a dangerous, possibly explosive substance.
26. Never put your face near the mouth of a container that holds chemicals. Never touch, taste, or smell a chemical unless you are instructed by your teacher to do so. Many chemicals are poisonous.
27. Use only those chemicals needed in the activity. Read and double-check labels on supply bottles before removing any chemicals. Take only as much as you need. Keep all containers closed when chemicals are not being used.
28. Dispose of all chemicals as instructed by your teacher. To avoid contamination, never return chemicals to their original containers. Never simply pour chemicals or other substances into the sink or trash containers.
29. Be extra careful when working with acids or bases. Pour all chemicals over the sink or a container, not over your work surface.
30. If you are instructed to test for odors, use a wafting motion to direct the odors to your nose. Do not inhale the fumes directly from the container.
31. When mixing an acid and water, always pour the water into the container first and then add the acid to the water. Never pour water into an acid.
32. Take extreme care not to spill any material in the laboratory. Wash chemical spills and splashes immediately with plenty of water. Immediately begin rinsing with water any acids that get on your skin or clothing, and notify your teacher of any acid spill at the same time.

Using Glassware Safely

33. Never force glass tubing or thermometers into a rubber stopper or rubber tubing. Have your teacher insert the glass tubing or thermometer if required for an activity.
34. If you are using a laboratory burner, use a wire screen to protect glassware from any flame. Never heat glassware that is not thoroughly dry on the outside.
35. Keep in mind that hot glassware looks cool. Never pick up glassware without first checking to see if it is hot. Use an oven mitt. See rule 24.
36. Never use broken or chipped glassware. If glassware breaks, notify your teacher and dispose of the glassware in the proper broken-glassware container. Never handle broken glass with your bare hands.
37. Never eat or drink from lab glassware.
38. Thoroughly clean glassware before putting it away.

Using Sharp Instruments

39. Handle scalpels or other sharp instruments with extreme care. Never cut material toward you; cut away from you.
40. Immediately notify your teacher if you cut your skin when working in the laboratory.

Animal and Plant Safety

41. Never perform experiments that cause pain, discomfort, or harm to mammals, birds, reptiles, fishes, or amphibians. This rule applies at home as well as in the classroom.
42. Animals should be handled only if absolutely necessary. Your teacher will instruct you as to how to handle each animal species brought into the classroom.
43. If you know that you are allergic to certain plants, molds, or animals, tell your teacher before doing an activity in which these are used.
44. During field work, protect your skin by wearing long pants, long sleeves, socks, and closed shoes. Know how to recognize the poisonous plants and fungi in your area, as well as plants with thorns, and avoid contact with them.
45. Never eat any part of an unidentified plant or fungus.
46. Wash your hands thoroughly after handling animals or the cage containing animals. Wash your hands when you are finished with any activity involving animal parts, plants, or soil.

End-of-Experiment Rules

47. After an experiment has been completed, clean up your work area and return all equipment to its proper place.
48. Dispose of waste materials as instructed by your teacher.
49. Wash your hands after every experiment.
50. Always turn off all burners or hot plates when they are not in use. Unplug hot plates and other electrical equipment. If you used a burner, check that the gas-line valve to the burner is off as well.

Appendix B

Identifying Common Minerals

GROUP 1
Metallic Luster, Mostly Dark-Colored

Mineral/ Formula	Hardness	Density (g/cm^3)	Luster	Streak	Color	Other Properties/Remarks
Pyrite FeS_2	6–6.5	5.0	Metallic	Greenish, brownish black	Light yellow	Harder than chalcopyrite and pyrrhotite; called "fool's gold," but harder than gold and very brittle
Magnetite Fe_3O_4	6	5.2	Metallic	Black	Iron black	Very magnetic; important iron ore; some varieties known as "lodestone"
Hematite Fe_2O_3	5.5–6.5	4.9–5.3	Metallic or earthy	Red or red brown	Reddish brown to black; also steel gray crystals	Most important ore of iron; known as "red ocher"; often used as red pigment in paint.
Pyrrhotite FeS	4	4.6	Metallic	Gray black	Brownish bronze	Less hard than pyrite: slightly magnetic
Sphalerite ZnS	3.5–4	3.9–4.1	Resinous	Brown to light yellow	Brown to yellow	Most important zinc ore
Chalcopyrite $CuFeS_2$	3.5–4	4.1–4.3	Metallic	Greenish black	Golden yellow, often tarnished	Most important copper ore; softer than pyrite and more yellow; more brittle than gold
Bornite Cu_5FeS_4	3	4.9–5.4	Metallic	Gray black	Copper, brown; turns to purple and black	Important copper ore; known as "peacock ore" because of iridescent purple color when exposed to air for a time
Copper Cu	2.5–3	8.9	Metallic	Copper red	Copper red to black	Can be pounded into various shapes and drawn into wires; used in making electrical wires, coins, pipes
Gold Au	2.5–3	19.3	Metallic	Yellow	Rich yellow	Can be pounded into various shapes and drawn into wires; does not tarnish; used in jewelry, coins, dental fillings
Silver Ag	2.5–3	10.0–11.0	Metallic	Silver to light gray	Silver white, tarnishes to black	Can be pounded into various shapes and drawn into wires; used in jewelry, coins, electrical wire
Galena PbS	2.5	7.4–7.6	Metallic	Lead gray	Lead gray	Main ore of lead; used in shields against radiation
Graphite C	1–2	2.3	Metallic to dull	Black	Black	Feels greasy; very soft; used as pencil "lead" and as a lubricant

GROUP 2
Nonmetallic Luster, Mostly Dark-Colored

Mineral/ Formula	Hardness	Density (g/cm^3)	Luster	Streak	Color	Other Properties/Remarks
Corundum Al_2O_3	9	3.9–4.1	Brilliant to glassy	White	Usually brown	Very hard; used as an abrasive; transparent crystals used as gems called "ruby" (red) and "sapphire" (blue and other colors)
Garnet $(Ca,Mg,Fe)_3(Al,Fe,Cr)_2(SiO_4)_3$	7–7.5	3.5–4.3	Glassy to resinous	White, light brown	Red, brown, black, green	A group of minerals used in jewelry, as a birthstone, and as an abrasive
Olivine $(Mg,Fe)_2SiO_4$	6.5–7	3.3–3.4	Glassy	White or gray	Olive green	Found in igneous rocks; sometimes used as a gem
Augite $Ca(Mg,Fe,Al)(AlSi)_2O_6$	5–6	3.2–3.4	Glassy	Greenish gray	Dark green to black	Found in igneous rocks
Hornblende $NaCa_2(Mg,Fe,Al)_5(Si,Al)_8O_{22}(OH)_2$	5–6	3.0–3.4	Glassy, silky	White to gray	Dark green to brown, black	Found in igneous and metamorphic rocks
Apatite $Ca_5(PO_4)_3F$	5	3.1–3.2	Glassy	White	Green, brown, red, blue, violet, yellow	Sometimes used as a gem; source of the phosphorus needed by plants
Azurite $Cu_3(CO_3)_2(OH)_2$	3.5–4	3.8	Glassy to dull	Pale blue	Intense blue	Ore of copper; used as a gem
Biotite $K(Mg,Fe)_3AlSiO_{10}(OH)_2$	2.5–3	2.8–3.4	Glassy or pearly	White to gray	Dark green, brown, or black	A type of mica, sometimes used as a lubricant
Serpentine $Mg_6Si_4O_{10}(OH)_8$	2–5	2.2–2.6	Greasy, waxy, silky	White	Usually green	Once used in insulation but found to cause cancer; used in fireproofing; can be in the form of asbestos
Limonite Mixture of hydrous iron oxides	1–5.5	2.8–4.3	Glassy to dull	Yellow brown	Brown black to brownish yellow	Ore of iron, also known as "yellow ocher," a pigment; a mixture that is not strictly a mineral
Bauxite Mixture of hydrous aluminum oxides	1–3	2.0–2.5	Dull to earthy	Colorless to gray	Brown, yellow, gray, white	Ore of aluminum, smells like clay when wet; a mixture that is not strictly a mineral

GROUP 3
Nonmetallic Luster, Mostly Light-Colored

Mineral/ Formula	Hardness	Density (g/cm^3)	Luster	Streak	Color	Other Properties/Remarks
Diamond C	10	3.5	Brilliant	White	Colorless and varied	Hardest known substance; used in jewelry, as an abrasive, in cutting instruments
Topaz $Al_2SiO_4(F,OH)_2$	8	3.5–3.6	Glassy	White	Straw yellow, pink, bluish, greenish	Valuable gem
Quartz SiO_2	7	2.6	Glassy, greasy	White	Colorless, white; any color when not pure	The second most abundant mineral; many varieties are gems (amethyst, cat's-eye, bloodstone, agate, jasper, onyx); used in making glass
Feldspar (K,Na,Ca) $(AlSi_3O_8)$	6	2.6	Glassy	Colorless, white	Colorless, white, various colors	As a family, the most abundant of all minerals; the different types of feldspar make up over 60 percent of Earth's crust
Fluorite CaF_2	4	3.0–3.3	Glassy	Colorless	Purple, light, green, yellow, bluish green, other colors	Some types are fluorescent (glow when exposed to ultraviolet light); used in making steel
Dolomite $CaMg(CO_3)_2$	3.5–4	2.8	Glassy or pearly	White	Colorless, white, pinkish, or light tints	Used in making concrete and cement; fizzes slowly in dilute hydrochloric acid
Calcite $CaCO_3$	3	2.7	Glassy	White to grayish	Colorless, white, pale tints	Easily scratched; bubbles in dilute hydrochloric acid; frequently fluorescent
Halite NaCl	2.5	2.1–2.6	Glassy	White	Colorless or white	Occurs as perfect cubic crystals; has salty taste
Gypsum $CaSO_4 \cdot 2H_2O$	2	2.3	Glassy, pearly, silky	White	Colorless, white, light tints	Very soft; used in manufacture of plaster of Paris; form known as alabaster used for statues
Sulfur S	2	2.0–2.1	Resinous to greasy	White	Yellow to yellowish brown	Used in making many medicines, in production of sulfuric acid, and in vulcanizing rubber
Talc $Mg_3Si_4O_{10}(OH)_2$	1	2.7–2.8	Pearly to greasy	White	Gray, white, greenish	Very soft; used in talcum powder; found mostly in metamorphic rocks; also called "soapstone"

Physical Map: California

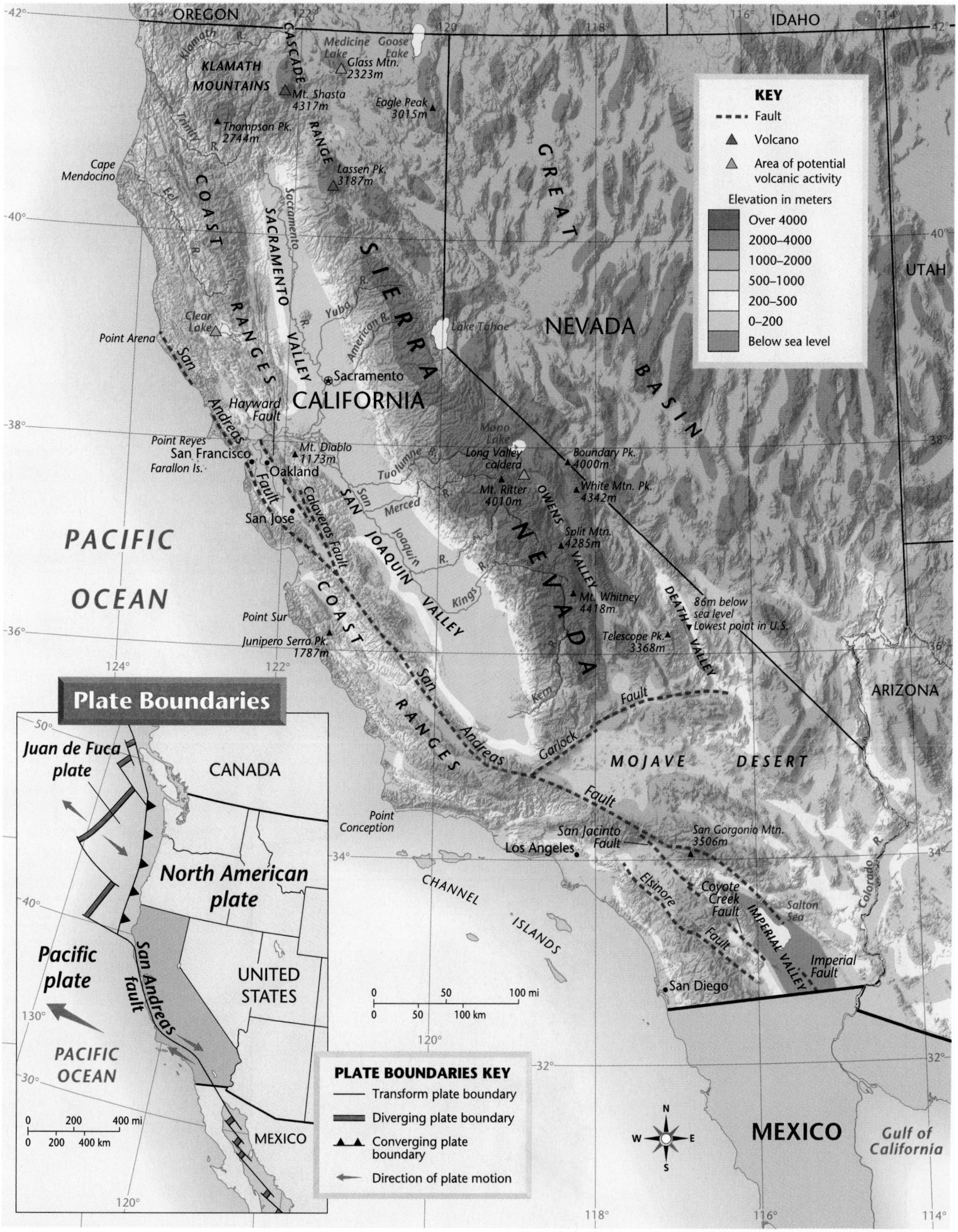
OREGON
IDAHO
UTAH
ARIZONA
NEVADA
CALIFORNIA
MEXICO
Gulf of California
PACIFIC OCEAN
KEY
Fault
Volcano
Area of potential volcanic activity
Elevation in meters
Over 4000
2000–4000
1000–2000
500–1000
200–500
0–200
Below sea level
Klamath R.
KLAMATH MOUNTAINS
CASCADE RANGE
Medicine Lake
Goose Lake
Glass Mtn. 2323m
Mt. Shasta 4317m
Eagle Peak 3015m
Thompson Pk. 2744m
Trinity R.
Lassen Pk. 3187m
Cape Mendocino
Eel R.
COAST RANGES
Sacramento R.
SACRAMENTO VALLEY
SIERRA NEVADA
GREAT BASIN
Yuba R.
American R.
Lake Tahoe
Clear Lake
Point Arena
San Andreas Fault
Sacramento
Hayward Fault
Point Reyes
San Francisco
Farallon Is.
Oakland
Mt. Diablo 1173m
Mono Lake
Long Valley caldera
Boundary Pk. 4000m
White Mtn. Pk. 4342m
Mt. Ritter 4010m
Tuolumne R.
Merced R.
San Joaquin R.
San Jose
Calaveras Fault
SAN JOAQUIN VALLEY
OWENS VALLEY
Split Mtn. 4285m
Mt. Whitney 4418m
Kings R.
DEATH VALLEY
86m below sea level
Lowest point in U.S.
Point Sur
Junipero Serra Pk. 1787m
Telescope Pk. 3368m
Kern R.
Garlock Fault
MOJAVE DESERT
Point Conception
San Jacinto Fault
San Gorgonio Mtn. 3506m
Los Angeles
CHANNEL ISLANDS
Coyote Creek Fault
Elsinore Fault
IMPERIAL VALLEY
Salton Sea
Colorado R.
Imperial Fault
San Diego
0 50 100 mi
0 50 100 km
Plate Boundaries
Juan de Fuca plate
CANADA
North American plate
Pacific plate
San Andreas fault
UNITED STATES
PACIFIC OCEAN
MEXICO
0 200 400 mi
0 200 400 km
PLATE BOUNDARIES KEY
Transform plate boundary
Diverging plate boundary
Converging plate boundary
Direction of plate motion
N
W
E
S

Physical Map: United States

CANADA
Vancouver
Cape Flattery
Strait of Juan de Fuca
Mt. Olympus 2428m
Seattle
Grand Coulee Dam
Franklin D. Roosevelt Lake
WASHINGTON
Columbia R.
Snake R.
Portland
Coast Ranges
Cascade Range
Blue Mts.
OREGON
Cape Blanco
Columbia Plateau
Cape Mendocino
Goose Lake
Shasta Lake
CALIFORNIA
Sacramento Valley
Sacramento R.
Lake Tahoe
San Francisco
Monterey Bay
Sierra Nevada
San Joaquin Valley
Coast Ranges
Mt. Whitney 4418m
Death Valley -86m
Pt. Conception
Los Angeles
Mojave Desert
Channel Islands
San Diego
Tijuana
Salton Sea
Imperial Valley
PACIFIC OCEAN
NEVADA
Great Basin
Pyramid Lake
Humboldt R.
Carson Sink
Ruby Mts.
Lake Mead
Hoover Dam
IDAHO
Salmon River Mts.
Snake R.
American Falls Res.
Bitterroot Range
MONTANA
Milk R.
Missouri R.
Fort Peck Lake
Yellowstone R.
Powder R.
Bighorn Mts.
Bighorn R.
Rocky Mountains
WYOMING
Pathfinder Res.
Seminoe Res.
Great Divide Basin
Great Salt Lake
Great Salt Lake Desert
Wasatch Range
Uinta Mts.
Utah Lake
Sevier Lake
UTAH
Green R.
Colorado Plateau
Glen Canyon Dam
Grand Canyon
Lake Powell
Little Colorado R.
ARIZONA
Parker Dam
Colorado R.
Phoenix
Salt R.
Gila R.
COLORADO
Denver
Front Range
Park Range
Mt. Elbert 4399m
Pikes Peak 4301m
Sangre de Cristo Mts.
S. Platte R.
Arkansas R.
NEW MEXICO
Elephant Butte Res.
Sacramento Mts.
Rio Grande
El Paso
Llano Estacado
Pecos R.
Great Plains
Lake Manitoba
Lake Sakakawea
NORTH DAKOTA
Lake Oahe
SOUTH DAKOTA
Black Hills
Niobrara R.
Platte R.
NEBRASKA
Republican R.
Smoky Hill
KANSAS
Canadian R.
Red R.
OK
TEXAS
Edwards Plateau
MEXICO
Monterrey
130°W
125°W
120°W
115°W
110°W
105°W
100°W
45°N
40°N
35°N
30°N
25°N
Kauai
Niihau
Oahu
Molokai
Pearl Harbor
Lanai
Maui
Kahoolawe
Hawaii
Mauna Loa 4169m
PACIFIC OCEAN
HAWAII
0 100 200 Miles
0 100 200 Kilometers
160°W
158°W
156°W
22°N
20°N
Chukchi Sea
Point Barrow
Beaufort Sea
RUSSIA
Bering Strait
Brooks Range
ARCTIC CIRCLE
Seward Peninsula
ALASKA
Norton Sound
St. Lawrence I.
Mt. McKinley 6194m
Alaska Range
Anchorage
Kenai Peninsula
CANADA
Nunivak I.
Bering Sea
Aleutian Islands
Alaska Peninsula
Kodiak I.
Gulf of Alaska
Alexander Archipelago
0 200 400 Miles
0 200 400 Kilometers
70°N
65°N
60°N
55°N
180°
175°W
170°W
165°W
160°W
155°W
150°W

UNITED STATES
Physical
International boundary
State boundary
Washington, D.C. National capital
Atlanta State capital
Detroit Major city
ELEVATION
Meters
Feet
Over 3000
Over 10,000
1500 to 3000
5,000 to 10,000
600 to 1500
2,000 to 5,000
300 to 600
1,000 to 2,000
150 to 300
500 to 1,000
0 to 150
0 to 500
Below sea level
Below sea level
WATER DEPTH
Less than 200
Less than 600
Greater than 200
Greater than 600
0 100 200 300 Miles
0 100 200 300 Kilometers
N
95°W
90°W
85°W
80°W
75°W
70°W
65°W
45°N
40°N
35°N
30°N
25°N
TROPIC OF CANCER
C A N A D A
Lake Winnipeg
Lake of the Woods
Red Lake
Lake Nipigon
Lake Superior
Gulf of St. Lawrence
Bay of Fundy
St. Lawrence R.
Montreal
Toronto
Lake Ontario
Niagara Falls
Lake Erie
Lake Huron
Georgian Bay
Lake Michigan
Upper Peninsula
Lower Peninsula
MINNESOTA
St. Paul
Minneapolis
Mississippi R.
Red R.
WISCONSIN
MICHIGAN
Detroit
Chicago
Cleveland
IOWA
Des Moines R.
Missouri R.
Rock R.
Illinois R.
Central Lowland
ILLINOIS
INDIANA
OHIO
Ohio R.
Wabash R.
Kansas R.
Kansas City
Missouri R.
Lake of the Ozarks
MISSOURI
Ozark Plateau
Table Rock Lake
Lake O' the Cherokees
KENTUCKY
Cumberland R.
TENNESSEE
Tennessee R.
Memphis
Boston Mts.
Arkansas R.
ARKANSAS
Ouachita Mts.
OKLAHOMA
Dallas
Toledo Bend Res.
Sam Rayburn Res.
Brazos R.
Colorado R.
Houston
Galveston Bay
Atchafalaya Bay
LOUISIANA
New Orleans
Mississippi River Delta
Gulf Coastal Plain
MISSISSIPPI
ALABAMA
Tombigbee R.
Chattahoochee R.
Mobile Bay
Apalachee Bay
GEORGIA
Atlanta
Clark Hill Lake
Savannah R.
Saluda R.
Altamaha R.
FLORIDA
Cape Canaveral
Tampa Bay
Lake Okeechobee
The Everglades
Miami
Cape Sable
Florida Keys
Straits of Florida
Dry Tortugas
Gulf of Mexico
Padre I.
CUBA
SOUTH CAROLINA
Charleston
Pee Dee R.
Atlantic Coastal Plain
Piedmont
NORTH CAROLINA
Roanoke R.
Pamlico Sound
Cape Hatteras
Albemarle Sound
VIRGINIA
James R.
Chesapeake Bay
WEST VIRGINIA
Cumberland Plateau
Appalachian Plateau
Appalachian Mountains
Allegheny Plateau
Potomac R.
Washington, D.C.
MARYLAND
DELAWARE
Delaware Bay
NEW JERSEY
PENNSYLVANIA
Susquehanna R.
NEW YORK
New York
Long Island
Hudson R.
Adirondack Mts.
Lake Champlain
Green Mts.
VERMONT
White Mts.
NEW HAMPSHIRE
MAINE
MASSACHUSETTS
Boston
Cape Cod
CONNECTICUT
RHODE ISLAND
ATLANTIC OCEAN

Glossary

A

aa A slow-moving type of lava that hardens to form rough chunks; cooler than pahoehoe. (p. 87)
abiotic factor A nonliving part of an ecosystem. (p. 580)
abrasion The grinding away of rock by other rock particles carried in water, ice, or wind. (pp. 199, 244)
abyssal plain A smooth, nearly flat region of the deep ocean floor. (p. 403)
acid rain Rain that is more acidic than normal, caused by the release of molecules of sulfur dioxide and nitrogen oxide into the air. (pp. 353, 449)
active Said of a volcano that is erupting or has shown signs of erupting in the near future. (p. 88)
active solar system A method of capturing the sun's energy and distributing it using pumps and fans. (p. 685)
adaptation The behaviors and physical characteristics of species that allow them to live successfully in their environments. (p. 594)
aftershock An earthquake that occurs after a larger earthquake in the same area. (p. 63)
air mass A huge body of air that has similar temperature, pressure, and humidity throughout. (p. 502)
air pressure A force that is the result of the weight of a column of air pushing down on an area. (p. 452)
alloy A solid mixture of two or more metals. (p. 128)
alluvial fan A wide, sloping deposit of sediment formed where a stream leaves a mountain range. (p. 235)
altitude Elevation above sea level. (p. 454)
anemometer An instrument used to measure wind speed. (p. 479)
aneroid barometer An instrument that measures changes in air pressure without using a liquid. Changes in the shape of an airtight metal box cause a needle on the barometer dial to move. (p. 453)
anticline An upward fold in rock formed by compression of Earth's crust. (p. 50)
anticyclone A high-pressure center of dry air. (p. 508)
aquaculture The practice of raising fish and other water organisms for food. (pp. 423, 657)
aquifer An underground layer of rock or soil that holds water. (p. 324)
artesian well A well in which water rises because of pressure within the aquifer. (p. 325)
asthenosphere The soft layer of the mantle on which the lithosphere floats. (p. 11)
atmosphere The mixture of gases that surrounds Earth. The outermost of the four spheres into which scientists divide Earth. (pp. 176, 440)
atoll A ring-shaped coral island found far from land. (pp. 151, 416)
atom The smallest unit of an element that retains the properties of that element. (p. 110)
aurora borealis A colorful, glowing display in the sky caused when particles from the sun strike oxygen and nitrogen atoms in the ionosphere; also called the Northern Lights. (p. 462)

B

barometer An instrument used to measure changes in air pressure. (p. 452)
basalt A dark, dense, igneous rock with a fine texture, found in oceanic crust. (p. 10)
base-isolated building A building mounted on bearings designed to absorb the energy of an earthquake. (p. 66)
batholith A mass of rock formed when a large body of magma cooled inside the crust. (p. 97)
beach Wave-washed sediment along a coast. (p. 255)
bedrock The solid layer of rock beneath the soil. (p. 207)
benthos Organisms that live on the bottom of the ocean or other body of water. (p. 409)
biodiversity The number of different species in an area. (p. 659)
biogeography The study of where organisms live. (p. 618)
bioluminescence The production of light by living things. (p. 419)
biomass fuel Fuel made from living things. (p. 688)
biome A group of ecosystems with similar climates and organisms. (p. 624)
biosphere All living things. One of the four spheres into which scientists divide Earth. (p. 176)
biotic factor A living part of an ecosystem. (p. 579)
birth rate The number of births in a population in a certain amount of time. (p. 587)
brackish Water that is partly salty and partly fresh, characteristic of estuaries. (p. 412)

C

caldera The large hole at the top of a volcano formed when the roof of a volcano's magma chamber collapses. (p. 94)
canopy A leafy roof formed by tall trees. (p. 625)
capillary action The combined force of attraction among water molecules and with the molecules of surrounding materials. (p. 277)
captive breeding The mating of endangered animals in zoos or preserves. (p. 666)
carnivore Consumer that eats only animals. (p. 608)
carrying capacity The largest population that an area can support. (p. 589)

cementation The process by which dissolved minerals crystallize and glue particles of sediment together into one mass. (p. 145)
chemical rock Sedimentary rock that forms when minerals crystallize from a solution. (p. 148)
chemical weathering The process that breaks down rock through chemical changes. (p. 201)
chlorofluorocarbons Chlorine compounds formerly used in air conditioners, refrigerators, and spray cans; also called CFCs. (p. 568)
cinder cone A steep, cone-shaped hill or mountain made of volcanic ash, cinders, and bombs piled up around a volcano's opening. (p. 94)
cirrus Wispy, feathery clouds made mostly of ice crystals that form at high levels, above about 6 kilometers. (p. 490)
clastic rock Sedimentary rock that forms when rock fragments are squeezed together under high pressure. (p. 146)
clear-cutting The process of cutting down all the trees in an area at once. (p. 654)
cleavage A mineral's ability to split easily along flat surfaces. (p. 115)
climate The average, year-after-year conditions of temperature, precipitation, winds, and clouds in an area. (pp. 388, 538, 621)
coagulation The process by which particles in a liquid clump together; a step in the water treatment process. (p. 337)
combustion The burning of a fuel. (p. 677)
commensalism A relationship between two species in which one species benefits and the other is neither helped nor harmed. (p. 599)
community All the different populations that live together in an area. (p. 582)
compaction The process by which sediments are pressed together under their own weight. (p. 145)
competition The struggle between organisms for the limited resources in a habitat. (p. 595)
composite volcano A tall, cone-shaped mountain in which layers of lava alternate with layers of ash and other volcanic materials. (p. 94)
compound A substance in which two or more elements are chemically joined. (p. 110)
compression Stress that squeezes rock until it folds or breaks. (p. 45)
concentration The amount of one substance in a certain volume of another substance. (p. 336)
condensation The process by which a gas, such as water vapor, changes to a liquid, such as water. (pp. 279, 489, 615)
conduction The transfer of heat by from one substance to another by direct contact of particles of matter. (pp. 16, 476)
coniferous trees Trees that produce their seeds in cones and have needle-shaped leaves. (p. 629)
conservation The process of using a resource wisely so it will not be used up. (p. 344)
conservation plowing Soil conservation method in which the dead stalks from the previous year's crop are left in the ground to hold the soil in place. (p. 218)
conservation viewpoint The belief that people should use natural resources as long as they do not destroy those resources. (p. 650)
constructive force A force that builds up mountains and landmasses on Earth's surface. (p. 7)
consumer An organism that obtains energy by feeding on other organisms. (p. 608)
continent A great landmass surrounded by oceans. (p. 7)
continental (air mass) A dry air mass that forms over land. (p. 502)
continental climate The climate of the centers of continents, with cold winters and warm or hot summers. (p. 540)
continental drift The hypothesis that the continents slowly move across Earth's surface. (pp. 19, 618)
continental glacier A glacier that covers much of a continent or large island. (p. 247)
continental shelf A gently sloping, shallow area of the ocean floor that extends outward from the edge of a continent. (p. 402)
continental slope A steep incline leading down from the edge of the continental shelf. (p. 402)
contour interval The difference in elevation from one contour line to the next. (p. 189)
contour line A line on a topographic map that connects points of equal elevation. (p. 189)
contour plowing Plowing fields along the curves of a slope to prevent soil loss. (p. 218)
control rod Cadmium rod used in a nuclear reactor to absorb neutrons from fission. (p. 694)
controlled experiment An experiment in which all factors except one are kept constant. (p. 717)
convection The transfer of heat by movements of a fluid. (pp. 16, 476)
convection current The movement of a fluid, caused by differences in temperature, that transfers heat from one part of the fluid to another. (p. 16)
convergent boundary A plate boundary where two plates move toward each other. (p. 36)
coral reef A structure of calcite skeletons built up by coral animals in warm, shallow ocean water. (p. 150)
Coriolis effect The way Earth's rotation makes winds in the Northern Hemisphere curve to the right and winds in the Southern Hemisphere curve to the left. (pp. 387, 483)

crater A bowl-shaped area that forms around a volcano's central opening. (p. 84)
crest The highest point of a wave. (p. 368)
crust The layer of rock that forms Earth's outer surface. (p. 10)
crystal A solid in which the atoms are arranged in a pattern that repeats again and again. (p. 110)
cumulus Clouds that form less than 2 kilometers above the ground and look like fluffy, rounded piles of cotton. (p. 490)
current A large stream of moving water that flows through the ocean. (p. 387)
cyclone A swirling center of low air pressure. (p. 507)

D

death rate The number of deaths in a population in a certain amount of time. (p. 587)
deciduous trees Trees that shed their leaves and grow new ones each year. (p. 628)
decomposer An organism that breaks down wastes and dead organisms. (pp. 211, 609)
deep-ocean trench A deep valley along the ocean floor through which oceanic crust slowly sinks towards the mantle. (p. 28)
deflation Wind erosion that removes surface materials. (p. 257)
deformation A change in the volume or shape of Earth's crust. (p. 45)
degree A unit used to measure distances around a circle. One degree equals 1/360 of a full circle. (p. 180)
delta A landform made of sediment that is deposited where a river flows into an ocean or lake. (pp. 235, 302)
density The amount of mass in a given space; mass per unit volume. (pp. 16, 451)
deposition The process by which sediment settles out of the water or wind that is carrying it, and is depostеd in a new location. (pp. 145, 225, 297)
desalination The process of obtaining fresh water from salt water by removing the salt. (p. 346)
desert A region that receives less than 25 centimeters of rain a year. (pp. 552, 626)
destructive force A force that slowly wears away mountains and other features on the surface of Earth. (p. 7)
development viewpoint The belief that humans should be able to freely use and benefit from all of Earth's resources. (p. 650)
dew point The temperature at which condensation begins. (p. 489)
digitizing Converting information to numbers for use by a computer. (p. 186)
dike A slab of volcanic rock formed when magma forces itself across rock layers. (p. 96)
dispersal The movement of organisms from one place to another. (p. 619)
divergent boundary A plate boundary where two plates move away from each other. (p. 35)
divide A ridge of land that separates one drainage basin or watershed from another. (pp. 233, 297)
dormant Said of a volcano that does not show signs of erupting in the near future. (p. 88)
drainage basin The land area from which a river and its tributaries collect their water. (p. 233)
drought(s) A water shortage caused by long periods of low precipitation in a particular area. (pp. 343, 496)
Dust Bowl The area of the Great Plains where wind erosion caused soil loss during the 1930s. (p. 217)

E

earthquake The shaking that results from the movement of rock beneath Earth's surface. (p. 44)
ecology The study of how living things interact with each other and their environment. (p. 582)
ecosystem All the living and nonliving things that interact in an area. (p. 578)
efficiency The percentage of energy that is used by a device to perform work. (p. 700)
El Niño An abnormal climate event that occurs every 2 to 7 years in the Pacific Ocean, causing changes in winds, currents, and weather patterns that can lead to dramatic climate changes. (pp. 391, 528)
electromagnetic wave A form of energy that can travel through space. (p. 468)
element A substance composed of a single kind of atom. (p. 110)
elevation Height above sea level. (p. 173)
emigration Leaving a population. (p. 588)
endangered species A species in danger of becoming extinct in the near future. (p. 662)
energy The ability to do work or cause change. (p. 243)
energy conservation The practice of reducing energy use. (p. 699)
energy pyramid A diagram that shows the amount of energy that moves from one feeding level to another in a food web. (p. 611)
epicenter The point on Earth's surface directly above an earthquake's focus. (p. 54)
equator An imaginary line that circles Earth halfway between the North and South poles. (p. 179)

erosion The process by which water, ice, wind, or gravity moves fragments of rock and soil. (pp. 145, 199, 225, 297)
estimate An approximation of a number based on reasonable assumptions. (p. 586)
estuary A habitat in a coastal inlet or bay where fresh water from rivers mixes with salty ocean water. (pp. 412, 633)
eutrophication The process by which nutrients in a lake build up over time, causing an increase in the growth of algae. (p. 309)
evacuate To move away temporarily. (p. 516)
evaporation The process by which molecules at the surface of a liquid, such as water, absorb enough energy to change to a gaseous state, such as water vapor. (pp. 279, 487, 614)
exosphere The outer layer of the thermosphere, extending outward into space. (p. 462)
exotic species Species that are carried to a new location by people. (p. 620)
extinct Said of a volcano that is unlikely to erupt again. (p. 88)
extinction The disappearance of all members of a species from Earth. (p. 662)
extrusive rock Igneous rock that forms from lava on Earth's surface. (p. 141)

F

fault A break in Earth's crust where slabs of rock slip past each other. (pp. 34, 46)
fault-block mountain A mountain that forms where a normal fault uplifts a block of rock. (p. 48)
filtration The process of passing water through a series of screens that allow the water through, but not larger solid particles. (p. 337)
fishery An area with a large population of valuable ocean organisms. (p. 656)
flash flood A sudden, violent flood that occurs within a few hours, or even minutes, of a heavy rainstorm. (p. 522)
flocs Sticky globs created by adding a chemical such as alum during water treatment. (p. 337)
flood plain A broad, flat valley through which a river flows. (pp. 234, 302)
fluorescence The property of a mineral in which the mineral glows under ultraviolet light. (p. 116)
focus The point beneath Earth's surface where rock breaks under stress and causes an earthquake. (p. 54)
fold A bend in rock that forms where part of Earth's crust is compressed. (p. 49)
foliated Term used to describe metamorphic rocks whose grains are arranged in parallel layers or bands. (p. 153)
food chain A series of events in which one organism eats another. (p. 609)
food web The pattern of overlapping food chains in a habitat or ecosystem. (pp. 409, 609)
footwall The block of rock that forms the lower half of a fault. (p. 46)
fossil A trace of an ancient organism that has been preserved in rock. (p. 20)
fossil fuel An energy-rich substance (such as coal, oil, or natural gas) formed from the remains of organisms. (p. 678)
fracture The way a mineral looks when it breaks apart in an irregular way. (p. 115)
frequency The number of waves that pass a specific point in a given amount of time. (p. 368)
friction The force that opposes the motion of one surface as it moves across another surface. (p. 245)
front The area where air masses meet and do not mix. (p. 505)
fuel rod Uranium rod that undergoes fission in a nuclear reactor. (p. 694)

G

gasohol A mixture of gasoline and alcohol. (p. 688)
gemstone A hard, colorful mineral that has a brilliant or glassy luster. (p. 125)
gene A structure in an organism's cells that carries its hereditary information. (p. 662)
geologist A scientist who studies the forces that make and shape planet Earth. (p. 7)
geology The study of planet Earth. (p. 7)
geothermal energy Heat energy in Earth's interior from water or steam that has been heated by magma. (pp. 89, 689)
geyser A type of hot spring that builds up pressure underground and erupts at regular intervals as a fountain of water and steam. (pp. 89, 326)
glacier A huge mass of ice and snow that moves slowly over the land. (pp. 247, 317)
Global Positioning System A method of finding latitude and longitude using satellites. (p. 191)
global warming A gradual increase in the temperature of Earth's atmosphere. (p. 566)
global winds Winds that blow steadily from specific directions over long distances. (p. 483)
globe A sphere that represents Earth's surface. (p. 177)
grain A particle of mineral or other rock that gives a rock its texture. (p. 137)
granite A usually light-colored rock that is found in continental crust. (p. 10)
grassland An area populated by grasses that gets 25 to 75 centimeters of rain each year. (p. 627)

greenhouse effect The process by which heat is trapped in the atmosphere by water vapor, carbon dioxide, methane, and other gases that form a "blanket" around Earth. (p. 471)
greenhouse gases Gases in the atmosphere that trap heat. (p. 566)
groin A stone or concrete wall built out from a beach to reduce erosion. (p. 371)
groundwater Water that fills the cracks and pores in underground soil and rock layers. (pp. 238, 274)
gully A large channel in soil formed by erosion. (p. 231)

H

habitat The place where an organism lives and that provides the things it needs to survive. (pp. 272, 579)
habitat destruction The loss of a natural habitat. (p. 663)
habitat fragmentation The breaking of a habitat into smaller, isolated pieces. (p. 663)
hanging wall The block of rock that forms the upper half of a fault. (p. 46)
hardness The level of the minerals calcium and magnesium in water. (p. 336)
headwaters The many small streams that come together at the source of the river. (p. 300)
heat The energy transferred from a hotter object to a cooler one. (p. 475)
heat transfer The movement of energy from a warmer object to a cooler object. (p. 15)
hemisphere One half of the sphere that makes up Earth's surface. (p. 179)
herbivore Consumer that eats only plants. (p. 608)
hibernation A low-energy state similar to sleep that some mammals enter in the winter. (p. 629)
holdfast A bundle of rootlike strands that attaches algae to the rocks. (p. 416)
host The organism that a parasite lives in or on in parasitism. (p. 600)
hot spot An area where magma from deep within the mantle melts through the crust above it. (p. 81)
hot spring A pool formed by groundwater that has risen to the surface after being heated by a nearby body of magma. (p. 89)
humid subtropical A wet and warm climate area on the edge of the tropics. (p. 554)
humidity A measure of the amount of water vapor in the air. (p. 488)
humus Dark-colored organic material in soil. (p. 208)
hurricane A tropical storm that has winds of 119 kilometers per hour or higher; typically about 600 kilometers across. (p. 514)
hydrocarbon A compound that contains carbon and hydrogen atoms. (p. 678)
hydroelectric power Electricity produced by the kinetic energy of water moving over a waterfall or dam. (pp. 358, 687)
hydrosphere Earth's water and ice. One of the four spheres into which scientists divide Earth. (p. 176)
hydrothermal vent An area where ocean water sinks through cracks in the ocean floor, is heated by the underlying magma, and rises again through the cracks. (p. 420)
hypothesis A possible explanation for a set of observations or answer to a scientific question. (p. 716)

I

ice ages Cold time periods in Earth's history, during which glaciers covered large parts of the surface. (pp. 248, 562)
ice wedging Process that splits rock when water seeps into cracks, then freezes and expands. (p. 200)
igneous rock A type of rock that forms from the cooling of molten rock at or below the surface. (p. 139)
immigration Moving into a population. (p. 588)
impermeable Characteristic of materials through which water does not easily pass, such as clay and granite. (p. 321)
infrared radiation A form of energy with wavelengths that are longer than visible light. (p. 469)
inner core A dense sphere of solid iron and nickel in the center of Earth. (p. 11)
inorganic Not formed from living things or the remains of living things. (p. 109)
insulation Building material that blocks heat transfer between the air inside and outside. (p. 701)
intertidal zone The area that stretches from the highest high-tide line on land out to the point exposed by the lowest low tide. (pp. 410, 634)
intrusive rock Igneous rock that forms when magma hardens beneath Earth's surface. (p. 141)
ionosphere The lower part of the thermosphere, where electrically charged particles called ions are found. (p. 462)
irrigation The process of supplying water to areas of land to make them suitable for growing crops. (p. 269)
island arc A string of islands formed by the volcanoes along a deep ocean trench. (p. 80)
isobars Lines on a map joining places that have the same air pressure. (p. 528)
isotherms Lines on a map joining places that have the same temperature. (p. 528)

J

jet streams Bands of high-speed winds about 10 kilometers above Earth's surface. (p. 486)

K

karst topography A type of landscape in rainy regions where there is limestone near the surface, characterized by caverns, sinkholes, and valleys. (p. 239)

kettle A small depression that forms when a chunk of ice is left in glacial till. (p. 250)

key A list of the symbols used on a map. (p. 178)

keystone species A species that influences the survival of many others in an ecosystem. (p. 661)

kinetic energy The form of energy an object has due to its motion. (pp. 243, 358)

L

land breeze The flow of air from land to a body of water. (p. 482)

landform A feature of topography formed by the processes that shape Earth's surface. (p. 173)

landform region A large area of land where the topography is similar. (p. 173)

latitude The distance north or south from the equator, measured in degrees. (pp. 180, 484)

lava Liquid magma that reaches the surface; also the rock formed when liquid lava hardens. (p. 78)

lava flow The area covered by lava as it pours out of a volcano's vent. (p. 84)

leach field The ground area around a septic tank through which wastewater filters after leaving the tank. (p. 341)

leeward The downwind side of mountains. (p. 543)

levee A long ridge formed by deposits of sediments alongside a river channel. (p. 304)

lightning A sudden spark, or energy discharge, caused when electrical charges jump between parts of a cloud or between a cloud and the ground. (p. 510)

limiting factor An environmental factor that prevents a population from increasing. (p. 589)

liquefaction The process by which an earthquake's violent movement suddenly turns loose soil into liquid mud. (p. 63)

lithosphere A rigid layer made up of the uppermost part of the mantle and the crust. One of four spheres into which scientists divide Earth. (pp. 10, 176)

litter The loose layer of dead plant leaves and stems on the surface of the soil. (p. 210)

load The amount of sediment that a river or stream carries. (p. 244)

loam Rich, fertile soil that is made up of about equal parts of clay, sand, and silt. (p. 208)

local winds Winds that blow over short distances. (p. 480)

loess A wind-formed deposit made of fine particles of clay and silt. (p. 258)

longitude The distance in degrees east or west of the prime meridian. (p. 181)

longshore drift The movement of water and sediment along a beach caused by waves coming into shore at an angle. (pp. 255, 370)

luster The way a mineral reflects light from its surface. (p. 113)

M

magma The molten mixture of rock-forming substances, gases, and water that makes up part of Earth's mantle. (pp. 78, 405)

magma chamber The pocket beneath a volcano where magma collects. (p. 84)

magnitude The measurement of an earthquake's strength based on seismic waves and movement along faults. (p. 57)

manipulated variable The one factor that a scientist changes during an experiment. (p. 717)

mantle The layer of hot, solid material between Earth's crust and core. (p. 10)

map A model of all or part of Earth's surface as seen from above. (p. 177)

map projection A framework of lines that helps to show landmasses on a flat surface. (p. 182)

marine climate The climate of some coastal regions, with relatively warm winters and cool summers. (p. 540)

maritime (air mass) A humid air mass that forms over oceans. (p. 502)

mass movement Any one of several processes by which gravity moves sediment downhill. (p. 225)

meander A looping curve formed in a river as it winds through its flood plain. (pp. 234, 302)

mechanical weathering The type of weathering in which rock is physically broken into smaller pieces. (p. 199)

meltdown A dangerous condition caused by overheating inside a nuclear reactor. (p. 695)

Mercalli scale A scale that rates earthquakes according to their intensity and how much damage they cause. (p. 57)

mercury barometer An instrument that measures changes in air pressure, consisting of a glass tube partially filled with mercury, with its open end resting in a dish of mercury. Air pressure pushing on the mercury in the dish forces the mercury in the tube higher. (p. 452)

mesosphere The middle layer of Earth's atmosphere; the layer in which most meteoroids burn up. (p. 458)

metamorphic rock A type of rock that forms from an existing rock that is changed by heat, pressure, or chemical reactions. (p. 139)
meteorologists Scientists who study the causes of weather and try to predict it. (p. 526)
microclimate The climate characteristic of a small, specific area; it may be different from the climate of the surrounding area. (p. 543)
mid-ocean ridge The undersea mountain chain where new ocean floor is produced; a divergent plate boundary. (pp. 24, 403)
mineral A naturally occurring, inorganic solid that has a crystal structure and a definite chemical composition. (p. 109)
Mohs hardness scale A scale ranking ten minerals from softest to hardest; used in testing the hardness of minerals. (p. 111)
moment magnitude scale A scale that rates earthquakes by estimating the total energy released by an earthquake. (p. 58)
monsoons Sea and land breezes over a large region that change direction with the seasons. (p. 482)
moraine A ridge formed by the till deposited at the edge of a glacier. (p. 249)
mountain A landform with high elevation and high relief. (p. 174)
mountain range A series of mountains that have the same general shape and structure. (p. 174)
mouth The point where a river flows into another body of water. (p. 302)
mutualism A relationship between two species in which both species benefit. (p. 599)

N

native species Species that have naturally evolved in an area. (p. 620)
natural selection Process by which individuals that are better adapted to the environment are more likely to survive and reproduce than others. (p. 594)
neap tide A tide with the least difference between low and high tide that occurs when the sun and moon pull at right angles to each other. (p. 377)
nekton Free-swimming animals that can move throughout the water column. (p. 409)
neritic zone The region of shallow water in the ocean that extends from the low-tide line out to the edge of the continental shelf. (pp. 415, 634)
niche An organism's particular role in an ecosystem, or how it makes its living. (p. 594)
nitrogen fixation The process of changing free nitrogen gas into a usable form. (p. 617)
nodule A lump formed when metals such as manganese build up around pieces of shell on the ocean floor. (p. 423)
nodules Bumps on the roots of certain plants that house nitrogen-fixing bacteria. (p. 617)
nonpoint source A widely spread source of pollution that is difficult to link to a specific point of origin, such as road runoff. (p. 351)
nonrenewable resource A natural resource that is not replaced as it is used. (p. 647)
normal fault A type of fault where the hanging wall slides downward; caused by tension in the crust. (p. 46)
nuclear fission The splitting of an atom's nucleus into smaller nuclei. (p. 693)
nuclear fusion The combining of two atomic nuclei into a single larger nucleus. (p. 696)
nucleus The central core of an atom that contains the protons and neutrons. (p. 693)

O

occluded Cut off, as the warm air mass at an occluded front is cut off from the ground by cooler air beneath it. (p. 507)
omnivore A consumer that eats both plants and animals. (p. 608)
open-ocean zone The area of the ocean beyond the edge of the continental shelf. (p. 415)
operational definition A statement that describes how a particular variable is to be measured or a term is to be defined. (p. 717)
ore Rock that contains a metal or economically useful mineral. (p. 125)
organic rock Sedimentary rock that forms where remains of organisms are deposited in thick layers. (p. 147)
outer core A layer of molten iron and nickel that surrounds the inner core of Earth. (p. 11)
oxbow lake The crescent-shaped, cutoff body of water that remains after a river carves a new channel. (pp. 234, 302)
ozone A form of oxygen that has three oxygen atoms in each molecule instead of the usual two. (p. 442)

P

P wave A type of seismic wave that compresses and expands the ground. (p. 55)
pahoehoe A hot, fast-moving type of lava that hardens to form smooth, ropelike coils. (p. 87)
Pangaea The name of the single landmass that broke apart 200 million years ago and gave rise to today's continents. (p. 19)
parasite The organism that benefits by living on or in a host in parasitism. (p. 600)
parasitism A relationship in which one organism lives on or inside another and harms it. (p. 600)

passive solar system A method of converting solar energy into heat without pumps or fans. (p. 685)
permafrost Permanently frozen soil found in the tundra climate region. (pp. 556, 630)
permeable Characteristic of materials such as sand and gravel which allow water to easily pass through them. (pp. 203, 321)
pesticide A chemical intended to kill insects and other organisms that damage crops. (p. 354)
petrochemical Compound made from oil. (p. 681)
petroleum Liquid fossil fuel; oil. (p. 680)
pH How acidic or basic a substance is, measured on a scale of 0 (very acidic) to 14 (very basic). (p. 335)
photochemical smog A brownish haze that is a mixture of ozone and other chemicals, formed when nitrogen oxides, hydrocarbons, and other pollutants react with each other in the presence of sunlight. (p. 448)
photosynthesis The process by which plants use water, plus carbon dioxide and energy from the sun, to make food. (pp. 271, 580)
pioneer species The first species to populate an area. (p. 639)
pipe A long tube through which magma moves from the magma chamber to Earth's surface. (p. 84)
pixels The tiny dots in a satellite image. (p. 185)
plain A landform made up of flat or gently rolling land with low relief. (p. 174)
plankton Tiny algae and animals that float in water and are carried by waves and currents. (p. 409)
plate A section of the lithosphere that slowly moves over the asthenosphere, carrying pieces of continental and oceanic crust. (pp. 32, 405)
plate tectonics The theory that pieces of Earth's lithosphere are in constant motion, driven by convection currents in the mantle. (p. 33)
plateau A landform that has a more or less level surface and is elevated high above sea level. (pp. 51, 175)
plucking The process by which a glacier picks up rocks as it flows over the land. (p. 248)
poaching Illegal hunting of wildlife. (p. 664)
point source A specific source of pollution that can be identified, such as a pipe. (p. 351)
polar (air mass) A cold air mass that forms north of 50° north latitude or south of 50° south latitude and has high air pressure. (p. 502)
polar molecule A molecule that has electrically charged areas. (p. 276)
polar zones The areas near both poles, from about 66.5° to 90° north and 66.5° to 90° south latitudes. (p. 539)
pollutants Harmful substances in the air, water, or soil. (p. 446)
pollution A change to the environment that has a negative effect on living things. (p. 647)
population All the members of one species in a particular area. (p. 581)
population density The number of individuals in a specific area. (p. 585)
pores Tiny openings in and between particles of rock and soil which may contain air or water. (p. 321)
porphyritic texture An igneous rock texture in which large crystals are scattered on a background of much smaller crystals. (p. 141)
potential energy Energy that is stored and available to be used later. (pp. 243, 358)
precipitation Forms of water such as rain, snow, sleet, or hail that fall from clouds and reach Earth's surface. (pp. 286, 493, 615)
predation An interaction in which one organism kills and eats another. (p. 596)
predator The organism that does the killing in predation. (p. 596)
preservation viewpoint The belief that all parts of the environment are equally important, no matter how useful they are to humans. (p. 650)
pressure The amount of force pushing on a surface or area. (pp. 9, 451)
prey An organism that is killed in predation. (p. 596)
primary succession The changes that occur in an area where no ecosystem had existed. (p. 639)
prime meridian The line that makes a half circle from the North Pole to the South Pole and that passes through Greenwich, England. (p. 180)
producer An organism that can make its own food. (p. 607)
psychrometer An instrument used to measure relative humidity, consisting of a wet-bulb thermometer and a dry-bulb thermometer. (p. 488)
pyroclastic flow The expulsion of ash, cinders, bombs, and gases during an explosive volcanic eruption. (p. 88)

R

radiation The direct transfer of energy through empty space by electromagnetic waves. (pp. 15, 468)
rain forest A forest in the tropical wet climate zone that gets plenty of rain all year. (p. 549)
rain gauge An instrument used to measure the amount of precipitation, consisting of an open-ended can topped by a collecting funnel and having a collecting tube and measuring scale inside. (p. 495)
reactor vessel The part of a nuclear reactor where nuclear fission occurs. (p. 694)
recharge New water that enters an aquifer from the surface. (p. 325)

refinery A factory where crude oil is separated into fuels and other products. (p. 681)

relative humidity The percentage of water vapor in the air compared to the maximum amount the air could hold at that temperature. (p. 488)

relief The difference in elevation between the highest and lowest parts of an area. (p. 173)

renewable resource A resource that is naturally replaced in a relatively short time. (p. 647)

reserve A known deposit of fuels. (p. 679)

reservoir A natural or artificial lake that stores water for human use. (p. 308)

responding variable The factor that changes as a result of changes to the manipulated variable in an experiment. (p. 717)

reverse fault A type of fault where the hanging wall slides upward. (p. 47)

Richter scale A scale that rates seismic waves as measured by a particular type of mechanical seismograph. (p. 57)

rift valley A deep valley that forms where two plates move apart. (p. 35)

rill A tiny groove in soil made by flowing water. (p. 231)

Ring of Fire A major belt of volcanoes that rims the Pacific Ocean. (p. 79)

rip current A rush of water that flows rapidly back to sea through a narrow opening. (p. 370)

river A large stream. (p. 232)

rock The material that forms Earth's hard surface. (p. 7)

rock cycle A series of processes on the surface and inside Earth that slowly change rocks from one kind to another. (p. 156)

runoff Water that flows over the ground surface rather than soaking into the ground. (pp. 231, 295)

S

S wave A type of seismic wave that moves the ground up and down or side to side. (p. 55)

salinity The total amount of dissolved salts in a water sample. (p. 379)

sand dune A deposit of wind-blown sand. (p. 256)

sandbar A ridge of sand deposited by waves as they slow down near shore. (p. 370)

satellite images Pictures of the land surface based on computer data collected from satellites. (p. 184)

saturated zone A layer of permeable rock or soil in which the cracks and pores are totally filled with water. (p. 321)

savanna A tropical grassland with scattered clumps of trees; found in the tropical wet-and-dry climate zone close to the equator. (pp. 552, 627)

scale Used to compare distance on a map or globe to distance on Earth's surface. (p. 177)

scattering Reflection of light in all directions. (p. 470)

scavenger A carnivore that feeds on the bodies of dead organisms. (p. 608)

scientific theory A well-tested concept that explains a wide range of observations. (p. 33)

sea breeze The flow of air from an ocean or lake to the land. (p. 482)

sea-floor spreading The process by which molten material adds new oceanic crust to the ocean floor. (pp. 25, 406)

seamount A mountain on the ocean floor that is completely underwater. (p. 403)

secondary succession The changes that occur after a disturbance in an ecosystem. (p. 640)

sediment(s) Small, solid particles of material from rocks or organisms which are moved by water or wind, resulting in erosion and deposition. (pp. 144, 225, 297)

sedimentary rock A type of rock that forms when particles from other rocks or the remains of plants and animals are pressed and cemented together. (p. 139)

seismic wave A vibration that travels through Earth carrying the energy released during an earthquake. (pp. 8, 54)

seismograph A device that records ground movements caused by seismic waves as they move through Earth. (p. 56)

selective cutting The process of cutting down only some trees in an area. (p. 654)

septic tank An underground tank containing bacteria that treat wastewater as it passes through. (p. 341)

sewage Water containing human wastes. (p. 339)

shearing Stress that pushes a mass of rock in opposite directions. (p. 45)

shield volcano A wide, gently sloping mountain made of layers of lava and formed by quiet eruptions. (p. 94)

silica A material that is formed from the elements oxygen and silicon; silica is found in magma. (p. 86)

sill A slab of volcanic rock formed when magma squeezes between layers of rock. (p. 96)

sludge Deposits of fine solids that settle out from wastewater during the treatment process. (p. 340)

smelting The process by which ore is melted to separate the useful metal from other elements. (p. 128)

sod A thick mass of grass roots and soil. (p. 215)

soil The loose, weathered material on Earth's surface in which plants can grow. (p. 207)

soil conservation The management of soil to prevent its destruction. (p. 218)

soil horizon A layer of soil that differs in color and texture from the layers above or below it. (p. 209)

solution A mixture in which one substance is dissolved in another. (pp. 120, 277)
solvent A substance that dissolves another substance, forming a solution. (p. 277)
sonar A system that determines the distance of an object under water by recording echoes of sound waves; gets its name from sound navigation and ranging. (pp. 24, 401)
species A group of organisms that are similar and reproduce to produce fertile offspring. (p. 581)
specific heat The amount of heat needed to increase the temperature of a certain mass of substance by 1°C. (p. 281)
spit A beach formed by longshore drift that projects like a finger out into the water. (p. 255)
spring A place where groundwater bubbles or flows out of cracks in the rocks. (p. 326)
spring tide A tide with the greatest difference between high and low tide that occurs when the sun and the moon are aligned in a line with Earth. (p. 376)
stalactite A calcite deposit that hangs from the roof of a cave. (p. 239)
stalagmite A cone-shaped calcite deposit that builds up from the floor of a cave. (p. 239)
state A form of matter; solid, liquid, or gas. (p. 278)
steppe A prairie or grassland found in the semiarid climate region. (p. 553)
storm A violent disturbance in the atmosphere. (p. 509)
storm surge A dome of water that sweeps across the coast where a hurricane lands. (p. 516)
stratosphere The second-lowest layer of Earth's atmosphere; the ozone layer is located in the upper stratosphere. (p. 458)
stratus Clouds that form in flat layers. (p. 490)
streak The color of a mineral's powder. (p. 112)
stream A channel through which water is continually flowing downhill. (p. 232)
stress A force that acts on rock to change its shape or volume. (p. 44)
strike-slip fault A type of fault where rocks on either side move past each other sideways with little up-or-down motion. (p. 46)
subarctic A climate zone that lies north of the humid continental climate zone, with short, cool summers and long, bitterly cold winters. (p. 555)
subduction The process by which oceanic crust sinks beneath a deep-ocean trench and back into the mantle at a convergent plate boundary. (p. 28)
submersible An underwater vehicle built of strong materials to resist pressure at depth. (p. 383)
subsoil The layer of soil beneath the topsoil that contains mostly clay and other minerals. (p. 209)
succession The series of predictable changes that occur in a community over time. (p. 638)
sunspots Dark, cooler regions on the surface of the sun. (p. 563)
surface tension The tightness across the surface of water that is caused by the polar molecules pulling on each other. (p. 276)
surface wave A type of seismic wave that forms when P waves and S waves reach Earth's surface. (p. 56)
sustainable yield A regular amount of a renewable resource that can be harvested without reducing the future supply. (p. 654)
symbiosis A close relationship between species that benefits at least one of the species. (p. 599)
symbols On a map, pictures used by mapmakers to stand for features on Earth's surface. (p. 178)
syncline A downward fold in rock formed by compression in Earth's crust. (p. 50)

T

taxol Chemical in Pacific yew tree bark that has cancer-fighting properties. (p. 669)
temperate zones The area between the tropical and polar zones, from about 23.5° to 66.5° north and 23.5° to 66.5° south latitudes. (p. 539)
temperature The average amount of energy of motion in the molecules of a substance. (p. 475)
tension Stress that stretches rock so that it becomes thinner in the middle. (p. 45)
texture The look and feel of a rock's surface determined by the size, shape, and pattern of a rock's grains. (p. 137)
thermal energy The energy of motion in the molecules of a substance. (p. 475)
thermometer An instrument used to measure temperature, consisting of a thin, glass tube with a bulb on one end that contains a liquid (usually mercury or alcohol). (p. 475)
thermosphere The outermost layer of Earth's atmosphere. (p. 461)
threatened species A species that could become endangered in the near future. (p. 662)
tides The daily rise and fall of Earth's waters on shores. (p. 375)
till The sediments deposited directly by a glacier. (p. 249)
topographic map A map that shows the surface features of an area. (p. 187)
topography The shape of the land determined by elevation, relief, and landforms. (p. 172)
topsoil Mixture of humus, clay, and other minerals that forms the topmost layer of soil. (p. 209)
tornado A rapidly whirling, funnel-shaped cloud that reaches down from a storm cloud to touch Earth's surface, usually leaving a destructive path. (p. 511)
transform boundary A plate boundary where two plates move past each other in opposite directions. (p. 34)

transpiration The process by which plants release water vapor through their leaves. (p. 285)

trench A deep canyon in the ocean floor. (p. 404)

tributary A stream that flows into a larger stream. (pp. 232, 296)

tropical (air mass) A warm air mass that forms in the tropics and has low air pressure. (p. 502)

tropical zone The area near the equator, between about 23.5° north latitude and 23.5° south latitude. (p. 539)

troposphere The lowest layer of Earth's atmosphere, where weather occurs. (p. 457)

trough The lowest point of a wave. (p. 369)

tsunami A giant wave caused by an earthquake on the ocean floor. (pp. 64, 373)

tundra A polar climate region, found across northern Alaska, Canada, and Russia, with short, cool summers and bitterly cold winters. (pp. 556, 630)

turbulence A type of movement of water in which, rather than moving downstream, the water moves every which way. (p. 246)

U

ultraviolet radiation A form of energy with wavelengths that are shorter than visible light. (p. 469)

understory A layer of shorter plants that grow in the shade of a forest canopy. (p. 625)

unsaturated zone A layer of rocks and soil above the water table in which the pores contain air as well as water. (p. 321)

upwelling An upward flow of cold water from the ocean depths. (p. 389)

V

valley glacier A long, narrow glacier that forms when snow and ice build up in a mountain valley. (p. 247)

variable Any factor that can change in an experiment. (p. 717)

vein A narrow slab of a mineral that is sharply different from the surrounding rock. (p. 120)

vent The opening through which molten rock and gas leave a volcano. (p. 84)

volcanic neck A deposit of hardened magma in a volcano's pipe. (p. 96)

volcano A weak spot in the crust where magma has come to the surface. (p. 78)

W

water cycle The continuous process by which water moves from Earth's surface to the atmosphere and back, passing through the living and nonliving parts of the environment. (pp. 284, 614)

water pollution The addition of any substance that has a negative effect on water or the living things that depend on the water. (p. 349)

water quality The degree of purity of water, determined by measuring the substances in water, besides water molecules. (p. 334)

water table The top of the saturated zone, or depth to the groundwater in an aquifer. (p. 321)

water vapor The invisible, gaseous form of water. (pp. 272, 443)

watershed The land area that supplies water to a river system. (p. 296)

wave The movement of energy through a body of water. (p. 367)

wave height The vertical distance from the crest of a wave to the trough. (p. 369)

wavelength The horizontal distance between two wave crests. (p. 368)

weather The condition of Earth's atmosphere at a particular time and place. (p. 440)

weathering The chemical and physical processes that break down rock at Earth's surface. (p. 198)

wetland An area of land that is covered with a shallow layer of water during some or all of the year. (p. 311)

wind The horizontal movement of air from an area of high pressure to an area of lower pressure. (p. 478)

wind-chill factor Increased cooling caused by the wind. (p. 479)

windward The side of mountains that faces the oncoming wind. (p. 543)

Index

Acknowledgments

Illustration

Carol Barber: 16
Patrice Rossi Calkin: 302, 310
Warren Cutler: 306–307, 314–315, 410–411
Kathleen Dempsey: 30, 38, 52, 60, 82, 98, 117, 130, 155, 160, 175, 183, 192, 204, 214, 240
John Edwards & Associates: 64, 180, 181t, 189, 202, 244, 245, 249, 253, 351, 368, 369, 370, 373, 375, 377, 389, 406, 415, 456, 470, 482t, 505, 506, 507, 515, 545, 566, 612, 621, 634–635, 677, 678, 685, 689, 695, 707
GeoSystems Global Corporation: 1m, 19, 20, 24b, 33, 41, 48t, 59, 60b, 71, 72, 79, 122, 173, 181B, 182, 213, 216, 217, 235, 248, 256, 273, 296, 315t, 387, 405, 422, 514, 517, 518, 529t, 541, 550–551, 562, 625, 626, 628, 630, 679, 706
Andrea Golden: 151, 276, 277, 279, 286, 288, 289, 313, 324, 574, 636t
Biruta Hansen: 582–583, 594
Jared D. Lee: 168–169t,
Map Quest.Com, Inc.: 731
Martucci Design: 61b, 75, 105, 188, 208, 272, 431, 441, 449, 469, 529b, 547, 558, 593, 631, 643, 647, 680, 699, 722, 723, 724
Matt Mayerchak: 40, 74, 104, 114, 132, 162, 194, 220, 260, 328, 362, 394, 464, 498, 570, 603, 642, 672, 720, 721
Karen Minot: 659
Paul Mirocha: 419
Morgan Cain & Associates: 12, 13, 14, 26, 27, 45, 50, 55tl, 56, 66, 67, 69, 70, 85, 95, 96, 142, 145, 191, 208, 210–211, 224, 226, 227, 233B, 246, 257, 338, 345, 354, 358, 452b, 453, 454, 471, 474, 476–477, 480, 483, 485, 493, 495, 567, 607, 681, 694, 696, 698
Morgan Cain & Associates (Chris Forsey): 3r, 17, 24t, 25, 28, 34, 35, 81, 400, 402–403, 417
Ortelius Design Inc.: 1m, 36, 37, 90, 91, 126, 127, 166: 178, 179, 268, 270, 271, 309, 348, 374, 391, 399, 407, 443, 482b, 508, 512-513, 535, 539, 542, 564, 571, 619
Judith Pinkham: 652, 691, 698t
Matthew Pippin: 55br, 65, 80, 120, 128, 209, 236–237, 250–251, 274, 285, 300–301, 321, 325, 329, 337, 340, 341, 359, 382, 452t, 459, 487, 491, 522, 614
Pond and Giles: 639, 640, 655
John Sanderson/Horizon Design: 504
Walter Stuart: 563, 610
Alan Witschonke: 710–711
J/B Woolsey Associates: 34, 46, 47, 48b, 49, 200, 231, 490, 523, 543, 584, 588, 595, 598, 609, 615, 616, 636, 663
J/B Woolsey Associates (Mark Desman): 418
Rose Zgodzinski: 380

Photography

Photo Research Kerri Hoar, Sue McDermott, PoYee McKenna Oster, Paula Wehde
Cover image David Muench Photography

Unit 1

Nature of Science
Page xxiv, 2, Paul Mann; **1,** Carol Prentice/U.S. Geological Survey.

Chapter 1
Pages 4–5, Earth Satellite Corporation/Science Photo Library/Photo Researchers; **6,** Gardar Palsson/Mats Wibe Lund; **7t, 7b, 7m,** W. Franke/Peter Arnold; **8,** Michael Nichols/Magnum; **9,** Tracy Frankel/The Image Bank; **10–11t,** Linde Waidhofer/Liaison International; **10m,** E. R. Degginger; **10b,** Breck P. Kent; **14,** Runk/Schoenberger/Grant Heilman; **15,** Richard Haynes; **18t,** Russ Lappa; **18b,** The Granger Collection, NY; **21,** Breck P. Kent; **22,** Bildarchiv Preussischer Kulturbesitz; **23,** Emory Kristof/National Geographic Image Collection; **26tl,** Woods Hole Oceanographic Institute/Sygma; **26tr,** USGS/HVO 3cp/U.S. Geological Survey; **27,** Scripps Oceanographic Institute; **29,** Norbert Wu; **30 all,** Richard Haynes; **31t,** Richard Haynes; **32t,** Russ Lappa; **39t,** The Granger Collection, NY.

Chapter 2
Pages 42–43, Science Museum/Michael Holford; **44,** Ben S. Kwiatkowski/Fundamental Photographs; **46t,** David Parker/Science Photo Library/Photo Researchers; **46b,** David Muench Photography; **47,** Sharon Gerig/Tom Stack & Associates; **48,** Stan Osolinski/TSI; **49,** Phillips Petroleum; **50–51,** Tom Bean; **53b, inset,** Richard Haynes; **54, 56t,** Richard Haynes; **56b,** Russell D. Curtis/Photo Researchers; **57,** Leonetto Medici/AP Photo; **58,** EERC/Berkeley; **62t,** Richard Haynes; **62b,** Natsuko Utsumi/Gamma Liaison; **63,** EERC/Berkeley; **66,** Esbin-Anderson/The Image Works; **68,** Terraphotographics/BPS; **73,** Science Museum/Michael Holford.

Chapter 3
Pages 76–77, Soames Summerhays/Photo Researchers; **78,** Savino/Sipa Press; **83 all,** Breck P. Kent; **84,** E. R. Degginger; **85,** B. Ingalls/NASA/Liaison International; **86t,** Ed Reschke/Peter Arnold; **86b,** E. R. Degginger; **87l,** Dave B. Fleetham/Tom Stack & Associates; **87r,** William Felger/Grant Heilman Photography; **88l, r,** Alberto Garcia/Saba Press; **89l, r,** Alberto Garcia/Saba Press; **89b,** Norbert Rosing/Animals Animals/Earth Scenes; **90tl,** North Wind; 90tr, Kim Heacox/Peter Arnold; **90b,** Robert Fried Photography; **91,** Alberto Garcia/Saba Press; **92l,** Pat Roqua/AP/Wide World; **92r,** Antonio Emerito/Sipa Press; **93t,** Richard Haynes; **93b,** Hela Lade/Peter Arnold; **94,** Greg Vaughn/Tom Stack & Associates; **95t,** Picture Perfect; **95b,** Manfred Gottschalk/Tom Stack & Associates; **96tl,** Brownie Harris/The Stock Market; **96bl,** Tom Bean/DRK Photo; **96br,** David Hosking/Photo Researchers; **97,** Bob Newman/Visual Unlimited; **99,** Richard Haynes; **100t, m,** NASA; **100b,** Chris Bjornberg/Photo Researchers; **101t, b,** 102, NASA; **103,** Norbert Rosing/Animals Animals/Earth Scenes.

Chapter 4
Pages 106–107, Thomas R. Taylor/Photo Researchers; **108t,** Richard Haynes; **108b,** Richard B. Levine; **109t,** Mark A. Schneider/Visuals Unlimited; **109m,** Ben Johnson/Science Photo Library/Photo Researchers; **109b,** E.R. Degginger; **110l,** Richard Treptow/Visuals Unlimited; **110r,** Gregory G. Dimijian/Photo Researchers; **110m,** McCutcheon/Visuals Unlimited; **111l,** Arne Hodalic/Corbis; **111r,** Breck P. Kent; **112,** Paul Silverman/Fundamental Photographs; **113l, r,** Breck P. Kent; **114 sulfur,** E. R. Degginger; **114 all others,** Breck P. Kent; **115l,** A. J. Copley/Visuals Unlimited; **115tr,** Paul Silverman/Fundamental Photographs; **116l, r,** E. R. Degginger; **118t,** Richard Haynes; **118b,** Gerhard Gscheidle/Peter Arnold; **119,** Jeffrey Scovil; **120l,** Ken Lucas/Visuals Unlimited; **120r,** Ted Clutter/Photo Researchers; **121,** Jay Syverson/Stock Boston; **123,** Nautilus Minerals Corp.; **124,** C. M. Dixon; **125t,** Runk/Schoenberger from Grant Heilman; **125b,** Mike Husar/DRK photo; **126t,** C. M. Dixon; **126bl,** Scala/Art Resource, NY; **126br,** C. M. Dixon; **127,** The Granger Collection, NY; **128t,** Charles D. Winters/Photo Researchers; **128b,** Russ Lappa; **129,** Visuals Unlimited; **130,** Richard Haynes; **131t, b, 133,** Breck P. Kent.

Chapter 5
Pages 134–135, Jim Nelson/Adventure Photo; **136t, m,** Breck P. Kent; **136b,** Jeff Zaroda/The Stock Market; **137tl, bl,** E. R. Degginger; **137tr, m,** Breck P. Kent; **137br,** Barry L. Runk/Grant Heilman; **138 slate, gneiss,** E. R. Degginger; **138 quartzite,** Jeff Scovil; **138 all others,** Breck P. Kent; **139,** Martin Rogers/Stock Boston; **140tl,** Breck P. Kent; **140tr,** Doug Martin/Photo Researchers; **140b,** Greg Vaughn/Tom Stack & Associates; **141tl, tm,** Breck P. Kent; **141tr,** E. R. Degginger; **142,** Alfred Pasieka/Science Photo Library/Photo Researchers; **143,** Michele & Tom Grimm/TSI; **144,** Clyde H. Smith/Peter Arnold; **146,** Specimen from North Museum/Franklin and Marshall College/Grant Heilman Photography; **147t,** E. R. Degginger; **147b,** Kevin Sink/Midwestock; **148,** Grant Heilman/Grant Heilman Photography; **149t,** Ted Clutter/Photo Researchers; **149b,** Stephen Frink/Waterhouse; **150,** Norbert Wu/The Stock Market; **150b,** Jean-Marc Truchet/TSI; **151,** Grant Heilman/Grant Heilman Photography; **152tl,** E. R. Degginger; **152bl,** Barry L. Runk/Grant Heilman Photography; **152br, 153bl,** Andrew J. Martinez/Photo Researchers; **154,** David Hosking/Photo Researchers; **156tl, tr,** Jeff Scovil; **156tm,** Breck P. Kent; **157,** Corbis; **158tl,** Tom Algire/Tom Stack & Associates; **158bl,** Breck P. Kent; **158br,** N. R. Rowan/Stock Boston; **159,** Breck P. Kent; **160t, m, b,** Russ Lappa; **161,** Greg Vaughn/Tom Stack & Associates; **163l, r,** E. R. Degginger; **163m,** Breck P. Kent.

Interdisciplinary Exploration
Page 164tl, Rosenfeld Imaged Ltd/Rainbow; **164br,** Michael Holford; **164–165m,** B. Daemmrich/The Image Works; **165 inset,** NASA/The Image Works; **166 border,** Marilyn "Angel" Wynn; **168b,** John Coletti/Stock Boston.

Unit 2

Chapter 6
Pages 170–171, Tom Bean; **172,** The Granger Collection, NY; **174t,** Tom Bean; **174b,** David Muench Photography; **176,** ESA/PLI/The Stock Market; **177 both,** Russ Lappa; **178t,** Bodleian Library, Oxford, U.K.; **178b,** The Granger Collection, NY; **179t, 179br,** The Granger Collection, NY; **179bl,** British Library, London/Bridgeman Art Library, London/Superstock; **184t,** Russ Lappa; **184b, 185 both,** Earth Satellite Corporation/Science Photo Library/Photo Researchers; **186tl,** Geographix; **186tr,** Bob Daemmrich/Stock Boston; **187t,** Richard Haynes; **187b,** Robert Rathe/Stock Boston; **189,** Paul Rezendes; **190,** U.S. Geological Survey;

191t, Ken M. Johns/Photo Researchers; **192,** Richard Haynes; **193,** ESA/PLI/The Stock Market; **195,** U.S. Geological Survey.

Chapter 7

Pages **196–197,** Mike Mazzaschi/Stock Boston; **198,** Russ Lappa; **199l,** Ron Watts/Westlight; **199r,** Jerry D. Greer; **200l,** Breck P. Kent/Animals Animals/Earth Scenes; **200r,** Susan Rayfield/Photo Researchers; **201l,** John Sohlden/Visuals Unlimited; **201m,** E. R. Degginger/Photo Researchers; **201r,** Gerald & Buff Corsi/Visuals Unlimited; **203t,** Chromosohm/Sohm/Photo Researchers; **203b,** Breck P. Kent/Animals Animals/Earth Scenes; **205,** Richard Haynes; **206,** John G. Ross/Photo Researchers; **207t,** Richard Haynes; **207b,** Rod Planck/TSI; **212,** J. M. Labat/Jacana/Photo Researchers; **214,** Richard T. Nowitz/Photo Researchers; **215t,** Richard Haynes; **215b,** Jim Brandenburg/Minden Pictures; **216,** Corbis; **217,** AP/Wide World Photos; **218t,** Larry Lefever/Grant Heilman Photography; **218b,** Jim Strawser/Grant Heilman Photography; **219t,** John G. Ross/Photo Researchers; **219b,** Ron Watts/Westlight.

Chapter 8

Pages 222–223 & 224, Jim Steinberg/Photo Researchers; **225,** Paul Sequeira/Photo Researchers; **226t,** Eric Vandeville/Gamma-Liaison Network; **226b,** Thomas G. Rampton/Grant Heilman Photography; **227,** Steven Holt; **228–229,** Richard Haynes; **230,** Photo Disc; **230–231,** Walter Bibikow/The Viesti Collection; **231t,** Runk Schoenberger/Grant Heilman Photography; **232,** Inga Spence/Tom Stack & Associates; **233,** David Ball/The Stock Market; **234l,** Glenn M. Oliver/Visuals Unlimited; **234r,** Georg Gerster/Photo Researchers; **235t,** Gerald and Buff Corsi/Visuals Unlimited; **235b,** NASA/SADO/Tom Stack & Associates; **238,** Chuck O'Rear/Westlight; **239,** St. Petersburg Times/Gamma-Liaison; **240,** Russ Lappa; **241,** Richard Haynes; **242,** Doug McKay/TSI; **243t,** Richard Haynes; **243b,** Eliot Cohen; **247t,** Richard Haynes; **247b,** Mark Kelley/Stock Boston; **249,** Grant Heilman Photography; **252,** Craig Tuttle/The Stock Market; **254,** Randy Wells/TSI; **255,** E.R.I.M./TSI; **256t,** Richard Haynes; **256b,** Jess Stock/TSI; **257,** Breck P. Kent; **258,** Connie Toops; **259,** Craig Tuttle/The Stock Market.

Unit 3

Nature of Science

Pages 262, 263, 264b, Courtesy of Cindy Lee Van Dover; **264t,** Emory Kristof/National Geographic Image Collection; **265,** Woods Hole Oceanographic Institution.

Chapter 9

Pages 266–267, Randy Linchs/Sharpshooters; **268b,** Uniphoto; **269tl,** Peter Menzel/Stock Boston; **269tr,** Foodpix; **270t,** O. Louis Mazzatenta/National Geographic Image Collection; **271b,** Liba Taylor/Corbis; **271t,** Tom Bean/TSI; **271b,** Gianni Dagli Orti/Corbis; **275,** Russ Lappa; **276b,** Stephen Dalton/Photo Researchers; **277 inset,** Tom Bean/The Stock Market; **277b,** Mark & Audry Gibson/The Stock Market; **279l,** Steven C. Kaufman/Peter Arnold; **279m,** Chris Soresen/the Stock Market; **279r,** Japack/Leo de Wys; **280b,** Neal Mishler/Natural Selection; **281t,** D. Adams/Picture Perfect Images; **281b,** Russ Lappa; **283b, 284t,** Richard Haynes; **284b,** Michael Giannechini/Photo Researchers; **286t,** John Shaw/Tom Stack & Associates; **287t, 289t,** Japack/Leo de Wys.

Chapter 10

Pages 292–293, Dave Johnston/Picture Cube; **294t,** Russ Lappa; **294 inset,** Wernher Krutein/Gamma-Liaison; **294m,** Superstock; **295,** Paul Barton/The Stock Market; **297,** Jacques Jangoux/TSI; **299,** Mark Thayer; **300l,** Michael Durham/ENP; **300b,** Darrell Gulin/TSI; **301l,** Harry Engels/Animals Animals; **301r,** Hal Horwitz/Corbis; **303 inset,** Gregory Foster/Gamma-Liaison; **303,** Bill Gillette/Gamma-Liaison; **304,** Les Stone/Sygma; **305t,** Russ Lappa; **305b,** Annie Griffiths Belt/Aurora; **308l,** David L. Brown/The Stock Market; **308r,** John Shaw/Tom Stack & Associates; **309,** George Holton/Photo Researchers; **31t,** Russ Lappa; **311b,** Helen Cruickshank/Photo Researchers; **312l,** Breck P. Kent/Animals Animals; **312r,** Greg Vaughn/Tom Stack & Associates; **313,** John Eastcott/Yva Momatiuk/Earth Scenes; **316,** Patrick M. Rose/Save the Manatee; **317t,** Richard Haynes; **317b,** Ralph A. Clevenger/Westlight; **318t,** Don Pitcher/Stock Boston; **318bl,** Hulton Getty/TSI; **318br,** Superstock; **319,** Ralph A. Clevenger/Westlight; **320t,** Richard Haynes; **320b,** Tim Olive/Sharpshooters; **323,** Mark Thayer; **326,** Barbara Filet/TSI; **327,** R. Clevenger/Westlight.

Chapter 11

Pages 330–331, Jeremy Horner/Corbis; **332,** Russ Lappa; **333,** Guy Marche/TSI; **334,** Michael Newman/Photo Edit; **339b,** Deborah Davis/Photo Edit; **339t,** Ted Horowitz/The Stock Market; **342t,** Russ Lappa; **342b,** Laura Sikes/Sygma; **343,** Calvin Larsen/Photo Researchers; **344,** Russ Lappa; **346t,** Peter Skinner/Photo Researchers; **346b, 347, 349t,** Russ Lappa; **349,** Seth Resnick/Stock Boston; **352,** Corbis/Bettmann; **353t,** Mugshots/The Stock Market; **353b,** Wayne Eastep/TSI; **355t,** Carson Baldwin/Earth Scenes; **355b,** John Eastcott/Yva Momatiuk/Stock Boston; **356,** Peter Essick/Aurora; **357t,** Russ Lappa; **357b,** I. Burgum/P. Boorman/TSI; **359b,** Robert K. Grubbs/Photo Network; **360,** George Gerster/Photo Researchers; **361b,** Deborah David/Photo Edit; **361t,** Mugshots/Stock Market.

Chapter 12

Pages 364–365, Seigried Layda/TSI; **366t,** Richard Haynes; **366–367b,** Aaron Chang/The Stock Market; **371t,** ©1996 The Art Institute of Chicago, Clarence Buckingham Collection; **371b,** Russ Lappa; **372t,** Eric Horan/Gamma Liaison; **372b,** Grace Davies/New England Stock; **374, 375,** Gene Ahrens/Bruce Coleman; **378,** Maher Attar/Sygma; **379t,** Richard Haynes; **379b,** Russ Lappa; **380,** Alon Reininger/The Stock Market; **381,** Corel; **383,** Russ Lappa; **385,** Mark Thayer; **386b,** Russ Lappa; **386t,** Richard Haynes; **388,** Raven/Explorer/Photo Researchers; **389br,** Carol Roessler/Animals Animals; **392,** Ryan Ott/AP Photo.

Chapter 13

Pages 396–397, Fred Bavendam; **398t,** Russ Lappa; **398b,** The Granger Collection; **399,** Courtesy, Peabody Essex Museum, Salem, MA; **400,** Norbert Wu/The Stock Market; **401t,** Scripps Oceanographic Institute; **401b,** Scott Camanzine/Photo Researchers; **404,** Ted Streshinsky/Corbis; **406,** Russ Lappa; **408,** Richard Dunoff/The Stock Market; **409tr,** E.R. Degginger/Photo Researchers; **409mr,** Tim Heller/Mo Yung Productions; **409br,** Doug Perrine/Innerspace Visions; **409bl,** F. Stuart Westmorland/Photo Researchers; **412bl,** Maresa Pryor/Earth Scenes; **160br,** Peter Weiman/Earth Scenes; **413t,** Lynda Richardson/Corbis; **413b,** Andy Mertinez/Photo Researchers; **414t,** Richard Haynes; **414b,** Jeff Foott/Tom Stack & Associates; **416l,** Chuck Davis/TSI; **416r,** Randy Morse/Tom Stack & Associates; **417,** Mike Bacon/Tom Stack & Associates; **418,** Norbert Wu; **420,** D. Foster/WHOI/Visuals Unlimited; **421t,** Richard Haynes; **421b,** Nathan Benn/Stock Boston; **423,** Russ Lappa; **424,** Arnulf Husmo/TSI; **425l,** Bob Torrez/TSI; **425r,** Bill Nation/Sygma; **426t,** Jake Evans/TSI; **426b,** Richard Haynes; **427,** Tim Hauf/Visuals Unlimited; **429l,** Doug Perrine/Innerspace Visions; **429r,** Randy Morse/Tom Stack & Associates.

Interdisciplinary Exploration

Page **433t,** The Granger Collection; **433m,** North Wind Picture Archives; **433b,** University Art Collection, Tulane; **435,** Richard Pasley/Liaison International; **436,** Art Resource; **437t,** North Wind Picture Archives; **437b,** Chromo Sohm/Photo Researchers.

Unit 4

Nature of Science

Page **572,** Jane Love/NASA; **573r,** Jose L. Pelaez/The Stock Market; **517,** NASA/Photo Researchers; **574b,** NASA; **574–575t,** NASA

Chapter 14

Pages **438–439,** Jay Simon/TSI; **440t,** Russ Lappa; **440b,** NASA/Photo Researchers; **442b,** Russ Lappa; **442t,** Richard Haynes; **443r,** George G. Dimijian/Photo Researchers; **444tl,** Eric Horan/Liaison International; **445,** Richard Haynes; **446t,** Russ Lappa; **446b,** Aaron Haupt/Photo Researchers; **447b,** Paul Lowe/Magnum Photos; **447t,** Biophoto Associates/Photo Researchers; **448,** Will McIntyre/Photo Researchers; **450, Steve Casimiro/Liaison International; 451t,** Russ Lappa; **451b,** Eric A. Kessler; **453t,** Ivan Bucher/Photo Researchers; **455,** Russ Lappa; **457t,** Russ Lappa; **457b,** Steve Vidler/Superstock; **458,** Mark C. Burnett/Photo Researchers; **460b,** Corbis-Bettmann; **460t,** The Granger Collection, NY; **461b,** NASA; **461t,** The National Archives/Corbis; **462,** Jack Finch/Science Photo Library/Photo Researchers; **463,** Biophoto Associates/Photo Researchers.

Chapter 15

Pages 466–467, William Johnson/Stock Boston; **468–469,** Photo Researchers; **473,** Richard Haynes; **474,** Russ Lappa; **475,** Russ Lappa; **476–477,** Daniel Cox/Allstock/PNI; **478t,** Russ Lappa; **478bl,** Victoria Hurst/Tom Stack & Associates; **478–479,** Gary Retherford/Photo Researchers; **479r,** Richard Haynes; 481, Richard Haynes; **482,** Steve McCurry/Magnum Photos; **484,** Scala/Art Resource, NY; **486,** Ken McVey/TSI; **487,** Russ Lappa; **488,** E.J. Tarbuck; **489,** Peter Arnold; **491t,** Michael Gadomski/GADOM/Bruce Coleman; **491tm,** Phil Degginger/Bruce Coleman; **491bm,** E. R. Degginger; **491b,** John Shaw/Bruce Coleman; **492,** Wendy Shattil/Bob Rozinski/Tom Stack & Associates; **493,** Richard Haynes; **494t,** AP/Wide World; **494b,** Nuridsany et Perennou/Photo Researchers; **494 inset,** Gerben Oppermans/TSI; **496,** Bill Frantz/TSI; **497l,** Gerben Oppermans/TSI; **497r,** Victoria Hurst/Tom Stack & Associates.

Chapter 16

Pages 500–501, Pete Turner/The Image Bank; **502t,** Russ Lappa; **502b,** Russ Lappa; **503,** Jim Corwin/TSI; **509t,** Russ Lappa; **509b,** Dirck Halstead/Liaison International; **510,** Dan Sudia/Photo Researchers; **511,** Schuster/Superstock;

512b, The Granger Collection, NY; **512t,** The Granger Collection, NY; **513l,** North Wind Picture Archives; **514,** Sheila Beougher/Liaison International; **515,** NASA-Goddard Laboratory for Atmospheres; **516,** Clore Collection, Tate Gallery, London/Art Resource, NY; **518,** NOAA; **520,** Tony Freeman/Photo Edit; **521t,** Richard Haynes; **521bl,** Keith Kent/Science Photo Library/Photo Researchers; **521br,** Grant V. Faint/The Image Bank; **524,** AP Photo/Pool/David J. Phillip; **525t,** Larry Lawfer; **525b,** Corel Corp.; **526,** AP Photo/David Umberger; **527,** NOAA; **529,** NOAA; **530–532,** AccuWeather, Inc.; **533l,** Schuster/Superstock; **533r,** Russ Lappa.

Chapter 17
Pages 536–537, David Muench; 538t, Richard Haynes; **538b,** Thomas D. Mangelsen/Peter Arnold; **540,** David Madison/Bruce Coleman; **542,** Duncan Wherrett/TSI; **543,** Chris Cheadle/TSI; **547,** Richard Haynes; **548t,** Russ Lappa; **548b,** Charlie Waite/TSI; **549,** Geogory G. Dimigian/Photo Researchers; **552t,** Thomas D. Mangelsen/Peter Arnold; **552b,** Alex S. MacLean/Peter Arnold; **553,** Stephen Johnson/TSI; **554t,** Ann Duncan/Tom Stack & Associates; **554b,** Margaret Gowan/TSI; **555,** Kennan Ward Photography/Corbis; **556t,** Art Wolfe/TSI; **556b,** Thomas Kitchin/Tom Stack & Associates; **557,** Photodisc, Inc.; **560,** 1996 Ira Block; **561r,** Tony Craddock/Science Photo Library/Photo Researchers; **561 inset,** George Godfrey/Animals Animals; **568,** NOAA; **569l,** Art Wolfe/TSI; **569r,** Tony Craddock/Science Photo Library/Photo Researchers.

Unit 5

Chapter 18
Pages 576–577, Tony Craddock/TSI; **578,** Richard Haynes; **578–579,** Shin Yoshino/Minden Pictures; **579,** Carr Clifton/Minden Pictures; **579 inset top,** Corel Corp.; **579 inset,** S. Nielsen/DRK Photo; **580,** John Cancalosi/Tom Stack & Associates; **581,** Patti Murray/Animals Animals; **585t,** Richard Haynes; **585b,** Michlo Hoshino/Minden Pictures; **586,** C. Allan Morgan/DRK Photo; **587t,** Rob Simpson/Visuals Unlimited; **587b,** Bas van Beek/Leo de Wys; **589,** Mitsuaki Iwago/Minden Pictures; **590t,** Dan Budnick/Woodfin Camp & Associates; **590b,** Russ Lappa; **592,** Gary Griffen/Animals Animals; **593,** J. Alcock/Visuals Unlimited; **595l,** Patti Murray/Animals Animals; **595tr,** Wayne Lankinen/DRK Photo; **595br,** Ron Willocks/Animals Animals; **596l,** Michael Fogden/DRK Photo; **596r,** D. Holden Bailey/Tom Stack & Associates; **597l,** Stephen J. Krasemann/DRK Photo; **597r,** Donald Specker/Animals Animals; **597b,** Jeanne White/Photo Researchers, **599,** Daryl Balfour/TSI; **600,** John Gerlach/DRK Photo; **601,** Tony Craddock/TSI.

Chapter 19
Pages 604–605, Tom McHugh/Steinhart Aquarium/Photo Researchers; **606t,** Richard Haynes; **606b,** Byron Jorjorian/TSI; **607,** Breck P. Kent/Animals Animals/Earth Scenes; **608l,** Stephen J. Krasemann/DRK Photo; **608tr,** John Cancalosi/DRK Photo; **608br,** John Netherton/Animals Animals; **609,** S. Nielsen/DRK Photo; **611,** Stephen J. Krasemann/DRK Photo; **613t,** Richard Haynes; **613b,** R.J. Erwin/DRK Photo; **617,** Dr. Jeremy Burgess/Science Photo Library/Photo Researchers; **618t,** Richard Haynes; **618b,** J. Cancalosi/DRK Photo; **619,** D. Cavagnaro/DRK Photo; **620,** Stephen G. Maka/DRK Photo; **621t,** John Canalosi/DRK Photo; **621b,** Russ Lappa; **623,** Richard Haynes; **624,** Russ Lappa; **625t,** Renee Lynn/TSI; **625m,** Frans Lanting/Minden Pictures; **625b,** Mark Hones/Minden Pictures; **626l,** Joe McDonald/DRK Photo; **626 inset,** Michael Fogden/DRK Photo; **627,** Art Wolfe/TSI; 628l, Carr Clifton/Minden Pictures; **628 inset, 629r,** Stephen J. Krasemann/DRK Photo; **629 inset,** Michael Quinton/Minden Pictures; **630, 631,** Michio Hoshino/Minden Pictures; **632l,** David Boyle/Animals Animals; **632r,** Kim Heacox/DRK Photo; **633l,** Stephen G. Maka/DRK Photo; **633r,** Steven David Miller/Animals Animals; **634l,** Anne Wertheim/Animals Animals; **634r,** Gregory Ochocki/Photo Researchers; 635l, Michael Nolan/Tom Stack & Associates; **635r,** Norbert Wu; **637l, 637r,** Russ Lappa; **638t, 638b,** Tom & Pat Leeson/Photo Researchers; **641,** John Cancalosi/DRK Photo.

Chapter 20
Pages 644–645, Gay Bumgarner/TSI; **646,** Frans Lanting/Minden Pictures; **647l,** Inga Spence/Tom Stack & Associates; **647r,** Charles D. Winters/Photo Researchers; **647b,** Key Sanders/TSI; **648t,** UPI/Corbis-Bettmann; **648b,** Corbis-Bettmann; **649t,** UPI/Corbis-Bettmann; **649bl,** Underwood & Underwood/Corbis-Bettmann; **649br,** William Campbell/Peter Arnold; **650,** Jeff Gnass/The Stock Market; **652,** Russ Lappa; **653,** Martin Rogers/Stock Boston; **654,** Gary Braasch/TSI; **656,** Tom Stewart/The Stock Market; **657,** Greg Vaughn/Tom Stack & Associates; **658,** Russ Lappa; **659,** Richard Haynes; **660tl,** Dave Watts/Tom Stack & Associates; **660tm,** Frans Lanting/Minden Pictures; **660tr,** George G. Dimijian/Photo Researchers; **660b,** Fred Bavendam/Minden Pictures; **661t,** Frans Lanting/Minden Pictures; **661b,** Jim Zipp/Photo Researchers; **662,** D. Cavagnaro/DRK Photo; **663,** Randy Wells/TSI; **664l,** John Shaw/Tom Stack & Associates; **664m,** Dan Suzio/Photo Researchers; **664tr,** Stephen J. Krasemann/DRK Photo; **664–665,** Phil A. Dotson/Photo Researchers; **665tm,** Frans Lanting/Minden Pictures; **665m,** David Liebman, **665r,** Lynn M. Stone/DRK Photo; **666l,** Roy Toft/Tom Stack & Associates; **666r,** Frans Lanting/Minden Pictures; **667,** Tom McHugh/Photo Researchers; **668t,** Richard Haynes; **668b,** Greg Vaughn/Tom Stack & Associates; **669l, 669r,** G. Payne/Liaison International; **670,** D. Cavagnaro/DRK Photo; **671,** Gary Braasch/TSI.

Chapter 21
Pages 674–675, Yamada Toshiro/TSI; **676,** M. L. Sinibaldi/The Stock Market; **679t,** Mike Abrahams/TSI; **679b,** Paul Harris/TSI; **680,** Jbboykin Oil Prod./The Stock Market; **682,** UPI/Corbis-Bettmann; **683,** Chad Ehlers/International Stock; **684,** Nadia MacKenzie/TSI; **686,** A & L Sinibaldi/TSI; **687,** Larry Ulrich/DRK Photo; **688,** Carlie Waite/TSI; **690,** NASA; **691,** Richard Haynes; **692,** Herb Swanson; **693t,** Russ Lappa; **693b,** Photograph by Johan Hagemeyer, courtesy AIP Emilio Segre Visual Archives; **696,** Y. Arthus-Bertrand/Peter Arnold; **697,** U.S. Dept. of Energy/Science Photo Library/Photo Researchers; **699,** Richard Haynes; **700l,** Mitch Kezar/TSI; **700r,** Leonard Lessin/Peter Arnold; **701,** Yves Marcoux/TSI; **702,** Wolf/Monkmeyer; **703l,** Nadia MacKenzie/TSI; **703r,** Yves Marcoux/TSI.

Interdisciplinary Exploration
Page 706tm, Frans Lanting/Minden Pictures; **706tr,** Alan Carey/Photo Researchers; **706bl,** Frans Lanting/Minden Pictures; **706br,** Roy Toft/Tom Stack & Associates; **707t,** Starin/Ardea London Ltd.; **707m,** Peter Steyn/Ardea London Ltd.; **707b,** Tom Brakefield/DRK Photo; **708t,** Dr. Migel Smith/ Earth Scenes; **708b,** Werner Forman Archive/Art Resource; **709l,** Christie's Images; **709r,** Jose Anzel/Aurora; **711,** Corbis-Bettmann.

Skills Handbook
Page **712,** Mike Moreland/Photo Network; **713t,** Foodpix; **713m,** Richard Haynes; **713b,** Russ Lappa; **716,** Richard Haynes; **718,** Ron Kimball; **719,** Renee Lynn/Photo Researchers.